Instructor's Solutions Manual

For

Serway and Jewett's

Physics

for Scientists and Engineers with Modern Physics

Sixth Edition, Volume Two

Ralph V. McGrew
Broome Community College

James A. Currie
Weston High School

Australia • Canada • Mexico • Singapore • Spain • United Kingdom • United States

Printed in the United States of America
1 2 3 4 5 6 7 07 06 05 04 03

Printer: Globus Printing Company, Inc.

0-534-40953-9

For more information about our products,
contact us at:
Thomson Learning Academic Resource Center
1-800-423-0563

For permission to use material from this text,
contact us by:
Phone: 1-800-730-2214
Fax: 1-800-731-2215
Web: http://www.thomsonrights.com

Brooks/Cole—Thomson Learning
10 Davis Drive
Belmont, CA 94002-3098
USA

Asia
Thomson Learning
5 Shenton Way #01-01
UIC Building
Singapore 068808

Australia/New Zealand
Thomson Learning
102 Dodds Street
Southbank, Victoria 3006
Australia

Canada
Nelson
1120 Birchmount Road
Toronto, Ontario M1K 5G4
Canada

Europe/Middle East/South Africa
Thomson Learning
High Holborn House
50/51 Bedford Row
London WC1R 4LR
United Kingdom

Latin America
Thomson Learning
Seneca, 53
Colonia Polanco
11560 Mexico D.F.
Mexico

Spain/Portugal
Paraninfo
Calle/Magallanes, 25
28015 Madrid, Spain

CONTENTS

PREFACE

This *Instructor's Solutions Manual* accompanies the sixth edition of the textbook *Physics for Scientists and Engineers* by Raymond A. Serway and John W. Jewett, Jr. It contains instructor's solutions for all of the end–of–chapter problems, with answers boxed; a list of answers to the even-numbered problems; and answers to the end–of–chapter questions. Problems new to this edition have asterisks next to their solutions.

The first word is *Instructor's*. Please do not give students access to this manual. Bear the following in mind:

- The publisher provides you with this copyrighted manual for your convenience, free of charge.
- Many teachers at many colleges use the textbook. Some use problems from it in graded homework and in examinations.
- Solutions in this manual are written for efficient communication with instructors, not for maximally effective help to students.
- Students never need to see solutions to all of the problems. The textbook is rich with examples. The *Student Solutions Manual and Study Guide* contains detailed solutions to about fifteen problems and several questions per chapter—those with their numbers boxed in the textbook. Of these, five per chapter are on the textbook's website.
- The useful life of this edition can continue only so long as the users maintain the integrity and security of the problem set and solutions.

You should take precautions to keep the manual as secure as possible. Within the context of a course using the textbook, we recognize that the teacher may use this manual to make answers and solutions to selected problems available for a limited time to students in the course. We ask you not to make the whole manual available to a student, not to make sections of it available at times when you are not teaching a course using the textbook, and not to make any sections of it available to the public, either physically or electronically.

As novice problem solvers are different from expert problem solvers, so the solutions in this manual are very different from solutions (such as those in the textbook examples) addressed to students. With the goals of communicating efficiently with you and of limiting the bulk of this manual, we have often omitted problem restatements, commentary, intermediate steps, and even initial steps that would make the solutions more clear to students. We generally answer questions briefly, without recitation of reasoning. Students profit from explicit help in understanding a problem, in representing it in different ways, in reasoning about it qualitatively, in planning a solution, and in evaluating a result for reasonableness. They will not get that help from this manual. Students need to see a problem situation in a context of direct experience with observed reality. They must understand the principles used in a problem solution as drawn from a remarkably small set of physical laws. Finally, their solutions must use techniques drawn from a comprehensible set of analysis models. If you provide students with solutions drawn from this manual, try including your own ideas in order to communicate most effectively with your students, and to reveal more of what really goes into solving a problem. We recommend following the *Conceptualize—Categorize—Analyze—Finalize* format introduced in the textbook. The classic book *How to Solve It* by George Polya [Princeton University Press] is especially good at explaining how a teacher can help a student who is actively working a problem, and how the student can learn a lot at the *Finalize* step of problem-solving by thinking critically about her solution.

- Problems in the text are varied in subject matter and in what they ask the student to do. Your choice of the questions and problems you assign strongly influences your students' perception of the course, what they learn, and how much they learn. Use of this manual may help you to make a thoughtful individual choice of questions and problems to assign. Two sorts of problems deserve further explanation:

- Each chapter contains at least one problem asking for estimates of data and an order-of-magnitude calculation. Solutions here look simple. Be prepared for students who have difficulty in deciding what quantities are relevant, in making estimates, and in believing that order-of-magnitude estimates have value. If you choose to include estimation problems in your course, we suggest examples, encouragement, working in pairs or groups, time to think, regularly repeated practice starting early in the course, and acceptance of different approaches. You may find that explicit study of Section 1.6 and assignment of Problem 56 in Chapter 1 and Problem 48 in Chapter 45 are necessary.
- While every chapter contains problems requiring symbolic solutions, each chapter contains a pair of adjacent problems stated in identical language, the first giving numerical data and asking for a numerical answer and the second asking for a symbolic solution. You can use either problem by itself. At any point in your course, for students who have learned to do numerical calculations but find difficulty with symbols, you can use both problems together. With your help, students will see that the same steps solve both problems, and that the symbolic problem can be much more instructive. For students who rely too much on an equation-solving calculator, you can assign both problems. With your help, students will see the need to do their algebra themselves.

When a problem quotes data to three significant digits, we quote answers to three significant digits. The last digit is uncertain, often depending, for example, on the precision of the values assumed for physical constants. If the calculation involves a chain of steps, we carry forward many digits in intermediate results, even though we write down only three digits. We "round off" only at the end of the calculation, never anywhere in the middle. The regularity of three significant digits in nearly all textbook problems can help students focus on physical concepts without distraction. We recognize that students may get the false impression that every physics problem should have values precise to three digits. You may assign your students to work more thoughtfully with laboratory measurements.

If you find errors in the textbook problems or solutions, please notify the first-named author at the address below. We will reply and will correct errors in future printings. We thank those who have helped to correct solutions since the publication of the last edition: the students Alexander Coto, John Liu, Karl Payne, and Eric Peterman, and the teachers David Aspnes, Robert Beichner, Joseph Biegen, Tom Devlin, Alfonso Diaz-Jimenez, Vasili Haralambous, Frank Hayes, Erika Hermon, Ken Menningen, Eugene Mosca, Margo Mulvihill, Henry Nebel, and Joseph Rudmin.

We are grateful to the staff at M and N Toscano for assembling and typing this manual and preparing diagrams and page layouts. Richard Miers checked the manual for accuracy. Their prompt and exacting work has contributed greatly to the book's correctness, clarity, and usefulness. Various solutions in this manual were written originally by Louis Cadwell, John R. Gordon, Lawrence Hmurcik, Henry Leap, Steve Van Wyk, Laurent Hodges, N. John DiNardo, Richard Cohen, Ronald Bieniek, Charles Teague, Duane Deardorff, Richard McGrew, and Michael Hones; and by Edward Adelson, Michael Browne, Andrew Duffy, Robert Forsythe, Perry Ganas, John Jewett, Boris Korsunsky, Edwin Lo, Clement Moses, Raymond Serway, and Jerzy Wrobel, who contributed new problems for this edition of the text. We thank Rebecca Heider and Alyssa White, Developmental Editors at Brooks/Cole Thomson Learning, who coordinated this project and provided resources for it.

Ralph McGrew, Engineering Science and Physics Department,
Broome Community College, Binghamton, NY 13902-1017
mcgrew_r@sunybroome.edu

James Currie
Weston High School, Weston, MA

23

Electric Fields

CHAPTER OUTLINE

ANSWERS TO QUESTIONS

Q23.1 A neutral atom is one that has no net charge. This means that it has the same number of electrons orbiting the nucleus as it has protons in the nucleus. A negatively charged atom has one or more excess electrons.

Q23.2 When the comb is nearby, molecules in the paper are polarized, similar to the molecules in the wall in Figure 23.5a, and the paper is attracted. During contact, charge from the comb is transferred to the paper by conduction. Then the paper has the same charge as the comb, and is repelled.

Q23.3 The clothes dryer rubs dissimilar materials together as it tumbles the clothes. Electrons are transferred from one kind of molecule to another. The charges on pieces of cloth, or on nearby objects charged by induction, can produce strong electric fields that promote the ionization process in the surrounding air that is necessary for a spark to occur. Then you hear or see the sparks.

Q23.4 To avoid making a spark. Rubber-soled shoes acquire a charge by friction with the floor and could discharge with a spark, possibly causing an explosion of any flammable material in the oxygen-enriched atmosphere.

Q23.5 Electrons are less massive and more mobile than protons. Also, they are more easily detached from atoms than protons.

Q23.6 The electric field due to the charged rod induces charges on near and far sides of the sphere. The attractive Coulomb force of the rod on the dissimilar charge on the close side of the sphere is larger than the repulsive Coulomb force of the rod on the like charge on the far side of the sphere. The result is a net attraction of the sphere to the rod. When the sphere touches the rod, charge is conducted between the rod and the sphere, leaving both the rod and the sphere like-charged. This results in a repulsive Coulomb force.

Q23.7 All of the constituents of air are nonpolar except for water. The polar water molecules in the air quite readily "steal" charge from a charged object, as any physics teacher trying to perform electrostatics demonstrations in the summer well knows. As a result—it is difficult to accumulate large amounts of excess charge on an object in a humid climate. During a North American winter, the cold, dry air allows accumulation of significant excess charge, giving the potential (pun intended) for a shocking (pun also intended) introduction to static electricity sparks.

Q23.8 Similarities: A force of gravity is proportional to the product of the intrinsic properties (masses) of two particles, and inversely proportional to the square of the separation distance. An electrical force exhibits the same proportionalities, with charge as the intrinsic property.

Differences: The electrical force can either attract or repel, while the gravitational force as described by Newton's law can only attract. The electrical force between elementary particles is vastly stronger than the gravitational force.

Q23.9 No. The balloon induces polarization of the molecules in the wall, so that a layer of positive charge exists near the balloon. This is just like the situation in Figure 23.5a, except that the signs of the charges are reversed. The attraction between these charges and the negative charges on the balloon is stronger than the repulsion between the negative charges on the balloon and the negative charges in the polarized molecules (because they are farther from the balloon), so that there is a net attractive force toward the wall. Ionization processes in the air surrounding the balloon provide ions to which excess electrons in the balloon can transfer, reducing the charge on the balloon and eventually causing the attractive force to be insufficient to support the weight of the balloon.

Q23.10 The electric field due to the charged rod induces a charge in the aluminum foil. If the rod is brought towards the aluminum from above, the top of the aluminum will have a negative charge induced on it, while the parts draping over the pencil can have a positive charge induced on them. These positive induced charges on the two parts give rise to a repulsive Coulomb force. If the pencil is a good insulator, the net charge on the aluminum can be zero.

Q23.11 So the electric field created by the test charge does not distort the electric field you are trying to measure, by moving the charges that create it.

Q23.12 With a very high budget, you could send first a proton and then an electron into an evacuated region in which the field exists. If the field is gravitational, both particles will experience a force in the same direction, while they will experience forces in opposite directions if the field is electric.

On a more practical scale, stick identical pith balls on each end of a toothpick. Charge one pith ball + and the other –, creating a large-scale dipole. Carefully suspend this dipole about its center of mass so that it can rotate freely. When suspended in the field in question, the dipole will rotate to align itself with an electric field, while it will not for a gravitational field. If the test device does not rotate, be sure to insert it into the field in more than one orientation in case it was aligned with the electric field when you inserted it on the first trial.

Q23.13 The student standing on the insulating platform is held at the same electrical potential as the generator sphere. Charge will only flow when there is a difference in potential. The student who unwisely touches the charged sphere is near zero electrical potential when compared to the charged sphere. When the student comes in contact with the sphere, charge will flow from the sphere to him or her until they are at the same electrical potential.

Q23.14 An electric field once established by a positive or negative charge extends in all directions from the charge. Thus, it can exist in empty space if that is what surrounds the charge. There is no material at point A in Figure 23.23(a), so there is no charge, nor is there a force. There would be a force if a charge were present at point A, however. A field does exist at point A.

Q23.15 If a charge distribution is small compared to the distance of a field point from it, the charge distribution can be modeled as a single particle with charge equal to the net charge of the distribution. Further, if a charge distribution is spherically symmetric, it will create a field at exterior points just as if all of its charge were a point charge at its center.

Q23.16 The direction of the electric field is the direction in which a positive test charge would feel a force when placed in the field. A charge will not experience two electrical forces at the same time, but the vector sum of the two. If electric field lines crossed, then a test charge placed at the point at which they cross would feel a force in two directions. Furthermore, the path that the test charge would follow if released at the point where the field lines cross would be indeterminate.

Q23.17 Both figures are drawn correctly. $\mathbf{E}_1$ and $\mathbf{E}_2$ are the electric fields separately created by the point charges q_1 and q_2 in Figure 23.14 or q and $-q$ in Figure 23.15, respectively. The net electric field is the vector sum of $\mathbf{E}_1$ and $\mathbf{E}_2$, shown as **E**. Figure 23.21 shows only one electric field line at each point away from the charge. At the point location of an object modeled as a point charge, the direction of the field is undefined, and so is its magnitude.

Q23.18 The electric forces on the particles have the same magnitude, but are in opposite directions. The electron will have a much larger acceleration (by a factor of about 2 000) than the proton, due to its much smaller mass.

Q23.19 The electric field around a point charge approaches infinity as r approaches zero.

Q23.20 Vertically downward.

Q23.21 Four times as many electric field lines start at the surface of the larger charge as end at the smaller charge. The extra lines extend away from the pair of charges. They may never end, or they may terminate on more distant negative charges. Figure 23.24 shows the situation for charges $+2q$ and $-q$.

Q23.22 At a point exactly midway between the two changes.

Q23.23 Linear charge density, λ, is charge per unit length. It is used when trying to determine the electric field created by a charged rod.

Surface charge density, σ, is charge per unit area. It is used when determining the electric field above a charged sheet or disk.

Volume charge density, ρ, is charge per unit volume. It is used when determining the electric field due to a uniformly charged sphere made of insulating material.

Q23.24 Yes, the path would still be parabolic. The electrical force on the electron is in the downward direction. This is similar to throwing a ball from the roof of a building horizontally or at some angle with the vertical. In both cases, the acceleration due to gravity is downward, giving a parabolic trajectory.

Q23.25 No. Life would be no different if electrons were + charged and protons were – charged. Opposite charges would still attract, and like charges would repel. The naming of + and – charge is merely a convention.

Q23.26 If the antenna were not grounded, electric charges in the atmosphere during a storm could place the antenna at a high positive or negative potential. The antenna would then place the television set inside the house at the high voltage, to make it a shock hazard. The wire to the ground keeps the antenna, the television set, and even the air around the antenna at close to zero potential.

Q23.27 People are all attracted to the Earth. If the force were electrostatic, people would all carry charge with the same sign and would repel each other. This repulsion is not observed. When we changed the charge on a person, as in the chapter-opener photograph, the person's weight would change greatly in magnitude or direction. We could levitate an airplane simply by draining away its electric charge. The failure of such experiments gives evidence that the attraction to the Earth is not due to electrical forces.

Q23.28 In special orientations the force between two dipoles can be zero or a force of repulsion. In general each dipole will exert a torque on the other, tending to align its axis with the field created by the first dipole. After this alignment, each dipole exerts a force of attraction on the other.

SOLUTIONS TO PROBLEMS

Section 23.1 Properties of Electric Charges

***P23.1** (a) The mass of an average neutral hydrogen atom is 1.007 9u. Losing one electron reduces its mass by a negligible amount, to

$$1.007\,9\left(1.660\times10^{-27}\text{ kg}\right)-9.11\times10^{-31}\text{ kg}=\boxed{1.67\times10^{-27}\text{ kg}}.$$

Its charge, due to loss of one electron, is

$$0-1\left(-1.60\times10^{-19}\text{ C}\right)=\boxed{+1.60\times10^{-19}\text{ C}}.$$

(b) By similar logic, charge $=\boxed{+1.60\times10^{-19}\text{ C}}$

$\text{mass}=22.99\left(1.66\times10^{-27}\text{ kg}\right)-9.11\times10^{-31}\text{ kg}=\boxed{3.82\times10^{-26}\text{ kg}}$

(c) charge of $\text{Cl}^-=\boxed{-1.60\times10^{-19}\text{ C}}$

$\text{mass}=35.453\left(1.66\times10^{-27}\text{ kg}\right)+9.11\times10^{-31}\text{ kg}=\boxed{5.89\times10^{-26}\text{ kg}}$

(d) charge of $\text{Ca}^{++}=-2\left(-1.60\times10^{-19}\text{ C}\right)=\boxed{+3.20\times10^{-19}\text{ C}}$

$\text{mass}=40.078\left(1.66\times10^{-27}\text{ kg}\right)-2\left(9.11\times10^{-31}\text{ kg}\right)=\boxed{6.65\times10^{-26}\text{ kg}}$

(e) charge of $\text{N}^{3-}=3\left(-1.60\times10^{-19}\text{ C}\right)=\boxed{-4.80\times10^{-19}\text{ C}}$

$\text{mass}=14.007\left(1.66\times10^{-27}\text{ kg}\right)+3\left(9.11\times10^{-31}\text{ kg}\right)=\boxed{2.33\times10^{-26}\text{ kg}}$

(f) charge of $\text{N}^{4+}=4\left(1.60\times10^{-19}\text{ C}\right)=\boxed{+6.40\times10^{-19}\text{ C}}$

$\text{mass}=14.007\left(1.66\times10^{-27}\text{ kg}\right)-4\left(9.11\times10^{-31}\text{ kg}\right)=\boxed{2.32\times10^{-26}\text{ kg}}$

(g) We think of a nitrogen nucleus as a seven-times ionized nitrogen atom.

$\text{charge}=7\left(1.60\times10^{-19}\text{ C}\right)=\boxed{1.12\times10^{-18}\text{ C}}$

$\text{mass}=14.007\left(1.66\times10^{-27}\text{ kg}\right)-7\left(9.11\times10^{-31}\text{ kg}\right)=\boxed{2.32\times10^{-26}\text{ kg}}$

(h) $\text{charge}=\boxed{-1.60\times10^{-19}\text{ C}}$

$\text{mass}=\left[2(1.007\,9)+15.999\right]1.66\times10^{-27}\text{ kg}+9.11\times10^{-31}\text{ kg}=\boxed{2.99\times10^{-26}\text{ kg}}$

P23.2 (a) $N = \left(\frac{10.0 \text{ grams}}{107.87 \text{ grams/mol}}\right)\left(6.02 \times 10^{23} \frac{\text{atoms}}{\text{mol}}\right)\left(47 \frac{\text{electrons}}{\text{atom}}\right) = \boxed{2.62 \times 10^{24}}$

(b) $\# \text{ electrons added} = \frac{Q}{e} = \frac{1.00 \times 10^{-3} \text{ C}}{1.60 \times 10^{-19} \text{ C/electron}} = 6.25 \times 10^{15}$

or $\boxed{2.38 \text{ electrons for every } 10^9 \text{ already present}}$.

Section 23.2 **Charging Objects by Induction**

Section 23.3 **Coulomb's Law**

P23.3 If each person has a mass of $\approx 70 \text{ kg}$ and is (almost) composed of water, then each person contains

$$N \cong \left(\frac{70\,000 \text{ grams}}{18 \text{ grams/mol}}\right)\left(6.02 \times 10^{23} \frac{\text{molecules}}{\text{mol}}\right)\left(10 \frac{\text{protons}}{\text{molecule}}\right) \cong 2.3 \times 10^{28} \text{ protons}.$$

With an excess of 1% electrons over protons, each person has a charge

$$q = 0.01\left(1.6 \times 10^{-19} \text{ C}\right)\left(2.3 \times 10^{28}\right) = 3.7 \times 10^{7} \text{ C}.$$

So $F = k_e \frac{q_1 q_2}{r^2} = \left(9 \times 10^9\right) \frac{\left(3.7 \times 10^7\right)^2}{0.6^2} \text{ N} = 4 \times 10^{25} \text{ N} \boxed{\sim 10^{26} \text{ N}}$.

This force is almost enough to lift a weight equal to that of the Earth:

$$Mg = 6 \times 10^{24} \text{ kg}\left(9.8 \text{ m/s}^2\right) = 6 \times 10^{25} \text{ N} \sim 10^{26} \text{ N}.$$

***P23.4** The force on one proton is $\mathbf{F} = \frac{k_e q_1 q_2}{r^2}$ away from the other proton. Its magnitude is

$$\left(8.99 \times 10^9 \text{ N} \cdot \text{m/C}^2\right)\left(\frac{1.6 \times 10^{-19} \text{ C}}{2 \times 10^{-15} \text{ m}}\right)^2 = \boxed{57.5 \text{ N}}.$$

P23.5 (a) $F_e = \frac{k_e q_1 q_2}{r^2} = \frac{\left(8.99 \times 10^9 \text{ N} \cdot \text{m}^2/\text{C}^2\right)\left(1.60 \times 10^{-19} \text{ C}\right)^2}{\left(3.80 \times 10^{-10} \text{ m}\right)^2} = \boxed{1.59 \times 10^{-9} \text{ N}}$ (repulsion)

(b) $F_g = \frac{G m_1 m_2}{r^2} = \frac{\left(6.67 \times 10^{-11} \text{ N} \cdot \text{m}^2/\text{C}^2\right)\left(1.67 \times 10^{-27} \text{ kg}\right)^2}{\left(3.80 \times 10^{-10} \text{ m}\right)^2} = \boxed{1.29 \times 10^{-45} \text{ N}}$

The electric force is $\boxed{\text{larger by } 1.24 \times 10^{36} \text{ times}}$.

(c) If $k_e \frac{q_1 q_2}{r^2} = G \frac{m_1 m_2}{r^2}$ with $q_1 = q_2 = q$ and $m_1 = m_2 = m$, then

$$\frac{q}{m} = \sqrt{\frac{G}{k_e}} = \sqrt{\frac{6.67 \times 10^{-11} \text{ N} \cdot \text{m}^2/\text{kg}^2}{8.99 \times 10^9 \text{ N} \cdot \text{m}^2/\text{C}^2}} = \boxed{8.61 \times 10^{-11} \text{ C/kg}}.$$

P23.6 We find the equal-magnitude charges on both spheres:

$$F = k_e \frac{q_1 q_2}{r^2} = k_e \frac{q^2}{r^2} \quad \text{so} \quad q = r\sqrt{\frac{F}{k_e}} = (1.00 \text{ m})\sqrt{\frac{1.00\times10^4 \text{ N}}{8.99\times10^9 \text{ N}\cdot\text{m}^2/\text{C}^2}} = 1.05\times10^{-3} \text{ C}.$$

The number of electron transferred is then

$$N_{\text{xfer}} = \frac{1.05\times10^{-3} \text{ C}}{1.60\times10^{-19} \text{ C}/e^-} = 6.59\times10^{15} \text{ electrons}.$$

The whole number of electrons in each sphere is

$$N_{\text{tot}} = \left(\frac{10.0 \text{ g}}{107.87 \text{ g/mol}}\right)\left(6.02\times10^{23} \text{ atoms/mol}\right)\left(47\ e^-/\text{atom}\right) = 2.62\times10^{24}\ e^-.$$

The fraction transferred is then

$$f = \frac{N_{\text{xfer}}}{N_{\text{tot}}} = \left(\frac{6.59\times10^{15}}{2.62\times10^{24}}\right) = \boxed{2.51\times10^{-9}} = 2.51 \text{ charges in every billion.}$$

P23.7

$$F_1 = k_e \frac{q_1 q_2}{r^2} = \frac{\left(8.99\times10^9 \text{ N}\cdot\text{m}^2/\text{C}^2\right)\left(7.00\times10^{-6} \text{ C}\right)\left(2.00\times10^{-6} \text{ C}\right)}{(0.500 \text{ m})^2} = 0.503 \text{ N}$$

$$F_2 = k_e \frac{q_1 q_2}{r^2} = \frac{\left(8.99\times10^9 \text{ N}\cdot\text{m}^2/\text{C}^2\right)\left(7.00\times10^{-6} \text{ C}\right)\left(4.00\times10^{-6} \text{ C}\right)}{(0.500 \text{ m})^2} = 1.01 \text{ N}$$

$$F_x = 0.503\cos 60.0° + 1.01\cos 60.0° = 0.755 \text{ N}$$

$$F_y = 0.503\sin 60.0° - 1.01\sin 60.0° = -0.436 \text{ N}$$

$$\mathbf{F} = (0.755 \text{ N})\hat{\mathbf{i}} - (0.436 \text{ N})\hat{\mathbf{j}} = \boxed{0.872 \text{ N at an angle of } 330°}$$

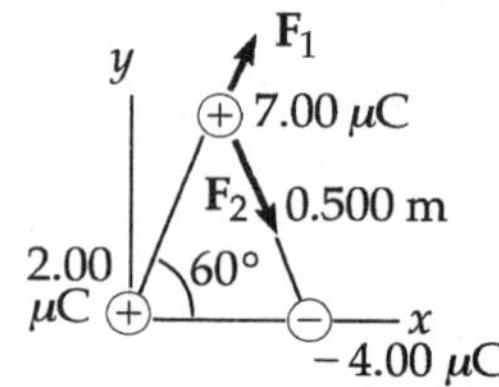

FIG. P23.7

P23.8

$$F = k_e \frac{q_1 q_2}{r^2} = \frac{\left(8.99\times10^9 \text{ N}\cdot\text{m}^2/\text{C}^2\right)\left(1.60\times10^{-19} \text{ C}\right)^2\left(6.02\times10^{23}\right)^2}{\left[2\left(6.37\times10^6 \text{ m}\right)\right]^2} = \boxed{514 \text{ kN}}$$

P23.9 (a) The force is one of $\boxed{\text{attraction}}$. The distance r in Coulomb's law is the distance between centers. The magnitude of the force is

$$F = \frac{k_e q_1 q_2}{r^2} = \left(8.99\times10^9 \text{ N}\cdot\text{m}^2/\text{C}^2\right)\frac{\left(12.0\times10^{-9} \text{ C}\right)\left(18.0\times10^{-9} \text{ C}\right)}{(0.300 \text{ m})^2} = \boxed{2.16\times10^{-5} \text{ N}}.$$

(b) The net charge of -6.00×10^{-9} C will be equally split between the two spheres, or -3.00×10^{-9} C on each. The force is one of $\boxed{\text{repulsion}}$, and its magnitude is

$$F = \frac{k_e q_1 q_2}{r^2} = \left(8.99\times10^9 \text{ N}\cdot\text{m}^2/\text{C}^2\right)\frac{\left(3.00\times10^{-9} \text{ C}\right)\left(3.00\times10^{-9} \text{ C}\right)}{(0.300 \text{ m})^2} = \boxed{8.99\times10^{-7} \text{ N}}.$$

P23.10 Let the third bead have charge Q and be located distance x from the left end of the rod. This bead will experience a net force given by

$$\mathbf{F} = \frac{k_e(3q)Q}{x^2}\hat{\mathbf{i}} + \frac{k_e(q)Q}{(d-x)^2}\left(-\hat{\mathbf{i}}\right).$$

The net force will be zero if $\frac{3}{x^2} = \frac{1}{(d-x)^2}$, or $d - x = \frac{x}{\sqrt{3}}$.

This gives an equilibrium position of the third bead of $x = \boxed{0.634d}$.

The equilibrium is $\boxed{\text{stable if the third bead has positive charge}}$.

P23.11 (a) $$F = \frac{k_e e^2}{r^2} = \left(8.99\times10^9\ \text{N}\cdot\text{m}^2/\text{C}^2\right)\frac{\left(1.60\times10^{-19}\ \text{C}\right)^2}{\left(0.529\times10^{-10}\ \text{m}\right)^2} = \boxed{8.22\times10^{-8}\ \text{N}}$$

(b) We have $F = \frac{mv^2}{r}$ from which

$$v = \sqrt{\frac{Fr}{m}} = \sqrt{\frac{8.22\times10^{-8}\ \text{N}\left(0.529\times10^{-10}\ \text{m}\right)}{9.11\times10^{-31}\ \text{kg}}} = \boxed{2.19\times10^6\ \text{m/s}}.$$

P23.12 The top charge exerts a force on the negative charge $\frac{k_e qQ}{\left(\frac{d}{2}\right)^2 + x^2}$ which is directed upward and to the left, at an angle of $\tan^{-1}\left(\frac{d}{2x}\right)$ to the x-axis. The two positive charges together exert force

$$\left(\frac{2k_e qQ}{\left(\frac{d^2}{4} + x^2\right)}\right)\left(\frac{(-x)\hat{\mathbf{i}}}{\left(\frac{d^2}{4} + x^2\right)^{1/2}}\right) = m\mathbf{a} \text{ or for } x \ll \frac{d}{2},\ \mathbf{a} \approx \frac{-2k_e qQ}{md^3/8}\mathbf{x}.$$

(a) The acceleration is equal to a negative constant times the excursion from equilibrium, as in $\mathbf{a} = -\omega^2\mathbf{x}$, so we have Simple Harmonic Motion with $\omega^2 = \frac{16k_e qQ}{md^3}$.

$$T = \frac{2\pi}{\omega} = \boxed{\frac{\pi}{2}\sqrt{\frac{md^3}{k_e qQ}}}$$, where m is the mass of the object with charge $-Q$.

(b) $$v_{\max} = \omega A = \boxed{4a\sqrt{\frac{k_e qQ}{md^3}}}$$

Section 23.4 The Electric Field

P23.13 For equilibrium, $\mathbf{F}_e = -\mathbf{F}_g$

or $q\mathbf{E} = -mg(-\hat{\mathbf{j}})$.

Thus, $\mathbf{E} = \frac{mg}{q}\hat{\mathbf{j}}$.

(a) $\mathbf{E} = \frac{mg}{q}\hat{\mathbf{j}} = \frac{(9.11\times10^{-31}\text{ kg})(9.80\text{ m/s}^2)}{(-1.60\times10^{-19}\text{ C})}\hat{\mathbf{j}} = \boxed{-(5.58\times10^{-11}\text{ N/C})\hat{\mathbf{j}}}$

(b) $\mathbf{E} = \frac{mg}{q}\hat{\mathbf{j}} = \frac{(1.67\times10^{-27}\text{ kg})(9.80\text{ m/s}^2)}{(1.60\times10^{-19}\text{ C})}\hat{\mathbf{j}} = \boxed{(1.02\times10^{-7}\text{ N/C})\hat{\mathbf{j}}}$

P23.14 $\sum F_y = 0:\ QE\hat{\mathbf{j}} + mg(-\hat{\mathbf{j}}) = 0$

$\therefore m = \frac{QE}{g} = \frac{(24.0\times10^{-6}\text{ C})(610\text{ N/C})}{9.80\text{ m/s}^2} = \boxed{1.49\text{ grams}}$

P23.15 The point is designated in the sketch. The magnitudes of the electric fields, E_1, (due to the -2.50×10^{-6} C charge) and E_2 (due to the 6.00×10^{-6} C charge) are

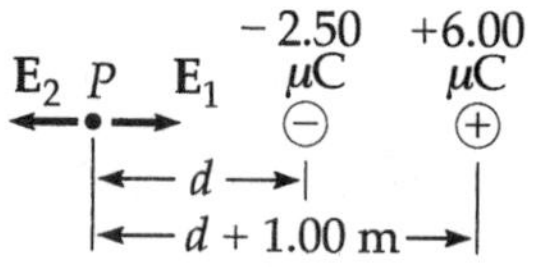

$$E_1 = \frac{k_e q}{r^2} = \frac{(8.99\times10^9\text{ N}\cdot\text{m}^2/\text{C}^2)(2.50\times10^{-6}\text{ C})}{d^2} \quad (1)$$

$$E_2 = \frac{k_e q}{r^2} = \frac{(8.99\times10^9\text{ N}\cdot\text{m}^2/\text{C}^2)(6.00\times10^{-6}\text{ C})}{(d+1.00\text{ m})^2} \quad (2)$$

FIG. P23.15

Equate the right sides of (1) and (2)

to get $(d+1.00\text{ m})^2 = 2.40d^2$

or $d + 1.00\text{ m} = \pm1.55d$

which yields $d = 1.82\text{ m}$

or $d = -0.392\text{ m}$.

The negative value for d is unsatisfactory because that locates a point between the charges where both fields are in the same direction.

Thus, $d = \boxed{1.82\text{ m to the left of the }-2.50\ \mu\text{C charge}}$.

P23.16 If we treat the concentrations as point charges,

$$\mathbf{E}_+ = k_e \frac{q}{r^2} = \left(8.99\times10^9 \text{ N}\cdot\text{m}^2/\text{C}^2\right)\frac{(40.0 \text{ C})}{(1\,000 \text{ m})^2}\left(-\hat{\mathbf{j}}\right) = 3.60\times10^5 \text{ N/C}\left(-\hat{\mathbf{j}}\right)(\text{downward})$$

$$\mathbf{E}_- = k_e \frac{q}{r^2} = \left(8.99\times10^9 \text{ N}\cdot\text{m}^2/\text{C}^2\right)\frac{(40.0 \text{ C})}{(1\,000 \text{ m})^2}\left(-\hat{\mathbf{j}}\right) = 3.60\times10^5 \text{ N/C}\left(-\hat{\mathbf{j}}\right)(\text{downward})$$

$$\mathbf{E} = \mathbf{E}_+ + \mathbf{E}_- = \boxed{7.20\times10^5 \text{ N/C downward}}$$

***P23.17** The first charge creates at the origin field $\frac{k_eQ}{a^2}$ to the right. Suppose the total field at the origin is to the right. Then q must be negative:

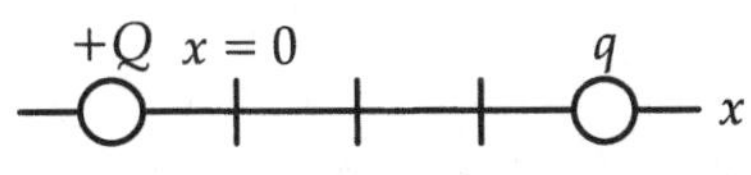

FIG. P23.17

$$\frac{k_eQ}{a^2}\hat{\mathbf{i}} + \frac{k_eq}{(3a)^2}\left(-\hat{\mathbf{i}}\right) = \frac{2k_eQ}{a^2}\hat{\mathbf{i}} \qquad \boxed{q = -9Q}.$$

In the alternative, the total field at the origin is to the left:

$$\frac{k_eQ}{a^2}\hat{\mathbf{i}} + \frac{k_eq}{9a^2}\left(-\hat{\mathbf{i}}\right) = \frac{2k_eQ}{a^2}\left(-\hat{\mathbf{i}}\right) \qquad \boxed{q = +27Q}.$$

P23.18 (a)

$$E_1 = \frac{k_eq}{r^2} = \frac{\left(8.99\times10^9\right)\left(7.00\times10^{-6}\right)}{(0.500)^2} = 2.52\times10^5 \text{ N/C}$$

$$E_2 = \frac{k_eq}{r^2} = \frac{\left(8.99\times10^9\right)\left(4.00\times10^{-6}\right)}{(0.500)^2} = 1.44\times10^5 \text{ N/C}$$

$$E_x = E_2 - E_1\cos60° = 1.44\times10^5 - 2.52\times10^5\cos60.0° = 18.0\times10^3 \text{ N/C}$$

$$E_y = -E_1\sin60.0° = -2.52\times10^5\sin60.0° = -218\times10^3 \text{ N/C}$$

$$\mathbf{E} = \left[18.0\hat{\mathbf{i}} - 218\hat{\mathbf{j}}\right]\times10^3 \text{ N/C} = \boxed{\left[18.0\hat{\mathbf{i}} - 218\hat{\mathbf{j}}\right] \text{ kN/C}}$$

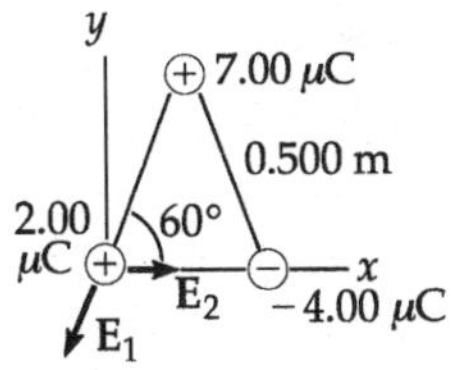

FIG. P23.18

(b)

$$\mathbf{F} = q\mathbf{E} = \left(2.00\times10^{-6} \text{ C}\right)\left(18.0\hat{\mathbf{i}} - 218\hat{\mathbf{j}}\right)\times10^3 \text{ N/C} = \left(36.0\hat{\mathbf{i}} - 436\hat{\mathbf{j}}\right)\times10^{-3} \text{ N} = \boxed{\left(36.0\hat{\mathbf{i}} - 436\hat{\mathbf{j}}\right) \text{ mN}}$$

P23.19 (a)

$$\mathbf{E}_1 = \frac{k_e|q_1|}{r_1^2}\left(-\hat{\mathbf{j}}\right) = \frac{\left(8.99\times10^9\right)\left(3.00\times10^{-9}\right)}{(0.100)^2}\left(-\hat{\mathbf{j}}\right) = -\left(2.70\times10^3 \text{ N/C}\right)\hat{\mathbf{j}}$$

$$\mathbf{E}_2 = \frac{k_e|q_2|}{r_2^2}\left(-\hat{\mathbf{i}}\right) = \frac{\left(8.99\times10^9\right)\left(6.00\times10^{-9}\right)}{(0.300)^2}\left(-\hat{\mathbf{i}}\right) = -\left(5.99\times10^2 \text{ N/C}\right)\hat{\mathbf{i}}$$

$$\mathbf{E} = \mathbf{E}_2 + \mathbf{E}_1 = \boxed{-\left(5.99\times10^2 \text{ N/C}\right)\hat{\mathbf{i}} - \left(2.70\times10^3 \text{ N/C}\right)\hat{\mathbf{j}}}$$

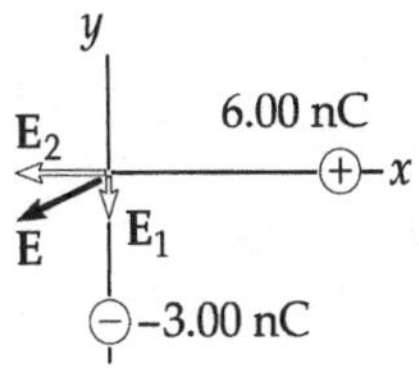

FIG. P23.19

(b)

$$\mathbf{F} = q\mathbf{E} = \left(5.00\times10^{-9} \text{ C}\right)\left(-599\hat{\mathbf{i}} - 2\,700\hat{\mathbf{j}}\right) \text{ N/C}$$

$$\mathbf{F} = \left(-3.00\times10^{-6}\hat{\mathbf{i}} - 13.5\times10^{-6}\hat{\mathbf{j}}\right) \text{ N} = \boxed{\left(-3.00\hat{\mathbf{i}} - 13.5\hat{\mathbf{j}}\right) \mu\text{N}}$$

P23.20 (a) $E = \frac{k_e q}{r^2} = \frac{(8.99 \times 10^9)(2.00 \times 10^{-6})}{(1.12)^2} = 14\,400 \text{ N/C}$

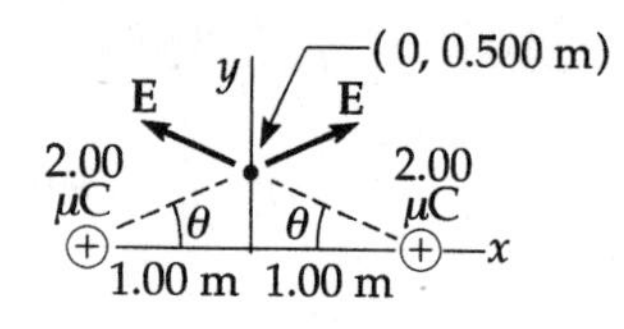

FIG. P23.20

$E_x = 0$ and $E_y = 2(14\,400)\sin 26.6° = 1.29 \times 10^4 \text{ N/C}$

so $\boxed{\mathbf{E} = 1.29 \times 10^4 \hat{\mathbf{j}} \text{ N/C}}$.

(b) $\mathbf{F} = q\mathbf{E} = (-3.00 \times 10^{-6})(1.29 \times 10^4 \hat{\mathbf{j}}) = \boxed{-3.86 \times 10^{-2} \hat{\mathbf{j}} \text{ N}}$

P23.21 (a) $\mathbf{E} = \frac{k_e q_1}{r_1^2}\hat{\mathbf{r}}_1 + \frac{k_e q_2}{r_2^2}\hat{\mathbf{r}}_2 + \frac{k_e q_3}{r_3^2}\hat{\mathbf{r}}_3 = \frac{k_e(2q)}{a^2}\hat{\mathbf{i}} + \frac{k_e(3q)}{2a^2}(\hat{\mathbf{i}}\cos 45.0° + \hat{\mathbf{j}}\sin 45.0°) + \frac{k_e(4q)}{a^2}\hat{\mathbf{j}}$

$\mathbf{E} = 3.06\frac{k_e q}{a^2}\hat{\mathbf{i}} + 5.06\frac{k_e q}{a^2}\hat{\mathbf{j}} = \boxed{5.91\frac{k_e q}{a^2} \text{ at } 58.8°}$

(b) $\mathbf{F} = q\mathbf{E} = \boxed{5.91\frac{k_e q^2}{a^2} \text{ at } 58.8°}$

P23.22 The electric field at any point x is

$$E = \frac{k_e q}{(x-a)^2} - \frac{k_e q}{(x-(-a))^2} = \frac{k_e q(4ax)}{(x^2 - a^2)^2}.$$

When x is much, much greater than a, we find $E \cong \boxed{\frac{4a(k_e q)}{x^3}}$.

P23.23 (a) One of the charges creates at P a field $\mathbf{E} = \frac{k_e Q/n}{R^2 + x^2}$ at an angle θ to the x-axis as shown.

When all the charges produce field, for $n > 1$, the components perpendicular to the x-axis add to zero.

The total field is $\frac{nk_e(Q/n)\hat{\mathbf{i}}}{R^2 + x^2}\cos\theta = \boxed{\frac{k_e Q x \hat{\mathbf{i}}}{(R^2 + x^2)^{3/2}}}$.

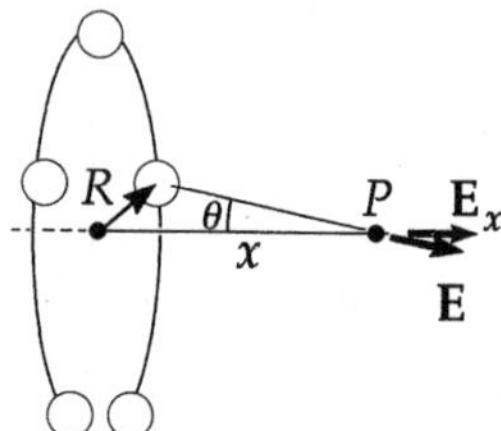

FIG. P23.23

(b) A circle of charge corresponds to letting n grow beyond all bounds, but the result does not depend on n. Smearing the charge around the circle does not change its amount or its distance from the field point, so it $\boxed{\text{does not change the field}}$.

P23.24 $\mathbf{E} = \sum \frac{k_e q}{r^2}\hat{\mathbf{r}} = \frac{k_e q}{a^2}(-\hat{\mathbf{i}}) + \frac{k_e q}{(2a)^2}(-\hat{\mathbf{i}}) + \frac{k_e q}{(3a)^2}(-\hat{\mathbf{i}}) + \ldots = \frac{-k_e q\hat{\mathbf{i}}}{a^2}\left(1 + \frac{1}{2^2} + \frac{1}{3^2} + \ldots\right) = \boxed{-\frac{\pi^2 k_e q}{6a^2}\hat{\mathbf{i}}}$

Section 23.5 **Electric Field of a Continuous Charge Distribution**

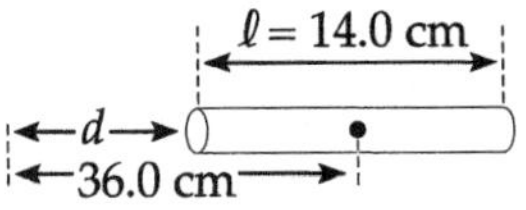

P23.25 $E = \frac{k_e \lambda \ell}{d(\ell + d)} = \frac{k_e (Q/\ell)\ell}{d(\ell + d)} = \frac{k_e Q}{d(\ell + d)} = \frac{(8.99 \times 10^9)(22.0 \times 10^{-6})}{(0.290)(0.140 + 0.290)}$

$\mathbf{E} = \boxed{1.59 \times 10^6 \text{ N/C, directed toward the rod.}}$

$\ell = 14.0$ cm
d
36.0 cm

FIG. P23.25

P23.26 $E = \int \frac{k_e dq}{x^2}$, where $dq = \lambda_0 dx$

$E = k_e \lambda_0 \int_{x_0}^{\infty} \frac{dx}{x^2} = k_e \lambda_0 \left(-\frac{1}{x} \right) \bigg|_{x_0}^{\infty} = \boxed{\frac{k_e \lambda_0}{x_0}}$ $\boxed{\text{The direction is } -\hat{\mathbf{i}} \text{ or left for } \lambda_0 > 0}$

P23.27 $E = \frac{k_e x Q}{\left(x^2 + a^2\right)^{3/2}} = \frac{(8.99 \times 10^9)(75.0 \times 10^{-6})x}{\left(x^2 + 0.100^2\right)^{3/2}} = \frac{6.74 \times 10^5 x}{\left(x^2 + 0.010\,0\right)^{3/2}}$

(a) At $x = 0.010\,0$ m, $\mathbf{E} = 6.64 \times 10^6 \hat{\mathbf{i}}$ N/C $= \boxed{6.64\hat{\mathbf{i}} \text{ MN/C}}$

(b) At $x = 0.050\,0$ m, $\mathbf{E} = 2.41 \times 10^7 \hat{\mathbf{i}}$ N/C $= \boxed{24.1\hat{\mathbf{i}} \text{ MN/C}}$

(c) At $x = 0.300$ m, $\mathbf{E} = 6.40 \times 10^6 \hat{\mathbf{i}}$ N/C $= \boxed{6.40\hat{\mathbf{i}} \text{ MN/C}}$

(d) At $x = 1.00$ m, $\mathbf{E} = 6.64 \times 10^5 \hat{\mathbf{i}}$ N/C $= \boxed{0.664\hat{\mathbf{i}} \text{ MN/C}}$

P23.28 $\mathbf{E} = \int d\mathbf{E} = \int_{x_0}^{\infty} \left[\frac{k_e \lambda_0 x_0 dx(-\hat{\mathbf{i}})}{x^3} \right] = -k_e \lambda_0 x_0 \hat{\mathbf{i}} \int_{x_0}^{\infty} x^{-3} dx = -k_e \lambda_0 x_0 \hat{\mathbf{i}} \left(-\frac{1}{2x^2} \bigg|_{x_0}^{\infty} \right) = \boxed{\frac{k_e \lambda_0}{2x_0} \left(-\hat{\mathbf{i}} \right)}$

P23.29 $E = \frac{k_e Q x}{\left(x^2 + a^2\right)^{3/2}}$

For a maximum, $\frac{dE}{dx} = Qk_e \left[\frac{1}{\left(x^2 + a^2\right)^{3/2}} - \frac{3x^2}{\left(x^2 + a^2\right)^{5/2}} \right] = 0$

$x^2 + a^2 - 3x^2 = 0$ or $x = \frac{a}{\sqrt{2}}$.

Substituting into the expression for E gives

$E = \frac{k_e Q a}{\sqrt{2}\left(\frac{3}{2} a^2\right)^{3/2}} = \frac{k_e Q}{3 \frac{\sqrt{3}}{2} a^2} = \boxed{\frac{2k_e Q}{3\sqrt{3} a^2}} = \boxed{\frac{Q}{6\sqrt{3}\pi \in_0 a^2}}$.

P23.30 $E = 2\pi k_e \sigma \left(1 - \frac{x}{\sqrt{x^2 + R^2}}\right)$

$$E = 2\pi\left(8.99\times10^9\right)\left(7.90\times10^{-3}\right)\left(1 - \frac{x}{\sqrt{x^2 + (0.350)^2}}\right) = 4.46\times10^8\left(1 - \frac{x}{\sqrt{x^2 + 0.123}}\right)$$

(a) At $x = 0.050\,0$ m, $E = 3.83\times10^8$ N/C $=$ $\boxed{383 \text{ MN/C}}$

(b) At $x = 0.100$ m, $E = 3.24\times10^8$ N/C $=$ $\boxed{324 \text{ MN/C}}$

(c) At $x = 0.500$ m, $E = 8.07\times10^7$ N/C $=$ $\boxed{80.7 \text{ MN/C}}$

(d) At $x = 2.00$ m, $E = 6.68\times10^8$ N/C $=$ $\boxed{6.68 \text{ MN/C}}$

P23.31 (a) From Example 23.9: $E = 2\pi k_e \sigma \left(1 - \frac{x}{\sqrt{x^2 + R^2}}\right)$

$\sigma = \frac{Q}{\pi R^2} = 1.84\times10^{-3}\ \text{C/m}^2$

$E = \left(1.04\times10^8 \text{ N/C}\right)(0.900) = 9.36\times10^7 \text{ N/C} = \boxed{93.6 \text{ MN/C}}$

appx: $E = 2\pi k_e \sigma =$ $\boxed{104 \text{ MN/C (about 11\% high)}}$

(b) $E = \left(1.04\times10^8 \text{ N/C}\right)\left(1 - \frac{30.0 \text{ cm}}{\sqrt{30.0^2 + 3.00^2} \text{ cm}}\right) = \left(1.04\times10^8 \text{ N/C}\right)(0.004\,96) = \boxed{0.516 \text{ MN/C}}$

appx: $E = k_e \frac{Q}{r^2} = \left(8.99\times10^9\right)\frac{5.20\times10^{-6}}{(0.30)^2} =$ $\boxed{0.519 \text{ MN/C (about 0.6\% high)}}$

P23.32 The electric field at a distance x is $E_x = 2\pi k_e \sigma \left[1 - \frac{x}{\sqrt{x^2 + R^2}}\right]$

This is equivalent to $E_x = 2\pi k_e \sigma \left[1 - \frac{1}{\sqrt{1 + R^2/x^2}}\right]$

For large x, $\frac{R^2}{x^2} << 1$ and $\sqrt{1 + \frac{R^2}{x^2}} \approx 1 + \frac{R^2}{2x^2}$

so $E_x = 2\pi k_e \sigma \left(1 - \frac{1}{\left[1 + R^2/\left(2x^2\right)\right]}\right) = 2\pi k_e \sigma \frac{\left(1 + R^2/\left(2x^2\right) - 1\right)}{\left[1 + R^2/\left(2x^2\right)\right]}$

Substitute $\sigma = \frac{Q}{\pi R^2}$, $E_x = \frac{k_e Q\left(1/x^2\right)}{\left[1 + R^2/\left(2x^2\right)\right]} = k_e Q\left(x^2 + \frac{R^2}{2}\right)$

But for $x >> R$, $\frac{1}{x^2 + R^2/2} \approx \frac{1}{x^2}$, so $\boxed{E_x \approx \frac{k_e Q}{x^2} \text{ for a disk at large distances}}$

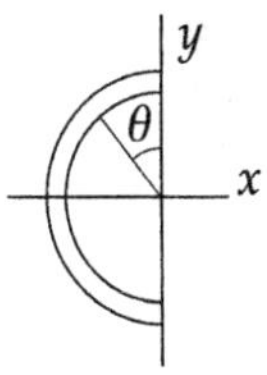

P23.33 Due to symmetry $E_y = \int dE_y = 0$, and $E_x = \int dE \sin\theta = k_e \int \frac{dq \sin\theta}{r^2}$

where $dq = \lambda ds = \lambda r d\theta$,

so that, $E_x = \frac{k_e \lambda}{r} \int_0^{\pi} \sin\theta d\theta = \frac{k_e \lambda}{r}(-\cos\theta)\Big|_0^{\pi} = \frac{2k_e \lambda}{r}$

where $\lambda = \frac{q}{L}$ and $r = \frac{L}{\pi}$.

Thus, $E_x = \frac{2k_e q \pi}{L^2} = \frac{2(8.99 \times 10^9 \text{ N}\cdot\text{m}^2/\text{C}^2)(7.50 \times 10^{-6} \text{ C})\pi}{(0.140 \text{ m})^2}$.

Solving, $E_x = 2.16 \times 10^7$ N/C.

Since the rod has a negative charge, $\mathbf{E} = (-2.16 \times 10^7 \hat{\mathbf{i}})$ N/C $= \boxed{-21.6\hat{\mathbf{i}} \text{ MN/C}}$.

FIG. P23.33

P23.34 (a) We define $x = 0$ at the point where we are to find the field. One ring, with thickness *dx*, has charge $\frac{Qdx}{h}$ and produces, at the chosen point, a field

$$d\mathbf{E} = \frac{k_e x}{(x^2 + R^2)^{3/2}} \frac{Qdx}{h} \hat{\mathbf{i}}.$$

The total field is

$$\mathbf{E} = \int_{\text{all charge}} d\mathbf{E} = \int_d^{d+h} \frac{k_e Q x dx}{h(x^2 + R^2)^{3/2}} \hat{\mathbf{i}} = \frac{k_e Q \hat{\mathbf{i}}}{2h} \int_{x=d}^{d+h} (x^2 + R^2)^{-3/2} 2x dx$$

$$\mathbf{E} = \frac{k_e Q \hat{\mathbf{i}}}{2h} \frac{(x^2 + R^2)^{-1/2}}{(-1/2)}\Bigg|_{x=d}^{d+h} = \boxed{\frac{k_e Q \hat{\mathbf{i}}}{h}\left[\frac{1}{(d^2 + R^2)^{1/2}} - \frac{1}{((d+h)^2 + R^2)^{1/2}}\right]}$$

(b) Think of the cylinder as a stack of disks, each with thickness *dx*, charge $\frac{Qdx}{h}$, and charge-per-area $\sigma = \frac{Qdx}{\pi R^2 h}$. One disk produces a field

$$d\mathbf{E} = \frac{2\pi k_e Q dx}{\pi R^2 h}\left(1 - \frac{x}{(x^2 + R^2)^{1/2}}\right)\hat{\mathbf{i}}.$$

So, $$\mathbf{E} = \int_{\text{all charge}} d\mathbf{E} = \int_{x=d}^{d+h} \frac{2k_e Q dx}{R^2 h}\left(1 - \frac{x}{(x^2 + R^2)^{1/2}}\right)\hat{\mathbf{i}}$$

$$\mathbf{E} = \frac{2k_e Q \hat{\mathbf{i}}}{R^2 h}\left[\int_d^{d+h} dx - \frac{1}{2}\int_{x=d}^{d+h} (x^2 + R^2)^{-1/2} 2x dx\right] = \frac{2k_e Q \hat{\mathbf{i}}}{R^2 h}\left[x\Big|_d^{d+h} - \frac{1}{2}\frac{(x^2 + R^2)^{1/2}}{1/2}\Bigg|_d^{d+h}\right]$$

$$\mathbf{E} = \frac{2k_e Q \hat{\mathbf{i}}}{R^2 h}\left[d + h - d - ((d+h)^2 + R^2)^{1/2} + (d^2 + R^2)^{1/2}\right]$$

$$\mathbf{E} = \boxed{\frac{2k_e Q \hat{\mathbf{i}}}{R^2 h}\left[h + (d^2 + R^2)^{1/2} - ((d+h)^2 + R^2)^{1/2}\right]}$$

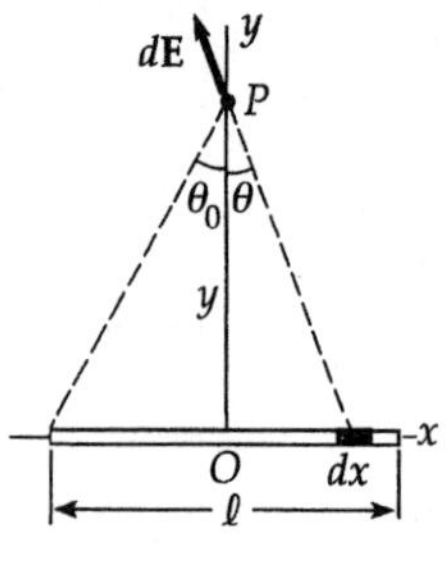

FIG. P23.35

P23.35 (a) The electric field at point P due to each element of length dx, is $dE = \frac{k_e dq}{x^2 + y^2}$ and is directed along the line joining the element to point P. By symmetry,

$E_x = \int dE_x = 0$ and since $dq = \lambda dx$,

$E = E_y = \int dE_y = \int dE\cos\theta$ where $\cos\theta = \frac{y}{\sqrt{x^2 + y^2}}$.

Therefore, $E = 2k_e\lambda y \int_0^{\ell/2} \frac{dx}{\left(x^2 + y^2\right)^{3/2}} = \boxed{\frac{2k_e\lambda\sin\theta_0}{y}}$.

(b) For a bar of infinite length, $\theta_0 = 90°$ and $E_y = \boxed{\frac{2k_e\lambda}{y}}$.

P23.36 (a) The whole surface area of the cylinder is $A = 2\pi r^2 + 2\pi rL = 2\pi r(r + L)$.

$Q = \sigma A = \left(15.0\times10^{-9}\ \text{C/m}^2\right)2\pi(0.025\,0\ \text{m})\left[0.025\,0\ \text{m} + 0.060\,0\ \text{m}\right] = \boxed{2.00\times10^{-10}\ \text{C}}$

(b) For the curved lateral surface only, $A = 2\pi rL$.

$Q = \sigma A = \left(15.0\times10^{-9}\ \text{C/m}^2\right)\left[2\pi(0.025\,0\ \text{m})(0.060\,0\ \text{m})\right] = \boxed{1.41\times10^{-10}\ \text{C}}$

(c) $Q = \rho V = \rho\pi r^2 L = \left(500\times10^{-9}\ \text{C/m}^3\right)\left[\pi(0.025\,0\ \text{m})^2(0.060\,0\ \text{m})\right] = \boxed{5.89\times10^{-11}\ \text{C}}$

P23.37 (a) Every object has the same volume, $V = 8(0.030\,0\ \text{m})^3 = 2.16\times10^{-4}\ \text{m}^3$.

For each, $Q = \rho V = \left(400\times10^{-9}\ \text{C/m}^3\right)\left(2.16\times10^{-4}\ \text{m}^3\right) = \boxed{8.64\times10^{-11}\ \text{C}}$

(b) We must count the $9.00\ \text{cm}^2$ squares painted with charge:

(i) $6\times4 = 24$ squares

$Q = \sigma A = \left(15.0\times10^{-9}\ \text{C/m}^2\right)24.0\left(9.00\times10^{-4}\ \text{m}^2\right) = \boxed{3.24\times10^{-10}\ \text{C}}$

(ii) 34 squares exposed

$Q = \sigma A = \left(15.0\times10^{-9}\ \text{C/m}^2\right)34.0\left(9.00\times10^{-4}\ \text{m}^2\right) = \boxed{4.59\times10^{-10}\ \text{C}}$

(iii) 34 squares

$Q = \sigma A = \left(15.0\times10^{-9}\ \text{C/m}^2\right)34.0\left(9.00\times10^{-4}\ \text{m}^2\right) = \boxed{4.59\times10^{-10}\ \text{C}}$

(iv) 32 squares

$Q = \sigma A = \left(15.0\times10^{-9}\ \text{C/m}^2\right)32.0\left(9.00\times10^{-4}\ \text{m}^2\right) = \boxed{4.32\times10^{-10}\ \text{C}}$

(c) (i) total edge length: $\ell = 24\times(0.030\,0\ \text{m})$

$Q = \lambda\ell = \left(80.0\times10^{-12}\ \text{C/m}\right)24\times(0.030\,0\ \text{m}) = \boxed{5.76\times10^{-11}\ \text{C}}$

(ii) $Q = \lambda\ell = \left(80.0\times10^{-12}\ \text{C/m}\right)44\times(0.030\,0\ \text{m}) = \boxed{1.06\times10^{-10}\ \text{C}}$

continued on next page

(iii) $Q = \lambda\ell = \left(80.0\times10^{-12}\text{ C/m}\right)64\times(0.030\,0\text{ m}) = \boxed{1.54\times10^{-10}\text{ C}}$

(iv) $Q = \lambda\ell = \left(80.0\times10^{-12}\text{ C/m}\right)40\times(0.030\,0\text{ m}) = \boxed{0.960\times10^{-10}\text{ C}}$

Section 23.6 **Electric Field Lines**

P23.38

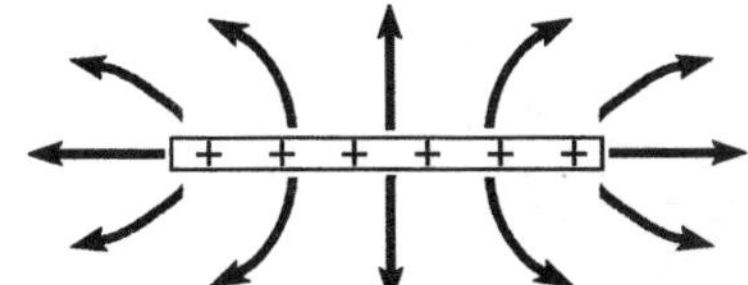

FIG. P23.38

P23.39

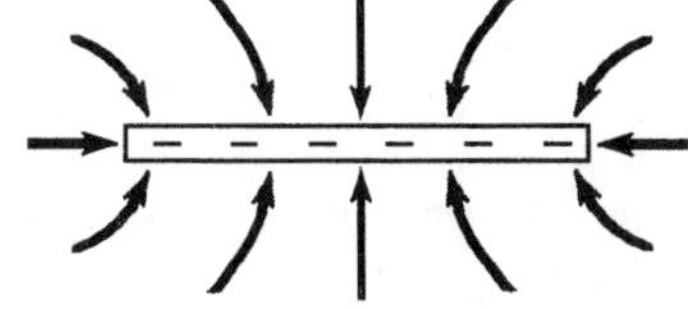

FIG. P23.39

P23.40 (a) $\dfrac{q_1}{q_2} = \dfrac{-6}{18} = \boxed{-\dfrac{1}{3}}$

(b) $\boxed{q_1 \text{ is negative, } q_2 \text{ is positive}}$

P23.41 (a) The electric field has the general appearance shown. It is zero $\boxed{\text{at the center}}$, where (by symmetry) one can see that the three charges individually produce fields that cancel out.

In addition to the center of the triangle, the electric field lines in the second figure to the right indicate three other points near the middle of each leg of the triangle where $E = 0$, but they are more difficult to find mathematically.

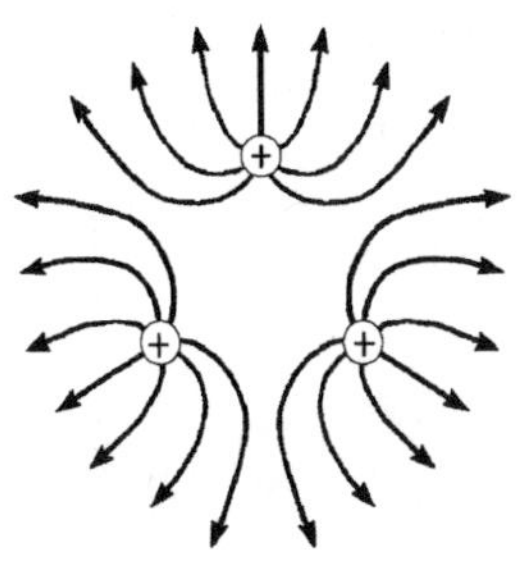

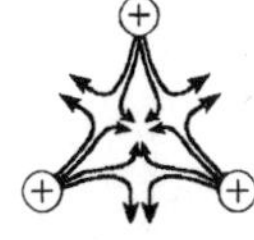

(b) You may need to review vector addition in Chapter Three. The electric field at point P can be found by adding the electric field vectors due to each of the two lower point charges: $\mathbf{E} = \mathbf{E}_1 + \mathbf{E}_2$.

The electric field from a point charge is $\mathbf{E} = k_e \dfrac{q}{r^2}\hat{\mathbf{r}}$.

As shown in the solution figure at right,

$\mathbf{E}_1 = k_e \dfrac{q}{a^2}$ to the right and upward at 60°

$\mathbf{E}_2 = k_e \dfrac{q}{a^2}$ to the left and upward at 60°

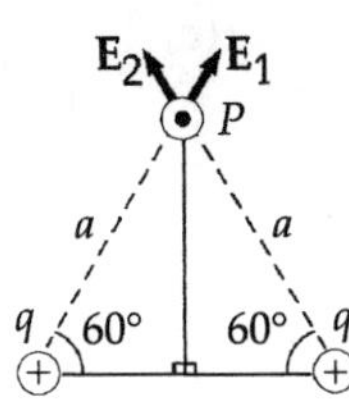

FIG. P23.41

$$\mathbf{E} = \mathbf{E}_1 + \mathbf{E}_2 = k_e \frac{q}{a^2}\left[\left(\cos 60°\,\hat{\mathbf{i}} + \sin 60°\,\hat{\mathbf{j}}\right) + \left(-\cos 60°\,\hat{\mathbf{i}} + \sin 60°\,\hat{\mathbf{j}}\right)\right] = k_e \frac{q}{a^2}\left[2\left(\sin 60°\,\hat{\mathbf{j}}\right)\right]$$

$$= \boxed{1.73 k_e \frac{q}{a^2}\hat{\mathbf{j}}}$$

Section 23.7 Motion of Charged Particles in a Uniform Electric Field

P23.42 $F = qE = ma \qquad a = \frac{qE}{m}$

$v_f = v_i + at \qquad v_f = \frac{qEt}{m}$

electron: $v_e = \frac{(1.602\times10^{-19})(520)(48.0\times10^{-9})}{9.11\times10^{-31}} = \boxed{4.39\times10^{6}\text{ m/s}}$

in a direction opposite to the field

proton: $v_p = \frac{(1.602\times10^{-19})(520)(48.0\times10^{-9})}{1.67\times10^{-27}} = \boxed{2.39\times10^{3}\text{ m/s}}$

in the same direction as the field

P23.43 (a) $a = \frac{qE}{m} = \frac{1.602\times10^{-19}(640)}{1.67\times10^{-27}} = \boxed{6.14\times10^{10}\text{ m/s}^2}$

(b) $v_f = v_i + at \qquad 1.20\times10^{6} = (6.14\times10^{10})t \qquad t = \boxed{1.95\times10^{-5}\text{ s}}$

(c) $x_f - x_i = \frac{1}{2}(v_i + v_f)t \qquad x_f = \frac{1}{2}(1.20\times10^{6})(1.95\times10^{-5}) = \boxed{11.7\text{ m}}$

(d) $K = \frac{1}{2}mv^2 = \frac{1}{2}(1.67\times10^{-27}\text{ kg})(1.20\times10^{6}\text{ m/s})^2 = \boxed{1.20\times10^{-15}\text{ J}}$

P23.44 (a) $|a| = \frac{qE}{m} = \frac{(1.602\times10^{-19})(6.00\times10^{5})}{(1.67\times10^{-27})} = 5.76\times10^{13}\text{ m/s so } \mathbf{a} = \boxed{-5.76\times10^{13}\hat{\mathbf{i}}\text{ m/s}^2}$

(b) $v_f = v_i + 2a(x_f - x_i)$

$0 = v_i^2 + 2(-5.76\times10^{13})(0.0700) \qquad \boxed{\mathbf{v}_i = 2.84\times10^{6}\hat{\mathbf{i}}\text{ m/s}}$

(c) $v_f = v_i + at$

$0 = 2.84\times10^{6} + (-5.76\times10^{13})t \qquad t = \boxed{4.93\times10^{-8}\text{ s}}$

P23.45 The required electric field will be $\boxed{\text{in the direction of motion}}$.

Work done $= \Delta K$

so, $-Fd = -\frac{1}{2}mv_i^2$ (since the final velocity $= 0$)

which becomes $eEd = K$

and $E = \boxed{\frac{K}{ed}}$.

P23.46 The acceleration is given by

$v_f^2 = v_i^2 + 2a(x_f - x_i)$ or $v_f^2 = 0 + 2a(-h)$.

Solving $a = -\dfrac{v_f^2}{2h}$.

Now $\sum \mathbf{F} = m\mathbf{a}: \quad -mg\hat{\mathbf{j}} + q\mathbf{E} = -\dfrac{mv_f^2\hat{\mathbf{j}}}{2h}$.

Therefore $q\mathbf{E} = \left(-\dfrac{mv_f^2}{2h} + mg\right)\hat{\mathbf{j}}$.

(a) Gravity alone would give the bead downward impact velocity

$$\sqrt{2(9.80 \text{ m/s}^2)(5.00 \text{ m})} = 9.90 \text{ m/s}.$$

To change this to 21.0 m/s down, a $\boxed{\text{downward}}$ electric field must exert a downward electric force.

(b) $$q = \frac{m}{E}\left(\frac{v_f^2}{2h} - g\right) = \frac{1.00 \times 10^{-3} \text{ kg}}{1.00 \times 10^4 \text{ N/C}}\left(\frac{\text{N} \cdot \text{s}^2}{\text{kg} \cdot \text{m}}\right)\left[\frac{(21.0 \text{ m/s})^2}{2(5.00 \text{ m})} - 9.80 \text{ m/s}^2\right] = \boxed{3.43\ \mu\text{C}}$$

P23.47 (a) $$t = \frac{x}{v_x} = \frac{0.050\,0}{4.50 \times 10^5} = 1.11 \times 10^{-7} \text{ s} = \boxed{111 \text{ ns}}$$

(b) $$a_y = \frac{qE}{m} = \frac{(1.602 \times 10^{-19})(9.60 \times 10^3)}{(1.67 \times 10^{-27})} = 9.21 \times 10^{11} \text{ m/s}^2$$

$y_f - y_i = v_{yi}t + \dfrac{1}{2}a_y t^2$: $\quad y_f = \dfrac{1}{2}(9.21 \times 10^{11})(1.11 \times 10^{-7})^2 = 5.68 \times 10^{-3} \text{ m} = \boxed{5.68 \text{ mm}}$

(c) $v_x = \boxed{4.50 \times 10^5 \text{ m/s}}$ $\quad v_{yf} = v_{yi} + a_y t = (9.21 \times 10^{11})(1.11 \times 10^{-7}) = \boxed{1.02 \times 10^5 \text{ m/s}}$

***P23.48** The particle feels a constant force: $\mathbf{F} = q\mathbf{E} = (1 \times 10^{-6} \text{ C})(2\,000 \text{ N/C})(-\hat{\mathbf{j}}) = 2 \times 10^{-3} \text{ N}(-\hat{\mathbf{j}})$

and moves with acceleration: $$\mathbf{a} = \frac{\sum \mathbf{F}}{m} = \frac{(2 \times 10^{-3} \text{ kg} \cdot \text{m/s}^2)(-\hat{\mathbf{j}})}{2 \times 10^{-16} \text{ kg}} = (1 \times 10^{13} \text{ m/s}^2)(-\hat{\mathbf{j}}).$$

Its x-component of velocity is constant at $(1.00 \times 10^5 \text{ m/s})\cos 37° = 7.99 \times 10^4 \text{ m/s}$. Thus it moves in a parabola opening downward. The maximum height it attains above the bottom plate is described by

$v_{yf}^2 = v_{yi}^2 + 2a_y(y_f - y_i)$: $\quad 0 = (6.02 \times 10^4 \text{ m/s})^2 - (2 \times 10^{13} \text{ m/s}^2)(y_f - 0)$

$$y_f = 1.81 \times 10^{-4} \text{ m}.$$

continued on next page

Since this is less than 10 mm, the particle does not strike the top plate, but moves in a symmetric parabola and strikes the bottom plate after a time given by

$y_f = y_i + v_{yi}t + \frac{1}{2}a_y t^2$ $\quad 0 = 0 + (6.02\times10^4 \text{ m/s})t + \frac{1}{2}(-1\times10^{13} \text{ m/s}^2)t^2$

since $t > 0$, $\quad t = 1.20\times10^{-8}$ s.

The particle's range is $\quad x_f = x_i + v_x t = 0 + (7.99\times10^4 \text{ m/s})(1.20\times10^{-8} \text{ s}) = 9.61\times10^{-4}$ m.

In sum,

The particle strikes the negative plate after moving in a parabola with a height of 0.181 mm and a width of 0.961 mm.

P23.49 $v_i = 9.55\times10^3$ m/s

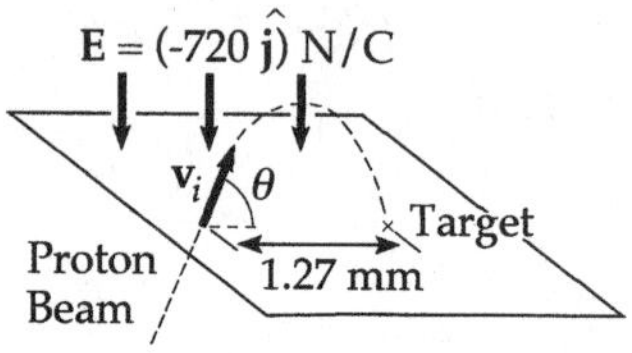

Target

E = (-720 ĵ) N/C

v_i θ

Proton Beam

1.27 mm

FIG. P23.49

(a) $a_y = \frac{eE}{m} = \frac{(1.60\times10^{-19})(720)}{(1.67\times10^{-27})} = 6.90\times10^{10} \text{ m/s}^2$

$R = \frac{v_i^2 \sin 2\theta}{a_y} = 1.27\times10^{-3}$ m so that

$$\frac{(9.55\times10^3)^2 \sin 2\theta}{6.90\times10^{10}} = 1.27\times10^{-3}$$

$\sin 2\theta = 0.961$ $\quad \theta = \boxed{36.9°}$ $\quad 90.0° - \theta = \boxed{53.1°}$

(b) $t = \frac{R}{v_{ix}} = \frac{R}{v_i \cos\theta}$ $\quad$ If $\theta = 36.9°$, $t = \boxed{167 \text{ ns}}$. $\quad$ If $\theta = 53.1°$, $t = \boxed{221 \text{ ns}}$.

Additional Problems

***P23.50** The two given charges exert equal-size forces of attraction on each other. If a third charge, positive or negative, were placed between them they could not be in equilibrium. If the third charge were at a point $x > 15$ cm, it would exert a stronger force on the 45 μC than on the -12 μC, and could not produce equilibrium for both. Thus the third charge must be at $x = -d < 0$. Its equilibrium requires

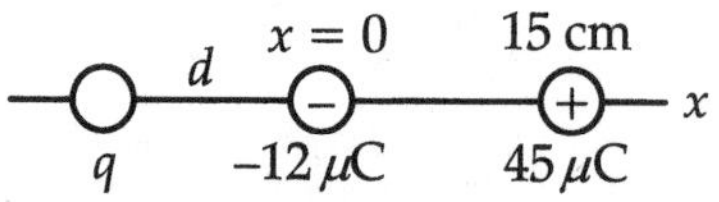

FIG. P23.50

$\frac{k_e q(12\ \mu\text{C})}{d^2} = \frac{k_e q(45\ \mu\text{C})}{(15 \text{ cm} + d)^2}$ $\quad \left(\frac{15 \text{ cm} + d}{d}\right)^2 = \frac{45}{12} = 3.75$

$15 \text{ cm} + d = 1.94d$ $\quad d = 16.0$ cm.

The third charge is at $\boxed{x = -16.0 \text{ cm}}$. The equilibrium of the -12 μC requires

$\frac{k_e q(12\ \mu\text{C})}{(16.0 \text{ cm})^2} = \frac{k_e(45\ \mu\text{C})12\ \mu\text{C}}{(15 \text{ cm})^2}$ $\quad \boxed{q = 51.3\ \mu\text{C}}$.

All six individual forces are now equal in magnitude, so we have equilibrium as required, and this is the only solution.

P23.51 The proton moves with acceleration $\left|a_p\right| = \dfrac{qE}{m} = \dfrac{\left(1.60\times10^{-19}\text{ C}\right)(640\text{ N/C})}{1.673\times10^{-27}\text{ kg}} = 6.13\times10^{10}\text{ m/s}^2$

while the e^- has acceleration $\left|a_e\right| = \dfrac{\left(1.60\times10^{-19}\text{ C}\right)(640\text{ N/C})}{9.110\times10^{-31}\text{ kg}} = 1.12\times10^{14}\text{ m/s}^2 = 1\,836a_p$.

(a) We want to find the distance traveled by the proton (i.e., $d = \frac{1}{2}a_pt^2$), knowing:

$$4.00\text{ cm} = \frac{1}{2}a_pt^2 + \frac{1}{2}a_et^2 = 1\,837\left(\frac{1}{2}a_pt^2\right).$$

Thus, $d = \dfrac{1}{2}a_pt^2 = \dfrac{4.00\text{ cm}}{1\,837} = \boxed{21.8\ \mu\text{m}}$.

(b) The distance from the positive plate to where the meeting occurs equals the distance the sodium ion travels (i.e., $d_{\text{Na}} = \frac{1}{2}a_{\text{Na}}t^2$). This is found from:

$4.00\text{ cm} = \frac{1}{2}a_{\text{Na}}t^2 + \frac{1}{2}a_{\text{Cl}}t^2$: $\quad 4.00\text{ cm} = \dfrac{1}{2}\left(\dfrac{eE}{22.99\text{ u}}\right)t^2 + \dfrac{1}{2}\left(\dfrac{eE}{35.45\text{ u}}\right)t^2$.

This may be written as $\quad 4.00\text{ cm} = \frac{1}{2}a_{\text{Na}}t^2 + \frac{1}{2}(0.649a_{\text{Na}})t^2 = 1.65\left(\frac{1}{2}a_{\text{Na}}t^2\right)$

so $\quad d_{\text{Na}} = \dfrac{1}{2}a_{\text{Na}}t^2 = \dfrac{4.00\text{ cm}}{1.65} = \boxed{2.43\text{ cm}}$.

P23.52 (a) The field, E_1, due to the 4.00×10^{-9} C charge is in the $-x$ direction.

$$\mathbf{E}_1 = \frac{k_eq}{r^2}\hat{\mathbf{r}} = \frac{\left(8.99\times10^9\text{ N}\cdot\text{m}^2/\text{C}^2\right)\left(-4.00\times10^{-9}\text{ C}\right)}{(2.50\text{ m})^2}\hat{\mathbf{i}}$$

$$= -5.75\hat{\mathbf{i}}\text{ N/C}$$

FIG. P23.52(a)

Likewise, E_2 and E_3, due to the 5.00×10^{-9} C charge and the 3.00×10^{-9} C charge are

$$\mathbf{E}_2 = \frac{k_eq}{r^2}\hat{\mathbf{r}} = \frac{\left(8.99\times10^9\text{ N}\cdot\text{m}^2/\text{C}^2\right)\left(5.00\times10^{-9}\text{ C}\right)}{(2.00\text{ m})^2}\hat{\mathbf{i}} = 11.2\text{ N/C }\hat{\mathbf{i}}$$

$$\mathbf{E}_3 = \frac{\left(8.99\times10^9\text{ N}\cdot\text{m}^2/\text{C}^2\right)\left(3.00\times10^{-9}\text{ C}\right)}{(1.20\text{ m})^2}\hat{\mathbf{i}} = 18.7\text{ N/C }\hat{\mathbf{i}}$$

$\mathbf{E}_R = \mathbf{E}_1 + \mathbf{E}_2 + \mathbf{E}_3 = \boxed{24.2\text{ N/C}}$ in $+x$ direction.

(b)

$$\mathbf{E}_1 = \frac{k_eq}{r^2}\hat{\mathbf{r}} = (-8.46\text{ N/C})\left(0.243\hat{\mathbf{i}} + 0.970\hat{\mathbf{j}}\right)$$

$$\mathbf{E}_2 = \frac{k_eq}{r^2}\hat{\mathbf{r}} = (11.2\text{ N/C})\left(+\hat{\mathbf{j}}\right)$$

$$\mathbf{E}_3 = \frac{k_eq}{r^2}\hat{\mathbf{r}} = (5.81\text{ N/C})\left(-0.371\hat{\mathbf{i}} + 0.928\hat{\mathbf{j}}\right)$$

$E_x = E_{1x} + E_{3x} = -4.21\hat{\mathbf{i}}\text{ N/C} \qquad E_y = E_{1y} + E_{2y} + E_{3y} = 8.43\hat{\mathbf{j}}\text{ N/C}$

$E_R = \boxed{9.42\text{ N/C}} \qquad \theta = \boxed{63.4°\text{ above } -x\text{ axis}}$

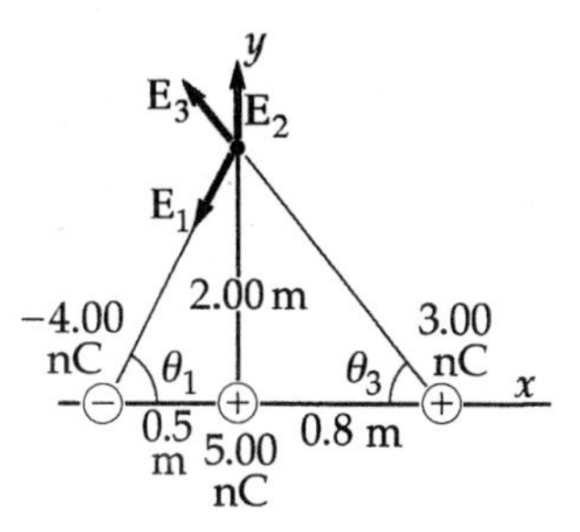

FIG. P23.52(b)

***P23.53** (a) Each ion moves in a quarter circle. The electric force causes the centripetal acceleration.

$$\sum F = ma \qquad qE = \frac{mv^2}{R} \qquad \boxed{E = \frac{mv^2}{qR}}$$

(b) For the x-motion, $v_{xf}^2 = v_{xi}^2 + 2a_x(x_f - x_i)$

$$0 = v^2 + 2a_x R \qquad a_x = -\frac{v^2}{2R} = \frac{F_x}{m} = \frac{qE_x}{m}$$

$E_x = -\dfrac{mv^2}{2qR}$. Similarly for the y-motion,

$$v^2 = 0 + 2a_y R \qquad a_y = +\frac{v^2}{2R} = \frac{qE_y}{m} \qquad E_y = \frac{mv^2}{2qR}$$

The magnitude of the field is

$$\sqrt{E_x^2 + E_y^2} = \boxed{\frac{mv^2}{\sqrt{2}qR} \text{ at } 135° \text{ counterclockwise from the } x\text{-axis}}.$$

P23.54 From the free-body diagram shown,

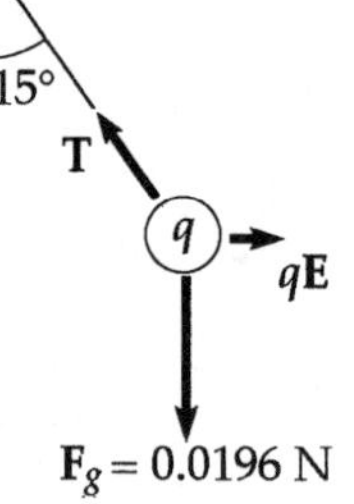

FIG. P23.54

$\sum F_y = 0$: $\qquad T\cos 15.0° = 1.96 \times 10^{-2}$ N.

So $\qquad T = 2.03 \times 10^{-2}$ N.

From $\sum F_x = 0$, we have $\qquad qE = T\sin 15.0°$

or $$q = \frac{T\sin 15.0°}{E} = \frac{\left(2.03 \times 10^{-2} \text{ N}\right)\sin 15.0°}{1.00 \times 10^3 \text{ N/C}} = 5.25 \times 10^{-6} \text{ C} = \boxed{5.25\ \mu\text{C}}.$$

P23.55 (a) Let us sum force components to find

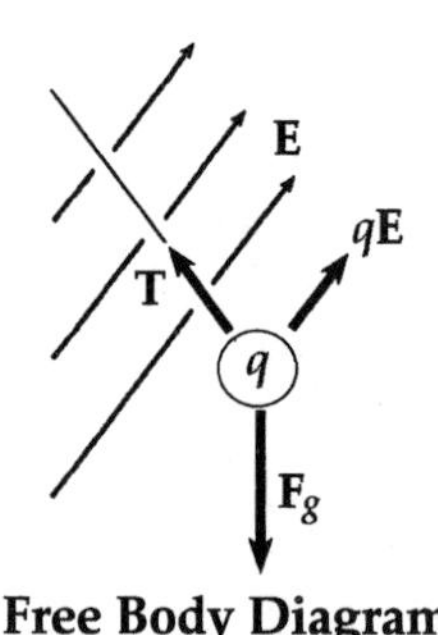

FIG. P23.55

$\sum F_x = qE_x - T\sin\theta = 0$, and $\sum F_y = qE_y + T\cos\theta - mg = 0$.

Combining these two equations, we get

$$q = \frac{mg}{\left(E_x \cot\theta + E_y\right)} = \frac{\left(1.00 \times 10^{-3}\right)(9.80)}{(3.00 \cot 37.0° + 5.00) \times 10^5} = 1.09 \times 10^{-8} \text{ C}$$
$$= \boxed{10.9 \text{ nC}}$$

(b) From the two equations for $\sum F_x$ and $\sum F_y$ we also find

$$T = \frac{qEx}{\sin 37.0°} = 5.44 \times 10^{-3} \text{ N} = \boxed{5.44 \text{ mN}}.$$

P23.56 This is the general version of the preceding problem. The known quantities are A, B, m, g, and θ. The unknowns are q and T.

The approach to this problem should be the same as for the last problem, but without numbers to substitute for the variables. Likewise, we can use the free body diagram given in the solution to problem 55.

Again, Newton's second law: $\sum F_x = -T\sin\theta + qA = 0$ (1)

and $\sum F_y = +T\cos\theta + qB - mg = 0$ (2)

(a) Substituting $T = \dfrac{qA}{\sin\theta}$, into Eq. (2), $\dfrac{qA\cos\theta}{\sin\theta} + qB = mg$.

Isolating q on the left, $\boxed{q = \dfrac{mg}{(A\cot\theta + B)}}$.

(b) Substituting this value into Eq. (1), $\boxed{T = \dfrac{mgA}{(A\cos\theta + B\sin\theta)}}$.

If we had solved this general problem first, we would only need to substitute the appropriate values in the equations for q and T to find the numerical results needed for problem 55. If you find this problem more difficult than problem 55, the little list at the first step is useful. It shows what symbols to think of as known data, and what to consider unknown. The list is a guide for deciding what to solve for in the analysis step, and for recognizing when we have an answer.

P23.57 $F = \dfrac{k_e q_1 q_2}{r^2}$: $\tan\theta = \dfrac{15.0}{60.0}$

$\theta = 14.0°$

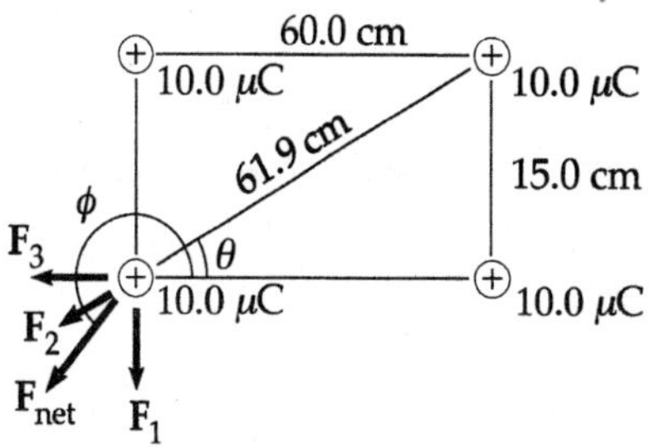

FIG. P23.57

$$F_1 = \frac{(8.99\times10^9)(10.0\times10^{-6})^2}{(0.150)^2} = 40.0\text{ N}$$

$$F_3 = \frac{(8.99\times10^9)(10.0\times10^{-6})^2}{(0.600)^2} = 2.50\text{ N}$$

$$F_2 = \frac{(8.99\times10^9)(10.0\times10^{-6})^2}{(0.619)^2} = 2.35\text{ N}$$

$$F_x = -F_3 - F_2\cos14.0° = -2.50 - 2.35\cos14.0° = -4.78\text{ N}$$

$$F_y = -F_1 - F_2\sin14.0° = -40.0 - 2.35\sin14.0° = -40.6\text{ N}$$

$$F_{net} = \sqrt{F_x^2 + F_y^2} = \sqrt{(4.78)^2 + (40.6)^2} = \boxed{40.9\text{ N}}$$

$$\tan\phi = \frac{F_y}{F_x} = \frac{-40.6}{-4.78}$$

$$\phi = \boxed{263°}$$

P23.58 From Figure A: $d\cos 30.0° = 15.0\text{ cm}$,

or $d = \dfrac{15.0\text{ cm}}{\cos 30.0°}$

From Figure B: $\theta = \sin^{-1}\left(\dfrac{d}{50.0\text{ cm}}\right)$

$$\theta = \sin^{-1}\left(\frac{15.0\text{ cm}}{50.0\text{ cm}(\cos 30.0°)}\right) = 20.3°$$

$$\frac{F_q}{mg} = \tan\theta$$

or $F_q = mg\tan 20.3°$ (1)

From Figure C: $F_q = 2F\cos 30.0°$

$$F_q = 2\left[\frac{k_e q^2}{(0.300\text{ m})^2}\right]\cos 30.0° \quad (2)$$

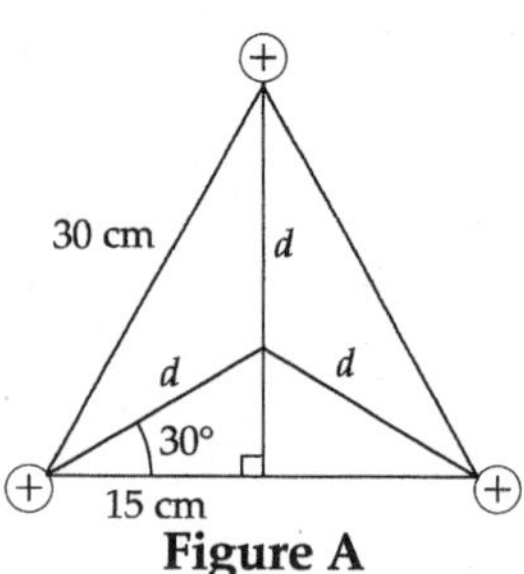

Figure A

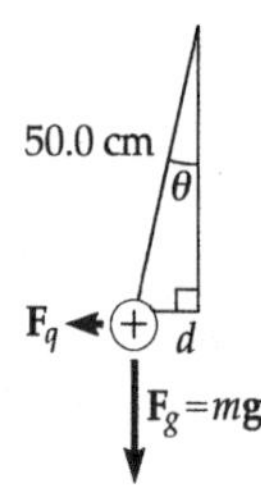

Figure B

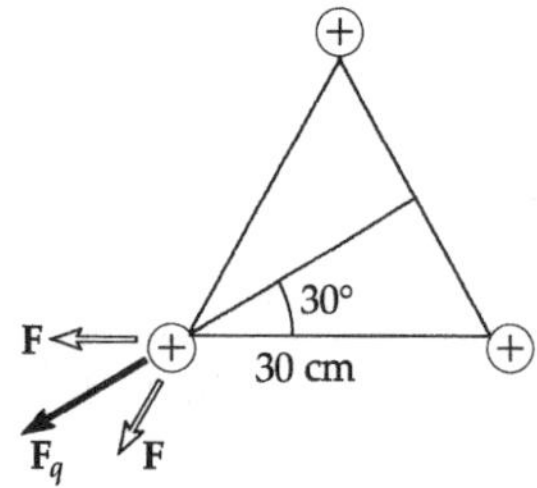

Figure C

FIG. P23.58

Combining equations (1) and (2),

$$2\left[\frac{k_e q^2}{(0.300\text{ m})^2}\right]\cos 30.0° = mg\tan 20.3°$$

$$q^2 = \frac{mg(0.300\text{ m})^2\tan 20.3°}{2k_e\cos 30.0°}$$

$$q^2 = \frac{\left(2.00\times10^{-3}\text{ kg}\right)\left(9.80\text{ m/s}^2\right)(0.300\text{ m})^2\tan 20.3°}{2\left(8.99\times10^9\text{ N}\cdot\text{m}^2/\text{C}^2\right)\cos 30.0°}$$

$$q = \sqrt{4.20\times10^{-14}\text{ C}^2} = 2.05\times10^{-7}\text{ C} = \boxed{0.205\ \mu\text{C}}$$

P23.59 Charge $\dfrac{Q}{2}$ resides on each block, which repel as point charges: $F = \dfrac{k_e(Q/2)(Q/2)}{L^2} = k(L - L_i)$.

Solving for Q, $Q = \boxed{2L\sqrt{\dfrac{k(L-L_i)}{k_e}}}$.

***P23.60** If we place one more charge q at the 29th vertex, the total force on the central charge will add up to zero: $\mathbf{F}_{28\text{ charges}} + \dfrac{k_e qQ}{a^2}$ away from vertex $29 = 0$ $\quad \mathbf{F}_{28\text{ charges}} = \boxed{\dfrac{k_e qQ}{a^2}\text{ toward vertex 29}}$.

P23.61 According to the result of Example 23.7, the left-hand rod creates this field at a distance d from its right-hand end:

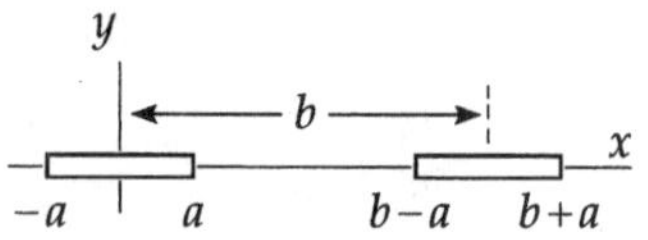

FIG. P23.61

$$E = \frac{k_e Q}{d(2a+d)}$$

$$dF = \frac{k_e QQ}{2a}\frac{dx}{d(d+2a)}$$

$$F = \frac{k_e Q^2}{2a}\int_{x=b-2a}^{b}\frac{dx}{x(x+2a)} = \frac{k_e Q^2}{2a}\left(-\frac{1}{2a}\ln\frac{2a+x}{x}\right)_{b-2a}^{b}$$

$$F = \frac{+k_e Q^2}{4a^2}\left(-\ln\frac{2a+b}{b} + \ln\frac{b}{b-2a}\right) = \frac{k_e Q^2}{4a^2}\ln\frac{b^2}{(b-2a)(b+2a)} = \boxed{\left(\frac{k_e Q^2}{4a^2}\right)\ln\left(\frac{b^2}{b^2-4a^2}\right)}$$

P23.62 At equilibrium, the distance between the charges is $r = 2(0.100 \text{ m})\sin 10.0° = 3.47 \times 10^{-2}$ m
Now consider the forces on the sphere with charge $+q$, and use $\sum F_y = 0$:

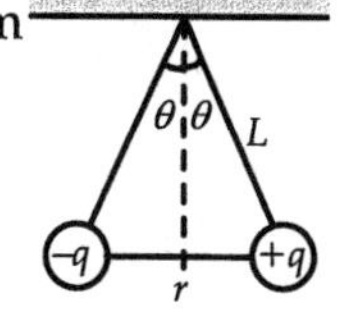

$$\sum F_y = 0: \qquad T\cos 10.0° = mg \text{, or } T = \frac{mg}{\cos 10.0°} \qquad (1)$$

$$\sum F_x = 0: \qquad F_{\text{net}} = F_2 - F_1 = T\sin 10.0° \qquad (2)$$

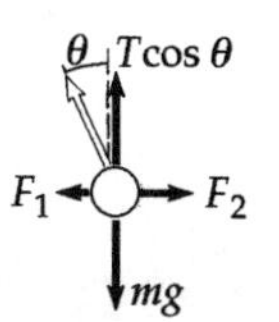

FIG. P23.62

F_{net} is the net electrical force on the charged sphere. Eliminate T from (2) by use of (1).

$$F_{\text{net}} = \frac{mg\sin 10.0°}{\cos 10.0°} = mg\tan 10.0° = \left(2.00 \times 10^{-3} \text{ kg}\right)\left(9.80 \text{ m/s}^2\right)\tan 10.0° = 3.46 \times 10^{-3} \text{ N}$$

F_{net} is the resultant of two forces, F_1 and F_2. F_1 is the attractive force on $+q$ exerted by $-q$, and F_2 is the force exerted on $+q$ by the external electric field.

$$F_{\text{net}} = F_2 - F_1 \text{ or } F_2 = F_{\text{net}} + F_1$$

$$F_1 = \left(8.99 \times 10^9 \text{ N}\cdot\text{m}^2/\text{C}^2\right)\frac{\left(5.00 \times 10^{-8} \text{ C}\right)\left(5.00 \times 10^{-8} \text{ C}\right)}{\left(3.47 \times 10^{-3} \text{ m}\right)^2} = 1.87 \times 10^{-2} \text{ N}$$

Thus, $F_2 = F_{\text{net}} + F_1$ yields $F_2 = 3.46 \times 10^{-3} \text{ N} + 1.87 \times 10^{-2} \text{ N} = 2.21 \times 10^{-2} \text{ N}$

and $F_2 = qE$, or $E = \frac{F_2}{q} = \frac{2.21 \times 10^{-2} \text{ N}}{5.00 \times 10^{-8} \text{ C}} = 4.43 \times 10^5 \text{ N/C} = \boxed{443 \text{ kN/C}}$.

P23.63 $Q = \int \lambda d\ell = \int_{-90.0°}^{90.0°} \lambda_0 \cos\theta R d\theta = \lambda_0 R \sin\theta\Big|_{-90.0°}^{90.0°} = \lambda_0 R[1-(-1)] = 2\lambda_0 R$

$Q = 12.0\ \mu\text{C} = (2\lambda_0)(0.600) \text{ m} = 12.0\ \mu\text{C}$ so $\lambda_0 = 10.0\ \mu\text{C/m}$

$$dF_y = \frac{1}{4\pi \in_0}\left(\frac{(3.00\ \mu\text{C})(\lambda d\ell)}{R^2}\right)\cos\theta = \frac{1}{4\pi \in_0}\left(\frac{(3.00\ \mu\text{C})\left(\lambda_0 \cos^2\theta R d\theta\right)}{R^2}\right)$$

$$F_y = \int_{-90.0°}^{90.0°}\left(8.99 \times 10^9 \text{ N}\cdot\text{m}^2/\text{C}^2\right)\frac{\left(3.00 \times 10^{-6} \text{ C}\right)\left(10.0 \times 10^{-6} \text{ C/m}\right)}{(0.600 \text{ m})}\cos^2\theta d\theta$$

$$F_y = \frac{8.99(30.0)}{0.600}\left(10^{-3} \text{ N}\right)\int_{-\pi/2}^{\pi/2}\left(\frac{1}{2} + \frac{1}{2}\cos 2\theta\right)d\theta$$

$$F_y = (0.450 \text{ N})\left(\frac{1}{2}\theta + \frac{1}{4}\sin 2\theta\Big|_{-\pi/2}^{\pi/2}\right) = \boxed{0.707 \text{ N}} \text{ Downward.}$$

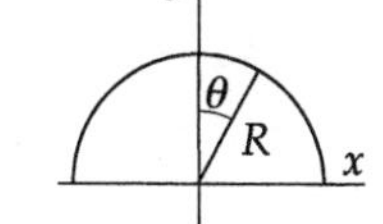

cos θ: 1, 0, −1, 0°, 360°

cos²θ: 1, 0, 0°, 360°

FIG. P23.63

Since the leftward and rightward forces due to the two halves of the semicircle cancel out, $F_x = 0$.

P23.64 At an equilibrium position, the net force on the charge Q is zero. The equilibrium position can be located by determining the angle θ corresponding to equilibrium.

In terms of lengths s, $\frac{1}{2}a\sqrt{3}$, and r, shown in Figure P23.64, the charge at the origin exerts an attractive force

$$\frac{k_e Qq}{\left(s + \frac{1}{2}a\sqrt{3}\right)^2}$$

continued on next page

The other two charges exert equal repulsive forces of magnitude $\frac{k_eQq}{r^2}$. The horizontal components of the two repulsive forces add, balancing the attractive force,

$$F_{\text{net}} = k_eQq\left[\frac{2\cos\theta}{r^2} - \frac{1}{\left(s+\frac{1}{2}a\sqrt{3}\right)^2}\right] = 0$$

From Figure P23.64 $\qquad r = \frac{\frac{1}{2}a}{\sin\theta} \qquad s = \frac{1}{2}a\cot\theta$

The equilibrium condition, in terms of θ, is $\qquad F_{\text{net}} = \left(\frac{4}{a^2}\right)k_eQq\left(2\cos\theta\sin^2\theta - \frac{1}{\left(\sqrt{3}+\cot\theta\right)^2}\right) = 0$.

Thus the equilibrium value of θ satisfies $\qquad 2\cos\theta\sin^2\theta\left(\sqrt{3}+\cot\theta\right)^2 = 1$.

One method for solving for θ is to tabulate the left side. To three significant figures a value of θ corresponding to equilibrium is 81.7°.

The distance from the vertical side of the triangle to the equilibrium position is

$$s = \frac{1}{2}a\cot 81.7° = \boxed{0.072\,9a}.$$

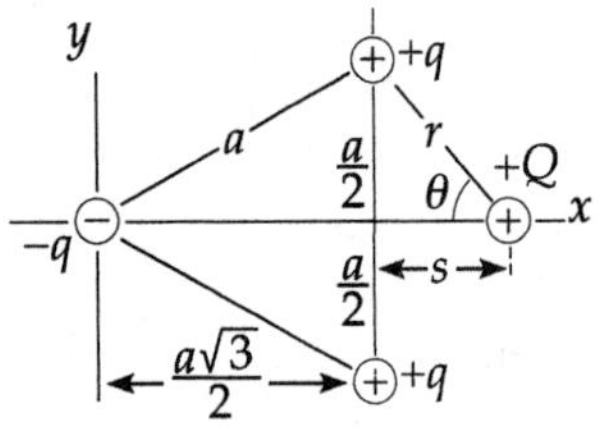

FIG. P23.64

θ	$2\cos\theta\sin^2\theta\left(\sqrt{3}+\cot\theta\right)^2$
60°	4
70°	2.654
80°	1.226
90°	0
81°	1.091
81.5°	1.024
81.7°	0.997

A second zero-field point is on the negative side of the *x*-axis, where $\theta = -9.16°$ and $s = -3.10a$.

P23.65 (a) From the 2*Q* charge we have $F_e - T_2\sin\theta_2 = 0$ and $mg - T_2\cos\theta_2 = 0$.

Combining these we find $\qquad \frac{F_e}{mg} = \frac{T_2\sin\theta_2}{T_2\cos\theta_2} = \tan\theta_2$.

From the *Q* charge we have $F_e = T_1\sin\theta_1 = 0$ and $mg - T_1\cos\theta_1 = 0$.

Combining these we find $\qquad \frac{F_e}{mg} = \frac{T_1\sin\theta_1}{T_1\cos\theta_1} = \tan\theta_1$ or $\boxed{\theta_2 = \theta_1}$.

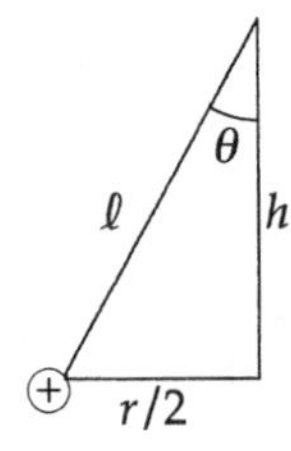

FIG. P23.65

(b) $F_e = \frac{k_e 2QQ}{r^2} = \frac{2k_eQ^2}{r^2}$

If we assume θ is small then $\qquad \tan\theta \approx \frac{r/2}{\ell}$.

Substitute expressions for F_e and $\tan\theta$ into either equation found in part (a) and solve for *r*.

$\frac{F_e}{mg} = \tan\theta$ then $\frac{2k_eQ^2}{r^2}\left(\frac{1}{mg}\right) \approx \frac{r}{2\ell}$ and solving for *r* we find $r \approx \left(\frac{4k_eQ^2\ell}{mg}\right)^{1/3}$.

P23.66 (a) The distance from each corner to the center of the square is

$$\sqrt{\left(\frac{L}{2}\right)^2+\left(\frac{L}{2}\right)^2}=\frac{L}{\sqrt{2}}.$$

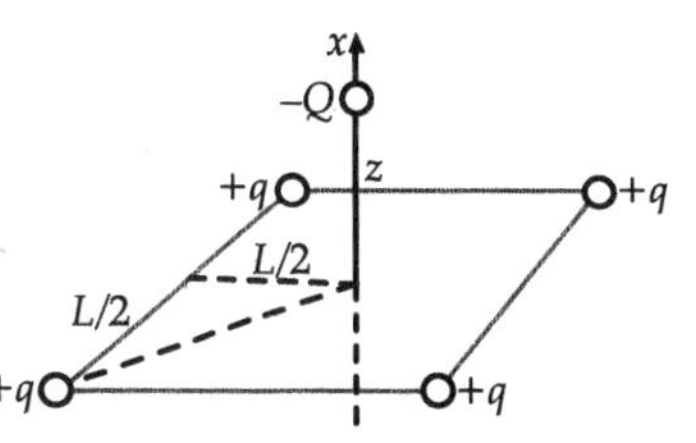

FIG. P23.66

The distance from each positive charge to $-Q$ is then $\sqrt{z^2+\frac{L^2}{2}}$. Each positive charge exerts a force directed along the line joining q and $-Q$, of magnitude $\frac{k_eQq}{z^2+L^2/2}$.

The line of force makes an angle with the z-axis whose cosine is $\frac{z}{\sqrt{z^2+L^2/2}}$

The four charges together exert forces whose x and y components add to zero, while the z-components add to $\mathbf{F}=\boxed{-\frac{4k_eQqz}{\left(z^2+L^2/2\right)^{3/2}}\hat{\mathbf{k}}}$

(b) For $z>>L$, the magnitude of this force is $F_z=-\frac{4k_eQqz}{\left(L^2/2\right)^{3/2}}=-\left(\frac{4(2)^{3/2}k_eQq}{L^3}\right)z=ma_z$

Therefore, the object's vertical acceleration is of the form $\boxed{a_z=-\omega^2z}$

with $\omega^2=\frac{4(2)^{3/2}k_eQq}{mL^3}=\frac{k_eQq\sqrt{128}}{mL^3}$.

Since the acceleration of the object is always oppositely directed to its excursion from equilibrium and in magnitude proportional to it, the object will execute simple harmonic motion with a period given by

$$T=\frac{2\pi}{\omega}=\frac{2\pi}{(128)^{1/4}}\sqrt{\frac{mL^3}{k_eQq}}=\boxed{\frac{\pi}{(8)^{1/4}}\sqrt{\frac{mL^3}{k_eQq}}}.$$

P23.67 (a) The total non-contact force on the cork ball is: $F=qE+mg=m\left(g+\frac{qE}{m}\right)$,

which is constant and directed downward. Therefore, it behaves like a simple pendulum in the presence of a modified uniform gravitational field with a period given by:

$$T=2\pi\sqrt{\frac{L}{g+qE/m}}=2\pi\sqrt{\frac{0.500\text{ m}}{9.80\text{ m/s}^2+\left[\left(2.00\times10^{-6}\text{ C}\right)\left(1.00\times10^{5}\text{ N/C}\right)/1.00\times10^{-3}\text{ kg}\right]}}$$

$$=\boxed{0.307\text{ s}}$$

(b) $\boxed{\text{Yes}}$. Without gravity in part (a), we get $T=2\pi\sqrt{\frac{L}{qE/m}}$

$$T=2\pi\sqrt{\frac{0.500\text{ m}}{\left(2.00\times10^{-6}\text{ C}\right)\left(1.00\times10^{5}\text{ N/C}\right)/1.00\times10^{-3}\text{ kg}}}=0.314\text{ s (a 2.28\% difference).}$$

P23.68 The bowl exerts a normal force on each bead, directed along the radius line or at 60.0° above the horizontal. Consider the free-body diagram of the bead on the left:

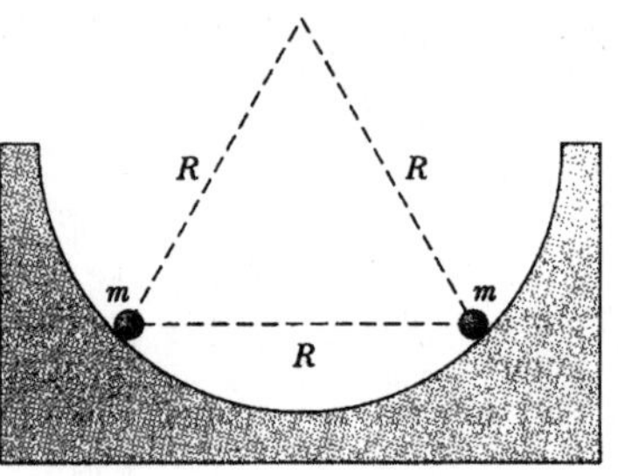

FIG. P23.68

$$\sum F_y = n\sin 60.0° - mg = 0,$$

or $$n = \frac{mg}{\sin 60.0°}.$$

Also, $$\sum F_x = -F_e + n\cos 60.0° = 0,$$

or $$\frac{k_e q^2}{R^2} = n\cos 60.0° = \frac{mg}{\tan 60.0°} = \frac{mg}{\sqrt{3}}.$$

Thus, $$q = \boxed{R\left(\frac{mg}{k_e\sqrt{3}}\right)^{1/2}}.$$

P23.69 (a) There are 7 terms which contribute:

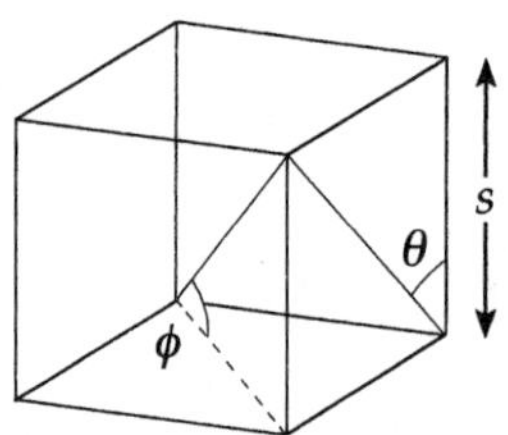

FIG. P23.69

3 are s away (along sides)

3 are $\sqrt{2}s$ away (face diagonals) and $\sin\theta = \frac{1}{\sqrt{2}} = \cos\theta$

1 is $\sqrt{3}s$ away (body diagonal) and $\sin\phi = \frac{1}{\sqrt{3}}$.

The component in each direction is the same by symmetry.

$$\mathbf{F} = \frac{k_e q^2}{s^2}\left[1 + \frac{2}{2\sqrt{2}} + \frac{1}{3\sqrt{3}}\right]\left(\hat{\mathbf{i}} + \hat{\mathbf{j}} + \hat{\mathbf{k}}\right) = \boxed{\frac{k_e q^2}{s^2}(1.90)\left(\hat{\mathbf{i}} + \hat{\mathbf{j}} + \hat{\mathbf{k}}\right)}$$

(b) $$F = \sqrt{F_x^2 + F_y^2 + F_z^2} = \boxed{3.29\frac{k_e q^2}{s^2} \text{ away from the origin}}$$

P23.70 (a) Zero contribution from the same face due to symmetry, opposite face contributes

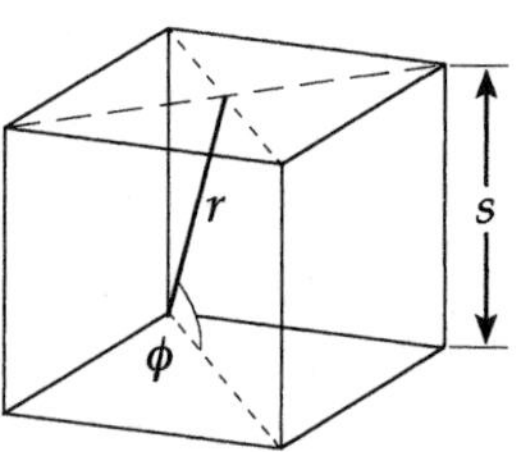

FIG. P23.70

$$4\left(\frac{k_e q}{r^2}\sin\phi\right) \text{ where } r = \sqrt{\left(\frac{s}{2}\right)^2 + \left(\frac{s}{2}\right)^2 + s^2} = \sqrt{1.5}s = 1.22s$$

$$\sin\phi = \frac{s}{r} \qquad E = 4\frac{k_e q s}{r^3} = \frac{4}{(1.22)^3}\frac{k_e q}{s^2} = \boxed{2.18\frac{k_e q}{s^2}}$$

(b) $\boxed{\text{The direction is the } \hat{\mathbf{k}} \text{ direction.}}$

P23.71 The field on the axis of the ring is calculated in Example 23.8, $E = E_x = \dfrac{k_e x Q}{\left(x^2+a^2\right)^{3/2}}$

The force experienced by a charge $-q$ placed along the axis of the ring is $F = -k_e Qq\left[\dfrac{x}{\left(x^2+a^2\right)^{3/2}}\right]$

and when $x << a$, this becomes $F = -\left(\dfrac{k_e Qq}{a^3}\right)x$

This expression for the force is in the form of Hooke's law, with an effective spring constant of $k = \dfrac{k_e Qq}{a^3}$

Since $\omega = 2\pi f = \sqrt{\dfrac{k}{m}}$, we have $f = \boxed{\dfrac{1}{2\pi}\sqrt{\dfrac{k_e Qq}{ma^3}}}$.

P23.72 $d\mathbf{E} = \dfrac{k_e\,dq}{x^2+(0.150\text{ m})^2}\left(\dfrac{-x\hat{\mathbf{i}}+0.150\text{ m}\hat{\mathbf{j}}}{\sqrt{x^2+(0.150\text{ m})^2}}\right) = \dfrac{k_e\lambda\left(-x\hat{\mathbf{i}}+0.150\text{ m}\hat{\mathbf{j}}\right)dx}{\left[x^2+(0.150\text{ m})^2\right]^{3/2}}$

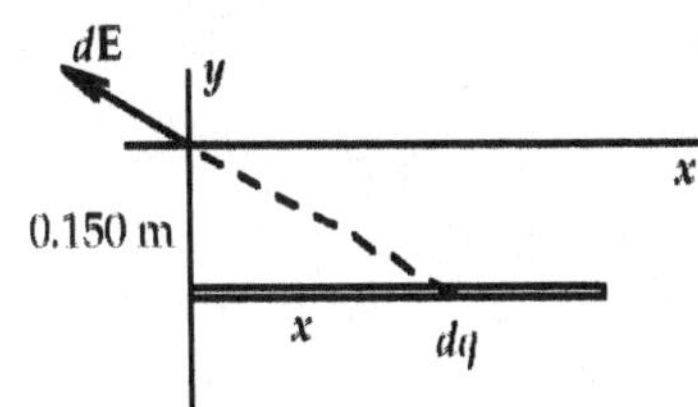

FIG. P23.72

$$\mathbf{E} = \int_{\text{all charge}} d\mathbf{E} = k_e\lambda\int_{x=0}^{0.400\text{ m}}\frac{\left(-x\hat{\mathbf{i}}+0.150\text{ m}\hat{\mathbf{j}}\right)dx}{\left[x^2+(0.150\text{ m})^2\right]^{3/2}}$$

$$\mathbf{E} = k_e\lambda\left[\left.\frac{+\hat{\mathbf{i}}}{\sqrt{x^2+(0.150\text{ m})^2}}\right|_0^{0.400\text{ m}} + \left.\frac{(0.150\text{ m})\hat{\mathbf{j}}x}{(0.150\text{ m})^2\sqrt{x^2+(0.150\text{ m})^2}}\right|_0^{0.400\text{ m}}\right]$$

$$\mathbf{E} = \left(8.99\times10^9\text{ N}\cdot\text{m}^2/\text{C}^2\right)\left(35.0\times10^{-9}\text{ C/m}\right)\left[\hat{\mathbf{i}}(2.34-6.67)\text{ m}^{-1}+\hat{\mathbf{j}}(6.24-0)\text{ m}^{-1}\right]$$

$$\mathbf{E} = \left(-1.36\hat{\mathbf{i}}+1.96\hat{\mathbf{j}}\right)\times10^3\text{ N/C} = \boxed{\left(-1.36\hat{\mathbf{i}}+1.96\hat{\mathbf{j}}\right)\text{ kN/C}}$$

P23.73 The electrostatic forces exerted on the two charges result in a net torque $\tau = -2Fa\sin\theta = -2Eqa\sin\theta$.

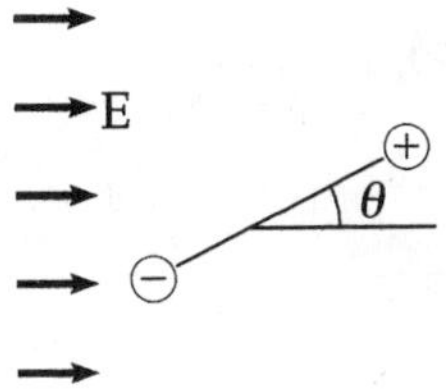

For small θ, $\sin\theta \approx \theta$ and using $p = 2qa$, we have $\tau = -Ep\theta$.

The torque produces an angular acceleration given by $\tau = I\alpha = I\dfrac{d^2\theta}{dt^2}$.

Combining these two expressions for torque, we have $\dfrac{d^2\theta}{dt^2}+\left(\dfrac{Ep}{I}\right)\theta = 0$.

FIG. P23.73

This equation can be written in the form $\dfrac{d^2\theta}{dt^2} = -\omega^2\theta$ where $\omega^2 = \dfrac{Ep}{I}$.

This is the same form as Equation 15.5 and the frequency of oscillation is found by comparison with Equation 15.11, or $f = \dfrac{1}{2\pi}\sqrt{\dfrac{pE}{I}} = \boxed{\dfrac{1}{2\pi}\sqrt{\dfrac{2qaE}{I}}}$.

ANSWERS TO EVEN PROBLEMS

P23.2 (a) 2.62×10^{24}; (b) 2.38 electrons for every 10^9 present

P23.4 57.5 N

P23.6 2.51×10^{-9}

P23.8 514 kN

P23.10 $x=0.634d$. The equilibrium is stable if the third bead has positive charge.

P23.12 (a) period $=\dfrac{\pi}{2}\sqrt{\dfrac{md^3}{k_eqQ}}$ where m is the mass of the object with charge $-Q$; (b) $4a\sqrt{\dfrac{k_eqQ}{md^3}}$

P23.14 1.49 g

P23.16 720 kN/C down

P23.18 (a) $\left[18.0\hat{\mathbf{i}}-218\hat{\mathbf{j}}\right]$ kN/C; (b) $\left(36.0\hat{\mathbf{i}}-436\hat{\mathbf{j}}\right)$ mN

P23.20 (a) $12.9\hat{\mathbf{j}}$ kN/C; (b) $-38.6\hat{\mathbf{j}}$ mN

P23.22 see the solution

P23.24 $-\dfrac{\pi^2k_eq}{6a^2}\hat{\mathbf{i}}$

P23.26 $\dfrac{k_e\lambda_0}{x_0}\left(-\hat{\mathbf{i}}\right)$

P23.28 $\dfrac{k_e\lambda_0}{2x_0}\left(-\hat{\mathbf{i}}\right)$

P23.30 (a) 383 MN/C away; (b) 324 MN/C away; (c) 80.7 MN/C away; (d) 6.68 MN/C away

P23.32 see the solution

P23.34 (a) $\dfrac{k_eQ\hat{\mathbf{i}}}{h}\left[\left(d^2+R^2\right)^{-1/2}-\left((d+h)^2+R^2\right)^{-1/2}\right]$; (b) $\dfrac{2k_eQ\hat{\mathbf{i}}}{R^2h}\left[h+\left(d^2+R^2\right)^{1/2}-\left((d+h)^2+R^2\right)^{1/2}\right]$

P23.36 (a) 200 pC; (b) 141 pC; (c) 58.9 pC

P23.38 see the solution

P23.40 (a) $-\dfrac{1}{3}$; (b) q_1 is negative and q_2 is positive

P23.42 electron: 4.39 Mm/s; proton: 2.39 km/s

P23.44 (a) $-57.6\hat{\mathbf{i}}$ Tm/s^2; (b) $2.84\hat{\mathbf{i}}$ Mm/s; (c) 49.3 ns

P23.46 (a) down; (b) 3.43 μC

P23.48 The particle strikes the negative plate after moving in a parabola 0.181 mm high and 0.961 mm.

P23.50 Possible only with +51.3 μC at $x=-16.0$ cm

P23.52 (a) 24.2 N/C at 0°; (b) 9.42 N/C at 117°

P23.54 5.25 μC

P23.56 (a) $\dfrac{mg}{A\cot\theta+B}$; (b) $\dfrac{mgA}{A\cos\theta+B\sin\theta}$

P23.58 0.205 μC

P23.60 $\dfrac{k_eqQ}{a^2}$ toward the 29th vertex

P23.62 $443\,\hat{\mathbf{i}}$ kN/C

P23.64 $0.072\,9a$

P23.66 see the solution; the period is $\dfrac{\pi}{8^{1/4}}\sqrt{\dfrac{mL^3}{k_eQq}}$

P23.68 $R\left(\dfrac{mg}{k_e\sqrt{3}}\right)^{1/2}$

P23.70 (a) see the solution; (b) $\hat{\mathbf{k}}$

P23.72 $\left(-1.36\hat{\mathbf{i}}+1.96\hat{\mathbf{j}}\right)$ kN/C

24

Gauss's Law

CHAPTER OUTLINE

ANSWERS TO QUESTIONS

Q24.1 The luminous flux on a given area is less when the sun is low in the sky, because the angle between the rays of the sun and the local area vector, $d\mathbf{A}$, is greater than zero. The cosine of this angle is reduced. The decreased flux results, on the average, in colder weather.

Q24.2 If the region is just a point, line, or plane, no. Consider two protons in otherwise empty space. The electric field is zero at the midpoint of the line joining the protons. If the field-free region is three-dimensional, then it can contain no charges, but it might be surrounded by electric charge. Consider the interior of a metal sphere carrying static charge.

Q24.3 The surface must enclose a positive total charge.

Q24.4 The net flux through any gaussian surface is zero. We can argue it two ways. Any surface contains zero charge so Gauss's law says the total flux is zero. The field is uniform, so the field lines entering one side of the closed surface come out the other side and the net flux is zero.

Q24.5 Gauss's law cannot tell the different values of the electric field at different points on the surface. When E is an unknown number, then we can say $\int E\cos\theta dA = E\int\cos\theta dA$. When $E(x, y, z)$ is an unknown function, then there is no such simplification.

Q24.6 The electric flux through a sphere around a point charge is independent of the size of the sphere. A sphere of larger radius has a larger area, but a smaller field at its surface, so that the product of field strength and area is independent of radius. If the surface is not spherical, some parts are closer to the charge than others. In this case as well, smaller projected areas go with stronger fields, so that the net flux is unaffected.

Q24.7 Faraday's visualization of electric field lines lends insight to this question. Consider a section of a vertical sheet carrying charge +1 coulomb. It has $\frac{1}{\epsilon_0}$ field lines pointing out from it horizontally to the right and left, all uniformly spaced. The lines have the same uniform spacing close to the sheet and far away, showing that the field has the same value at all distances.

Q24.8 Consider any point, zone, or object where electric field lines begin. Surround it with a close-fitting gaussian surface. The lines will go outward through the surface to constitute positive net flux. Then Gauss's law asserts that positive net charge must be inside the surface: it is where the lines begin. Similarly, any place where electric field lines end must be just inside a gaussian surface passing net negative flux, and must be a negative charge.

Q24.9 Inject some charge at arbitrary places within a conducting object. Every bit of the charge repels every other bit, so each bit runs away as far as it can, stopping only when it reaches the outer surface of the conductor.

Q24.10 If the person is uncharged, the electric field inside the sphere is zero. The interior wall of the shell carries no charge. The person is not harmed by touching this wall. If the person carries a (small) charge q, the electric field inside the sphere is no longer zero. Charge $-q$ is induced on the inner wall of the sphere. The person will get a (small) shock when touching the sphere, as all the charge on his body jumps to the metal.

Q24.11 The electric fields outside are identical. The electric fields inside are very different. We have $\mathbf{E} = 0$ everywhere inside the conducting sphere while E decreases gradually as you go below the surface of the sphere with uniform volume charge density.

Q24.12 There is zero force. The huge charged sheet creates a uniform field. The field can polarize the neutral sheet, creating in effect a film of opposite charge on the near face and a film with an equal amount of like charge on the far face of the neutral sheet. Since the field is uniform, the films of charge feel equal-magnitude forces of attraction and repulsion to the charged sheet. The forces add to zero.

Q24.13 Gauss's law predicts, as described in section 24.4, that excess charge on a conductor will reside on the surface of the conductor. If a car is left charged by a lightning strike, then that charge will remain on the outside of the car, not harming the occupants. It turns out that during the lightning strike, the current also remains on the outside of the conductor. Note that it is not necessarily safe to be in a fiberglass car or a convertible during a thunderstorm.

SOLUTIONS TO PROBLEMS

Section 24.1 **Electric Flux**

P24.1 (a) $\Phi_E = EA\cos\theta = \left(3.50\times10^3\right)(0.350\times0.700)\cos 0° = \boxed{858\ \text{N}\cdot\text{m}^2/\text{C}}$

(b) $\theta = 90.0°$ $\boxed{\Phi_E = 0}$

(c) $\Phi_E = \left(3.50\times10^3\right)(0.350\times0.700)\cos 40.0° = \boxed{657\ \text{N}\cdot\text{m}^2/\text{C}}$

P24.2 $\Phi_E = EA\cos\theta = \left(2.00\times10^4\ \text{N/C}\right)\left(18.0\ \text{m}^2\right)\cos 10.0° = \boxed{355\ \text{kN}\cdot\text{m}^2/\text{C}}$

P24.3 $\Phi_E = EA\cos\theta$ $A = \pi r^2 = \pi(0.200)^2 = 0.126\ \text{m}^2$

$5.20\times10^5 = E(0.126)\cos 0°$ $E = 4.14\times10^6\ \text{N/C} = \boxed{4.14\ \text{MN/C}}$

P24.4 (a) $A' = (10.0\text{ cm})(30.0\text{ cm})$

$A' = 300\text{ cm}^2 = 0.030\,0\text{ m}^2$

$\Phi_{E,\,A'} = EA'\cos\theta$

$\Phi_{E,\,A'} = \left(7.80\times10^4\right)(0.030\,0)\cos180°$

$\Phi_{E,\,A'} = \boxed{-2.34\text{ kN}\cdot\text{m}^2/\text{C}}$

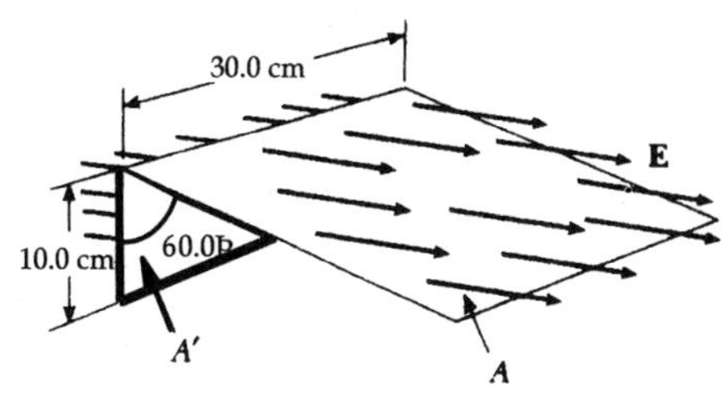

FIG. P24.4

(b) $\Phi_{E,\,A} = EA\cos\theta = \left(7.80\times10^4\right)(A)\cos60.0°$

$A = (30.0\text{ cm})(w) = (30.0\text{ cm})\left(\dfrac{10.0\text{ cm}}{\cos60.0°}\right) = 600\text{ cm}^2 = 0.060\,0\text{ m}^2$

$\Phi_{E,\,A} = \left(7.80\times10^4\right)(0.060\,0)\cos60.0° = \boxed{+2.34\text{ kN}\cdot\text{m}^2/\text{C}}$

(c) The bottom and the two triangular sides all lie *parallel* to **E**, so $\Phi_E = 0$ for each of these. Thus,

$\Phi_{E,\,\text{total}} = -2.34\text{ kN}\cdot\text{m}^2/\text{C} + 2.34\text{ kN}\cdot\text{m}^2/\text{C} + 0 + 0 + 0 = \boxed{0}$.

P24.5 (a) $\Phi_E = \mathbf{E}\cdot\mathbf{A} = \left(a\hat{\mathbf{i}} + b\hat{\mathbf{j}}\right)\cdot A\hat{\mathbf{i}} = \boxed{aA}$

(b) $\Phi_E = \left(a\hat{\mathbf{i}} + b\hat{\mathbf{j}}\right)\cdot A\hat{\mathbf{j}} = \boxed{bA}$

(c) $\Phi_E = \left(a\hat{\mathbf{i}} + b\hat{\mathbf{j}}\right)\cdot A\hat{\mathbf{k}} = \boxed{0}$

P24.6 Only the charge inside radius R contributes to the total flux.

$\Phi_E = \boxed{\dfrac{q}{\epsilon_0}}$

P24.7 $\Phi_E = EA\cos\theta$ through the base

$\Phi_E = (52.0)(36.0)\cos180° = -1.87\text{ kN}\cdot\text{m}^2/\text{C}$.

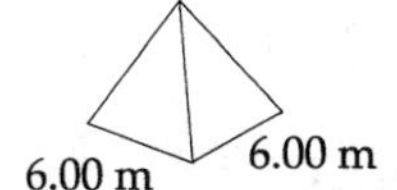

FIG. P24.7

Note the same number of electric field lines go through the base as go through the pyramid's surface (not counting the base).

For the slanting surfaces, $\boxed{\Phi_E = +1.87\text{ kN}\cdot\text{m}^2/\text{C}}$.

P24.8 The flux entering the closed surface equals the flux exiting the surface. The flux entering the left side of the cone is $\Phi_E = \int\mathbf{E}\cdot d\mathbf{A} = \boxed{ERh}$. This is the same as the flux that exits the right side of the cone. Note that for a uniform field only the cross sectional area matters, not shape.

Section 24.2 Gauss's Law

P24.9 (a) $\Phi_E = \frac{q_{in}}{\epsilon_0} = \frac{(+5.00\ \mu C - 9.00\ \mu C + 27.0\ \mu C - 84.0\ \mu C)}{8.85 \times 10^{-12}\ C^2/N \cdot m^2} = -6.89 \times 10^6\ N \cdot m^2/C^2$

$\Phi_E = \boxed{-6.89\ MN \cdot m^2/C}$

(b) Since the net electric flux is negative, more lines enter than leave the surface.

P24.10 (a) $E = \frac{k_e Q}{r^2}$: $\quad 8.90 \times 10^2 = \frac{(8.99 \times 10^9)Q}{(0.750)^2}$

But Q is negative since **E** points inward. $\quad Q = -5.56 \times 10^{-8}\ C = \boxed{-55.6\ nC}$

(b) The $\boxed{\text{negative}}$ charge has a $\boxed{\text{spherically symmetric}}$ charge distribution.

P24.11 $\Phi_E = \frac{q_{in}}{\epsilon_0}$

Through S_1 $\quad \Phi_E = \frac{-2Q+Q}{\epsilon_0} = \boxed{-\frac{Q}{\epsilon_0}}$

Through S_2 $\quad \Phi_E = \frac{+Q-Q}{\epsilon_0} = \boxed{0}$

Through S_3 $\quad \Phi_E = \frac{-2Q+Q-Q}{\epsilon_0} = \boxed{-\frac{2Q}{\epsilon_0}}$

Through S_4 $\quad \Phi_E = \boxed{0}$

P24.12 (a) One-half of the total flux created by the charge q goes through the plane. Thus,

$\Phi_{E,\ plane} = \frac{1}{2}\Phi_{E,\ total} = \frac{1}{2}\left(\frac{q}{\epsilon_0}\right) = \boxed{\frac{q}{2\ \epsilon_0}}$.

(b) The square looks like an infinite plane to a charge *very close* to the surface. Hence,

$\Phi_{E,\ square} \approx \Phi_{E,\ plane} = \boxed{\frac{q}{2\ \epsilon_0}}$.

(c) $\boxed{\text{The plane and the square look the same to the charge.}}$

P24.13 The flux through the curved surface is equal to the flux through the flat circle, $\boxed{E_0 \pi r^2}$.

P24.14 (a) $\Phi_{E,\ shell} = \frac{q_{in}}{\epsilon_0} = \frac{12.0 \times 10^{-6}}{8.85 \times 10^{-12}} = 1.36 \times 10^6\ N \cdot m^2/C = \boxed{1.36\ MN \cdot m^2/C}$

(b) $\Phi_{E,\ half\ shell} = \frac{1}{2}(1.36 \times 10^6\ N \cdot m^2/C) = 6.78 \times 10^5\ N \cdot m^2/C = \boxed{678\ kN \cdot m^2/C}$

(c) $\boxed{\text{No,}}$ the same number of field lines will pass through each surface, no matter how the radius changes.

P24.15 (a) With δ very small, all points on the hemisphere are nearly at a distance R from the charge, so the field everywhere on the curved surface is $\dfrac{k_e Q}{R^2}$ radially outward (normal to the surface). Therefore, the flux is this field strength times the area of half a sphere:

$$\Phi_{\text{curved}} = \int \mathbf{E} \cdot d\mathbf{A} = E_{\text{local}} A_{\text{hemisphere}}$$

$$\Phi_{\text{curved}} = \left(k_e \frac{Q}{R^2}\right)\left(\frac{1}{2} 4\pi R^2\right) = \frac{1}{4\pi \epsilon_0} Q(2\pi) = \boxed{\frac{+Q}{2\epsilon_0}}$$

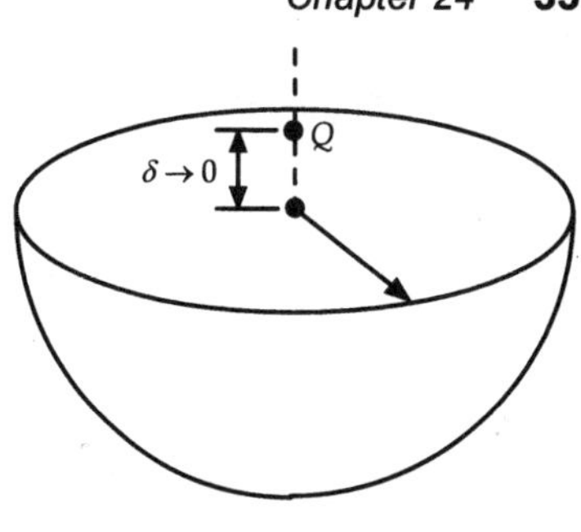

FIG. P24.15

(b) The closed surface encloses zero charge so Gauss's law gives

$$\Phi_{\text{curved}} + \Phi_{\text{flat}} = 0 \quad \text{or} \quad \Phi_{\text{flat}} = -\Phi_{\text{curved}} = \boxed{\frac{-Q}{2\epsilon_0}}.$$

***P24.16** Consider as a gaussian surface a box with horizontal area A, lying between 500 and 600 m elevation.

$$\oint \mathbf{E} \cdot d\mathbf{A} = \frac{q}{\epsilon_0}: \qquad (+120 \text{ N/C})A + (-100 \text{ N/C})A = \frac{\rho A(100 \text{ m})}{\epsilon_0}$$

$$\rho = \frac{(20 \text{ N/C})(8.85 \times 10^{-12} \text{ C}^2/\text{N} \cdot \text{m}^2)}{100 \text{ m}} = \boxed{1.77 \times 10^{-12} \text{ C/m}^3}$$

The charge is $\boxed{\text{positive}}$, to produce the net outward flux of electric field.

P24.17 The total charge is $Q - 6|q|$. The total outward flux from the cube is $\dfrac{Q - 6|q|}{\epsilon_0}$, of which one-sixth goes through each face:

$$(\Phi_E)_{\text{one face}} = \frac{Q - 6|q|}{6\epsilon_0}$$

$$(\Phi_E)_{\text{one face}} = \frac{Q - 6|q|}{6\epsilon_0} = \frac{(5.00 - 6.00) \times 10^{-6} \text{ C} \cdot \text{N} \cdot \text{m}^2}{6 \times 8.85 \times 10^{-12} \text{ C}^2} = \boxed{-18.8 \text{ kN} \cdot \text{m}^2/\text{C}}.$$

P24.18 The total charge is $Q - 6|q|$. The total outward flux from the cube is $\dfrac{Q - 6|q|}{\epsilon_0}$, of which one-sixth goes through each face:

$$(\Phi_E)_{\text{one face}} = \boxed{\frac{Q - 6|q|}{6\epsilon_0}}.$$

P24.19 If $R \le d$, the sphere encloses no charge and $\Phi_E = \dfrac{q_{\text{in}}}{\epsilon_0} = \boxed{0}$.

If $R > d$, the length of line falling within the sphere is $2\sqrt{R^2 - d^2}$

so $\quad \Phi_E = \boxed{\dfrac{2\lambda\sqrt{R^2 - d^2}}{\epsilon_0}}$.

P24.20 $\Phi_{E,\text{ hole}} = \mathbf{E}\cdot\mathbf{A}_{\text{hole}} = \left(\frac{k_e Q}{R^2}\right)\left(\pi r^2\right) = \left(\frac{\left(8.99\times10^9\ \text{N}\cdot\text{m}^2/\text{C}^2\right)\left(10.0\times10^{-6}\ \text{C}\right)}{(0.100\ \text{m})^2}\right)\pi\left(1.00\times10^{-3}\ \text{m}\right)^2$

$$\Phi_{E,\text{ hole}} = \boxed{28.2\ \text{N}\cdot\text{m}^2/\text{C}}$$

P24.21 $\Phi_E = \frac{q_{\text{in}}}{\epsilon_0} = \frac{170\times10^{-6}\ \text{C}}{8.85\times10^{-12}\ \text{C}^2/\text{N}\cdot\text{m}^2} = 1.92\times10^7\ \text{N}\cdot\text{m}^2/\text{C}$

(a) $(\Phi_E)_{\text{one face}} = \frac{1}{6}\Phi_E = \frac{1.92\times10^7\ \text{N}\cdot\text{m}^2/\text{C}}{6}$ $\qquad (\Phi_E)_{\text{one face}} = \boxed{3.20\ \text{MN}\cdot\text{m}^2/\text{C}}$

(b) $\Phi_E = \boxed{19.2\ \text{MN}\cdot\text{m}^2/\text{C}}$

(c) The answer to (a) would change because the flux through each face of the cube would not be equal with an asymmetric charge distribution. The sides of the cube nearer the charge would have more flux and the ones further away would have less. The answer to (b) would remain the same, since the overall flux would remain the same.

P24.22 No charge is inside the cube. The net flux through the cube is zero. Positive flux comes out through the three faces meeting at g. These three faces together fill solid angle equal to one-eighth of a sphere as seen from q, and together pass flux $\frac{1}{8}\left(\frac{q}{\epsilon_0}\right)$. Each face containing a intercepts equal flux going into the cube:

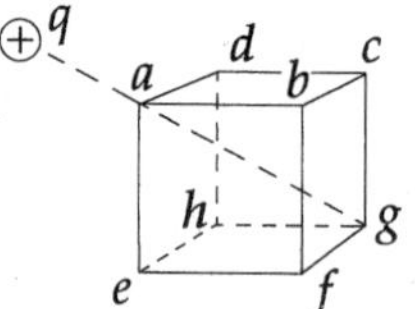

FIG. P24.22

$$0 = \Phi_{E,\text{ net}} = 3\Phi_{E,\text{ abcd}} + \frac{q}{8\epsilon_0}$$

$$\Phi_{E,\text{ abcd}} = \boxed{\frac{-q}{24\epsilon_0}}$$

Section 24.3 **Application of Gauss's Law to Various Charge Distributions**

P24.23 The charge distributed through the nucleus creates a field at the surface equal to that of a point charge at its center: $E = \frac{k_e q}{r^2}$

$$E = \frac{\left(8.99\times10^9\ \text{Nm}^2/\text{C}^2\right)\left(82\times1.60\times10^{-19}\ \text{C}\right)}{\left[(208)^{1/3}1.20\times10^{-15}\ \text{m}\right]^2}$$

$E = \boxed{2.33\times10^{21}\ \text{N/C}}$ away from the nucleus

P24.24 (a) $E = \frac{k_e Qr}{a^3} = \boxed{0}$

(b) $E = \frac{k_e Qr}{a^3} = \frac{(8.99\times10^9)(26.0\times10^{-6})(0.100)}{(0.400)^3} = \boxed{365\text{ kN/C}}$

(c) $E = \frac{k_e Q}{r^2} = \frac{(8.99\times10^9)(26.0\times10^{-6})}{(0.400)^2} = \boxed{1.46\text{ MN/C}}$

(d) $E = \frac{k_e Q}{r^2} = \frac{(8.99\times10^9)(26.0\times10^{-6})}{(0.600)^2} = \boxed{649\text{ kN/C}}$

The direction for each electric field is $\boxed{\text{radially outward}}$.

***P24.25** $mg = qE = q\left(\frac{\sigma}{2\in_0}\right) = q\left(\frac{Q/A}{2\in_0}\right)$ $\qquad \frac{Q}{A} = \frac{2\in_0 mg}{q} = \frac{2(8.85\times10^{-12})(0.01)(9.8)}{-0.7\times10^{-6}} = \boxed{-2.48\ \mu\text{C/m}^2}$

P24.26 (a) $E = \frac{2k_e\lambda}{r}$ $\qquad 3.60\times10^4 = \frac{2(8.99\times10^9)(Q/2.40)}{0.190}$

$Q = +9.13\times10^{-7}\text{ C} = \boxed{+913\text{ nC}}$

(b) $\mathbf{E} = \boxed{0}$

***P24.27** The volume of the spherical shell is

$\frac{4}{3}\pi\left[(0.25\text{ m})^3 - (0.20\text{ m})^3\right] = 3.19\times10^{-2}\text{ m}^3$.

Its charge is

$\rho V = (-1.33\times10^{-6}\text{ C/m}^3)(3.19\times10^{-2}\text{ m}^3) = -4.25\times10^{-8}\text{ C}$.

The net charge inside a sphere containing the proton's path as its equator is

$-60\times10^{-9}\text{ C} - 4.25\times10^{-8}\text{ C} = -1.02\times10^{-7}\text{ C}$.

The electric field is radially inward with magnitude

$$\frac{k_e|q|}{r^2} = \frac{|q|}{\in_0 4\pi r^2} = \frac{8.99\times10^9\text{ Nm}^2(1.02\times10^{-7}\text{ C})}{\text{C}^2(0.25\text{ m})^2} = 1.47\times10^4\text{ N/C}.$$

For the proton

$\sum F = ma \qquad eE = \frac{mv^2}{r}$

$$v = \left(\frac{eEr}{m}\right)^{1/2} = \left(\frac{1.60\times10^{-19}\text{ C}(1.47\times10^4\text{ N/C})0.25\text{ m}}{1.67\times10^{-27}\text{ kg}}\right)^{1/2} = \boxed{5.94\times10^5\text{ m/s}}.$$

P24.28 $\sigma = (8.60\times10^{-6}\ \text{C/cm}^2)\left(\dfrac{100\ \text{cm}}{\text{m}}\right)^2 = 8.60\times10^{-2}\ \text{C/m}^2$

$$E = \frac{\sigma}{2\epsilon_0} = \frac{8.60\times10^{-2}}{2(8.85\times10^{-12})} = \boxed{4.86\times10^9\ \text{N/C away from the wall}}$$

The field is essentially uniform as long as the distance from the center of the wall to the field point is much less than the dimensions of the wall.

P24.29 If ρ is positive, the field must be radially outward. Choose as the gaussian surface a cylinder of length L and radius r, contained inside the charged rod. Its volume is $\pi r^2 L$ and it encloses charge $\rho\pi r^2 L$. Because the charge distribution is long, no electric flux passes through the circular end caps; $\mathbf{E}\cdot d\mathbf{A} = EdA\cos 90.0° = 0$. The curved surface has $\mathbf{E}\cdot d\mathbf{A} = EdA\cos 0°$, and E must be the same strength everywhere over the curved surface.

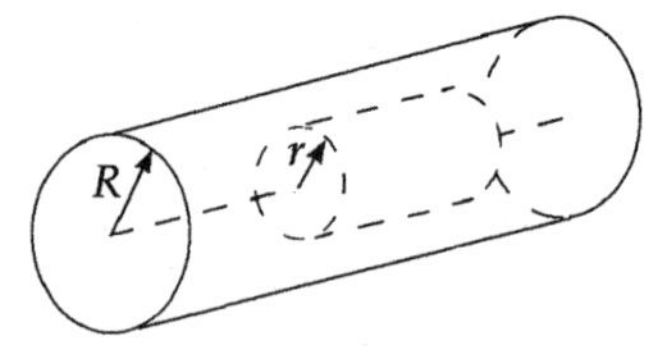

FIG. P24.29

Gauss's law, $\oint \mathbf{E}\cdot d\mathbf{A} = \dfrac{q}{\epsilon_0}$, becomes $E\displaystyle\int_{\substack{\text{Curved}\\\text{Surface}}} dA = \frac{\rho\pi r^2 L}{\epsilon_0}$.

Now the lateral surface area of the cylinder is $2\pi rL$:

$E(2\pi r)L = \dfrac{\rho\pi r^2 L}{\epsilon_0}$. Thus, $\mathbf{E} = \boxed{\dfrac{\rho r}{2\epsilon_0}\ \text{radially away from the cylinder axis}}$.

***P24.30** Let ρ represent the charge density. For the field inside the sphere at $r_1 = 5$ cm we have

$$E_1 4\pi r_1^2 = \frac{q_{\text{inside}}}{\epsilon_0} = \frac{4\pi r_1^3\rho}{3\epsilon_0} \qquad E_1 = \frac{r_1\rho}{3\epsilon_0}$$

$$\rho = \frac{3\epsilon_0 E_1}{r_1} = \frac{3(8.85\times10^{-12}\ \text{C}^2)(-86\times10^3\ \text{N})}{0.05\ \text{m}\quad \text{Nm}^2 \quad \text{C}} = -4.57\times10^{-5}\ \text{C/m}^3.$$

Now for the field outside at $r_3 = 15$ cm

$$E_3 4\pi r_3^2 = \frac{4\pi r_2^3\rho}{3\epsilon_0}$$

$$E_3 = \frac{k_e}{r_3^2}\frac{4}{3}\frac{\pi(0.10\ \text{m})^3(-4.57\times10^{-5}\ \text{C})}{\text{m}^3} = \frac{8.99\times10^9\ \text{Nm}^2(-1.91\times10^{-7}\ \text{C})}{(0.15\ \text{m})^2\text{C}^2} = -7.64\times10^4\ \text{N/C}$$

$\mathbf{E}_3 = \boxed{76.4\ \text{kN/C}}$ radially inward

P24.31 (a) $\mathbf{E} = \boxed{0}$

(b) $E = \dfrac{k_e Q}{r^2} = \dfrac{(8.99\times10^9)(32.0\times10^{-6})}{(0.200)^2} = 7.19\ \text{MN/C}$ $\quad\mathbf{E} = \boxed{7.19\ \text{MN/C radially outward}}$

P24.32 The distance between centers is $2\times5.90\times10^{-15}$ m. Each produces a field as if it were a point charge at its center, and each feels a force as if all its charge were a point at its center.

$$F = \frac{k_e q_1 q_2}{r^2} = (8.99\times10^9\ \text{N}\cdot\text{m}^2/\text{C}^2)\frac{(46)^2(1.60\times10^{-19}\ \text{C})^2}{(2\times5.90\times10^{-15}\ \text{m})^2} = 3.50\times10^3\ \text{N} = \boxed{3.50\ \text{kN}}$$

P24.33 Consider two balloons of diameter 0.2 m, each with mass 1 g, hanging apart with a 0.05 m separation on the ends of strings making angles of 10° with the vertical.

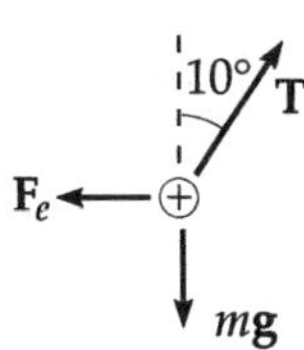

FIG. P24.33

(a) $\sum F_y = T\cos 10° - mg = 0 \Rightarrow T = \dfrac{mg}{\cos 10°}$

$\sum F_x = T\sin 10° - F_e = 0 \Rightarrow F_e = T\sin 10°$, so

$$F_e = \left(\frac{mg}{\cos 10°}\right)\sin 10° = mg\tan 10° = (0.001\text{ kg})\left(9.8\text{ m/s}^2\right)\tan 10°$$

$$F_e \approx 2\times 10^{-3}\text{ N} \boxed{\sim 10^{-3}\text{ N or 1 mN}}$$

(b) $F_e = \dfrac{k_e q^2}{r^2}$

$$2\times 10^{-3}\text{ N} \approx \frac{\left(8.99\times 10^9\text{ N}\cdot\text{m}^2/\text{C}^2\right)q^2}{(0.25\text{ m})^2}$$

$$q \approx 1.2\times 10^{-7}\text{ C} \boxed{\sim 10^{-7}\text{ C or 100 nC}}$$

(c) $$E = \frac{k_e q}{r^2} \approx \frac{\left(8.99\times 10^9\text{ N}\cdot\text{m}^2/\text{C}^2\right)\left(1.2\times 10^{-7}\text{ C}\right)}{(0.25\text{ m})^2} \approx 1.7\times 10^4\text{ N/C} \boxed{\sim 10\text{ kN/C}}$$

(d) $$\Phi_E = \frac{q}{\epsilon_0} \approx \frac{1.2\times 10^{-7}\text{ C}}{8.85\times 10^{-12}\text{ C}^2/\text{N}\cdot\text{m}^2} = 1.4\times 10^4\text{ N}\cdot\text{m}^2/\text{C} \boxed{\sim 10\text{ kN}\cdot\text{m}^2/\text{C}}$$

***P24.34** The charge density is determined by $Q = \frac{4}{3}\pi a^3\rho$ $\qquad \rho = \dfrac{3Q}{4\pi a^3}$

(a) The flux is that created by the enclosed charge within radius r:

$$\Phi_E = \frac{q_{\text{in}}}{\epsilon_0} = \frac{4\pi r^3\rho}{3\epsilon_0} = \frac{4\pi r^3 3Q}{3\epsilon_0 4\pi a^3} = \boxed{\frac{Qr^3}{\epsilon_0 a^3}}$$

(b) $\Phi_E = \boxed{\dfrac{Q}{\epsilon_0}}$. Note that the answers to parts (a) and (b) agree at $r = a$.

(c)

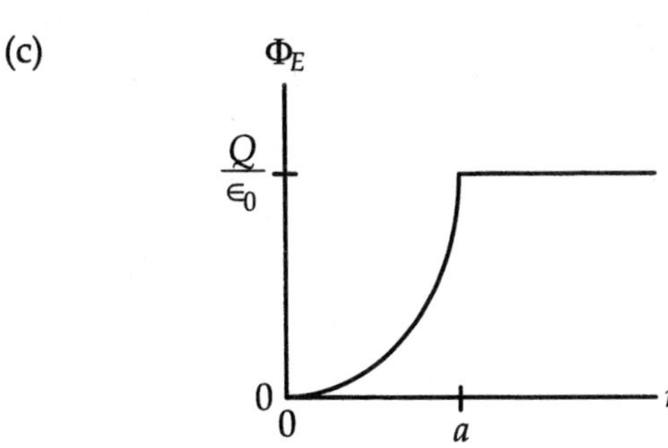

FIG. P24.34(c)

P24.35 (a) $$E = \frac{2k_e\lambda}{r} = \frac{2\left(8.99\times10^9\ \text{N}\cdot\text{m}^2/\text{C}^2\right)\left[\left(2.00\times10^{-6}\ \text{C}\right)/7.00\ \text{m}\right]}{0.100\ \text{m}}$$

$$E = \boxed{51.4\ \text{kN/C, radially outward}}$$

(b) $$\Phi_E = EA\cos\theta = E(2\pi r\ell)\cos 0°$$

$$\Phi_E = \left(5.14\times10^4\ \text{N/C}\right)2\pi(0.100\ \text{m})(0.020\,0\ \text{m})(1.00) = \boxed{646\ \text{N}\cdot\text{m}^2/\text{C}}$$

P24.36 (a) $$\rho = \frac{Q}{\frac{4}{3}\pi a^3} = \frac{5.70\times10^{-6}}{\frac{4}{3}\pi(0.040\,0)^3} = 2.13\times10^{-2}\ \text{C/m}^3$$

$$q_{\text{in}} = \rho\left(\frac{4}{3}\pi r^3\right) = \left(2.13\times10^{-2}\right)\left(\frac{4}{3}\pi\right)(0.020\,0)^3 = 7.13\times10^{-7}\ \text{C} = \boxed{713\ \text{nC}}$$

(b) $$q_{\text{in}} = \rho\left(\frac{4}{3}\pi r^3\right) = \left(2.13\times10^{-2}\right)\left(\frac{4}{3}\pi\right)(0.040\,0)^3 = \boxed{5.70\ \mu\text{C}}$$

P24.37 $$E = \frac{\sigma}{2\epsilon_0} = \frac{9.00\times10^{-6}\ \text{C/m}^2}{2\left(8.85\times10^{-12}\ \text{C}^2/\text{N}\cdot\text{m}^2\right)} = \boxed{508\ \text{kN/C, upward}}$$

P24.38 Note that the electric field in each case is directed radially inward, toward the filament.

(a) $$E = \frac{2k_e\lambda}{r} = \frac{2\left(8.99\times10^9\ \text{N}\cdot\text{m}^2/\text{C}^2\right)\left(90.0\times10^{-6}\ \text{C/m}\right)}{0.100\ \text{m}} = \boxed{16.2\ \text{MN/C}}$$

(b) $$E = \frac{2k_e\lambda}{r} = \frac{2\left(8.99\times10^9\ \text{N}\cdot\text{m}^2/\text{C}^2\right)\left(90.0\times10^{-6}\ \text{C/m}\right)}{0.200\ \text{m}} = \boxed{8.09\ \text{MN/C}}$$

(c) $$E = \frac{2k_e\lambda}{r} = \frac{2\left(8.99\times10^9\ \text{N}\cdot\text{m}^2/\text{C}^2\right)\left(90.0\times10^{-6}\ \text{C/m}\right)}{1.00\ \text{m}} = \boxed{1.62\ \text{MN/C}}$$

Section 24.4 **Conductors in Electrostatic Equilibrium**

P24.39 $$\oint E\,dA = E(2\pi rl) = \frac{q_{\text{in}}}{\epsilon_0} \qquad E = \frac{q_{\text{in}}/l}{2\pi\epsilon_0 r} = \frac{\lambda}{2\pi\epsilon_0 r}$$

(a) $r = 3.00$ cm $\qquad \mathbf{E} = \boxed{0}$

(b) $r = 10.0$ cm $$\mathbf{E} = \frac{30.0\times10^{-9}}{2\pi\left(8.85\times10^{-12}\right)(0.100)} = \boxed{5\,400\ \text{N/C, outward}}$$

(c) $r = 100$ cm $$\mathbf{E} = \frac{30.0\times10^{-9}}{2\pi\left(8.85\times10^{-12}\right)(1.00)} = \boxed{540\ \text{N/C, outward}}$$

P24.40 From Gauss's Law, $EA = \frac{Q}{\epsilon_0}$

$$\sigma = \frac{Q}{A} = \epsilon_0 E = \left(8.85 \times 10^{-12}\right)(-130) = -1.15 \times 10^{-9}\ \text{C/m}^2 = \boxed{-1.15\ \text{nC/m}^2}$$

P24.41 The fields are equal. The Equation 24.9 $E = \frac{\sigma_{\text{conductor}}}{\epsilon_0}$ for the field outside the aluminum looks different from Equation 24.8 $E = \frac{\sigma_{\text{insulator}}}{2\epsilon_0}$ for the field around glass. But its charge will spread out to cover both sides of the aluminum plate, so the density is $\sigma_{\text{conductor}} = \frac{Q}{2A}$. The glass carries charge only on area A, with $\sigma_{\text{insulator}} = \frac{Q}{A}$. The two fields are $\frac{Q}{2A\epsilon_0}$ the same in magnitude, and both are perpendicular to the plates, vertically upward if Q is positive.

***P24.42** (a) All of the charge sits on the surface of the copper sphere at radius 15 cm. The field inside is $\boxed{\text{zero}}$.

(b) The charged sphere creates field at exterior points as if it were a point charge at the center:

$$\mathbf{E} = \frac{k_e q}{r^2}\ \text{away} = \frac{\left(8.99 \times 10^9\ \text{Nm}^2\right)\left(40 \times 10^{-9}\ \text{C}\right)}{\text{C}^2 (0.17\ \text{m})^2}\ \text{outward} = \boxed{1.24 \times 10^4\ \text{N/C outward}}$$

(c) $$\mathbf{E} = \frac{\left(8.99 \times 10^9\ \text{Nm}^2\right)\left(40 \times 10^{-9}\ \text{C}\right)}{\text{C}^2 (0.75\ \text{m})^2}\ \text{outward} = \boxed{639\ \text{N/C outward}}$$

(d) All three answers would be the same.

P24.43 (a) $E = \frac{\sigma}{\epsilon_0}$ $\qquad \sigma = \left(8.00 \times 10^4\right)\left(8.85 \times 10^{-12}\right) = 7.08 \times 10^{-7}\ \text{C/m}^2$

$\sigma = \boxed{708\ \text{nC/m}^2}$, positive on one face and negative on the other.

(b) $\sigma = \frac{Q}{A}$ $\qquad Q = \sigma A = \left(7.08 \times 10^{-7}\right)(0.500)^2\ \text{C}$

$Q = 1.77 \times 10^{-7}\ \text{C} = \boxed{177\ \text{nC}}$, positive on one face and negative on the other.

P24.44 (a) $\mathbf{E} = \boxed{0}$

(b) $$E = \frac{k_e Q}{r^2} = \frac{\left(8.99 \times 10^9\right)\left(8.00 \times 10^{-6}\right)}{(0.030\,0)^2} = 7.99 \times 10^7\ \text{N/C} \qquad \mathbf{E} = \boxed{79.9\ \text{MN/C radially outward}}$$

(c) $\mathbf{E} = \boxed{0}$

(d) $$E = \frac{k_e Q}{r^2} = \frac{\left(8.99 \times 10^9\right)\left(4.00 \times 10^{-6}\right)}{(0.070\,0)^2} = 7.34 \times 10^6\ \text{N/C} \qquad \mathbf{E} = \boxed{7.34\ \text{MN/C radially outward}}$$

P24.45 The charge divides equally between the identical spheres, with charge $\frac{Q}{2}$ on each. Then they repel like point charges at their centers:

$$F=\frac{k_e(Q/2)(Q/2)}{(L+R+R)^2}=\frac{k_eQ^2}{4(L+2R)^2}=\frac{8.99\times10^9\ \text{N}\cdot\text{m}^2\left(60.0\times10^{-6}\ \text{C}\right)^2}{4\ \text{C}^2(2.01\ \text{m})^2}=\boxed{2.00\ \text{N}}.$$

P24.46 The electric field on the surface of a conductor varies inversely with the radius of curvature of the surface. Thus, the field is most intense where the radius of curvature is smallest and vice-versa. The local charge density and the electric field intensity are related by

$$E=\frac{\sigma}{\epsilon_0}\qquad\text{or}\qquad\sigma=\epsilon_0 E.$$

(a) Where the radius of curvature is the greatest,

$$\sigma=\epsilon_0 E_{\text{min}}=\left(8.85\times10^{-12}\ \text{C}^2/\text{N}\cdot\text{m}^2\right)\left(2.80\times10^4\ \text{N/C}\right)=\boxed{248\ \text{nC/m}^2}.$$

(b) Where the radius of curvature is the smallest,

$$\sigma=\epsilon_0 E_{\text{max}}=\left(8.85\times10^{-12}\ \text{C}^2/\text{N}\cdot\text{m}^2\right)\left(5.60\times10^4\ \text{N/C}\right)=\boxed{496\ \text{nC/m}^2}.$$

P24.47 (a) Inside surface: consider a cylindrical surface within the metal. Since E inside the conducting shell is zero, the total charge inside the gaussian surface must be zero, so the inside charge/length $=-\lambda$.

$0=\lambda\ell+q_{\text{in}}$ so $\frac{q_{\text{in}}}{\ell}=\boxed{-\lambda}$

Outside surface: The total charge on the metal cylinder is $2\lambda\ell=q_{\text{in}}+q_{\text{out}}$

$q_{\text{out}}=2\lambda\ell+\lambda\ell$ so the outside charge/length is $\boxed{3\lambda}$.

(b) $$E=\frac{2k_e(3\lambda)}{r}=\frac{6k_e\lambda}{r}=\boxed{\frac{3\lambda}{2\pi\epsilon_0 r}\ \text{radially outward}}$$

P24.48 (a) $$E=\frac{k_eQ}{r^2}=\frac{\left(8.99\times10^9\right)\left(6.40\times10^{-6}\right)}{(0.150)^2}=\boxed{2.56\ \text{MN/C, radially inward}}$$

(b) $\boxed{E=0}$

P24.49 (a) The charge density on each of the surfaces (upper and lower) of the plate is:

$$\sigma=\frac{1}{2}\left(\frac{q}{A}\right)=\frac{1}{2}\frac{\left(4.00\times10^{-8}\ \text{C}\right)}{(0.500\ \text{m})^2}=8.00\times10^{-8}\ \text{C/m}^2=\boxed{80.0\ \text{nC/m}^2}.$$

(b) $$\mathbf{E}=\left(\frac{\sigma}{\epsilon_0}\right)\hat{\mathbf{k}}=\left(\frac{8.00\times10^{-8}\ \text{C/m}^2}{8.85\times10^{-12}\ \text{C}^2/\text{N}\cdot\text{m}^2}\right)\hat{\mathbf{k}}=\boxed{(9.04\ \text{kN/C})\hat{\mathbf{k}}}$$

(c) $\mathbf{E}=\boxed{(-9.04\ \text{kN/C})\hat{\mathbf{k}}}$

P24.50 (a) The charge $+q$ at the center induces charge $-q$ on the inner surface of the conductor, where its surface density is:

$$\sigma_a = \boxed{\frac{-q}{4\pi a^2}}.$$

(b) The outer surface carries charge $Q+q$ with density

$$\sigma_b = \boxed{\frac{Q+q}{4\pi b^2}}.$$

P24.51 Use Gauss's Law to evaluate the electric field in each region, recalling that the electric field is zero everywhere within conducting materials. The results are:

$\boxed{E = 0 \text{ inside the sphere and within the material of the shell}}$

$\boxed{E = k_e \frac{Q}{r^2} \text{ between the sphere and shell, directed radially inward}}$

$\boxed{E = k_e \frac{2Q}{r^2} \text{ outside the shell, directed radially outward}}$.

Charge $\boxed{-Q \text{ is on the outer surface of the sphere}}$.

Charge $\boxed{+Q \text{ is on the inner surface of the shell}}$,

and $\boxed{+2Q \text{ is on the outer surface of the shell.}}$

P24.52 An approximate sketch is given at the right. Note that the electric field lines should be perpendicular to the conductor both inside and outside.

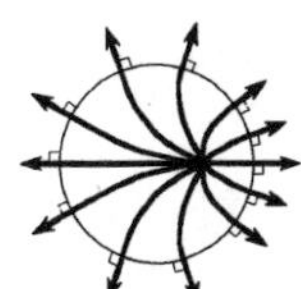

FIG. P24.52

Section 24.5 Formal Derivation of Gauss's Law

P24.53 (a) Uniform **E**, pointing radially outward, so $\Phi_E = EA$. The arc length is $ds = Rd\theta$, and the circumference is $2\pi r = 2\pi R\sin\theta$

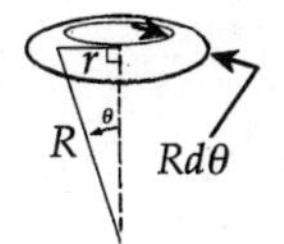

FIG. P24.53

$$A = \int 2\pi r ds = \int_0^\theta (2\pi R\sin\theta)Rd\theta = 2\pi R^2 \int_0^\theta \sin\theta d\theta = 2\pi R^2(-\cos\theta)\Big|_0^\theta = 2\pi R^2(1-\cos\theta)$$

$$\Phi_E = \frac{1}{4\pi \epsilon_0}\frac{Q}{R^2}\cdot 2\pi R^2(1-\cos\theta) = \boxed{\frac{Q}{2\epsilon_0}(1-\cos\theta)} \quad \text{[independent of R!]}$$

(b) For $\theta = 90.0°$ (hemisphere): $\Phi_E = \frac{Q}{2\epsilon_0}(1-\cos 90°) = \boxed{\frac{Q}{2\epsilon_0}}$.

(c) For $\theta = 180°$ (entire sphere): $\Phi_E = \frac{Q}{2\epsilon_0}(1-\cos 180°) = \boxed{\frac{Q}{\epsilon_0}}$ [Gauss's Law].

Additional Problems

P24.54 In general, $\mathbf{E} = ay\hat{\mathbf{i}} + bz\hat{\mathbf{j}} + cx\hat{\mathbf{k}}$

In the xy plane, $z = 0$ and $\mathbf{E} = ay\hat{\mathbf{i}} + cx\hat{\mathbf{k}}$

$$\Phi_E = \int \mathbf{E}\cdot d\mathbf{A} = \int \left(ay\hat{\mathbf{i}} + cx\hat{\mathbf{k}}\right)\cdot\hat{\mathbf{k}}\,dA$$

$$\Phi_E = ch\int_{x=0}^{w} x\,dx = ch\left.\frac{x^2}{2}\right|_{x=0}^{w} = \boxed{\frac{chw^2}{2}}$$

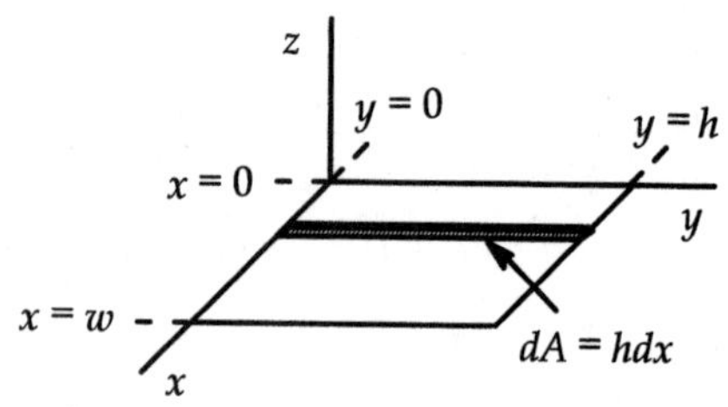

FIG. P24.54

P24.55 (a) $q_{in} = +3Q - Q = \boxed{+2Q}$

(b) The charge distribution is spherically symmetric and $q_{in} > 0$. Thus, the field is directed $\boxed{\text{radially outward}}$.

(c) $E = \dfrac{k_e q_{in}}{r^2} = \boxed{\dfrac{2k_eQ}{r^2}}$ for $r \ge c$.

(d) Since all points within this region are located inside conducting material, $\boxed{E = 0}$ for $b < r < c$.

(e) $\Phi_E = \int \mathbf{E}\cdot d\mathbf{A} = 0 \Rightarrow q_{in} = \epsilon_0\,\Phi_E = \boxed{0}$

(f) $q_{in} = \boxed{+3Q}$

(g) $E = \dfrac{k_e q_{in}}{r^2} = \boxed{\dfrac{3k_eQ}{r^2}}$ (radially outward) for $a \le r < b$.

(h) $q_{in} = \rho V = \left(\dfrac{+3Q}{\frac{4}{3}\pi a^3}\right)\left(\dfrac{4}{3}\pi r^3\right) = \boxed{+3Q\dfrac{r^3}{a^3}}$

(i) $E = \dfrac{k_e q_{in}}{r^2} = \dfrac{k_e}{r^2}\left(+3Q\dfrac{r^3}{a^3}\right) = \boxed{3k_eQ\dfrac{r}{a^3}}$ (radially outward) for $0 \le r \le a$.

(j) From part (d), $E = 0$ for $b < r < c$. Thus, for a spherical gaussian surface with $b < r < c$, $q_{in} = +3Q + q_{inner} = 0$ where q_{inner} is the charge on the inner surface of the conducting shell. This yields $q_{inner} = \boxed{-3Q}$.

(k) Since the total charge on the conducting shell is $q_{net} = q_{outer} + q_{inner} = -Q$, we have $q_{outer} = -Q - q_{inner} = -Q - (-3Q) = \boxed{+2Q}$.

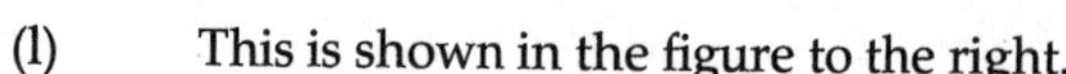

(l) This is shown in the figure to the right.

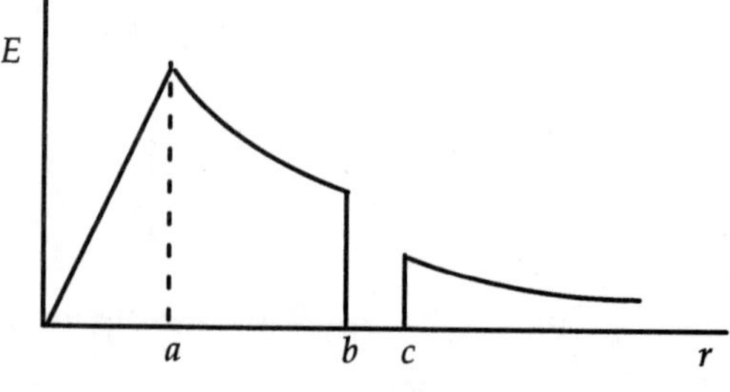

FIG. P24.55(l)

P24.56 The sphere with large charge creates a strong field to polarize the other sphere. That means it pushes the excess charge over to the far side, leaving charge of the opposite sign on the near side. This patch of opposite charge is smaller in amount but located in a stronger external field, so it can feel a force of attraction that is larger than the repelling force felt by the larger charge in the weaker field on the other side.

P24.57 (a) $\oint \mathbf{E}\cdot d\mathbf{A} = E\left(4\pi r^2\right) = \dfrac{q_{in}}{\epsilon_0}$

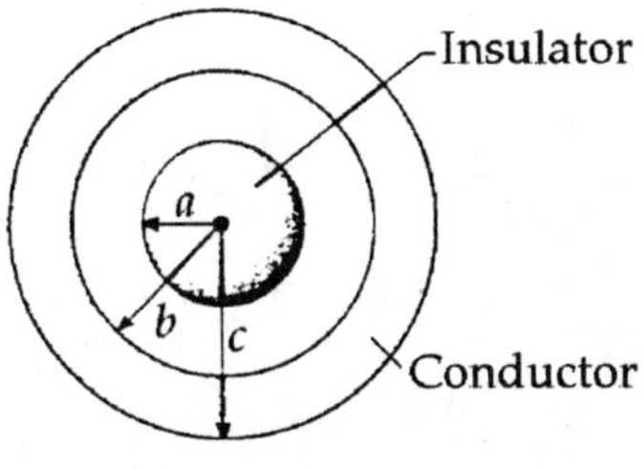

For $r < a$, $q_{in} = \rho\left(\dfrac{4}{3}\pi r^3\right)$

so $E = \boxed{\dfrac{\rho r}{3\epsilon_0}}$.

For $a < r < b$ and $c < r$, $q_{in} = Q$.

So $E = \boxed{\dfrac{Q}{4\pi r^2 \epsilon_0}}$.

For $b \le r \le c$, $E = 0$, since $\boxed{E=0}$ inside a conductor.

FIG. P24.57

(b) Let $q_1 =$ induced charge on the inner surface of the hollow sphere. Since $E = 0$ inside the conductor, the total charge enclosed by a spherical surface of radius $b \le r \le c$ must be zero.

Therefore, $q_1 + Q = 0$ and $\sigma_1 = \dfrac{q_1}{4\pi b^2} = \boxed{\dfrac{-Q}{4\pi b^2}}$.

Let $q_2 =$ induced charge on the outside surface of the hollow sphere. Since the hollow sphere is uncharged, we require

$q_1 + q_2 = 0$ and $\sigma_2 = \dfrac{q_1}{4\pi c^2} = \boxed{\dfrac{Q}{4\pi c^2}}$.

P24.58 $\oint \mathbf{E}\cdot d\mathbf{A} = E\left(4\pi r^2\right) = \dfrac{q_{in}}{\epsilon_0}$

(a) $\left(-3.60\times10^3 \text{ N/C}\right)4\pi(0.100 \text{ m})^2 = \dfrac{Q}{8.85\times10^{-12} \text{ C}^2/\text{N}\cdot\text{m}^2}$ $(a < r < b)$

$Q = -4.00\times10^{-9} \text{ C} = \boxed{-4.00 \text{ nC}}$

(b) We take Q' to be the net charge on the hollow sphere. Outside c,

$\left(+2.00\times10^2 \text{ N/C}\right)4\pi(0.500 \text{ m})^2 = \dfrac{Q+Q'}{8.85\times10^{-12} \text{ C}^2/\text{N}\cdot\text{m}^2}$ $(r > c)$

$Q + Q' = +5.56\times10^{-9}$ C, so $Q' = +9.56\times10^{-9} \text{ C} = \boxed{+9.56 \text{ nC}}$

(c) For $b < r < c$: $E = 0$ and $q_{in} = Q + Q_1 = 0$ where Q_1 is the total charge on the inner surface of the hollow sphere. Thus, $Q_1 = -Q = \boxed{+4.00 \text{ nC}}$.

Then, if Q_2 is the total charge on the outer surface of the hollow sphere,

$Q_2 = Q' - Q_1 = 9.56 \text{ nC} - 4.0 \text{ nC} = \boxed{+5.56 \text{ nC}}$.

***P24.59** The vertical velocity component of the moving charge increases according to

$$m\frac{dv_y}{dt}=F_y \qquad m\frac{dv_y}{dx}\frac{dx}{dt}=qE_y.$$

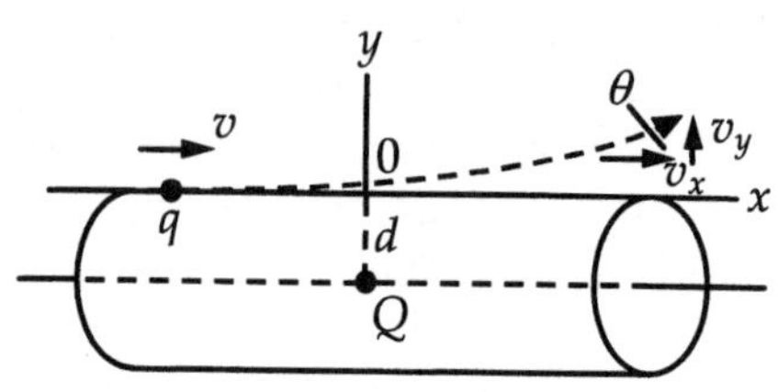

FIG. P24.59

Now $\frac{dx}{dt}=v_x$ has the nearly constant value v. So

$$dv_y=\frac{q}{mv}E_y dx \qquad v_y=\int_0^{v_y}dv_y=\frac{q}{mv}\int_{-\infty}^{\infty}E_y dx.$$

The radially outward compnent of the electric field varies along the x axis, but is described by

$$\int_{-\infty}^{\infty}E_y dA=\int_{-\infty}^{\infty}E_y(2\pi d)dx=\frac{Q}{\epsilon_0}.$$

So $\int_{-\infty}^{\infty}E_y dx=\frac{Q}{2\pi d\,\epsilon_0}$ and $v_y=\frac{qQ}{mv2\pi d\,\epsilon_0}$. The angle of deflection is described by

$$\tan\theta=\frac{v_y}{v}=\frac{qQ}{2\pi\,\epsilon_0\,dmv^2} \qquad \boxed{\theta=\tan^{-1}\frac{qQ}{2\pi\,\epsilon_0\,dmv^2}}.$$

P24.60 First, consider the field at distance $r<R$ from the center of a uniform sphere of positive charge $(Q=+e)$ with radius R.

$$\left(4\pi r^2\right)E=\frac{q_{\text{in}}}{\epsilon_0}=\frac{\rho V}{\epsilon_0}=\left(\frac{+e}{\frac{4}{3}\pi R^3}\right)\frac{\frac{4}{3}\pi r^3}{\epsilon_0} \quad \text{so } E=\left(\frac{e}{4\pi\,\epsilon_0\,R^3}\right)r \text{ directed outward}$$

(a) The force exerted on a point charge $q=-e$ located at distance r from the center is then

$$F=qE=-e\left(\frac{e}{4\pi\,\epsilon_0\,R^3}\right)r=-\left(\frac{e^2}{4\pi\,\epsilon_0\,R^3}\right)r=\boxed{-Kr}.$$

(b) $$K=\frac{e^2}{4\pi\,\epsilon_0\,R^3}=\boxed{\frac{k_e e^2}{R^3}}$$

(c) $$F_r=m_e a_r=-\left(\frac{k_e e^2}{R^3}\right)r\text{, so } a_r=-\left(\frac{k_e e^2}{m_e R^3}\right)r=-\omega^2 r$$

Thus, the motion is simple harmonic with frequency $f=\frac{\omega}{2\pi}=\boxed{\frac{1}{2\pi}\sqrt{\frac{k_e e^2}{m_e R^3}}}$.

(d) $$f=2.47\times10^{15}\text{ Hz}=\frac{1}{2\pi}\sqrt{\frac{\left(8.99\times10^9\text{ N}\cdot\text{m}^2/\text{C}^2\right)\left(1.60\times10^{-19}\text{ C}\right)^2}{\left(9.11\times10^{-31}\text{ kg}\right)R^3}}$$

which yields $R^3=1.05\times10^{-30}\text{ m}^3$, or $R=1.02\times10^{-10}\text{ m}=\boxed{102\text{ pm}}$.

P24.61 The field direction is radially outward perpendicular to the axis. The field strength depends on r but not on the other cylindrical coordinates θ or z. Choose a Gaussian cylinder of radius r and length L. If $r < a$,

$$\Phi_E = \frac{q_{\text{in}}}{\epsilon_0} \quad \text{and} \quad E(2\pi rL) = \frac{\lambda L}{\epsilon_0}$$

$$E = \frac{\lambda}{2\pi r \epsilon_0} \quad \text{or} \quad \boxed{\mathbf{E} = \frac{\lambda}{2\pi r \epsilon_0}\hat{\mathbf{r}} \quad (r < a)}.$$

If $a < r < b$,

$$E(2\pi rL) = \frac{\lambda L + \rho\pi(r^2 - a^2)L}{\epsilon_0}$$

$$\boxed{\mathbf{E} = \frac{\lambda + \rho\pi(r^2 - a^2)}{2\pi r \epsilon_0}\hat{\mathbf{r}} \quad (a < r < b)}.$$

If $r > b$,

$$E(2\pi rL) = \frac{\lambda L + \rho\pi(b^2 - a^2)L}{\epsilon_0}$$

$$\boxed{\mathbf{E} = \frac{\lambda + \rho\pi(b^2 - a^2)}{2\pi r \epsilon_0}\hat{\mathbf{r}} \quad (r > b)}.$$

P24.62 Consider the field due to a single sheet and let E_+ and E_- represent the fields due to the positive and negative sheets. The field at any distance from each sheet has a magnitude given by Equation 24.8:

$$|E_+| = |E_-| = \frac{\sigma}{2\epsilon_0}.$$

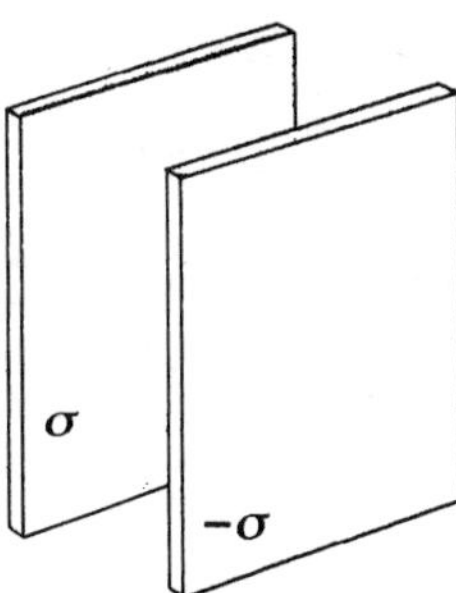

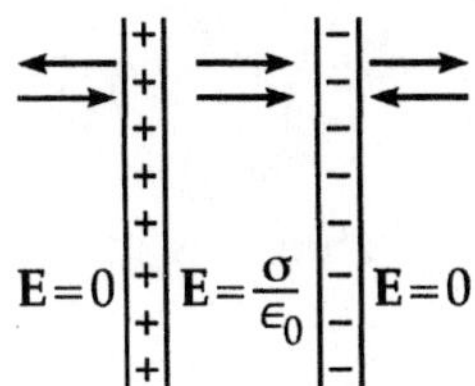

FIG. P24.62

(a) To the left of the positive sheet, E_+ is directed toward the left and E_- toward the right and the net field over this region is $\mathbf{E} = \boxed{0}$.

(b) In the region between the sheets, E_+ and E_- are both directed toward the right and the net field is

$$\mathbf{E} = \boxed{\frac{\sigma}{\epsilon_0} \text{ to the right}}.$$

(c) To the right of the negative sheet, E_+ and E_- are again oppositely directed and $\mathbf{E} = \boxed{0}$.

P24.63 The magnitude of the field due to the each sheet given by Equation 24.8 is

$$E = \frac{\sigma}{2\in_0} \text{ directed perpendicular to the sheet.}$$

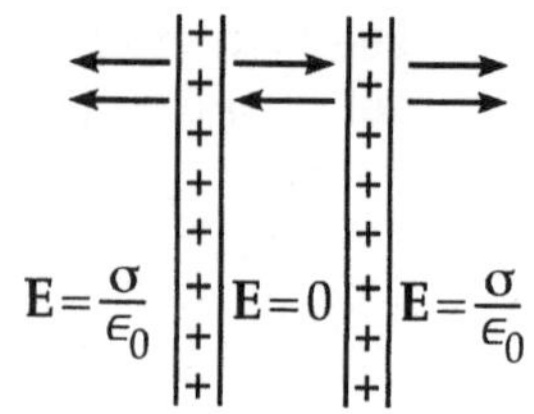

FIG. P24.63

(a) In the region to the left of the pair of sheets, both fields are directed toward the left and the net field is

$$\mathbf{E} = \boxed{\frac{\sigma}{\in_0} \text{ to the left}}.$$

(b) In the region between the sheets, the fields due to the individual sheets are oppositely directed and the net field is

$$\mathbf{E} = \boxed{0}.$$

(c) In the region to the right of the pair of sheets, both are fields are directed toward the right and the net field is

$$\mathbf{E} = \boxed{\frac{\sigma}{\in_0} \text{ to the right}}.$$

P24.64 The resultant field within the cavity is the superposition of two fields, one $\mathbf{E}_+$ due to a uniform sphere of positive charge of radius $2a$, and the other $\mathbf{E}_-$ due to a sphere of negative charge of radius a centered within the cavity.

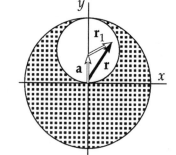

$$\frac{4}{3}\left(\frac{\pi r^3 \rho}{\in_0}\right) = 4\pi r^2 E_+ \qquad \text{so} \qquad \mathbf{E}_+ = \frac{\rho r}{3\in_0}\hat{\mathbf{r}} = \frac{\rho \mathbf{r}}{3\in_0}$$

$$-\frac{4}{3}\left(\frac{\pi r_1^3 \rho}{\in_0}\right) = 4\pi r_1^2 E_- \qquad \text{so} \qquad \mathbf{E}_- = \frac{\rho r_1}{3\in_0}\left(-\hat{\mathbf{r}}_1\right) = \frac{-\rho}{3\in_0}\mathbf{r}_1.$$

FIG. P24.64

Since $\mathbf{r} = \mathbf{a} + \mathbf{r}_1$, $\quad \mathbf{E}_- = \frac{-\rho(\mathbf{r}-\mathbf{a})}{3\in_0}$

$$\mathbf{E} = \mathbf{E}_+ + \mathbf{E}_- = \frac{\rho \mathbf{r}}{3\in_0} - \frac{\rho \mathbf{r}}{3\in_0} + \frac{\rho \mathbf{a}}{3\in_0} = \frac{\rho \mathbf{a}}{3\in_0} = 0\hat{\mathbf{i}} + \frac{\rho a}{3\in_0}\hat{\mathbf{j}}.$$

Thus, $\boxed{E_x = 0}$

and $\boxed{E_y = \frac{\rho a}{3\in_0}}$ at all points within the cavity.

***P24.65** Consider the charge distribution to be an unbroken charged spherical shell with uniform charge density σ and a circular disk with charge per area $-\sigma$. The total field is that due to the whole sphere, $\frac{Q}{4\pi\in_0 R^2} = \frac{4\pi R^2\sigma}{4\pi\varepsilon_0 R^2} = \frac{\sigma}{\in_0}$ outward plus the field of the disk $-\frac{\sigma}{2\in_0} = \frac{\sigma}{2\in_0}$ radially inward. The total field is $\frac{\sigma}{\in_0} - \frac{\sigma}{2\in_0} = \boxed{\frac{\sigma}{2\in_0} \text{ outward}}$.

P24.66 The electric field throughout the region is directed along x; therefore, **E** will be perpendicular to dA over the four faces of the surface which are perpendicular to the yz plane, and E will be parallel to dA over the two faces which are parallel to the yz plane. Therefore,

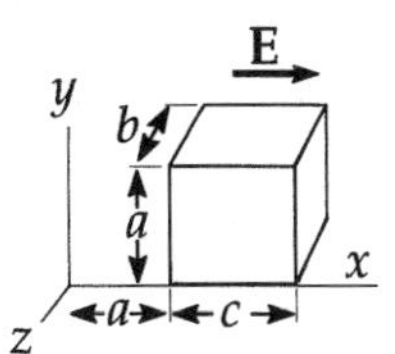

FIG. P24.66

$$\Phi_E = -\left(E_x\big|_{x=a}\right)A + \left(E_x\big|_{x=a+c}\right)A = -\left(3+2a^2\right)ab + \left(3+2(a+c)^2\right)ab = 2abc(2a+c).$$

Substituting the given values for a, b, and c, we find $\Phi_E = \boxed{0.269\ \text{N}\cdot\text{m}^2/\text{C}}$.

$Q = \epsilon_0 \Phi_E = 2.38\times10^{-12}\ \text{C} = \boxed{2.38\ \text{pC}}$

P24.67 $\oint \mathbf{E}\cdot d\mathbf{A} = E\left(4\pi r^2\right) = \dfrac{q_{\text{in}}}{\epsilon_0}$

(a) For $r > R$, $q_{\text{in}} = \int_0^R Ar^2\left(4\pi r^2\right)dr = 4\pi\dfrac{AR^5}{5}$

and $E = \boxed{\dfrac{AR^5}{5\epsilon_0 r^2}}$.

(b) For $r < R$, $q_{\text{in}} = \int_0^r Ar^2\left(4\pi r^2\right)dr = \dfrac{4\pi Ar^5}{5}$

and $E = \boxed{\dfrac{Ar^3}{5\epsilon_0}}$.

P24.68 The total flux through a surface enclosing the charge Q is $\dfrac{Q}{\epsilon_0}$. The flux through the disk is

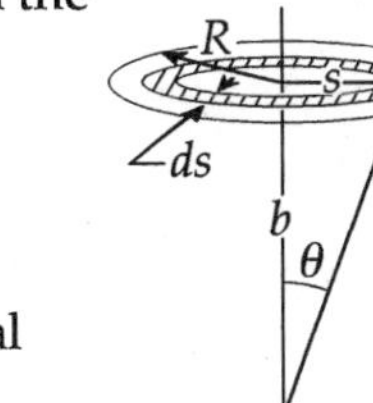

FIG. P24.68

$\Phi_{\text{disk}} = \int \mathbf{E}\cdot d\mathbf{A}$

where the integration covers the area of the disk. We must evaluate this integral and set it equal to $\dfrac{\frac{1}{4}Q}{\epsilon_0}$ to find how b and R are related. In the figure, take $d\mathbf{A}$ to be the area of an annular ring of radius s and width ds. The flux through $d\mathbf{A}$ is

$\mathbf{E}\cdot d\mathbf{A} = EdA\cos\theta = E(2\pi s\,ds)\cos\theta$.

The magnitude of the electric field has the same value at all points within the annular ring,

$$E = \frac{1}{4\pi\epsilon_0}\frac{Q}{r^2} = \frac{1}{4\pi\epsilon_0}\frac{Q}{s^2+b^2} \quad \text{and} \quad \cos\theta = \frac{b}{r} = \frac{b}{\left(s^2+b^2\right)^{1/2}}.$$

Integrate from $s = 0$ to $s = R$ to get the flux through the entire disk.

$$\Phi_{E,\,\text{disk}} = \frac{Qb}{2\epsilon_0}\int_0^R \frac{s\,ds}{\left(s^2+b^2\right)^{3/2}} = \frac{Qb}{2\epsilon_0}\left[-\left(s^2+b^2\right)^{1/2}\right]_0^R = \frac{Q}{2\epsilon_0}\left[1-\frac{b}{\left(R^2+b^2\right)^{1/2}}\right]$$

The flux through the disk equals $\dfrac{Q}{4\epsilon_0}$ provided that $\dfrac{b}{\left(R^2+b^2\right)^{1/2}} = \dfrac{1}{2}$.

This is satisfied if $\boxed{R = \sqrt{3}b}$.

P24.69 $\oint \mathbf{E}\cdot d\mathbf{A} = \frac{q_{\text{in}}}{\epsilon_0} = \frac{1}{\epsilon_0}\int_0^r \frac{a}{r} 4\pi r^2 dr$

$$E 4\pi r^2 = \frac{4\pi a}{\epsilon_0}\int_0^r r\,dr = \frac{4\pi a}{\epsilon_0}\frac{r^2}{2}$$

$$\boxed{E = \frac{a}{2\epsilon_0}} = \text{constant magnitude}$$

(The direction is radially outward from center for positive a; radially inward for negative a.)

P24.70 In this case the charge density is *not uniform*, and Gauss's law is written as $\oint \mathbf{E}\cdot d\mathbf{A} = \frac{1}{\epsilon_0}\int \rho\,dV$. We use a gaussian surface which is a cylinder of radius r, length ℓ, and is coaxial with the charge distribution.

(a) When $r < R$, this becomes $E(2\pi r\ell) = \frac{\rho_0}{\epsilon_0}\int_0^r \left(a - \frac{r}{b}\right) dV$. The element of volume is a cylindrical shell of radius r, length ℓ, and thickness dr so that $dV = 2\pi r\ell\,dr$.

$$E(2\pi r\ell) = \left(\frac{2\pi r^2 \ell \rho_0}{\epsilon_0}\right)\left(\frac{a}{2} - \frac{r}{3b}\right) \text{ so inside the cylinder, } E = \boxed{\frac{\rho_0 r}{2\epsilon_0}\left(a - \frac{2r}{3b}\right)}.$$

(b) When $r > R$, Gauss's law becomes

$$E(2\pi r\ell) = \frac{\rho_0}{\epsilon_0}\int_0^R \left(a - \frac{r}{b}\right)(2\pi r\ell\,dr) \text{ or outside the cylinder, } E = \boxed{\frac{\rho_0 R^2}{2\epsilon_0 r}\left(a - \frac{2R}{3b}\right)}.$$

P24.71 (a) Consider a cylindrical shaped gaussian surface perpendicular to the yz plane with one end in the yz plane and the other end containing the point x:

Use Gauss's law: $\oint \mathbf{E}\cdot d\mathbf{A} = \frac{q_{\text{in}}}{\epsilon_0}$

By symmetry, the electric field is zero in the yz plane and is perpendicular to $d\mathbf{A}$ over the wall of the gaussian cylinder. Therefore, the only contribution to the integral is over the end cap containing the point x:

$$\oint \mathbf{E}\cdot d\mathbf{A} = \frac{q_{\text{in}}}{\epsilon_0} \text{ or } EA = \frac{\rho(Ax)}{\epsilon_0}$$

so that at distance x from the mid-line of the slab, $\boxed{E = \frac{\rho x}{\epsilon_0}}$.

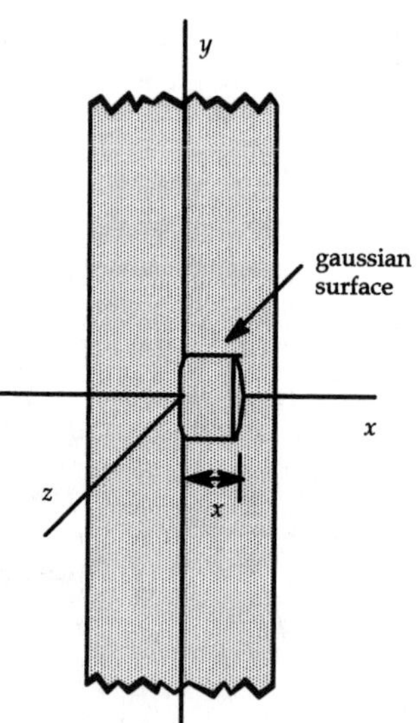

FIG. P24.71

(b) $a = \frac{F}{m_e} = \frac{(-e)E}{m_e} = -\left(\frac{\rho e}{m_e \epsilon_0}\right)x$

The acceleration of the electron is of the form $a = -\omega^2 x$ with $\omega = \sqrt{\frac{\rho e}{m_e \epsilon_0}}$.

Thus, the motion is simple harmonic with frequency $f = \frac{\omega}{2\pi} = \boxed{\frac{1}{2\pi}\sqrt{\frac{\rho e}{m_e \epsilon_0}}}$.

P24.72 Consider the gaussian surface described in the solution to problem 71.

(a) For $x > \frac{d}{2}$, $dq = \rho dV = \rho A dx = CAx^2 dx$

$$\int \mathbf{E} \cdot d\mathbf{A} = \frac{1}{\epsilon_0} \int dq$$

$$EA = \frac{CA}{\epsilon_0} \int_0^{d/2} x^2 dx = \frac{1}{3}\left(\frac{CA}{\epsilon_0}\right)\left(\frac{d^3}{8}\right)$$

$$E = \frac{Cd^3}{24 \epsilon_0} \quad \text{or} \quad \boxed{\mathbf{E} = \frac{Cd^3}{24 \epsilon_0}\hat{\mathbf{i}} \text{ for } x > \frac{d}{2}; \quad \mathbf{E} = -\frac{Cd^3}{24 \epsilon_0}\hat{\mathbf{i}} \text{ for } x < -\frac{d}{2}}$$

(b) For $-\frac{d}{2} < x < \frac{d}{2}$ $\int \mathbf{E} \cdot d\mathbf{A} = \frac{1}{\epsilon_0} \int dq = \frac{CA}{\epsilon_0} \int_0^x x^2 dx = \frac{CAx^3}{3 \epsilon_0}$

$$\boxed{\mathbf{E} = \frac{Cx^3}{3 \epsilon_0}\hat{\mathbf{i}} \text{ for } x > 0; \quad \mathbf{E} = -\frac{Cx^3}{3 \epsilon_0}\hat{\mathbf{i}} \text{ for } x < 0}$$

P24.73 (a) A point mass m creates a gravitational acceleration $\mathbf{g} = -\frac{Gm}{r^2}\hat{\mathbf{r}}$ at a distance r.

The flux of this field through a sphere is $\oint \mathbf{g} \cdot d\mathbf{A} = -\frac{Gm}{r^2}\left(4\pi r^2\right) = -4\pi Gm$.

Since the r has divided out, we can visualize the field as unbroken field lines. The same flux would go through any other closed surface around the mass. If there are several or no masses inside a closed surface, each creates field to make its own contribution to the net flux according to

$$\boxed{\oint \mathbf{g} \cdot d\mathbf{A} = -4\pi G m_{\text{in}}}.$$

(b) Take a spherical gaussian surface of radius r. The field is inward so

$$\oint \mathbf{g} \cdot d\mathbf{A} = g4\pi r^2 \cos 180° = -g4\pi r^2$$

and $-4\pi G m_{\text{in}} = -4\pi G \frac{4}{3}\pi r^3 \rho$.

Then, $-g4\pi r^2 = -4\pi G \frac{4}{3}\pi r^3 \rho$ and $g = \frac{4}{3}\pi r \rho G$.

Or, since $\rho = \frac{M_E}{\frac{4}{3}\pi R_E^3}$, $g = \frac{M_E G r}{R_E^3}$ or $\boxed{\mathbf{g} = \frac{M_E G r}{R_E^3} \text{ inward}}$.

ANSWERS TO EVEN PROBLEMS

P24.2 $355 \text{ kN} \cdot \text{m}^2/\text{C}$

P24.4 (a) $-2.34 \text{ kN} \cdot \text{m}^2/\text{C}$; (b) $+2.34 \text{ kN} \cdot \text{m}^2/\text{C}$; (c) 0

P24.6 $\frac{q}{\epsilon_0}$

P24.8 ERh

P24.10 (a) -55.6 nC; (b) The negative charge has a spherically symmetric distribution.

P24.12 (a) $\frac{q}{2 \epsilon_0}$; (b) $\frac{q}{2 \epsilon_0}$; (c) Plane and square both subtend a solid angle of a hemisphere at the charge.

P24.14 (a) $1.36 \text{ MN} \cdot \text{m}^2/\text{C}$; (b) $678 \text{ kN} \cdot \text{m}^2/\text{C}$; (c) No; see the solution.

P24.16 1.77 $\mathrm{pC/m^3}$ positive

P24.18 $\dfrac{Q-6|q|}{6\in_0}$

P24.20 28.2 $\mathrm{N\cdot m^2/C}$

P24.22 $\dfrac{-q}{24\in_0}$

P24.24 (a) 0; (b) 365 kN/C; (c) 1.46 MN/C; (d) 649 kN/C

P24.26 (a) 913 nC; (b) 0

P24.28 4.86 GN/C away from the wall. It is constant close to the wall

P24.30 76.4 kN/C radially inward

P24.32 3.50 kN

P24.34 (a) $\dfrac{Qr^3}{\in_0 a^3}$; (b) $\dfrac{Q}{\in_0}$; (c) see the solution

P24.36 713 nC; (b) 5.70 μC

P24.38 (a) 16.2 MN/C toward the filament; (b) 8.09 MN/C toward the filament; (c) 1.62 MN/C toward the filament

P24.40 $-1.15\ \mathrm{nC/m^2}$

P24.42 (a) 0; (b) 12.4 kN/C radially outward; (c) 639 N/C radially outward; (d) Nothing would change.

P24.44 (a) 0; (b) 79.9 MN/C radially outward; (c) 0; (d) 7.34 MN/C radially outward

P24.46 (a) 248 $\mathrm{nC/m^2}$; (b) 496 $\mathrm{nC/m^2}$

P24.48 (a) 2.56 MN/C radially inward; (b) 0

P24.50 (a) $\dfrac{-q}{4\pi a^2}$; (b) $\dfrac{Q+q}{4\pi b^2}$

P24.52 see the solution

P24.54 $\dfrac{chw^2}{2}$

P24.56 see the solution

P24.58 (a) -4.00 nC; (b) $+9.56$ nC; (c) $+4.00$ nC and $+5.56$ nC

P24.60 (a, b) see the solution; (c) $\dfrac{1}{2\pi}\sqrt{\dfrac{k_e e^2}{m_e R^3}}$; (d) 102 pm

P24.62 (a) 0; (b) $\dfrac{\sigma}{\in_0}$ to the right; (c) 0

P24.64 see the solution

P24.66 0.269 $\mathrm{N\cdot m^2/C}$; 2.38 pC

P24.68 see the solution

P24.70 (a) $\dfrac{\rho_0 r}{2\in_0}\left(a-\dfrac{2r}{3b}\right)$; (b) $\dfrac{\rho_0 R^2}{2\in_0 r}\left(a-\dfrac{2R}{3b}\right)$

P24.72 (a) $\mathbf{E}=\dfrac{Cd^3}{24\in_0}\hat{\mathbf{i}}$ for $x>\dfrac{d}{2}$; $\mathbf{E}=-\dfrac{Cd^3}{24\in_0}\hat{\mathbf{i}}$ for $x<-\dfrac{d}{2}$; (b) $\mathbf{E}=\dfrac{Cx^3}{3\in_0}\hat{\mathbf{i}}$ for $x>0$; $\mathbf{E}=-\dfrac{Cx^3}{3\in_0}\hat{\mathbf{i}}$ for $x<0$

25

Electric Potential

CHAPTER OUTLINE

ANSWERS TO QUESTIONS

Q25.1 When one object B with electric charge is immersed in the electric field of another charge or charges A, the system possesses electric potential energy. The energy can be measured by seeing how much work the field does on the charge B as it moves to a reference location. We choose not to visualize A's effect on B as an action-at-a-distance, but as the result of a two-step process: Charge A creates electric potential throughout the surrounding space. Then the potential acts on B to inject the system with energy.

Q25.2 The potential energy increases. When an outside agent makes it move in the direction of the field, the charge moves to a region of lower electric potential. Then the product of its negative charge with a lower number of volts gives a higher number of joules. Keep in mind that a negative charge feels an electric force in the *opposite* direction to the field, while the potential is the work done on the charge to move it in a field per unit charge.

Q25.3 To move like charges together from an infinite separation, at which the potential energy of the system of two charges is zero, requires *work* to be done on the system by an outside agent. Hence energy is stored, and potential energy is positive. As charges with opposite signs move together from an infinite separation, energy is released, and the potential energy of the set of charges becomes negative.

Q25.4 The charge can be moved along any path parallel to the y-z plane, namely perpendicular to the field.

Q25.5 The electric field always points in the direction of the greatest change in electric potential. This is implied by the relationships $E_x = -\frac{\partial V}{\partial x}$, $E_y = -\frac{\partial V}{\partial y}$ and $E_z = -\frac{\partial V}{\partial z}$.

Q25.6 (a) The equipotential surfaces are nesting coaxial cylinders around an infinite line of charge.

(b) The equipotential surfaces are nesting concentric spheres around a uniformly charged sphere.

Q25.7 If there were a potential difference between two points on the conductor, the free electrons in the conductor would move until the potential difference disappears.

Q25.8 No. The uniformly charged sphere, whether hollow or solid metal, is an equipotential volume. Since there is no electric field, this means that there is no *change* in electrical potential. The potential at every point inside is the same as the value of the potential at the surface.

Q25.9 Infinitely far away from a line of charge, the line will not look like a point. In fact, without any distinguishing features, it is not possible to tell the distance from an infinitely long line of charge. Another way of stating the answer: The potential would diverge to infinity at any finite distance, if it were zero infinitely far away.

Q25.10 The smaller sphere will. In the solution to the example referred to, equation 1 states that each will have the same ratio of charge to radius, $\frac{q}{r}$. In this case, the charge density is a surface charge density, $\frac{q}{4\pi r^2}$, so the smaller-radius sphere will have the greater charge density.

Q25.11 The main factor is the radius of the dome. One often overlooked aspect is also the humidity of the air—drier air has a larger dielectric breakdown strength, resulting in a higher attainable electric potential. If other grounded objects are nearby, the maximum potential might be reduced.

Q25.12 The intense—often oscillating—electric fields around high voltage lines is large enough to ionize the air surrounding the cables. When the molecules recapture their electrons, they release that energy in the form of light.

Q25.13 A sharp point in a charged conductor would imply a large electric field in that region. An electric discharge could most easily take place at that sharp point.

Q25.14 Use a conductive box to shield the equipment. Any stray electric field will cause charges on the outer surface of the conductor to rearrange and cancel the stray field inside the volume it encloses.

Q25.15 No charge stays on the inner sphere in equilibrium. If there were any, it would create an electric field in the wire to push more charge to the outer sphere. All of the charge is on the outer sphere. Therefore, zero charge is on the inner sphere and 10.0 μC is on the outer sphere.

Q25.16 The grounding wire can be touched equally well to any point on the sphere. Electrons will drain away into the ground and the sphere will be left positively charged. The ground, wire, and sphere are all conducting. They together form an equipotential volume at zero volts during the contact. However close the grounding wire is to the negative charge, electrons have no difficulty in moving within the metal through the grounding wire to ground. The ground can act as an infinite source or sink of electrons. In this case, it is an electron sink.

SOLUTIONS TO PROBLEMS

Section 25.1 Potential Difference and Electric Potential

P25.1 $\Delta V = -14.0\ \text{V}$ and $Q = -N_A e = -\left(6.02\times10^{23}\right)\left(1.60\times10^{-19}\right) = -9.63\times10^{4}\ \text{C}$

$\Delta V = \frac{W}{Q}$, so $W = Q\Delta V = \left(-9.63\times10^{4}\ \text{C}\right)\left(-14.0\ \text{J/C}\right) = \boxed{1.35\ \text{MJ}}$

P25.2 $\Delta K = q|\Delta V|$ $\quad 7.37 \times 10^{-17} = q(115)$

$\boxed{q = 6.41 \times 10^{-19} \text{ C}}$

P25.3 (a) Energy of the proton-field system is conserved as the proton moves from high to low potential, which can be defined for this problem as moving from 120 V down to 0 V.

$$K_i + U_i + \Delta E_{\text{mech}} = K_f + U_f \qquad 0 + qV + 0 = \frac{1}{2}mv_p^2 + 0$$

$$\left(1.60 \times 10^{-19} \text{ C}\right)(120 \text{ V})\left(\frac{1 \text{ J}}{1 \text{ V} \cdot \text{C}}\right) = \frac{1}{2}\left(1.67 \times 10^{-27} \text{ kg}\right)v_p^2$$

$$v_p = \boxed{1.52 \times 10^5 \text{ m/s}}$$

(b) The electron will gain speed in moving the other way,

from $V_i = 0$ to $V_f = 120$ V: $\quad K_i + U_i + \Delta E_{\text{mech}} = K_f + U_f$

$$0 + 0 + 0 = \frac{1}{2}mv_e^2 + qV$$

$$0 = \frac{1}{2}\left(9.11 \times 10^{-31} \text{ kg}\right)v_e^2 + \left(-1.60 \times 10^{-19} \text{ C}\right)(120 \text{ J/C})$$

$$v_e = \boxed{6.49 \times 10^6 \text{ m/s}}$$

P25.4 $W = \Delta K = -q\Delta V$

$$0 - \frac{1}{2}\left(9.11 \times 10^{-31} \text{ kg}\right)\left(4.20 \times 10^5 \text{ m/s}\right)^2 = -\left(-1.60 \times 10^{-19} \text{ C}\right)\Delta V$$

From which, $\Delta V = \boxed{-0.502 \text{ V}}$.

Section 25.2 **Potential Difference in a Uniform Electric Field**

P25.5 (a) We follow the path from (0, 0) to (20.0 cm, 0) to (20.0 cm, 50.0 cm).

$\Delta U = -$(work done)

$\Delta U = -$(work from origin to (20.0 cm, 0)) $-$ (work from (20.0 cm, 0) to (20.0 cm, 50.0 cm))

Note that the last term is equal to 0 because the force is perpendicular to the displacement.

$$\Delta U = -(qE_x)\Delta x = -\left(12.0 \times 10^{-6} \text{ C}\right)(250 \text{ V/m})(0.200 \text{ m}) = \boxed{-6.00 \times 10^{-4} \text{ J}}$$

(b) $$\Delta V = \frac{\Delta U}{q} = -\frac{6.00 \times 10^{-4} \text{ J}}{12.0 \times 10^{-6} \text{ C}} = -50.0 \text{ J/C} = \boxed{-50.0 \text{ V}}$$

P25.6 $$E = \frac{|\Delta V|}{d} = \frac{25.0 \times 10^3 \text{ J/C}}{1.50 \times 10^{-2} \text{ m}} = 1.67 \times 10^6 \text{ N/C} = \boxed{1.67 \text{ MN/C}}$$

P25.7 $\Delta U = -\frac{1}{2}m\left(v_f^2 - v_i^2\right) = -\frac{1}{2}\left(9.11\times10^{-31}\text{ kg}\right)\left[\left(1.40\times10^5\text{ m/s}\right)^2 - \left(3.70\times10^6\text{ m/s}\right)^2\right] = 6.23\times10^{-18}\text{ J}$

$\Delta U = q\Delta V$: $\quad +6.23\times10^{-18} = \left(-1.60\times10^{-19}\right)\Delta V$

$\Delta V = \boxed{-38.9\text{ V. The origin is at highest potential.}}$

P25.8 (a) $|\Delta V| = Ed = \left(5.90\times10^3\text{ V/m}\right)(0.010\,0\text{ m}) = \boxed{59.0\text{ V}}$

(b) $\frac{1}{2}mv_f^2 = |q\Delta V|$: $\quad \frac{1}{2}\left(9.11\times10^{-31}\right)v_f^2 = \left(1.60\times10^{-19}\right)(59.0)$

$v_f = \boxed{4.55\times10^6\text{ m/s}}$

P25.9 $V_B - V_A = -\int_A^B \mathbf{E}\cdot d\mathbf{s} = -\int_A^C \mathbf{E}\cdot d\mathbf{s} - \int_C^B \mathbf{E}\cdot d\mathbf{s}$

$V_B - V_A = (-E\cos180°)\int_{-0.300}^{0.500} dy - (E\cos90.0°)\int_{-0.200}^{0.400} dx$

$V_B - V_A = (325)(0.800) = \boxed{+260\text{ V}}$

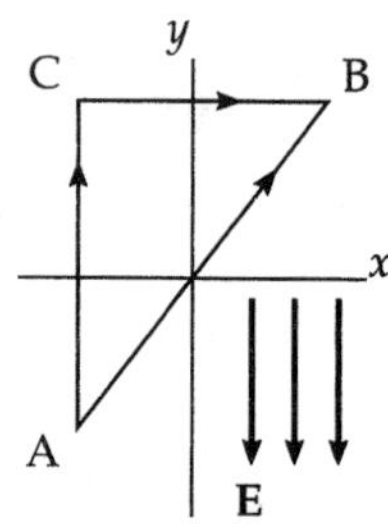

FIG. P25.9

***P25.10** Assume the opposite. Then at some point A on some equipotential surface the electric field has a nonzero component E_p in the plane of the surface. Let a test charge start from point A and move some distance on the surface in the direction of the field component. Then $\Delta V = -\int_A^B \mathbf{E}\cdot d\mathbf{s}$ is nonzero. The electric potential charges across the surface and it is not an equipotential surface. The contradiction shows that our assumption is false, that $E_p = 0$, and that the field is perpendicular to the equipotential surface.

P25.11 (a) Arbitrarily choose $V = 0$ at 0. Then at other points

$V = -Ex$ and $U_e = QV = -QEx$.

Between the endpoints of the motion,

$(K + U_s + U_e)_i = (K + U_s + U_e)_f$

$0 + 0 + 0 = 0 + \frac{1}{2}kx_{max}^2 - QEx_{max}$ so $x_{max} = \boxed{\frac{2QE}{k}}$.

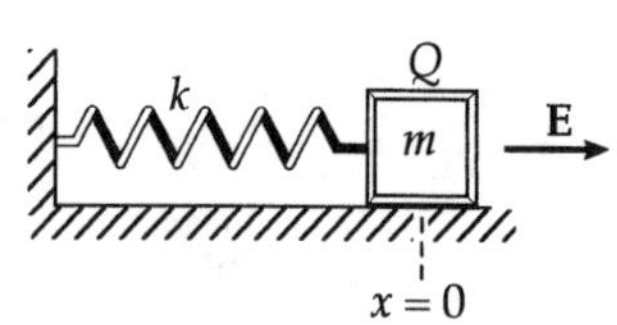

FIG. P25.11

(b) At equilibrium,

$\sum F_x = -F_s + F_e = 0$ or $kx = QE$.

So the equilibrium position is at $x = \boxed{\frac{QE}{k}}$.

continued on next page

(c) The block's equation of motion is $\sum F_x = -kx + QE = m\dfrac{d^2x}{dt^2}$.

Let $x' = x - \dfrac{QE}{k}$, or $x = x' + \dfrac{QE}{k}$,

so the equation of motion becomes:

$$-k\left(x' + \frac{QE}{k}\right) + QE = m\frac{d^2(x + QE/k)}{dt^2}, \text{ or } \frac{d^2x'}{dt^2} = -\left(\frac{k}{m}\right)x'.$$

This is the equation for simple harmonic motion $a_{x'} = -\omega^2 x'$

with $\omega = \sqrt{\dfrac{k}{m}}$.

The period of the motion is then $T = \dfrac{2\pi}{\omega} = \boxed{2\pi\sqrt{\dfrac{m}{k}}}$.

(d) $(K + U_s + U_e)_i + \Delta E_{\text{mech}} = (K + U_s + U_e)_f$

$$0 + 0 + 0 - \mu_k mgx_{\max} = 0 + \frac{1}{2}kx_{\max}^2 - QEx_{\max}$$

$$x_{\max} = \boxed{\frac{2(QE - \mu_k mg)}{k}}$$

P25.12 For the entire motion, $y_f - y_i = v_{yi}t + \dfrac{1}{2}a_y t^2$

$$0 - 0 = v_i t + \frac{1}{2}a_y t^2 \quad \text{so} \quad a_y = -\frac{2v_i}{t}$$

$\sum F_y = ma_y$: $\quad -mg - qE = -\dfrac{2mv_i}{t}$

$$E = \frac{m}{q}\left(\frac{2v_i}{t} - g\right) \quad \text{and} \quad \mathbf{E} = -\frac{m}{q}\left(\frac{2v_i}{t} - g\right)\hat{\mathbf{j}}.$$

For the upward flight: $v_{yf}^2 = v_{yi}^2 + 2a_y(y_f - y_i)$

$$0 = v_i^2 + 2\left(-\frac{2v_i}{t}\right)(y_{\max} - 0) \quad \text{and} \quad y_{\max} = \frac{1}{4}v_i t$$

$$\Delta V = -\int_0^{y_{\max}} \mathbf{E} \cdot d\mathbf{y} = +\frac{m}{q}\left(\frac{2v_i}{t} - g\right)y\Big|_0^{y_{\max}} = \frac{m}{q}\left(\frac{2v_i}{t} - g\right)\left(\frac{1}{4}v_i t\right)$$

$$\Delta V = \frac{2.00 \text{ kg}}{5.00 \times 10^{-6} \text{ C}}\left(\frac{2(20.1 \text{ m/s})}{4.10 \text{ s}} - 9.80 \text{ m/s}^2\right)\left[\frac{1}{4}(20.1 \text{ m/s})(4.10 \text{ s})\right] = \boxed{40.2 \text{ kV}}$$

P25.13 Arbitrarily take $V = 0$ at the initial point. Then at distance d downfield, where L is the rod length, $V = -Ed$ and $U_e = -\lambda LEd$.

(a) $(K + U)_i = (K + U)_f$

$$0 + 0 = \frac{1}{2}\mu Lv^2 - \lambda LEd$$

$$v = \sqrt{\frac{2\lambda Ed}{\mu}} = \sqrt{\frac{2(40.0 \times 10^{-6} \text{ C/m})(100 \text{ N/C})(2.00 \text{ m})}{(0.100 \text{ kg/m})}} = \boxed{0.400 \text{ m/s}}$$

(b) $\boxed{\text{The same.}}$

P25.14 Arbitrarily take $V=0$ at point *P*. Then (from Equation 25.8) the potential at the original position of the charge is $-\mathbf{E}\cdot\mathbf{s}=-EL\cos\theta$. At the final point *a*, $V=-EL$. Suppose the table is frictionless: $(K+U)_i=(K+U)_f$

$$0-qEL\cos\theta=\frac{1}{2}mv^2-qEL$$

$$v=\sqrt{\frac{2qEL(1-\cos\theta)}{m}}=\sqrt{\frac{2\left(2.00\times10^{-6}\text{ C}\right)(300\text{ N/C})(1.50\text{ m})(1-\cos 60.0°)}{0.010\,0\text{ kg}}}=\boxed{0.300\text{ m/s}}$$

Section 25.3 Electric Potential and Potential Energy Due to Point Charges

P25.15 (a) The potential at 1.00 cm is $V_1=k_e\frac{q}{r}=\frac{\left(8.99\times10^9\text{ N}\cdot\text{m}^2/\text{C}^2\right)\left(1.60\times10^{-19}\text{ C}\right)}{1.00\times10^{-2}\text{ m}}=\boxed{1.44\times10^{-7}\text{ V}}$.

(b) The potential at 2.00 cm is $V_2=k_e\frac{q}{r}=\frac{\left(8.99\times10^9\text{ N}\cdot\text{m}^2/\text{C}^2\right)\left(1.60\times10^{-19}\text{ C}\right)}{2.00\times10^{-2}\text{ m}}=0.719\times10^{-7}\text{ V}$.

Thus, the difference in potential between the two points is $\Delta V=V_2-V_1=\boxed{-7.19\times10^{-8}\text{ V}}$.

(c) The approach is the same as above except the charge is -1.60×10^{-19} C. This changes the sign of each answer, with its magnitude remaining the same.

That is, the potential at 1.00 cm is $\boxed{-1.44\times10^{-7}\text{ V}}$.

The potential at 2.00 cm is -0.719×10^{-7} V, so $\Delta V=V_2-V_1=\boxed{7.19\times10^{-8}\text{ V}}$.

P25.16 (a) Since the charges are equal and placed symmetrically, $\boxed{F=0}$.

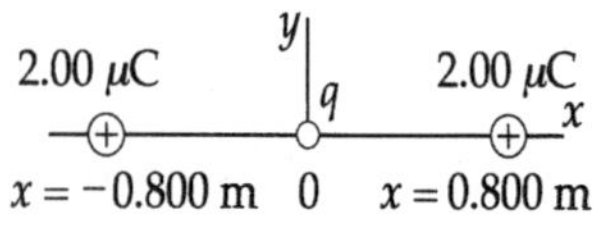

(b) Since $F=qE=0$, $\boxed{E=0}$.

FIG. P25.16

(c) $V=2k_e\frac{q}{r}=2\left(8.99\times10^9\text{ N}\cdot\text{m}^2/\text{C}^2\right)\left(\frac{2.00\times10^{-6}\text{ C}}{0.800\text{ m}}\right)$

$V=4.50\times10^4\text{ V}=\boxed{45.0\text{ kV}}$

P25.17 (a) $E=\frac{|Q|}{4\pi\epsilon_0 r^2}$

$V=\frac{Q}{4\pi\epsilon_0 r}$

$r=\frac{|V|}{|E|}=\frac{3\,000\text{ V}}{500\text{ V/m}}=\boxed{6.00\text{ m}}$

(b) $V=-3\,000\text{ V}=\frac{Q}{4\pi\epsilon_0(6.00\text{ m})}$

$Q=\frac{-3\,000\text{ V}}{\left(8.99\times10^9\text{ V}\cdot\text{m/C}\right)}(6.00\text{ m})=\boxed{-2.00\ \mu\text{C}}$

P25.18 (a) $E_x = \dfrac{k_e q_1}{x^2} + \dfrac{k_e q_2}{(x-2.00)^2} = 0$ becomes $E_x = k_e\left(\dfrac{+q}{x^2} + \dfrac{-2q}{(x-2.00)^2}\right) = 0$.

Dividing by k_e, $2qx^2 = q(x-2.00)^2$ $x^2 + 4.00x - 4.00 = 0$.

Therefore $E = 0$ when $x = \dfrac{-4.00 \pm \sqrt{16.0+16.0}}{2} = \boxed{-4.83\text{ m}}$.

(Note that the positive root does not correspond to a physically valid situation.)

(b) $V = \dfrac{k_e q_1}{x} + \dfrac{k_e q_2}{2.00-x} = 0$ or $V = k_e\left(\dfrac{+q}{x} - \dfrac{2q}{2.00-x}\right) = 0$.

Again solving for x, $2qx = q(2.00-x)$.

For $0 \le x \le 2.00$ $V = 0$ when $x = \boxed{0.667\text{ m}}$

and $\dfrac{q}{|x|} = \dfrac{-2q}{|2-x|}$. For $x < 0$ $x = \boxed{-2.00\text{ m}}$.

P25.19 $V = \sum_i k\dfrac{q_i}{r_i}$

$V = (8.99\times10^9)(7.00\times10^{-6})\left[\dfrac{-1}{0.010\,0} - \dfrac{1}{0.010\,0} + \dfrac{1}{0.038\,7}\right]$

$V = \boxed{-1.10\times10^7\text{ V} = -11.0\text{ MV}}$

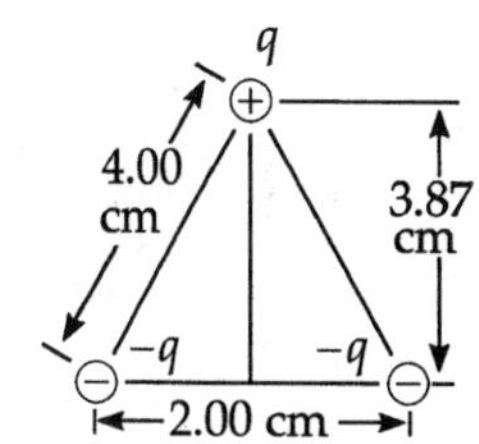

FIG. P25.19

P25.20 (a) $U = \dfrac{qQ}{4\pi\epsilon_0 r} = \dfrac{(5.00\times10^{-9}\text{ C})(-3.00\times10^{-9}\text{ C})(8.99\times10^9\text{ V}\cdot\text{m/C})}{(0.350\text{ m})} = \boxed{-3.86\times10^{-7}\text{ J}}$

The minus sign means it takes 3.86×10^{-7} J to pull the two charges apart from 35 cm to a much larger separation.

(b) $V = \dfrac{Q_1}{4\pi\epsilon_0 r_1} + \dfrac{Q_2}{4\pi\epsilon_0 r_2}$

$= \dfrac{(5.00\times10^{-9}\text{ C})(8.99\times10^9\text{ V}\cdot\text{m/C})}{0.175\text{ m}} + \dfrac{(-3.00\times10^{-9}\text{ C})(8.99\times10^9\text{ V}\cdot\text{m/C})}{0.175\text{ m}}$

$V = \boxed{103\text{ V}}$

P25.21 $U_e = q_4 V_1 + q_4 V_2 + q_4 V_3 = q_4 \left(\frac{1}{4\pi \in_0} \right) \left(\frac{q_1}{r_1} + \frac{q_2}{r_2} + \frac{q_3}{r_3} \right)$

$$U_e = \left(10.0 \times 10^{-6} \text{ C}\right)^2 \left(8.99 \times 10^9 \text{ N} \cdot \text{m}^2/\text{C}^2\right) \left(\frac{1}{0.600 \text{ m}} + \frac{1}{0.150 \text{ m}} + \frac{1}{\sqrt{(0.600 \text{ m})^2 + (0.150 \text{ m})^2}} \right)$$

$$U_e = \boxed{8.95 \text{ J}}$$

P25.22 (a) $V = \frac{k_e q_1}{r_1} + \frac{k_e q_2}{r_2} = 2\left(\frac{k_e q}{r} \right)$

$$V = 2\left(\frac{\left(8.99 \times 10^9 \text{ N} \cdot \text{m}^2/\text{C}^2\right)\left(2.00 \times 10^{-6} \text{ C}\right)}{\sqrt{(1.00 \text{ m})^2 + (0.500 \text{ m})^2}} \right)$$

$$V = 3.22 \times 10^4 \text{ V} = \boxed{32.2 \text{ kV}}$$

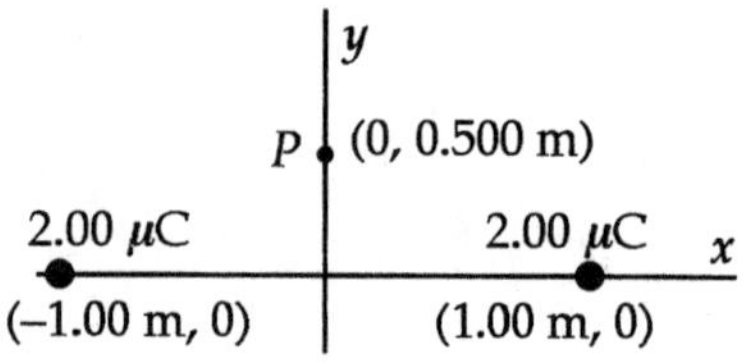

FIG. P25.22

(b) $U = qV = \left(-3.00 \times 10^{-6} \text{ C}\right)\left(3.22 \times 10^4 \text{ J/C}\right) = \boxed{-9.65 \times 10^{-2} \text{ J}}$

P25.23 $U = U_1 + U_2 + U_3 + U_4$

$$U = 0 + U_{12} + (U_{13} + U_{23}) + (U_{14} + U_{24} + U_{34})$$

$$U = 0 + \frac{k_e Q^2}{s} + \frac{k_e Q^2}{s}\left(\frac{1}{\sqrt{2}} + 1 \right) + \frac{k_e Q^2}{s}\left(1 + \frac{1}{\sqrt{2}} + 1 \right)$$

$$U = \frac{k_e Q^2}{s}\left(4 + \frac{2}{\sqrt{2}} \right) = \boxed{5.41 \frac{k_e Q^2}{s}}$$

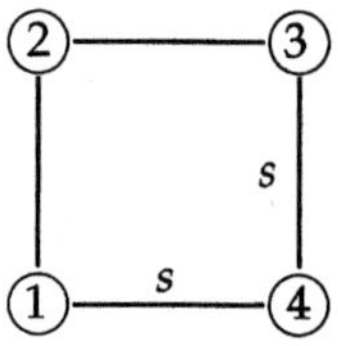

FIG. P25.23

An alternate way to get the term $\left(4 + \frac{2}{\sqrt{2}} \right)$ is to recognize that there are 4 side pairs and 2 face diagonal pairs.

P25.24 Each charge creates equal potential at the center. The total potential is:

$$V = 5\left[\frac{k_e(-q)}{R} \right] = \boxed{-\frac{5k_e q}{R}}.$$

P25.25 (a) Each charge separately creates positive potential everywhere. The total potential produced by the three charges together is then the sum of three positive terms. There is $\boxed{\text{no point}}$ located at a finite distance from the charges, at which this total potential is zero.

(b) $V = \frac{k_e q}{a} + \frac{k_e q}{a} = \boxed{\frac{2k_e q}{a}}$

P25.26 Consider the two spheres as a system.

(a) Conservation of momentum: $0 = m_1 v_1 \hat{\mathbf{i}} + m_2 v_2 \left(-\hat{\mathbf{i}}\right)$ or $v_2 = \dfrac{m_1 v_1}{m_2}$

By conservation of energy, $0 = \dfrac{k_e(-q_1)q_2}{d} = \dfrac{1}{2}m_1 v_1^2 + \dfrac{1}{2}m_2 v_2^2 + \dfrac{k_e(-q_1)q_2}{r_1 + r_2}$

and $\dfrac{k_e q_1 q_2}{r_1 + r_2} - \dfrac{k_e q_1 q_2}{d} = \dfrac{1}{2}m_1 v_1^2 + \dfrac{1}{2}\dfrac{m_1^2 v_1^2}{m_2}$

$$v_1 = \sqrt{\frac{2m_2 k_e q_1 q_2}{m_1(m_1 + m_2)}\left(\frac{1}{r_1 + r_2} - \frac{1}{d}\right)}$$

$$v_1 = \sqrt{\frac{2(0.700\text{ kg})\left(8.99\times 10^9 \text{ N}\cdot\text{m}^2/\text{C}^2\right)\left(2\times 10^{-6}\text{ C}\right)\left(3\times 10^{-6}\text{ C}\right)}{(0.100\text{ kg})(0.800\text{ kg})}\left(\frac{1}{8\times 10^{-3}\text{ m}} - \frac{1}{1.00\text{ m}}\right)}$$

$$= \boxed{10.8\text{ m/s}}$$

$$v_2 = \frac{m_1 v_1}{m_2} = \frac{0.100\text{ kg}(10.8\text{ m/s})}{0.700\text{ kg}} = \boxed{1.55\text{ m/s}}$$

(b) If the spheres are metal, electrons will move around on them with negligible energy loss to place the centers of excess charge on the insides of the spheres. Then just before they touch, the effective distance between charges will be less than $r_1 + r_2$ and the spheres will really be moving $\boxed{\text{faster than calculated in (a)}}$.

P25.27 Consider the two spheres as a system.

(a) Conservation of momentum: $0 = m_1 v_1 \hat{\mathbf{i}} + m_2 v_2 \left(-\hat{\mathbf{i}}\right)$

or $v_2 = \dfrac{m_1 v_1}{m_2}$.

By conservation of energy, $0 = \dfrac{k_e(-q_1)q_2}{d} = \dfrac{1}{2}m_1 v_1^2 + \dfrac{1}{2}m_2 v_2^2 + \dfrac{k_e(-q_1)q_2}{r_1 + r_2}$

and $\dfrac{k_e q_1 q_2}{r_1 + r_2} - \dfrac{k_e q_1 q_2}{d} = \dfrac{1}{2}m_1 v_1^2 + \dfrac{1}{2}\dfrac{m_1^2 v_1^2}{m_2}$.

$$v_1 = \boxed{\sqrt{\frac{2m_2 k_e q_1 q_2}{m_1(m_1 + m_2)}\left(\frac{1}{r_1 + r_2} - \frac{1}{d}\right)}}$$

$$v_2 = \left(\frac{m_1}{m_2}\right)v_1 = \boxed{\sqrt{\frac{2m_1 k_e q_1 q_2}{m_2(m_1 + m_2)}\left(\frac{1}{r_1 + r_2} - \frac{1}{d}\right)}}$$

(b) If the spheres are metal, electrons will move around on them with negligible energy loss to place the centers of excess charge on the insides of the spheres. Then just before they touch, the effective distance between charges will be less than $r_1 + r_2$ and the spheres will really be moving $\boxed{\text{faster than calculated in (a)}}$.

***P25.28** (a) In an empty universe, the 20-nC charge can be placed at its location with no energy investment. At a distance of 4 cm, it creates a potential

$$V_1 = \frac{k_e q_1}{r} = \frac{\left(8.99\times10^9\ \text{N}\cdot\text{m}^2/\text{C}^2\right)\left(20\times10^{-9}\ \text{C}\right)}{0.04\ \text{m}} = 4.50\ \text{kV}.$$

To place the 10-nC charge there we must put in energy

$$U_{12} = q_2 V_1 = \left(10\times10^{-9}\ \text{C}\right)\left(4.5\times10^3\ \text{V}\right) = 4.50\times10^{-5}\ \text{J}.$$

Next, to bring up the –20-nC charge requires energy

$$U_{23} + U_{13} = q_3 V_2 + q_3 V_1 = q_3\left(V_2 + V_1\right)$$

$$= -20\times10^{-9}\ \text{C}\left(8.99\times10^9\ \text{N}\cdot\text{m}^2/\text{C}^2\right)\left(\frac{10\times10^{-9}\ \text{C}}{0.04\ \text{m}} + \frac{20\times10^{-9}\ \text{C}}{0.08\ \text{m}}\right)$$

$$= -4.50\times10^{-5}\ \text{J} - 4.50\times10^{-5}\ \text{J}$$

The total energy of the three charges is

$$U_{12} + U_{23} + U_{13} = \boxed{-4.50\times10^{-5}\ \text{J}}.$$

(b) The three fixed charges create this potential at the location where the fourth is released:

$$V = V_1 + V_2 + V_3 = \left(8.99\times10^9\ \text{N}\cdot\text{m}^2/\text{C}^2\right)\left(\frac{20\times10^{-9}}{\sqrt{0.04^2 + 0.03^2}} + \frac{10\times10^{-9}}{0.03} - \frac{20\times10^{-9}}{0.05}\right)\ \text{C/m}$$

$$V = 3.00\times10^3\ \text{V}$$

Energy of the system of four charged objects is conserved as the fourth charge flies away:

$$\left(\frac{1}{2}mv^2 + qV\right)_i = \left(\frac{1}{2}mv^2 + qV\right)_f$$

$$0 + \left(40\times10^{-9}\ \text{C}\right)\left(3.00\times10^3\ \text{V}\right) = \frac{1}{2}\left(2.00\times10^{-13}\ \text{kg}\right)v^2 + 0$$

$$v = \sqrt{\frac{2\left(1.20\times10^{-4}\ \text{J}\right)}{2\times10^{-13}\ \text{kg}}} = \boxed{3.46\times10^4\ \text{m/s}}$$

***P25.29** The original electrical potential energy is

$$U_e = qV = q\frac{k_e q}{d}.$$

In the final configuration we have mechanical equilibrium. The spring and electrostatic forces on each charge are $-k(2d) + q\frac{k_e q}{(3d)^2} = 0$. Then $k = \frac{k_e q^2}{18d^3}$. In the final configuration the total potential energy is $\frac{1}{2}kx^2 + qV = \frac{1}{2}\frac{k_e q^2}{18d^3}(2d)^2 + q\frac{k_e q}{3d} = \frac{4}{9}\frac{k_e q^2}{d}$. The missing energy must have become internal energy, as the system is isolated: $\frac{k_e q^2}{d} = \frac{4k_e q^2}{9d} + \Delta E_{\text{int}}$

$$\boxed{\Delta E_{\text{int}} = \frac{5}{9}\frac{k_e q^2}{d}}.$$

P25.30 (a) $$V(x)=\frac{k_eQ_1}{r_1}+\frac{k_eQ_2}{r_2}=\frac{k_e(+Q)}{\sqrt{x^2+a^2}}+\frac{k_e(+Q)}{\sqrt{x^2+(-a)^2}}$$

$$V(x)=\frac{2k_eQ}{\sqrt{x^2+a^2}}=\frac{k_eQ}{a}\left(\frac{2}{\sqrt{(x/a)^2+1}}\right)$$

$$\frac{V(x)}{(k_eQ/a)}=\boxed{\frac{2}{\sqrt{(x/a)^2+1}}}$$

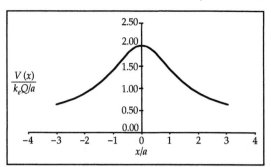

FIG. P25.30(a)

(b) $$V(y)=\frac{k_eQ_1}{r_1}+\frac{k_eQ_2}{r_2}=\frac{k_e(+Q)}{|y-a|}+\frac{k_e(-Q)}{|y+a|}$$

$$V(y)=\frac{k_eQ}{a}\left(\frac{1}{|y/a-1|}-\frac{1}{|y/a+1|}\right)$$

$$\frac{V(y)}{(k_eQ/a)}=\boxed{\left(\frac{1}{|y/a-1|}-\frac{1}{|y/a+1|}\right)}$$

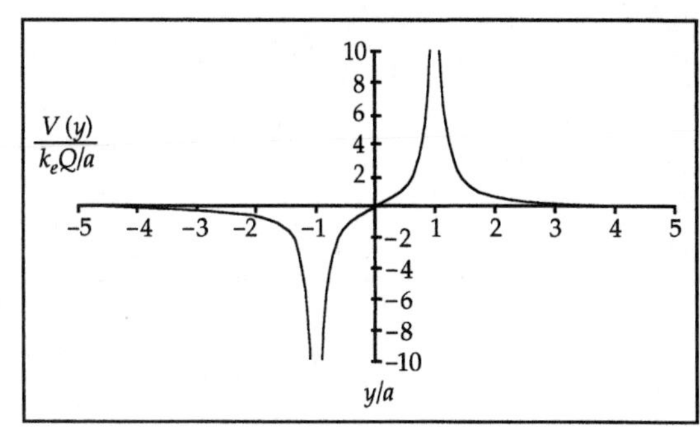

FIG. P25.30(b)

P25.31 $V=\frac{k_eQ}{r}$ so $r=\frac{k_eQ}{V}=\frac{(8.99\times10^9\ \text{N}\cdot\text{m}^2/\text{C}^2)(8.00\times10^{-9}\ \text{C})}{V}=\frac{72.0\ \text{V}\cdot\text{m}}{V}$.

For $V=100$ V, 50.0 V, and 25.0 V, $\boxed{r=0.720\ \text{m},\ 1.44\ \text{m, and } 2.88\ \text{m}}$.

The radii are $\boxed{\text{inversely proportional}}$ to the potential.

P25.32 Using conservation of energy for the alpha particle-nucleus system,

we have $K_f+U_f=K_i+U_i$.

But $U_i=\frac{k_eq_\alpha q_{\text{gold}}}{r_i}$

and $r_i\approx\infty$.

Thus, $U_i=0$.

Also $K_f=0$ ($v_f=0$ at turning point),

so $U_f=K_i$

or $\frac{k_eq_\alpha q_{\text{gold}}}{r_{\min}}=\frac{1}{2}m_\alpha v_\alpha^2$

$$r_{\min}=\frac{2k_eq_\alpha q_{\text{gold}}}{m_\alpha v_\alpha^2}=\frac{2(8.99\times10^9\ \text{N}\cdot\text{m}^2/\text{C}^2)(2)(79)(1.60\times10^{-19}\ \text{C})^2}{(6.64\times10^{-27}\ \text{kg})(2.00\times10^7\ \text{m/s})^2}=2.74\times10^{-14}\ \text{m}=\boxed{27.4\ \text{fm}}.$$

P25.33 Using conservation of energy

we have: $\frac{k_e eQ}{r_1} = \frac{k_e qQ}{r_2} + \frac{1}{2}mv^2$

which gives: $v = \sqrt{\frac{2k_e eQ}{m}\left(\frac{1}{r_1} - \frac{1}{r_2}\right)}$

or $v = \sqrt{\frac{(2)(8.99\times10^9 \text{ N}\cdot\text{m}^2/\text{C}^2)(-1.60\times10^{-19}\text{ C})(10^{-9}\text{ C})}{9.11\times10^{-31}\text{ kg}}\left(\frac{1}{0.030\,0\text{ m}} - \frac{1}{0.020\,0\text{ m}}\right)}$.

Thus, $v = \boxed{7.26\times10^6 \text{ m/s}}$.

P25.34 $U = \sum \frac{k_e q_i q_j}{r_{ij}}$, summed over all pairs of (i, j) where $i \neq j$.

$$U = k_e\left[\frac{q(-2q)}{b} + \frac{(-2q)(3q)}{a} + \frac{(2q)(3q)}{b} + \frac{q(2q)}{a} + \frac{q(3q)}{\sqrt{a^2+b^2}} + \frac{2q(-2q)}{\sqrt{a^2+b^2}}\right]$$

$$U = k_e q^2\left[\frac{-2}{0.400} - \frac{6}{0.200} + \frac{6}{0.400} + \frac{2}{0.200} + \frac{3}{0.447} - \frac{4}{0.447}\right]$$

$$U = (8.99\times10^9)(6.00\times10^{-6})^2\left[\frac{4}{0.400} - \frac{4}{0.200} - \frac{1}{0.447}\right] = \boxed{-3.96\text{ J}}$$

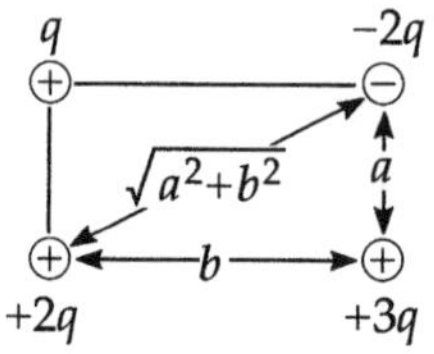

FIG. P25.34

P25.35 Each charge moves off on its diagonal line. All charges have equal speeds.

$$\sum(K+U)_i = \sum(K+U)_f$$

$$0 + \frac{4k_e q^2}{L} + \frac{2k_e q^2}{\sqrt{2}L} = 4\left(\frac{1}{2}mv^2\right) + \frac{4k_e q^2}{2L} + \frac{2k_e q^2}{2\sqrt{2}L}$$

$$\left(2 + \frac{1}{\sqrt{2}}\right)\frac{k_e q^2}{L} = 2mv^2$$

$$\boxed{v = \sqrt{\left(1 + \frac{1}{\sqrt{8}}\right)\frac{k_e q^2}{mL}}}$$

P25.36 A cube has 12 edges and 6 faces. Consequently, there are 12 edge pairs separated by s, $2\times6 = 12$ face diagonal pairs separated by $\sqrt{2}s$ and 4 interior diagonal pairs separated $\sqrt{3}s$.

$$U = \frac{k_e q^2}{s}\left[12 + \frac{12}{\sqrt{2}} + \frac{4}{\sqrt{3}}\right] = \boxed{22.8\frac{k_e q^2}{s}}$$

Section 25.4 Obtaining the Value of the Electric Field from the Electric Potential

P25.37 $V = a + bx = 10.0\text{ V} + (-7.00\text{ V/m})x$

(a) At $x = 0$, $V = \boxed{10.0\text{ V}}$

At $x = 3.00$ m, $V = \boxed{-11.0\text{ V}}$

At $x = 6.00$ m, $V = \boxed{-32.0\text{ V}}$

(b) $E = -\frac{dV}{dx} = -b = -(-7.00\text{ V/m}) = \boxed{7.00\text{ N/C in the } +x \text{ direction}}$

P25.38 (a) For $r < R$ $V = \frac{k_e Q}{R}$

$$E_r = -\frac{dV}{dr} = \boxed{0}$$

(b) For $r \geq R$ $V = \frac{k_e Q}{r}$

$$E_r = -\frac{dV}{dr} = -\left(-\frac{k_e Q}{r^2}\right) = \boxed{\frac{k_e Q}{r^2}}$$

P25.39 $V = 5x - 3x^2 y + 2yz^2$

Evaluate E at $(1, 0, -2)$

$$E_x = -\frac{\partial V}{\partial x} = \boxed{-5 + 6xy} = -5 + 6(1)(0) = -5$$

$$E_y = -\frac{\partial V}{\partial y} = \boxed{+3x^2 - 2z^2} = 3(1)^2 - 2(-2)^2 = -5$$

$$E_z = -\frac{\partial V}{\partial z} = \boxed{-4yz} = -4(0)(-2) = 0$$

$$E = \sqrt{E_x^2 + E_y^2 + E_z^2} = \sqrt{(-5)^2 + (-5)^2 + 0^2} = \boxed{7.07 \text{ N/C}}$$

P25.40 (a) $\boxed{E_A > E_B \text{ since } E = \frac{\Delta V}{\Delta s}}$

(b) $E_B = -\frac{\Delta V}{\Delta s} = -\frac{(6-2) \text{ V}}{2 \text{ cm}} = \boxed{200 \text{ N/C}}$ down

(c) The figure is shown to the right, with sample field lines sketched in.

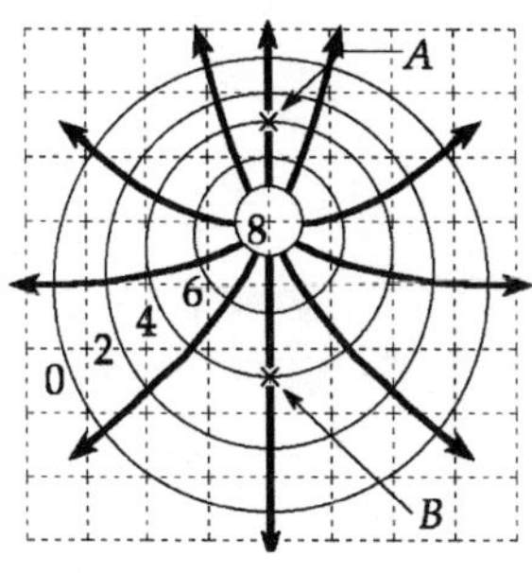

FIG. P25.40

P25.41 $$E_y = -\frac{\partial V}{\partial y} = -\frac{\partial}{\partial y}\left[\frac{k_e Q}{\ell} \ln\left(\frac{\ell + \sqrt{\ell^2 + y^2}}{y}\right)\right]$$

$$E_y = \frac{k_e Q}{\ell y}\left[1 - \frac{y^2}{\ell^2 + y^2 + \ell\sqrt{\ell^2 + y^2}}\right] = \boxed{\frac{k_e Q}{y\sqrt{\ell^2 + y^2}}}$$

Section 25.5 Electric Potential Due to Continuous Charge Distributions

P25.42 $$\Delta V = V_{2R} - V_0 = \frac{k_e Q}{\sqrt{R^2 + (2R)^2}} - \frac{k_e Q}{R} = \frac{k_e Q}{R}\left(\frac{1}{\sqrt{5}} - 1\right) = \boxed{-0.553 \frac{k_e Q}{R}}$$

P25.43 (a) $[\alpha]=\left[\dfrac{\lambda}{x}\right]=\dfrac{\text{C}}{\text{m}}\cdot\left(\dfrac{1}{\text{m}}\right)=\boxed{\dfrac{\text{C}}{\text{m}^2}}$

(b) $V=k_e\int\dfrac{dq}{r}=k_e\int\dfrac{\lambda dx}{r}=k_e\alpha\int_0^L\dfrac{xdx}{d+x}=\boxed{k_e\alpha\left[L-d\ln\left(1+\dfrac{L}{d}\right)\right]}$

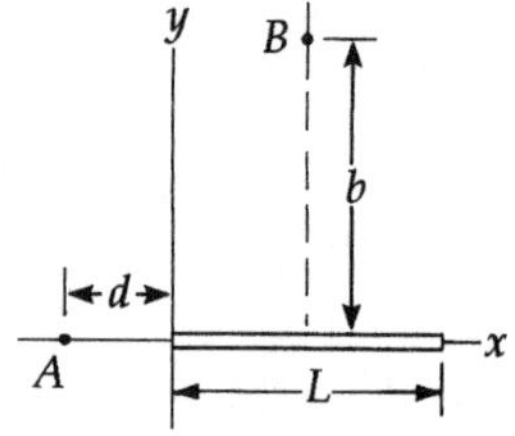

FIG. P25.43

P25.44 $V=\int\dfrac{k_e dq}{r}=k_e\int\dfrac{\alpha x dx}{\sqrt{b^2+(L/2-x)^2}}$

Let $z=\dfrac{L}{2}-x$.

Then $x=\dfrac{L}{2}-z$, and $dx=-dz$

$$V=k_e\alpha\int\frac{(L/2-z)(-dz)}{\sqrt{b^2+z^2}}=-\frac{k_e\alpha L}{2}\int\frac{dz}{\sqrt{b^2+z^2}}+k_e\alpha\int\frac{zdz}{\sqrt{b^2+z^2}}=-\frac{k_e\alpha L}{2}\ln\left(z+\sqrt{z^2+b^2}\right)+k_e\alpha\sqrt{z^2+b^2}$$

$$V=-\frac{k_e\alpha L}{2}\ln\left[\left(\frac{L}{2}-x\right)+\sqrt{\left(\frac{L}{2}-x\right)^2+b^2}\right]_0^L+k_e\alpha\sqrt{\left(\frac{L}{2}-x\right)^2+b^2}\,\Bigg|_0^L$$

$$V=-\frac{k_e\alpha L}{2}\ln\left[\frac{L/2-L+\sqrt{(L/2)^2+b^2}}{L/2+\sqrt{(L/2)^2+b^2}}\right]+k_e\alpha\left[\sqrt{\left(\frac{L}{2}-L\right)^2+b^2}-\sqrt{\left(\frac{L}{2}\right)^2+b^2}\right]$$

$$V=\boxed{-\frac{k_e\alpha L}{2}\ln\left[\frac{\sqrt{b^2+(L^2/4)}-L/2}{\sqrt{b^2+(L^2/4)}+L/2}\right]}$$

P25.45 $V=\int dV=\dfrac{1}{4\pi\epsilon_0}\int\dfrac{dq}{r}$

All bits of charge are at the same distance from O.

So $V=\dfrac{1}{4\pi\epsilon_0}\left(\dfrac{Q}{R}\right)=\left(8.99\times10^9\ \text{N}\cdot\text{m}^2/\text{C}^2\right)\left(\dfrac{-7.50\times10^{-6}\ \text{C}}{0.140\ \text{m}/\pi}\right)=\boxed{-1.51\ \text{MV}}$.

P25.46 $dV=\dfrac{k_e dq}{\sqrt{r^2+x^2}}$ where $dq=\sigma dA=\sigma 2\pi r dr$

$V=2\pi\sigma k_e\int_a^b\dfrac{rdr}{\sqrt{r^2+x^2}}=\boxed{2\pi k_e\sigma\left[\sqrt{x^2+b^2}-\sqrt{x^2+a^2}\right]}$

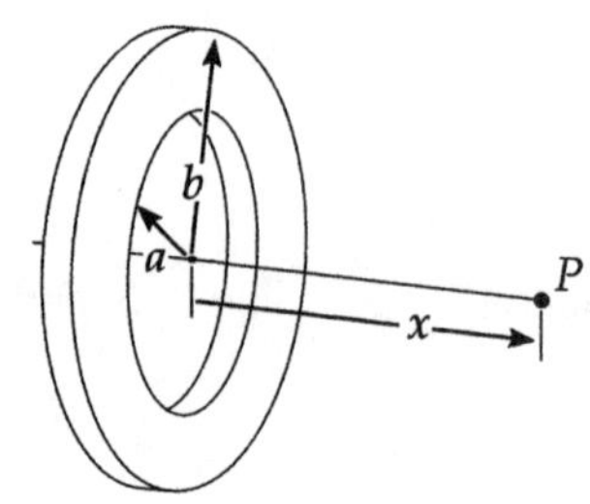

FIG. P25.46

P25.47 $$V = k_e \int_{\text{all charge}} \frac{dq}{r} = k_e \int_{-3R}^{-R} \frac{\lambda dx}{-x} + k_e \int_{\text{semicircle}} \frac{\lambda ds}{R} + k_e \int_{R}^{3R} \frac{\lambda dx}{x}$$

$$V = -k_e \lambda \ln(-x)\Big|_{-3R}^{-R} + \frac{k_e \lambda}{R} \pi R + k_e \lambda \ln x\Big|_{R}^{3R}$$

$$V = k_e \ln \frac{3R}{R} + k_e \lambda \pi + k_e \ln 3 = \boxed{k_e \lambda(\pi + 2\ln 3)}$$

Section 25.6 **Electric Potential Due to a Charged Conductor**

P25.48 Substituting given values into $V = \frac{k_e q}{r}$

$$7.50 \times 10^3 \text{ V} = \frac{\left(8.99 \times 10^9 \text{ N} \cdot \text{m}^2/\text{C}^2\right)q}{0.300 \text{ m}}.$$

Substituting $q = 2.50 \times 10^{-7}$ C,

$$N = \frac{2.50 \times 10^{-7} \text{ C}}{1.60 \times 10^{-19} \text{ C}/e^-} = \boxed{1.56 \times 10^{12} \text{ electrons}}.$$

P25.49 (a) $E = \boxed{0}$;

$$V = \frac{k_e q}{R} = \frac{\left(8.99 \times 10^9\right)\left(26.0 \times 10^{-6}\right)}{0.140} = \boxed{1.67 \text{ MV}}$$

(b) $$E = \frac{k_e q}{r^2} = \frac{\left(8.99 \times 10^9\right)\left(26.0 \times 10^{-6}\right)}{(0.200)^2} = \boxed{5.84 \text{ MN/C}} \text{ away}$$

$$V = \frac{k_e q}{R} = \frac{\left(8.99 \times 10^9\right)\left(26.0 \times 10^{-6}\right)}{0.200} = \boxed{1.17 \text{ MV}}$$

(c) $$E = \frac{k_e q}{R^2} = \frac{\left(8.99 \times 10^9\right)\left(26.0 \times 10^{-6}\right)}{(0.140)^2} = \boxed{11.9 \text{ MN/C}} \text{ away}$$

$$V = \frac{k_e q}{R} = \boxed{1.67 \text{ MV}}$$

***P25.50** (a) Both spheres must be at the same potential according to $\frac{k_e q_1}{r_1} = \frac{k_e q_2}{r_2}$

where also $q_1 + q_2 = 1.20 \times 10^{-6}$ C.

Then
$$q_1 = \frac{q_2 r_1}{r_2}$$
$$\frac{q_2 r_1}{r_2} + q_2 = 1.20 \times 10^{-6} \text{ C}$$
$$q_2 = \frac{1.20 \times 10^{-6} \text{ C}}{1 + 6 \text{ cm}/2 \text{ cm}} = 0.300 \times 10^{-6} \text{ C on the smaller sphere}$$
$$q_1 = 1.20 \times 10^{-6} \text{ C} - 0.300 \times 10^{-6} \text{ C} = 0.900 \times 10^{-6} \text{ C}$$
$$V = \frac{k_e q_1}{r_1} = \frac{(8.99 \times 10^9 \text{ N}\cdot\text{m}^2/\text{C}^2)(0.900 \times 10^{-6} \text{ C})}{6 \times 10^{-2} \text{ m}} = \boxed{1.35 \times 10^5 \text{ V}}$$

(b) Outside the larger sphere,
$$\mathbf{E}_1 = \frac{k_e q_1}{r_1^2}\hat{\mathbf{r}} = \frac{V_1}{r_1}\hat{\mathbf{r}} = \frac{1.35 \times 10^5 \text{ V}}{0.06 \text{ m}}\hat{\mathbf{r}} = \boxed{2.25 \times 10^6 \text{ V/m away}}.$$

Outside the smaller sphere,
$$\mathbf{E}_2 = \frac{1.35 \times 10^5 \text{ V}}{0.02 \text{ m}}\hat{\mathbf{r}} = \boxed{6.74 \times 10^6 \text{ V/m away}}.$$

The smaller sphere carries less charge but creates a much stronger electric field than the larger sphere.

Section 25.7 The Milliken Oil Drop Experiment

Section 25.8 Application of Electrostatistics

P25.51 (a) $E_{\text{max}} = 3.00 \times 10^6 \text{ V/m} = \frac{k_e Q}{r^2} = \frac{k_e Q}{r}\left(\frac{1}{r}\right) = V_{\text{max}}\left(\frac{1}{r}\right)$

$V_{\text{max}} = E_{\text{max}} r = 3.00 \times 10^6 (0.150) = \boxed{450 \text{ kV}}$

(b) $\frac{k_e Q_{\text{max}}}{r^2} = E_{\text{max}}$ $\left\{\text{or } \frac{k_e Q_{\text{max}}}{r} = V_{\text{max}}\right\}$ $Q_{\text{max}} = \frac{E_{\text{max}} r^2}{k_e} = \frac{3.00 \times 10^6 (0.150)^2}{8.99 \times 10^9} = \boxed{7.51 \ \mu\text{C}}$

P25.52 $V = \frac{k_e q}{r}$ and $E = \frac{k_e q}{r^2}$. Since $E = \frac{V}{r}$,

(b) $r = \frac{V}{E} = \frac{6.00 \times 10^5 \text{ V}}{3.00 \times 10^6 \text{ V/m}} = \boxed{0.200 \text{ m}}$ and

(a) $q = \frac{Vr}{k_e} = \boxed{13.3 \ \mu\text{C}}$

Additional Problems

P25.53 $U = qV = k_e \dfrac{q_1 q_2}{r_{12}} = \left(8.99 \times 10^9\right) \dfrac{(38)(54)\left(1.60 \times 10^{-19}\right)^2}{(5.50 + 6.20) \times 10^{-15}} = 4.04 \times 10^{-11} \text{ J} = \boxed{253 \text{ MeV}}$

P25.54 (a) To make a spark 5 mm long in dry air between flat metal plates requires potential difference

$$\Delta V = Ed = \left(3 \times 10^6 \text{ V/m}\right)\left(5 \times 10^{-3} \text{ m}\right) = 1.5 \times 10^4 \text{ V} \boxed{\sim 10^4 \text{ V}}.$$

(b) The area of your skin is perhaps 1.5 m^2, so model your body as a sphere with this surface area. Its radius is given by $1.5 \text{ m}^2 = 4\pi r^2$, $r = 0.35 \text{ m}$. We require that you are at the potential found in part (a):

$$V = \frac{k_e q}{r} \qquad q = \frac{Vr}{k_e} = \frac{1.5 \times 10^4 \text{ V}(0.35 \text{ m})}{8.99 \times 10^9 \text{ N}\cdot\text{m}^2/\text{C}^2}\left(\frac{\text{J}}{\text{V}\cdot\text{C}}\right)\left(\frac{\text{N}\cdot\text{m}}{\text{J}}\right)$$

$$q = 5.8 \times 10^{-7} \text{ C} \boxed{\sim 10^{-6} \text{ C}}.$$

P25.55 (a) $U = \dfrac{k_e q_1 q_2}{r} = \dfrac{-\left(8.99 \times 10^9\right)\left(1.60 \times 10^{-19}\right)^2}{0.052\,9 \times 10^{-9}} = -4.35 \times 10^{-18} \text{ J} = \boxed{-27.2 \text{ eV}}$

(b) $U = \dfrac{k_e q_1 q_2}{r} = \dfrac{-\left(8.99 \times 10^9\right)\left(1.60 \times 10^{-19}\right)^2}{2^2\left(0.052\,9 \times 10^{-9}\right)} = \boxed{-6.80 \text{ eV}}$

(c) $U = \dfrac{k_e q_1 q_2}{r} = \dfrac{-k_e e^2}{\infty} = \boxed{0}$

P25.56 From Example 25.5, the potential created by the ring at the electron's starting point is

$$V_i = \frac{k_e Q}{\sqrt{x_i^2 + a^2}} = \frac{k_e(2\pi\lambda a)}{\sqrt{x_i^2 + a^2}}$$

while at the center, it is $V_f = 2\pi k_e \lambda$. From conservation of energy,

$$0 + (-eV_i) = \frac{1}{2} m_e v_f^2 + (-eV_f)$$

$$v_f^2 = \frac{2e}{m_e}\left(V_f - V_i\right) = \frac{4\pi e k_e \lambda}{m_e}\left(1 - \frac{a}{\sqrt{x_i^2 + a^2}}\right)$$

$$v_f^2 = \frac{4\pi\left(1.60 \times 10^{-19}\right)\left(8.99 \times 10^9\right)\left(1.00 \times 10^{-7}\right)}{9.11 \times 10^{-31}}\left(1 - \frac{0.200}{\sqrt{(0.100)^2 + (0.200)^2}}\right)$$

$$v_f = \boxed{1.45 \times 10^7 \text{ m/s}}$$

***P25.57** The plates create uniform electric field to the right in the picture, with magnitude $\frac{V_0-(-V_0)}{d}=\frac{2V_0}{d}$. Assume the ball swings a small distance x to the right. It moves to a place where the voltage created by the plates is lower by $-Ex=-\frac{2V_0}{d}x$. Its ground connection maintains it at $V=0$ by allowing charge q to flow from ground onto the ball, where $-\frac{2V_0x}{d}+\frac{k_eq}{R}=0 \qquad q=\frac{2V_0xR}{k_ed}$. Then the ball feels electric force $F=qE=\frac{4V_0^2xR}{k_ed^2}$ to the right. For equilibrium this must be balanced by the horizontal component of string tension according to $T\cos\theta=mg \qquad T\sin\theta=\frac{4V_0^2xR}{k_ed^2}$

$\tan\theta=\frac{4V_0^2xR}{k_ed^2mg}=\frac{x}{L}$ for small x. Then $V_0=\left(\frac{k_ed^2mg}{4RL}\right)^{1/2}$.

If V_0 is less than this value, the only equilibrium position of the ball is hanging straight down. If V_0 exceeds this value the ball will swing over to one plate or the other.

P25.58 (a) Take the origin at the point where we will find the potential. One ring, of width dx, has charge $\frac{Qdx}{h}$ and, according to Example 25.5, creates potential

$$dV=\frac{k_eQdx}{h\sqrt{x^2+R^2}}.$$

The whole stack of rings creates potential

$$V=\int_{\text{all charge}}dV=\int_d^{d+h}\frac{k_eQdx}{h\sqrt{x^2+R^2}}=\frac{k_eQ}{h}\ln\left(x+\sqrt{x^2+R^2}\right)\Big|_d^{d+h}=\boxed{\frac{k_eQ}{h}\ln\left(\frac{d+h+\sqrt{(d+h)^2+R^2}}{d+\sqrt{d^2+R^2}}\right)}.$$

(b) A disk of thickness dx has charge $\frac{Qdx}{h}$ and charge-per-area $\frac{Qdx}{\pi R^2h}$. According to Example 25.6, it creates potential

$$dV=2\pi k_e\frac{Qdx}{\pi R^2h}\left(\sqrt{x^2+R^2}-x\right).$$

Integrating,

$$V=\int_d^{d+h}\frac{2k_eQ}{R^2h}\left(\sqrt{x^2+R^2}\,dx-xdx\right)=\frac{2k_eQ}{R^2h}\left[\frac{1}{2}x\sqrt{x^2+R^2}+\frac{R^2}{2}\ln\left(x+\sqrt{x^2+R^2}\right)-\frac{x^2}{2}\right]_d^{d+h}$$

$$V=\boxed{\frac{k_eQ}{R^2h}\left[(d+h)\sqrt{(d+h)^2+R^2}-d\sqrt{d^2+R^2}-2dh-h^2+R^2\ln\left(\frac{d+h+\sqrt{(d+h)^2+R^2}}{d+\sqrt{d^2+R^2}}\right)\right]}$$

P25.59 $W=\int_0^Q Vdq$

where $V=\frac{k_eq}{R}$.

Therefore, $W=\boxed{\frac{k_eQ^2}{2R}}$.

P25.60 The positive plate by itself creates a field $E = \frac{\sigma}{2\in_0} = \frac{36.0\times10^{-9}\ \text{C/m}^2}{2\left(8.85\times10^{-12}\ \text{C}^2/\text{N}\cdot\text{m}^2\right)} = 2.03\ \text{kN/C}$ away from the + plate. The negative plate by itself creates the same size field and between the plates it is in the same direction. Together the plates create a uniform field $4.07\ \text{kN/C}$ in the space between.

(a) Take $V = 0$ at the negative plate. The potential at the positive plate is then

$$V - 0 = -\int_0^{12.0\ \text{cm}} (-4.07\ \text{kN/C})dx.$$

The potential difference between the plates is $V = \left(4.07\times10^3\ \text{N/C}\right)(0.120\ \text{m}) = \boxed{488\ \text{V}}$.

(b) $$\left(\frac{1}{2}mv^2 + qV\right)_i = \left(\frac{1}{2}mv^2 + qV\right)_f$$

$$qV = \left(1.60\times10^{-19}\ \text{C}\right)(488\ \text{V}) = \frac{1}{2}mv_f^2 = \boxed{7.81\times10^{-17}\ \text{J}}$$

(c) $$v_f = \boxed{306\ \text{km/s}}$$

(d) $$v_f^2 = v_i^2 + 2a\left(x_f - x_i\right)$$

$$\left(3.06\times10^5\ \text{m/s}\right)^2 = 0 + 2a(0.120\ \text{m})$$

$$a = \boxed{3.90\times10^{11}\ \text{m/s}^2}$$

(e) $$\sum F = ma = \left(1.67\times10^{-27}\ \text{kg}\right)\left(3.90\times10^{11}\ \text{m/s}^2\right) = \boxed{6.51\times10^{-16}\ \text{N}}$$

(f) $$E = \frac{F}{q} = \frac{6.51\times10^{-16}\ \text{N}}{1.60\times10^{-19}\ \text{C}} = \boxed{4.07\ \text{kN/C}}$$

P25.61 (a) $V_B - V_A = -\int_A^B \mathbf{E}\cdot d\mathbf{s}$ and the field at distance r from a uniformly charged rod (where $r >$ radius of charged rod) is

$$E = \frac{\lambda}{2\pi\in_0 r} = \frac{2k_e\lambda}{r}.$$

In this case, the field between the central wire and the coaxial cylinder is directed perpendicular to the line of charge so that

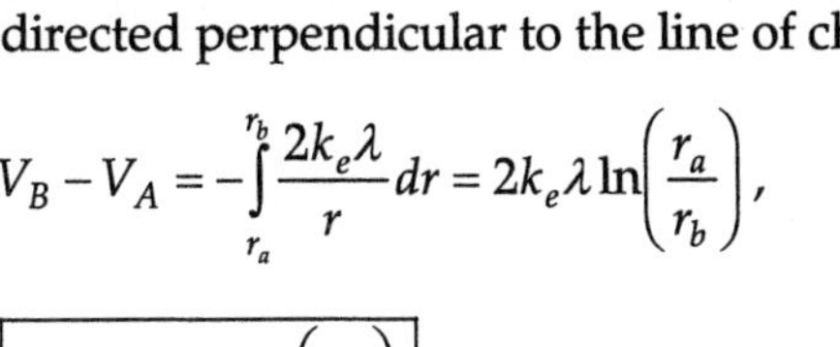

$$V_B - V_A = -\int_{r_a}^{r_b} \frac{2k_e\lambda}{r}dr = 2k_e\lambda\ln\left(\frac{r_a}{r_b}\right),$$

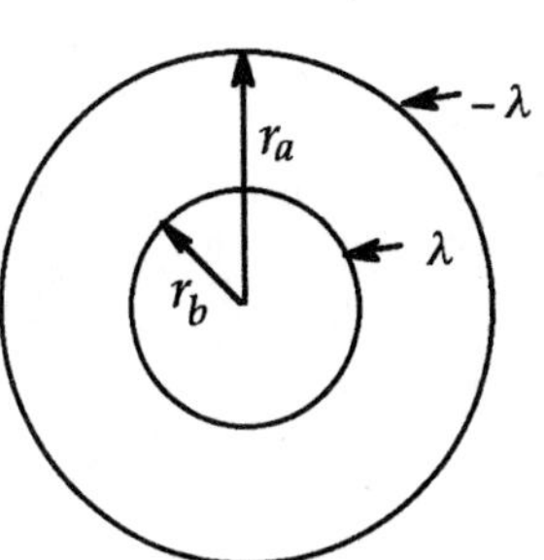

FIG. P25.61

or $$\boxed{\Delta V = 2k_e\lambda\ln\left(\frac{r_a}{r_b}\right)}.$$

continued on next page

(b) From part (a), when the outer cylinder is considered to be at zero potential, the potential at a distance r from the axis is

$$V = 2k_e\lambda \ln\left(\frac{r_a}{r}\right).$$

The field at r is given by

$$E = -\frac{\partial V}{\partial r} = -2k_e\lambda\left(\frac{r}{r_a}\right)\left(-\frac{r_a}{r^2}\right) = \frac{2k_e\lambda}{r}.$$

But, from part (a), $2k_e\lambda = \dfrac{\Delta V}{\ln(r_a/r_b)}$.

Therefore, $\boxed{E = \dfrac{\Delta V}{\ln(r_a/r_b)}\left(\dfrac{1}{r}\right)}$.

P25.62 (a) From Problem 61,

$$E = \frac{\Delta V}{\ln(r_a/r_b)}\frac{1}{r}.$$

We require just outside the central wire

$$5.50\times10^6\ \text{V/m} = \frac{50.0\times10^3\ \text{V}}{\ln(0.850\ \text{m}/r_b)}\left(\frac{1}{r_b}\right)$$

or $$\left(110\ \text{m}^{-1}\right)r_b \ln\left(\frac{0.850\ \text{m}}{r_b}\right) = 1.$$

We solve by homing in on the required value

r_b (m)	0.0100	0.00100	0.00150	0.00145	0.00143	0.00142
$\left(110\ \text{m}^{-1}\right)r_b \ln\left(\frac{0.850\ \text{m}}{r_b}\right)$	4.89	0.740	1.05	1.017	1.005	0.999

Thus, to three significant figures,

$$r_b = \boxed{1.42\ \text{mm}}.$$

(b) At r_a,

$$E = \frac{50.0\ \text{kV}}{\ln(0.850\ \text{m}/0.001\,42\ \text{m})}\left(\frac{1}{0.850\ \text{m}}\right) = \boxed{9.20\ \text{kV/m}}.$$

P25.63 $$V_2 - V_1 = -\int_{r_1}^{r_2}\mathbf{E}\cdot d\mathbf{r} = -\int_{r_1}^{r_2}\frac{\lambda}{2\pi\epsilon_0 r}dr$$

$$V_2 - V_1 = \boxed{\frac{-\lambda}{2\pi\epsilon_0}\ln\left(\frac{r_2}{r_1}\right)}$$

***P25.64** Take the illustration presented with the problem as an initial picture. No external horizontal forces act on the set of four balls, so its center of mass stays fixed at the location of the center of the square. As the charged balls 1 and 2 swing out and away from each other, balls 3 and 4 move up with equal y-components of velocity. The maximum-kinetic-energy point is illustrated. System energy is conserved:

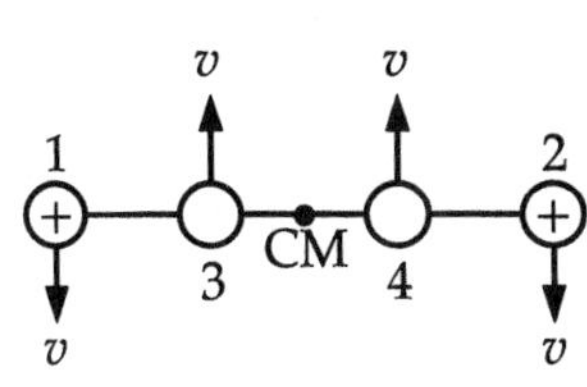

FIG. P25.64

$$\frac{k_e q^2}{a} = \frac{k_e q^2}{3a} + \frac{1}{2}mv^2 + \frac{1}{2}mv^2 + \frac{1}{2}mv^2 + \frac{1}{2}mv^2$$

$$\frac{2k_e q^2}{3a} = 2mv^2 \qquad \boxed{v = \sqrt{\frac{k_e q^2}{3am}}}$$

P25.65 For the given charge distribution, $V(x, y, z) = \dfrac{k_e(q)}{r_1} + \dfrac{k_e(-2q)}{r_2}$

where $r_1 = \sqrt{(x+R)^2 + y^2 + z^2}$ and $r_2 = \sqrt{x^2 + y^2 + z^2}$.

The surface on which $V(x, y, z) = 0$

is given by $k_e q\left(\dfrac{1}{r_1} - \dfrac{2}{r_2}\right) = 0$, or $2r_1 = r_2$.

This gives: $4(x+R)^2 + 4y^2 + 4z^2 = x^2 + y^2 + z^2$

which may be written in the form: $x^2 + y^2 + z^2 + \left(\dfrac{8}{3}R\right)x + (0)y + (0)z + \left(\dfrac{4}{3}R^2\right) = 0$. [1]

The general equation for a sphere of radius a centered at (x_0, y_0, z_0) is:

$$(x - x_0)^2 + (y - y_0)^2 + (z - z_0)^2 - a^2 = 0$$

or $x^2 + y^2 + z^2 + (-2x_0)x + (-2y_0)y + (-2z_0)z + \left(x_0^2 + y_0^2 + z_0^2 - a^2\right) = 0$. [2]

Comparing equations [1] and [2], it is seen that the equipotential surface for which $V = 0$ is indeed a sphere and that:

$$-2x_0 = \frac{8}{3}R;\ -2y_0 = 0;\ -2z_0 = 0;\ x_0^2 + y_0^2 + z_0^2 - a^2 = \frac{4}{3}R^2.$$

Thus, $x_0 = -\dfrac{4}{3}R$, $y_0 = z_0 = 0$, and $a^2 = \left(\dfrac{16}{9} - \dfrac{4}{3}\right)R^2 = \dfrac{4}{9}R^2$.

The equipotential surface is therefore a sphere centered at $\boxed{\left(-\dfrac{4}{3}R, 0, 0\right)}$, having a radius $\boxed{\dfrac{2}{3}R}$.

P25.66 (a) From Gauss's law, $\boxed{E_A = 0}$ (no charge within)

$$E_B = k_e \frac{q_A}{r^2} = \left(8.99\times10^9\right)\frac{\left(1.00\times10^{-8}\right)}{r^2} = \boxed{\left(\frac{89.9}{r^2}\right)\text{ V/m}}$$

$$E_C = k_e \frac{\left(q_A + q_B\right)}{r} = \left(8.99\times10^9\right)\frac{\left(-5.00\times10^{-9}\right)}{r^2} = \boxed{\left(-\frac{45.0}{r^2}\right)\text{ V/m}}$$

(b) $$V_C = k_e \frac{\left(q_A + q_B\right)}{r} = \left(8.99\times10^9\right)\frac{\left(-5.00\times10^{-9}\right)}{r} = \boxed{\left(-\frac{45.0}{r}\right)\text{ V}}$$

$$\therefore \text{At } r_2,\ V = -\frac{45.0}{0.300} = -150\text{ V}$$

$$\text{Inside } r_2,\ V_B = -150\text{ V} + \int_{r_2}^{r}\frac{89.9}{r^2}dr = -150 + 89.9\left(\frac{1}{r} - \frac{1}{0.300}\right) = \boxed{\left(-450 + \frac{89.9}{r}\right)\text{ V}}$$

$$\therefore \text{At } r_1,\ V = -450 + \frac{89.9}{0.150} = +150\text{ V so } \boxed{V_A = +150\text{ V}}.$$

P25.67 From Example 25.5, the potential at the center of the ring is $V_i = \frac{k_eQ}{R}$ and the potential at an infinite distance from the ring is $V_f = 0$. Thus, the initial and final potential energies of the point charge-ring system are:

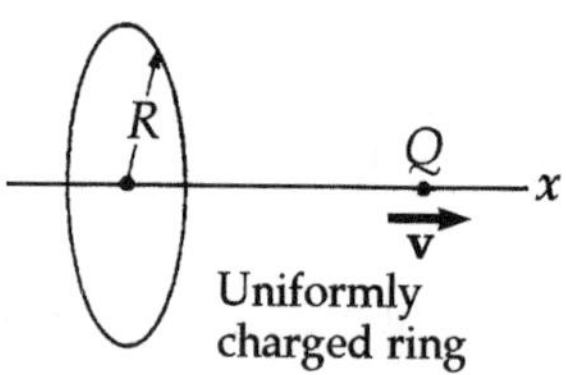

FIG. P25.67

$$U_i = QV_i = \frac{k_eQ^2}{R}$$

and $$U_f = QV_f = 0.$$

From conservation of energy,

$$K_f + U_f = K_i + U_i$$

or $$\frac{1}{2}Mv_f^2 + 0 = 0 + \frac{k_eQ^2}{R}$$

giving $$v_f = \boxed{\sqrt{\frac{2k_eQ^2}{MR}}}.$$

P25.68 $$V = k_e \int_a^{a+L} \frac{\lambda dx}{\sqrt{x^2+b^2}} = k_e\lambda \ln\left[x + \sqrt{\left(x^2+b^2\right)}\right]_a^{a+L} = \boxed{k_e\lambda \ln\left[\frac{a+L+\sqrt{(a+L)^2+b^2}}{a+\sqrt{a^2+b^2}}\right]}$$

***P25.69** (a) $V = \dfrac{k_e q}{r_1} - \dfrac{k_e q}{r_2} = \dfrac{k_e q}{r_1 r_2}(r_2 - r_1)$

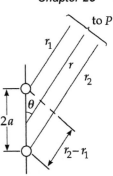

From the figure, for $r >> a$, $r_2 - r_1 \cong 2a\cos\theta$.

Then $V \cong \dfrac{k_e q}{r_1 r_2} 2a\cos\theta \cong \dfrac{k_e p\cos\theta}{r^2}$.

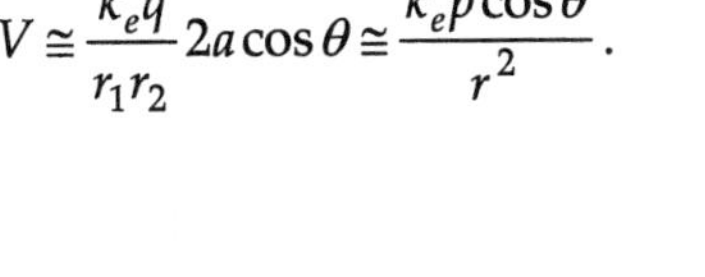

FIG. P25.69

(b) $E_r = -\dfrac{\partial V}{\partial r} = \boxed{\dfrac{2k_e p\cos\theta}{r^3}}$

In spherical coordinates, the θ component of the gradient is $\dfrac{1}{r}\left(\dfrac{\partial}{\partial\theta}\right)$.

Therefore, $E_\theta = -\dfrac{1}{r}\left(\dfrac{\partial V}{\partial\theta}\right) = \boxed{\dfrac{k_e p\sin\theta}{r^3}}$.

For $r >> a$ $E_r(0°) = \dfrac{2k_e p}{r^3}$

and $E_r(90°) = 0$,

$E_\theta(0°) = 0$

and $E_\theta(90°) = \dfrac{k_e p}{r^3}$.

These results are $\boxed{\text{reasonable for } r >> a}$. Their directions are as shown in Figure 25.13 (c). However, for $\boxed{r \to 0,\ E(0) \to \infty. \text{ This is unreasonable,}}$ since r is not much greater than a if it is 0.

(c) $\boxed{V = \dfrac{k_e p y}{\left(x^2 + y^2\right)^{3/2}}}$

and $\boxed{E_x = -\dfrac{\partial V}{\partial x} = \dfrac{3k_e p x y}{\left(x^2 + y^2\right)^{5/2}}}$

$\boxed{E_y = -\dfrac{\partial V}{\partial y} = \dfrac{k_e p\left(2y^2 - x^2\right)}{\left(x^2 + y^2\right)^{5/2}}}$

P25.70 Inside the sphere, $E_x = E_y = E_z = 0$.

Outside, $E_x = -\frac{\partial V}{\partial x} = -\frac{\partial}{\partial x}\left(V_0 - E_0 z + E_0 a^3 z\left(x^2+y^2+z^2\right)^{-3/2}\right)$

So $E_x = -\left[0 + 0 + E_0 a^3 z\left(-\frac{3}{2}\right)\left(x^2+y^2+z^2\right)^{-5/2}(2x)\right] = \boxed{3E_0 a^3 xz\left(x^2+y^2+z^2\right)^{-5/2}}$

$$E_y = -\frac{\partial V}{\partial y} = -\frac{\partial}{\partial y}\left(V_0 - E_0 z + E_0 a^3 z\left(x^2+y^2+z^2\right)^{-3/2}\right)$$

$$E_y = -E_0 a^3 z\left(-\frac{3}{2}\right)\left(x^2+y^2+z^2\right)^{-5/2} 2y = \boxed{3E_0 a^3 yz\left(x^2+y^2+z^2\right)^{-5/2}}$$

$$E_z = -\frac{\partial V}{\partial z} = E_0 - E_0 a^3 z\left(-\frac{3}{2}\right)\left(x^2+y^2+z^2\right)^{-5/2}(2z) - E_0 a^3\left(x^2+y^2+z^2\right)^{-3/2}$$

$$E_z = \boxed{E_0 + E_0 a^3\left(2z^2 - x^2 - y^2\right)\left(x^2+y^2+z^2\right)^{-5/2}}$$

P25.71 For an element of area which is a ring of radius r and width dr, $dV = \frac{k_e dq}{\sqrt{r^2+x^2}}$.

$dq = \sigma dA = Cr(2\pi r dr)$ and

$$V = C(2\pi k_e)\int_0^R \frac{r^2 dr}{\sqrt{r^2+x^2}} = \boxed{C(\pi k_e)\left[R\sqrt{R^2+x^2} + x^2 \ln\left(\frac{x}{R+\sqrt{R^2+x^2}}\right)\right]}.$$

P25.72 $dU = V dq$ where the potential $V = \frac{k_e q}{r}$.

The element of charge in a shell is $dq = \rho$ (volume element) or $dq = \rho\left(4\pi r^2 dr\right)$ and the charge q in a sphere of radius r is

$$q = 4\pi\rho\int_0^r r^2 dr = \rho\left(\frac{4\pi r^3}{3}\right).$$

Substituting this into the expression for dU, we have

$$dU = \left(\frac{k_e q}{r}\right)dq = k_e\rho\left(\frac{4\pi r^3}{3}\right)\left(\frac{1}{r}\right)\rho\left(4\pi r^2 dr\right) = k_e\left(\frac{16\pi^2}{3}\right)\rho^2 r^4 dr$$

$$U = \int dU = k_e\left(\frac{16\pi^2}{3}\right)\rho^2\int_0^R r^4 dr = k_e\left(\frac{16\pi^2}{15}\right)\rho^2 R^5$$

But the *total* charge, $Q = \rho\frac{4}{3}\pi R^3$. Therefore, $\boxed{U = \frac{3}{5}\frac{k_e Q^2}{R}}$.

***P25.73** (a) The whole charge on the cube is $q=\left(100\times10^{-6}\ \text{C/m}^3\right)(0.1\ \text{m})^3=10^{-7}\ \text{C}$. Divide up the cube into 64 or more elements. The little cube labeled a creates at P potential $\dfrac{k_e q}{64\sqrt{6.25^2+1.25^2+1.25^2}\,10^{-2}\ \text{m}}$. The others in the horizontal row behind it contribute

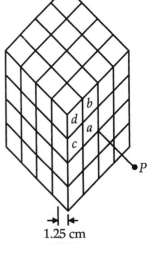

$$\frac{k_e q}{64\left(10^{-2}\ \text{m}\right)}\left(\frac{1}{\sqrt{8.75^2+3.125}}+\frac{1}{\sqrt{11.25^2+3.125}}+\frac{1}{\sqrt{13.75^2+3.125}}\right).$$

The little cubes in the rows containing b and c add

$$\frac{2k_e q}{64\left(10^{-2}\ \text{m}\right)}\left[\left(6.25^2+1.25^2+3.75^2\right)^{-1/2}+\left(8.75^2+15.625\right)^{-1/2}+\left(11.25^2+15.625\right)^{-1/2}+\left(13.75^2+15.625\right)^{-1/2}\right]$$

and the bits in row d make potential at P

$$\frac{k_e q}{64\left(10^{-2}\ \text{m}\right)}\left[\left(6.25^2+28.125\right)^{-1/2}+\ldots+\left(13.75^2+28.125\right)^{-1/2}\right].$$

FIG. P25.73

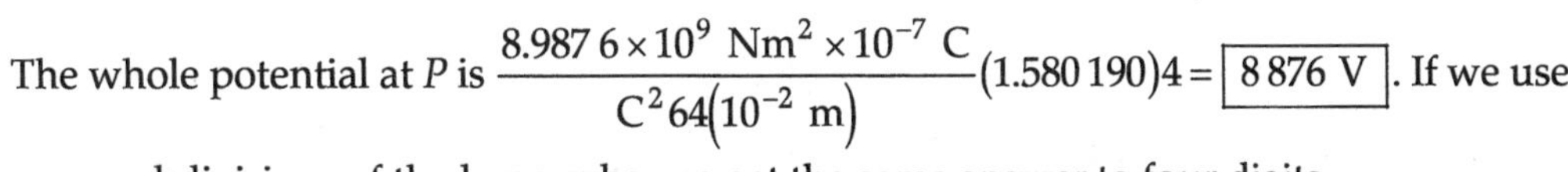

The whole potential at P is $\dfrac{8.987\,6\times10^9\ \text{Nm}^2\times10^{-7}\ \text{C}}{\text{C}^2\,64\left(10^{-2}\ \text{m}\right)}(1.580\,190)4=\boxed{8\,876\ \text{V}}$. If we use more subdivisions of the large cube, we get the same answer to four digits.

(b) A sphere centered at the same point would create potential

$$\frac{k_e q}{r}=\frac{8.987\,6\times10^9\ \text{Nm}^2\times10^{-7}\ \text{C}}{\text{C}^2\quad 10^{-1}\ \text{m}}=8\,988\ \text{V},\ \boxed{\text{larger by }112\ \text{V}}.$$

ANSWERS TO EVEN PROBLEMS

P25.2 6.41×10^{-19} C

P25.4 –0.502 V

P25.6 1.67 MN/C

P25.8 (a) 59.0 V; (b) 4.55 Mm/s

P25.10 see the solution

P25.12 40.2 kV

P25.14 0.300 m/s

P25.16 (a) 0; (b) 0; (c) 45.0 kV

P25.18 (a) –4.83 m; (b) 0.667 m and –2.00 m

P25.20 (a) –386 nJ; (b) 103 V

P25.22 (a) 32.2 kV; (b) –96.5 mJ

P25.24 $-\dfrac{5k_e q}{R}$

P25.26 (a) 10.8 m/s and 1.55 m/s; (b) greater

P25.28 (a) –45.0 μJ; (b) 34.6 km/s

P25.30 see the solution

P25.32 27.4 fm

P25.34 –3.96 J

P25.36 $22.8\dfrac{k_e q^2}{s}$

P25.38 (a) 0; (b) $\frac{k_e Q}{r^2}$ radially outward

P25.40 (a) larger at A; (b) 200 N/C down; (c) see the solution

P25.42 $-0.553\frac{k_e Q}{R}$

P25.44 $-\frac{k_e \alpha L}{2}\ln\left[\frac{\sqrt{b^2+(L^2/4)}-L/2}{\sqrt{b^2+(L^2/4)}+L/2}\right]$

P25.46 $2\pi k_e \sigma\left[\sqrt{x^2+b^2}-\sqrt{x^2+a^2}\right]$

P25.48 1.56×10^{12} electrons

P25.50 (a) 135 kV; (b) 2.25 MV/m away from the large sphere and 6.74 MV/m away from the small sphere

P25.52 (a) 13.3 μC; (b) 0.200 m

P25.54 (a) $\sim 10^4$ V; (b) $\sim 10^{-6}$ C

P25.56 14.5 Mm/s

P25.58 (a) $\frac{k_e Q}{h}\ln\left(\frac{d+h+\sqrt{(d+h)^2+R^2}}{d+\sqrt{d^2+R^2}}\right)$;

(b) $\frac{k_e Q}{R^2 h}\left[(d+h)\sqrt{(d+h)^2+R^2}-d\sqrt{d^2+R^2}-2dh-h^2+R^2\ln\left(\frac{d+h+\sqrt{(d+h)^2+R^2}}{d+\sqrt{d^2+R^2}}\right)\right]$

P25.60 (a) 488 V; (b) 7.81×10^{-17} J; (c) 306 km/s; (d) 390 Gm/s^2 toward the negative plate; (e) 6.51×10^{-16} N toward the negative plate; (f) 4.07 kN/C toward the negative plate

P25.62 (a) 1.42 mm; (b) 9.20 kV/m

P25.64 $\left(\frac{k_e q^2}{3am}\right)^{1/2}$

P25.66 (a) $\mathbf{E}_A = 0$; $\mathbf{E}_B = \left(\frac{89.9}{r^2}\right)$ V/m radially outward; $\mathbf{E}_C = \left(-\frac{45.0}{r^2}\right)$ V/m radially outward;

(b) $V_A = 150$ V; $V_B = \left(-450+\frac{89.9}{r}\right)$ V; $V_C = \left(-\frac{45.0}{r}\right)$ V

P25.68 $k_e\lambda\ln\left[\frac{a+L+\sqrt{(a+L)^2+b^2}}{a+\sqrt{a^2+b^2}}\right]$

P25.70 $E_x = 3E_0 a^3 xz\left(x^2+y^2+z^2\right)^{-5/2}$;

$E_y = 3E_0 a^3 yz\left(x^2+y^2+z^2\right)^{-5/2}$;

$E_z = E_0 + \frac{E_0 a^3\left(2z^2-x^2-y^2\right)}{\left(x^2+y^2+z^2\right)^{5/2}}$ outside and

$\mathbf{E} = 0$ inside

P25.72 $\frac{3}{5}\frac{k_e Q^2}{R}$

26

Capacitance and Dielectrics

CHAPTER OUTLINE

ANSWERS TO QUESTIONS

Q26.1 Nothing happens to the charge if the wires are disconnected. If the wires are connected to each other, charges in the single conductor which now exists move between the wires and the plates until the entire conductor is at a single potential and the capacitor is discharged.

Q26.2 336 km. The plate area would need to be $\frac{1}{\epsilon_0}$ m^2.

Q26.3 The parallel-connected capacitors store more energy, since they have higher equivalent capacitance.

Q26.4 Seventeen combinations:

Individual C_1, C_2, C_3

Parallel $C_1+C_2+C_3,\ C_1+C_2,\ C_1+C_3,\ C_2+C_3$

Series-Parallel $\left(\frac{1}{C_1}+\frac{1}{C_2}\right)^{-1}+C_3,\ \left(\frac{1}{C_1}+\frac{1}{C_3}\right)^{-1}+C_2,\ \left(\frac{1}{C_2}+\frac{1}{C_3}\right)^{-1}+C_1$

$$\left(\frac{1}{C_1+C_2}+\frac{1}{C_3}\right)^{-1},\ \left(\frac{1}{C_1+C_3}+\frac{1}{C_2}\right)^{-1},\ \left(\frac{1}{C_2+C_3}+\frac{1}{C_1}\right)^{-1}$$

Series $\left(\frac{1}{C_1}+\frac{1}{C_2}+\frac{1}{C_3}\right)^{-1},\ \left(\frac{1}{C_1}+\frac{1}{C_2}\right)^{-1},\ \left(\frac{1}{C_2}+\frac{1}{C_3}\right)^{-1},\ \left(\frac{1}{C_1}+\frac{1}{C_3}\right)^{-1}$

Q26.5 This arrangement would decrease the potential difference between the plates of any individual capacitor by a factor of 2, thus decreasing the possibility of dielectric breakdown. Depending on the application, this could be the difference between the life or death of some other (most likely more expensive) electrical component connected to the capacitors.

Q26.6 No—not just using rules about capacitors in series or in parallel. See Problem 72 for an example. If connections can be made to a combination of capacitors at more than two points, the combination may be irreducible.

Q26.7 A capacitor stores energy in the electric field between the plates. This is most easily seen when using a "dissectable" capacitor. If the capacitor is charged, carefully pull it apart into its component pieces. One will find that very little residual charge remains on each plate. When reassembled, the capacitor is suddenly "recharged"—by induction—due to the electric field set up and "stored" in the dielectric. This proves to be an instructive classroom demonstration, especially when you ask a student to reconstruct the capacitor without supplying him/her with any rubber gloves or other insulating material. (Of course, this is *after* they sign a liability waiver).

Q26.8 The work you do to pull the plates apart becomes additional electric potential energy stored in the capacitor. The charge is constant and the capacitance decreases but the potential difference increases to drive up the potential energy $\frac{1}{2}Q\Delta V$. The electric field between the plates is constant in strength but fills more volume as you pull the plates apart.

Q26.9 A capacitor stores energy in the electric field inside the dielectric. Once the external voltage source is removed—provided that there is no external resistance through which the capacitor can discharge—the capacitor can hold onto this energy for a very long time. To make the capacitor safe to handle, you can discharge the capacitor through a conductor, such as a screwdriver, provided that you only touch the insulating handle. If the capacitor is a large one, it is best to use an external resistor to discharge the capacitor more slowly to prevent damage to the dielectric, or welding of the screwdriver to the terminals of the capacitor.

Q26.10 The work done, $W = Q\Delta V$, is the work done by an external agent, like a battery, to move a charge through a potential difference, ΔV. To determine the energy in a charged capacitor, we must add the work done to move bits of charge from one plate to the other. Initially, there is no potential difference between the plates of an uncharged capacitor. As more charge is transferred from one plate to the other, the potential difference increases as shown in Figure 26.12, meaning that more work is needed to transfer each additional bit of charge. The total work is the area under the curve of Figure 26.12, and thus $W = \frac{1}{2}Q\Delta V$.

Q26.11 Energy is proportional to voltage squared. It gets four times larger.

Q26.12 Let $C =$ the capacitance of an individual capacitor, and C_s represent the equivalent capacitance of the group in series. While being charged in parallel, each capacitor receives charge

$$Q = C\Delta V_{\text{charge}} = \left(500\times10^{-4}\text{ F}\right)(800\text{ V}) = 0.400\text{ C}.$$

While being discharged in series, $\Delta V_{\text{discharge}} = \frac{Q}{C_s} = \frac{Q}{C/10} = \frac{0.400\text{ C}}{5.00\times10^{-5}\text{ F}} = 8.00\text{ kV}$

(or 10 times the original voltage).

Q26.13 Put a material with higher dielectric strength between the plates, or evacuate the space between the plates. At very high voltages, you may want to cool off the plates or choose to make them of a different chemically stable material, because atoms in the plates themselves can ionize, showing *thermionic emission* under high electric fields.

Q26.14 The potential difference must decrease. Since there is no external power supply, the charge on the capacitor, Q, will remain constant—that is assuming that the resistance of the meter is sufficiently large. Adding a dielectric *increases* the capacitance, which must therefore *decrease* the potential difference between the plates.

Q26.15 Each polar molecule acts like an electric "compass" needle, aligning itself with the external electric field set up by the charged plates. The contribution of these electric dipoles pointing in the same direction reduces the net electric field. As each dipole falls into a configuration of lower potential energy it can contribute to increasing the internal energy of the material.

Q26.16 The material of the dielectric may be able to support a larger electric field than air, without breaking down to pass a spark between the capacitor plates.

Q26.17 The dielectric strength is a measure of the potential difference per unit length that a dielectric can withstand without having individual molecules ionized, leaving in its wake a conducting path from plate to plate. For example, dry air has a dielectric strength of about 3 MV/m. The dielectric constant in effect describes the contribution of the electric dipoles of the polar molecules in the dielectric to the electric field once aligned.

Q26.18 In water, the oxygen atom and one hydrogen atom considered alone have an electric dipole moment that points from the hydrogen to the oxygen. The other O-H pair has its own dipole moment that points again toward the oxygen. Due to the geometry of the molecule, these dipole moments add to have a non-zero component along the axis of symmetry and pointing toward the oxygen.

A non-polarized molecule could either have no intrinsic dipole moments, or have dipole moments that add to zero. An example of the latter case is CO_2. The molecule is structured so that each CO pair has a dipole moment, but since both dipole moments have the same magnitude and opposite direction—due to the linear geometry of the molecule—the entire molecule has no dipole moment.

Q26.19 Heating a dielectric will decrease its dielectric constant, decreasing the capacitance of a capacitor. When you heat a material, the average kinetic energy per molecule increases. If you refer back to the answer to Question 26.15, each polar molecule will no longer be nicely aligned with the applied electric field, but will begin to "dither"—rock back and forth—effectively decreasing its contribution to the overall field.

Q26.20 The primary choice would be the dielectric. You would want to chose a dielectric that has a large dielectric constant and dielectric strength, such as strontium titanate, where $\kappa \approx 233$ (Table 26.1). A convenient choice could be thick plastic or mylar. Secondly, geometry would be a factor. To maximize capacitance, one would want the individual plates as close as possible, since the capacitance is proportional to the inverse of the plate separation—hence the need for a dielectric with a high dielectric strength. Also, one would want to build, instead of a single parallel plate capacitor, several capacitors in parallel. This could be achieved through "stacking" the plates of the capacitor. For example, you can alternately lay down sheets of a conducting material, such as aluminum foil, sandwiched between your sheets of insulating dielectric. Making sure that none of the conducting sheets are in contact with their next neighbors, connect every other plate together. Figure Q26.20 illustrates this idea.

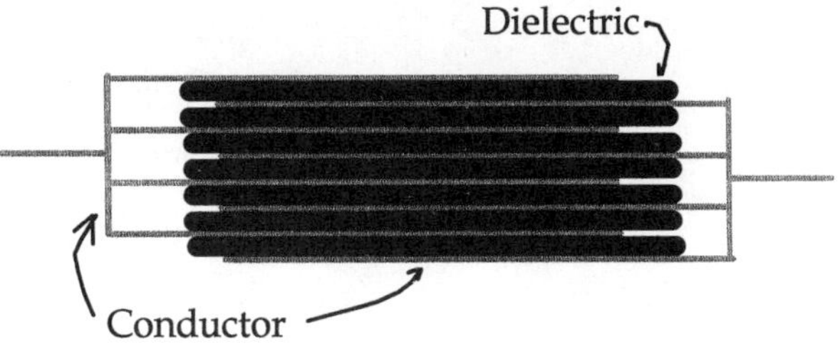

FIG. Q26.20

This technique is often used when "home-brewing" signal capacitors for radio applications, as they can withstand huge potential differences without flashover (without either discharge between plates around the dielectric or dielectric breakdown). One variation on this technique is to sandwich together flexible materials such as aluminum roof flashing and thick plastic, so the whole product can be rolled up into a "capacitor burrito" and placed in an insulating tube, such as a PVC pipe, and then filled with motor oil (again to prevent flashover).

SOLUTIONS TO PROBLEMS

Section 26.1 Definition of Capacitance

P26.1 (a) $Q = C\Delta V = \left(4.00\times10^{-6}\text{ F}\right)(12.0\text{ V}) = 4.80\times10^{-5}\text{ C} = \boxed{48.0\ \mu\text{C}}$

(b) $Q = C\Delta V = \left(4.00\times10^{-6}\text{ F}\right)(1.50\text{ V}) = 6.00\times10^{-6}\text{ C} = \boxed{6.00\ \mu\text{C}}$

P26.2 (a) $C = \dfrac{Q}{\Delta V} = \dfrac{10.0\times10^{-6}\text{ C}}{10.0\text{ V}} = 1.00\times10^{-6}\text{ F} = \boxed{1.00\ \mu\text{F}}$

(b) $\Delta V = \dfrac{Q}{C} = \dfrac{100\times10^{-6}\text{ C}}{1.00\times10^{-6}\text{ F}} = \boxed{100\text{ V}}$

Section 26.2 Calculating Capacitance

P26.3 $E = \dfrac{k_e q}{r^2}$: $\quad q = \dfrac{\left(4.90\times10^{4}\text{ N/C}\right)(0.210\text{ m})^2}{\left(8.99\times10^{9}\text{ N}\cdot\text{m}^2/\text{C}^2\right)} = 0.240\ \mu\text{C}$

(a) $\sigma = \dfrac{q}{A} = \dfrac{0.240\times10^{-6}}{4\pi(0.120)^2} = \boxed{1.33\ \mu\text{C/m}^2}$

(b) $C = 4\pi\in_0 r = 4\pi\left(8.85\times10^{-12}\right)(0.120) = \boxed{13.3\text{ pF}}$

P26.4 (a) $C = 4\pi\in_0 R$

$R = \dfrac{C}{4\pi\in_0} = k_e C = \left(8.99\times10^{9}\text{ N}\cdot\text{m}^2/\text{C}^2\right)\left(1.00\times10^{-12}\text{ F}\right) = \boxed{8.99\text{ mm}}$

(b) $C = 4\pi\in_0 R = \dfrac{4\pi\left(8.85\times10^{-12}\text{ C}^2\right)\left(2.00\times10^{-3}\text{ m}\right)}{\text{N}\cdot\text{m}^2} = \boxed{0.222\text{ pF}}$

(c) $Q = CV = \left(2.22\times10^{-13}\text{ F}\right)(100\text{ V}) = \boxed{2.22\times10^{-11}\text{ C}}$

P26.5 (a) $\dfrac{Q_1}{Q_2} = \dfrac{R_1}{R_2}$

$Q_1 + Q_2 = \left(1 + \dfrac{R_1}{R_2}\right)Q_2 = 3.50Q_2 = 7.00\ \mu\text{C}$

$\boxed{Q_2 = 2.00\ \mu\text{C}}\ \boxed{Q_1 = 5.00\ \mu\text{C}}$

(b) $V_1 = V_2 = \dfrac{Q_1}{C_1} = \dfrac{Q_2}{C_2} = \dfrac{5.00\ \mu\text{C}}{\left(8.99\times10^{9}\text{ m/F}\right)^{-1}(0.500\text{ m})} = 8.99\times10^{4}\text{ V} = \boxed{89.9\text{ kV}}$

P26.6 $C = \dfrac{\kappa \in_0 A}{d} = \dfrac{(1.00)\left(8.85\times10^{-12}\ \text{C}^2\right)\left(1.00\times10^3\ \text{m}\right)^2}{\text{N}\cdot\text{m}^2(800\ \text{m})} = \boxed{11.1\ \text{nF}}$

The potential between ground and cloud is

$$\Delta V = Ed = \left(3.00\times10^6\ \text{N/C}\right)(800\ \text{m}) = 2.40\times10^9\ \text{V}$$

$$Q = C(\Delta V) = \left(11.1\times10^{-9}\ \text{C/V}\right)\left(2.40\times10^9\ \text{V}\right) = \boxed{26.6\ \text{C}}$$

P26.7 (a) $\Delta V = Ed$

$$E = \frac{20.0\ \text{V}}{1.80\times10^{-3}\ \text{m}} = \boxed{11.1\ \text{kV/m}}$$

(b) $E = \dfrac{\sigma}{\in_0}$

$$\sigma = \left(1.11\times10^4\ \text{N/C}\right)\left(8.85\times10^{-12}\ \text{C}^2/\text{N}\cdot\text{m}^2\right) = \boxed{98.3\ \text{nC/m}^2}$$

(c) $C = \dfrac{\in_0 A}{d} = \dfrac{\left(8.85\times10^{-12}\ \text{C}^2/\text{N}\cdot\text{m}^2\right)\left(7.60\ \text{cm}^2\right)(1.00\ \text{m}/100\ \text{cm})^2}{1.80\times10^{-3}\ \text{m}} = \boxed{3.74\ \text{pF}}$

(d) $\Delta V = \dfrac{Q}{C}$

$$Q = (20.0\ \text{V})\left(3.74\times10^{-12}\ \text{F}\right) = \boxed{74.7\ \text{pC}}$$

P26.8 $C = \dfrac{\kappa \in_0 A}{d} = 60.0\times10^{-15}\ \text{F}$

$$d = \frac{\kappa \in_0 A}{C} = \frac{(1)\left(8.85\times10^{-12}\right)\left(21.0\times10^{-12}\right)}{60.0\times10^{-15}}$$

$$d = 3.10\times10^{-9}\ \text{m} = \boxed{3.10\ \text{nm}}$$

P26.9 $Q = \dfrac{\in_0 A}{d}(\Delta V)$ $\qquad \dfrac{Q}{A} = \sigma = \dfrac{\in_0 (\Delta V)}{d}$

$$d = \frac{\in_0 (\Delta V)}{\sigma} = \frac{\left(8.85\times10^{-12}\ \text{C}^2/\text{N}\cdot\text{m}^2\right)(150\ \text{V})}{\left(30.0\times10^{-9}\ \text{C/cm}^2\right)\left(1.00\times10^4\ \text{cm}^2/\text{m}^2\right)} = \boxed{4.42\ \mu\text{m}}$$

P26.10 With $\theta = \pi$, the plates are out of mesh and the overlap area is zero. With $\theta = 0$, the overlap area is that of a semi-circle, $\frac{\pi R^2}{2}$. By proportion, the effective area of a single sheet of charge is $\frac{(\pi - \theta)R^2}{2}$.

When there are two plates in each comb, the number of adjoining sheets of positive and negative charge is 3, as shown in the sketch. When there are N plates on each comb, the number of parallel capacitors is $2N - 1$ and the total capacitance is

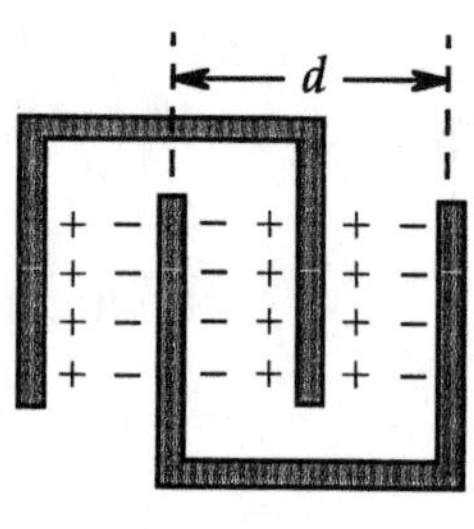

FIG. P26.10

$$C = (2N-1)\frac{\epsilon_0 A_{\text{effective}}}{\text{distance}} = \frac{(2N-1)\epsilon_0(\pi - \theta)R^2/2}{d/2} = \boxed{\frac{(2N-1)\epsilon_0(\pi-\theta)R^2}{d}}.$$

P26.11 (a) $C = \frac{\ell}{2k_e \ln\left(\frac{b}{a}\right)} = \frac{50.0}{2\left(8.99\times10^9\right)\ln\left(\frac{7.27}{2.58}\right)} = \boxed{2.68 \text{ nF}}$

(b) Method 1: $\Delta V = 2k_e \lambda \ln\left(\frac{b}{a}\right)$

$$\lambda = \frac{q}{\ell} = \frac{8.10\times10^{-6} \text{ C}}{50.0 \text{ m}} = 1.62\times10^{-7} \text{ C/m}$$

$$\Delta V = 2\left(8.99\times10^9\right)\left(1.62\times10^{-7}\right)\ln\left(\frac{7.27}{2.58}\right) = \boxed{3.02 \text{ kV}}$$

Method 2: $\Delta V = \frac{Q}{C} = \frac{8.10\times10^{-6}}{2.68\times10^{-9}} = \boxed{3.02 \text{ kV}}$

P26.12 Let the radii be b and a with $b = 2a$. Put charge Q on the inner conductor and $-Q$ on the outer. Electric field exists only in the volume between them. The potential of the inner sphere is $V_a = \frac{k_e Q}{a}$; that of the outer is $V_b = \frac{k_e Q}{b}$. Then

$$V_a - V_b = \frac{k_e Q}{a} - \frac{k_e Q}{b} = \frac{Q}{4\pi\epsilon_0}\left(\frac{b-a}{ab}\right) \text{ and } C = \frac{Q}{V_a - V_b} = \frac{4\pi\epsilon_0 ab}{b-a}.$$

Here $C = \frac{4\pi\epsilon_0 2a^2}{a} = 8\pi\epsilon_0 a \qquad a = \frac{C}{8\pi\epsilon_0}$.

The intervening volume is

$$\text{Volume} = \frac{4}{3}\pi b^3 - \frac{4}{3}\pi a^3 = 7\left(\frac{4}{3}\pi a^3\right) = 7\left(\frac{4}{3}\pi\right)\frac{C^3}{8^3\pi^3\epsilon_0^3} = \frac{7C^3}{384\pi^2\epsilon_0^3}$$

$$\text{Volume} = \frac{7\left(20.0\times10^{-6} \text{ C}^2/\text{N}\cdot\text{m}\right)^3}{384\pi^2\left(8.85\times10^{-12} \text{ C}^2/\text{N}\cdot\text{m}^2\right)^3} = \boxed{2.13\times10^{16} \text{ m}^3}.$$

The outer sphere is 360 km in diameter.

P26.13 (a) $C = \frac{ab}{k_e(b-a)} = \frac{(0.070\,0)(0.140)}{\left(8.99\times10^9\right)(0.140 - 0.070\,0)} = \boxed{15.6 \text{ pF}}$

(b) $C = \frac{Q}{\Delta V} \qquad \Delta V = \frac{Q}{C} = \frac{4.00\times10^{-6} \text{ C}}{15.6\times10^{-12} \text{ F}} = \boxed{256 \text{ kV}}$

P26.14 $\sum F_y = 0$: $T\cos\theta - mg = 0$

$\sum F_x = 0$: $T\sin\theta - Eq = 0$

Dividing, $\tan\theta = \frac{Eq}{mg}$

so $E = \frac{mg}{q}\tan\theta$

and $\Delta V = Ed = \boxed{\frac{mgd\tan\theta}{q}}$.

P26.15 $C = 4\pi \in_0 R = 4\pi\left(8.85\times10^{-12}\ \text{C/N}\cdot\text{m}^2\right)\left(6.37\times10^6\ \text{m}\right) = \boxed{7.08\times10^{-4}\ \text{F}}$

Section 26.3 **Combinations of Capacitors**

P26.16 (a) Capacitors in parallel add. Thus, the equivalent capacitor has a value of

$$C_{eq} = C_1 + C_2 = 5.00\ \mu\text{F} + 12.0\ \mu\text{F} = \boxed{17.0\ \mu\text{F}}.$$

(b) The potential difference across each branch is the same and equal to the voltage of the battery.

$$\Delta V = \boxed{9.00\ \text{V}}$$

(c) $Q_5 = C\Delta V = (5.00\ \mu\text{F})(9.00\ \text{V}) = \boxed{45.0\ \mu\text{C}}$

and $Q_{12} = C\Delta V = (12.0\ \mu\text{F})(9.00\ \text{V}) = \boxed{108\ \mu\text{C}}$

P26.17 (a) In series capacitors add as

$$\frac{1}{C_{eq}} = \frac{1}{C_1} + \frac{1}{C_2} = \frac{1}{5.00\ \mu\text{F}} + \frac{1}{12.0\ \mu\text{F}}$$

and $C_{eq} = \boxed{3.53\ \mu\text{F}}$.

(c) The charge on the equivalent capacitor is $Q_{eq} = C_{eq}\Delta V = (3.53\ \mu\text{F})(9.00\ \text{V}) = 31.8\ \mu\text{C}$.

Each of the series capacitors has this same charge on it.

So $Q_1 = Q_2 = \boxed{31.8\ \mu\text{C}}$.

(b) The potential difference across each is $\Delta V_1 = \frac{Q_1}{C_1} = \frac{31.8\ \mu\text{C}}{5.00\ \mu\text{F}} = \boxed{6.35\ \text{V}}$

and $\Delta V_2 = \frac{Q_2}{C_2} = \frac{31.8\ \mu\text{C}}{12.0\ \mu\text{F}} = \boxed{2.65\ \text{V}}$.

P26.18 The circuit reduces first according to the rule for capacitors in series, as shown in the figure, then according to the rule for capacitors in parallel, shown below.

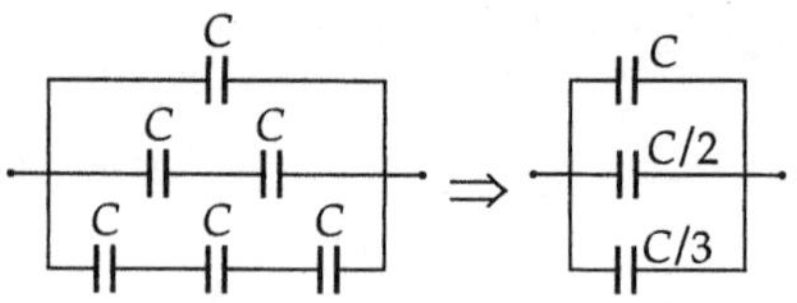

$$C_{eq}=C\left(1+\frac{1}{2}+\frac{1}{3}\right)=\frac{11}{6}C=\boxed{1.83C}$$

FIG. P26.18

P26.19 $C_p=C_1+C_2$ $\qquad \dfrac{1}{C_s}=\dfrac{1}{C_1}+\dfrac{1}{C_2}$

Substitute $C_2=C_p-C_1$ $\qquad \dfrac{1}{C_s}=\dfrac{1}{C_1}+\dfrac{1}{C_p-C_1}=\dfrac{C_p-C_1+C_1}{C_1\left(C_p-C_1\right)}$.

Simplifying, $\qquad C_1^2-C_1C_p+C_pC_s=0$.

$$C_1=\frac{C_p\pm\sqrt{C_p^2-4C_pC_s}}{2}=\frac{1}{2}C_p\pm\sqrt{\frac{1}{4}C_p^2-C_pC_s}$$

We choose arbitrarily the + sign. (This choice can be arbitrary, since with the case of the minus sign, we would get the same two answers with their names interchanged.)

$$C_1=\frac{1}{2}C_p+\sqrt{\frac{1}{4}C_p^2-C_pC_s}=\frac{1}{2}(9.00\text{ pF})+\sqrt{\frac{1}{4}(9.00\text{ pF})^2-(9.00\text{ pF})(2.00\text{ pF})}=\boxed{6.00\text{ pF}}$$

$$C_2=C_p-C_1=\frac{1}{2}C_p-\sqrt{\frac{1}{4}C_p^2-C_pC_s}=\frac{1}{2}(9.00\text{ pF})-1.50\text{ pF}=\boxed{3.00\text{ pF}}$$

P26.20 $C_p=C_1+C_2$

and $\qquad \dfrac{1}{C_s}=\dfrac{1}{C_1}+\dfrac{1}{C_2}$.

Substitute $\qquad C_2=C_p-C_1$: $\qquad \dfrac{1}{C_s}=\dfrac{1}{C_1}+\dfrac{1}{C_p-C_1}=\dfrac{C_p-C_1+C_1}{C_1\left(C_p-C_1\right)}$.

Simplifying, $\qquad C_1^2-C_1C_p+C_pC_s=0$

and $\qquad C_1=\dfrac{C_p\pm\sqrt{C_p^2-4C_pC_s}}{2}=\boxed{\dfrac{1}{2}C_p+\sqrt{\dfrac{1}{4}C_p^2-C_pC_s}}$

where the positive sign was arbitrarily chosen (choosing the negative sign gives the same values for the capacitances, with the names reversed).

Then, from $\qquad C_2=C_p-C_1$

$$C_2=\boxed{\frac{1}{2}C_p-\sqrt{\frac{1}{4}C_p^2-C_pC_s}}.$$

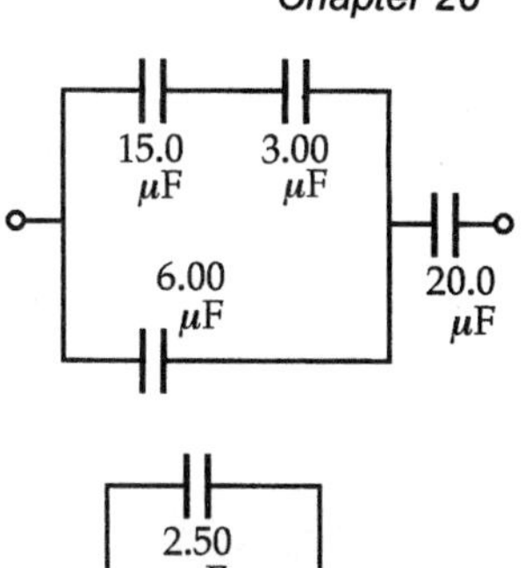

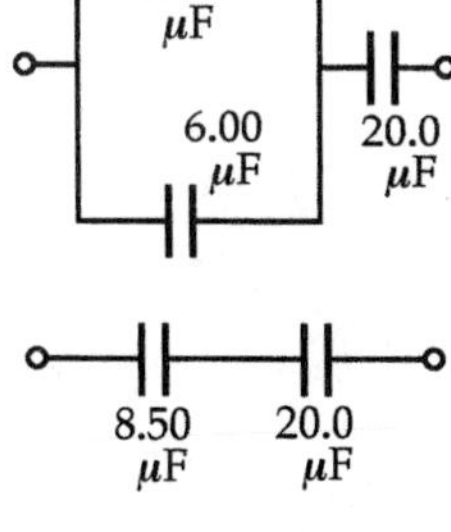

P26.21 (a) $\dfrac{1}{C_s} = \dfrac{1}{15.0} + \dfrac{1}{3.00}$

$C_s = 2.50\ \mu\text{F}$

$C_p = 2.50 + 6.00 = 8.50\ \mu\text{F}$

$C_{eq} = \left(\dfrac{1}{8.50\ \mu\text{F}} + \dfrac{1}{20.0\ \mu\text{F}}\right)^{-1} = \boxed{5.96\ \mu\text{F}}$

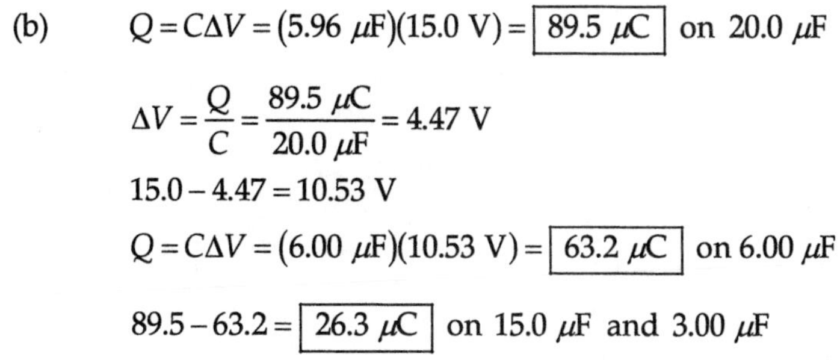

(b) $Q = C\Delta V = (5.96\ \mu\text{F})(15.0\ \text{V}) = \boxed{89.5\ \mu\text{C}}$ on $20.0\ \mu\text{F}$

$\Delta V = \dfrac{Q}{C} = \dfrac{89.5\ \mu\text{C}}{20.0\ \mu\text{F}} = 4.47\ \text{V}$

$15.0 - 4.47 = 10.53\ \text{V}$

$Q = C\Delta V = (6.00\ \mu\text{F})(10.53\ \text{V}) = \boxed{63.2\ \mu\text{C}}$ on $6.00\ \mu\text{F}$

$89.5 - 63.2 = \boxed{26.3\ \mu\text{C}}$ on $15.0\ \mu\text{F}$ and $3.00\ \mu\text{F}$

8.50 μF 20.0 μF

FIG. P26.21

***P26.22** (a) Capacitors 2 and 3 are in parallel and present equivalent capacitance 6C. This is in series with capacitor 1, so the battery sees capacitance $\left[\dfrac{1}{3C} + \dfrac{1}{6C}\right]^{-1} = \boxed{2C}$.

(b) If they were initially unchanged, C_1 stores the same charge as C_2 and C_3 together. With greater capacitance, C_3 stores more charge than C_2. Then $\boxed{Q_1 > Q_3 > Q_2}$.

(c) The $(C_2 || C_3)$ equivalent capacitor stores the same charge as C_1. Since it has greater capacitance, $\Delta V = \dfrac{Q}{C}$ implies that it has smaller potential difference across it than C_1. In parallel with each other, C_2 and C_3 have equal voltages: $\boxed{\Delta V_1 > \Delta V_2 = \Delta V_3}$.

(d) If C_3 is increased, the overall equivalent capacitance increases. More charge moves through the battery and Q increases. As ΔV_1 increases, ΔV_2 must decrease so Q_2 decreases. Then Q_3 must increase even more: $\boxed{Q_3 \text{ and } Q_1 \text{ increase; } Q_2 \text{ decreases}}$.

P26.23 $C = \dfrac{Q}{\Delta V}$ so $6.00 \times 10^{-6} = \dfrac{Q}{20.0}$

and $Q = \boxed{120\ \mu\text{C}}$

$Q_1 = 120\ \mu\text{C} - Q_2$

and $\Delta V = \dfrac{Q}{C}$: $\dfrac{120 - Q_2}{C_1} = \dfrac{Q_2}{C_2}$

or $\dfrac{120 - Q_2}{6.00} = \dfrac{Q_2}{3.00}$

$(3.00)(120 - Q_2) = (6.00)Q_2$

$Q_2 = \dfrac{360}{9.00} = \boxed{40.0\ \mu\text{C}}$ $Q_1 = 120\ \mu\text{C} - 40.0\ \mu\text{C} = \boxed{80.0\ \mu\text{C}}$

ΔV C1 C2 S1 S2

FIG. P26.23

P26.24 (a) In $\boxed{\text{series}}$, to reduce the effective capacitance:

$$\frac{1}{32.0\ \mu\text{F}}=\frac{1}{34.8\ \mu\text{F}}+\frac{1}{C_s}$$

$$C_s=\frac{1}{2.51\times10^{-3}/\mu\text{F}}=\boxed{398\ \mu\text{F}}$$

(b) In $\boxed{\text{parallel}}$, to increase the total capacitance:

$$29.8\ \mu\text{F}+C_p=32.0\ \mu\text{F}$$

$$C_p=\boxed{2.20\ \mu\text{F}}$$

P26.25 $$nC=\frac{100}{\underbrace{\frac{1}{C}+\frac{1}{C}+\frac{1}{C}+\cdots}_{n\text{ capacitors}}}=\frac{100}{n/C}$$

$$nC=\frac{100C}{n}\quad\text{so } n^2=100 \text{ and } n=\boxed{10}$$

***P26.26** For C_1 connected by itself, $C_1\Delta V=30.8\ \mu\text{C}$ where ΔV is the battery voltage: $\Delta V=\frac{30.8\ \mu\text{C}}{C_1}$.

For C_1 and C_2 in series:

$$\left(\frac{1}{1/C_1+1/C_2}\right)\Delta V=23.1\ \mu\text{C}$$

substituting, $\frac{30.8\ \mu\text{C}}{C_1}=\frac{23.1\ \mu\text{C}}{C_1}+\frac{23.1\ \mu\text{C}}{C_2}$ $\qquad C_1=0.333C_2$.

For C_1 and C_3 in series:

$$\left(\frac{1}{1/C_1+1/C_3}\right)\Delta V=25.2\ \mu\text{C}$$

$\frac{30.8\ \mu\text{C}}{C_1}=\frac{25.2\ \mu\text{C}}{C_1}+\frac{25.2\ \mu\text{C}}{C_3}$ $\qquad C_1=0.222C_3$.

For all three:

$$Q=\left(\frac{1}{1/C_1+1/C_2+1/C_3}\right)\Delta V=\frac{C_1\Delta V}{1+C_1/C_2+C_1/C_3}=\frac{30.8\ \mu\text{C}}{1+0.333+0.222}=\boxed{19.8\ \mu\text{C}}.$$

This is the charge on each one of the three.

P26.27 $$C_s=\left(\frac{1}{5.00}+\frac{1}{10.0}\right)^{-1}=3.33\ \mu\text{F}$$

$$C_{p1}=2(3.33)+2.00=8.66\ \mu\text{F}$$

$$C_{p2}=2(10.0)=20.0\ \mu\text{F}$$

$$C_{eq}=\left(\frac{1}{8.66}+\frac{1}{20.0}\right)^{-1}=\boxed{6.04\ \mu\text{F}}$$

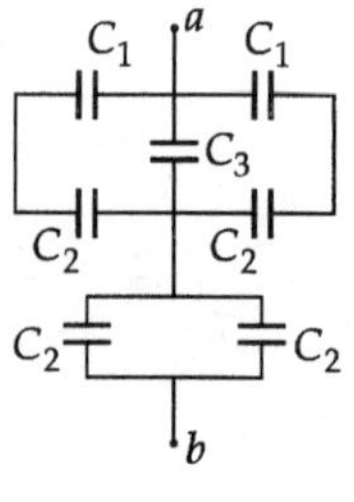

FIG. P26.27

P26.28 $Q_{eq} = C_{eq}(\Delta V) = (6.04\times10^{-6}\text{ F})(60.0\text{ V}) = 3.62\times10^{-4}\text{ C}$

$$Q_{p1} = Q_{eq},\text{ so }\Delta V_{p1} = \frac{Q_{eq}}{C_{p1}} = \frac{3.62\times10^{-4}\text{ C}}{8.66\times10^{-6}\text{ F}} = 41.8\text{ V}$$

$$Q_3 = C_3(\Delta V_{p1}) = (2.00\times10^{-6}\text{ F})(41.8\text{ V}) = \boxed{83.6\ \mu\text{C}}$$

P26.29 $C_s = \left(\frac{1}{5.00}+\frac{1}{7.00}\right)^{-1} = 2.92\ \mu\text{F}$

$C_p = 2.92 + 4.00 + 6.00 = \boxed{12.9\ \mu\text{F}}$

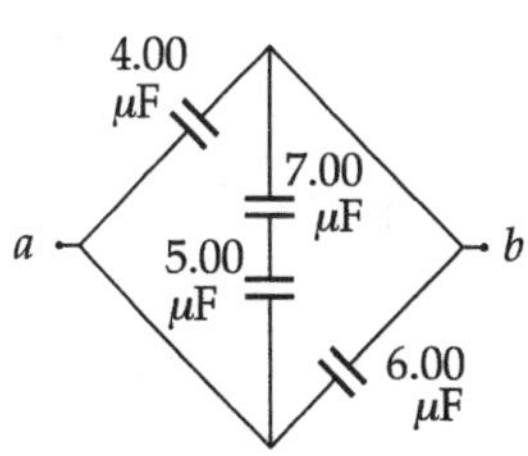

FIG. P26.29

***P26.30** According to the suggestion, the combination of capacitors shown is equivalent to [capacitor C between x and y]

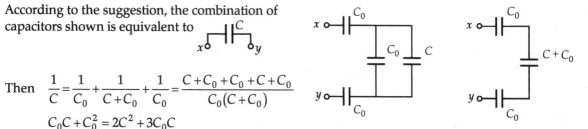

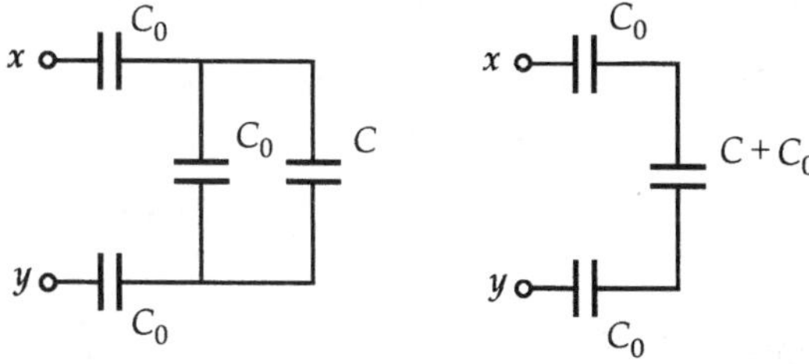

FIG. P26.30

Then $\frac{1}{C} = \frac{1}{C_0}+\frac{1}{C+C_0}+\frac{1}{C_0} = \frac{C+C_0+C_0+C+C_0}{C_0(C+C_0)}$

$$C_0C + C_0^2 = 2C^2 + 3C_0C$$

$$2C^2 + 2C_0C - C_0^2 = 0$$

$$C = \frac{-2C_0 \pm \sqrt{4C_0^2 + 4(2C_0^2)}}{4}$$

Only the positive root is physical

$$\boxed{C = \frac{C_0}{2}\left(\sqrt{3}-1\right)}$$

Section 26.4 Energy Stored in a Charged Capacitor

P26.31 (a) $U = \frac{1}{2}C(\Delta V)^2 = \frac{1}{2}(3.00\ \mu\text{F})(12.0\text{ V})^2 = \boxed{216\ \mu\text{J}}$

(b) $U = \frac{1}{2}C(\Delta V)^2 = \frac{1}{2}(3.00\ \mu\text{F})(6.00\text{ V})^2 = \boxed{54.0\ \mu\text{J}}$

P26.32 $U = \frac{1}{2}C\Delta V^2$

$$\Delta V = \sqrt{\frac{2U}{C}} = \sqrt{\frac{2(300\text{ J})}{30\times10^{-6}\text{ C/V}}} = \boxed{4.47\times10^{3}\text{ V}}$$

P26.33 $U = \frac{1}{2}C(\Delta V)^2$

The circuit diagram is shown at the right.

100 V 25.0 μF 5.00 μF

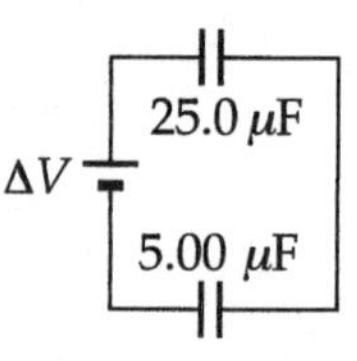

FIG. P26.33

(a) $C_p = C_1 + C_2 = 25.0\ \mu\text{F} + 5.00\ \mu\text{F} = 30.0\ \mu\text{F}$

$$U = \frac{1}{2}\left(30.0 \times 10^{-6}\right)(100)^2 = \boxed{0.150\ \text{J}}$$

(b) $C_s = \left(\frac{1}{C_1} + \frac{1}{C_2}\right)^{-1} = \left(\frac{1}{25.0\ \mu\text{F}} + \frac{1}{5.00\ \mu\text{F}}\right)^{-1} = 4.17\ \mu\text{F}$

$$U = \frac{1}{2}C(\Delta V)^2$$

$$\Delta V = \sqrt{\frac{2U}{C}} = \sqrt{\frac{2(0.150)}{4.17 \times 10^{-6}}} = \boxed{268\ \text{V}}$$

P26.34 Use $U = \frac{1}{2}\frac{Q^2}{C}$ and $C = \frac{\epsilon_0 A}{d}$.

If $d_2 = 2d_1$, $C_2 = \frac{1}{2}C_1$. Therefore, the $\boxed{\text{stored energy doubles}}$.

***P26.35** (a) $Q = C\Delta V = \left(150 \times 10^{-12}\ \text{F}\right)\left(10 \times 10^3\ \text{V}\right) = \boxed{1.50 \times 10^{-6}\ \text{C}}$

(b) $U = \frac{1}{2}C(\Delta V)^2$

$$\Delta V = \sqrt{\frac{2U}{C}} = \sqrt{\frac{2\left(250 \times 10^{-6}\ \text{J}\right)}{150 \times 10^{-12}\ \text{F}}} = \boxed{1.83 \times 10^3\ \text{V}}$$

P26.36 $u = \frac{U}{V} = \frac{1}{2}\epsilon_0 E^2$

$$\frac{1.00 \times 10^{-7}}{V} = \frac{1}{2}\left(8.85 \times 10^{-12}\right)(3\,000)^2$$

$$V = \boxed{2.51 \times 10^{-3}\ \text{m}^3} = \left(2.51 \times 10^{-3}\ \text{m}^3\right)\left(\frac{1\,000\ \text{L}}{\text{m}^3}\right) = \boxed{2.51\ \text{L}}$$

P26.37 $W = U = \int F dx$

$$\text{so } F = \frac{dU}{dx} = \frac{d}{dx}\left(\frac{Q^2}{2C}\right) = \frac{d}{dx}\left(\frac{Q^2 x}{2\epsilon_0 A}\right) = \boxed{\frac{Q^2}{2\epsilon_0 A}}$$

P26.38 With switch closed, distance $d' = 0.500d$ and capacitance $C' = \frac{\epsilon_0 A}{d'} = \frac{2\epsilon_0 A}{d} = 2C$.

(a) $Q = C'(\Delta V) = 2C(\Delta V) = 2\left(2.00\times10^{-6}\ \text{F}\right)(100\ \text{V}) = \boxed{400\ \mu\text{C}}$

(b) The force stretching out one spring is

$$F = \frac{Q^2}{2\epsilon_0 A} = \frac{4C^2(\Delta V)^2}{2\epsilon_0 A} = \frac{2C^2(\Delta V)^2}{(\epsilon_0 A/d)d} = \frac{2C(\Delta V)^2}{d}.$$

One spring stretches by distance $x = \frac{d}{4}$, so

$$k = \frac{F}{x} = \frac{2C(\Delta V)^2}{d}\left(\frac{4}{d}\right) = \frac{8C(\Delta V)^2}{d^2} = \frac{8\left(2.00\times10^{-6}\ \text{F}\right)(100\ \text{V})^2}{\left(8.00\times10^{-3}\ \text{m}\right)^2} = \boxed{2.50\ \text{kN/m}}.$$

P26.39 The energy transferred is $H_{\text{ET}} = \frac{1}{2}Q\Delta V = \frac{1}{2}(50.0\ \text{C})\left(1.00\times10^{8}\ \text{V}\right) = 2.50\times10^{9}\ \text{J}$

and 1% of this (or $\Delta E_{\text{int}} = 2.50\times10^{7}\ \text{J}$) is absorbed by the tree. If m is the amount of water boiled away,

then $\Delta E_{\text{int}} = m(4\,186\ \text{J/kg}\cdot{}^\circ\text{C})(100^\circ\text{C} - 30.0^\circ\text{C}) + m\left(2.26\times10^{6}\ \text{J/kg}\right) = 2.50\times10^{7}\ \text{J}$

giving $m = \boxed{9.79\ \text{kg}}$.

***P26.40** (a) $U = \frac{1}{2}C(\Delta V)^2 + \frac{1}{2}C(\Delta V)^2 = \boxed{C(\Delta V)^2}$

(b) The altered capacitor has capacitance $C' = \frac{C}{2}$. The total charge is the same as before:

$$C(\Delta V) + C(\Delta V) = C(\Delta V') + \frac{C}{2}(\Delta V') \qquad \boxed{\Delta V' = \frac{4\Delta V}{3}}.$$

(c) $U' = \frac{1}{2}C\left(\frac{4\Delta V}{3}\right)^2 + \frac{1}{2}\frac{1}{2}C\left(\frac{4\Delta V}{3}\right)^2 = \boxed{4C\frac{(\Delta V)^2}{3}}$

(d) The extra energy comes from work put into the system by the agent pulling the capacitor plates apart.

P26.41 $U = \frac{1}{2}C(\Delta V)^2$ where $C = 4\pi\epsilon_0 R = \frac{R}{k_e}$ and $\Delta V = \frac{k_e Q}{R} - 0 = \frac{k_e Q}{R}$

$$U = \frac{1}{2}\left(\frac{R}{k_e}\right)\left(\frac{k_e Q}{R}\right)^2 = \boxed{\frac{k_e Q^2}{2R}}$$

***P26.42** (a) The total energy is $U = U_1 + U_2 = \frac{1}{2}\frac{q_1^2}{C_1} + \frac{1}{2}\frac{q_2^2}{C_2} = \frac{1}{2}\frac{q_1^2}{4\pi \in_0 R_1} + \frac{1}{2}\frac{(Q-q_1)^2}{4\pi \in_0 R^2}$.

For a minimum we set $\frac{dU}{dq_1} = 0$:

$$\frac{1}{2}\frac{2q_1}{4\pi \in_0 R_1} + \frac{1}{2}\frac{2(Q-q_1)}{4\pi \in_0 R_2}(-1) = 0$$

$$R_2 q_1 = R_1 Q - R_1 q_1 \qquad \boxed{q_1 = \frac{R_1 Q}{R_1 + R_2}}$$

Then $q_2 = Q - q_1 = \boxed{\frac{R_2 Q}{R_1 + R_2} = q_2}$.

(b) $$V_1 = \frac{k_e q_1}{R_1} = \frac{k_e R_1 Q}{R_1(R_1 + R_2)} = \frac{k_e Q}{R_1 + R_2}$$

$$V_2 = \frac{k_e q_2}{R_2} = \frac{k_e R_2 Q}{R_2(R_1 + R_2)} = \frac{k_e Q}{R_1 + R_2}$$

and $V_1 - V_2 = 0$.

Section 26.5 Capacitors with Dielectrics

P26.43 (a) $$C = \frac{\kappa \in_0 A}{d} = \frac{2.10\left(8.85 \times 10^{-12} \text{ F/m}\right)\left(1.75 \times 10^{-4} \text{ m}^2\right)}{4.00 \times 10^{-5} \text{ m}} = 8.13 \times 10^{-11} \text{ F} = \boxed{81.3 \text{ pF}}$$

(b) $$\Delta V_{max} = E_{max} d = \left(60.0 \times 10^6 \text{ V/m}\right)\left(4.00 \times 10^{-5} \text{ m}\right) = \boxed{2.40 \text{ kV}}$$

P26.44 $Q_{max} = C\Delta V_{max}$,

but $\Delta V_{max} = E_{max} d$.

Also, $C = \frac{\kappa \in_0 A}{d}$.

Thus, $Q_{max} = \frac{\kappa \in_0 A}{d}(E_{max} d) = \kappa \in_0 A E_{max}$.

(a) With air between the plates, $\kappa = 1.00$

and $E_{max} = 3.00 \times 10^6$ V/m.

Therefore,

$$Q_{max} = \kappa \in_0 A E_{max} = \left(8.85 \times 10^{-12} \text{ F/m}\right)\left(5.00 \times 10^{-4} \text{ m}^2\right)\left(3.00 \times 10^6 \text{ V/m}\right) = \boxed{13.3 \text{ nC}}.$$

(b) With polystyrene between the plates, $\kappa = 2.56$ and $E_{max} = 24.0 \times 10^6$ V/m.

$$Q_{max} = \kappa \in_0 A E_{max} = 2.56\left(8.85 \times 10^{-12} \text{ F/m}\right)\left(5.00 \times 10^{-4} \text{ m}^2\right)\left(24.0 \times 10^6 \text{ V/m}\right) = \boxed{272 \text{ nC}}$$

P26.45 $C = \frac{\kappa \in_0 A}{d}$

or $95.0 \times 10^{-9} = \frac{3.70\left(8.85 \times 10^{-12}\right)(0.070\,0)\ell}{0.025\,0 \times 10^{-3}}$

$\ell = \boxed{1.04 \text{ m}}$

P26.46 Consider two sheets of aluminum foil, each 40 cm by 100 cm, with one sheet of plastic between them. Suppose the plastic has $\kappa \cong 3$, $E_{\max} \sim 10^7$ V/m and thickness 1 mil $= \frac{2.54 \text{ cm}}{1\,000}$. Then,

$$C = \frac{\kappa \in_0 A}{d} \sim \frac{3\left(8.85 \times 10^{-12} \text{ C}^2/\text{N}\cdot\text{m}^2\right)\left(0.4 \text{ m}^2\right)}{2.54 \times 10^{-5} \text{ m}} \sim \boxed{10^{-6} \text{ F}}$$

$$\Delta V_{\max} = E_{\max} d \sim \left(10^7 \text{ V/m}\right)\left(2.54 \times 10^{-5} \text{ m}\right) \sim \boxed{10^2 \text{ V}}$$

P26.47 Originally, $C = \frac{\in_0 A}{d} = \frac{Q}{(\Delta V)_i}$.

(a) The charge is the same before and after immersion, with value $Q = \frac{\in_0 A(\Delta V)_i}{d}$.

$$Q = \frac{\left(8.85 \times 10^{-12} \text{ C}^2/\text{N}\cdot\text{m}^2\right)\left(25.0 \times 10^{-4} \text{ m}^2\right)(250 \text{ V})}{\left(1.50 \times 10^{-2} \text{ m}\right)} = \boxed{369 \text{ pC}}$$

(b) Finally,

$$C_f = \frac{\kappa \in_0 A}{d} = \frac{Q}{(\Delta V)_f} \qquad C_f = \frac{80.0\left(8.85 \times 10^{-12} \text{ C}^2/\text{N}\cdot\text{m}^2\right)\left(25.0 \times 10^{-4} \text{ m}^2\right)}{\left(1.50 \times 10^{-2} \text{ m}\right)} = \boxed{118 \text{ pF}}$$

$$(\Delta V)_f = \frac{Qd}{\kappa \in_0 A} = \frac{\in_0 A(\Delta V)_i d}{\kappa \in_0 Ad} = \frac{(\Delta V)_i}{\kappa} = \frac{250 \text{ V}}{80.0} = \boxed{3.12 \text{ V}}.$$

(c) Originally, $U_i = \frac{1}{2}C(\Delta V)_i^2 = \frac{\in_0 A(\Delta V)_i^2}{2d}$.

Finally, $U_f = \frac{1}{2}C_f(\Delta V)_f^2 = \frac{\kappa \in_0 A(\Delta V)_i^2}{2d\kappa^2} = \frac{\in_0 A(\Delta V)_i^2}{2d\kappa}$.

So, $\Delta U = U_f - U_i = \frac{-\in_0 A(\Delta V)_i^2(\kappa - 1)}{2d\kappa}$

$$\Delta U = -\frac{\left(8.85 \times 10^{-12} \text{ C}^2/\text{N}\cdot\text{m}^2\right)\left(25.0 \times 10^{-4} \text{ m}^2\right)(250 \text{ V})^2(79.0)}{2\left(1.50 \times 10^{-2} \text{ m}\right)(80.0)} = \boxed{-45.5 \text{ nJ}}.$$

P26.48 (a) $C = \kappa C_0 = \dfrac{\kappa \in_0 A}{d} = \dfrac{(173)(8.85\times10^{-12})(1.00\times10^{-4}\ \text{m}^2)}{0.100\times10^{-3}\ \text{m}} = \boxed{1.53\ \text{nF}}$

(b) The battery delivers the free charge

$Q = C(\Delta V) = (1.53\times10^{-9}\ \text{F})(12.0\ \text{V}) = \boxed{18.4\ \text{nC}}$.

(c) The surface density of free charge is

$\sigma = \dfrac{Q}{A} = \dfrac{18.4\times10^{-9}\ \text{C}}{1.00\times10^{-4}\ \text{m}^2} = \boxed{1.84\times10^{-4}\ \text{C/m}^2}$.

The surface density of polarization charge is

$\sigma_p = \sigma\left(1-\dfrac{1}{\kappa}\right) = \sigma\left(1-\dfrac{1}{173}\right) = \boxed{1.83\times10^{-4}\ \text{C/m}^2}$.

(d) We have $E = \dfrac{E_0}{\kappa}$ and $E_0 = \dfrac{\Delta V}{d}$; hence,

$E = \dfrac{\Delta V}{\kappa d} = \dfrac{12.0\ \text{V}}{(173)(1.00\times10^{-4}\ \text{m})} = \boxed{694\ \text{V/m}}$.

P26.49 The given combination of capacitors is equivalent to the circuit diagram shown to the right.

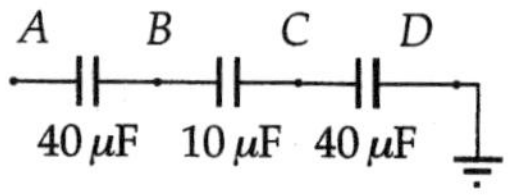

FIG. P26.49

Put charge Q on point A. Then,

$$Q = (40.0\ \mu\text{F})\Delta V_{AB} = (10.0\ \mu\text{F})\Delta V_{BC} = (40.0\ \mu\text{F})\Delta V_{CD}.$$

So, $\Delta V_{BC} = 4\Delta V_{AB} = 4\Delta V_{CD}$, and the center capacitor will break down first, at $\Delta V_{BC} = 15.0\ \text{V}$. When this occurs,

$$\Delta V_{AB} = \Delta V_{CD} = \frac{1}{4}(\Delta V_{BC}) = 3.75\ \text{V}$$

and $V_{AD} = V_{AB} + V_{BC} + V_{CD} = 3.75\ \text{V} + 15.0\ \text{V} + 3.75\ \text{V} = \boxed{22.5\ \text{V}}$.

Section 26.6 Electric Dipole in an Electric Field

P26.50 (a) The displacement from negative to positive charge is

$2\mathbf{a} = (-1.20\hat{\mathbf{i}} + 1.10\hat{\mathbf{j}})\ \text{mm} - (1.40\hat{\mathbf{i}} - 1.30\hat{\mathbf{j}})\ \text{mm} = (-2.60\hat{\mathbf{i}} + 2.40\hat{\mathbf{j}})\times10^{-3}\ \text{m}.$

The electric dipole moment is

$\mathbf{p} = 2\mathbf{a}q = (3.50\times10^{-9}\ \text{C})(-2.60\hat{\mathbf{i}} + 2.40\hat{\mathbf{j}})\times10^{-3}\ \text{m} = \boxed{(-9.10\hat{\mathbf{i}} + 8.40\hat{\mathbf{j}})\times10^{-12}\ \text{C}\cdot\text{m}}$.

(b) $\boldsymbol{\tau} = \mathbf{p}\times\mathbf{E} = \left[(-9.10\hat{\mathbf{i}} + 8.40\hat{\mathbf{j}})\times10^{-12}\ \text{C}\cdot\text{m}\right]\times\left[(7.80\hat{\mathbf{i}} - 4.90\hat{\mathbf{j}})\times10^{3}\ \text{N/C}\right]$

$\boldsymbol{\tau} = (+44.6\hat{\mathbf{k}} - 65.5\hat{\mathbf{k}})\times10^{-9}\ \text{N}\cdot\text{m} = \boxed{-2.09\times10^{-8}\ \text{N}\cdot\text{m}\hat{\mathbf{k}}}$

continued on next page

(c) $U = -\mathbf{p}\cdot\mathbf{E} = -\left[\left(-9.10\hat{\mathbf{i}} + 8.40\hat{\mathbf{j}}\right)\times 10^{-12}\ \text{C}\cdot\text{m}\right]\cdot\left[\left(7.80\hat{\mathbf{i}} - 4.90\hat{\mathbf{j}}\right)\times 10^{3}\ \text{N/C}\right]$

$$U = (71.0 + 41.2)\times 10^{-9}\ \text{J} = \boxed{112\ \text{nJ}}$$

(d) $|\mathbf{p}| = \sqrt{(9.10)^2 + (8.40)^2}\times 10^{-12}\ \text{C}\cdot\text{m} = 12.4\times 10^{-12}\ \text{C}\cdot\text{m}$

$$|\mathbf{E}| = \sqrt{(7.80)^2 + (4.90)^2}\times 10^{3}\ \text{N/C} = 9.21\times 10^{3}\ \text{N/C}$$

$$U_{\max} = |\mathbf{p}||\mathbf{E}| = 114\ \text{nJ},\qquad U_{\min} = -114\ \text{nJ}$$

$$U_{\max} - U_{\min} = \boxed{228\ \text{nJ}}$$

P26.51 (a) Let x represent the coordinate of the negative charge. Then $x + 2a\cos\theta$ is the coordinate of the positive charge. The force on the negative charge is $\mathbf{F}_- = -qE(x)\hat{\mathbf{i}}$. The force on the positive charge is

$$\mathbf{F}_+ = +qE(x + 2a\cos\theta)\hat{\mathbf{i}} \approx qE(x)\hat{\mathbf{i}} + q\frac{dE}{dx}(2a\cos\theta)\hat{\mathbf{i}}.$$

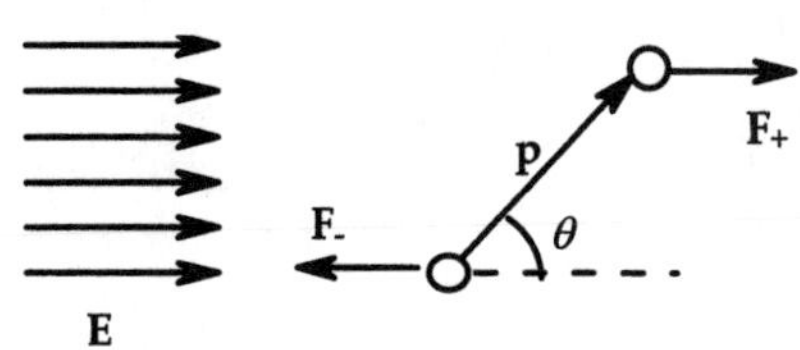

FIG. P26.51(a)

The force on the dipole is altogether $\mathbf{F} = \mathbf{F}_- + \mathbf{F}_+ = q\frac{dE}{dx}(2a\cos\theta)\hat{\mathbf{i}} = \boxed{p\frac{dE}{dx}\cos\theta\,\hat{\mathbf{i}}}$.

(b) The balloon creates field along the x-axis of $\frac{k_e q}{x^2}\hat{\mathbf{i}}$.

Thus, $\frac{dE}{dx} = \frac{(-2)k_e q}{x^3}$.

At $x = 16.0$ cm, $\frac{dE}{dx} = \frac{(-2)\left(8.99\times 10^{9}\right)\left(2.00\times 10^{-6}\right)}{(0.160)^3} = \boxed{-8.78\ \text{MN/C}\cdot\text{m}}$

$$\mathbf{F} = \left(6.30\times 10^{-9}\ \text{C}\cdot\text{m}\right)\left(-8.78\times 10^{6}\ \text{N/C}\cdot\text{m}\right)\cos 0^\circ\,\hat{\mathbf{i}} = \boxed{-55.3\hat{\mathbf{i}}\ \text{mN}}$$

Section 26.7 An Atomic Description of Dielectrics

P26.52 $2\pi r\ell E = \frac{q_{\text{in}}}{\epsilon_0}$

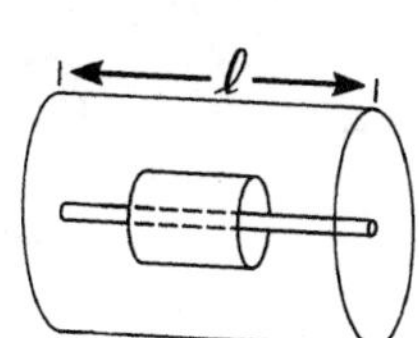

FIG. P26.52

so $E = \frac{\lambda}{2\pi r\,\epsilon_0}$

$$\Delta V = -\int_{r_1}^{r_2}\mathbf{E}\cdot d\mathbf{r} = \int_{r_1}^{r_2}\frac{\lambda}{2\pi r\,\epsilon_0}dr = \frac{\lambda}{2\pi\epsilon_0}\ln\left(\frac{r_1}{r_2}\right)$$

$$\frac{\lambda_{\max}}{2\pi\epsilon_0} = E_{\max} r_{\text{inner}}$$

$$\Delta V = \left(1.20\times 10^{6}\ \text{V/m}\right)\left(0.100\times 10^{-3}\ \text{m}\right)\ln\left(\frac{25.0}{0.200}\right)$$

$$\Delta V_{\max} = \boxed{579\ \text{V}}$$

P26.53 (a) Consider a gaussian surface in the form of a cylindrical pillbox with ends of area $A' << A$ parallel to the sheet. The side wall of the cylinder passes no flux of electric field since this surface is everywhere parallel to the field. Gauss's law becomes

$$EA' + EA' = \frac{Q}{\in A}A', \text{ so } \boxed{E = \frac{Q}{2\in A}} \text{ directed away from the positive sheet.}$$

(b) In the space between the sheets, each creates field $\frac{Q}{2\in A}$ away from the positive and toward the negative sheet. Together, they create a field of

$$\boxed{E = \frac{Q}{\in A}}.$$

(c) Assume that the field is in the positive x-direction. Then, the potential of the positive plate relative to the negative plate is

$$\Delta V = -\int_{-\text{plate}}^{+\text{plate}} \mathbf{E}\cdot d\mathbf{s} = -\int_{-\text{plate}}^{+\text{plate}} \frac{Q}{\in A}\hat{\mathbf{i}}\cdot\left(-\hat{\mathbf{i}}dx\right) = \boxed{+\frac{Qd}{\in A}}.$$

(d) Capacitance is defined by: $C = \frac{Q}{\Delta V} = \frac{Q}{Qd/\in A} = \boxed{\frac{\in A}{d} = \frac{\kappa \in_0 A}{d}}$.

Additional Problems

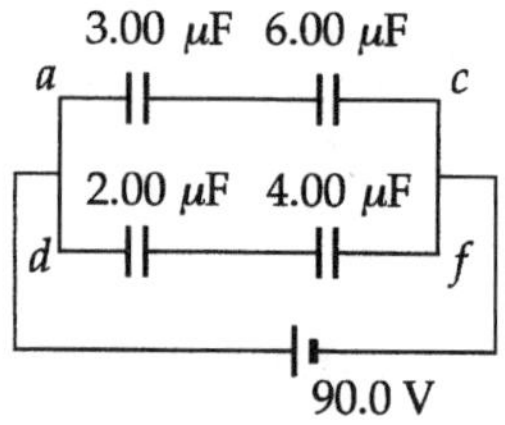

P26.54 (a) $C = \left[\frac{1}{3.00} + \frac{1}{6.00}\right]^{-1} + \left[\frac{1}{2.00} + \frac{1}{4.00}\right]^{-1} = \boxed{3.33\ \mu\text{F}}$

(c) $Q_{ac} = C_{ac}\left(\Delta V_{ac}\right) = (2.00\ \mu\text{F})(90.0\ \text{V}) = 180\ \mu\text{C}$

Therefore, $Q_3 = Q_6 = \boxed{180\ \mu\text{C}}$

$Q_{df} = C_{df}\left(\Delta V_{df}\right) = (1.33\ \mu\text{F})(90.0\ \text{V}) = \boxed{120\ \mu\text{C}}$

3.00 μF 6.00 μF
a c
2.00 μF 4.00 μF
d f
90.0 V

FIG. P26.54

(b) $\Delta V_3 = \frac{Q_3}{C_3} = \frac{180\ \mu\text{C}}{3.00\ \mu\text{F}} = \boxed{60.0\ \text{V}}$

$\Delta V_6 = \frac{Q_6}{C_6} = \frac{180\ \mu\text{C}}{6.00\ \mu\text{F}} = \boxed{30.0\ \text{V}}$

$\Delta V_2 = \frac{Q_2}{C_2} = \frac{120\ \mu\text{C}}{2.00\ \mu\text{F}} = \boxed{60.0\ \text{V}}$

$\Delta V_4 = \frac{Q_4}{C_4} = \frac{120\ \mu\text{C}}{4.00\ \mu\text{F}} = \boxed{30.0\ \text{V}}$

(d) $U_T = \frac{1}{2}C_{eq}(\Delta V)^2 = \frac{1}{2}\left(3.33\times10^{-6}\right)(90.0\ \text{V})^2 = \boxed{13.4\ \text{mJ}}$

***P26.55** (a) Each face of P_2 carries charge, so the three-plate system is equivalent to

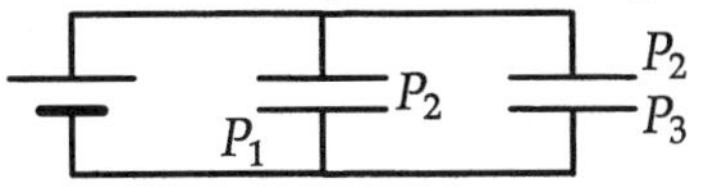

P_1 P_2 P_2 P_3

Each capacitor by itself has capacitance

$$C = \frac{\kappa \in_0 A}{d} = \frac{1(8.85\times10^{-12}\ \text{C}^2)7.5\times10^{-4}\ \text{m}^2}{\text{N}\cdot\text{m}^2\ \ 1.19\times10^{-3}\ \text{m}} = 5.58\ \text{pF}.$$

Then equivalent capacitance $= 5.58 + 5.58 = \boxed{11.2\ \text{pF}}$.

(b) $Q = C\Delta V + C\Delta V = 11.2\times10^{-12}\ \text{F}(12\ \text{V}) = \boxed{134\ \text{pC}}$

(c) Now P_3 has charge on two surfaces and in effect three capacitors are in parallel:

$C = 3(5.58\ \text{pF}) = \boxed{16.7\ \text{pF}}$.

(d) Only one face of P_4 carries charge:

$Q = C\Delta V = 5.58\times10^{-12}\ \text{F}(12\ \text{V}) = \boxed{66.9\ \text{pC}}$.

***P26.56** From the example about a cylindrical capacitor,

$$V_b - V_a = -2k_e\lambda \ln\frac{b}{a}$$

$$V_b - 345\ \text{kV} = -2\left(8.99\times10^9\ \text{Nm}^2/\text{C}^2\right)\left(1.40\times10^{-6}\ \text{C/m}\right)\ln\frac{12\ \text{m}}{0.024\ \text{m}}$$

$$= -2(8.99)\left(1.4\times10^3\ \text{J/C}\right)\ln 500$$

$$= -1.5643\times10^5\ \text{V}$$

$$V_b = 3.45\times10^5\ \text{V} - 1.56\times10^5\ \text{V} = \boxed{1.89\times10^5\ \text{V}}$$

***P26.57** Imagine the center plate is split along its midplane and pulled apart. We have two capacitors in parallel, supporting the same ΔV and carrying total charge Q. The upper has capacitance $C_1 = \frac{\in_0 A}{d}$ and the lower $C_2 = \frac{\in_0 A}{2d}$. Charge flows from ground onto each of the outside plates so that $Q_1 + Q_2 = Q$ $\quad \Delta V_1 = \Delta V_2 = \Delta V$.

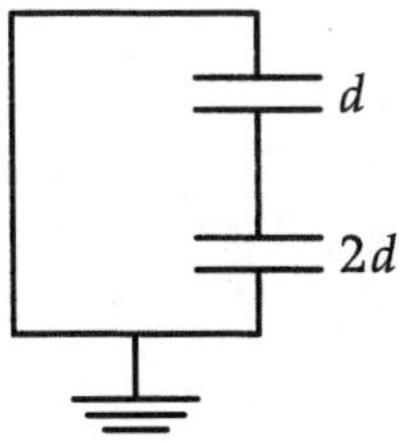

d

$2d$

FIG. P26.57

Then $\frac{Q_1}{C_1} = \frac{Q_2}{C_2} = \frac{Q_1 d}{\in_0 A} = \frac{Q_2 2d}{\in_0 A}$ $\quad Q_1 = 2Q_2 \quad 2Q_2 + Q_2 = Q$.

(a) $Q_2 = \frac{Q}{3}$. $\boxed{\text{On the lower plate the charge is } -\frac{Q}{3}.}$

$Q_1 = \frac{2Q}{3}$. $\boxed{\text{On the upper plate the charge is } -\frac{2Q}{3}.}$

(b) $\Delta V = \frac{Q_1}{C_1} = \boxed{\frac{2Qd}{3 \in_0 A}}$

P26.58 (a) We use Equation 26.11 to find the potential energy of the capacitor. As we will see, the potential difference ΔV changes as the dielectric is withdrawn. The initial and final energies are $U_i = \frac{1}{2}\left(\frac{Q^2}{C_i}\right)$ and $U_f = \frac{1}{2}\left(\frac{Q^2}{C_f}\right)$.

But the initial capacitance (with the dielectric) is $C_i = \kappa C_f$. Therefore, $U_f = \frac{1}{2}\kappa\left(\frac{Q^2}{C_i}\right)$.

Since the work done by the external force in removing the dielectric equals the change in potential energy, we have $W = U_f - U_i = \frac{1}{2}\kappa\left(\frac{Q^2}{C_i}\right) - \frac{1}{2}\left(\frac{Q^2}{C_i}\right) = \frac{1}{2}\left(\frac{Q^2}{C_i}\right)(\kappa - 1)$.

To express this relation in terms of potential difference ΔV_i, we substitute $Q = C_i(\Delta V_i)$, and evaluate: $W = \frac{1}{2}C_i(\Delta V_i)^2(\kappa - 1) = \frac{1}{2}(2.00\times10^{-9}\text{ F})(100\text{ V})^2(5.00-1.00) = \boxed{4.00\times10^{-5}\text{ J}}$.

The positive result confirms that the final energy of the capacitor is greater than the initial energy. The extra energy comes from the work done *on* the system by the external force that pulled out the dielectric.

(b) The final potential difference across the capacitor is $\Delta V_f = \frac{Q}{C_f}$.

Substituting $C_f = \frac{C_i}{\kappa}$ and $Q = C_i(\Delta V_i)$ gives $\Delta V_f = \kappa\Delta V_i = 5.00(100\text{ V}) = \boxed{500\text{ V}}$.

Even though the capacitor is isolated and its charge remains constant, the potential difference across the plates does increase in this case.

P26.59 $\kappa = 3.00$, $E_{max} = 2.00\times10^8\text{ V/m} = \frac{\Delta V_{max}}{d}$

For $C = \frac{\kappa \epsilon_0 A}{d} = 0.250\times10^{-6}\text{ F}$

$$A = \frac{Cd}{\kappa\epsilon_0} = \frac{C\Delta V_{max}}{\kappa\epsilon_0 E_{max}} = \frac{(0.250\times10^{-6})(4\,000)}{3.00(8.85\times10^{-12})(2.00\times10^8)} = \boxed{0.188\text{ m}^2}$$

***P26.60** The original kinetic energy of the particle is

$$K = \frac{1}{2}mv^2 = \frac{1}{2}(2\times10^{-16}\text{ kg})(2\times10^6\text{ m/s})^2 = 4.00\times10^{-4}\text{ J}.$$

The potential difference across the capacitor is $\Delta V = \frac{Q}{C} = \frac{1\,000\ \mu\text{C}}{10\ \mu\text{F}} = 100\text{ V}$.

For the particle to reach the negative plate, the particle-capacitor system would need energy

$$U = q\Delta V = (-3\times10^6\text{ C})(-100\text{ V}) = 3.00\times10^{-4}\text{ J}.$$

Since its original kinetic energy is greater than this, $\boxed{\text{the particle will reach the negative plate}}$.

As the particle moves, the system keeps constant total energy

$$(K+U)_{\text{at +plate}} = (K+U)_{\text{at −plate}}: \quad 4.00\times10^{-4}\text{ J} + (-3\times10^{-6}\text{ C})(+100\text{ V}) = \frac{1}{2}(2\times10^{-16})v_f^2 + 0$$

$$v_f = \sqrt{\frac{2(1.00\times10^{-4}\text{ J})}{2\times10^{-16}\text{ kg}}} = \boxed{1.00\times10^6\text{ m/s}}.$$

P26.61 (a) $C_1 = \frac{\kappa_1 \in_0 A/2}{d}$; $C_2 = \frac{\kappa_2 \in_0 A/2}{d/2}$; $C_3 = \frac{\kappa_3 \in_0 A/2}{d/2}$

$$\left(\frac{1}{C_2}+\frac{1}{C_3}\right)^{-1} = \frac{C_2 C_3}{C_2+C_3} = \frac{\in_0 A}{d}\left(\frac{\kappa_2\kappa_3}{\kappa_2+\kappa_3}\right)$$

$$C = C_1 + \left(\frac{1}{C_2}+\frac{1}{C_3}\right)^{-1} = \boxed{\frac{\in_0 A}{d}\left(\frac{\kappa_1}{2}+\frac{\kappa_2\kappa_3}{\kappa_2+\kappa_3}\right)}$$

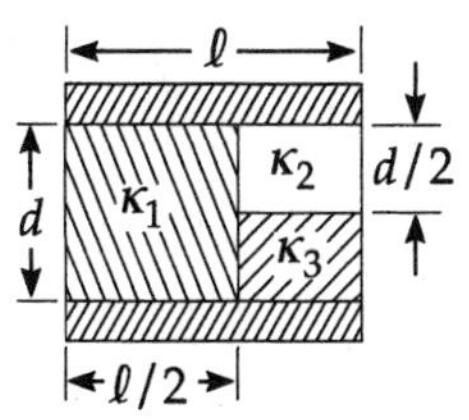

FIG. P26.61

(b) Using the given values we find: $C_{\text{total}} = 1.76 \times 10^{-12}\ \text{F} = \boxed{1.76\ \text{pF}}$.

***P26.62** The initial charge on the larger capacitor is

$$Q = C\Delta V = 10\ \mu\text{F}(15\ \text{V}) = 150\ \mu\text{C}.$$

An additional charge q is pushed through the 50-V battery, giving the smaller capacitor charge q and the larger charge $150\ \mu\text{C} + q$.

Then

$$50\ \text{V} = \frac{q}{5\ \mu\text{F}} + \frac{150\ \mu\text{C} + q}{10\ \mu\text{F}}$$

$$500\ \mu\text{C} = 2q + 150\ \mu\text{C} + q$$

$$q = 117\ \mu\text{C}$$

So across the 5-μF capacitor $\Delta V = \frac{q}{C} = \frac{117\ \mu\text{C}}{5\ \mu\text{F}} = \boxed{23.3\ \text{V}}$.

Across the 10-μF capacitor $\Delta V = \frac{150\ \mu\text{C} + 117\ \mu\text{C}}{10\ \mu\text{F}} = \boxed{26.7\ \text{V}}$.

P26.63 (a) Put charge Q on the sphere of radius a and $-Q$ on the other sphere. Relative to $V = 0$ at infinity,

the potential at the surface of a is $V_a = \frac{k_e Q}{a} - \frac{k_e Q}{d}$

and the potential of b is $V_b = \frac{-k_e Q}{b} + \frac{k_e Q}{d}$.

The difference in potential is $V_a - V_b = \frac{k_e Q}{a} + \frac{k_e Q}{b} - \frac{k_e Q}{d} - \frac{k_e Q}{d}$

and $C = \frac{Q}{V_a - V_b} = \boxed{\left(\frac{4\pi \in_0}{(1/a)+(1/b)-(2/d)}\right)}$.

(b) As $d \to \infty$, $\frac{1}{d}$ becomes negligible compared to $\frac{1}{a}$. Then,

$C = \frac{4\pi \in_0}{1/a + 1/b}$ and $\frac{1}{C} = \boxed{\frac{1}{4\pi \in_0 a} + \frac{1}{4\pi \in_0 b}}$

as for two spheres in series.

P26.64 (a) $C=\frac{\epsilon_0}{d}\left[(\ell-x)\ell+\kappa\ell x\right]=\boxed{\frac{\epsilon_0}{d}\left[\ell^2+\ell x(\kappa-1)\right]}$

(b) $U=\frac{1}{2}C(\Delta V)^2=\boxed{\frac{1}{2}\left(\frac{\epsilon_0(\Delta V)^2}{d}\right)\left[\ell^2+\ell x(\kappa-1)\right]}$

(c) $\mathbf{F}=-\left(\frac{dU}{dx}\right)\hat{\mathbf{i}}=\boxed{\frac{\epsilon_0(\Delta V)^2}{2d}\ell(\kappa-1)\text{ to the left}}$ (out of the capacitor)

(d) $F=\frac{(2\,000)^2\left(8.85\times10^{-12}\right)(0.050\,0)(4.50-1)}{2\left(2.00\times10^{-3}\right)}=\boxed{1.55\times10^{-3}\text{ N}}$

P26.65 The portion of the capacitor nearly filled by metal has

capacitance $\frac{\kappa\epsilon_0(\ell x)}{d}\to\infty$

and stored energy $\frac{Q^2}{2C}\to0$.

The unfilled portion has

capacitance $\frac{\epsilon_0\ell(\ell-x)}{d}$.

The charge on this portion is $Q=\frac{(\ell-x)Q_0}{\ell}$.

(a) The stored energy is

$$U=\frac{Q^2}{2C}=\frac{\left[(\ell-x)Q_0/\ell\right]^2}{2\epsilon_0\ell(\ell-x)/d}=\boxed{\frac{Q_0^2(\ell-x)d}{2\epsilon_0\ell^3}}.$$

(b) $F=-\frac{dU}{dx}=-\frac{d}{dx}\left(\frac{Q_0^2(\ell-x)d}{2\epsilon_0\ell^3}\right)=+\frac{Q_0^2d}{2\epsilon_0\ell^3}$

$\mathbf{F}=\boxed{\frac{Q_0^2d}{2\epsilon_0\ell^3}\text{ to the right}}$ (into the capacitor)

(c) Stress $=\frac{F}{\ell d}=\boxed{\frac{Q_0^2}{2\epsilon_0\ell^4}}$

(d) $u=\frac{1}{2}\epsilon_0E^2=\frac{1}{2}\epsilon_0\left(\frac{\sigma}{\epsilon_0}\right)^2=\frac{1}{2}\epsilon_0\left(\frac{Q_0}{\epsilon_0\ell^2}\right)^2=\boxed{\frac{Q_0^2}{2\epsilon_0\ell^4}}$

P26.66 Gasoline: $(126\,000 \text{ Btu/gal})(1\,054 \text{ J/Btu})\left(\dfrac{1.00 \text{ gal}}{3.786\times10^{-3} \text{ m}^3}\right)\left(\dfrac{1.00 \text{ m}^3}{670 \text{ kg}}\right) = 5.24\times10^{7} \text{ J/kg}$

Battery: $\dfrac{(12.0 \text{ J/C})(100 \text{ C/s})(3\,600 \text{ s})}{16.0 \text{ kg}} = 2.70\times10^{5} \text{ J/kg}$

Capacitor: $\dfrac{\frac{1}{2}(0.100 \text{ F})(12.0 \text{ V})^2}{0.100 \text{ kg}} = 72.0 \text{ J/kg}$

Gasoline has 194 times the specific energy content of the battery and 727 000 times that of the capacitor.

P26.67 Call the unknown capacitance C_u

$$Q = C_u(\Delta V_i) = (C_u + C)(\Delta V_f)$$

$$\boxed{C_u = \frac{C(\Delta V_f)}{(\Delta V_i)-(\Delta V_f)}} = \frac{(10.0\ \mu\text{F})(30.0 \text{ V})}{(100 \text{ V} - 30.0 \text{ V})} = \boxed{4.29\ \mu\text{F}}$$

***P26.68** She can clip together a series combination of parallel combinations of two 100-μF capacitors. The equivalent capacitance is $\dfrac{1}{(200\ \mu\text{F})^{-1} + (200\ \mu\text{F})^{-1}} = 100\ \mu\text{F}$. When 90 V is connected across the combination, only $\boxed{45 \text{ V}}$ appears across each individual capacitor.

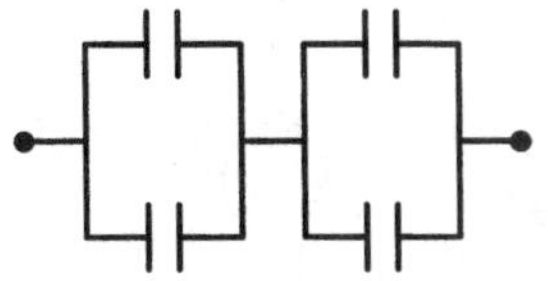

FIG. P26.68

P26.69 (a) $C_0 = \dfrac{\epsilon_0 A}{d} = \dfrac{Q_0}{\Delta V_0}$

When the dielectric is inserted at constant voltage,

$$C = \kappa C_0 = \frac{Q}{\Delta V_0};$$

$$U_0 = \frac{C_0(\Delta V_0)^2}{2}$$

$$U = \frac{C(\Delta V_0)^2}{2} = \frac{\kappa C_0(\Delta V_0^2)}{2}$$

and $\dfrac{U}{U_0} = \kappa$.

The extra energy comes from (part of the) electrical work done by the battery in separating the extra charge.

(b) $Q_0 = C_0 \Delta V_0$

and $Q = C\Delta V_0 = \kappa C_0 \Delta V_0$

so $\boxed{\dfrac{Q}{Q_0} = \kappa}$.

P26.70 The vertical orientation sets up two capacitors in parallel, with equivalent capacitance

$$C_p = \frac{\epsilon_0 (A/2)}{d} + \frac{\kappa \epsilon_0 (A/2)}{d} = \left(\frac{\kappa+1}{2}\right)\frac{\epsilon_0 A}{d}$$

where A is the area of either plate and d is the separation of the plates. The horizontal orientation produces two capacitors in series. If f is the fraction of the horizontal capacitor filled with dielectric, the equivalent capacitance is

$$\frac{1}{C_s} = \frac{fd}{\kappa \epsilon_0 A} + \frac{(1-f)d}{\epsilon_0 A} = \left[\frac{f+\kappa(1-f)}{\kappa}\right]\frac{d}{\epsilon_0 A}, \text{ or } C_s = \left[\frac{\kappa}{f+\kappa(1-f)}\right]\frac{\epsilon_0 A}{d}.$$

Requiring that $C_p = C_s$ gives $\frac{\kappa+1}{2} = \frac{\kappa}{f+\kappa(1-f)}$, or $(\kappa+1)[f+\kappa(1-f)] = 2\kappa$.

For $\kappa = 2.00$, this yields $3.00[2.00-(1.00)f] = 4.00$, with the solution $f = \boxed{\frac{2}{3}}$.

P26.71 Initially (capacitors charged in parallel),

$$q_1 = C_1(\Delta V) = (6.00\ \mu\text{F})(250\ \text{V}) = 1\,500\ \mu\text{C}$$

$$q_2 = C_2(\Delta V) = (2.00\ \mu\text{F})(250\ \text{V}) = 500\ \mu\text{C}.$$

After reconnection (positive plate to negative plate),

$$q'_{\text{total}} = q_1 - q_2 = 1\,000\ \mu\text{C} \text{ and } \Delta V' = \frac{q'_{\text{total}}}{C_{\text{total}}} = \frac{1\,000\ \mu\text{C}}{8.00\ \mu\text{F}} = 125\ \text{V}.$$

Therefore,

$$q'_1 = C_1(\Delta V') = (6.00\ \mu\text{F})(125\ \text{V}) = \boxed{750\ \mu\text{C}}$$

$$q'_2 = C_2(\Delta V') = (2.00\ \mu\text{F})(125\ \text{V}) = \boxed{250\ \mu\text{C}}.$$

P26.72 Assume a potential difference across a and b, and notice that the potential difference across the $8.00\ \mu\text{F}$ capacitor must be zero by symmetry. Then the equivalent capacitance can be determined from the following circuit:

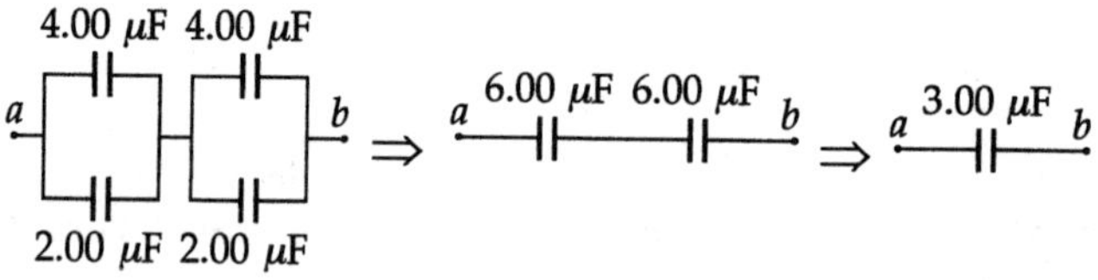

FIG. P26.72

$$C_{ab} = \boxed{3.00\ \mu\text{F}}.$$

P26.73 E_{max} occurs at the inner conductor's surface.

$$E_{max} = \frac{2k_e\lambda}{a} \text{ from Equation 24.7.}$$

$$\Delta V = 2k_e\lambda \ln\left(\frac{b}{a}\right) \text{ from Example 26.2}$$

$$E_{max} = \frac{\Delta V}{a\ln(b/a)}$$

$$\Delta V_{max} = E_{max} a \ln\left(\frac{b}{a}\right) = \left(18.0\times10^{6}\text{ V/m}\right)\left(0.800\times10^{-3}\text{ m}\right)\ln\left(\frac{3.00}{0.800}\right) = \boxed{19.0\text{ kV}}.$$

P26.74 $E = \frac{2\kappa\lambda}{a}$; $\Delta V = 2\kappa\lambda \ln\left(\frac{b}{a}\right)$

$$\Delta V_{max} = E_{max} a \ln\left(\frac{b}{a}\right)$$

$$\frac{dV_{max}}{da} = E_{max}\left[\ln\left(\frac{b}{a}\right) + a\left(\frac{1}{b/a}\right)\left(-\frac{b}{a^2}\right)\right] = 0$$

$$\ln\left(\frac{b}{a}\right) = 1 \text{ or } \frac{b}{a} = e^{1} \text{ so } \boxed{a = \frac{b}{e}}$$

P26.75 By symmetry, the potential difference across 3C is zero, so the circuit reduces to

$$C_{eq} = \left(\frac{1}{2C} + \frac{1}{4C}\right)^{-1} = \frac{8}{6}C = \boxed{\frac{4}{3}C}.$$

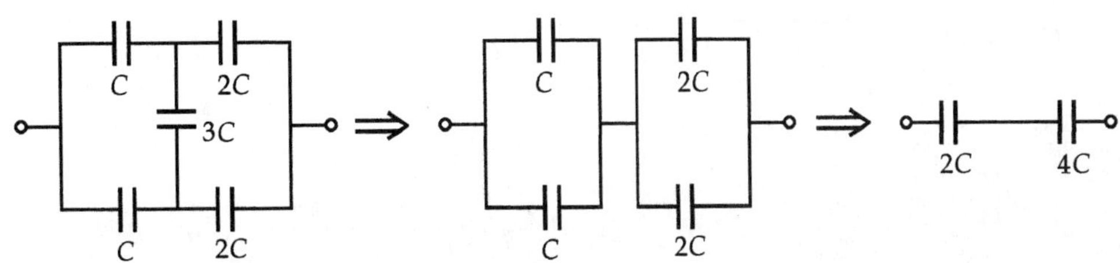

FIG. P26.75

P26.76 The electric field due to the charge on the positive wire is perpendicular to the wire, radial, and of magnitude

$$E_+ = \frac{\lambda}{2\pi \epsilon_0 r}.$$

The potential difference between wires due to the presence of this charge is

$$\Delta V_1 = -\int_{-\text{wire}}^{+\text{wire}} \mathbf{E}\cdot d\mathbf{r} = -\frac{\lambda}{2\pi \epsilon_0}\int_{D-d}^{d}\frac{dr}{r} = \frac{\lambda}{2\pi \epsilon_0}\ln\left(\frac{D-d}{d}\right).$$

The presence of the linear charge density $-\lambda$ on the negative wire makes an identical contribution to the potential difference between the wires. Therefore, the total potential difference is

$$\Delta V = 2(\Delta V_1) = \frac{\lambda}{\pi \epsilon_0}\ln\left(\frac{D-d}{d}\right)$$

and the capacitance of this system of two wires, each of length ℓ, is

$$C = \frac{Q}{\Delta V} = \frac{\lambda \ell}{\Delta V} = \frac{\lambda \ell}{(\lambda/\pi \epsilon_0)\ln[(D-d)/d]} = \frac{\pi \epsilon_0 \ell}{\ln[(D-d)/d]}.$$

The capacitance per unit length is: $\boxed{\frac{C}{\ell} = \frac{\pi \epsilon_0}{\ln[(D-d)/d]}}$.

***P26.77** The condition that we are testing is that the capacitance increases by less than 10%, or,

$$\frac{C'}{C} < 1.10.$$

Substituting the expressions for C and C' from Example 26.2, we have,

$$\frac{C'}{C} = \frac{\dfrac{\ell}{2k_e \ln\left(\frac{b}{1.10a}\right)}}{\dfrac{\ell}{2k_e \ln\left(\frac{b}{a}\right)}} = \frac{\ln\left(\frac{b}{a}\right)}{\ln\left(\frac{b}{1.10a}\right)} < 1.10.$$

This becomes,

$$\ln\left(\frac{b}{a}\right) < 1.10\ln\left(\frac{b}{1.10a}\right) = 1.10\ln\left(\frac{b}{a}\right) + 1.10\ln\left(\frac{1}{1.10}\right) = 1.10\ln\left(\frac{b}{a}\right) - 1.10\ln(1.10).$$

We can rewrite this as,

$$-0.10\ln\left(\frac{b}{a}\right) < -1.10\ln(1.10)$$

$$\ln\left(\frac{b}{a}\right) > 11.0\ln(1.10) = \ln(1.10)^{11.0}$$

where we have reversed the direction of the inequality because we multiplied the whole expression by –1 to remove the negative signs. Comparing the arguments of the logarithms on both sides of the inequality, we see that,

$$\frac{b}{a} > (1.10)^{11.0} = 2.85.$$

Thus, if $b > 2.85a$, the increase in capacitance is less than 10% and it is more effective to increase ℓ.

ANSWERS TO EVEN PROBLEMS

P26.2 (a) $1.00\ \mu\text{F}$; (b) $100\ \text{V}$

P26.4 (a) $8.99\ \text{mm}$; (b) $0.222\ \text{pF}$; (c) $22.2\ \text{pC}$

P26.6 $11.1\ \text{nF}$; $26.6\ \text{C}$

P26.8 $3.10\ \text{nm}$

P26.10 $\dfrac{(2N-1)\in_0(\pi-\theta)R^2}{d}$

P26.12 $2.13\times10^{16}\ \text{m}^3$

P26.14 $\dfrac{mgd\tan\theta}{q}$

P26.16 (a) $17.0\ \mu\text{F}$; (b) $9.00\ \text{V}$; (c) $45.0\ \mu\text{C}$ and $108\ \mu\text{C}$

P26.18 $1.83C$

P26.20 $\dfrac{C_p}{2}+\sqrt{\dfrac{C_p^2}{4}-C_pC_s}$ and $\dfrac{C_p}{2}-\sqrt{\dfrac{C_p^2}{4}-C_pC_s}$

P26.22 (a) $2C$; (b) $Q_1>Q_3>Q_2$; (c) $\Delta V_1>\Delta V_2=\Delta V_3$; (d) Q_3 and Q_1 increase and Q_2 decreases

P26.24 (a) $398\ \mu\text{F}$ in series; (b) $2.20\ \mu\text{F}$ in parallel

P26.26 $19.8\ \mu\text{C}$

P26.28 $83.6\ \mu\text{C}$

P26.30 $\left(\sqrt{3}-1\right)\dfrac{C_0}{2}$

P26.32 $4.47\ \text{kV}$

P26.34 energy doubles

P26.36 $2.51\times10^{-3}\ \text{m}^3=2.51\ \text{L}$

P26.38 (a) $400\ \mu\text{C}$; (b) $2.50\ \text{kN/m}$

P26.40 (a) $C(\Delta V)^2$; (b) $\dfrac{4\Delta V}{3}$; (c) $4C\dfrac{(\Delta V)^2}{3}$; (d) Positive work is done on the system by the agent pulling the plates apart.

P26.42 (a) $q_1=\dfrac{R_1Q}{R_1+R_2}$ and $q_2=\dfrac{R_2Q}{R_1+R_2}$; (b) see the solution

P26.44 (a) $13.3\ \text{nC}$; (b) $272\ \text{nC}$

P26.46 $\sim10^{-6}\ \text{F}$ and $\sim10^{2}\ \text{V}$ for two 40 cm by 100 cm sheets of aluminum foil sandwiching a thin sheet of plastic.

P26.48 (a) $1.53\ \text{nF}$; (b) $18.4\ \text{nC}$; (c) $184\ \mu\text{C/m}^2$ free; $183\ \mu\text{C/m}^2$ induced; (d) $694\ \text{V/m}$

P26.50 (a) $\left(-9.10\hat{\mathbf{i}}+8.40\hat{\mathbf{j}}\right)\ \text{pC}\cdot\text{m}$; (b) $-20.9\ \text{nN}\cdot\text{m}\hat{\mathbf{k}}$; (c) $112\ \text{nJ}$; (d) $228\ \text{nJ}$

P26.52 $579\ \text{V}$

P26.54 (a) $3.33\ \mu\text{F}$; (b) $\Delta V_3=60.0\ \text{V}$; $\Delta V_6=30.0\ \text{V}$; $\Delta V_2=60.0\ \text{V}$; $\Delta V_4=30.0\ \text{V}$; (c) $Q_3=Q_6=180\ \mu\text{C}$; $Q_2=Q_4=120\ \mu\text{C}$; (d) $13.4\ \text{mJ}$

P26.56 $189\ \text{kV}$

P26.58 (a) $40.0\ \mu\text{J}$; (b) $500\ \text{V}$

P26.60 yes; $1.00\ \text{Mm/s}$

P26.62 $23.3\ \text{V}$; $26.7\ \text{V}$

P26.64 (a) $\dfrac{\in_0\left[\ell^2+\ell x(\kappa-1)\right]}{d}$; (b) $\dfrac{\in_0(\Delta V)^2\left[\ell^2+\ell x(\kappa-1)\right]}{2d}$; (c) $\dfrac{\in_0(\Delta V)^2\ell(\kappa-1)}{2d}$ to the left; (d) $1.55\ \text{mN}$ left

P26.66 Gasoline has 194 times the specific energy content of the battery, and 727 000 times that of the capacitor.

P26.68 see the solution; 45 V

P26.70 $\frac{2}{3}$

P26.72 3.00 μF

P26.74 see the solution

P26.76 see the solution

27

Current and Resistance

CHAPTER OUTLINE

ANSWERS TO QUESTIONS

Q27.1 Individual vehicles—cars, trucks and motorcycles—would correspond to charge. The number of vehicles that pass a certain point in a given time would correspond to the current.

Q27.2 Voltage is a measure of potential difference, not of current. "Surge" implies a flow—and only charge, in coulombs, can flow through a system. It would also be correct to say that the victim carried a certain current, in amperes.

Q27.3 Geometry and resistivity. In turn, the resistivity of the material depends on the temperature.

Q27.4 Resistance is a physical property of the conductor based on the material of which it is made and its size and shape, including the locations where current is put in and taken out. Resistivity is a physical property only of the material of which the resistor is made.

Q27.5 The radius of wire B is $\sqrt{3}$ times the radius of wire A, to make its cross–sectional area 3 times larger.

Q27.6 Not all conductors obey Ohm's law at all times. For example, consider an experiment in which a variable potential difference is applied across an incandescent light bulb, and the current is measured. At very low voltages, the filament follows Ohm's law nicely. But then long before the filament begins to glow, the plot of $\frac{\Delta V}{I}$ becomes non-linear, because the resistivity is temperature-dependent.

Q27.7 A conductor is not in electrostatic equilibrium when it is carrying a current, duh! If charges are placed on an isolated conductor, the electric fields established in the conductor by the charges will cause the charges to move until they are in positions such that there is zero electric field throughout the conductor. A conductor carrying a steady current is not an isolated conductor—its ends must be connected to a source of emf, such as a battery. The battery maintains a potential difference across the conductor and, therefore, an electric field in the conductor. The steady current is due to the response of the electrons in the conductor due to this constant electric field.

Q27.8 The bottom of the rods on the *Jacob's Ladder* are close enough so that the supplied voltage is sufficient to produce dielectric breakdown of the air. The initial spark at the bottom includes a tube of ionized air molecules. Since this tube containing ions is warmer than the air around it, it is buoyed up by the surrounding air and begins to rise. The ions themselves significantly decrease the resistivity of the air. They significantly lower the dielectric strength of the air, marking longer sparks possible. Internal resistance in the power supply will typically make its terminal voltage drop, so that it cannot produce a spark across the bottom ends of the rods. A single "continuous" spark, therefore will rise up, becoming longer and longer, until the potential difference is not large enough to sustain dielectric breakdown of the air. Once the initial spark stops, another one will form at the bottom, where again, the supplied potential difference is sufficient to break down the air.

Q27.9 The conductor does not follow Ohm's law, and must have a resistivity that is current-dependent, or more likely temperature-dependent.

Q27.10 A power supply would correspond to a water pump; a resistor corresponds to a pipe of a certain diameter, and thus resistance to flow; charge corresponds to the water itself; potential difference corresponds to difference in height between the ends of a pipe or the ports of a water pump.

Q27.11 The amplitude of atomic vibrations increases with temperature. Atoms can then scatter electrons more efficiently.

Q27.12 In a metal, the conduction electrons are not strongly bound to individual ion cores. They can move in response to an applied electric field to constitute an electric current. Each metal ion in the lattice of a microcrystal exerts Coulomb forces on its neighbors. When one ion is vibrating rapidly, it can set its neighbors into vibration. This process represents energy moving though the material by heat.

Q27.13 The resistance of copper *increases* with temperature, while the resistance of silicon *decreases* with increasing temperature. The conduction electrons are scattered more by vibrating atoms when copper heats up. Silicon's charge carrier density increases as temperature increases and more atomic electrons are promoted to become conduction electrons.

Q27.14 A current will continue to exist in a superconductor without voltage because there is no resistance loss.

Q27.15 Superconductors have no resistance when they are below a certain critical temperature. For most superconducting materials, this critical temperature is close to absolute zero. It requires expensive refrigeration, often using liquid helium. Liquid nitrogen at 77 K is much less expensive. Recent discoveries of materials that have higher critical temperatures suggest the possibility of developing superconductors that do not require expensive cooling systems.

Q27.16 In a normal metal, suppose that we could proceed to a limit of zero resistance by lengthening the average time between collisions. The classical model of conduction then suggests that a constant applied voltage would cause constant acceleration of the free electrons, and a current steadily increasing in time.

On the other hand, we can actually switch to zero resistance by substituting a superconducting wire for the normal metal. In this case, the drift velocity of electrons is established by vibrations of atoms in the crystal lattice; the maximum current is limited; and it becomes impossible to establish a potential difference across the superconductor.

Q27.17 Because there are so many electrons in a conductor (approximately 10^{28} electrons/m^3) the average velocity of charges is very slow. When you connect a wire to a potential difference, you establish an electric field everywhere in the wire nearly instantaneously, to make electrons start drifting everywhere all at once.

Q27.18 Current moving through a wire is analogous to a longitudinal wave moving through the electrons of the atoms. The wave speed depends on the speed at which the disturbance in the electric field can be communicated between neighboring atoms, not on the drift velocities of the electrons themselves. If you leave a direct-current light bulb on for a reasonably short time, it is likely that no single electron will enter one end of the filament and leave at the other end.

Q27.19 More power is delivered to the resistor with the smaller resistance, since $\mathcal{P} = \frac{\Delta V^2}{R}$.

Q27.20 The 25 W bulb has a higher resistance. The 100 W bulb carries more current.

Q27.21 One ampere–hour is 3 600 coulombs. The ampere–hour rating is the quantity of charge that the battery can lift though its nominal potential difference.

Q27.22 Choose the voltage of the power supply you will use to drive the heater. Next calculate the required resistance R as $\frac{\Delta V^2}{\mathcal{P}}$. Knowing the resistivity ρ of the material, choose a combination of wire length and cross–sectional area to make $\left(\frac{\ell}{A}\right) = \left(\frac{R}{\rho}\right)$. You will have to pay for less material if you make both ℓ and A smaller, but if you go too far the wire will have too little surface area to radiate away the energy; then the resistor will melt.

SOLUTIONS TO PROBLEMS

Section 27.1 Electric Current

P27.1 $I = \frac{\Delta Q}{\Delta t}$ $\qquad \Delta Q = I\Delta t = \left(30.0 \times 10^{-6}\ \text{A}\right)(40.0\ \text{s}) = 1.20 \times 10^{-3}\ \text{C}$

$$N = \frac{Q}{e} = \frac{1.20 \times 10^{-3}\ \text{C}}{1.60 \times 10^{-19}\ \text{C/electron}} = \boxed{7.50 \times 10^{15}\ \text{electrons}}$$

P27.2 The molar mass of silver $= 107.9\ \text{g/mole}$ and the volume V is

$$V = (\text{area})(\text{thickness}) = \left(700 \times 10^{-4}\ \text{m}^2\right)\left(0.133 \times 10^{-3}\ \text{m}\right) = 9.31 \times 10^{-6}\ \text{m}^3.$$

The mass of silver deposited is $m_{\text{Ag}} = \rho V = \left(10.5 \times 10^3\ \text{kg/m}^3\right)\left(9.31 \times 10^{-6}\ \text{m}^3\right) = 9.78 \times 10^{-2}\ \text{kg}$.

And the number of silver atoms deposited is

$$N = \left(9.78 \times 10^{-2}\ \text{kg}\right)\left(\frac{6.02 \times 10^{23}\ \text{atoms}}{107.9\ \text{g}}\right)\left(\frac{1\,000\ \text{g}}{1\ \text{kg}}\right) = 5.45 \times 10^{23}\ \text{atoms}$$

$$I = \frac{\Delta V}{R} = \frac{12.0\ \text{V}}{1.80\ \Omega} = 6.67\ \text{A} = 6.67\ \text{C/s}$$

$$\Delta t = \frac{\Delta Q}{I} = \frac{Ne}{I} = \frac{\left(5.45 \times 10^{23}\right)\left(1.60 \times 10^{-19}\ \text{C}\right)}{6.67\ \text{C/s}} = 1.31 \times 10^4\ \text{s} = \boxed{3.64\ \text{h}}$$

P27.3 $Q(t)=\int_0^t Idt = I_0\tau\left(1-e^{-t/\tau}\right)$

(a) $Q(\tau)=I_0\tau\left(1-e^{-1}\right)=\boxed{(0.632)I_0\tau}$

(b) $Q(10\tau)=I_0\tau\left(1-e^{-10}\right)=\boxed{(0.999\,95)I_0\tau}$

(c) $Q(\infty)=I_0\tau\left(1-e^{-\infty}\right)=\boxed{I_0\tau}$

P27.4 (a) Using $\frac{k_e e^2}{r^2}=\frac{mv^2}{r}$, we get: $v=\sqrt{\frac{k_e e^2}{mr}}=\boxed{2.19\times10^6\ \text{m/s}}$.

(b) The time for the electron to revolve around the proton once is:

$$t=\frac{2\pi r}{v}=\frac{2\pi\left(5.29\times10^{-11}\ \text{m}\right)}{\left(2.19\times10^6\ \text{m/s}\right)}=1.52\times10^{-16}\ \text{s}.$$

The total charge flow in this time is 1.60×10^{-19} C, so the current is

$$I=\frac{1.60\times10^{-19}\ \text{C}}{1.52\times10^{-16}\ \text{s}}=1.05\times10^{-3}\ \text{A}=\boxed{1.05\ \text{mA}}.$$

P27.5 The period of revolution for the sphere is $T=\frac{2\pi}{\omega}$, and the average current represented by this revolving charge is $I=\frac{q}{T}=\boxed{\frac{q\omega}{2\pi}}$.

P27.6 $q=4t^3+5t+6$

$$A=\left(2.00\ \text{cm}^2\right)\left(\frac{1.00\ \text{m}}{100\ \text{cm}}\right)^2=2.00\times10^{-4}\ \text{m}^2$$

(a) $I(1.00\ \text{s})=\left.\frac{dq}{dt}\right|_{t=1.00\ \text{s}}=\left.\left(12t^2+5\right)\right|_{t=1.00\ \text{s}}=\boxed{17.0\ \text{A}}$

(b) $J=\frac{I}{A}=\frac{17.0\ \text{A}}{2.00\times10^{-4}\ \text{m}^2}=\boxed{85.0\ \text{kA/m}^2}$

P27.7 $I=\frac{dq}{dt}$

$$q=\int dq=\int Idt=\int_0^{1/240\ \text{s}}(100\ \text{A})\sin\left(\frac{120\pi t}{\text{s}}\right)dt$$

$$q=\frac{-100\ \text{C}}{120\pi}\left[\cos\left(\frac{\pi}{2}\right)-\cos 0\right]=\frac{+100\ \text{C}}{120\pi}=\boxed{0.265\ \text{C}}$$

P27.8 (a) $J = \frac{I}{A} = \frac{5.00\text{ A}}{\pi\left(4.00 \times 10^{-3}\text{ m}\right)^2} = \boxed{99.5\text{ kA/m}^2}$

(b) $J_2 = \frac{1}{4}J_1;\ \frac{I}{A_2} = \frac{1}{4}\frac{I}{A_1}$

$A_1 = \frac{1}{4}A_2$ so $\pi\left(4.00 \times 10^{-3}\right)^2 = \frac{1}{4}\pi r_2^2$

$r_2 = 2\left(4.00 \times 10^{-3}\right) = 8.00 \times 10^{-3}\text{ m} = \boxed{8.00\text{ mm}}$

P27.9 (a) $J = \frac{I}{A} = \frac{8.00 \times 10^{-6}\text{ A}}{\pi\left(1.00 \times 10^{-3}\text{ m}\right)^2} = \boxed{2.55\text{ A/m}^2}$

(b) From $J = nev_d$, we have $n = \frac{J}{ev_d} = \frac{2.55\text{ A/m}^2}{\left(1.60 \times 10^{-19}\text{ C}\right)\left(3.00 \times 10^8\text{ m/s}\right)} = \boxed{5.31 \times 10^{10}\text{ m}^{-3}}$.

(c) From $I = \frac{\Delta Q}{\Delta t}$, we have $\Delta t = \frac{\Delta Q}{I} = \frac{N_A e}{I} = \frac{\left(6.02 \times 10^{23}\right)\left(1.60 \times 10^{-19}\text{ C}\right)}{8.00 \times 10^{-6}\text{ A}} = \boxed{1.20 \times 10^{10}\text{ s}}$.

(This is about 382 years!)

P27.10 (a) The speed of each deuteron is given by $K = \frac{1}{2}mv^2$

$\left(2.00 \times 10^6\right)\left(1.60 \times 10^{-19}\text{ J}\right) = \frac{1}{2}\left(2 \times 1.67 \times 10^{-27}\text{ kg}\right)v^2$ and $v = 1.38 \times 10^7\text{ m/s}$.

The time between deuterons passing a stationary point is t in $I = \frac{q}{t}$

$10.0 \times 10^{-6}\text{ C/s} = 1.60 \times 10^{-19}\text{ C}/t$ or $t = 1.60 \times 10^{-14}\text{ s}$.

So the distance between them is $vt = \left(1.38 \times 10^7\text{ m/s}\right)\left(1.60 \times 10^{-14}\text{ s}\right) = \boxed{2.21 \times 10^{-7}\text{ m}}$.

(b) One nucleus will put its nearest neighbor at potential

$$V = \frac{k_e q}{r} = \frac{\left(8.99 \times 10^9\text{ N}\cdot\text{m}^2/\text{C}^2\right)\left(1.60 \times 10^{-19}\text{ C}\right)}{2.21 \times 10^{-7}\text{ m}} = 6.49 \times 10^{-3}\text{ V}.$$

This is very small compared to the 2 MV accelerating potential, so repulsion within the beam is a small effect.

P27.11 We use $I = nqAv_d$ n is the number of charge carriers per unit volume, and is identical to the number of atoms per unit volume. We assume a contribution of 1 free electron per atom in the relationship above. For aluminum, which has a molar mass of 27, we know that Avogadro's number of atoms, N_A, has a mass of 27.0 g. Thus, the mass per atom is

$$\frac{27.0\text{ g}}{N_A} = \frac{27.0\text{ g}}{6.02\times 10^{23}} = 4.49\times 10^{-23}\text{ g/atom}.$$

Thus,
$$n = \frac{\text{density of aluminum}}{\text{mass per atom}} = \frac{2.70\text{ g/cm}^3}{4.49\times 10^{-23}\text{ g/atom}}$$

$$n = 6.02\times 10^{22}\text{ atoms/cm}^3 = 6.02\times 10^{28}\text{ atoms/m}^3.$$

Therefore,
$$v_d = \frac{I}{nqA} = \frac{5.00\text{ A}}{\left(6.02\times 10^{28}\text{ m}^{-3}\right)\left(1.60\times 10^{-19}\text{ C}\right)\left(4.00\times 10^{-6}\text{ m}^2\right)} = 1.30\times 10^{-4}\text{ m/s}$$

or,
$$v_d = \boxed{0.130\text{ mm/s}}.$$

Section 27.2 Resistance

***P27.12** $J = \sigma E = \frac{E}{\rho} = \frac{0.740\text{ V/m}}{2.44\times 10^{-8}\ \Omega\cdot\text{m}}\left(\frac{1\ \Omega\cdot\text{A}}{1\text{ V}}\right) = \boxed{3.03\times 10^{7}\text{ A/m}^2}$

P27.13 $I = \frac{\Delta V}{R} = \frac{120\text{ V}}{240\ \Omega} = 0.500\text{ A} = \boxed{500\text{ mA}}$

P27.14 (a) Applying its definition, we find the resistance of the rod,

$$R = \frac{\Delta V}{I} = \frac{15.0\text{ V}}{4.00\times 10^{-3}\text{ A}} = 3\,750\ \Omega = \boxed{3.75\text{ k}\Omega}.$$

(b) The length of the rod is determined from the definition of resistivity: $R = \frac{\rho\ell}{A}$. Solving for ℓ and substituting numerical values for R, A, and the value of ρ given for carbon in Table 27.1, we obtain

$$\ell = \frac{RA}{\rho} = \frac{\left(3.75\times 10^{3}\ \Omega\right)\left(5.00\times 10^{-6}\text{ m}^2\right)}{\left(3.50\times 10^{-5}\ \Omega\cdot\text{m}\right)} = \boxed{536\text{ m}}.$$

P27.15 $\Delta V = IR$

and $R = \frac{\rho\ell}{A}$:
$$A = (0.600\text{ mm})^2\left(\frac{1.00\text{ m}}{1\,000\text{ mm}}\right)^2 = 6.00\times 10^{-7}\text{ m}^2$$

$\Delta V = \frac{I\rho\ell}{A}$:
$$I = \frac{\Delta VA}{\rho\ell} = \frac{(0.900\text{ V})\left(6.00\times 10^{-7}\text{ m}^2\right)}{\left(5.60\times 10^{-8}\ \Omega\cdot\text{m}\right)(1.50\text{ m})}$$

$$I = \boxed{6.43\text{ A}}$$

P27.16 $J=\frac{I}{\pi r^2}=\sigma E=\frac{3.00\text{ A}}{\pi(0.012\,0\text{ m})^2}=\sigma(120\text{ N/C})$

$\sigma=55.3(\Omega\cdot\text{m})^{-1}$ $\rho=\frac{1}{\sigma}=\boxed{0.018\,1\ \Omega\cdot\text{m}}$

P27.17 (a) Given $M=\rho_d V=\rho_d A\ell$ where $\rho_d\equiv$ mass density,

we obtain: $A=\frac{M}{\rho_d\ell}$. Taking $\rho_r\equiv$ resistivity, $R=\frac{\rho_r\ell}{A}=\frac{\rho_r\ell}{M/\rho_d\ell}=\frac{\rho_r\rho_d\ell^2}{M}$.

Thus, $\ell=\sqrt{\frac{MR}{\rho_r\rho_d}}=\sqrt{\frac{(1.00\times10^{-3})(0.500)}{(1.70\times10^{-8})(8.92\times10^3)}}$ $\ell=\boxed{1.82\text{ m}}$.

(b) $V=\frac{M}{\rho_d}$, or $\pi r^2\ell=\frac{M}{\rho_d}$.

Thus, $r=\sqrt{\frac{M}{\pi\rho_d\ell}}=\sqrt{\frac{1.00\times10^{-3}}{\pi(8.92\times10^3)(1.82)}}$ $r=1.40\times10^{-4}\text{ m}$.

The diameter is twice this distance: diameter $=\boxed{280\ \mu\text{m}}$.

***P27.18** The volume of the gram of gold is given by $\rho=\frac{m}{V}$

$$V=\frac{m}{\rho}=\frac{10^{-3}\text{ kg}}{19.3\times10^3\text{ kg/m}^3}=5.18\times10^{-8}\text{ m}^3=A(2.40\times10^3\text{ m})$$

$$A=2.16\times10^{-11}\text{ m}^2$$

$$R=\frac{\rho\ell}{A}=\frac{2.44\times10^{-8}\ \Omega\cdot\text{m}(2.4\times10^3\text{ m})}{2.16\times10^{-11}\text{ m}^2}=\boxed{2.71\times10^6\ \Omega}$$

P27.19 (a) Suppose the rubber is 10 cm long and 1 mm in diameter.

$$R=\frac{\rho\ell}{A}=\frac{4\rho\ell}{\pi d^2}\sim\frac{4(10^{13}\ \Omega\cdot\text{m})(10^{-1}\text{ m})}{\pi(10^{-3}\text{ m})^2}=\boxed{\sim10^{18}\ \Omega}$$

(b) $$R=\frac{4\rho\ell}{\pi d^2}\sim\frac{4(1.7\times10^{-8}\ \Omega\cdot\text{m})(10^{-3}\text{ m})}{\pi(2\times10^{-2}\text{ m})^2}\boxed{\sim10^{-7}\ \Omega}$$

(c) $$I=\frac{\Delta V}{R}\sim\frac{10^2\text{ V}}{10^{18}\ \Omega}\boxed{\sim10^{-16}\text{ A}}$$

$$I\sim\frac{10^2\text{ V}}{10^{-7}\ \Omega}\boxed{\sim10^9\text{ A}}$$

P27.20 The distance between opposite faces of the cube is $\ell = \left(\dfrac{90.0\text{ g}}{10.5\text{ g/cm}^3}\right)^{1/3} = 2.05\text{ cm}$.

(a) $$R = \frac{\rho\ell}{A} = \frac{\rho\ell}{\ell^2} = \frac{\rho}{\ell} = \frac{1.59\times10^{-8}\ \Omega\cdot\text{m}}{2.05\times10^{-2}\text{ m}} = 7.77\times10^{-7}\ \Omega = \boxed{777\text{ n}\Omega}$$

(b) $$I = \frac{\Delta V}{R} = \frac{1.00\times10^{-5}\text{ V}}{7.77\times10^{-7}\ \Omega} = 12.9\text{ A}$$

$$n = \frac{10.5\text{ g/cm}^3}{107.87\text{ g/mol}}\left(6.02\times10^{23}\text{ electrons/mol}\right)$$

$$n = \left(5.86\times10^{22}\text{ electrons/cm}^3\right)\left(\frac{1.00\times10^6\text{ cm}^3}{1.00\text{ m}^3}\right) = 5.86\times10^{28}/\text{m}^3$$

$$I = nqvA \text{ and } v = \frac{I}{nqA} = \frac{12.9\text{ C/s}}{\left(5.86\times10^{28}/\text{m}^3\right)\left(1.60\times10^{-19}\text{ C}\right)\left(0.020\,5\text{ m}\right)^2} = \boxed{3.28\ \mu\text{m/s}}$$

P27.21 Originally, $R = \dfrac{\rho\ell}{A}$. Finally, $R_f = \dfrac{\rho(\ell/3)}{3A} = \dfrac{\rho\ell}{9A} = \boxed{\dfrac{R}{9}}$.

P27.22 $$\frac{\rho_{\text{Al}}\ell}{\pi(r_{\text{Al}})^2} = \frac{\rho_{\text{Cu}}\ell}{\pi(r_{\text{Cu}})^2}$$

$$\frac{r_{\text{Al}}}{r_{\text{Cu}}} = \sqrt{\frac{\rho_{\text{Al}}}{\rho_{\text{Cu}}}} = \sqrt{\frac{2.82\times10^{-8}}{1.70\times10^{-8}}} = \boxed{1.29}$$

P27.23 $J = \sigma E$ so $\sigma = \dfrac{J}{E} = \dfrac{6.00\times10^{-13}\text{ A/m}^2}{100\text{ V/m}} = \boxed{6.00\times10^{-15}\ (\Omega\cdot\text{m})^{-1}}$

P27.24 $$R = \frac{\rho_1\ell_1}{A_1} + \frac{\rho_2\ell_2}{A_2} = \frac{\rho_1\ell_1 + \rho_2\ell_2}{d^2}$$

$$R = \frac{\left(4.00\times10^{-3}\ \Omega\cdot\text{m}\right)(0.250\text{ m}) + \left(6.00\times10^{-3}\ \Omega\cdot\text{m}\right)(0.400\text{ m})}{\left(3.00\times10^{-3}\text{ m}\right)^2} = \boxed{378\ \Omega}$$

Section 27.3 A Model for Electrical Conduction

P27.25 $$\rho = \frac{m}{nq^2\tau}$$

so $$\tau = \frac{m}{\rho nq^2} = \frac{\left(9.11\times10^{-31}\right)}{\left(1.70\times10^{-8}\right)\left(8.49\times10^{28}\right)\left(1.60\times10^{-19}\right)} = 2.47\times10^{-14}\text{ s}$$

$$v_d = \frac{qE}{m}\tau$$

so $$7.84\times10^{-4} = \frac{\left(1.60\times10^{-19}\right)E\left(2.47\times10^{-14}\right)}{9.11\times10^{-31}}$$

Therefore, $E = \boxed{0.181\text{ V/m}}$.

P27.26 (a) n is $\boxed{\text{unaffected}}$

(b) $|J| = \frac{I}{A} \propto I$

so it $\boxed{\text{doubles}}$.

(c) $J = nev_d$

so v_d $\boxed{\text{doubles}}$.

(d) $\tau = \frac{m\sigma}{nq^2}$ is $\boxed{\text{unchanged}}$ as long as σ does not change due to a temperature change in the conductor.

P27.27 From Equation 27.17,

$$\tau = \frac{m_e}{nq^2\rho} = \frac{9.11\times10^{-31}}{\left(8.49\times10^{28}\right)\left(1.60\times10^{-19}\right)^2\left(1.70\times10^{-8}\right)} = 2.47\times10^{-14}\text{ s}$$

$$\ell = v\tau = \left(8.60\times10^5\text{ m/s}\right)\left(2.47\times10^{-14}\text{ s}\right) = 2.12\times10^{-8}\text{ m} = \boxed{21.2\text{ nm}}$$

Section 27.4 **Resistance and Temperature**

P27.28 At the low temperature T_C we write $R_C = \frac{\Delta V}{I_C} = R_0\left[1+\alpha\left(T_C - T_0\right)\right]$ where $T_0 = 20.0°\text{C}$.

At the high temperature T_h, $R_h = \frac{\Delta V}{I_h} = \frac{\Delta V}{1\text{ A}} = R_0\left[1+\alpha\left(T_h - T_0\right)\right]$.

Then $$\frac{(\Delta V)/(1.00\text{ A})}{(\Delta V)/I_C} = \frac{1+\left(3.90\times10^{-3}\right)(38.0)}{1+\left(3.90\times10^{-3}\right)(-108)}$$

and $$I_C = (1.00\text{ A})\left(\frac{1.15}{0.579}\right) = \boxed{1.98\text{ A}}.$$

P27.29 $R = R_0\left[1+\alpha(\Delta T)\right]$ gives $140\ \Omega = (19.0\ \Omega)\left[1+\left(4.50\times10^{-3}/°\text{C}\right)\Delta T\right]$.

Solving, $\Delta T = 1.42\times10^3\ °\text{C} = T - 20.0°\text{C}$.

And, the final temperature is $\boxed{T = 1.44\times10^3\ °\text{C}}$.

P27.30 $R = R_c + R_n = R_c\left[1+\alpha_c(T-T_0)\right] + R_n\left[1+\alpha_n(T-T_0)\right]$

$$0 = R_c\alpha_c(T-T_0) + R_n\alpha_n(T-T_0) \text{ so } R_c = -R_n\frac{\alpha_n}{\alpha_c}$$

$$R = -R_n\frac{\alpha_n}{\alpha_c} + R_n$$

$$R_n = R\left(1-\frac{\alpha_n}{\alpha_c}\right)^{-1} \qquad R_c = R\left(1-\frac{\alpha_c}{\alpha_n}\right)^{-1}$$

$$R_n = 10.0\text{ k}\Omega\left[1-\frac{\left(0.400\times10^{-3}/^\circ\text{C}\right)}{\left(-0.500\times10^{-3}/^\circ\text{C}\right)}\right]^{-1}$$

$$\boxed{R_n = 5.56\text{ k}\Omega} \quad \text{and} \quad \boxed{R_c = 4.44\text{ k}\Omega}$$

P27.31 (a) $\rho = \rho_0\left[1+\alpha(T-T_0)\right] = \left(2.82\times10^{-8}\ \Omega\cdot\text{m}\right)\left[1+3.90\times10^{-3}(30.0^\circ)\right] = \boxed{3.15\times10^{-8}\ \Omega\cdot\text{m}}$

(b) $J = \dfrac{E}{\rho} = \dfrac{0.200\text{ V/m}}{3.15\times10^{-8}\ \Omega\cdot\text{m}} = \boxed{6.35\times10^{6}\text{ A/m}^2}$

(c) $I = JA = J\left(\dfrac{\pi d^2}{4}\right) = \left(6.35\times10^{6}\text{ A/m}^2\right)\left[\dfrac{\pi\left(1.00\times10^{-4}\text{ m}\right)^2}{4}\right] = \boxed{49.9\text{ mA}}$

(d) $n = \dfrac{6.02\times10^{23}\text{ electrons}}{\left[26.98\text{ g}/\left(2.70\times10^{6}\text{ g/m}^3\right)\right]} = 6.02\times10^{28}\text{ electrons/m}^3$

$$v_d = \frac{J}{ne} = \frac{\left(6.35\times10^{6}\text{ A/m}^2\right)}{\left(6.02\times10^{28}\text{ electrons/m}^3\right)\left(1.60\times10^{-19}\text{ C}\right)} = \boxed{659\ \mu\text{m/s}}$$

(e) $\Delta V = E\ell = (0.200\text{ V/m})(2.00\text{ m}) = \boxed{0.400\text{ V}}$

P27.32 For aluminum,

$$\alpha_E = 3.90\times10^{-3}\ {}^\circ\text{C}^{-1} \qquad \text{(Table 27.1)}$$

$$\alpha = 24.0\times10^{-6}\ {}^\circ\text{C}^{-1} \qquad \text{(Table 19.1)}$$

$$R = \frac{\rho\ell}{A} = \frac{\rho_0(1+\alpha_E\Delta T)\ell(1+\alpha\Delta T)}{A(1+\alpha\Delta T)^2} = R_0\frac{(1+\alpha_E\Delta T)}{(1+\alpha\Delta T)} = (1.234\ \Omega)\left(\frac{1.39}{1.002\,4}\right) = \boxed{1.71\ \Omega}$$

P27.33 $R = R_0[1+\alpha T]$

$$R - R_0 = R_0\alpha\Delta T$$

$$\frac{R-R_0}{R_0} = \alpha\Delta T = \left(5.00\times10^{-3}\right)25.0 = \boxed{0.125}$$

P27.34 Assuming linear change of resistance with temperature, $R = R_0(1+\alpha\Delta T)$

$$R_{77\text{ K}} = (1.00\ \Omega)\left[1+\left(3.92\times10^{-3}\right)(-216°\text{C})\right] = \boxed{0.153\ \Omega}.$$

P27.35 $\rho = \rho_0(1+\alpha\Delta T)$ or $\Delta T_W = \dfrac{1}{\alpha_W}\left(\dfrac{\rho_W}{\rho_{0W}}-1\right)$

Require that $\rho_W = 4\rho_{0_{Cu}}$ so that $\Delta T_W = \left(\dfrac{1}{4.50\times10^{-3}/°\text{C}}\right)\left(\dfrac{4\left(1.70\times10^{-8}\right)}{5.60\times10^{-8}}-1\right) = 47.6°\text{C}$.

Therefore, $T_W = 47.6°\text{C} + T_0 = \boxed{67.6°\text{C}}$.

Section 27.5 **Superconductors**

Problem 48 in Chapter 43 can be assigned with this section.

Section 27.6 **Electric Power**

P27.36 $I = \dfrac{\mathcal{P}}{\Delta V} = \dfrac{600\text{ W}}{120\text{ V}} = \boxed{5.00\text{ A}}$

and $R = \dfrac{\Delta V}{I} = \dfrac{120\text{ V}}{5.00\text{ A}} = \boxed{24.0\ \Omega}$.

***P27.37** $\mathcal{P} = I\Delta V = 500\times10^{-6}\text{ A}\left(15\times10^{3}\text{ V}\right) = \boxed{7.50\text{ W}}$

P27.38 $\mathcal{P} = 0.800(1\,500\text{ hp})(746\text{ W/hp}) = 8.95\times10^{5}\text{ W}$

$\mathcal{P} = I\Delta V$ $\quad 8.95\times10^{5} = I(2\,000)$ $\quad I = \boxed{448\text{ A}}$

P27.39 The heat that must be added to the water is

$Q = mc\Delta T = (1.50\text{ kg})(4\,186\text{ J/kg°C})(40.0°\text{C}) = 2.51\times10^{5}\text{ J}$.

Thus, the power supplied by the heater is

$$\mathcal{P} = \frac{W}{\Delta t} = \frac{Q}{\Delta t} = \frac{2.51\times10^{5}\text{ J}}{600\text{ s}} = 419\text{ W}$$

and the resistance is $R = \dfrac{(\Delta V)^2}{\mathcal{P}} = \dfrac{(110\text{ V})^2}{419\text{ W}} = \boxed{28.9\ \Omega}$.

***P27.40** The battery takes in energy by electric transmission

$$\mathcal{P}\Delta t = (\Delta V)I(\Delta t) = 2.3 \text{ J/C}\left(13.5\times10^{-3}\text{ C/s}\right)4.2\text{ h}\left(\frac{3\,600\text{ s}}{1\text{ h}}\right) = 469\text{ J}.$$

It puts out energy by electric transmission

$$(\Delta V)I(\Delta t) = 1.6\text{ J/C}\left(18\times10^{-3}\text{ C/s}\right)2.4\text{ h}\left(\frac{3\,600\text{ s}}{1\text{ h}}\right) = 249\text{ J}.$$

(a) $\text{efficiency} = \dfrac{\text{useful output}}{\text{total input}} = \dfrac{249\text{ J}}{469\text{ J}} = \boxed{0.530}$

(b) The only place for the missing energy to go is into internal energy:

$469\text{ J} = 249\text{ J} + \Delta E_{\text{int}}$

$\Delta E_{\text{int}} = \boxed{221\text{ J}}$

(c) We imagine toasting the battery over a fire with 221 J of heat input:

$Q = mc\Delta T$

$\Delta T = \dfrac{Q}{mc} = \dfrac{221\text{ J}}{0.015\text{ kg}}\dfrac{\text{kg}^\circ\text{C}}{975\text{ J}} = \boxed{15.1^\circ\text{C}}$

P27.41 $\dfrac{\mathcal{P}}{\mathcal{P}_0} = \dfrac{(\Delta V)^2/R}{(\Delta V_0)^2/R} = \left(\dfrac{\Delta V}{\Delta V_0}\right)^2 = \left(\dfrac{140}{120}\right)^2 = 1.361$

$$\Delta\% = \left(\frac{\mathcal{P}-\mathcal{P}_0}{\mathcal{P}_0}\right)(100\%) = \left(\frac{\mathcal{P}}{\mathcal{P}_0}-1\right)(100\%) = (1.361-1)100\% = \boxed{36.1\%}$$

P27.42 $\mathcal{P} = I(\Delta V) = \dfrac{(\Delta V)^2}{R} = 500\text{ W}$

$R = \dfrac{(110\text{ V})^2}{(500\text{ W})} = 24.2\ \Omega$

(a) $R = \dfrac{\rho}{A}\ell$ so $\ell = \dfrac{RA}{\rho} = \dfrac{(24.2\ \Omega)\pi\left(2.50\times10^{-4}\text{ m}\right)^2}{1.50\times10^{-6}\ \Omega\cdot\text{m}} = \boxed{3.17\text{ m}}$

(b) $R = R_0[1+\alpha\Delta T] = 24.2\ \Omega\left[1+\left(0.400\times10^{-3}\right)(1\,180)\right] = 35.6\ \Omega$

$\mathcal{P} = \dfrac{(\Delta V)^2}{R} = \dfrac{(110)^2}{35.6} = \boxed{340\text{ W}}$

P27.43 $R=\frac{\rho\ell}{A}=\frac{\left(1.50\times10^{-6}\ \Omega\cdot\text{m}\right)25.0\text{ m}}{\pi\left(0.200\times10^{-3}\text{ m}\right)^2}=298\ \Omega$

$\Delta V=IR=(0.500\text{ A})(298\ \Omega)=149\text{ V}$

(a) $E=\frac{\Delta V}{\ell}=\frac{149\text{ V}}{25.0\text{ m}}=\boxed{5.97\text{ V/m}}$

(b) $\mathcal{P}=(\Delta V)I=(149\text{ V})(0.500\text{ A})=\boxed{74.6\text{ W}}$

(c) $R=R_0\left[1+\alpha(T-T_0)\right]=298\ \Omega\left[1+\left(0.400\times10^{-3}/^\circ\text{C}\right)320^\circ\text{C}\right]=337\ \Omega$

$I=\frac{\Delta V}{R}=\frac{(149\text{ V})}{(337\ \Omega)}=0.443\text{ A}$

$\mathcal{P}=(\Delta V)I=(149\text{ V})(0.443\text{ A})=\boxed{66.1\text{ W}}$

P27.44 (a) $\Delta U=q(\Delta V)=It(\Delta V)=(55.0\text{ A}\cdot\text{h})(12.0\text{ V})\left(\frac{1\text{ C}}{1\text{ A}\cdot\text{s}}\right)\left(\frac{1\text{ J}}{1\text{ V}\cdot\text{C}}\right)\left(\frac{1\text{ W}\cdot\text{s}}{1\text{ J}}\right)=660\text{ W}\cdot\text{h}=\boxed{0.660\text{ kWh}}$

(b) $\text{Cost }=0.660\text{ kWh}\left(\frac{\$0.060\,0}{1\text{ kWh}}\right)=\boxed{3.96¢}$

P27.45 $\mathcal{P}=I(\Delta V)\qquad \Delta V=IR$

$\mathcal{P}=\frac{(\Delta V)^2}{R}=\frac{(10.0)^2}{120}=\boxed{0.833\text{ W}}$

***P27.46** (a) The resistance of 1 m of 12-gauge copper wire is

$R=\frac{\rho\ell}{A}=\frac{\rho\ell}{\pi(d/2)^2}=\frac{4\rho\ell}{\pi d^2}=\frac{4\left(1.7\times10^{-8}\ \Omega\cdot\text{m}\right)1\text{ m}}{\pi\left(0.205\,3\times10^{-2}\text{ m}\right)^2}=5.14\times10^{-3}\ \Omega.$

The rate of internal energy production is $\mathcal{P}=I\Delta V=I^2R=(20\text{ A})^2 5.14\times10^{-3}\ \Omega=\boxed{2.05\text{ W}}$.

(b) $\mathcal{P}_{\text{Al}}=I^2R=\frac{I^2 4\rho_{\text{Al}}\ell}{\pi d^2}$

$\frac{\mathcal{P}_{\text{Al}}}{\mathcal{P}_{\text{Cu}}}=\frac{\rho_{\text{Al}}}{\rho_{\text{Cu}}}\qquad \mathcal{P}_{\text{Al}}=\frac{2.82\times10^{-8}\ \Omega\cdot\text{m}}{1.7\times10^{-8}\ \Omega\cdot\text{m}}2.05\text{ W}=\boxed{3.41\text{ W}}$

Aluminum of the same diameter will get hotter than copper.

***P27.47** The energy taken in by electric transmission for the fluorescent lamp is

$$\mathcal{P}\Delta t = 11 \text{ J/s}(100 \text{ h})\left(\frac{3\,600 \text{ s}}{1 \text{ h}}\right) = 3.96 \times 10^6 \text{ J}$$

$$\text{cost} = 3.96 \times 10^6 \text{ J}\left(\frac{\$0.08}{\text{kWh}}\right)\left(\frac{\text{k}}{1\,000}\right)\left(\frac{\text{W}\cdot\text{s}}{\text{J}}\right)\left(\frac{\text{h}}{3\,600 \text{ s}}\right) = \$0.088$$

For the incandescent bulb,

$$\mathcal{P}\Delta t = 40 \text{ W}(100 \text{ h})\left(\frac{3\,600 \text{ s}}{1 \text{ h}}\right) = 1.44 \times 10^7 \text{ J}$$

$$\text{cost} = 1.44 \times 10^7 \text{ J}\left(\frac{\$0.08}{3.6 \times 10^6 \text{ J}}\right) = \$0.32$$

$$\text{saving} = \$0.32 - \$0.088 = \boxed{\$0.232}$$

P27.48 The total clock power is

$$\left(270 \times 10^6 \text{ clocks}\right)\left(2.50 \ \frac{\text{J/s}}{\text{clock}}\right)\left(\frac{3\,600 \text{ s}}{1 \text{ h}}\right) = 2.43 \times 10^{12} \text{ J/h}.$$

From $e = \frac{W_{out}}{Q_{in}}$, the power input to the generating plants must be:

$$\frac{Q_{in}}{\Delta t} = \frac{W_{out}/\Delta t}{e} = \frac{2.43 \times 10^{12} \text{ J/h}}{0.250} = 9.72 \times 10^{12} \text{ J/h}$$

and the rate of coal consumption is

$$\text{Rate} = \left(9.72 \times 10^{12} \text{ J/h}\right)\left(\frac{1.00 \text{ kg coal}}{33.0 \times 10^6 \text{ J}}\right) = 2.95 \times 10^5 \text{ kg coal/h} = \boxed{295 \text{ metric ton/h}}.$$

P27.49 $\mathcal{P} = I(\Delta V) = (1.70 \text{ A})(110 \text{ V}) = 187 \text{ W}$

Energy used in a 24-hour day $= (0.187 \text{ kW})(24.0 \text{ h}) = 4.49 \text{ kWh}$

$$\therefore \text{cost} = 4.49 \text{ kWh}\left(\frac{\$0.060\,0}{\text{kWh}}\right) = \$0.269 = \boxed{26.9¢}$$

P27.50 $\mathcal{P} = I\Delta V = (2.00 \text{ A})(120 \text{ V}) = 240 \text{ W}$

$\Delta E_{int} = (0.500 \text{ kg})(4\,186 \text{ J/kg}\cdot°\text{C})(77.0°\text{C}) = 161 \text{ kJ}$

$$\Delta t = \frac{\Delta E_{int}}{\mathcal{P}} = \frac{1.61 \times 10^5 \text{ J}}{240 \text{ W}} = \boxed{672 \text{ s}}$$

P27.51 At operating temperature,

(a) $\mathcal{P} = I\Delta V = (1.53\text{ A})(120\text{ V}) = \boxed{184\text{ W}}$

(b) Use the change in resistance to find the final operating temperature of the toaster.

$$R = R_0(1+\alpha\Delta T) \qquad \frac{120}{1.53} = \frac{120}{1.80}\left[1+\left(0.400\times10^{-3}\right)\Delta T\right]$$

$$\Delta T = 441°\text{C} \qquad T = 20.0°\text{C} + 441°\text{C} = \boxed{461°\text{C}}$$

***P27.52** You pay the electric company for energy transferred in the amount $E = \mathcal{P}\Delta t$

(a) $$\mathcal{P}\Delta t = 40\text{ W}(2\text{ weeks})\left(\frac{7\text{ d}}{1\text{ week}}\right)\left(\frac{86\,400\text{ s}}{1\text{ d}}\right)\left(\frac{1\text{ J}}{1\text{ W}\cdot\text{s}}\right) = 48.4\text{ MJ}$$

$$\mathcal{P}\Delta t = 40\text{ W}(2\text{ weeks})\left(\frac{7\text{ d}}{1\text{ week}}\right)\left(\frac{24\text{ h}}{1\text{ d}}\right)\left(\frac{\text{k}}{1\,000}\right) = 13.4\text{ kWh}$$

$$\mathcal{P}\Delta t = 40\text{ W}(2\text{ weeks})\left(\frac{7\text{ d}}{1\text{ week}}\right)\left(\frac{24\text{ h}}{1\text{ d}}\right)\left(\frac{\text{k}}{1\,000}\right)\left(\frac{0.12\text{ \$}}{\text{kWh}}\right) = \boxed{\$1.61}$$

(b) $$\mathcal{P}\Delta t = 970\text{ W}(3\text{ min})\left(\frac{1\text{ h}}{60\text{ min}}\right)\left(\frac{\text{k}}{1\,000}\right)\left(\frac{0.12\text{ \$}}{\text{kWh}}\right) = \boxed{\$0.005\,82} = 0.582¢$$

(c) $$\mathcal{P}\Delta t = 5\,200\text{ W}(40\text{ min})\left(\frac{1\text{ h}}{60\text{ min}}\right)\left(\frac{\text{k}}{1\,000}\right)\left(\frac{0.12\text{ \$}}{\text{kWh}}\right) = \boxed{\$0.416}$$

P27.53 Consider a 400-W blow dryer used for ten minutes daily for a year. The energy transferred to the dryer is

$$\mathcal{P}\Delta t = (400\text{ J/s})(600\text{ s/d})(365\text{ d}) \approx 9\times10^7\text{ J}\left(\frac{1\text{ kWh}}{3.6\times10^6\text{ J}}\right) \approx 20\text{ kWh}.$$

We suppose that electrically transmitted energy costs on the order of ten cents per kilowatt-hour. Then the cost of using the dryer for a year is on the order of

$$\text{Cost} \cong (20\text{ kWh})(\$0.10/\text{kWh}) = \$2 \boxed{\sim\$1}.$$

Additional Problems

P27.54 (a) $I=\frac{\Delta V}{R}$ so $\mathcal{P}=I\Delta V=\frac{(\Delta V)^2}{R}$

$R=\frac{(\Delta V)^2}{\mathcal{P}}=\frac{(120\text{ V})^2}{25.0\text{ W}}=\boxed{576\ \Omega}$ and $R=\frac{(\Delta V)^2}{\mathcal{P}}=\frac{(120\text{ V})^2}{100\text{ W}}=\boxed{144\ \Omega}$

(b) $I=\frac{\mathcal{P}}{\Delta V}=\frac{25.0\text{ W}}{120\text{ V}}=0.208\text{ A}=\frac{Q}{\Delta t}=\frac{1.00\text{ C}}{\Delta t}$

$\Delta t=\frac{1.00\text{ C}}{0.208\text{ A}}=\boxed{4.80\text{ s}}$

The bulb takes in charge at high potential and puts out the same amount of charge at low potential.

(c) $\mathcal{P}=25.0\text{ W}=\frac{\Delta U}{\Delta t}=\frac{1.00\text{ J}}{\Delta t}$ $\Delta t=\frac{1.00\text{ J}}{25.0\text{ W}}=\boxed{0.040\,0\text{ s}}$

The bulb takes in energy by electrical transmission and puts out the same amount of energy by heat and light.

(d) $\Delta U=\mathcal{P}\Delta t=(25.0\text{ J/s})(86\,400\text{ s/d})(30.0\text{ d})=64.8\times10^{8}\text{ J}$

The electric company sells $\boxed{\text{energy}}$.

$\text{Cost}=64.8\times10^{6}\text{ J}\left(\frac{\$0.070\,0}{\text{kWh}}\right)\left(\frac{\text{k}}{1\,000}\right)\left(\frac{\text{W}\cdot\text{s}}{\text{J}}\right)\left(\frac{\text{h}}{3\,600\text{ s}}\right)=\boxed{\$1.26}$

$\text{Cost per joule}=\frac{\$0.070\,0}{\text{kWh}}\left(\frac{\text{kWh}}{3.60\times10^{6}\text{ J}}\right)=\boxed{\$1.94\times10^{-8}/\text{J}}$

***P27.55** The original stored energy is $U_i=\frac{1}{2}Q\Delta V_i=\frac{1}{2}\frac{Q^2}{C}$.

(a) When the switch is closed, charge Q distributes itself over the plates of C and 3C in parallel, presenting equivalent capacitance 4C. Then the final potential difference is $\boxed{\Delta V_f=\frac{Q}{4C}}$ for both.

(b) The smaller capacitor then carries charge $C\Delta V_f=\frac{Q}{4C}C=\boxed{\frac{Q}{4}}$. The larger capacitor carries charge $3C\frac{Q}{4C}=\boxed{\frac{3Q}{4}}$.

(c) The smaller capacitor stores final energy $\frac{1}{2}C(\Delta V_f)^2=\frac{1}{2}C\left(\frac{Q}{4C}\right)^2=\boxed{\frac{Q^2}{32C}}$. The larger capacitor possesses energy $\frac{1}{2}3C\left(\frac{Q}{4C}\right)^2=\boxed{\frac{3Q^2}{32C}}$.

(d) The total final energy is $\frac{Q^2}{32C}+\frac{3Q^2}{32C}=\frac{Q^2}{8C}$. The loss of potential energy is the energy appearing as internal energy in the resistor: $\frac{Q^2}{2C}=\frac{Q^2}{8C}+\Delta E_{\text{int}}$ $\Delta E_{\text{int}}=\boxed{\frac{3Q^2}{8C}}$.

P27.56 We find the drift velocity from $I = nqv_dA = nqv_d\pi r^2$

$$v_d = \frac{I}{nq\pi r^2} = \frac{1\,000\text{ A}}{8.49\times10^{28}\text{ m}^{-3}\left(1.60\times10^{-19}\text{ C}\right)\pi\left(10^{-2}\text{ m}\right)^2} = 2.34\times10^{-4}\text{ m/s}$$

$$v = \frac{x}{t} \qquad t = \frac{x}{v} = \frac{200\times10^3\text{ m}}{2.34\times10^{-4}\text{ m/s}} = 8.54\times10^8\text{ s} = \boxed{27.0\text{ yr}}$$

P27.57 We begin with the differential equation $\alpha = \frac{1}{\rho}\frac{d\rho}{dT}$.

(a) Separating variables, $\int_{\rho_0}^{\rho}\frac{d\rho}{\rho} = \int_{T_0}^{T}\alpha dT$

$\ln\left(\frac{\rho}{\rho_0}\right) = \alpha(T-T_0)$ and $\boxed{\rho = \rho_0 e^{\alpha(T-T_0)}}$.

(b) From the series expansion $e^x \cong 1+x$, $(x<<1)$,

$\boxed{\rho \cong \rho_0\left[1+\alpha(T-T_0)\right]}$.

P27.58 The resistance of one wire is $\left(\frac{0.500\ \Omega}{\text{mi}}\right)(100\text{ mi}) = 50.0\ \Omega$.

The whole wire is at nominal 700 kV away from ground potential, but the potential difference between its two ends is

$IR = (1\,000\text{ A})(50.0\ \Omega) = 50.0\text{ kV}$.

Then it radiates as heat power $\mathcal{P} = (\Delta V)I = \left(50.0\times10^3\text{ V}\right)(1\,000\text{ A}) = \boxed{50.0\text{ MW}}$.

P27.59 $\rho = \frac{RA}{\ell} = \frac{(\Delta V)}{I}\frac{A}{\ell}$

ℓ (m)	R (Ω)	ρ ($\Omega\cdot$m)
0.540	10.4	1.41×10^{-6}
1.028	21.1	1.50×10^{-6}
1.543	31.8	1.50×10^{-6}

$\bar{\rho} = \boxed{1.47\times10^{-6}\ \Omega\cdot\text{m}}$ (in agreement with tabulated value of $1.50\times10^{-6}\ \Omega\cdot\text{m}$ in Table 27.1)

P27.60 2 wires $\rightarrow \ell = 100$ m

$$R = \frac{0.108\ \Omega}{300\text{ m}}(100\text{ m}) = 0.036\,0\ \Omega$$

(a) $(\Delta V)_{\text{home}} = (\Delta V)_{\text{line}} - IR = 120 - (110)(0.036\,0) = \boxed{116\text{ V}}$

(b) $\mathcal{P} = I(\Delta V) = (110\text{ A})(116\text{ V}) = \boxed{12.8\text{ kW}}$

(c) $\mathcal{P}_{\text{wires}} = I^2R = (110\text{ A})^2(0.036\,0\ \Omega) = \boxed{436\text{ W}}$

P27.61 (a) $$\mathbf{E}=-\frac{dV}{dx}\hat{\mathbf{i}}=-\frac{(0-4.00)\text{ V}}{(0.500-0)\text{ m}}=\boxed{8.00\hat{\mathbf{i}}\text{ V/m}}$$

(b) $$R=\frac{\rho\ell}{A}=\frac{\left(4.00\times10^{-8}\ \Omega\cdot\text{m}\right)(0.500\text{ m})}{\pi\left(1.00\times10^{-4}\text{ m}\right)^2}=\boxed{0.637\ \Omega}$$

(c) $$I=\frac{\Delta V}{R}=\frac{4.00\text{ V}}{0.637\ \Omega}=\boxed{6.28\text{ A}}$$

(d) $$\mathbf{J}=\frac{I}{A}\hat{\mathbf{i}}=\frac{6.28\text{ A}}{\pi\left(1.00\times10^{-4}\text{ m}\right)^2}=2.00\times10^8\hat{\mathbf{i}}\text{ A/m}^2=\boxed{200\hat{\mathbf{i}}\text{ MA/m}^2}$$

(e) $$\rho\mathbf{J}=\left(4.00\times10^{-8}\ \Omega\cdot\text{m}\right)\left(2.00\times10^8\hat{\mathbf{i}}\text{ A/m}^2\right)=8.00\hat{\mathbf{i}}\text{ V/m}=\mathbf{E}$$

P27.62 (a) $$\mathbf{E}=-\frac{dV(x)}{dx}\hat{\mathbf{i}}=\boxed{\frac{V}{L}\hat{\mathbf{i}}}$$

(b) $$R=\frac{\rho\ell}{A}=\boxed{\frac{4\rho L}{\pi d^2}}$$

(c) $$I=\frac{\Delta V}{R}=\boxed{\frac{V\pi d^2}{4\rho L}}$$

(d) $$\mathbf{J}=\frac{I}{A}\hat{\mathbf{i}}=\boxed{\frac{V}{\rho L}\hat{\mathbf{i}}}$$

(e) $$\rho\mathbf{J}=\frac{V}{L}\hat{\mathbf{i}}=\boxed{\mathbf{E}}$$

P27.63 $R=R_0\left[1+\alpha(T-T_0)\right]$ so $T=T_0+\frac{1}{\alpha}\left[\frac{R}{R_0}-1\right]=T_0+\frac{1}{\alpha}\left[\frac{I_0}{I}-1\right]$.

In this case, $I=\frac{I_0}{10}$, so $T=T_0+\frac{1}{\alpha}(9)=20°+\frac{9}{0.004\,50/°\text{C}}=\boxed{2\,020°\text{C}}$.

P27.64 $R=\frac{\Delta V}{I}=\frac{12.0}{I}=\frac{6.00}{(I-3.00)}$ thus $12.0I-36.0=6.00I$ and $I=6.00\text{ A}$.

Therefore, $R=\frac{12.0\text{ V}}{6.00\text{ A}}=\boxed{2.00\ \Omega}$.

P27.65 (a) $\mathcal{P} = I\Delta V$

so $I = \dfrac{\mathcal{P}}{\Delta V} = \dfrac{8.00 \times 10^3 \text{ W}}{12.0 \text{ V}} = \boxed{667 \text{ A}}$.

(b) $\Delta t = \dfrac{\Delta U}{\mathcal{P}} = \dfrac{2.00 \times 10^7 \text{ J}}{8.00 \times 10^3 \text{ W}} = 2.50 \times 10^3 \text{ s}$

and $\Delta x = v\Delta t = (20.0 \text{ m/s})(2.50 \times 10^3 \text{ s}) = \boxed{50.0 \text{ km}}$.

P27.66 (a) We begin with $R = \dfrac{\rho \ell}{A} = \dfrac{\rho_0[1+\alpha(T-T_0)]\ell_0[1+\alpha'(T-T_0)]}{A_0[1+2\alpha'(T-T_0)]}$,

which reduces to $R = \boxed{\dfrac{R_0[1+\alpha(T-T_0)][1+\alpha'(T-T_0)]}{[1+2\alpha'(T-T_0)]}}$.

(b) For copper: $\rho_0 = 1.70 \times 10^{-8}\ \Omega\cdot\text{m}$, $\alpha = 3.90 \times 10^{-3}\ {}^\circ\text{C}^{-1}$, and $\alpha' = 17.0 \times 10^{-6}\ {}^\circ\text{C}^{-1}$

$$R_0 = \frac{\rho_0 \ell_0}{A_0} = \frac{(1.70 \times 10^{-8})(2.00)}{\pi(0.100 \times 10^{-3})^2} = \boxed{1.08\ \Omega}.$$

The simple formula for R gives:

$$R = (1.08\ \Omega)\left[1+(3.90 \times 10^{-3}\ {}^\circ\text{C}^{-1})(100^\circ\text{C} - 20.0^\circ\text{C})\right] = \boxed{1.420\ \Omega}$$

while the more complicated formula gives:

$$R = \frac{(1.08\ \Omega)\left[1+(3.90 \times 10^{-3}\ {}^\circ\text{C}^{-1})(80.0^\circ\text{C})\right]\left[1+(17.0 \times 10^{-6}\ {}^\circ\text{C}^{-1})(80.0^\circ\text{C})\right]}{\left[1+2(17.0 \times 10^{-6}\ {}^\circ\text{C}^{-1})(80.0^\circ\text{C})\right]} = \boxed{1.418\ \Omega}.$$

P27.67 Let α be the temperature coefficient at 20.0°C, and α' be the temperature coefficient at 0 °C. Then $\rho = \rho_0[1+\alpha(T-20.0^\circ\text{C})]$, and $\rho = \rho'[1+\alpha'(T-0^\circ\text{C})]$ must both give the correct resistivity at any temperature T. That is, we must have:

$$\rho_0[1+\alpha(T-20.0^\circ\text{C})] = \rho'[1+\alpha'(T-0^\circ\text{C})]. \quad (1)$$

Setting $T = 0$ in equation (1) yields: $\rho' = \rho_0[1-\alpha(20.0^\circ\text{C})]$,

and setting $T = 20.0^\circ\text{C}$ in equation (1) gives: $\rho_0 = \rho'[1+\alpha'(20.0^\circ\text{C})]$.

Put ρ' from the first of these results into the second to obtain:

$$\rho_0 = \rho_0[1-\alpha(20.0^\circ\text{C})][1+\alpha'(20.0^\circ\text{C})].$$

continued on next page

Therefore $$1+\alpha'(20.0°\text{C})=\frac{1}{1-\alpha(20.0°\text{C})}$$

which simplifies to $$\alpha'=\frac{\alpha}{\left[1-\alpha(20.0°\text{C})\right]}.$$

From this, the temperature coefficient, based on a reference temperature of 0°C, may be computed for any material. For example, using this, $\boxed{\text{Table 27.1 becomes at 0°C}}$:

Material	Temp Coefficients at 0°C
Silver	$4.1\times10^{-3}/°\text{C}$
Copper	$4.2\times10^{-3}/°\text{C}$
Gold	$3.6\times10^{-3}/°\text{C}$
Aluminum	$4.2\times10^{-3}/°\text{C}$
Tungsten	$4.9\times10^{-3}/°\text{C}$
Iron	$5.6\times10^{-3}/°\text{C}$
Platinum	$4.25\times10^{-3}/°\text{C}$
Lead	$4.2\times10^{-3}/°\text{C}$
Nichrome	$0.4\times10^{-3}/°\text{C}$
Carbon	$-0.5\times10^{-3}/°\text{C}$
Germanium	$-24\times10^{-3}/°\text{C}$
Silicon	$-30\times10^{-3}/°\text{C}$

P27.68 (a) A thin cylindrical shell of radius r, thickness dr, and length L contributes resistance

$$dR=\frac{\rho d\ell}{A}=\frac{\rho dr}{(2\pi r)L}=\left(\frac{\rho}{2\pi L}\right)\frac{dr}{r}.$$

The resistance of the whole annulus is the series summation of the contributions of the thin shells:

$$R=\frac{\rho}{2\pi L}\int_{r_a}^{r_b}\frac{dr}{r}=\boxed{\frac{\rho}{2\pi L}\ln\left(\frac{r_b}{r_a}\right)}.$$

(b) In this equation $$\frac{\Delta V}{I}=\frac{\rho}{2\pi L}\ln\left(\frac{r_b}{r_a}\right)$$

we solve for $$\boxed{\rho=\frac{2\pi L\Delta V}{I\ln(r_b/r_a)}}.$$

P27.69 Each speaker receives 60.0 W of power. Using $\mathscr{P} = I^2 R$, we then have

$$I = \sqrt{\frac{\mathscr{P}}{R}} = \sqrt{\frac{60.0\text{ W}}{4.00\ \Omega}} = 3.87\text{ A}.$$

The system is $\boxed{\text{not adequately protected}}$ since the $\boxed{\text{fuse should be set to melt at 3.87 A, or less}}$.

P27.70 $\Delta V = -E \cdot \ell$ or $dV = -E \cdot dx$

$\Delta V = -IR = -E \cdot \ell$

$$I = \frac{dq}{dt} = \frac{E \cdot \ell}{R} = \frac{A}{\rho \ell} E \cdot \ell = \frac{A}{\rho} E = -\sigma A \frac{dV}{dx} = \boxed{\sigma A \left| \frac{dV}{dx} \right|}$$

Current flows in the direction of decreasing voltage. Energy flows as heat in the direction of decreasing temperature.

P27.71 $R = \int \frac{\rho dx}{A} = \int \frac{\rho dx}{wy}$ where $y = y_1 + \frac{y_2 - y_1}{L} x$

$$R = \frac{\rho}{w} \int_0^L \frac{dx}{y_1 + \left[(y_2 - y_1)/L\right] x} = \frac{\rho L}{w(y_2 - y_1)} \ln\left[y_1 + \frac{y_2 - y_1}{L} x \right]_0^L$$

$$R = \boxed{\frac{\rho L}{w(y_2 - y_1)} \ln\left(\frac{y_2}{y_1}\right)}$$

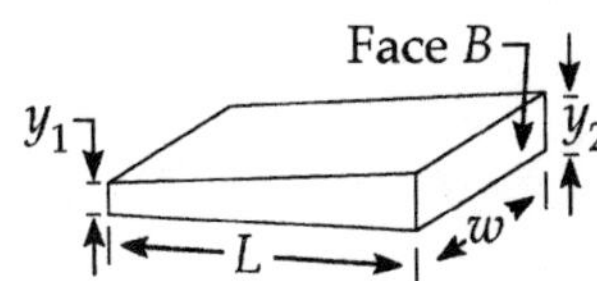

FIG. P27.71

P27.72 From the geometry of the longitudinal section of the resistor shown in the figure, we see that

$$\frac{(b-r)}{y} = \frac{(b-a)}{h}.$$

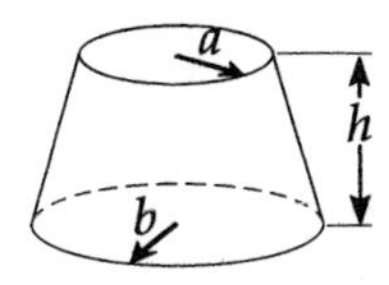

FIG. P27.72

From this, the radius at a distance y from the base is $r = (a-b)\frac{y}{h} + b$.

For a disk-shaped element of volume $dR = \frac{\rho dy}{\pi r^2}$: $R = \frac{\rho}{\pi} \int_0^h \frac{dy}{\left[(a-b)(y/h) + b\right]^2}$.

Using the integral formula $\int \frac{du}{(au+b)^2} = -\frac{1}{a(au+b)}$, $\boxed{R = \frac{\rho}{\pi} \frac{h}{ab}}$.

***P27.73** (a) The resistance of the dielectric block is $R = \frac{\rho \ell}{A} = \frac{d}{\sigma A}$.

The capacitance of the capacitor is $C = \frac{\kappa \epsilon_0 A}{d}$.

Then $RC = \frac{d}{\sigma A} \frac{\kappa \epsilon_0 A}{d} = \frac{\kappa \epsilon_0}{\sigma}$ is a characteristic of the material only.

(b) $$R = \frac{\kappa \epsilon_0}{\sigma C} = \frac{\rho \kappa \epsilon_0}{C} = \frac{75 \times 10^{16}\ \Omega \cdot \text{m}(3.78) 8.85 \times 10^{-12}\ \text{C}^2}{14 \times 10^{-9}\ \text{F}\ \ \text{N} \cdot \text{m}^2} = \boxed{1.79 \times 10^{15}\ \Omega}$$

P27.74 $I = I_0\left[\exp\left(\frac{e\Delta V}{k_BT}\right) - 1\right]$ and $R = \frac{\Delta V}{I}$

with $I_0 = 1.00 \times 10^{-9}$ A, $e = 1.60 \times 10^{-19}$ C, and $k_B = 1.38 \times 10^{-23}$ J/K.

The following includes a partial table of calculated values and a graph for each of the specified temperatures.

(i) For $T = 280$ K:

ΔV(V)	I(A)	$R(\Omega)$
0.400	0.015 6	25.6
0.440	0.081 8	5.38
0.480	0.429	1.12
0.520	2.25	0.232
0.560	11.8	0.047 6
0.600	61.6	0.009 7

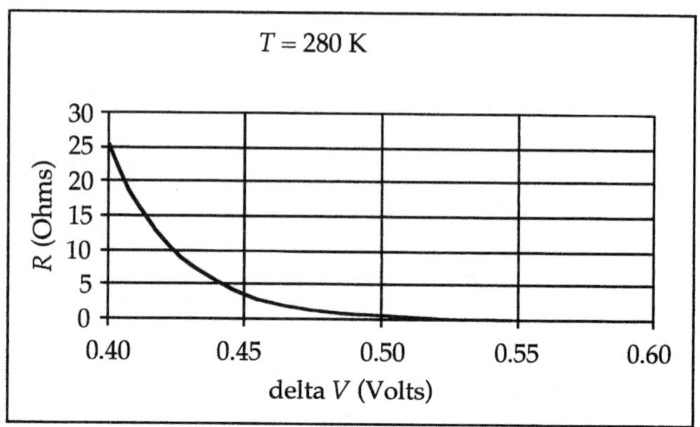

FIG. P27.74(i)

(ii) For $T = 300$ K:

ΔV(V)	I(A)	$R(\Omega)$
0.400	0.005	77.3
0.440	0.024	18.1
0.480	0.114	4.22
0.520	0.534	0.973
0.560	2.51	0.223
0.600	11.8	0.051

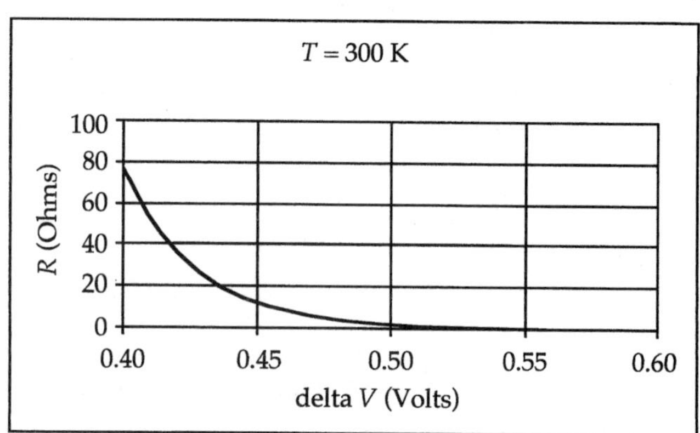

FIG. P27.74(ii)

(iii) For $T = 320$ K:

ΔV(V)	I(A)	$R(\Omega)$
0.400	0.002 0	203
0.440	0.008 4	52.5
0.480	0.035 7	13.4
0.520	0.152	3.42
0.560	0.648	0.864
0.600	2.76	0.217

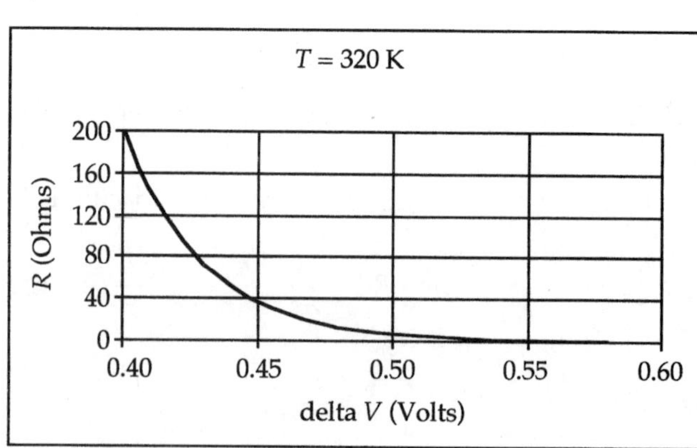

FIG. P27.74(iii)

***P27.75** (a) Think of the device as two capacitors in parallel. The one on the left has $\kappa_1 = 1$, $A_1 = \left(\frac{\ell}{2}+x\right)\ell$. The equivalent capacitance is

$$\frac{\kappa_1 \in_0 A_1}{d}+\frac{\kappa_2 \in_0 A_2}{d}=\frac{\in_0 \ell}{d}\left(\frac{\ell}{2}+x\right)+\frac{\kappa \in_0 \ell}{d}\left(\frac{\ell}{2}-x\right)=\boxed{\frac{\in_0 \ell}{2d}(\ell+2x+\kappa\ell-2\kappa x)}.$$

(b) The charge on the capacitor is $Q = C\Delta V$

$$Q=\frac{\in_0 \ell\Delta V}{2d}(\ell+2x+\kappa\ell-2\kappa x).$$

The current is

$$I=\frac{dQ}{dt}=\frac{dQ}{dx}\frac{dx}{dt}=\frac{\in_0 \ell\Delta V}{2d}(0+2+0-2\kappa)v=-\frac{\in_0 \ell\Delta V v}{d}(\kappa-1).$$

The negative value indicates that the current drains charge from the capacitor. Positive current is $\boxed{\text{clockwise } \frac{\in_0 \ell\Delta V v}{d}(\kappa-1)}$.

ANSWERS TO EVEN PROBLEMS

P27.2 3.64 h

P27.4 (a) see the solution; (b) 1.05 mA

P27.6 (a) 17.0 A; (b) 85.0 kA/m^2

P27.8 (a) 99.5 kA/m^2; (b) 8.00 mm

P27.10 (a) 221 nm; (b) no; see the solution

P27.12 30.3 MA/m^2

P27.14 (a) 3.75 kΩ; (b) 536 m

P27.16 0.018 1 Ω·m

P27.18 2.71 MΩ

P27.20 (a) 777 nΩ; (b) 3.28 μm/s

P27.22 $\frac{r_{Al}}{r_{Cu}} = 1.29$

P27.24 378 Ω

P27.26 (a) nothing; (b) doubles; (c) doubles; (d) nothing

P27.28 1.98 A

P27.30 carbon, 4.44 kΩ; nichrome, 5.56 kΩ

P27.32 1.71 Ω

P27.34 0.153 Ω

P27.36 5.00 A, 24.0 Ω

P27.38 448 A

P27.40 (a) 0.530; (b) 221 J; (c) 15.1°C

P27.42 (a) 3.17 m; (b) 340 W

P27.44 (a) 0.660 kWh; (b) 3.96¢

P27.46 (a) 2.05 W; (b) 3.41 W; no

P27.48 295 metric ton/h

P27.50 672 s

P27.52 (a) \$1.61; (b) \$0.005 82; (c) \$0.416

P27.54 (a) 576 Ω and 144 Ω;
(b) 4.80 s; The charge is the same. The charge-field system is in a lower-energy configuration.
(c) 0.040 0 s; The energy enters by electric transmission and exits by heat and electromagnetic radiation;
(d) \$1.26; energy; 1.94×10^{-8} \$/J

P27.56 27.0 yr

P27.58 50.0 MW

P27.60 (a) 116 V ; (b) 12.8 kW ; (c) 436 W

P27.62 (a) $\mathbf{E}=\frac{V\hat{\mathbf{i}}}{L}$; (b) $R=\frac{4\rho L}{\pi d^2}$; (c) $I=\frac{V\pi d^2}{4\rho L}$; (d) $\mathbf{J}=\frac{V\hat{\mathbf{i}}}{\rho L}$; (e) see the solution

P27.64 2.00 Ω

P27.66 (a) see the solution;
(b) 1.418 Ω nearly agrees with 1.420 Ω

P27.68 (a) $R=\frac{\rho}{2\pi L}\ln\frac{r_b}{r_a}$; (b) $\rho=\frac{2\pi L\Delta V}{I\ln(r_b/r_a)}$

P27.70 see the solution

P27.72 see the solution

P27.74 see the solution

28

Direct Current Circuits

CHAPTER OUTLINE

ANSWERS TO QUESTIONS

Q28.1 The load resistance in a circuit is the effective resistance of all of the circuit elements excluding the emf source. In energy terms, it can be used to determine the energy delivered to the load by electrical transmission and there appearing as internal energy to raise the temperature of the resistor. The internal resistance of a battery represents the limitation on the efficiency of the chemical reaction that takes place in the battery to supply current to the load. The emf of the battery represents its conversion of chemical energy into energy which it puts out by electric transmission; the battery also creates internal energy within itself, in an amount that can be computed from its internal resistance. We model the internal resistance as constant for a given battery, but it may increase greatly as the battery ages. It may increase somewhat with increasing current demand by the load. For a load described by Ohm's law, the load resistance is a precisely fixed value.

Q28.2 The potential difference between the terminals of a battery will equal the emf of the battery when there is no current in the battery. At this time, the current though, and hence the potential drop across the internal resistance is zero. This only happens when there is no load placed on the battery—that includes measuring the potential difference with a voltmeter! The terminal voltage will exceed the emf of the battery when current is driven backward through the battery, in at its positive terminal and out at its negative terminal.

Q28.3 No. If there is one battery in a circuit, the current inside it will be from its negative terminal to its positive terminal. Whenever a battery is delivering energy to a circuit, it will carry current in this direction. On the other hand, when another source of emf is charging the battery in question, it will have a current pushed through it from its positive terminal to its negative terminal.

Q28.4 Connect the resistors in series. Resistors of 5.0 kΩ, 7.5 kΩ and 2.2 kΩ connected in series present equivalent resistance 14.7 kΩ.

Q28.5 Connect the resistors in parallel. Resistors of 5.0 kΩ, 7.5 kΩ and 2.2 kΩ connected in parallel present equivalent resistance 1.3 kΩ.

Q28.6

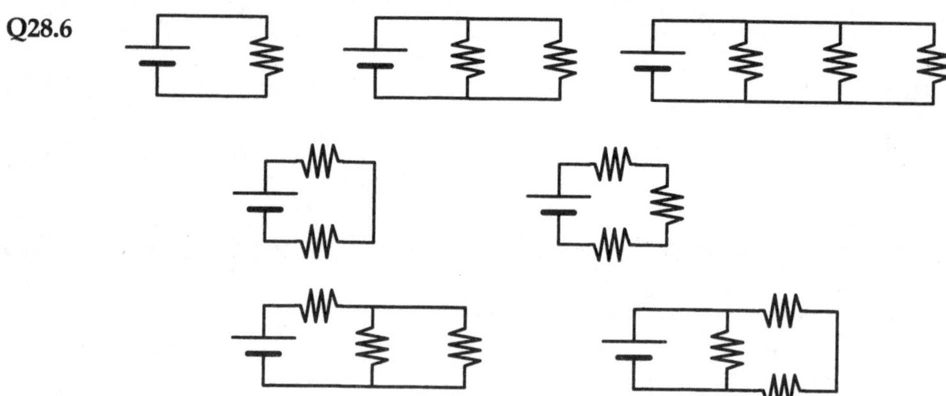

Q28.7 In series, the current is the same through each resistor. Without knowing individual resistances, nothing can be determined about potential differences or power.

Q28.8 In parallel, the potential difference is the same across each resistor. Without knowing individual resistances, nothing can be determined about current or power.

Q28.9 In this configuration, the power delivered to one individual resistor is significantly less than if only one equivalent resistor were used. This decreases the possibility of component failure, and possible electrical disaster to some more expensive circuit component than a resistor.

Q28.10 Each of the two conductors in the extension cord itself has a small resistance. The longer the extension cord, the larger the resistance. Taken into account in the circuit, the extension cord will reduce the current from the power supply, and also will absorb energy itself in the form of internal energy, leaving less power available to the light bulb.

Q28.11 The whole wire is very nearly at one uniform potential. There is essentially zero *difference* in potential between the bird's feet. Then negligible current goes through the bird. The resistance through the bird's body between its feet is much larger than the resistance through the wire between the same two points.

Q28.12 The potential difference across a resistor is positive when it is measured *against* the direction of the current in the resistor.

Q28.13 The bulb will light up for a while immediately after the switch is closed. As the capacitor charges, the bulb gets progressively dimmer. When the capacitor is fully charged the current in the circuit is zero and the bulb does not glow at all. If the value of RC is small, this whole process might occupy a very short time interval.

Q28.14 An ideal ammeter has zero resistance. An ideal voltmeter has infinite resistance. Real meters cannot attain these values, but do approach these values to the degree that they do not alter the current or potential difference that is being measured within the accuracy of the meter. Hooray for experimental uncertainty!

Q28.15 A short circuit can develop when the last bit of insulation frays away between the two conductors in a lamp cord. Then the two conductors touch each other, opening a low-resistance branch in parallel with the lamp. The lamp will immediately go out, carrying no current and presenting no danger. A very large current exists in the power supply, the house wiring, and the rest of the lamp cord up to the contact point. Before it blows the fuse or pops the circuit breaker, the large current can quickly raise the temperature in the short-circuit path.

Q28.16 A wire or cable in a transmission line is thick and made of material with very low resistivity. Only when its length is very large does its resistance become significant. To transmit power over a long distance it is most efficient to use low current at high voltage, minimizing the I^2R power loss in the transmission line. Alternating current, as opposed to the direct current we study first, can be stepped up in voltage and then down again, with high-efficiency transformers at both ends of the power line.

Q28.17 Car headlights are in parallel. If they were in series, both would go out when the filament of one failed. An important safety factor would be lost.

Q28.18 Kirchhoff's junction rule expresses conservation of electric charge. If the total current into a point were different from the total current out, then charge would be continuously created or annihilated at that point.

Kirchhoff's loop rule expresses conservation of energy. For a single-loop circle with two resistors, the loop rule reads $+\varepsilon - IR_1 - IR_2 = 0$. This is algebraically equivalent to $q\varepsilon = qIR_1 + qIR_2$, where $q = I\Delta t$ is the charge passing a point in the loop in the time interval Δt. The equivalent equation states that the power supply injects energy into the circuit equal in amount to that which the resistors degrade into internal energy.

Q28.19 At their normal operating temperatures, from $\mathcal{P} = \dfrac{\Delta V^2}{R}$, the bulbs present resistances $R = \dfrac{\Delta V^2}{\mathcal{P}} = \dfrac{(120\text{ V})^2}{60\text{ W}} = 240\ \Omega$, and $\dfrac{(120\text{ V})^2}{75\text{ W}} = 190\ \Omega$, and $\dfrac{(120\text{ V})^2}{200\text{ W}} = 72\ \Omega$. The nominal 60 W lamp has greatest resistance. When they are connected in series, they all carry the same small current. Here the highest-resistance bulb glows most brightly and the one with lowest resistance is faintest. This is just the reverse of their order of intensity if they were connected in parallel, as they are designed to be.

Q28.20 Answer their question with a challenge. If the student is just looking at a diagram, provide the materials to build the circuit. If you are looking at a circuit where the second bulb really is fainter, get the student to unscrew them both and interchange them. But check that the student's understanding of potential has not been impaired: if you patch past the first bulb to short it out, the second gets brighter.

Q28.21 Series, because the circuit breaker trips and opens the circuit when the current in that circuit loop exceeds a certain preset value. The circuit breaker must be in series to sense the appropriate current (see Fig. 28.30).

Q28.22 The hospital maintenance worker is right. A hospital room is full of electrical grounds, including the bed frame. If your grandmother touched the faulty knob and the bed frame at the same time, she could receive quite a jolt, as there would be a potential difference of 120 V across her. If the 120 V is DC, the shock could send her into ventricular fibrillation, and the hospital staff could use the defibrillator you read about in Section 26.4. If the 120 V is AC, which is most likely, the current could produce external and internal burns along the path of conduction. Likely no one got a shock from the radio back at home because her bedroom contained no electrical grounds—no conductors connected to zero volts. Just like the bird in Question 28.11, granny could touch the "hot" knob without getting a shock so long as there was no path to ground to supply a potential difference across her. A new appliance in the bedroom or a flood could make the radio lethal. Repair it or discard it. Enjoy the news from Lake Wobegon on the new plastic radio.

Q28.23 So long as you only grab one wire, and you do not touch anything that is grounded, you are safe (see Question 28.11). If the wire breaks, *let go!* If you continue to hold on to the wire, there will be a large—and rather lethal—potential difference between the wire and your feet when you hit the ground. Since your body can have a resistance of about 10 kΩ, the current in you would be sufficient to ruin your day.

Q28.24 Both 120-V and 240-V lines can deliver injurious or lethal shocks, but there is a somewhat better safety factor with the lower voltage. To say it a different way, the insulation on a 120-V line can be thinner. On the other hand, a 240-V device carries less current to operate a device with the same power, so the conductor itself can be thinner. Finally, as we will see in Chapter 33, the last step-down transformer can also be somewhat smaller if it has to go down only to 240 volts from the high voltage of the main power line.

Q28.25 As Luigi Galvani showed with his experiment with frogs' legs, muscles contract when electric current exists in them. If an electrician contacts a "live" wire, the muscles in his hands and fingers will contract, making his hand clench. If he touches the wire with the front of his hand, his hand will clench around the wire, and he may not be able to let go. Also, the back of his hand may be drier than his palm, so an actual shock may be much weaker.

Q28.26 Grab an insulator, like a stick or baseball bat, and bat for a home run. Hit the wire away from the person or hit them away from the wire. If you grab the person, you will learn very quickly about electrical circuits by becoming part of one.

Q28.27 A high voltage can lead to a high current when placed in a circuit. A device cannot supply a high current—or any current—unless connected to a load. A more accurate sign saying *potentially high current* would just confuse the poor physics student who already has problems distinguishing between electrical potential and current.

Q28.28 The two greatest factors are the potential difference between the wire and your feet, and the conductivity of the kite string. This is why Ben Franklin's experiment with lightning and flying a kite was so dangerous. Several scientists died trying to reproduce Franklin's results.

Q28.29 Suppose $\varepsilon = 12\text{ V}$ and each lamp has $R = 2\ \Omega$. Before the switch is closed the current is $\dfrac{12\text{ V}}{6\ \Omega} = 2\text{ A}$. The potential difference across each lamp is $(2\text{ A})(2\ \Omega) = 4\text{ V}$. The power of each lamp is $(2\text{ A})(4\text{ V}) = 8\text{ W}$, totaling 24 W for the circuit. Closing the switch makes the switch and the wires connected to it a zero-resistance branch. All of the current through A and B will go through the switch and (b) lamp C goes out, with zero voltage across it. With less total resistance, the (c) current in the battery $\dfrac{12\text{ V}}{4\ \Omega} = 3\text{ A}$ becomes larger than before and (a) lamps A and B get brighter. (d) The voltage across each of A and B is $(3\text{ A})(2\ \Omega) = 6\text{ V}$, larger than before. Each converts power $(3\text{ A})(6\text{ V}) = 18\text{ W}$, totaling 36 W, which is (e) an increase.

Q28.30 The starter motor draws a significant amount of current from the battery while it is starting the car. This, coupled with the internal resistance of the battery, decreases the output voltage of the battery below its the nominal 12 V emf. Then the current in the headlights decreases.

Q28.31 Two runs in series: . Three runs in parallel: 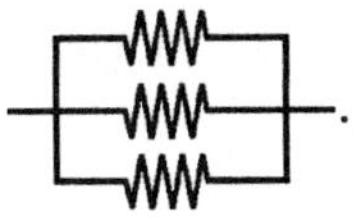. Junction of one lift and two runs: 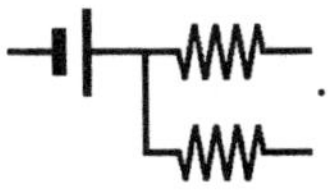.

Gustav Robert Kirchhoff, Professor of Physics at Heidelberg and Berlin, was master of the obvious. A junction rule: The number of skiers coming into any junction must be equal to the number of skiers leaving. A loop rule: the total change in altitude must be zero for any skier completing a closed path.

SOLUTIONS TO PROBLEMS

Section 28.1 Electromotive Force

P28.1 (a) $\mathcal{P} = \dfrac{(\Delta V)^2}{R}$

becomes $20.0\text{ W} = \dfrac{(11.6\text{ V})^2}{R}$

so $R = \boxed{6.73\ \Omega}$.

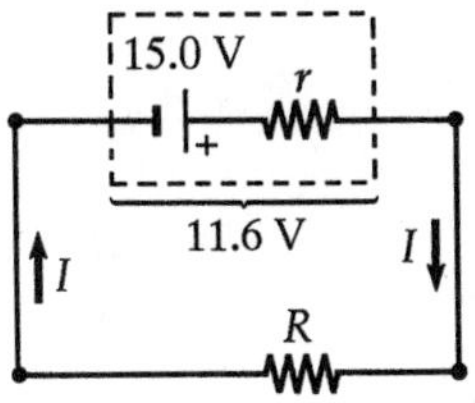

FIG. P28.1

(b) $\Delta V = IR$

so $11.6\text{ V} = I(6.73\ \Omega)$

and $I = 1.72\text{ A}$

$\varepsilon = IR + Ir$

so $15.0\text{ V} = 11.6\text{ V} + (1.72\text{ A})r$

$r = \boxed{1.97\ \Omega}$.

P28.2 (a) $\Delta V_{\text{term}} = IR$

becomes $10.0\text{ V} = I(5.60\ \Omega)$

so $I = \boxed{1.79\text{ A}}$.

(b) $\Delta V_{\text{term}} = \varepsilon - Ir$

becomes $10.0\text{ V} = \varepsilon - (1.79\text{ A})(0.200\ \Omega)$

so $\varepsilon = \boxed{10.4\text{ V}}$.

P28.3 The total resistance is $R = \dfrac{3.00\text{ V}}{0.600\text{ A}} = 5.00\ \Omega$.

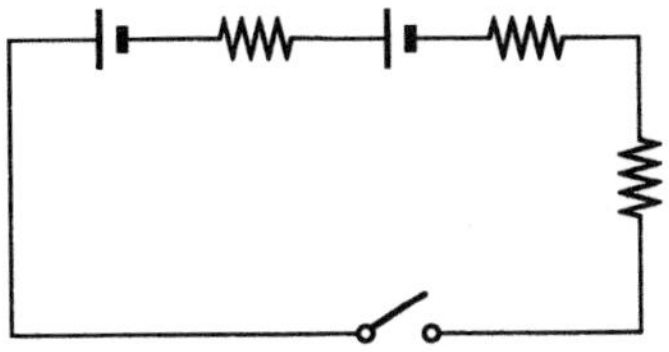

FIG. P28.3

(a) $R_{\text{lamp}} = R - r_{\text{batteries}} = 5.00\ \Omega - 0.408\ \Omega = \boxed{4.59\ \Omega}$

(b) $\dfrac{\mathcal{P}_{\text{batteries}}}{\mathcal{P}_{\text{total}}} = \dfrac{(0.408\ \Omega)I^2}{(5.00\ \Omega)I^2} = 0.081\,6 = \boxed{8.16\%}$

P28.4 (a) Here $\varepsilon = I(R+r)$, so $I = \dfrac{\varepsilon}{R+r} = \dfrac{12.6\text{ V}}{(5.00\ \Omega + 0.080\,0\ \Omega)} = 2.48\text{ A}$.

Then, $\Delta V = IR = (2.48\text{ A})(5.00\ \Omega) = \boxed{12.4\text{ V}}$.

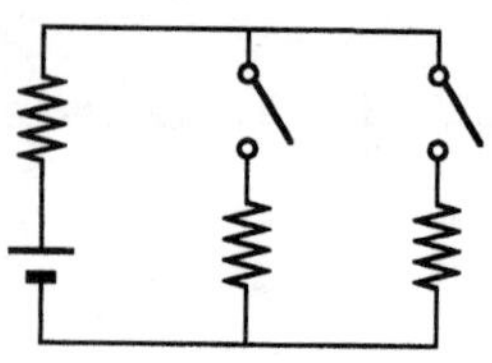

FIG. P28.4

(b) Let I_1 and I_2 be the currents flowing through the battery and the headlights, respectively.

Then, $I_1 = I_2 + 35.0\text{ A}$, and $\varepsilon - I_1 r - I_2 r = 0$

so $\varepsilon = (I_2 + 35.0\text{ A})(0.080\,0\ \Omega) + I_2(5.00\ \Omega) = 12.6\text{ V}$

giving $I_2 = 1.93\text{ A}$.

Thus, $\Delta V_2 = (1.93\text{ A})(5.00\ \Omega) = \boxed{9.65\text{ V}}$.

Section 28.2 **Resistors in Series and Parallel**

P28.5 $\Delta V = I_1 R_1 = (2.00\text{ A})R_1$ and $\Delta V = I_2(R_1 + R_2) = (1.60\text{ A})(R_1 + 3.00\ \Omega)$

Therefore, $(2.00\text{ A})R_1 = (1.60\text{ A})(R_1 + 3.00\ \Omega)$ or $R_1 = \boxed{12.0\ \Omega}$.

P28.6 (a) $R_p = \dfrac{1}{(1/7.00\ \Omega) + (1/10.0\ \Omega)} = 4.12\ \Omega$

$R_s = R_1 + R_2 + R_3 = 4.00 + 4.12 + 9.00 = \boxed{17.1\ \Omega}$

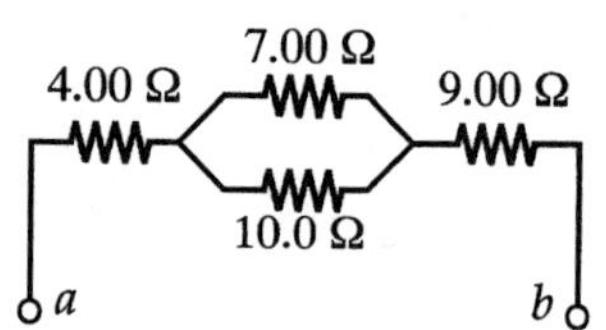

FIG. P28.6

(b) $\Delta V = IR$

$34.0\text{ V} = I(17.1\ \Omega)$

$I = \boxed{1.99\text{ A}}$ for $4.00\ \Omega$, $9.00\ \Omega$ resistors.

Applying $\Delta V = IR$, $(1.99\text{ A})(4.12\ \Omega) = 8.18\text{ V}$

$8.18\text{ V} = I(7.00\ \Omega)$

so $I = \boxed{1.17\text{ A}}$ for $7.00\ \Omega$ resistor

$8.18\text{ V} = I(10.0\ \Omega)$

so $I = \boxed{0.818\text{ A}}$ for $10.0\ \Omega$ resistor.

P28.7 For the bulb in use as intended,

$$I = \frac{\mathscr{P}}{\Delta V} = \frac{75.0\text{ W}}{120\text{ V}} = 0.625\text{ A}$$

and

$$R = \frac{\Delta V}{I} = \frac{120\text{ V}}{0.625\text{ A}} = 192\ \Omega.$$

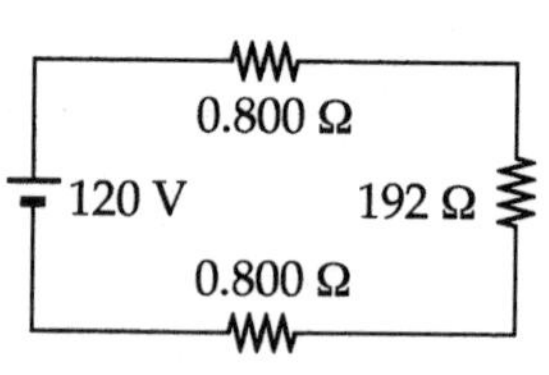

FIG. P28.7

Now, presuming the bulb resistance is unchanged,

$$I = \frac{120\text{ V}}{193.6\ \Omega} = 0.620\text{ A}.$$

Across the bulb is $\Delta V = IR = 192\ \Omega(0.620\text{ A}) = 119\text{ V}$

so its power is $\mathscr{P} = I\Delta V = 0.620\text{ A}(119\text{ V}) = \boxed{73.8\text{ W}}$.

P28.8 $120\text{ V} = IR_{\text{eq}} = I\left(\dfrac{\rho\ell}{A_1}+\dfrac{\rho\ell}{A_2}+\dfrac{\rho\ell}{A_3}+\dfrac{\rho\ell}{A_4}\right)$, or $I\rho\ell = \dfrac{(120\text{ V})}{\left(\frac{1}{A_1}+\frac{1}{A_2}+\frac{1}{A_3}+\frac{1}{A_4}\right)}$

$$\Delta V_2 = \frac{I\rho\ell}{A_2} = \frac{(120\text{ V})}{A_2\left(\frac{1}{A_1}+\frac{1}{A_2}+\frac{1}{A_3}+\frac{1}{A_4}\right)} = \boxed{29.5\text{ V}}$$

P28.9 If we turn the given diagram on its side, we find that it is the same as figure (a). The 20.0 Ω and 5.00 Ω resistors are in series, so the first reduction is shown in (b). In addition, since the 10.0 Ω, 5.00 Ω, and 25.0 Ω resistors are then in parallel, we can solve for their equivalent resistance as:

$$R_{\text{eq}} = \frac{1}{\left(\frac{1}{10.0\ \Omega}+\frac{1}{5.00\ \Omega}+\frac{1}{25.0\ \Omega}\right)} = 2.94\ \Omega.$$

This is shown in figure (c), which in turn reduces to the circuit shown in figure (d).

Next, we work backwards through the diagrams applying $I = \dfrac{\Delta V}{R}$ and $\Delta V = IR$ alternately to every resistor, real and equivalent. The 12.94 Ω resistor is connected across 25.0 V, so the current through the battery in every diagram is

$$I = \frac{\Delta V}{R} = \frac{25.0\text{ V}}{12.94\ \Omega} = 1.93\text{ A}.$$

In figure (c), this 1.93 A goes through the 2.94 Ω equivalent resistor to give a potential difference of:

$$\Delta V = IR = (1.93\text{ A})(2.94\ \Omega) = 5.68\text{ V}.$$

From figure (b), we see that this potential difference is the same across ΔV_{ab}, the 10 Ω resistor, and the 5.00 Ω resistor.

(b) Therefore, $\Delta V_{ab} = \boxed{5.68\text{ V}}$.

(a) Since the current through the 20.0 Ω resistor is also the current through the 25.0 Ω line *ab*,

$$I = \frac{\Delta V_{ab}}{R_{ab}} = \frac{5.68\text{ V}}{25.0\ \Omega} = 0.227\text{ A} = \boxed{227\text{ mA}}.$$

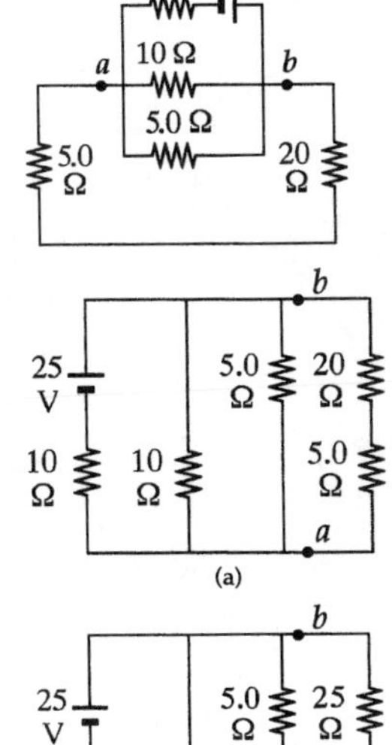

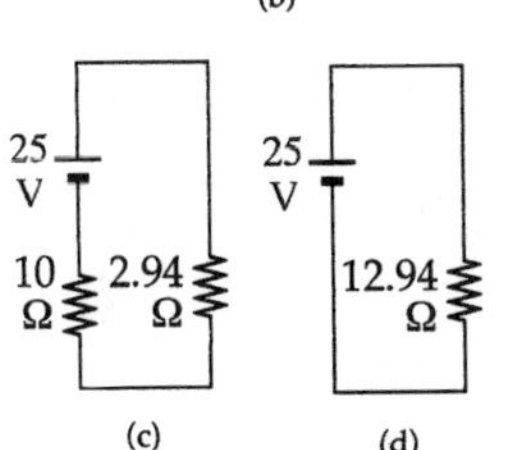

FIG. P28.9

***P28.10** We assume that the metal wand makes low-resistance contact with the person's hand and that the resistance through the person's body is negligible compared to the resistance R_{shoes} of the shoe soles. The equivalent resistance seen by the power supply is $1.00\text{ M}\Omega + R_{\text{shoes}}$. The current through both resistors is $\dfrac{50.0\text{ V}}{1.00\text{ M}\Omega + R_{\text{shoes}}}$. The voltmeter displays

$$\Delta V = I(1.00\text{ M}\Omega) = \frac{50.0\text{ V}(1.00\text{ M}\Omega)}{1.00\text{ M}\Omega + R_{\text{shoes}}} = \Delta V.$$

(a) We solve to obtain

$$50.0\text{ V}(1.00\text{ M}\Omega) = \Delta V(1.00\text{ M}\Omega) + \Delta V(R_{\text{shoes}})$$

$$R_{\text{shoes}} = \frac{1.00\text{ M}\Omega(50.0-\Delta V)}{\Delta V}.$$

(b) With $R_{\text{shoes}} \to 0$, the current through the person's body is

$$\frac{50.0\text{ V}}{1.00\text{ M}\Omega} = 50.0\ \mu\text{A} \qquad \boxed{\text{The current will never exceed } 50\ \mu\text{A}}.$$

P28.11 (a) Since all the current in the circuit must pass through the series 100 Ω resistor, $\mathcal{P} = I^2R$

$$\mathcal{P}_{max} = RI_{max}^2$$

so $$I_{max} = \sqrt{\frac{\mathcal{P}}{R}} = \sqrt{\frac{25.0\text{ W}}{100\ \Omega}} = 0.500\text{ A}$$

$$R_{eq} = 100\ \Omega + \left(\frac{1}{100} + \frac{1}{100}\right)^{-1}\ \Omega = 150\ \Omega$$

$$\Delta V_{max} = R_{eq}I_{max} = \boxed{75.0\text{ V}}$$

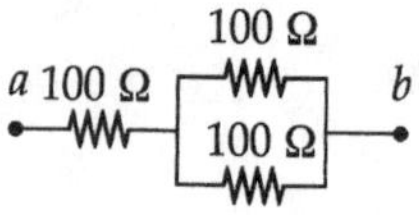

FIG. P28.11

(b) $$\mathcal{P} = I\Delta V = (0.500\text{ A})(75.0\text{ V}) = \boxed{37.5\text{ W}}\text{ total power}$$

$$\mathcal{P}_1 = \boxed{25.0\text{ W}}$$

$$\mathcal{P}_2 = \mathcal{P}_3 = RI^2(100\ \Omega)(0.250\text{ A})^2 = \boxed{6.25\text{ W}}$$

P28.12 Using 2.00-Ω, 3.00-Ω, 4.00-Ω resistors, there are 7 series, 4 parallel, and 6 mixed combinations:

Series		Parallel	Mixed
2.00 Ω	6.00 Ω	0.923 Ω	1.56 Ω
3.00 Ω	7.00 Ω	1.20 Ω	2.00 Ω
4.00 Ω	9.00 Ω	1.33 Ω	2.22 Ω
5.00 Ω		1.71 Ω	3.71 Ω
			4.33 Ω
			5.20 Ω

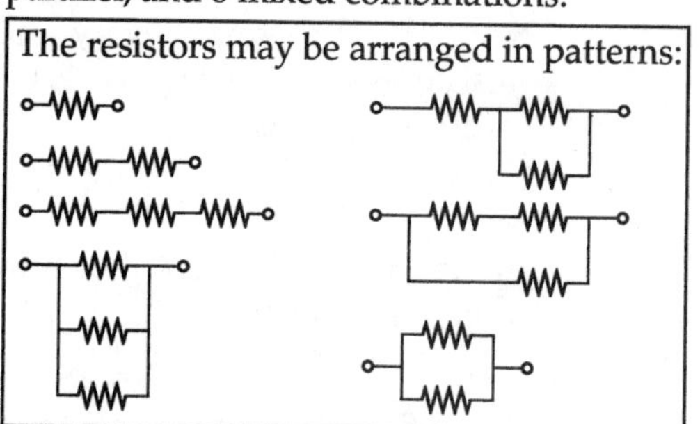

P28.13 The potential difference is the same across either combination.

$$\Delta V = IR = 3I\frac{1}{\left(\frac{1}{R} + \frac{1}{500}\right)} \quad \text{so} \quad R\left(\frac{1}{R} + \frac{1}{500}\right) = 3$$

$$1 + \frac{R}{500} = 3 \quad \text{and} \quad R = 1\,000\ \Omega = \boxed{1.00\text{ k}\Omega}.$$

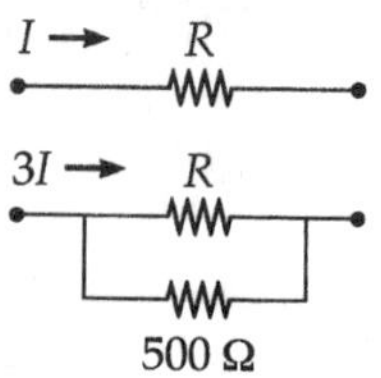

FIG. P28.13

***P28.14** *When S is open*, R_1, R_2, R_3 are in series with the battery. Thus:

$$R_1 + R_2 + R_3 = \frac{6\text{ V}}{10^{-3}\text{ A}} = 6\text{ k}\Omega. \tag{1}$$

When S is closed in position 1, the parallel combination of the two R_2's is in series with R_1, R_3, and the battery. Thus:

$$R_1 + \frac{1}{2}R_2 + R_3 = \frac{6\text{ V}}{1.2\times10^{-3}\text{ A}} = 5\text{ k}\Omega. \tag{2}$$

When S is closed in position 2, R_1 and R_2 are in series with the battery. R_3 is shorted. Thus:

$$R_1 + R_2 = \frac{6\text{ V}}{2\times10^{-3}\text{ A}} = 3\text{ k}\Omega. \tag{3}$$

From (1) and (3): $R_3 = 3\text{ k}\Omega$.

Subtract (2) from (1): $R_2 = 2\text{ k}\Omega$.

From (3): $R_1 = 1\text{ k}\Omega$.

Answers: $\boxed{R_1 = 1.00\text{ k}\Omega,\ R_2 = 2.00\text{ k}\Omega,\ R_3 = 3.00\text{ k}\Omega}$.

P28.15 $R_p = \left(\dfrac{1}{3.00} + \dfrac{1}{1.00}\right)^{-1} = 0.750\ \Omega$

$R_s = (2.00 + 0.750 + 4.00)\ \Omega = 6.75\ \Omega$

$I_{\text{battery}} = \dfrac{\Delta V}{R_s} = \dfrac{18.0\ \text{V}}{6.75\ \Omega} = 2.67\ \text{A}$

$\mathcal{P} = I^2R$: $\quad \mathcal{P}_2 = (2.67\ \text{A})^2(2.00\ \Omega)$

$\mathcal{P}_2 = \boxed{14.2\ \text{W}}$ in $2.00\ \Omega$

$\mathcal{P}_4 = (2.67\ \text{A})^2(4.00\ \text{A}) = \boxed{28.4\ \text{W}}$ in $4.00\ \Omega$

$\Delta V_2 = (2.67\ \text{A})(2.00\ \Omega) = 5.33\ \text{V}$,

$\Delta V_4 = (2.67\ \text{A})(4.00\ \Omega) = 10.67\ \text{V}$

$\Delta V_p = 18.0\ \text{V} - \Delta V_2 - \Delta V_4 = 2.00\ \text{V}(= \Delta V_3 = \Delta V_1)$

$\mathcal{P}_3 = \dfrac{(\Delta V_3)^2}{R_3} = \dfrac{(2.00\ \text{V})^2}{3.00\ \Omega} = \boxed{1.33\ \text{W}}$ in $3.00\ \Omega$

$\mathcal{P}_1 = \dfrac{(\Delta V_1)}{R_1} = \dfrac{(2.00\ \text{V})^2}{1.00\ \Omega} = \boxed{4.00\ \text{W}}$ in $1.00\ \Omega$

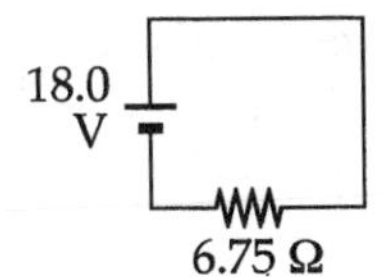

FIG. P28.15

P28.16 Denoting the two resistors as x and y,

$x + y = 690$, and $\dfrac{1}{150} = \dfrac{1}{x} + \dfrac{1}{y}$

$$\frac{1}{150} = \frac{1}{x} + \frac{1}{690 - x} = \frac{(690 - x) + x}{x(690 - x)}$$

$$x^2 - 690x + 103\,500 = 0$$

$$x = \frac{690 \pm \sqrt{(690)^2 - 414\,000}}{2}$$

$x = \boxed{470\ \Omega}$ $\qquad y = \boxed{220\ \Omega}$

***P28.17** A certain quantity of energy $\Delta E_{\text{int}} = \mathcal{P}(\text{time})$ is required to raise the temperature of the water to $100°\text{C}$. For the power delivered to the heaters we have $\mathcal{P} = I\Delta V = \dfrac{(\Delta V)^2}{R}$ where (ΔV) is a constant.

Thus comparing coils 1 and 2, we have for the energy $\dfrac{(\Delta V)^2 \Delta t}{R_1} = \dfrac{(\Delta V)^2 2\Delta t}{R_2}$. Then $R_2 = 2R_1$.

(a) When connected in parallel, the coils present equivalent resistance

$R_p = \dfrac{1}{1/R_1 + 1/R_2} = \dfrac{1}{1/R_1 + 1/2R_1} = \dfrac{2R_1}{3}$. Now $\dfrac{(\Delta V)^2 \Delta t}{R_1} = \dfrac{(\Delta V)^2 \Delta t_p}{2R_1/3}$ $\qquad \Delta t_p = \boxed{\dfrac{2\Delta t}{3}}$.

(b) For the series connection, $R_s = R_1 + R_2 = R_1 + 2R_1 = 3R_1$ and $\dfrac{(\Delta V)^2 \Delta t}{R_1} = \dfrac{(\Delta V)^2 \Delta t_s}{3R_1}$

$\Delta t_s = \boxed{3\Delta t}$.

P28.18 (a) $\Delta V = IR$: $33.0\text{ V} = I_1(11.0\ \Omega)$ $33.0\text{ V} = I_2(22.0\ \Omega)$

$I_3 = 3.00\text{ A}$ $I_2 = 1.50\text{ A}$

$\mathcal{P} = I^2R$: $\mathcal{P}_1 = (3.00\text{ A})^2(11.0\ \Omega)$ $\mathcal{P}_2 = (1.50\text{ A})^2(22.0\ \Omega)$

$\mathcal{P}_1 = 99.0\text{ W}$ $\mathcal{P}_2 = 49.5\text{ W}$

The 11.0-Ω resistor uses more power.

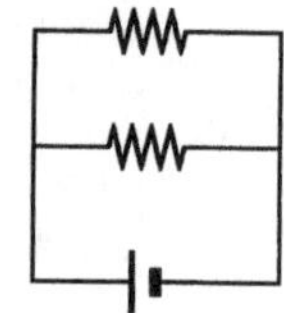

FIG. P28.18(a)

(b) $\mathcal{P}_1 + \mathcal{P}_2 = \boxed{148\text{ W}}$ $\mathcal{P} = I(\Delta V) = (4.50)(33.0) = \boxed{148\text{ W}}$

(c) $R_s = R_1 + R_2 = 11.0\ \Omega + 22.0\ \Omega = 33.0\ \Omega$

$\Delta V = IR$: $33.0\text{ V} = I(33.0\ \Omega)$, so $I = 1.00\text{ A}$

$\mathcal{P} = I^2R$: $\mathcal{P}_1 = (1.00\text{ A})^2(11.0\ \Omega)$ $\mathcal{P}_2 = (1.00\text{ A})^2(22.0\ \Omega)$

$\mathcal{P}_1 = 11.0\text{ W}$ $\mathcal{P}_2 = 22.0\text{ W}$

The 22.0-Ω resistor uses more power.

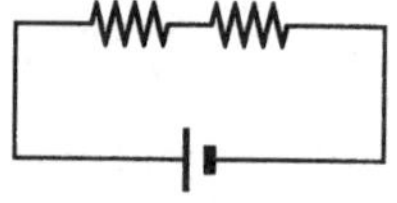

FIG. P28.18(c)

(d) $\mathcal{P}_1 + \mathcal{P}_2 = I^2(R_1 + R_2) = (1.00\text{ A})^2(33.0\ \Omega) = \boxed{33.0\text{ W}}$

$\mathcal{P} = I(\Delta V) = (1.00\text{ A})(33.0\text{ V}) = \boxed{33.0\text{ W}}$

(e) The parallel configuration uses more power.

***P28.19** (a) The resistors 2, 3, and 4 can be combined to a single $2R$ resistor. This is in series with resistor 1, with resistance R, so the equivalent resistance of the whole circuit is $3R$. In series, potential difference is shared in proportion to the resistance, so resistor 1 gets $\frac{1}{3}$ of the battery voltage and the 2-3-4 parallel combination get $\frac{2}{3}$ of the battery voltage. This is the potential difference across resistor 4, but resistors 2 and 3 must share this voltage. $\frac{1}{3}$ goes to 2 and $\frac{2}{3}$ to 3. The ranking by potential difference is $\boxed{\Delta V_4 > \Delta V_3 > \Delta V_1 > \Delta V_2}$.

(b) Based on the reasoning above the potential differences are

$$\boxed{\Delta V_1 = \frac{\varepsilon}{3},\ \Delta V_2 = \frac{2\varepsilon}{9},\ \Delta V_3 = \frac{4\varepsilon}{9},\ \Delta V_4 = \frac{2\varepsilon}{3}}.$$

(c) All the current goes through resistor 1, so it gets the most. The current then splits at the parallel combination. Resistor 4 gets more than half, because the resistance in that branch is less than in the other branch. Resistors 2 and 3 have equal currents because they are in series. The ranking by current is $\boxed{I_1 > I_4 > I_2 = I_3}$.

(d) Resistor 1 has a current of I. Because the resistance of 2 and 3 in series is twice that of resistor 4, twice as much current goes through 4 as through 2 and 3. The current through the resistors are $\boxed{I_1 = I,\ I_2 = I_3 = \frac{I}{3},\ I_4 = \frac{2I}{3}}$.

continued on next page

(e) Increasing resistor 3 increases the equivalent resistance of the entire circuit. The current in the circuit, which is the current through resistor 1, decreases. This decreases the potential difference across resistor 1, increasing the potential difference across the parallel combination. With a larger potential difference the current through resistor 4 is increased. With more current through 4, and less in the circuit to start with, the current through resistors 2 and 3 must decrease. To summarize, $\boxed{I_4 \text{ increases and } I_1, I_2, \text{ and } I_3 \text{ decrease}}$.

(f) If resistor 3 has an infinite resistance it blocks any current from passing through that branch, and the circuit effectively is just resistor 1 and resistor 4 in series with the battery. The circuit now has an equivalent resistance of $4R$. The current in the circuit drops to $\frac{3}{4}$ of the original current because the resistance has increased by $\frac{4}{3}$. All this current passes through resistors 1 and 4, and none passes through 2 or 3. Therefore $\boxed{I_1 = \frac{3I}{4}, I_2 = I_3 = 0, I_4 = \frac{3I}{4}}$.

Section 28.3 Kirchhoff's Rules

P28.20 $+15.0 - (7.00)I_1 - (2.00)(5.00) = 0$

$5.00 = 7.00I_1$ so $\boxed{I_1 = 0.714 \text{ A}}$

$I_3 = I_1 + I_2 = 2.00 \text{ A}$

$0.714 + I_2 = 2.00$ so $\boxed{I_2 = 1.29 \text{ A}}$

$+\varepsilon - 2.00(1.29) - 5.00(2.00) = 0$ $\boxed{\varepsilon = 12.6 \text{ V}}$

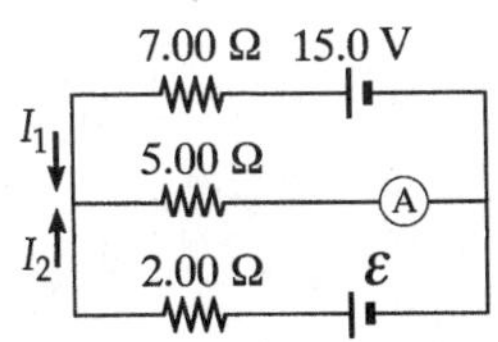

FIG. P28.20

P28.21 We name currents I_1, I_2, and I_3 as shown.

From Kirchhoff's current rule, $I_3 = I_1 + I_2$.

Applying Kirchhoff's voltage rule to the loop containing I_2 and I_3,

$12.0 \text{ V} - (4.00)I_3 - (6.00)I_2 - 4.00 \text{ V} = 0$

$8.00 = (4.00)I_3 + (6.00)I_2$

Applying Kirchhoff's voltage rule to the loop containing I_1 and I_2,

$-(6.00)I_2 - 4.00 \text{ V} + (8.00)I_1 = 0$ $\quad (8.00)I_1 = 4.00 + (6.00)I_2$.

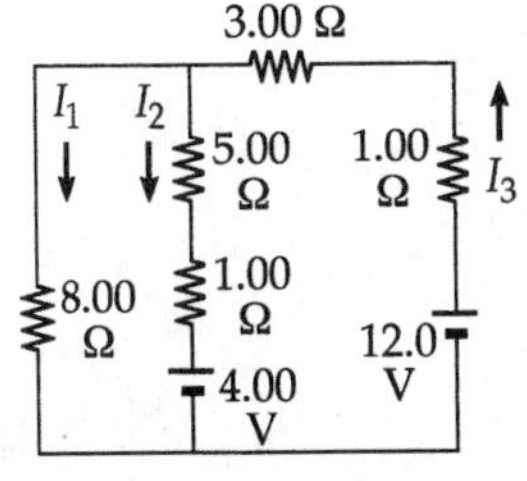

FIG. P28.21

Solving the above linear system, we proceed to the pair of simultaneous equations:

$$\begin{cases} 8 = 4I_1 + 4I_2 + 6I_2 \\ 8I_1 = 4 + 6I_2 \end{cases} \quad \text{or} \quad \begin{cases} 8 = 4I_1 + 10I_2 \\ I_2 = 1.33I_1 - 0.667 \end{cases}$$

and to the single equation $8 = 4I_1 + 13.3I_1 - 6.67$

$$I_1 = \frac{14.7 \text{ V}}{17.3 \ \Omega} = 0.846 \text{ A}. \quad \text{Then} \quad I_2 = 1.33(0.846 \text{ A}) - 0.667$$

and $\quad I_3 = I_1 + I_2 \quad$ give $\quad \boxed{I_1 = 846 \text{ mA}, I_2 = 462 \text{ mA}, I_3 = 1.31 \text{ A}}$.

All currents are in the directions indicated by the arrows in the circuit diagram.

P28.22 The solution figure is shown to the right.

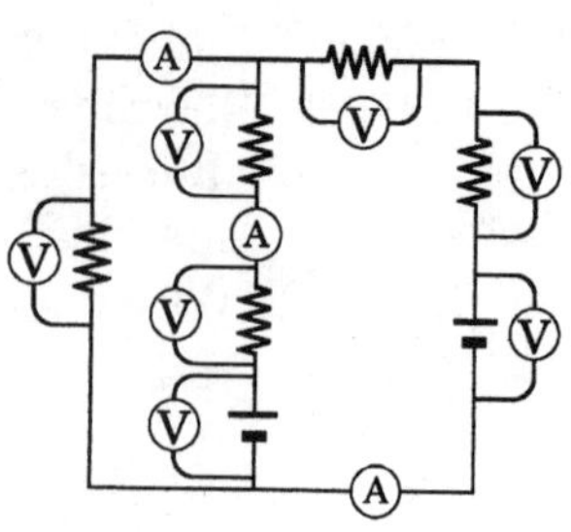

FIG. P28.22

P28.23 We use the results of Problem 28.21.

(a) By the 4.00-V battery: $\Delta U = (\Delta V)I\Delta t = (4.00 \text{ V})(-0.462 \text{ A})120 \text{ s} = \boxed{-222 \text{ J}}$.

By the 12.0-V battery: $(12.0 \text{ V})(1.31 \text{ A})120 \text{ s} = \boxed{1.88 \text{ kJ}}$.

(b) By the 8.00-Ω resistor: $I^2R\Delta t = (0.846 \text{ A})^2(8.00 \ \Omega)120 \text{ s} = \boxed{687 \text{ J}}$.

By the 5.00-Ω resistor: $(0.462 \text{ A})^2(5.00 \ \Omega)120 \text{ s} = \boxed{128 \text{ J}}$.

By the 1.00-Ω resistor: $(0.462 \text{ A})^2(1.00 \ \Omega)120 \text{ s} = \boxed{25.6 \text{ J}}$.

By the 3.00-Ω resistor: $(1.31 \text{ A})^2(3.00 \ \Omega)120 \text{ s} = \boxed{616 \text{ J}}$.

By the 1.00-Ω resistor: $(1.31 \text{ A})^2(1.00 \ \Omega)120 \text{ s} = \boxed{205 \text{ J}}$.

(c) $-222 \text{ J} + 1.88 \text{ kJ} = \boxed{1.66 \text{ kJ}}$ from chemical to electrical.

$687 \text{ J} + 128 \text{ J} + 25.6 \text{ J} + 616 \text{ J} + 205 \text{ J} = 1.66 \text{ kJ}$ from electrical to internal.

P28.24 We name the currents I_1, I_2, and I_3 as shown.

[1] $70.0 - 60.0 - I_2(3.00 \text{ k}\Omega) - I_1(2.00 \text{ k}\Omega) = 0$

[2] $80.0 - I_3(4.00 \text{ k}\Omega) - 60.0 - I_2(3.00 \text{ k}\Omega) = 0$

[3] $I_2 = I_1 + I_3$

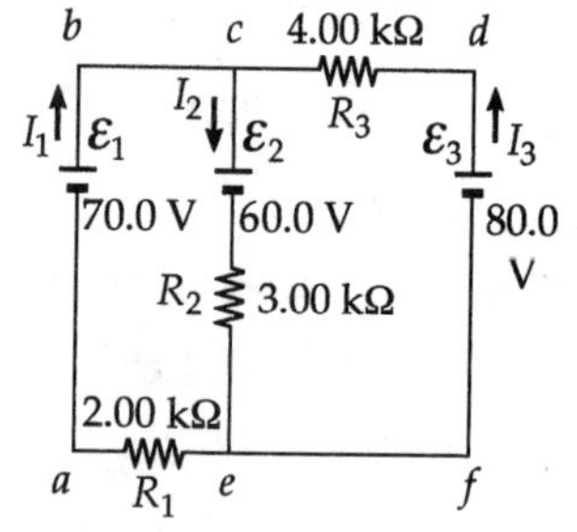

FIG. P28.24

(a) Substituting for I_2 and solving the resulting simultaneous equations yields

$I_1 = \boxed{0.385 \text{ mA}}$ (through R_1)

$I_3 = \boxed{2.69 \text{ mA}}$ (through R_3)

$I_2 = \boxed{3.08 \text{ mA}}$ (through R_2)

(b) $\Delta V_{cf} = -60.0 \text{ V} - (3.08 \text{ mA})(3.00 \text{ k}\Omega) = \boxed{-69.2 \text{ V}}$

$\boxed{\text{Point } c \text{ is at higher potential.}}$

P28.25 Label the currents in the branches as shown in the first figure. Reduce the circuit by combining the two parallel resistors as shown in the second figure.

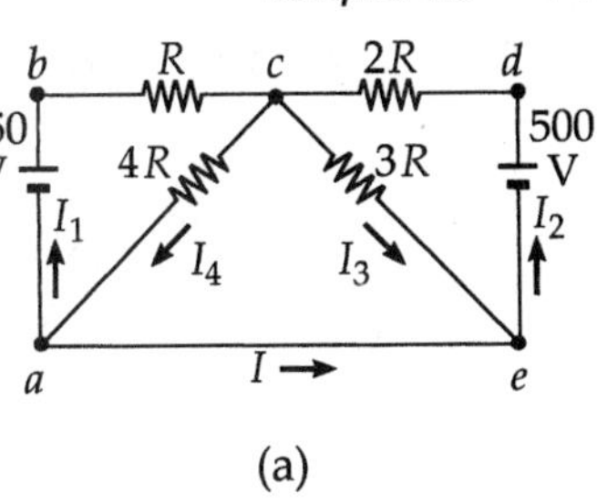

Apply Kirchhoff's loop rule to both loops in Figure (b) to obtain:

$$(2.71R)I_1 + (1.71R)I_2 = 250$$

and $$(1.71R)I_1 + (3.71R)I_2 = 500.$$

With $R = 1\,000\ \Omega$, simultaneous solution of these equations yields:

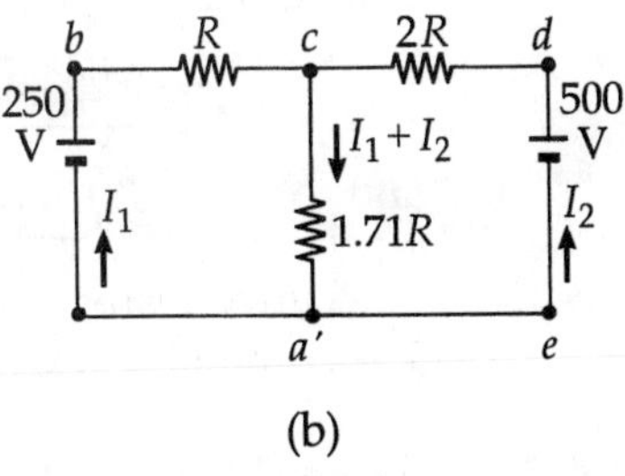

$$I_1 = 10.0\ \text{mA}$$

and $$I_2 = 130.0\ \text{mA}.$$

From Figure (b), $V_c - V_a = (I_1 + I_2)(1.71R) = 240\ \text{V}$.

Thus, from Figure (a), $I_4 = \dfrac{V_c - V_a}{4R} = \dfrac{240\ \text{V}}{4\,000\ \Omega} = 60.0\ \text{mA}$.

Finally, applying Kirchhoff's point rule at point a in Figure (a) gives:

FIG. P28.25

$$I = I_4 - I_1 = 60.0\ \text{mA} - 10.0\ \text{mA} = +50.0\ \text{mA},$$

or $$I = \boxed{50.0\ \text{mA from point } a \text{ to point } e}.$$

P28.26 Name the currents as shown in the figure to the right. Then $w + x + z = y$. Loop equations are

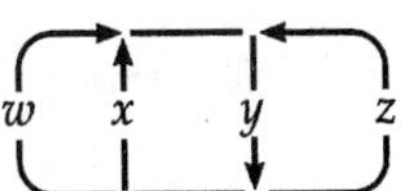

FIG. P28.26

$$-200w - 40.0 + 80.0x = 0$$
$$-80.0x + 40.0 + 360 - 20.0y = 0$$
$$+360 - 20.0y - 70.0z + 80.0 = 0$$

Eliminate y by substitution.
$$\begin{cases} x = 2.50w + 0.500 \\ 400 - 100x - 20.0w - 20.0z = 0 \\ 440 - 20.0w - 20.0x - 90.0z = 0 \end{cases}$$

Eliminate x.
$$\begin{cases} 350 - 270w - 20.0z = 0 \\ 430 - 70.0w - 90.0z = 0 \end{cases}$$

Eliminate $z = 17.5 - 13.5w$ to obtain $430 - 70.0w - 1\,575 + 1\,215w = 0$

$$w = \frac{70.0}{70.0} = \boxed{1.00\ \text{A upward in } 200\ \Omega}.$$

Now $$z = \boxed{4.00\ \text{A upward in } 70.0\ \Omega}$$

$$x = \boxed{3.00\ \text{A upward in } 80.0\ \Omega}$$

$$y = \boxed{8.00\ \text{A downward in } 20.0\ \Omega}$$

and for the 200 Ω, $\Delta V = IR = (1.00\ \text{A})(200\ \Omega) = \boxed{200\ \text{V}}$.

P28.27 Using Kirchhoff's rules,

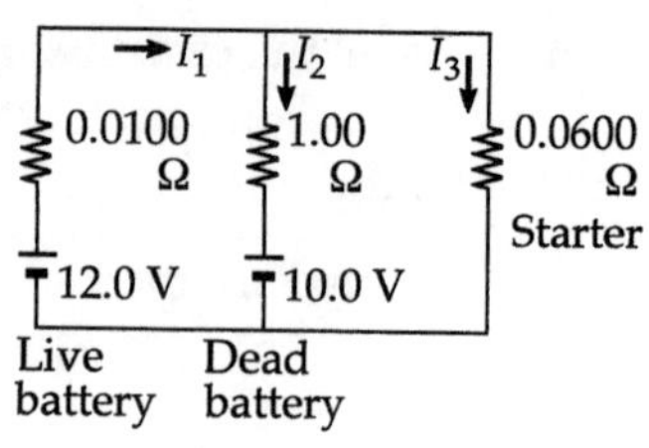

FIG. P28.27

$$12.0-(0.0100)I_1-(0.0600)I_3=0$$
$$10.0+(1.00)I_2-(0.0600)I_3=0$$

and $I_1=I_2+I_3$

$$12.0-(0.0100)I_2-(0.0700)I_3=0$$
$$10.0+(1.00)I_2-(0.0600)I_3=0$$

Solving simultaneously,

$I_2=$ $\boxed{0.283 \text{ A downward}}$ in the dead battery

and $I_3=$ $\boxed{171 \text{ A downward}}$ in the starter.

The currents are forward in the live battery and in the starter, relative to normal starting operation. The current is backward in the dead battery, tending to charge it up.

P28.28
$$\Delta V_{ab}=(1.00)I_1+(1.00)(I_1-I_2)$$
$$\Delta V_{ab}=(1.00)I_1+(1.00)I_2+(5.00)(I-I_1+I_2)$$
$$\Delta V_{ab}=(3.00)(I-I_1)+(5.00)(I-I_1+I_2)$$

Let $I=1.00$ A, $I_1=x$, and $I_2=y$.

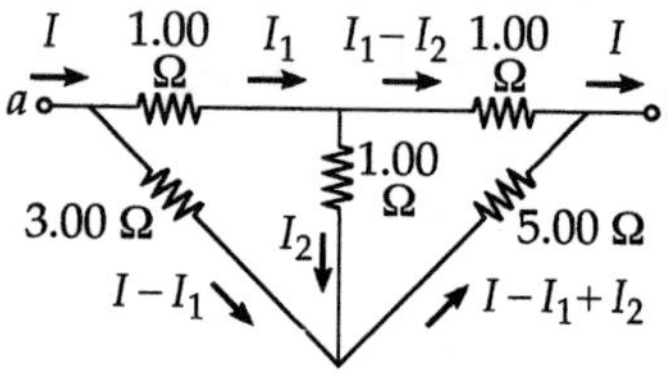

Then, the three equations become:

$\Delta V_{ab}=2.00x-y$, or $y=2.00x-\Delta V_{ab}$

$\Delta V_{ab}=-4.00x+6.00y+5.00$

and $\Delta V_{ab}=8.00-8.00x+5.00y$.

Substituting the first into the last two gives:

$7.00\Delta V_{ab}=8.00x+5.00$ and $6.00\Delta V_{ab}=2.00x+8.00$.

Solving these simultaneously yields $\Delta V_{ab}=\frac{27}{17}$ V.

Then, $R_{ab}=\frac{\Delta V_{ab}}{I}=\frac{\frac{27}{17}\text{ V}}{1.00\text{ A}}$ or $\boxed{R_{ab}=\frac{27}{17}\ \Omega}$.

FIG. P28.28

P28.29 We name the currents I_1, I_2, and I_3 as shown.

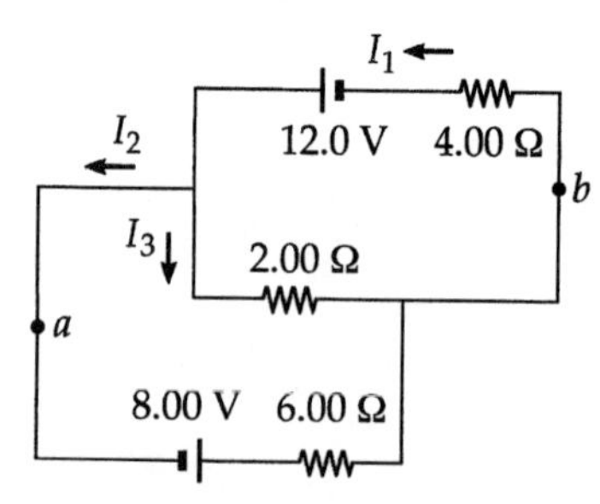

FIG. P28.29

(a) $I_1=I_2+I_3$

Counterclockwise around the top loop,

$12.0\text{ V}-(2.00\ \Omega)I_3-(4.00\ \Omega)I_1=0$.

Traversing the bottom loop,

$8.00\text{ V}-(6.00\ \Omega)I_2+(2.00\ \Omega)I_3=0$

$I_1=3.00-\frac{1}{2}I_3$, $I_2=\frac{4}{3}+\frac{1}{3}I_3$, and $\boxed{I_3=909\text{ mA}}$.

(b) $V_a-(0.909\text{ A})(2.00\ \Omega)=V_b$

$V_b-V_a=\boxed{-1.82\text{ V}}$

P28.30 We apply Kirchhoff's rules to the second diagram.

$$50.0-2.00I_1-2.00I_2=0 \qquad (1)$$

$$20.0-2.00I_3+2.00I_2=0 \qquad (2)$$

$$I_1=I_2+I_3 \qquad (3)$$

Substitute (3) into (1), and solve for I_1, I_2, and I_3

$I_1=20.0\text{ A};\ I_2=5.00\text{ A};\ I_3=15.0\text{ A}.$

Then apply $\mathcal{P}=I^2R$ to each resistor:

$(2.00\ \Omega)_1$: $\mathcal{P}=I_1^2(2.00\ \Omega)=(20.0\text{ A})^2(2.00\ \Omega)=\boxed{800\text{ W}}$

$(4.00\ \Omega)$: $\mathcal{P}=\left(\dfrac{5.00}{2}\text{ A}\right)^2(4.00\ \Omega)=\boxed{25.0\text{ W}}$

(Half of I_2 goes through each)

$(2.00\ \Omega)_3$: $\mathcal{P}=I_3^2(2.00\ \Omega)=(15.0\text{ A})^2(2.00\ \Omega)=\boxed{450\text{ W}}$.

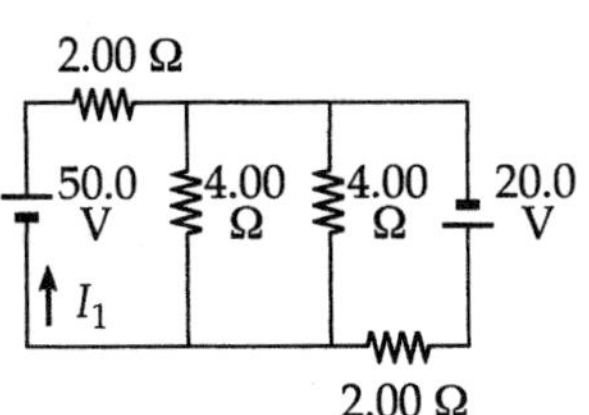

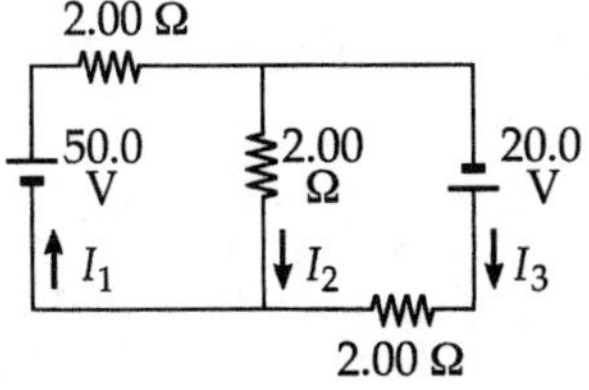

FIG. P28.30

Section 28.4 *RC* Circuits

P28.31 (a) $RC=\left(1.00\times10^{6}\ \Omega\right)\left(5.00\times10^{-6}\text{ F}\right)=\boxed{5.00\text{ s}}$

(b) $Q=C\varepsilon=\left(5.00\times10^{-6}\text{ C}\right)(30.0\text{ V})=\boxed{150\ \mu\text{C}}$

(c) $I(t)=\dfrac{\varepsilon}{R}e^{-t/RC}=\left(\dfrac{30.0}{1.00\times10^{6}}\right)\exp\left[\dfrac{-10.0}{\left(1.00\times10^{6}\right)\left(5.00\times10^{-6}\right)}\right]=\boxed{4.06\ \mu\text{A}}$

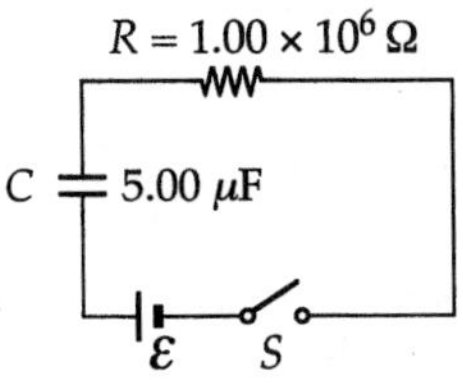

FIG. P28.31

P28.32 (a) $I(t)=-I_0e^{-t/RC}$

$$I_0=\frac{Q}{RC}=\frac{5.10\times10^{-6}\text{ C}}{(1\,300\ \Omega)\left(2.00\times10^{-9}\text{ F}\right)}=1.96\text{ A}$$

$$I(t)=-(1.96\text{ A})\exp\left[\frac{-9.00\times10^{-6}\text{ s}}{(1\,300\ \Omega)\left(2.00\times10^{-9}\text{ F}\right)}\right]=\boxed{-61.6\text{ mA}}$$

(b) $q(t)=Qe^{-t/RC}=(5.10\ \mu\text{C})\exp\left[\dfrac{-8.00\times10^{-6}\text{ s}}{(1\,300\ \Omega)\left(2.00\times10^{-9}\text{ F}\right)}\right]=\boxed{0.235\ \mu\text{C}}$

(c) The magnitude of the maximum current is $I_0=\boxed{1.96\text{ A}}$.

P28.33 $U=\dfrac{1}{2}C(\Delta V)^2$ and $\Delta V=\dfrac{Q}{C}$.

Therefore, $U=\dfrac{Q^2}{2C}$ and when the charge decreases to half its original value, the stored energy is one-quarter its original value: $\boxed{U_f=\dfrac{1}{4}U_0}$.

P28.34 $q(t)=Q\left[1-e^{-t/RC}\right]$ so $\dfrac{q(t)}{Q}=1-e^{-t/RC}$

$0.600=1-e^{-0.900/RC}$ or $e^{-0.900/RC}=1-0.600=0.400$

$\dfrac{-0.900}{RC}=\ln(0.400)$ thus $RC=\dfrac{-0.900}{\ln(0.400)}=\boxed{0.982\text{ s}}$.

***P28.35** We are to calculate

$$\int_0^\infty e^{-2t/RC}dt=-\frac{RC}{2}\int_0^\infty e^{-2t/RC}\left(-\frac{2dt}{RC}\right)=-\frac{RC}{2}e^{-2t/RC}\Big|_0^\infty=-\frac{RC}{2}\left[e^{-\infty}-e^0\right]=-\frac{RC}{2}[0-1]=\boxed{+\frac{RC}{2}}.$$

P28.36 (a) $\tau=RC=\left(1.50\times10^5\ \Omega\right)\left(10.0\times10^{-6}\text{ F}\right)=\boxed{1.50\text{ s}}$

(b) $\tau=\left(1.00\times10^5\ \Omega\right)\left(10.0\times10^{-6}\text{ F}\right)=\boxed{1.00\text{ s}}$

(c) The battery carries current $\dfrac{10.0\text{ V}}{50.0\times10^3\ \Omega}=200\ \mu\text{A}$.

The 100 kΩ carries current of magnitude $I=I_0e^{-t/RC}=\left(\dfrac{10.0\text{ V}}{100\times10^3\ \Omega}\right)e^{-t/1.00\text{ s}}$.

So the switch carries downward current $\boxed{200\ \mu\text{A}+(100\ \mu\text{A})e^{-t/1.00\text{ s}}}$.

P28.37 (a) Call the potential at the left junction V_L and at the right V_R. After a "long" time, the capacitor is fully charged.

$V_L=8.00$ V because of voltage divider:

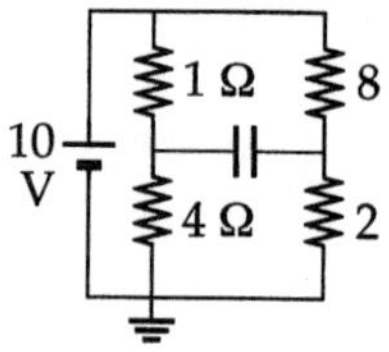

$$I_L=\frac{10.0\text{ V}}{5.00\ \Omega}=2.00\text{ A}$$

$$V_L=10.0\text{ V}-(2.00\text{ A})(1.00\ \Omega)=8.00\text{ V}$$

FIG. P28.37(a)

Likewise, $V_R=\left(\dfrac{2.00\ \Omega}{2.00\ \Omega+8.00\ \Omega}\right)(10.0\text{ V})=2.00\text{ V}$

or $I_R=\dfrac{10.0\text{ V}}{10.0\ \Omega}=1.00\text{ A}$

$V_R=(10.0\text{ V})-(8.00\ \Omega)(1.00\text{ A})=2.00\text{ V}$.

Therefore, $\Delta V=V_L-V_R=8.00-2.00=\boxed{6.00\text{ V}}$.

(b) Redraw the circuit $R=\dfrac{1}{(1/9.00\ \Omega)+(1/6.00\ \Omega)}=3.60\ \Omega$

$RC=3.60\times10^{-6}$ s

and $e^{-t/RC}=\dfrac{1}{10}$

so $t=RC\ln10=\boxed{8.29\ \mu\text{s}}$.

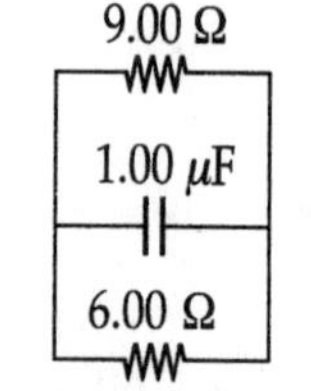

FIG. P28.37(b)

***P28.38** (a) We model the person's body and street shoes as shown. For the discharge to reach 100 V,

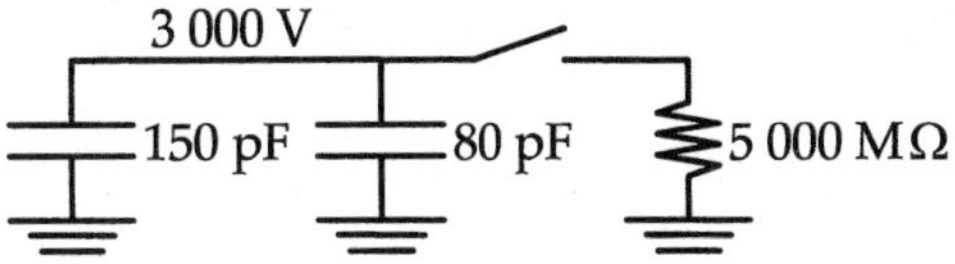

$$q(t)=Qe^{-t/RC}=C\Delta V(t)=C\Delta V_0 e^{-t/RC}$$

$$\frac{\Delta V}{\Delta V_0}=e^{-t/RC} \qquad \frac{\Delta V_0}{\Delta V}=e^{+t/RC} \qquad \frac{t}{RC}=\ln\left(\frac{\Delta V_0}{\Delta V}\right)$$

3 000 V
150 pF
80 pF
5 000 MΩ

FIG. P28.38(a)

$$t=RC\ln\left(\frac{\Delta V_0}{\Delta V}\right)=5\,000\times10^6\ \Omega\left(230\times10^{-12}\ \text{F}\right)\ln\left(\frac{3\,000}{100}\right)=\boxed{3.91\ \text{s}}$$

(b) $$t=1\times10^6\ \text{V/A}\left(230\times10^{-12}\ \text{C/V}\right)\ln 30=\boxed{782\ \mu\text{s}}$$

P28.39 (a) $$\tau=RC=\left(4.00\times10^6\ \Omega\right)\left(3.00\times10^{-6}\ \text{F}\right)=\boxed{12.0\ \text{s}}$$

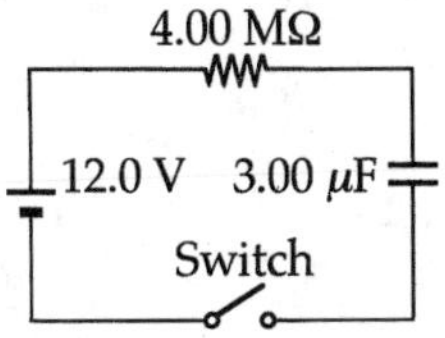

(b) $$I=\frac{\mathcal{E}}{R}e^{-t/RC}=\frac{12.0}{4.00\times10^6}e^{-t/12.0\ \text{s}}$$

$$q=C\mathcal{E}\left[1-e^{-t/RC}\right]=3.00\times10^{-6}(12.0)\left[1-e^{-t/12.0}\right]$$

$$\boxed{q=36.0\ \mu\text{C}\left[1-e^{-t/12.0}\right]} \quad \boxed{I=3.00\ \mu\text{A}e^{-t/12.0}}$$

4.00 MΩ
12.0 V
3.00 μF
Switch

FIG. P28.39

P28.40 $\Delta V_0=\dfrac{Q}{C}$

Then, if $q(t)=Qe^{-t/RC}$ $\qquad \Delta V(t)=(\Delta V_0)e^{-t/RC}$

and $\qquad \dfrac{\Delta V(t)}{(\Delta V_0)}=e^{-t/RC}.$

When $\Delta V(t)=\dfrac{1}{2}(\Delta V_0)$, then $\qquad e^{-t/RC}=\dfrac{1}{2}$

$$-\frac{t}{RC}=\ln\left(\frac{1}{2}\right)=-\ln 2.$$

Thus, $$\boxed{R=\frac{t}{C(\ln 2)}}.$$

Section 28.5 Electrical Meters

P28.41 $\Delta V=I_g r_g=\left(I-I_g\right)R_p$, or $R_p=\dfrac{I_g r_g}{\left(I-I_g\right)}=\dfrac{I_g(60.0\ \Omega)}{\left(I-I_g\right)}$

Therefore, to have $I=0.100\ \text{A}=100\ \text{mA}$ when $I_g=0.500\ \text{mA}$:

$$R_p=\frac{(0.500\ \text{mA})(60.0\ \Omega)}{99.5\ \text{mA}}=\boxed{0.302\ \Omega}.$$

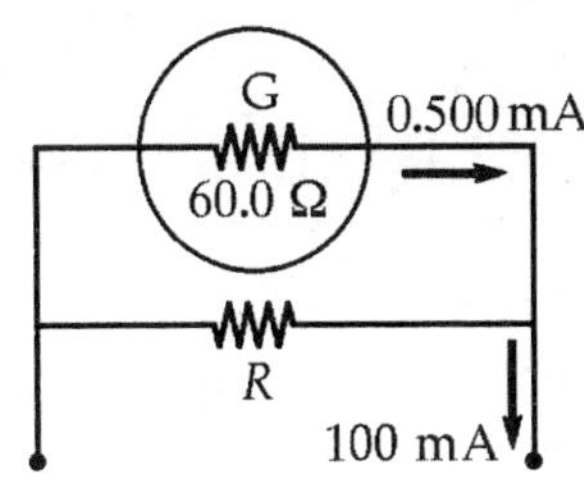

FIG. P28.41

P28.42 Applying Kirchhoff's loop rule, $-I_g(75.0\ \Omega)+\left(I-I_g\right)R_p=0$.

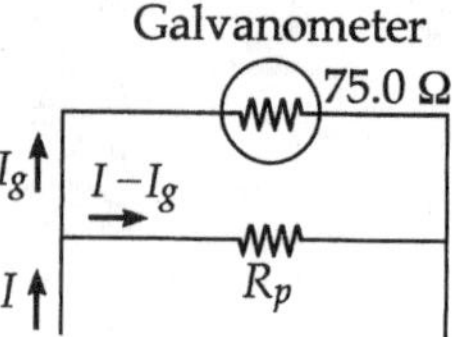

FIG. P28.42

Therefore, if $I=1.00$ A when $I_g=1.50$ mA,

$$R_p=\frac{I_g(75.0\ \Omega)}{\left(I-I_g\right)}=\frac{\left(1.50\times10^{-3}\text{ A}\right)(75.0\ \Omega)}{1.00\text{ A}-1.50\times10^{-3}\text{ A}}=\boxed{0.113\ \Omega}.$$

P28.43 Series Resistor → Voltmeter

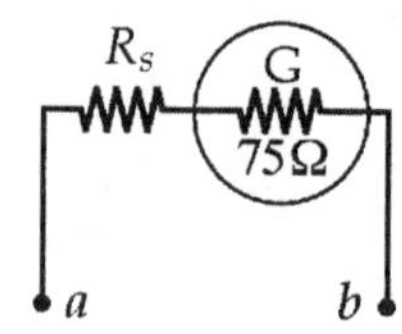

FIG. P28.43

$\Delta V=IR$: $\quad 25.0=1.50\times10^{-3}\left(R_s+75.0\right)$

Solving, $\boxed{R_s=16.6\text{ k}\Omega}$.

P28.44 (a) In Figure (a), the emf sees an equivalent resistance of $200.00\ \Omega$.

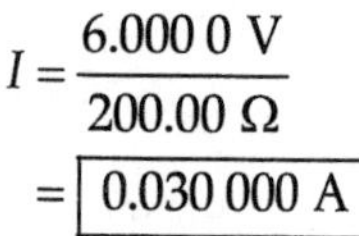

$$I=\frac{6.0000\text{ V}}{200.00\ \Omega}=\boxed{0.030000\text{ A}}$$

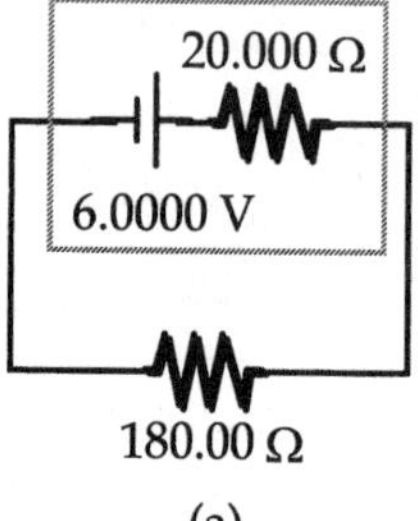

(a)

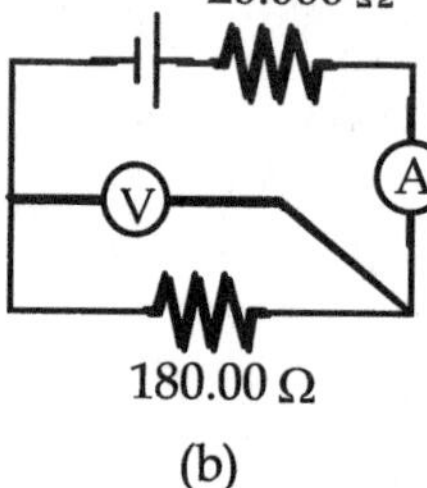

(b)

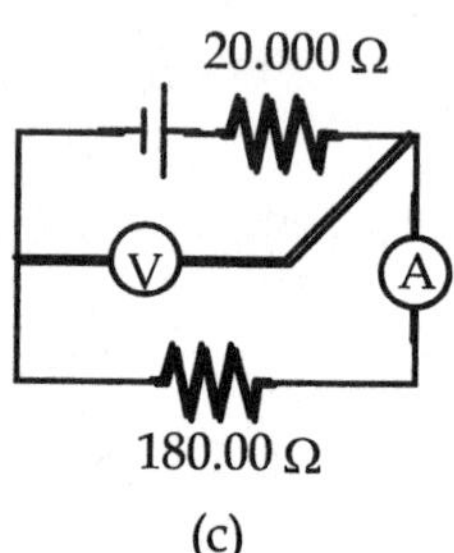

(c)

FIG. P28.44

The terminal potential difference is $\Delta V=IR=(0.030000\text{ A})(180.00\ \Omega)=\boxed{5.4000\text{ V}}$.

(b) In Figure (b), $R_{eq}=\left(\frac{1}{180.00\ \Omega}+\frac{1}{20000\ \Omega}\right)^{-1}=178.39\ \Omega$.

The equivalent resistance across the emf is $178.39\ \Omega+0.50000\ \Omega+20.000\ \Omega=198.89\ \Omega$.

The ammeter reads $I=\frac{\varepsilon}{R}=\frac{6.0000\text{ V}}{198.89\ \Omega}=\boxed{0.030167\text{ A}}$

and the voltmeter reads $\Delta V=IR=(0.030167\text{ A})(178.39\ \Omega)=\boxed{5.3816\text{ V}}$.

(c) In Figure (c), $\left(\frac{1}{180.50\ \Omega}+\frac{1}{20000\ \Omega}\right)^{-1}=178.89\ \Omega$.

Therefore, the emf sends current through $R_{\text{tot}}=178.89\ \Omega+20.000\ \Omega=198.89\ \Omega$.

The current through the battery is $I=\frac{6.0000\text{ V}}{198.89\ \Omega}=0.030168\text{ A}$

but not all of this goes through the ammeter.

The voltmeter reads $\Delta V=IR=(0.030168\text{ A})(178.89\ \Omega)=\boxed{5.3966\text{ V}}$.

The ammeter measures current $I=\frac{\Delta V}{R}=\frac{5.3966\text{ V}}{180.50\ \Omega}=\boxed{0.029898\text{ A}}$.

The connection shown in Figure (c) is better than that shown in Figure (b) for accurate readings.

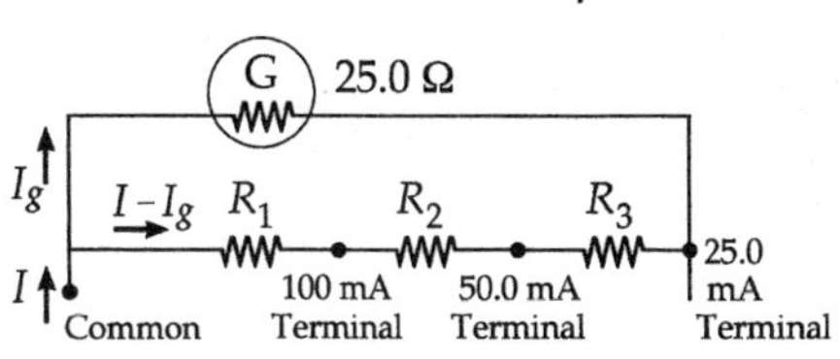

FIG. P28.45

P28.45 Consider the circuit diagram shown, realizing that $I_g = 1.00$ mA. For the 25.0 mA scale:

$$(24.0\text{ mA})(R_1 + R_2 + R_3) = (1.00\text{ mA})(25.0\ \Omega)$$

or $$R_1 + R_2 + R_3 = \left(\frac{25.0}{24.0}\right)\Omega. \qquad (1)$$

For the 50.0 mA scale: $$(49.0\text{ mA})(R_1 + R_2) = (1.00\text{ mA})(25.0\ \Omega + R_3)$$

or $$49.0(R_1 + R_2) = 25.0\ \Omega + R_3. \qquad (2)$$

For the 100 mA scale: $$(99.0\text{ mA})R_1 = (1.00\text{ mA})(25.0\ \Omega + R_2 + R_3)$$

or $$99.0R_1 = 25.0\ \Omega + R_2 + R_3. \qquad (3)$$

Solving (1), (2), and (3) simultaneously yields

$$\boxed{R_1 = 0.260\ \Omega,\ R_2 = 0.261\ \Omega,\ R_3 = 0.521\ \Omega}.$$

P28.46 $\Delta V = IR$

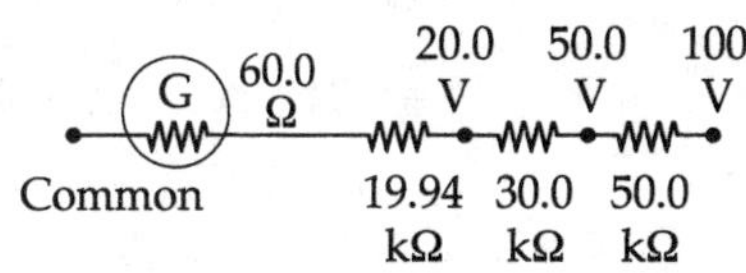

FIG. P28.46

(a) $$20.0\text{ V} = \left(1.00\times10^{-3}\text{ A}\right)(R_1 + 60.0\ \Omega)$$

$$R_1 = 1.994\times10^4\ \Omega = \boxed{19.94\text{ k}\Omega}$$

(b) $$50.0\text{ V} = \left(1.00\times10^{-3}\text{ A}\right)(R_2 + R_1 + 60.0\ \Omega) \qquad R_2 = \boxed{30.0\text{ k}\Omega}$$

(c) $$100\text{ V} = \left(1.00\times10^{-3}\text{ A}\right)(R_3 + R_1 + 60.0\ \Omega) \qquad R_3 = \boxed{50.0\text{ k}\Omega}$$

P28.47 *Ammeter:* $$I_g r = \left(0.500\text{ A} - I_g\right)(0.220\ \Omega)$$

or $$I_g(r + 0.220\ \Omega) = 0.110\text{ V} \qquad (1)$$

Voltmeter: $$2.00\text{ V} = I_g(r + 2\,500\ \Omega) \qquad (2)$$

Solve (1) and (2) simultaneously to find:

$$I_g = \boxed{0.756\text{ mA}} \text{ and } r = \boxed{145\ \Omega}.$$

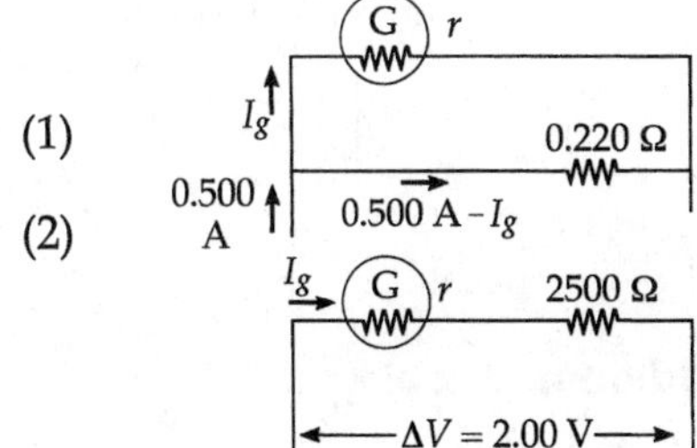

FIG. P28.47

Section 28.6 Household Wiring and Electrical Safety

P28.48 (a) $$\mathcal{P} = I^2R = I^2\left(\frac{\rho\ell}{A}\right) = \frac{(1.00\text{ A})^2\left(1.70\times10^{-8}\ \Omega\cdot\text{m}\right)(16.0\text{ ft})(0.304\,8\text{ m/ft})}{\pi\left(0.512\times10^{-3}\text{ m}\right)^2} = \boxed{0.101\text{ W}}$$

(b) $$\mathcal{P} = I^2R = 100(0.101\ \Omega) = \boxed{10.1\text{ W}}$$

P28.49 (a) $\mathscr{P} = I\Delta V$: So for the Heater, $I = \frac{\mathscr{P}}{\Delta V} = \frac{1\,500 \text{ W}}{120 \text{ V}} = \boxed{12.5 \text{ A}}$.

For the Toaster, $I = \frac{750 \text{ W}}{120 \text{ V}} = \boxed{6.25 \text{ A}}$.

And for the Grill, $I = \frac{1\,000 \text{ W}}{120 \text{ V}} = \boxed{8.33 \text{ A}}$.

(b) $12.5 + 6.25 + 8.33 = \boxed{27.1 \text{ A}}$

The current draw is greater than 25.0 amps, so this circuit breaker would not be sufficient.

P28.50 $I_{\text{Al}}^2 R_{\text{Al}} = I_{\text{Cu}}^2 R_{\text{Cu}}$ so $I_{\text{Al}} = \sqrt{\frac{R_{\text{Cu}}}{R_{\text{Al}}}} I_{\text{Cu}} = \sqrt{\frac{\rho_{\text{Cu}}}{\rho_{\text{Al}}}} I_{\text{Cu}} = \sqrt{\frac{1.70}{2.82}}(20.0) = 0.776(20.0) = \boxed{15.5 \text{ A}}$

P28.51 (a) Suppose that the insulation between either of your fingers and the conductor adjacent is a chunk of rubber with contact area 4 mm^2 and thickness 1 mm. Its resistance is

$$R = \frac{\rho \ell}{A} \approx \frac{\left(10^{13} \ \Omega \cdot \text{m}\right)\left(10^{-3} \ \text{m}\right)}{4 \times 10^{-6} \ \text{m}^2} \approx 2 \times 10^{15} \ \Omega.$$

The current will be driven by 120 V through total resistance (series)

$2 \times 10^{15} \ \Omega + 10^4 \ \Omega + 2 \times 10^{15} \ \Omega \approx 5 \times 10^{15} \ \Omega$.

It is: $I = \frac{\Delta V}{R} \sim \frac{120 \text{ V}}{5 \times 10^{15} \ \Omega} \boxed{\sim 10^{-14} \text{ A}}$.

(b) The resistors form a voltage divider, with the center of your hand at potential $\frac{V_h}{2}$, where V_h is the potential of the "hot" wire. The potential difference between your finger and thumb is $\Delta V = IR \sim \left(10^{-14} \text{ A}\right)\left(10^4 \ \Omega\right) \sim 10^{-10} \text{ V}$. So the points where the rubber meets your fingers are at potentials of

$\boxed{\sim \frac{V_h}{2} + 10^{-10} \text{ V}}$ and $\boxed{\sim \frac{V_h}{2} - 10^{-10} \text{ V}}$.

Additional Problems

P28.52 The set of four batteries boosts the electric potential of each bit of charge that goes through them by $4 \times 1.50 \text{ V} = 6.00 \text{ V}$. The chemical energy they store is

$$\Delta U = q\Delta V = (240 \text{ C})(6.00 \ \text{J/C}) = 1\,440 \text{ J}.$$

The radio draws current $I = \frac{\Delta V}{R} = \frac{6.00 \text{ V}}{200 \ \Omega} = 0.030\,0 \text{ A}$.

So, its power is $\mathscr{P} = (\Delta V)I = (6.00 \text{ V})(0.030\,0 \text{ A}) = 0.180 \text{ W} = 0.180 \ \text{J/s}$.

Then for the time the energy lasts, we have $\mathscr{P} = \frac{E}{\Delta t}$: $\Delta t = \frac{E}{\mathscr{P}} = \frac{1\,440 \text{ J}}{0.180 \ \text{J/s}} = 8.00 \times 10^3 \text{ s}$.

We could also compute this from $I = \frac{Q}{\Delta t}$: $\Delta t = \frac{Q}{I} = \frac{240 \text{ C}}{0.030\,0 \text{ A}} = 8.00 \times 10^3 \text{ s} = \boxed{2.22 \text{ h}}$.

P28.53 $I = \frac{\varepsilon}{R+r}$, so $\mathcal{P} = I^2 R = \frac{\varepsilon^2 R}{(R+r)^2}$ or $(R+r)^2 = \left(\frac{\varepsilon^2}{\mathcal{P}}\right) R$.

Let $x \equiv \frac{\varepsilon^2}{\mathcal{P}}$, then $(R+r)^2 = xR$ or $R^2 + (2r - x)R - r^2 = 0$.

With $r = 1.20\ \Omega$, this becomes $R^2 + (2.40 - x)R - 1.44 = 0$,

which has solutions of $R = \frac{-(2.40 - x) \pm \sqrt{(2.40 - x)^2 - 5.76}}{2}$.

(a) With $\varepsilon = 9.20$ V and $\mathcal{P} = 12.8$ W, $x = 6.61$:

$$R = \frac{+4.21 \pm \sqrt{(4.21)^2 - 5.76}}{2} = \boxed{3.84\ \Omega} \text{ or } \boxed{0.375\ \Omega}.$$

(b) For $\varepsilon = 9.20$ V and $\mathcal{P} = 21.2$ W, $x \equiv \frac{\varepsilon^2}{\mathcal{P}} = 3.99$

$$R = \frac{+1.59 \pm \sqrt{(1.59)^2 - 5.76}}{2} = \frac{1.59 \pm \sqrt{-3.22}}{2}.$$

The equation for the load resistance yields a complex number, so **there is no resistance** that will extract 21.2 W from this battery. The maximum power output occurs when $R = r = 1.20\ \Omega$, and that maximum is: $\mathcal{P}_{max} = \frac{\varepsilon^2}{4r} = 17.6$ W.

P28.54 Using Kirchhoff's loop rule for the closed loop, $+12.0 - 2.00I - 4.00I = 0$, so $I = 2.00$ A

$V_b - V_a = +4.00\text{ V} - (2.00\text{ A})(4.00\ \Omega) - (0)(10.0\ \Omega) = -4.00$ V.

Thus, $|\Delta V_{ab}| = \boxed{4.00\text{ V}}$ and **point *a* is at thc higher potential**.

P28.55 (a) $R_{eq} = 3R$ $\quad I = \frac{\varepsilon}{3R}$ $\quad \mathcal{P}_{series} = \varepsilon I = \boxed{\frac{\varepsilon^2}{3R}}$

(b) $R_{eq} = \frac{1}{(1/R)+(1/R)+(1/R)} = \frac{R}{3}$ $\quad I = \frac{3\varepsilon}{R}$ $\quad \mathcal{P}_{parallel} = \varepsilon I = \boxed{\frac{3\varepsilon^2}{R}}$

(c) Nine times more power is converted in the **parallel** connection.

***P28.56** (a) We model the generator as a constant-voltage power supply. Connect two light bulbs across it in series. Each bulb is designed to carry current $I = \frac{\mathcal{P}}{\Delta V} = \frac{100\text{ W}}{120\text{ V}} = 0.833$ A. Each has resistance $R = \frac{\Delta V}{I} = \frac{120\text{ V}}{0.833\text{ A}} = 144\ \Omega$. In the 240-V circuit the equivalent resistance is $144\ \Omega + 144\ \Omega = 288\ \Omega$. The current is $I = \frac{\Delta V}{R} = \frac{240\text{ V}}{288\ \Omega} = \boxed{0.833\text{ A}}$ and the generator delivers power $\mathcal{P} = I\Delta V = 0.833\text{ A}(240\text{ V}) = \boxed{200\text{ W}}$.

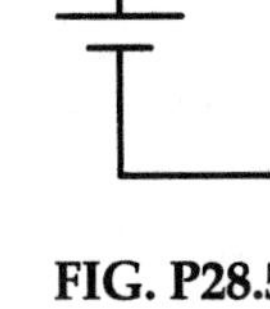

FIG. P28.56(a)

continued on next page

(b) The hot pot is designed to carry current

$$I = \frac{\mathcal{P}}{\Delta V} = \frac{500\text{ W}}{120\text{ V}} = 4.17\text{ A}.$$

It has resistance

$$R = \frac{\Delta V}{I} = \frac{120\text{ V}}{4.17\text{ A}} = 28.8\ \Omega.$$

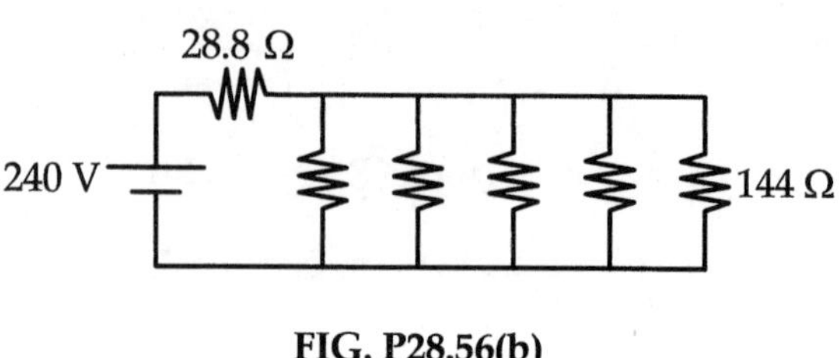

FIG. P28.56(b)

In terms of current, since $\frac{4.17\text{ A}}{0.833\text{ A}} = 5$, we can place five light bulbs in parallel and the hot pot in series with their combination. The current in the generator is then $\boxed{4.17\text{ A}}$ and it delivers power $\mathcal{P} = I\Delta V = 4.17\text{ A}(240\text{ V}) = \boxed{1\,000\text{ W}}$.

P28.57 The current in the simple loop circuit will be $I = \frac{\varepsilon}{R + r}$.

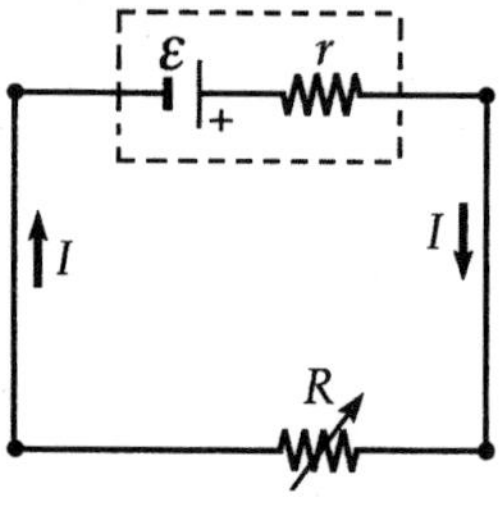

FIG. P28.57

(a) $\Delta V_{ter} = \varepsilon - Ir = \frac{\varepsilon R}{R + r}$ and $\Delta V_{ter} \to \varepsilon$ as $\boxed{R \to \infty}$.

(b) $I = \frac{\varepsilon}{R + r}$ and $I \to \frac{\varepsilon}{r}$ as $\boxed{R \to 0}$.

(c) $\mathcal{P} = I^2 R = \varepsilon^2 \frac{R}{(R + r)^2}$ $\qquad \frac{d\mathcal{P}}{dR} = \frac{-2\varepsilon^2 R}{(R + r)^3} + \frac{\varepsilon^2}{(R + r)^2} = 0$

Then $2R = R + r$ and $\boxed{R = r}$.

P28.58 The potential difference across the capacitor $\Delta V(t) = \Delta V_{max}\left(1 - e^{-t/RC}\right)$.

Using 1 Farad $= 1\ \text{s}/\Omega$, $\qquad 4.00\text{ V} = (10.0\text{ V})\left[1 - e^{-(3.00\text{ s})/\left[R\left(10.0\times 10^{-6}\ \text{s}/\Omega\right)\right]}\right]$.

Therefore, $\qquad 0.400 = 1.00 - e^{-\left(3.00\times 10^5\ \Omega\right)/R}$.

Or $\qquad e^{-\left(3.00\times 10^5\ \Omega\right)/R} = 0.600$.

Taking the natural logarithm of both sides, $\qquad -\frac{3.00\times 10^5\ \Omega}{R} = \ln(0.600)$

and $\qquad R = -\frac{3.00\times 10^5\ \Omega}{\ln(0.600)} = +5.87\times 10^5\ \Omega = \boxed{587\text{ k}\Omega}$.

P28.59 Let the two resistances be x and y.

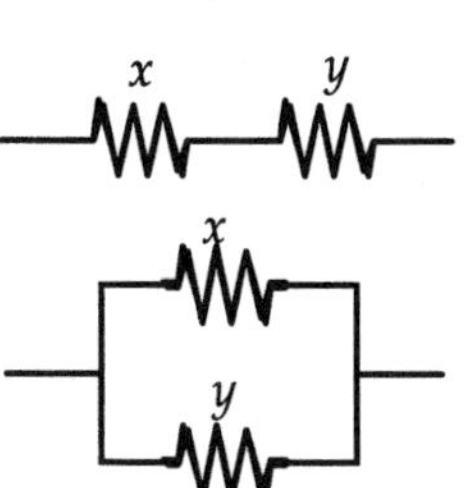

FIG. P28.59

Then, $R_s = x + y = \frac{\mathscr{P}_s}{I^2} = \frac{225\ \text{W}}{(5.00\ \text{A})^2} = 9.00\ \Omega \qquad y = 9.00\ \Omega - x$

and $R_p = \frac{xy}{x+y} = \frac{\mathscr{P}_p}{I^2} = \frac{50.0\ \text{W}}{(5.00\ \text{A})^2} = 2.00\ \Omega$

so $\frac{x(9.00\ \Omega - x)}{x + (9.00\ \Omega - x)} = 2.00\ \Omega \qquad x^2 - 9.00x + 18.0 = 0.$

Factoring the second equation, $(x - 6.00)(x - 3.00) = 0$

so $x = 6.00\ \Omega$ or $x = 3.00\ \Omega$.

Then, $y = 9.00\ \Omega - x$ gives $y = 3.00\ \Omega$ or $y = 6.00\ \Omega$.

The two resistances are found to be $\boxed{6.00\ \Omega}$ and $\boxed{3.00\ \Omega}$.

P28.60 Let the two resistances be x and y.

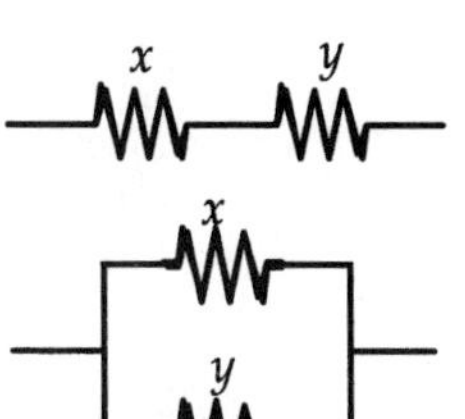

FIG. P28.60

Then, $R_s = x + y = \frac{\mathscr{P}_s}{I^2}$ and $R_p = \frac{xy}{x+y} = \frac{\mathscr{P}_p}{I^2}$.

From the first equation, $y = \frac{\mathscr{P}_s}{I^2} - x$, and the second

becomes $\frac{x\left(\mathscr{P}_s/I^2 - x\right)}{x + \left(\mathscr{P}_s/I^2 - x\right)} = \frac{\mathscr{P}_p}{I^2}$ or $x^2 - \left(\frac{\mathscr{P}_s}{I^2}\right)x + \frac{\mathscr{P}_s\mathscr{P}_p}{I^4} = 0$.

Using the quadratic formula, $x = \frac{\mathscr{P}_s \pm \sqrt{\mathscr{P}_s^2 - 4\mathscr{P}_s\mathscr{P}_p}}{2I^2}$.

Then, $y = \frac{\mathscr{P}_s}{I^2} - x$ gives $y = \frac{\mathscr{P}_s \mp \sqrt{\mathscr{P}_s^2 - 4\mathscr{P}_s\mathscr{P}_p}}{2I^2}$.

The two resistances are $\boxed{\frac{\mathscr{P}_s + \sqrt{\mathscr{P}_s^2 - 4\mathscr{P}_s\mathscr{P}_p}}{2I^2}}$ and $\boxed{\frac{\mathscr{P}_s - \sqrt{\mathscr{P}_s^2 - 4\mathscr{P}_s\mathscr{P}_p}}{2I^2}}$.

P28.61 (a) 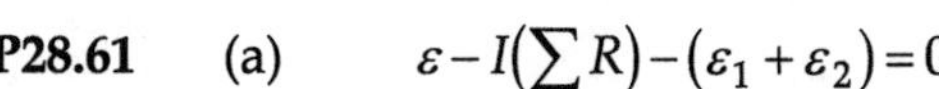

$\varepsilon - I\left(\sum R\right) - (\varepsilon_1 + \varepsilon_2) = 0$

$40.0\ \text{V} - (4.00\ \text{A})\left[(2.00 + 0.300 + 0.300 + R)\Omega\right] - (6.00 + 6.00)\ \text{V} = 0;$ so $R = \boxed{4.40\ \Omega}$

(b) Inside the supply, $\mathscr{P} = I^2R = (4.00\ \text{A})^2(2.00\ \Omega) = \boxed{32.0\ \text{W}}$.

Inside both batteries together, $\mathscr{P} = I^2R = (4.00\ \text{A})^2(0.600\ \Omega) = \boxed{9.60\ \text{W}}$.

For the limiting resistor, $\mathscr{P} = (4.00\ \text{A})^2(4.40\ \Omega) = \boxed{70.4\ \text{W}}$.

(c) $\mathscr{P} = I(\varepsilon_1 + \varepsilon_2) = (4.00\ \text{A})\left[(6.00 + 6.00)\ \text{V}\right] = \boxed{48.0\ \text{W}}$

***P28.62** (a) $\Delta V_1 = \Delta V_2 \qquad I_1R_1 = I_2R_2$

$$I = I_1 + I_2 = I_1 + \frac{I_1R_1}{R_2} = I_1\frac{R_2 + R_1}{R_2}$$

$$\boxed{I_1 = \frac{IR_2}{R_1 + R_2}}$$

$$I_2 = \frac{I_1R_1}{R_2} = \boxed{\frac{IR_1}{R_1 + R_2} = I_2}$$

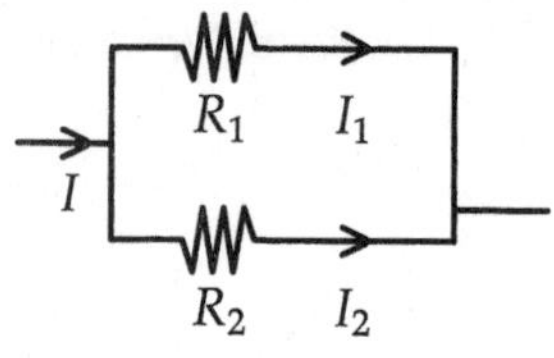

FIG. P28.62(a)

(b) The power delivered to the pair is $\mathscr{P} = I_1^2R_1 + I_2^2R_2 = I_1^2R_1 + (I - I_1)^2R_2$. For minimum power we want to find I_1 such that $\frac{d\mathscr{P}}{dI_1} = 0$.

$$\frac{d\mathscr{P}}{dI_1} = 2I_1R_1 + 2(I - I_1)(-1)R_2 = 0 \qquad I_1R_1 - IR_2 + I_1R_2 = 0$$

$$I_1 = \frac{IR_2}{R_1 + R_2}$$

This is the same condition as that found in part (a).

P28.63 Let R_m = measured value, R = actual value,

I_R = current through the resistor R

I = current measured by the ammeter.

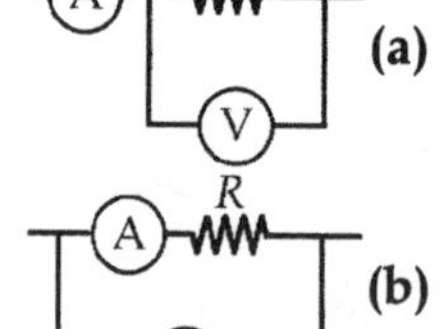

FIG. P28.63

(a) When using circuit (a), $I_RR = \Delta V = 20\,000(I - I_R)$ or $R = 20\,000\left[\frac{I}{I_R} - 1\right]$.

But since $I = \frac{\Delta V}{R_m}$ and $I_R = \frac{\Delta V}{R}$, we have $\frac{I}{I_R} = \frac{R}{R_m}$

and $$R = 20\,000\frac{(R - R_m)}{R_m}. \qquad (1)$$

When $R > R_m$, we require $\frac{(R - R_m)}{R} \le 0.050\,0$.

Therefore, $R_m \ge R(1 - 0.050\,0)$ and from (1) we find $\boxed{R \le 1\,050\ \Omega}$.

(b) When using circuit (b), $I_RR = \Delta V - I_R(0.5\ \Omega)$.

But since $I_R = \frac{\Delta V}{R_m}$, $$R_m = (0.500 + R). \qquad (2)$$

When $R_m > R$, we require $\frac{(R_m - R)}{R} \le 0.050\,0$.

From (2) we find $\boxed{R \ge 10.0\ \Omega}$.

P28.64 The battery supplies energy at a changing rate $\frac{dE}{dt} = \mathcal{P} = \mathcal{E}I = \mathcal{E}\left(\frac{\mathcal{E}}{R}e^{-1/RC}\right)$.

Then the total energy put out by the battery is $\int dE = \int_{t=0}^{\infty} \frac{\mathcal{E}^2}{R}\exp\left(-\frac{t}{RC}\right)dt$

$$\int dE = \frac{\mathcal{E}^2}{R}(-RC)\int_0^{\infty} \exp\left(-\frac{t}{RC}\right)\left(-\frac{dt}{RC}\right) = -\mathcal{E}^2 C \exp\left(-\frac{t}{RC}\right)\Big|_0^{\infty} = -\mathcal{E}^2 C[0-1] = \mathcal{E}^2 C.$$

The power delivered to the resistor is $\frac{dE}{dt} = \mathcal{P} = \Delta V_R I = I^2 R = R\frac{\mathcal{E}^2}{R^2}\exp\left(-\frac{2t}{RC}\right)$.

So the total internal energy appearing in the resistor is $\int dE = \int_0^{\infty} \frac{\mathcal{E}^2}{R}\exp\left(-\frac{2t}{RC}\right)dt$

$$\int dE = \frac{\mathcal{E}^2}{R}\left(-\frac{RC}{2}\right)\int_0^{\infty} \exp\left(-\frac{2t}{RC}\right)\left(-\frac{2dt}{RC}\right) = -\frac{\mathcal{E}^2 C}{2}\exp\left(-\frac{2t}{RC}\right)\Big|_0^{\infty} = -\frac{\mathcal{E}^2 C}{2}[0-1] = \frac{\mathcal{E}^2 C}{2}.$$

The energy finally stored in the capacitor is $U = \frac{1}{2}C(\Delta V)^2 = \frac{1}{2}C\mathcal{E}^2$. Thus, energy of the circuit is conserved $\mathcal{E}^2 C = \frac{1}{2}\mathcal{E}^2 C + \frac{1}{2}\mathcal{E}^2 C$ and resistor and capacitor share equally in the energy from the battery.

P28.65 (a) $q = C\Delta V\left(1 - e^{-t/RC}\right)$

$$q = \left(1.00\times10^{-6}\text{ F}\right)(10.0\text{ V})\left[1 - e^{-10.0/\left[\left(2.00\times10^{6}\right)\left(1.00\times10^{-6}\right)\right]}\right] = \boxed{9.93\ \mu\text{C}}$$

(b) $I = \frac{dq}{dt} = \left(\frac{\Delta V}{R}\right)e^{-t/RC}$

$$I = \left(\frac{10.0\text{ V}}{2.00\times10^{6}\ \Omega}\right)e^{-5.00} = 3.37\times10^{-8}\text{ A} = \boxed{33.7\text{ nA}}$$

(c) $\frac{dU}{dt} = \frac{d}{dt}\left(\frac{1}{2}\frac{q^2}{C}\right) = \left(\frac{q}{C}\right)\frac{dq}{dt} = \left(\frac{q}{C}\right)I$

$$\frac{dU}{dt} = \left(\frac{9.93\times10^{-6}\text{ C}}{1.00\times10^{-6}\text{ C/V}}\right)\left(3.37\times10^{-8}\text{ A}\right) = 3.34\times10^{-7}\text{ W} = \boxed{334\text{ nW}}$$

(d) $\mathcal{P}_{\text{battery}} = I\mathcal{E} = \left(3.37\times10^{-8}\text{ A}\right)(10.0\text{ V}) = 3.37\times10^{-7}\text{ W} = \boxed{337\text{ nW}}$

P28.66 Start at the point when the voltage has just reached $\frac{2}{3}\Delta V$ and the switch has just closed. The voltage is $\frac{2}{3}\Delta V$ and is decaying towards 0 V with a time constant R_2C

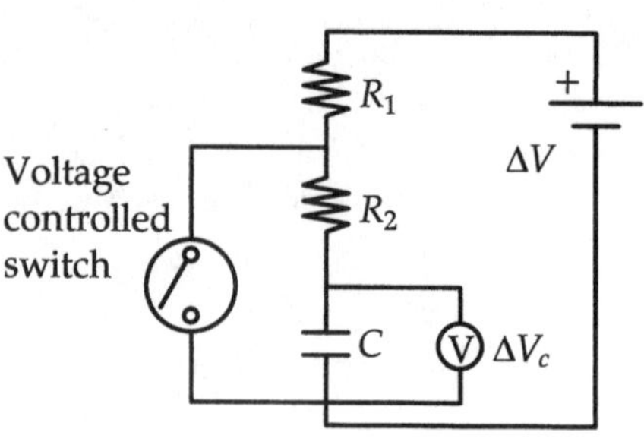

$$\Delta V_C(t) = \left[\frac{2}{3}\Delta V\right]e^{-t/R_2C}.$$

We want to know when $\Delta V_C(t)$ will reach $\frac{1}{3}\Delta V$.

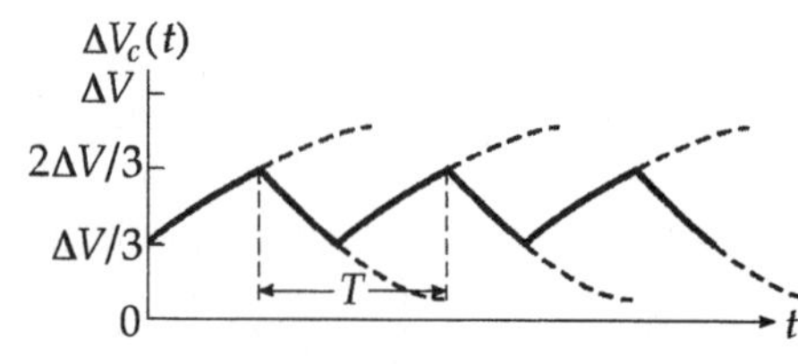

Therefore, $\frac{1}{3}\Delta V = \left[\frac{2}{3}\Delta V\right]e^{-t/R_2C}$

or $e^{-t/R_2C} = \frac{1}{2}$

or $t_1 = R_2C\ln 2$.

FIG. P28.66

After the switch opens, the voltage is $\frac{1}{3}\Delta V$, increasing toward ΔV with time constant $(R_1 + R_2)C$:

$$\Delta V_C(t) = \Delta V - \left[\frac{2}{3}\Delta V\right]e^{-t/(R_1+R_2)C}.$$

When $\Delta V_C(t) = \frac{2}{3}\Delta V$

$\frac{2}{3}\Delta V = \Delta V - \frac{2}{3}\Delta V e^{-t/(R_1+R_2)C}$ or $e^{-t/(R_1+R_2)C} = \frac{1}{2}$.

So $t_2 = (R_1 + R_2)C\ln 2$ and $T = t_1 + t_2 = \boxed{(R_1 + 2R_2)C\ln 2}$.

P28.67 (a) First determine the resistance of each light bulb: $\mathcal{P} = \frac{(\Delta V)^2}{R}$

$$R = \frac{(\Delta V)^2}{\mathcal{P}} = \frac{(120\text{ V})^2}{60.0\text{ W}} = 240\ \Omega.$$

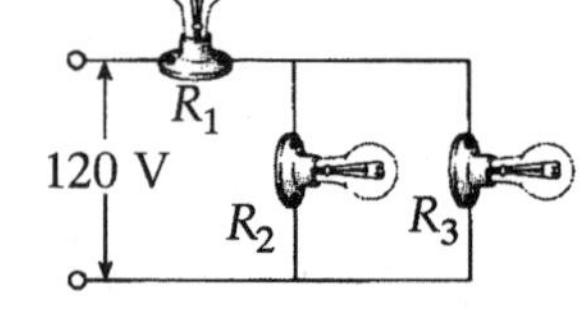

FIG. P28.67

We obtain the equivalent resistance R_{eq} of the network of light bulbs by identifying series and parallel equivalent resistances:

$$R_{eq} = R_1 + \frac{1}{(1/R_2) + (1/R_3)} = 240\ \Omega + 120\ \Omega = 360\ \Omega.$$

The total power dissipated in the 360 Ω is $\mathcal{P} = \frac{(\Delta V)^2}{R_{eq}} = \frac{(120\text{ V})^2}{360\ \Omega} = \boxed{40.0\text{ W}}$.

(b) The current through the network is given by $\mathcal{P} = I^2R_{eq}$: $I = \sqrt{\frac{\mathcal{P}}{R_{eq}}} = \sqrt{\frac{40.0\text{ W}}{360\ \Omega}} = \frac{1}{3}\text{ A}$.

The potential difference across R_1 is $\Delta V_1 = IR_1 = \left(\frac{1}{3}\text{ A}\right)(240\ \Omega) = \boxed{80.0\text{ V}}$.

The potential difference ΔV_{23} across the parallel combination of R_2 and R_3 is

$$\Delta V_{23} = IR_{23} = \left(\frac{1}{3}\text{ A}\right)\left(\frac{1}{(1/240\ \Omega) + (1/240\ \Omega)}\right) = \boxed{40.0\text{ V}}.$$

***P28.68** (a) With the switch closed, current exists in a simple series circuit as shown. The capacitors carry no current. For R_2 we have

$$\mathcal{P} = I^2 R_2 \qquad I = \sqrt{\frac{\mathcal{P}}{R_2}} = \sqrt{\frac{2.40 \text{ V}\cdot\text{A}}{7\,000 \text{ V/A}}} = 18.5 \text{ mA}.$$

I

$R_1 = 4\text{ k}\Omega$ $\quad 3\mu\text{F} = C_1$

$R_2 = 7\text{ k}\Omega$ $\quad 6\mu\text{F} = C_2$

FIG. P28.68(a)

The potential difference across R_1 and C_1 is

$$\Delta V = IR_1 = \left(1.85\times10^{-2} \text{ A}\right)\left(4\,000 \text{ V/A}\right) = 74.1 \text{ V}.$$

The charge on C_1

$$Q = C_1 \Delta V = \left(3.00\times10^{-6} \text{ C/V}\right)(74.1 \text{ V}) = \boxed{222\ \mu\text{C}}.$$

The potential difference across R_2 and C_2 is

$$\Delta V = IR_2 = \left(1.85\times10^{-2} \text{ A}\right)\left(7\,000\ \Omega\right) = 130 \text{ V}.$$

The charge on C_2

$$Q = C_2 \Delta V = \left(6.00\times10^{-6} \text{ C/V}\right)(130 \text{ V}) = 778\ \mu\text{C}.$$

The battery emf is

$$IR_{eq} = I(R_1 + R_2) = 1.85\times10^{-2} \text{ A}(4\,000 + 7\,000) \text{ V/A} = 204 \text{ V}.$$

(b) In equilibrium after the switch has been opened, no current exists. The potential difference across each resistor is zero. The full 204 V appears across both capacitors. The new charge C_2

$$Q = C_2 \Delta V = \left(6.00\times10^{-6} \text{ C/V}\right)(204 \text{ V}) = 1\,222\ \mu\text{C}$$

for a change of $1\,222\ \mu\text{C} - 778\ \mu\text{C} = \boxed{444\ \mu\text{C}}$.

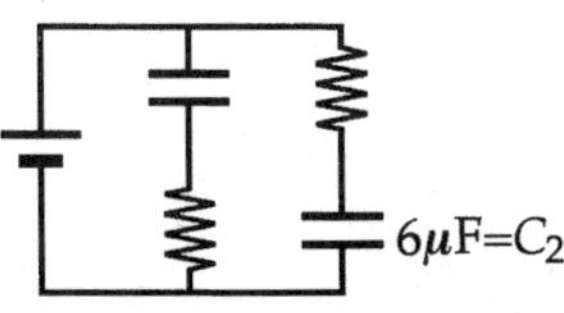

FIG. P28.68(b)

***P28.69** The battery current is

$$(150 + 45 + 14 + 4) \text{ mA} = 213 \text{ mA}.$$

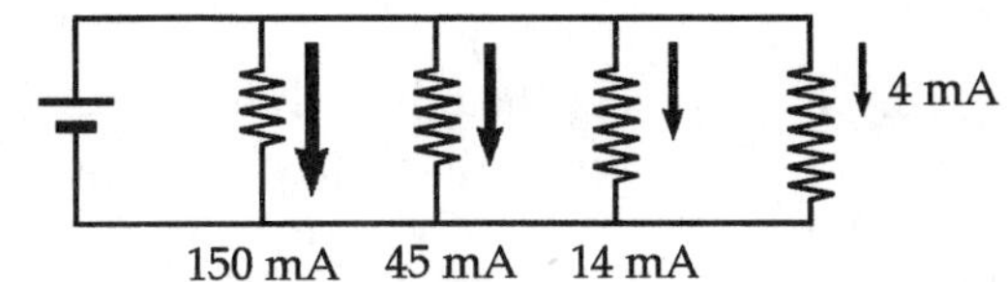

FIG. P28.69

(a) The resistor with highest resistance is that carrying 4 mA. Doubling its resistance will reduce the current it carries to 2 mA. Then the total current is

$(150 + 45 + 14 + 2) \text{ mA} = 211 \text{ mA}$, nearly the same as before. The ratio is $\frac{211}{213} = \boxed{0.991}$.

(b) The resistor with least resistance carries 150 mA. Doubling its resistance changes this current to 75 mA and changes the total to

$(75 + 45 + 14 + 4) \text{ mA} = 138 \text{ mA}$. The ratio is $\frac{138}{213} = \boxed{0.648}$, representing a much larger reduction (35.2% instead of 0.9%).

(c) This problem is precisely analogous. As a battery maintained a potential difference in parts (a) and (b), a furnace maintains a temperature difference here. Energy flow by heat is analogous to current and takes place through thermal resistances in parallel. Each resistance can have its "*R*-value" increased by adding insulation. Doubling the thermal resistance of the attic door will produce only a negligible (0.9%) saving in fuel. Doubling the thermal resistance of $\boxed{\text{the ceiling}}$ will produce a much larger saving. The ceiling originally has the smallest thermal resistance.

***P28.70** From the hint, the equivalent resistance of

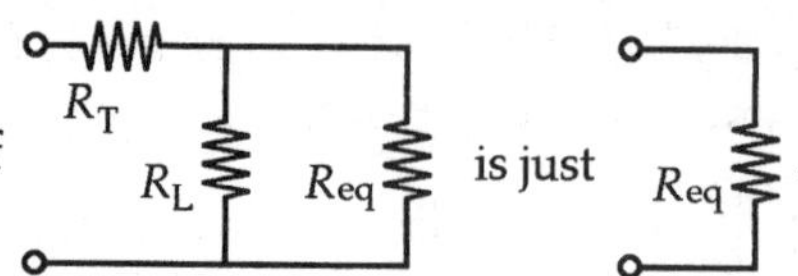

That is,
$$R_T + \frac{1}{1/R_L + 1/R_{eq}} = R_{eq}$$

$$R_T + \frac{R_L R_{eq}}{R_L + R_{eq}} = R_{eq}$$

$$R_T R_L + R_T R_{eq} + R_L R_{eq} = R_L R_{eq} + R_{eq}^2$$

$$R_{eq}^2 - R_T R_{eq} - R_T R_L = 0$$

$$R_{eq} = \frac{R_T \pm \sqrt{R_T^2 - 4(1)(-R_T R_L)}}{2(1)}$$

Only the + sign is physical:

$$R_{eq} = \frac{1}{2}\left(\sqrt{4R_T R_L + R_T^2} + R_T\right).$$

For example, if $R_T = 1\ \Omega$.

And $R_L = 20\ \Omega,\ R_{eq} = 5\ \Omega$.

P28.71 (a) After steady-state conditions have been reached, there is no DC current through the capacitor.

Thus, for R_3: $\boxed{I_{R_3} = 0 \text{ (steady-state)}}$.

For the other two resistors, the steady-state current is simply determined by the 9.00-V emf across the 12-kΩ and 15-kΩ resistors in series:

For R_1 and R_2:
$$I_{(R_1+R_2)} = \frac{\mathcal{E}}{R_1 + R_2} = \frac{9.00\text{ V}}{(12.0\text{ k}\Omega + 15.0\text{ k}\Omega)} = \boxed{333\ \mu\text{A (steady-state)}}.$$

(b) After the transient currents have ceased, the potential difference across C is the same as the potential difference across $R_2 (= IR_2)$ because there is no voltage drop across R_3. Therefore, the charge Q on C is

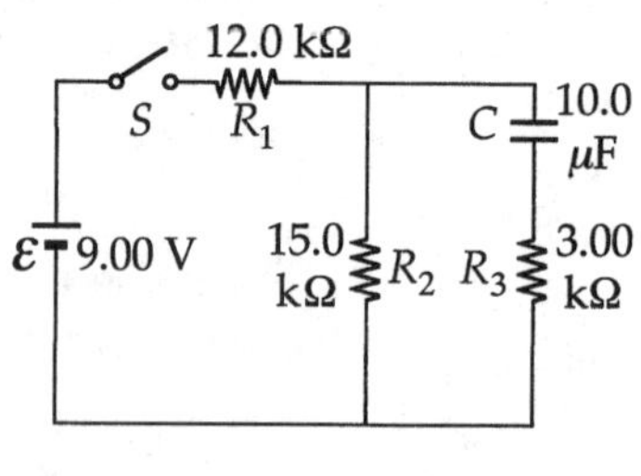

FIG. P28.71(b)

$$Q = C(\Delta V)_{R_2} = C(IR_2) = (10.0\ \mu\text{F})(333\ \mu\text{A})(15.0\text{ k}\Omega)$$
$$= \boxed{50.0\ \mu\text{C}}.$$

continued on next page

(c) When the switch is opened, the branch containing R_1 is no longer part of the circuit. The capacitor discharges through $(R_2 + R_3)$ with a time constant of $(R_2 + R_3)C = (15.0\text{ k}\Omega + 3.00\text{ k}\Omega)(10.0\ \mu\text{F}) = 0.180\text{ s}$. The initial current I_i in this discharge circuit is determined by the initial potential difference across the capacitor applied to $(R_2 + R_3)$ in series:

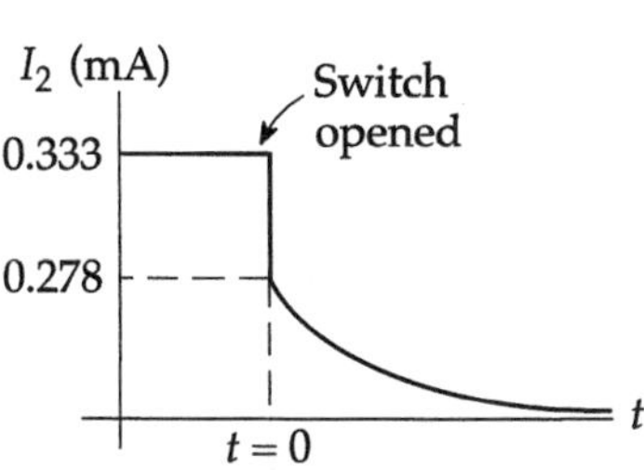

FIG. P28.71(c)

$$I_i = \frac{(\Delta V)_C}{(R_2 + R_3)} = \frac{IR_2}{(R_2 + R_3)} = \frac{(333\ \mu\text{A})(15.0\text{ k}\Omega)}{(15.0\text{ k}\Omega + 3.00\text{ k}\Omega)} = 278\ \mu\text{A}.$$

Thus, when the switch is opened, the current through R_2 changes instantaneously from 333 μA (downward) to 278 μA (downward) as shown in the graph. Thereafter, it decays according to

$$I_{R_2} = I_i e^{-t/(R_2+R_3)C} = \boxed{(278\ \mu\text{A})e^{-t/(0.180\text{ s})}\ (\text{for } t > 0)}.$$

(d) The charge q on the capacitor decays from Q_i to $\frac{Q_i}{5}$ according to

$$q = Q_i e^{-t/(R_2+R_3)C}$$

$$\frac{Q_i}{5} = Q_i e^{(-t/0.180\text{ s})}$$

$$5 = e^{t/0.180\text{ s}}$$

$$\ln 5 = \frac{t}{180\text{ ms}}$$

$$t = (0.180\text{ s})(\ln 5) = \boxed{290\text{ ms}}$$

***P28.72** (a) First let us flatten the circuit on a 2-D plane as shown; then reorganize it to a format easier to read. Notice that the five resistors on the top are in the same connection as those in Example 28.5; the same argument tells us that the middle resistor can be removed without affecting the circuit. The remaining resistors over the three parallel branches have equivalent resistance

$$R_{eq} = \left(\frac{1}{20} + \frac{1}{20} + \frac{1}{10}\right)^{-1} = \boxed{5.00\ \Omega}.$$

(b) So the current through the battery is

$$\frac{\Delta V}{R_{eq}} = \frac{12.0\text{ V}}{5.00\ \Omega} = \boxed{2.40\text{ A}}.$$

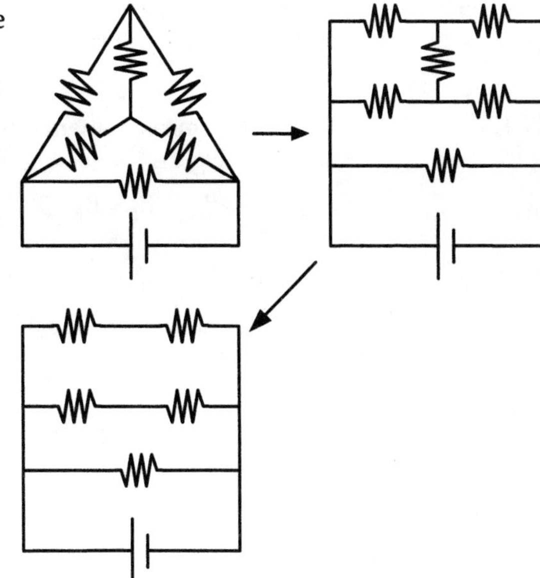

FIG. P28.72(a)

P28.73 $\Delta V = \varepsilon e^{-t/RC}$

so $\ln\left(\frac{\varepsilon}{\Delta V}\right) = \left(\frac{1}{RC}\right)t$.

A plot of $\ln\left(\frac{\varepsilon}{\Delta V}\right)$ versus t should be a straight line with slope equal to $\frac{1}{RC}$.

Using the given data values:

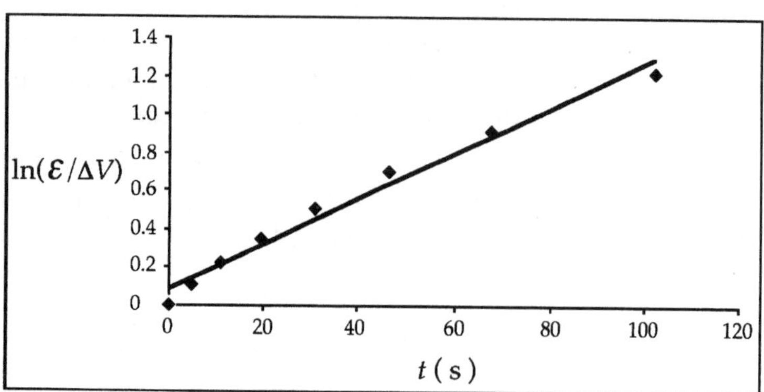

FIG. P28.73

t(s)	ΔV(V)	$\ln(\varepsilon/\Delta V)$
0	6.19	0
4.87	5.55	0.109
11.1	4.93	0.228
19.4	4.34	0.355
30.8	3.72	0.509
46.6	3.09	0.695
67.3	2.47	0.919
102.2	1.83	1.219

(a) A least-square fit to this data yields the graph above.

$\sum x_i = 282$, $\sum x_i^2 = 1.86 \times 10^4$,

$\sum x_i y_i = 244$, $\sum y_i = 4.03$, $N = 8$

$$\text{Slope} = \frac{N\left(\sum x_i y_i\right) - \left(\sum x_i\right)\left(\sum y_i\right)}{N\left(\sum x_i^2\right) - \left(\sum x_i\right)^2} = 0.011\,8$$

$$\text{Intercept} = \frac{\left(\sum x_i^2\right)\left(\sum y_i\right) - \left(\sum x_i\right)\left(\sum x_i y_i\right)}{N\left(\sum x_i^2\right) - \left(\sum x_i\right)^2} = 0.088\,2$$

The equation of the best fit line is: $\boxed{\ln\left(\frac{\varepsilon}{\Delta V}\right) = (0.011\,8)t + 0.088\,2}$.

(b) Thus, the time constant is $\tau = RC = \frac{1}{\text{slope}} = \frac{1}{0.011\,8} = \boxed{84.7 \text{ s}}$

and the capacitance is $C = \frac{\tau}{R} = \frac{84.7 \text{ s}}{10.0 \times 10^6\ \Omega} = \boxed{8.47\ \mu\text{F}}$.

P28.74 (a) For the first measurement, the equivalent circuit is as shown in Figure 1.

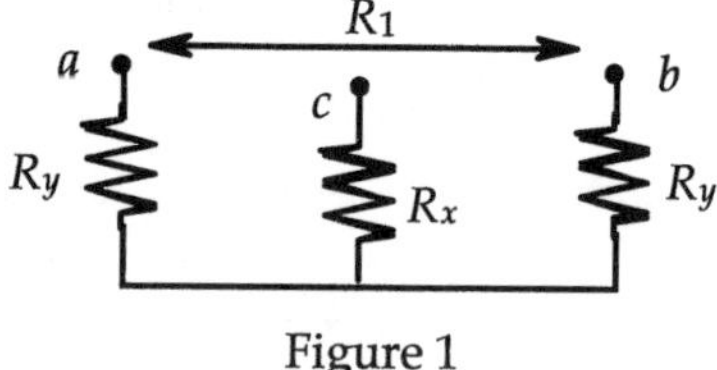

Figure 1

$$R_{ab} = R_1 = R_y + R_y = 2R_y$$

so $R_y = \frac{1}{2}R_1$. (1)

For the second measurement, the equivalent circuit is shown in Figure 2.

Thus, $R_{ac} = R_2 = \frac{1}{2}R_y + R_x$. (2)

Substitute (1) into (2) to obtain:

$$R_2 = \frac{1}{2}\left(\frac{1}{2}R_1\right) + R_x, \text{ or } \boxed{R_x = R_2 - \frac{1}{4}R_1}.$$

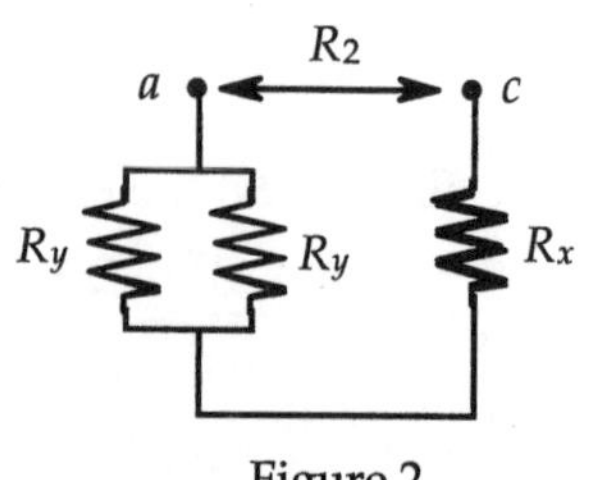

Figure 2

FIG. P28.74

(b) If $R_1 = 13.0\ \Omega$ and $R_2 = 6.00\ \Omega$, then $\boxed{R_x = 2.75\ \Omega}$.

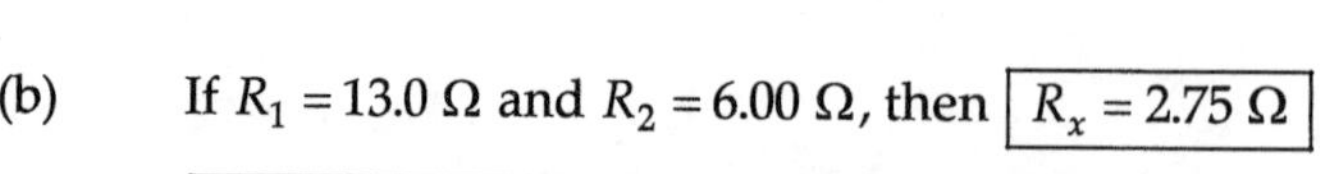

The antenna is inadequately grounded since this exceeds the limit of $2.00\ \Omega$.

P28.75 The total resistance between points b and c is:

$$R=\frac{(2.00\text{ k}\Omega)(3.00\text{ k}\Omega)}{2.00\text{ k}\Omega+3.00\text{ k}\Omega}=1.20\text{ k}\Omega.$$

The total capacitance between points d and e is:

$C=2.00\ \mu\text{F}+3.00\ \mu\text{F}=5.00\ \mu\text{F}$.

The potential difference between point d and e in this series RC circuit at any time is:

$$\Delta V=\varepsilon\left[1-e^{-t/RC}\right]=(120.0\text{ V})\left[1-e^{-1\,000t/6}\right].$$

Therefore, the charge on each capacitor between points d and e is:

$$q_1=C_1\Delta V=(2.00\ \mu\text{F})(120.0\text{ V})\left[1-e^{-1\,000t/6}\right]=\boxed{(240\ \mu\text{C})\left[1-e^{-1\,000t/6}\right]}$$

and $q_2=C_2(\Delta V)=(3.00\ \mu\text{F})(120.0\text{ V})\left[1-e^{-1\,000t/6}\right]=\boxed{(360\ \mu\text{C})\left[1-e^{-1\,000t/6}\right]}$.

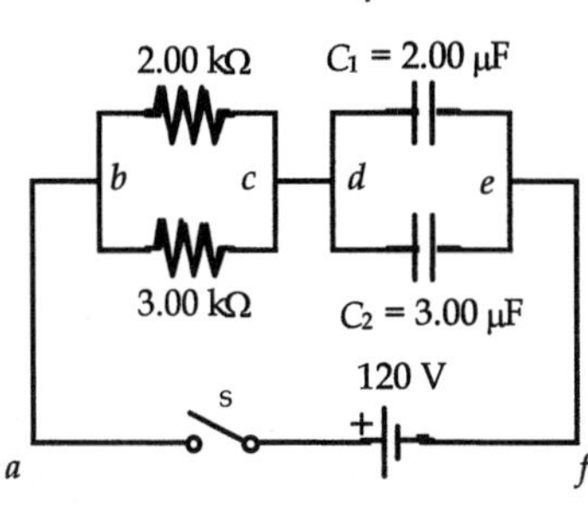

FIG. P28.75

***P28.76** (a) Let i represent the current in the battery and i_c the current charging the capacitor. Then $i-i_c$ is the current in the voltmeter. The loop rule applied to the inner loop is $+\varepsilon-iR-\frac{q}{C}=0$. The loop rule for the outer perimeter is $\varepsilon-iR-(i-i_c)r=0$. With $i_c=\frac{dq}{dt}$, this becomes $\varepsilon-iR-ir+\frac{dq}{dt}r=0$. Between the two loop equations we eliminate $i=\frac{\varepsilon}{R}-\frac{q}{RC}$ by substitution to obtain

$$\varepsilon-(R+r)\left(\frac{\varepsilon}{R}-\frac{q}{RC}\right)+\frac{dq}{dt}r=0$$

$$\varepsilon-\frac{R+r}{R}\varepsilon+\frac{R+r}{RC}q+\frac{dq}{dt}r=0$$

$$-\frac{r}{R+r}\varepsilon+\frac{q}{C}+\frac{Rr}{R+r}\frac{dq}{dt}=0$$

This is the differential equation required.

(b) To solve we follow the same steps as on page 875.

$$\frac{dq}{dt}=\frac{\varepsilon}{R}-\frac{R+r}{RrC}q=-\frac{R+r}{RrC}\left(q-\frac{\varepsilon rC}{R+r}\right)$$

$$\int_0^q\frac{dq}{q-\varepsilon rC/(R+r)}=-\frac{R+r}{RrC}\int_0^t dt \qquad \ln\left(q-\frac{\varepsilon rc}{R+r}\right)\Bigg|_0^q=-\frac{R+r}{RrC}t\Bigg|_0^t$$

$$\ln\left(\frac{q-\varepsilon rc/(R+r)}{-\varepsilon rc/(R+r)}\right)=-\frac{R+r}{RrC}t \qquad q-\frac{\varepsilon rc}{R+r}=-\frac{\varepsilon rc}{R+r}e^{[-(R+r)/RrC]t}$$

$$q=\frac{r}{r+R}C\varepsilon\left(1-e^{-t/R_{eq}C}\right)\text{ where }R_{eq}=\frac{Rr}{R+r}$$

The voltage across the capacitor is $V_C=\frac{q}{C}=\frac{r}{r+R}\varepsilon\left(1-e^{-t/R_{eq}C}\right)$.

(c) As $t\to\infty$ the capacitor voltage approaches $\frac{r}{r+R}\varepsilon(1-0)=\frac{r\varepsilon}{r+R}$. If the switch is then opened, the capacitor discharges through the voltmeter. Its voltage decays exponentially according to $\boxed{\frac{r\varepsilon}{r+R}e^{-t/rC}}$.

ANSWERS TO EVEN PROBLEMS

P28.2 (a) 1.79 A; (b) 10.4 V

P28.4 (a) 12.4 V; (b) 9.65 V

P28.6 (a) 17.1 Ω; (b) 1.99 A in 4 Ω and 9 Ω; 1.17 A in 7 Ω; 0.818 A in 10 Ω

P28.8 29.5 V

P28.10 (a) see the solution; (b) no

P28.12 see the solution

P28.14 $R_1 = 1.00$ kΩ; $R_2 = 2.00$ kΩ; $R_3 = 3.00$ kΩ

P28.16 470 Ω and 220 Ω

P28.18 (a) 11.0 Ω; (b) and (d) see the solution; (c) 220 Ω; (e) Parallel

P28.20 $I_1 = 714$ mA; $I_2 = 1.29$ A; $\varepsilon = 12.6$ V

P28.22 see the solution

P28.24 (a) 0.385 mA in R_1; 2.69 mA in R_3; 3.08 mA in R_2; (b) c higher by 69.2 V

P28.26 1.00 A up in 200 Ω; 4.00 A up in 70 Ω; 3.00 A up in 80 Ω; 8.00 A down in 20 Ω; 200 V

P28.28 see the solution

P28.30 800 W to the left-hand resistor; 25.0 W to each 4 Ω; 450 W to the right-hand resistor

P28.32 (a) −61.6 mA; (b) 0.235 μC; (c) 1.96 A

P28.34 0.982 s

P28.36 (a) 1.50 s; (b) 1.00 s; (c) $200\ \mu\text{A} + (100\ \mu\text{A})e^{-t/1.00\text{ s}}$

P28.38 (a) 3.91 s; (b) 0.782 ms

P28.40 $\dfrac{t}{C\ln 2}$

P28.42 0.113 Ω

P28.44 (a) 30.000 mA, 5.400 0 V; (b) 30.167 mA, 5.381 6 V; (c) 29.898 mA; 5.396 6 V

P28.46 see the solution

P28.48 (a) 0.101 W; (b) 10.1 W

P28.50 15.5 A

P28.52 2.22 h

P28.54 a is 4.00 V higher

P28.56 (a) see the solution; 833 mA; 200 W; (b) see the solution; 4.17 A; 1.00 kW

P28.58 587 kΩ

P28.60 $\dfrac{\mathcal{P}_s + \sqrt{\mathcal{P}_s^2 - 4\mathcal{P}_s\mathcal{P}_p}}{2I^2}$ and $\dfrac{\mathcal{P}_s - \sqrt{\mathcal{P}_s^2 - 4\mathcal{P}_s\mathcal{P}_p}}{2I^2}$

P28.62 (a) $I_1 = \dfrac{IR_2}{(R_1 + R_2)}$; $I_2 = \dfrac{IR_1}{R_1 + R_2}$; (b) see the solution

P28.64 see the solution

P28.66 $(R_1 + 2R_2)C\ln 2$

P28.68 (a) 222 μC; (b) increase by 444 μC

P28.70 see the solution

P28.72 (a) 5.00 Ω; (b) 2.40 A

P28.74 (a) $R_x = R_2 - \dfrac{R_1}{4}$; (b) no; $R_x = 2.75$ Ω

P28.76 (a) and (b) see the solution; (c) $\dfrac{r\varepsilon}{r+R}e^{-t/rC}$

29

Magnetic Fields

CHAPTER OUTLINE

ANSWERS TO QUESTIONS

Q29.1 The force is in the $+y$ direction. No, the proton will not continue with constant velocity, but will move in a circular path in the x-y plane. The magnetic force will always be perpendicular to the magnetic field and also to the velocity of the proton. As the velocity changes direction, the magnetic force on the proton does too.

Q29.2 If they are projected in the same direction into the same magnetic field, the charges are of opposite sign.

Q29.3 Not necessarily. If the magnetic field is parallel or antiparallel to the velocity of the charged particle, then the particle will experience no magnetic force.

Q29.4 One particle veers in a circular path clockwise in the page, while the other veers in a counterclockwise circular path. If the magnetic field is into the page, the electron goes clockwise and the proton counterclockwise.

Q29.5 Send the particle through the uniform field and look at its path. If the path of the particle is parabolic, then the field must be electric, as the electric field exerts a constant force on a charged particle. If you shoot a proton through an electric field, it will feel a constant force in the same direction as the electric field—it's similar to throwing a ball through a gravitational field. If the path of the particle is helical or circular, then the field is magnetic—see Question 29.1. If the path of the particle is straight, then observe the speed of the particle. If the particle accelerates, then the field is electric, as a constant force on a proton with or against its motion will make its speed change. If the speed remains constant, then the field is magnetic—see Question 29.3.

Q29.6 Similarities: Both can alter the velocity of a charged particle moving through the field. Both exert forces directly proportional to the charge of the particle feeling the force. Positive and negative charges feel forces in opposite directions. Differences: The direction of the electric force is parallel or antiparallel to the direction of the electric field, but the direction of the magnetic force is perpendicular to the magnetic field and to the velocity of the charged particle. Electric forces can accelerate a charged particle from rest or stop a moving particle, but magnetic forces cannot.

Q29.7 Since $\mathbf{F}_B = q(\mathbf{v} \times \mathbf{B})$, then the acceleration produced by a magnetic field on a particle of mass m is $\mathbf{a}_B = \frac{q}{m}(\mathbf{v} \times \mathbf{B})$. For the acceleration to change the speed, a component of the acceleration must be in the direction of the velocity. The cross product tells us that the acceleration must be perpendicular to the velocity, and thus can only change the direction of the velocity.

Q29.8 The magnetic field in a cyclotron essentially keeps the charged particle in the electric field for a longer period of time, and thus experiencing a larger change in speed from the electric field, by forcing it in a spiral path. Without the magnetic field, the particle would have to move in a straight line through an electric field over a distance that is very large compared to the size of the cyclotron.

Q29.9 (a) The $q\mathbf{v} \times \mathbf{B}$ force on each electron is down. Since electrons are negative, $\mathbf{v} \times \mathbf{B}$ must be up. With $\mathbf{v}$ to the right, $\mathbf{B}$ must be into the page, away from you.

(b) Reversing the current in the coils would reverse the direction of $\mathbf{B}$, making it toward you. Then $\mathbf{v} \times \mathbf{B}$ is in the direction **right** × **toward you** = **down,** and $q\mathbf{v} \times \mathbf{B}$ will make the electron beam curve up.

Q29.10 If the current is in a direction *parallel* or *antiparallel* to the magnetic field, then there is no force.

Q29.11 Yes. If the magnetic field is perpendicular to the plane of the loop, then it exerts no torque on the loop.

Q29.12 If you can hook a spring balance to the particle and measure the force on it in a known electric field, then $q = \frac{F}{E}$ will tell you its charge. You cannot hook a spring balance to an electron. Measuring the acceleration of small particles by observing their deflection in known electric and magnetic fields can tell you the charge-to-mass ratio, but not separately the charge or mass. Both an acceleration produced by an electric field and an acceleration caused by a magnetic field depend on the properties of the particle only by being proportional to the ratio $\frac{q}{m}$.

Q29.13 If the current loop feels a torque, it must be caused by a magnetic field. If the current loop feels no torque, try a different orientation—the torque is zero if the field is along the axis of the loop.

Q29.14 The Earth's magnetic field exerts force on a charged incoming cosmic ray, tending to make it spiral around a magnetic field line. If the particle energy is low enough, the spiral will be tight enough that the particle will first hit some matter as it follows a field line down into the atmosphere or to the surface at a high geographic latitude.

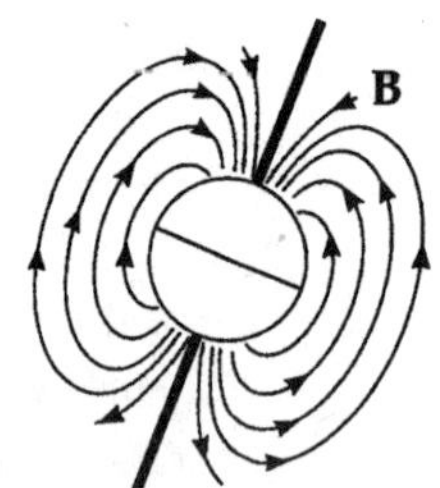

FIG. Q29.14

Q29.15 The net force is zero, but not the net torque.

Q29.16 Only a non-uniform field can exert a non-zero force on a magnetic dipole. If the dipole is aligned with the field, the direction of the resultant force is in the direction of increasing field strength.

Q29.17 The proton will veer upward when it enters the field and move in a counter-clockwise semicircular arc. An electron would turn downward and move in a clockwise semicircular arc of smaller radius than that of the proton, due to its smaller mass.

Q29.18 Particles of higher speeds will travel in semicircular paths of proportionately larger radius. They will take just the same time to travel farther with their higher speeds. As shown in Equation 29.15, the time it takes to follow the path is independent of particle's speed.

Q29.19 The spiral tracks are left by charged particles gradually losing kinetic energy. A straight path might be left by an uncharged particle that managed to leave a trail of bubbles, or it might be the imperceptibly curving track of a very fast charged particle.

Q29.20 No. Changing the velocity of a particle requires an accelerating force. The magnetic force is proportional to the speed of the particle. If the particle is not moving, there can be no magnetic force on it.

Q29.21 Increase the current in the probe. If the material is a semiconductor, raising its temperature may increase the density of mobile charge carriers in it.

SOLUTIONS TO PROBLEMS

Section 29.1 Magnetic Fields and Forces

P29.1 (a) up

(b) out of the page, since the charge is negative.

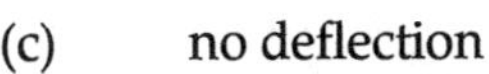

(c) no deflection

(d) into the page

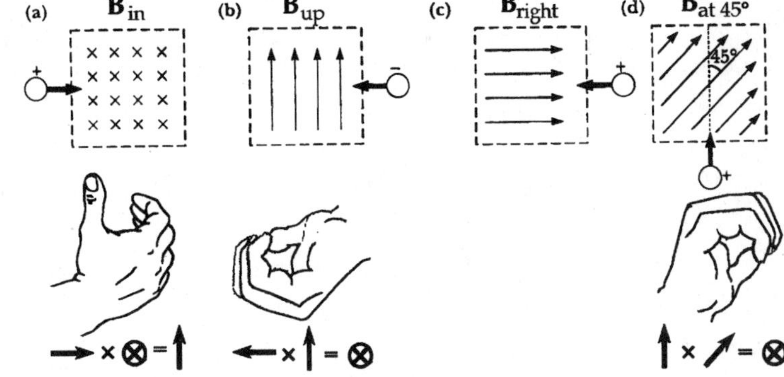

FIG. P29.1

P29.2 At the equator, the Earth's magnetic field is horizontally north. Because an electron has negative charge, $\mathbf{F} = q\mathbf{v} \times \mathbf{B}$ is opposite in direction to $\mathbf{v} \times \mathbf{B}$. Figures are drawn looking down.

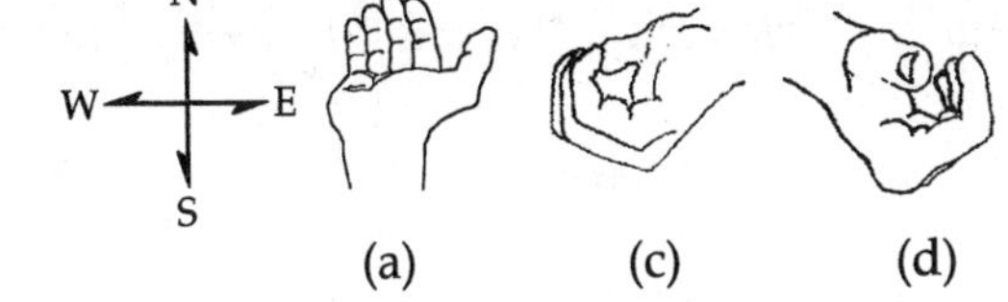

FIG. P29.2

(a) Down × North = East, so the force is directed $\boxed{\text{West}}$.

(b) North × North $= \sin 0° = 0$: $\boxed{\text{Zero deflection}}$.

(c) West × North = Down, so the force is directed $\boxed{\text{Up}}$.

(d) Southeast × North = Up, so the force is $\boxed{\text{Down}}$.

P29.3 $\mathbf{F}_B = q\mathbf{v}\times\mathbf{B}$; $|\mathbf{F}_B|(-\hat{\mathbf{j}}) = -e|\mathbf{v}|\hat{\mathbf{i}}\times\mathbf{B}$

Therefore, $B = |\mathbf{B}|(-\hat{\mathbf{k}})$ which indicates the $\boxed{\text{negative } z \text{ direction}}$.

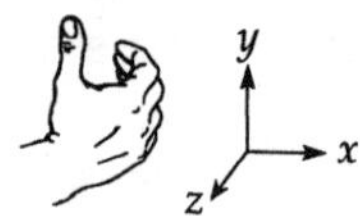

FIG. P29.3

P29.4 (a) $F_B = qvB\sin\theta = (1.60\times10^{-19}\text{ C})(3.00\times10^{6}\text{ m/s})(3.00\times10^{-1}\text{ T})\sin 37.0°$

$F_B = \boxed{8.67\times10^{-14}\text{ N}}$

(b) $a = \frac{F}{m} = \frac{8.67\times10^{-14}\text{ N}}{1.67\times10^{-27}\text{ kg}} = \boxed{5.19\times10^{13}\text{ m/s}^2}$

P29.5 $F = ma = (1.67\times10^{-27}\text{ kg})(2.00\times10^{13}\text{ m/s}^2) = 3.34\times10^{-14}\text{ N} = qvB\sin 90°$

$B = \frac{F}{qv} = \frac{3.34\times10^{-14}\text{ N}}{(1.60\times10^{-19}\text{ C})(1.00\times10^{7}\text{ m/s})} = \boxed{2.09\times10^{-2}\text{ T}}$

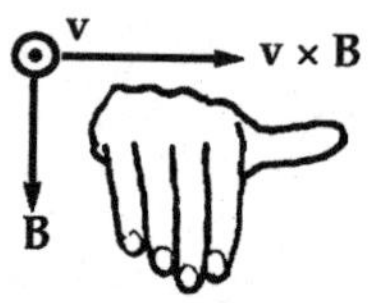

The right-hand rule shows that B must be in the $-y$ direction to yield a force in the $+x$ direction when v is in the z direction.

FIG. P29.5

P29.6 First find the speed of the electron.

$\Delta K = \frac{1}{2}mv^2 = e\Delta V = \Delta U$: $\quad v = \sqrt{\frac{2e\Delta V}{m}} = \sqrt{\frac{2(1.60\times10^{-19}\text{ C})(2\,400\text{ J/C})}{(9.11\times10^{-31}\text{ kg})}} = 2.90\times10^{7}\text{ m/s}$

(a) $F_{B,\,\max} = qvB = (1.60\times10^{-19}\text{ C})(2.90\times10^{7}\text{ m/s})(1.70\text{ T}) = \boxed{7.90\times10^{-12}\text{ N}}$

(b) $F_{B,\,\min} = \boxed{0}$ occurs when **v** is either parallel to or anti-parallel to **B**.

P29.7 $F_B = qvB\sin\theta$ so $8.20\times10^{-13}\text{ N} = (1.60\times10^{-19}\text{ C})(4.00\times10^{6}\text{ m/s})(1.70\text{ T})\sin\theta$

$\sin\theta = 0.754$ and $\theta = \sin^{-1}(0.754) = \boxed{48.9°\text{ or }131°}$.

P29.8 Gravitational force: $F_g = mg = (9.11\times10^{-31}\text{ kg})(9.80\text{ m/s}^2) = \boxed{8.93\times10^{-30}\text{ N down}}$.

Electric force: $F_e = qE = (-1.60\times10^{-19}\text{ C})(100\text{ N/C down}) = \boxed{1.60\times10^{-17}\text{ N up}}$.

Magnetic force: $\mathbf{F}_B = q\mathbf{v}\times\mathbf{B} = (-1.60\times10^{-19}\text{ C})(6.00\times10^{6}\text{ m/s }\hat{\mathbf{E}})\times(50.0\times10^{-6}\text{ N}\cdot\text{s/C}\cdot\text{m }\hat{\mathbf{N}})$.

$\mathbf{F}_B = -4.80\times10^{-17}\text{ N up} = \boxed{4.80\times10^{-17}\text{ N down}}$.

P29.9 $\mathbf{F}_B = q\mathbf{v}\times\mathbf{B}$

$$\mathbf{v}\times\mathbf{B} = \begin{vmatrix} \hat{\mathbf{i}} & \hat{\mathbf{j}} & \hat{\mathbf{k}} \\ +2 & -4 & +1 \\ +1 & +2 & -3 \end{vmatrix} = (12-2)\hat{\mathbf{i}} + (1+6)\hat{\mathbf{j}} + (4+4)\hat{\mathbf{k}} = 10\hat{\mathbf{i}} + 7\hat{\mathbf{j}} + 8\hat{\mathbf{k}}$$

$$|\mathbf{v}\times\mathbf{B}| = \sqrt{10^2+7^2+8^2} = 14.6\ \text{T}\cdot\text{m/s}$$

$$|\mathbf{F}_B| = q|\mathbf{v}\times\mathbf{B}| = \left(1.60\times10^{-19}\ \text{C}\right)\left(14.6\ \text{T}\cdot\text{m/s}\right) = \boxed{2.34\times10^{-18}\ \text{N}}$$

P29.10 $q\mathbf{E} = \left(-1.60\times10^{-19}\ \text{C}\right)(20.0\ \text{N/C})\hat{\mathbf{k}} = \left(-3.20\times10^{-18}\ \text{N}\right)\hat{\mathbf{k}}$

$$\sum\mathbf{F} = q\mathbf{E} + q\mathbf{v}\times\mathbf{B} = m\mathbf{a}$$

$$\left(-3.20\times10^{-18}\ \text{N}\right)\hat{\mathbf{k}} - 1.60\times10^{-19}\ \text{C}\left(1.20\times10^{4}\ \text{m/s}\,\hat{\mathbf{i}}\right)\times\mathbf{B} = \left(9.11\times10^{-31}\right)\left(2.00\times10^{12}\ \text{m/s}^2\right)\hat{\mathbf{k}}$$

$$-\left(3.20\times10^{-18}\ \text{N}\right)\hat{\mathbf{k}} - \left(1.92\times10^{-15}\ \text{C}\cdot\text{m/s}\right)\hat{\mathbf{i}}\times\mathbf{B} = \left(1.82\times10^{-18}\ \text{N}\right)\hat{\mathbf{k}}$$

$$\left(1.92\times10^{-15}\ \text{C}\cdot\text{m/s}\right)\hat{\mathbf{i}}\times\mathbf{B} = -\left(5.02\times10^{-18}\ \text{N}\right)\hat{\mathbf{k}}$$

The magnetic field $\boxed{\text{may have any } x\text{-component}}$. $B_z = \boxed{0}$ and $B_y = \boxed{-2.62\ \text{mT}}$.

Section 29.2 Magnetic Force Acting on a Current-Carrying Conductor

P29.11 $F_B = ILB\sin\theta$ with $F_B = F_g = mg$

$mg = ILB\sin\theta$ so $\frac{m}{L}g = IB\sin\theta$

$I = 2.00\ \text{A}$ and $\frac{m}{L} = (0.500\ \text{g/cm})\left(\frac{100\ \text{cm/m}}{1\,000\ \text{g/kg}}\right) = 5.00\times10^{-2}\ \text{kg/m}.$

Thus $\left(5.00\times10^{-2}\right)(9.80) = (2.00)B\sin 90.0°$

$B = \boxed{0.245\ \text{Tesla}}$ with the direction given by right-hand rule: $\boxed{\text{eastward}}$.

FIG. P29.11

P29.12 $\mathbf{F}_B = I\boldsymbol{\ell}\times\mathbf{B} = (2.40\ \text{A})(0.750\ \text{m})\hat{\mathbf{i}}\times(1.60\ \text{T})\hat{\mathbf{k}} = \boxed{\left(-2.88\hat{\mathbf{j}}\right)\ \text{N}}$

P29.13 (a) $F_B = ILB\sin\theta = (5.00\ \text{A})(2.80\ \text{m})(0.390\ \text{T})\sin 60.0° = \boxed{4.73\ \text{N}}$

(b) $F_B = (5.00\ \text{A})(2.80\ \text{m})(0.390\ \text{T})\sin 90.0° = \boxed{5.46\ \text{N}}$

(c) $F_B = (5.00\ \text{A})(2.80\ \text{m})(0.390\ \text{T})\sin 120° = \boxed{4.73\ \text{N}}$

P29.14 $\dfrac{|\mathbf{F}_B|}{\ell} = \dfrac{mg}{\ell} = \dfrac{I|\boldsymbol{\ell} \times \mathbf{B}|}{\ell}$

$$I = \frac{mg}{B\ell} = \frac{(0.040\,0\text{ kg/m})(9.80\text{ m/s}^2)}{3.60\text{ T}} = \boxed{0.109\text{ A}}$$

The direction of I in the bar is $\boxed{\text{to the right}}$.

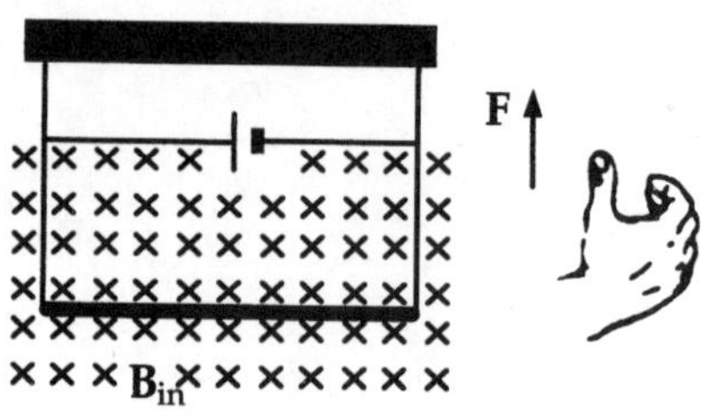

FIG. P29.14

P29.15 The rod feels force $\mathbf{F}_B = I(\mathbf{d} \times \mathbf{B}) = Id(\hat{\mathbf{k}}) \times B(-\hat{\mathbf{j}}) = IdB(\hat{\mathbf{i}})$.

The work-energy theorem is $(K_{\text{trasn}} + K_{\text{rot}})_i + \Delta E = (K_{\text{trans}} + K_{\text{rot}})_f$

$$0 + 0 + F_s \cos\theta = \frac{1}{2}mv^2 + \frac{1}{2}I\omega^2$$

$$IdBL\cos 0° = \frac{1}{2}mv^2 + \frac{1}{2}\left(\frac{1}{2}mR^2\right)\left(\frac{v}{R}\right)^2 \text{ and } IdBL = \frac{3}{4}mv^2$$

$$v = \sqrt{\frac{4IdBL}{3m}} = \sqrt{\frac{4(48.0\text{ A})(0.120\text{ m})(0.240\text{ T})(0.450\text{ m})}{3(0.720\text{ kg})}} = \boxed{1.07\text{ m/s}}.$$

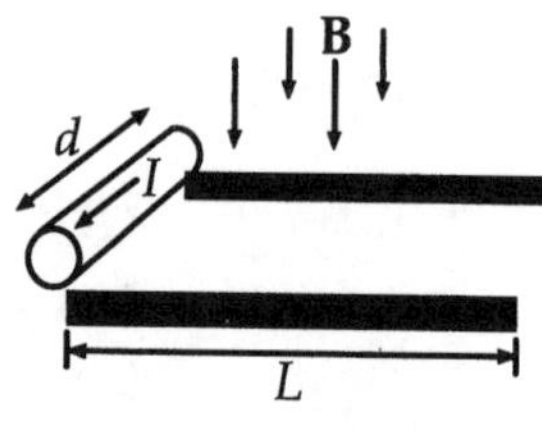

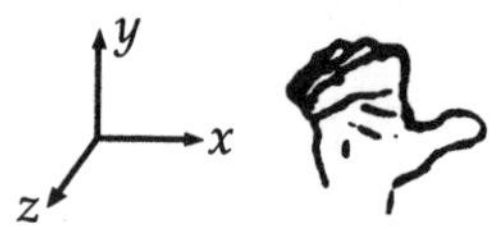

FIG. P29.15

P29.16 The rod feels force $\mathbf{F}_B = I(\mathbf{d} \times \mathbf{B}) = Id(\hat{\mathbf{k}}) \times B(-\hat{\mathbf{j}}) = IdB(\hat{\mathbf{i}})$.

The work-energy theorem is $(K_{\text{trans}} + K_{\text{rot}})_i + \Delta E = (K_{\text{trans}} + K_{\text{rot}})_f$

$$0 + 0 + Fs\cos\theta = \frac{1}{2}mv^2 + \frac{1}{2}I\omega^2$$

$$IdBL\cos 0° = \frac{1}{2}mv^2 + \frac{1}{2}\left(\frac{1}{2}mR^2\right)\left(\frac{v}{R}\right)^2 \text{ and } v = \boxed{\sqrt{\frac{4IdBL}{3m}}}.$$

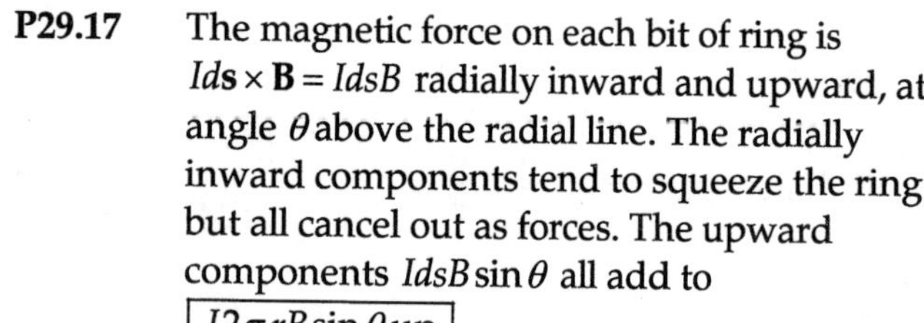

P29.17 The magnetic force on each bit of ring is $Id\mathbf{s} \times \mathbf{B} = IdsB$ radially inward and upward, at angle θ above the radial line. The radially inward components tend to squeeze the ring but all cancel out as forces. The upward components $IdsB\sin\theta$ all add to $\boxed{I2\pi rB\sin\theta \text{ up}}$.

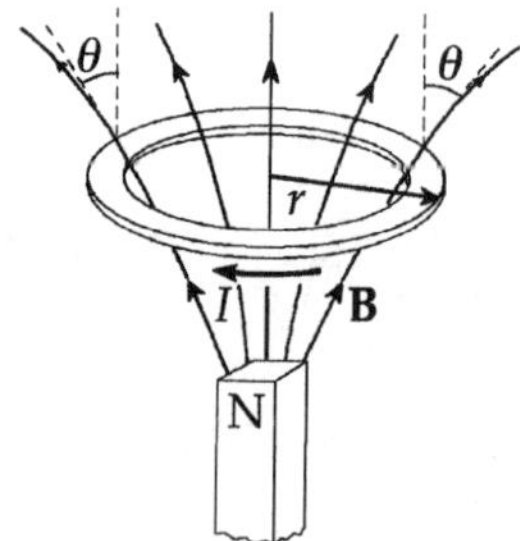

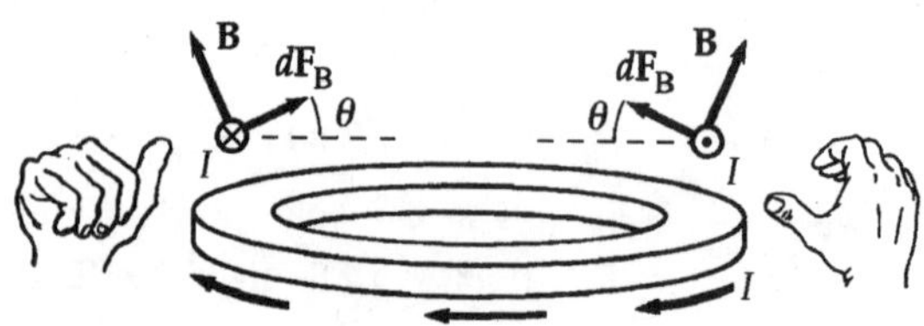

FIG. P29.17

P29.18 For each segment, $I = 5.00$ A and $\mathbf{B} = 0.020\,0\ \text{N/A}\cdot\text{m}\,\hat{\mathbf{j}}$.

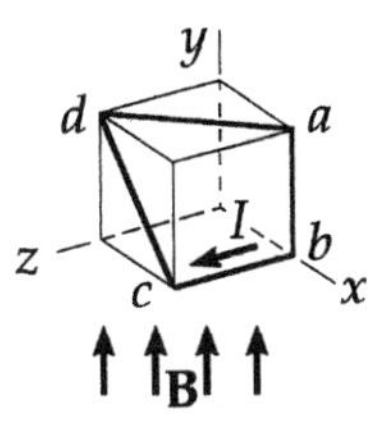

FIG. P29.18

Segment	ℓ	$\mathbf{F}_B = I(\ell \times \mathbf{B})$
ab	$-0.400\text{ m}\,\hat{\mathbf{j}}$	$\boxed{0}$
bc	$0.400\text{ m}\,\hat{\mathbf{k}}$	$\boxed{(40.0\text{ mN})(-\hat{\mathbf{i}})}$
cd	$-0.400\text{ m}\,\hat{\mathbf{i}} + 0.400\text{ m}\,\hat{\mathbf{j}}$	$\boxed{(40.0\text{ mN})(-\hat{\mathbf{k}})}$
da	$0.400\text{ m}\,\hat{\mathbf{i}} - 0.400\text{ m}\,\hat{\mathbf{k}}$	$\boxed{(40.0\text{ mN})(\hat{\mathbf{k}} + \hat{\mathbf{i}})}$

P29.19 Take the x-axis east, the y-axis up, and the z-axis south. The field is

FIG. P29.19

$$\mathbf{B} = (52.0\ \mu\text{T})\cos 60.0°(-\hat{\mathbf{k}}) + (52.0\ \mu\text{T})\sin 60.0°(-\hat{\mathbf{j}}).$$

The current then has equivalent length: $\mathbf{L}' = 1.40\text{ m}(-\hat{\mathbf{k}}) + 0.850\text{ m}(\hat{\mathbf{j}})$

$$\mathbf{F}_B = I\mathbf{L}' \times \mathbf{B} = (0.035\,0\text{ A})(0.850\hat{\mathbf{j}} - 1.40\hat{\mathbf{k}})\text{ m} \times (-45.0\hat{\mathbf{j}} - 26.0\hat{\mathbf{k}})10^{-6}\text{ T}$$

$$\mathbf{F}_B = 3.50 \times 10^{-8}\text{ N}(-22.1\hat{\mathbf{i}} - 63.0\hat{\mathbf{i}}) = 2.98 \times 10^{-6}\text{ N}(-\hat{\mathbf{i}}) = \boxed{2.98\ \mu\text{N west}}$$

Section 29.3 Torque on a Current Loop in a Uniform Magnetic Field

P29.20 (a) $2\pi r = 2.00$ m

so $r = 0.318$ m

$$\mu = IA = (17.0 \times 10^{-3}\text{ A})\left[\pi(0.318)^2\text{ m}^2\right] = \boxed{5.41\text{ mA}\cdot\text{m}^2}$$

(b) $\boldsymbol{\tau} = \boldsymbol{\mu} \times \mathbf{B}$

so $\tau = (5.41 \times 10^{-3}\text{ A}\cdot\text{m}^2)(0.800\text{ T}) = \boxed{4.33\text{ mN}\cdot\text{m}}$

P29.21 $\tau = \mu B \sin\theta$ so $4.60 \times 10^{-3}\text{ N}\cdot\text{m} = \mu(0.250)\sin 90.0°$

$$\mu = 1.84 \times 10^{-2}\text{ A}\cdot\text{m}^2 = \boxed{18.4\text{ mA}\cdot\text{m}^2}$$

P29.22 (a) Let θ represent the unknown angle; L, the total length of the wire; and d, the length of one side of the square coil. Then, using the definition of magnetic moment and the right-hand rule in Figure 29.15, we find

$\mu = NAI$: $\qquad \mu = \left(\frac{L}{4d}\right)d^2 I$ at angle θ with the horizontal.

At equilibrium, $\qquad \sum \boldsymbol{\tau} = (\boldsymbol{\mu} \times \mathbf{B}) - (\mathbf{r} \times m\mathbf{g}) = 0$

$$\left(\frac{ILBd}{4}\right)\sin(90.0°-\theta) - \left(\frac{mgd}{2}\right)\sin\theta = 0$$

and $\qquad \left(\frac{mgd}{2}\right)\sin\theta = \left(\frac{ILBd}{4}\right)\cos\theta$

$$\theta = \tan^{-1}\left(\frac{ILB}{2mg}\right) = \tan^{-1}\left(\frac{(3.40\text{ A})(4.00\text{ m})(0.010\,0\text{ T})}{2(0.100\text{ kg})(9.80\text{ m/s}^2)}\right) = \boxed{3.97°}.$$

(b) $\tau_m = \left(\frac{ILBd}{4}\right)\cos\theta = \frac{1}{4}(3.40\text{ A})(4.00\text{ m})(0.010\,0\text{ T})(0.100\text{ m})\cos 3.97° = \boxed{3.39\text{ mN}\cdot\text{m}}$

P29.23 $\tau = NBAI\sin\phi$

$\tau = 100(0.800\text{ T})(0.400 \times 0.300\text{ m}^2)(1.20\text{ A})\sin 60°$

$\tau = \boxed{9.98\text{ N}\cdot\text{m}}$

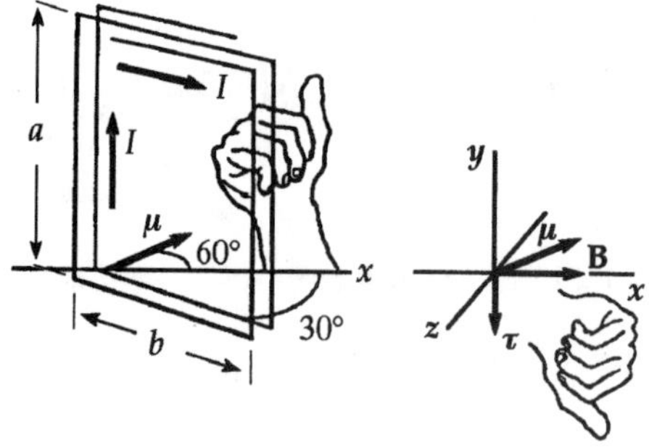

FIG. P29.23

Note that ϕ is the angle between the magnetic moment and the **B** field. The loop will rotate so as to align the magnetic moment with the **B** field. Looking down along the y-axis, the loop will rotate in a $\boxed{\text{clockwise}}$ direction.

P29.24 From $\boldsymbol{\tau} = \boldsymbol{\mu} \times \mathbf{B} = I\mathbf{A} \times \mathbf{B}$, the magnitude of the torque is $IAB\sin 90.0°$.

(a) Each side of the triangle is $\frac{40.0\text{ cm}}{3}$.

Its altitude is $\sqrt{13.3^2 - 6.67^2}\text{ cm} = 11.5\text{ cm}$ and its area is

$A = \frac{1}{2}(11.5\text{ cm})(13.3\text{ cm}) = 7.70 \times 10^{-3}\text{ m}^2$.

Then $\tau = (20.0\text{ A})(7.70 \times 10^{-3}\text{ m}^2)(0.520\text{ N}\cdot\text{s/C}\cdot\text{m}) = \boxed{80.1\text{ mN}\cdot\text{m}}$.

(b) Each side of the square is 10.0 cm and its area is $100\text{ cm}^2 = 10^{-2}\text{ m}^2$.

$\tau = (20.0\text{ A})(10^{-2}\text{ m}^2)(0.520\text{ T}) = \boxed{0.104\text{ N}\cdot\text{m}}$

(c) $r = \frac{0.400\text{ m}}{2\pi} = 0.063\,7\text{ m}$

$A = \pi r^2 = 1.27 \times 10^{-2}\text{ m}^2$

$\tau = (20.0\text{ A})(1.27 \times 10^{-2}\text{ m}^2)(0.520) = \boxed{0.132\text{ N}\cdot\text{m}}$

(d) The circular loop experiences the largest torque.

P29.25 Choose $U=0$ when the dipole moment is at $\theta=90.0°$ to the field. The field exerts torque of magnitude $\mu B\sin\theta$ on the dipole, tending to turn the dipole moment in the direction of decreasing θ. According to Equations 8.16 and 10.22, the potential energy of the dipole-field system is given by

$$U-0=\int_{90.0°}^{\theta}\mu B\sin\theta\,d\theta=\mu B(-\cos\theta)\Big|_{90.0°}^{\theta}=-\mu B\cos\theta+0 \quad \text{or} \quad \boxed{U=-\boldsymbol{\mu}\cdot\mathbf{B}}.$$

P29.26 (a) The field exerts torque on the needle tending to align it with the field, so the minimum energy orientation of the needle is:

$\boxed{\text{pointing north at 48.0° below the horizontal}}$

where its energy is $U_{\min}=-\mu B\cos 0°=-\left(9.70\times10^{-3}\text{ A}\cdot\text{m}^2\right)\left(55.0\times10^{-6}\text{ T}\right)=-5.34\times10^{-7}\text{ J}$.

It has maximum energy when pointing in the opposite direction,

$\boxed{\text{south at 48.0° above the horizontal}}$

where its energy is $U_{\max}=-\mu B\cos 180°=+\left(9.70\times10^{-3}\text{ A}\cdot\text{m}^2\right)\left(55.0\times10^{-6}\text{ T}\right)=+5.34\times10^{-7}\text{ J}$.

(b) $U_{\min}+W=U_{\max}$: $W=U_{\max}-U_{\min}=+5.34\times10^{-7}\text{ J}-\left(-5.34\times10^{-7}\text{ J}\right)=\boxed{1.07\ \mu\text{J}}$

P29.27 (a) $\tau=\boldsymbol{\mu}\times\mathbf{B}$, so $\tau=|\boldsymbol{\mu}\times\mathbf{B}|=\mu B\sin\theta=NIAB\sin\theta$

$$\tau_{\max}=NIAB\sin 90.0°=1(5.00\text{ A})\left[\pi(0.050\,0\text{ m})^2\right]\left(3.00\times10^{-3}\text{ T}\right)=\boxed{118\ \mu\text{N}\cdot\text{m}}$$

(b) $U=-\mu\cdot\mathbf{B}$, so $-\mu B\le U\le+\mu B$

Since $\mu B=(NIA)B=1(5.00\text{ A})\left[\pi(0.050\,0\text{ m})^2\right]\left(3.00\times10^{-3}\text{ T}\right)=118\ \mu\text{J}$,

the range of the potential energy is: $\boxed{-118\ \mu\text{J}\le U\le+118\ \mu\text{J}}$.

***P29.28** (a) $|\boldsymbol{\tau}|=|\boldsymbol{\mu}\times\mathbf{B}|=NIAB\sin\theta$

$$\tau_{\max}=80\left(10^{-2}\text{ A}\right)(0.025\text{ m}\cdot0.04\text{ m})(0.8\text{ N/A}\cdot\text{m})\sin 90°=\boxed{6.40\times10^{-4}\text{ N}\cdot\text{m}}$$

(b) $$\mathcal{P}_{\max}=\tau_{\max}\omega=6.40\times10^{-4}\text{ N}\cdot\text{m}(3\,600\text{ rev/min})\left(\frac{2\pi\text{ rad}}{1\text{ rev}}\right)\left(\frac{1\text{ min}}{60\text{ s}}\right)=\boxed{0.241\text{ W}}$$

(c) In one half revolution the work is

$$W=U_{\max}-U_{\min}=-\mu B\cos 180°-(-\mu B\cos 0°)=2\mu B$$
$$=2NIAB=2\left(6.40\times10^{-4}\text{ N}\cdot\text{m}\right)=1.28\times10^{-3}\text{ J}$$

In one full revolution, $W=2\left(1.28\times10^{-3}\text{ J}\right)=\boxed{2.56\times10^{-3}\text{ J}}$.

(d) $$\mathcal{P}_{\text{avg}}=\frac{W}{\Delta t}=\frac{2.56\times10^{-3}\text{ J}}{(1/60)\text{ s}}=\boxed{0.154\text{ W}}$$

The peak power in (b) is greater by the factor $\frac{\pi}{2}$.

Section 29.4 Motion of a Charged Particle in a Uniform Magnetic Field

P29.29 (a) $B = 50.0\times10^{-6}\text{ T};\ v = 6.20\times10^{6}\text{ m/s}$

Direction is given by the right-hand-rule: $\boxed{\text{southward}}$

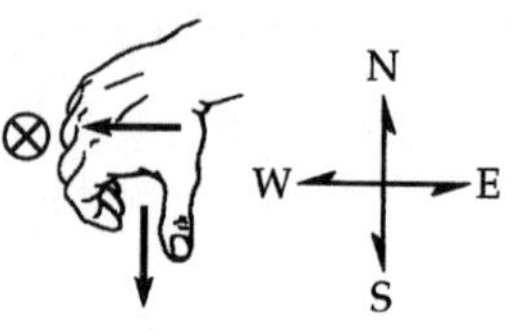

FIG. P29.29

$$F_B = qvB\sin\theta$$

$$F_B = \left(1.60\times10^{-19}\text{ C}\right)\left(6.20\times10^{6}\text{ m/s}\right)\left(50.0\times10^{-6}\text{ T}\right)\sin 90.0^\circ$$

$$= \boxed{4.96\times10^{-17}\text{ N}}$$

(b) $$F = \frac{mv^2}{r}\text{ so } r = \frac{mv^2}{F} = \frac{\left(1.67\times10^{-27}\text{ kg}\right)\left(6.20\times10^{6}\text{ m/s}\right)^2}{4.96\times10^{-17}\text{ N}} = \boxed{1.29\text{ km}}$$

P29.30 $\frac{1}{2}mv^2 = q(\Delta V)$ $\quad\frac{1}{2}\left(3.20\times10^{-26}\text{ kg}\right)v^2 = \left(1.60\times10^{-19}\text{ C}\right)(833\text{ V})$ $\quad v = 91.3\text{ km/s}$

The magnetic force provides the centripetal force: $qvB\sin\theta = \frac{mv^2}{r}$

$$r = \frac{mv}{qB\sin 90.0^\circ} = \frac{\left(3.20\times10^{-26}\text{ kg}\right)\left(9.13\times10^{4}\text{ m/s}\right)}{\left(1.60\times10^{-19}\text{ C}\right)(0.920\text{ N}\cdot\text{s/C}\cdot\text{m})} = \boxed{1.98\text{ cm}}.$$

P29.31 For each electron, $|q|vB\sin 90.0^\circ = \frac{mv^2}{r}$ and $v = \frac{eBr}{m}$.

The electrons have no internal structure to absorb energy, so the collision must be perfectly elastic:

$$K = \frac{1}{2}mv_{1i}^2 + 0 = \frac{1}{2}mv_{1f}^2 + \frac{1}{2}mv_{2f}^2$$

$$K = \frac{1}{2}m\left(\frac{e^2B^2R_1^2}{m^2}\right) + \frac{1}{2}m\left(\frac{e^2B^2R_2^2}{m^2}\right) = \frac{e^2B^2}{2m}\left(R_1^2 + R_2^2\right)$$

$$K = \frac{e\left(1.60\times10^{-19}\text{ C}\right)(0.0440\text{ N}\cdot\text{s/C}\cdot\text{m})^2}{2\left(9.11\times10^{-31}\text{ kg}\right)}\left[(0.0100\text{ m})^2 + (0.0240\text{ m})^2\right] = \boxed{115\text{ keV}}$$

P29.32 We begin with $qvB = \frac{mv^2}{R}$, so $v = \frac{qRB}{m}$.

The time to complete one revolution is $T = \frac{2\pi R}{v} = \frac{2\pi R}{qRB/m} = \frac{2\pi m}{qB}$.

Solving for B, $B = \frac{2\pi m}{qT} = \boxed{6.56\times10^{-2}\text{ T}}$.

P29.33 $q(\Delta V) = \frac{1}{2}mv^2$ or $v = \sqrt{\frac{2q(\Delta V)}{m}}$.

Also, $qvB = \frac{mv^2}{r}$ so $r = \frac{mv}{qB} = \frac{m}{qB}\sqrt{\frac{2q(\Delta V)}{m}} = \sqrt{\frac{2m(\Delta V)}{qB^2}}$.

Therefore, $r_p^2 = \frac{2m_p(\Delta V)}{eB^2}$

$$r_d^2 = \frac{2m_d(\Delta V)}{q_d B^2} = \frac{2(2m_p)(\Delta V)}{eB^2} = 2\left(\frac{2m_p(\Delta V)}{eB^2}\right) = 2r_p^2$$

and $r_\alpha^2 = \frac{2m_\alpha(\Delta V)}{q_\alpha B^2} = \frac{2(4m_p)(\Delta V)}{(2e)B^2} = 2\left(\frac{2m_p(\Delta V)}{eB^2}\right) = 2r_p^2$.

The conclusion is: $\boxed{r_\alpha = r_d = \sqrt{2}r_p}$.

P29.34 (a) We begin with $qvB = \frac{mv^2}{R}$

or $qRB = mv$.

But $L = mvR = qR^2B$.

Therefore, $R = \sqrt{\frac{L}{qB}} = \sqrt{\frac{4.00 \times 10^{-25}\ \text{J}\cdot\text{s}}{(1.60 \times 10^{-19}\ \text{C})(1.00 \times 10^{-3}\ \text{T})}} = 0.050\,0\ \text{m} = \boxed{5.00\ \text{cm}}$.

(b) Thus, $v = \frac{L}{mR} = \frac{4.00 \times 10^{-25}\ \text{J}\cdot\text{s}}{(9.11 \times 10^{-31}\ \text{kg})(0.050\,0\ \text{m})} = \boxed{8.78 \times 10^6\ \text{m/s}}$.

P29.35 $\omega = \frac{qB}{m} = \frac{(1.60 \times 10^{-19}\ \text{C})(5.20\ \text{T})}{1.67 \times 10^{-27}\ \text{kg}} = \boxed{4.98 \times 10^8\ \text{rad/s}}$

P29.36 $\frac{1}{2}mv^2 = q(\Delta V)$ so $v = \sqrt{\frac{2q(\Delta V)}{m}}$

$r = \frac{mv}{qB}$ so $r = \frac{m\sqrt{2q(\Delta V)/m}}{qB}$

$r^2 = \frac{m}{q}\cdot\frac{2(\Delta V)}{B^2}$ and $(r')^2 = \frac{m'}{q'}\cdot\frac{2(\Delta V)}{B^2}$

$m = \frac{qB^2r^2}{2(\Delta V)}$ and $(m') = \frac{(q')B^2(r')^2}{2(\Delta V)}$ so $\frac{m'}{m} = \frac{q'}{q}\cdot\frac{(r')^2}{r^2} = \left(\frac{2e}{e}\right)\left(\frac{2R}{R}\right)^2 = \boxed{8}$

P29.37 $E = \frac{1}{2}mv^2 = e\Delta V$

and $evB\sin 90° = \frac{mv^2}{R}$

$$B = \frac{mv}{eR} = \frac{m}{eR}\sqrt{\frac{2e\Delta V}{m}} = \frac{1}{R}\sqrt{\frac{2m\Delta V}{e}}$$

$$B = \frac{1}{5.80\times 10^{10}\text{ m}}\sqrt{\frac{2\left(1.67\times 10^{-27}\text{ kg}\right)\left(10.0\times 10^{6}\text{ V}\right)}{1.60\times 10^{-19}\text{ C}}} = \boxed{7.88\times 10^{-12}\text{ T}}$$

***P29.38** (a) At the moment shown in Figure 29.21, the particle must be moving upward in order for the magnetic force on it to be into the page, toward the center of this turn of its spiral path. Throughout its motion it circulates clockwise.

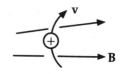

FIG. P29.38(a)

(b) After the particle has passed the middle of the bottle and moves into the region of increasing magnetic field, the magnetic force on it has a component to the left (as well as a radially inward component) as shown. This force in the $-x$ direction slows and reverses the particle's motion along the axis.

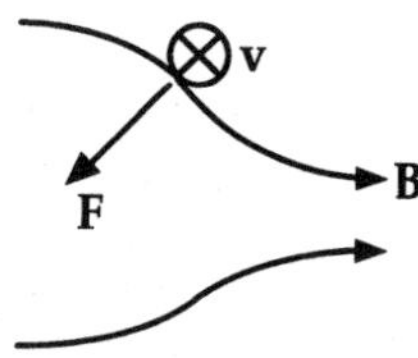

FIG. P29.38(b)

(c) The magnetic force is perpendicular to the velocity and does no work on the particle. The particle keeps constant kinetic energy. As its axial velocity component decreases, its tangential velocity component increases.

(d) The orbiting particle constitutes a loop of current in the yz plane and therefore a magnetic dipole moment $IA = \frac{q}{T}A$ in the $-x$ direction. It is like a little bar magnet with its N pole on the left.

FIG. P29.38(d)

(e) Problem 17 showed that a nonuniform magnetic field exerts a net force on a magnetic dipole. When the dipole is aligned opposite to the external field, the force pushes it out of the region of stronger field. Here it is to the left, a force of repulsion of one magnetic south pole on another south pole.

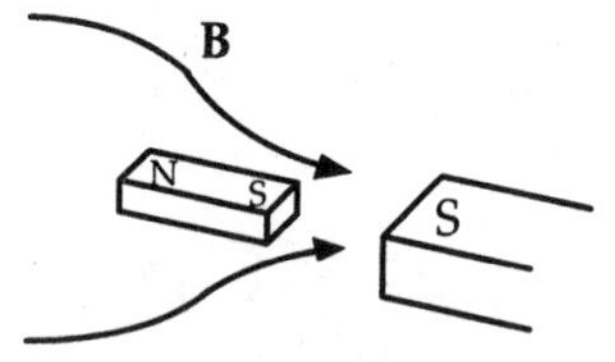

FIG. P29.38(e)

P29.39 $r = \frac{mv}{qB}$ so $m = \frac{rqB}{v} = \frac{(7.94 \times 10^{-3}\ \text{m})(1.60 \times 10^{-19}\ \text{C})(1.80\ \text{T})}{4.60 \times 10^{5}\ \text{m/s}}$

$$m = 4.97 \times 10^{-27}\ \text{kg}\left(\frac{1\ \text{u}}{1.66 \times 10^{-27}\ \text{kg}}\right) = \boxed{2.99\ \text{u}}$$

The particle is singly ionized: either a tritium ion, $\boxed{{}_1^3\text{H}^+}$, or a helium ion, $\boxed{{}_2^3\text{He}^+}$.

Section 29.5 Applications Involving Charged Particles Moving in a Magnetic Field

P29.40 $F_B = F_e$

so $qvB = qE$

where $v = \sqrt{\frac{2K}{m}}$ and K is kinetic energy of the electron.

$$E = vB = \sqrt{\frac{2K}{m}}B = \sqrt{\frac{2(750)(1.60 \times 10^{-19})}{9.11 \times 10^{-31}}}(0.015\,0) = \boxed{244\ \text{kV/m}}$$

P29.41 $K = \frac{1}{2}mv^2 = q(\Delta V)$ so $v = \sqrt{\frac{2q(\Delta V)}{m}}$

$|\mathbf{F}_B| = |q\mathbf{v} \times \mathbf{B}| = \frac{mv^2}{r}$ $r = \frac{mv}{qB} = \frac{m}{q}\frac{\sqrt{2q(\Delta V)/m}}{B} = \frac{1}{B}\sqrt{\frac{2m(\Delta V)}{q}}$

(a) $$r_{238} = \sqrt{\frac{2(238 \times 1.66 \times 10^{-27})2\,000}{1.60 \times 10^{-19}}}\left(\frac{1}{1.20}\right) = 8.28 \times 10^{-2}\ \text{m} = \boxed{8.28\ \text{cm}}$$

(b) $r_{235} = \boxed{8.23\ \text{cm}}$

$$\frac{r_{238}}{r_{235}} = \sqrt{\frac{m_{238}}{m_{235}}} = \sqrt{\frac{238.05}{235.04}} = 1.006\,4$$

The ratios of the orbit radius for different ions are independent of ΔV and B.

P29.42 In the velocity selector: $v = \frac{E}{B} = \frac{2\,500\ \text{V/m}}{0.035\,0\ \text{T}} = 7.14 \times 10^{4}\ \text{m/s}$.

In the deflection chamber: $r = \frac{mv}{qB} = \frac{(2.18 \times 10^{-26}\ \text{kg})(7.14 \times 10^{4}\ \text{m/s})}{(1.60 \times 10^{-19}\ \text{C})(0.035\,0\ \text{T})} = \boxed{0.278\ \text{m}}$.

P29.43 (a) $F_B = qvB = \dfrac{mv^2}{R}$

$$\omega = \frac{v}{R} = \frac{qBR}{mR} = \frac{qB}{m} = \frac{(1.60\times10^{-19}\ \text{C})(0.450\ \text{T})}{1.67\times10^{-27}\ \text{kg}} = \boxed{4.31\times10^{7}\ \text{rad/s}}$$

(b) $$v = \frac{qBR}{m} = \frac{(1.60\times10^{-19}\ \text{C})(0.450\ \text{T})(1.20\ \text{m})}{1.67\times10^{-27}\ \text{kg}} = \boxed{5.17\times10^{7}\ \text{m/s}}$$

P29.44 $K = \dfrac{1}{2}mv^2$: $\quad (34.0\times10^{6}\ \text{eV})(1.60\times10^{-19}\ \text{J/eV}) = \dfrac{1}{2}(1.67\times10^{-27}\ \text{kg})v^2$

$v = 8.07\times10^{7}\ \text{m/s}$ $\quad r = \dfrac{mv}{qB} = \dfrac{(1.67\times10^{-27}\ \text{kg})(8.07\times10^{7}\ \text{m/s})}{(1.60\times10^{-19}\ \text{C})(5.20\ \text{T})} = \boxed{0.162\ \text{m}}$

***P29.45** Note that the "cyclotron frequency" is an angular speed. The motion of the proton is described by $\sum F = ma$:

$$|q|vB\sin 90° = \frac{mv^2}{r}$$

$$|q|B = m\frac{v}{r} = m\omega$$

(a) $$\omega = \frac{|q|B}{m} = \frac{(1.60\times10^{-19}\ \text{C})(0.8\ \text{N}\cdot\text{s/C}\cdot\text{m})}{(1.67\times10^{-27}\ \text{kg})}\left(\frac{\text{kg}\cdot\text{m}}{\text{N}\cdot\text{s}^2}\right) = \boxed{7.66\times10^{7}\ \text{rad/s}}$$

(b) $$v = \omega r = (7.66\times10^{7}\ \text{rad/s})(0.350\ \text{m})\left(\frac{1}{1\ \text{rad}}\right) = \boxed{2.68\times10^{7}\ \text{m/s}}$$

(c) $$K = \frac{1}{2}mv^2 = \frac{1}{2}(1.67\times10^{-27}\ \text{kg})(2.68\times10^{7}\ \text{m/s})^2\left(\frac{1\ \text{eV}}{1.6\times10^{-19}\ \text{J}}\right) = \boxed{3.76\times10^{6}\ \text{eV}}$$

(d) The proton gains 600 eV twice during each revolution, so the number of revolutions is

$$\frac{3.76\times10^{6}\ \text{eV}}{2(600\ \text{eV})} = \boxed{3.13\times10^{3}\ \text{revolutions}}.$$

(e) $\theta = \omega t$ $\quad t = \dfrac{\theta}{\omega} = \dfrac{3.13\times10^{3}\ \text{rev}}{7.66\times10^{7}\ \text{rad/s}}\left(\dfrac{2\pi\,\text{rad}}{1\ \text{rev}}\right) = \boxed{2.57\times10^{-4}\ \text{s}}$

P29.46 $F_B = qvB = \dfrac{mv^2}{r}$

$$B = \frac{mv}{qr} = \frac{4.80\times10^{-16}\ \text{kg}\cdot\text{m/s}}{(1.60\times10^{-19}\ \text{C})(1\,000\ \text{m})} = \boxed{3.00\ \text{T}}$$

P29.47 $\theta = \tan^{-1}\left(\frac{25.0}{10.0}\right) = 68.2°$ and $R = \frac{1.00 \text{ cm}}{\sin 68.2°} = 1.08 \text{ cm}$.

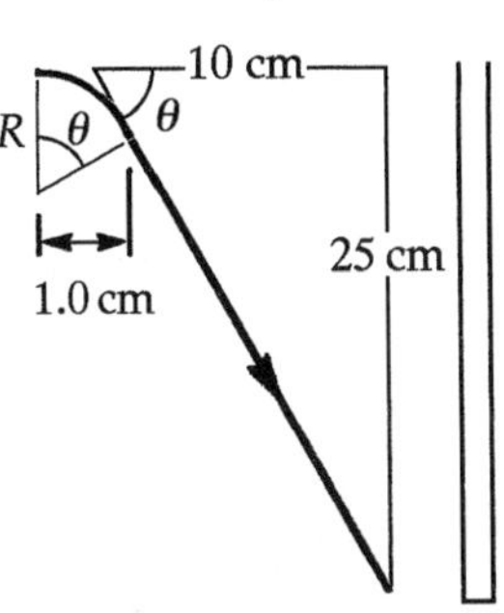

FIG. P29.47

Ignoring relativistic correction, the kinetic energy of the electrons is

$$\frac{1}{2}mv^2 = q\Delta V \quad \text{so} \quad v = \sqrt{\frac{2q\Delta V}{m}} = 1.33 \times 10^8 \text{ m/s}.$$

From Newton's second law $\frac{mv^2}{R} = qvB$, we find the magnetic field

$$B = \frac{mv}{|q|R} = \frac{(9.11 \times 10^{-31} \text{ kg})(1.33 \times 10^8 \text{ m/s})}{(1.60 \times 10^{-19} \text{ C})(1.08 \times 10^{-2} \text{ m})} = \boxed{70.1 \text{ mT}}.$$

Section 29.6 The Hall Effect

P29.48 (a) $R_H \equiv \frac{1}{nq}$ so $n = \frac{1}{qR_H} = \frac{1}{(1.60 \times 10^{-19} \text{ C})(0.840 \times 10^{-10} \text{ m}^3/\text{C})} = \boxed{7.44 \times 10^{28} \text{ m}^{-3}}$

(b) $\Delta V_H = \frac{IB}{nqt}$

$$B = \frac{nqt(\Delta V_H)}{I} = \frac{(7.44 \times 10^{28} \text{ m}^{-3})(1.60 \times 10^{-19} \text{ C})(0.200 \times 10^{-3} \text{ m})(15.0 \times 10^{-6} \text{ V})}{20.0 \text{ A}} = \boxed{1.79 \text{ T}}$$

P29.49 Since $\Delta V_H = \frac{IB}{nqt}$, and given that $I = 50.0 \text{ A}$, $B = 1.30 \text{ T}$, and $t = 0.330 \text{ mm}$, the number of charge carriers per unit volume is

$$n = \frac{IB}{e(\Delta V_H)t} = \boxed{1.28 \times 10^{29} \text{ m}^{-3}}$$

The number density of atoms we compute from the density:

$$n_0 = \frac{8.92 \text{ g}}{\text{cm}^3}\left(\frac{1 \text{ mole}}{63.5 \text{ g}}\right)\left(\frac{6.02 \times 10^{23} \text{ atoms}}{\text{mole}}\right)\left(\frac{10^6 \text{ cm}^3}{1 \text{ m}^3}\right) = 8.46 \times 10^{28} \text{ atom/m}^3$$

So the number of conduction electrons per atom is

$$\frac{n}{n_0} = \frac{1.28 \times 10^{29}}{8.46 \times 10^{28}} = \boxed{1.52}$$

P29.50 (a) $\Delta V_H = \frac{IB}{nqt}$ so $\frac{nqt}{I} = \frac{B}{\Delta V_H} = \frac{0.080\,0\text{ T}}{0.700 \times 10^{-6}\text{ V}} = 1.14 \times 10^5\text{ T/V}.$

Then, the unknown field is $B = \left(\frac{nqt}{I}\right)(\Delta V_H)$

$$B = \left(1.14 \times 10^5\text{ T/V}\right)\left(0.330 \times 10^{-6}\text{ V}\right) = 0.037\,7\text{ T} = \boxed{37.7\text{ mT}}.$$

(b) $\frac{nqt}{I} = 1.14 \times 10^5\text{ T/V}$ so $n = \left(1.14 \times 10^5\text{ T/V}\right)\frac{I}{qt}$

$$n = \left(1.14 \times 10^5\text{ T/V}\right)\frac{0.120\text{ A}}{\left(1.60 \times 10^{-19}\text{ C}\right)\left(2.00 \times 10^{-3}\text{ m}\right)} = \boxed{4.29 \times 10^{25}\text{ m}^{-3}}.$$

P29.51 $B = \frac{nqt(\Delta V_H)}{I} = \frac{\left(8.49 \times 10^{28}\text{ m}^{-3}\right)\left(1.60 \times 10^{-19}\text{ C}\right)\left(5.00 \times 10^{-3}\text{ m}\right)\left(5.10 \times 10^{-12}\text{ V}\right)}{8.00\text{ A}}$

$$B = 4.33 \times 10^{-5}\text{ T} = \boxed{43.3\ \mu\text{T}}$$

Additional Problems

P29.52 (a) The boundary between a region of strong magnetic field and a region of zero field cannot be perfectly sharp, but we ignore the thickness of the transition zone. In the field the electron moves on an arc of a circle:

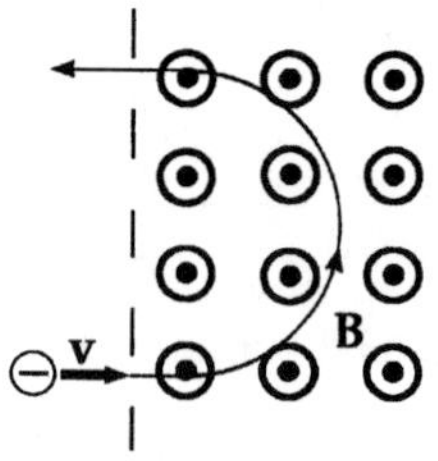

$\sum F = ma:$

$$|q|vB\sin 90° = \frac{mv^2}{r}$$

$$\frac{v}{r} = \omega = \frac{|q|B}{m} = \frac{\left(1.60 \times 10^{-19}\text{ C}\right)\left(10^{-3}\text{ N}\cdot\text{s/C}\cdot\text{m}\right)}{\left(9.11 \times 10^{-31}\text{ kg}\right)} = 1.76 \times 10^8\text{ rad/s}$$

FIG. P29.52(a)

The time for one half revolution is,

from $\Delta\theta = \omega\Delta t$

$$\Delta t = \frac{\Delta\theta}{\omega} = \frac{\pi\text{ rad}}{1.76 \times 10^8\text{ rad/s}} = \boxed{1.79 \times 10^{-8}\text{ s}}.$$

(b) The maximum depth of penetration is the radius of the path.

Then $v = \omega r = \left(1.76 \times 10^8\text{ s}^{-1}\right)(0.02\text{ m}) = 3.51 \times 10^6\text{ m/s}$

and

$$K = \frac{1}{2}mv^2 = \frac{1}{2}\left(9.11 \times 10^{-31}\text{ kg}\right)\left(3.51 \times 10^6\text{ m/s}\right)^2 = 5.62 \times 10^{-18}\text{ J} = \frac{5.62 \times 10^{-18}\text{ J}\cdot\text{e}}{1.60 \times 10^{-19}\text{ C}}$$

$$= \boxed{35.1\text{ eV}}.$$

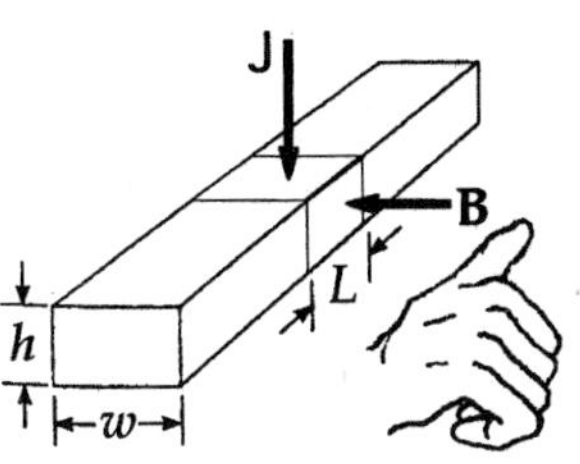

FIG. P29.53

P29.53 (a) Define vector **h** to have the downward direction of the current, and vector **L** to be along the pipe into the page as shown. The electric current experiences a magnetic force.

$I(\mathbf{h}\times\mathbf{B})$ in the direction of **L**.

(b) The sodium, consisting of ions and electrons, flows along the pipe transporting no net charge. But inside the section of length L, electrons drift upward to constitute downward electric current $J\times(\text{area}) = JLw$.

The current then feels a magnetic force $I|\mathbf{h}\times\mathbf{B}| = JLwhB\sin 90°$.

This force along the pipe axis will make the fluid move, exerting pressure

$$\frac{F}{\text{area}} = \frac{JLwhB}{hw} = \boxed{JLB}.$$

P29.54 $\sum F_y = 0$: $\quad +n - mg = 0$

$\sum F_x = 0$: $\quad -\mu_k n + IB\sin 90.0° = 0$

$$B = \frac{\mu_k mg}{Id} = \frac{0.100(0.200\text{ kg})(9.80\text{ m/s}^2)}{(10.0\text{ A})(0.500\text{ m})} = \boxed{39.2\text{ mT}}$$

P29.55 The magnetic force on each proton, $\mathbf{F}_B = q\mathbf{v}\times\mathbf{B} = qvB\sin 90°$ downward perpendicular to velocity, causes centripetal acceleration, guiding it into a circular path of radius r, with

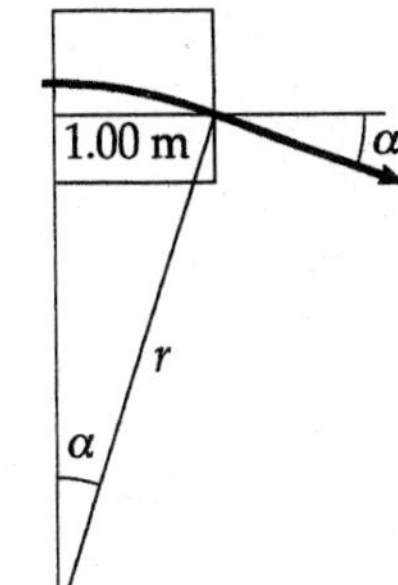

FIG. P29.55

$$qvB = \frac{mv^2}{r}$$

and $$r = \frac{mv}{qB}.$$

We compute this radius by first finding the proton's speed:

$$K = \frac{1}{2}mv^2$$

$$v = \sqrt{\frac{2K}{m}} = \sqrt{\frac{2(5.00\times10^6\text{ eV})(1.60\times10^{-19}\text{ J/eV})}{1.67\times10^{-27}\text{ kg}}} = 3.10\times10^7\text{ m/s}.$$

Now, $$r = \frac{mv}{qB} = \frac{(1.67\times10^{-27}\text{ kg})(3.10\times10^7\text{ m/s})}{(1.60\times10^{-19}\text{ C})(0.050\,0\text{ N}\cdot\text{s/C}\cdot\text{m})} = 6.46\text{ m}.$$

(b) From the figure, observe that

$$\sin\alpha = \frac{1.00\text{ m}}{r} = \frac{1\text{ m}}{6.46\text{ m}}$$

$$\boxed{\alpha = 8.90°}$$

(a) The magnitude of the proton momentum stays constant, and its final y component is

$$-(1.67\times10^{-27}\text{ kg})(3.10\times10^7\text{ m/s})\sin 8.90° = \boxed{-8.00\times10^{-21}\text{ kg}\cdot\text{m/s}}.$$

P29.56 (a) If $\mathbf{B} = B_x\hat{\mathbf{i}} + B_y\hat{\mathbf{j}} + B_z\hat{\mathbf{k}}$, $\mathbf{F}_B = q\mathbf{v}\times\mathbf{B} = e(v_i\hat{\mathbf{i}})\times(B_x\hat{\mathbf{i}} + B_y\hat{\mathbf{j}} + B_z\hat{\mathbf{k}}) = 0 + ev_iB_y\hat{\mathbf{k}} - ev_iB_z\hat{\mathbf{j}}$.

Since the force actually experienced is $\mathbf{F}_B = F_i\hat{\mathbf{j}}$, observe that

$$\boxed{B_x \text{ could have any value}}, \boxed{B_y = 0}, \text{ and } \boxed{B_z = -\frac{F_i}{ev_i}}.$$

(b) If $\mathbf{v} = -v_i\hat{\mathbf{i}}$, then $\mathbf{F}_B = q\mathbf{v}\times\mathbf{B} = e(-v_i\hat{\mathbf{i}})\times\left(B_x\hat{\mathbf{i}} + 0\hat{\mathbf{j}} - \frac{F_i}{ev_i}\hat{\mathbf{k}}\right) = \boxed{-F_i\hat{\mathbf{j}}}$.

(c) If $q = -e$ and $\mathbf{v} = v_i\hat{\mathbf{i}}$, then $\mathbf{F}_B = q\mathbf{v}\times\mathbf{B} = -e(v_i\hat{\mathbf{i}})\times\left(B_x\hat{\mathbf{i}} + 0\hat{\mathbf{j}} - \frac{F_i}{ev_i}\hat{\mathbf{k}}\right) = \boxed{-F_i\hat{\mathbf{j}}}$.

Reversing either the velocity or the sign of the charge reverses the force.

P29.57 (a) The net force is the Lorentz force given by

$$\mathbf{F} = q\mathbf{E} + q\mathbf{v}\times\mathbf{B} = q(\mathbf{E} + \mathbf{v}\times\mathbf{B})$$

$$\mathbf{F} = (3.20\times10^{-19})\left[(4\hat{\mathbf{i}} - 1\hat{\mathbf{j}} - 2\hat{\mathbf{k}}) + (2\hat{\mathbf{i}} + 3\hat{\mathbf{j}} - 1\hat{\mathbf{k}})\times(2\hat{\mathbf{i}} + 4\hat{\mathbf{j}} + 1\hat{\mathbf{k}})\right] \text{ N}$$

Carrying out the indicated operations, we find:

$$\mathbf{F} = \boxed{(3.52\hat{\mathbf{i}} - 1.60\hat{\mathbf{j}})\times10^{-18} \text{ N}}.$$

(b) $$\theta = \cos^{-1}\left(\frac{F_x}{F}\right) = \cos^{-1}\left(\frac{3.52}{\sqrt{(3.52)^2 + (1.60)^2}}\right) = \boxed{24.4°}$$

P29.58 A key to solving this problem is that reducing the normal force will reduce the friction force: $F_B = BIL$ or $B = \frac{F_B}{IL}$.

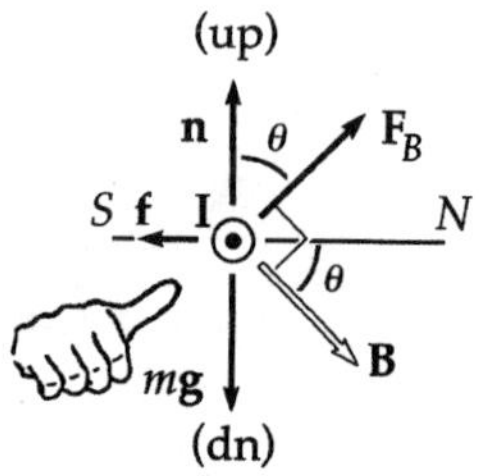

FIG. P29.58

When the wire is just able to move, $\sum F_y = n + F_B\cos\theta - mg = 0$

so $n = mg - F_B\cos\theta$

and $f = \mu(mg - F_B\cos\theta)$.

Also, $\sum F_x = F_B\sin\theta - f = 0$

so $F_B\sin\theta = f$: $F_B\sin\theta = \mu(mg - F_B\cos\theta)$ and $F_B = \frac{\mu mg}{\sin\theta + \mu\cos\theta}$.

We minimize B by minimizing F_B: $\frac{dF_B}{d\theta} = (\mu mg)\frac{\cos\theta - \mu\sin\theta}{(\sin\theta + \mu\cos\theta)^2} = 0 \Rightarrow \mu\sin\theta = \cos\theta$.

Thus, $\theta = \tan^{-1}\left(\frac{1}{\mu}\right) = \tan^{-1}(5.00) = 78.7°$ for the smallest field, and

$$B = \frac{F_B}{IL} = \left(\frac{\mu g}{I}\right)\frac{(m/L)}{\sin\theta + \mu\cos\theta}$$

$$B_{min} = \left[\frac{(0.200)(9.80 \text{ m/s}^2)}{1.50 \text{ A}}\right]\frac{0.100 \text{ kg/m}}{\sin 78.7° + (0.200)\cos 78.7°} = 0.128 \text{ T}$$

$$\boxed{B_{min} = 0.128 \text{ T pointing north at an angle of } 78.7° \text{ below the horizontal}}$$

***P29.59** The electrons are all fired from the electron gun with the same speed v in

$$U_i = K_f \qquad qV = \frac{1}{2}mv^2 \qquad (-e)(-\Delta V) = \frac{1}{2}m_e v^2 \qquad v = \sqrt{\frac{2e\Delta V}{m_e}}$$

For ϕ small, $\cos\phi$ is nearly equal to 1. The time T of passage of each electron in the chamber is given by

$$d = vT \qquad T = d\left(\frac{m_e}{2e\Delta V}\right)^{1/2}$$

Each electron moves in a different helix, around a different axis. If each completes just one revolution within the chamber, it will be in the right place to pass through the exit port. Its transverse velocity component $v_\perp = v\sin\phi$ swings around according to $F_\perp = ma_\perp$

$$qv_\perp B\sin 90° = \frac{mv_\perp^2}{r} \qquad eB = \frac{m_e v_\perp}{r} = m_e\omega = m_e\frac{2\pi}{T} \qquad T = \frac{m_e 2\pi}{eB} = d\left(\frac{m_e}{2e\Delta V}\right)^{1/2}$$

Then $\dfrac{2\pi}{B}\left(\dfrac{m_e}{e}\right)^{1/2} = \dfrac{d}{(2\Delta V)^{1/2}}$ $\boxed{B = \dfrac{2\pi}{d}\left(\dfrac{2m_e\Delta V}{e}\right)^{1/2}}$.

***P29.60** Let v_i represent the original speed of the alpha particle. Let v_α and v_p represent the particles' speeds after the collision. We have conservation of momentum $4m_p v_i = 4m_p v_\alpha + m_p v_p$ and the relative velocity equation $v_i - 0 = v_p - v_\alpha$. Eliminating v_i,

$$4v_p - 4v_\alpha = 4v_\alpha + v_p \qquad 3v_p = 8v_\alpha \qquad v_\alpha = \frac{3}{8}v_p.$$

For the proton's motion in the magnetic field,

$$\sum F = ma \qquad ev_p B\sin 90° = \frac{m_p v_p^2}{R} \qquad \frac{eBR}{m_p} = v_p.$$

For the alpha particle,

$$2ev_\alpha B\sin 90° = \frac{4m_p v_\alpha^2}{r_\alpha} \qquad r_\alpha = \frac{2m_p v_\alpha}{eB} \qquad r_\alpha = \frac{2m_p}{eB}\frac{3}{8}v_p = \frac{2m_p}{eB}\frac{3}{8}\frac{eBR}{m_p} = \boxed{\frac{3}{4}R}.$$

P29.61 Let Δx_1 be the elongation due to the weight of the wire and let Δx_2 be the additional elongation of the springs when the magnetic field is turned on. Then $F_{\text{magnetic}} = 2k\Delta x_2$ where k is the force constant of the spring and can be determined from $k = \dfrac{mg}{2\Delta x_1}$. (The factor 2 is included in the two previous equations since there are 2 springs in parallel.) Combining these two equations, we find

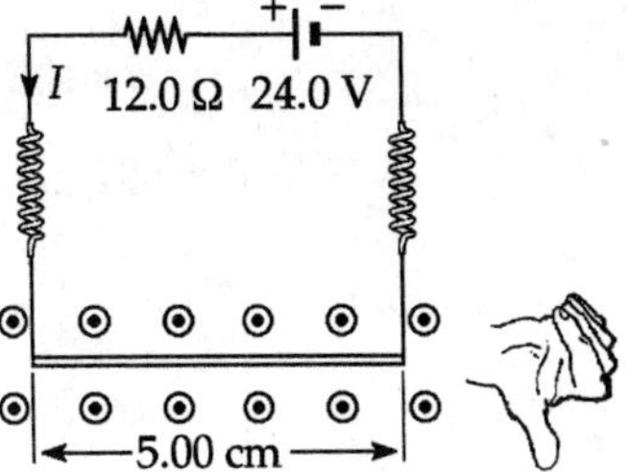

FIG. P29.61

$$F_{\text{magnetic}} = 2\left(\frac{mg}{2\Delta x_1}\right)\Delta x_2 = \frac{mg\Delta x_2}{\Delta x_1}; \text{ but } |\mathbf{F}_B| = I|\mathbf{L}\times\mathbf{B}| = ILB.$$

Therefore, where $I = \dfrac{24.0\text{ V}}{12.0\ \Omega} = 2.00\text{ A}$, $B = \dfrac{mg\Delta x_2}{IL\Delta x_1} = \dfrac{(0.100)(9.80)\left(3.00\times10^{-3}\right)}{(2.00)(0.050\,0)\left(5.00\times10^{-3}\right)} = \boxed{0.588\text{ T}}$.

P29.62 Suppose the input power is

$120\text{ W} = (120\text{ V})I$: $\boxed{I \sim 1\text{ A} = 10^0\text{ A}}$.

Suppose $\omega = 2\,000\text{ rev/min}\left(\frac{1\text{ min}}{60\text{ s}}\right)\left(\frac{2\pi\text{ rad}}{1\text{ rev}}\right) \sim 200\text{ rad/s}$

and the output power is $20\text{ W} = \tau\omega = \tau(200\text{ rad/s})$ $\boxed{\tau \sim 10^{-1}\text{ N}\cdot\text{m}}$.

Suppose the area is about $(3\text{ cm}) \times (4\text{ cm})$, or $\boxed{A \sim 10^{-3}\text{ m}^2}$.

Suppose that the field is $\boxed{B \sim 10^{-1}\text{ T}}$.

Then, the number of turns in the coil may be found from $\tau \cong NIAB$:

$$0.1\text{ N}\cdot\text{m} \sim N(1\text{ C/s})\left(10^{-3}\text{ m}^2\right)\left(10^{-1}\text{ N}\cdot\text{s/C}\cdot\text{m}\right)$$

giving $\boxed{N \sim 10^3}$.

***P29.63** The sphere is in translational equilibrium, thus

$f_s - Mg\sin\theta = 0$. (1)

The sphere is in rotational equilibrium. If torques are taken about the center of the sphere, the magnetic field produces a clockwise torque of magnitude $\mu B\sin\theta$, and the frictional force a counterclockwise torque of magnitude f_sR, where R is the radius of the sphere. Thus:

$f_sR - \mu B\sin\theta = 0$. (2)

From (1): $f_s = Mg\sin\theta$. Substituting this in (2) and canceling out $\sin\theta$, one obtains

$\mu B = MgR$. (3)

FIG. P29.63

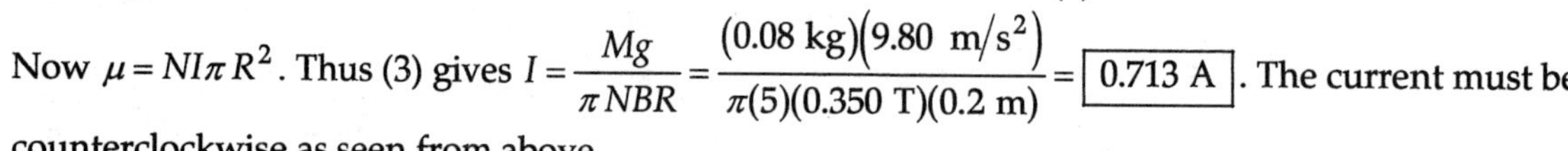

Now $\mu = NI\pi R^2$. Thus (3) gives $I = \frac{Mg}{\pi NBR} = \frac{(0.08\text{ kg})(9.80\text{ m/s}^2)}{\pi(5)(0.350\text{ T})(0.2\text{ m})} = \boxed{0.713\text{ A}}$. The current must be counterclockwise as seen from above.

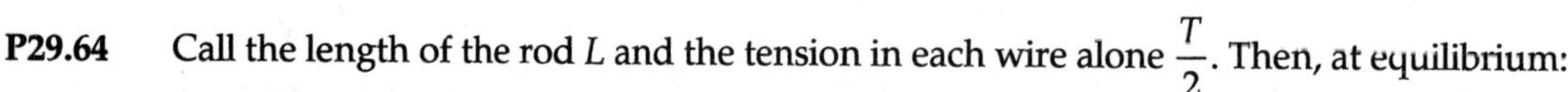

P29.64 Call the length of the rod L and the tension in each wire alone $\frac{T}{2}$. Then, at equilibrium:

$\sum F_x = T\sin\theta - ILB\sin 90.0° = 0$ or $T\sin\theta = ILB$

$\sum F_y = T\cos\theta - mg = 0$, or $T\cos\theta = mg$

$\tan\theta = \frac{ILB}{mg} = \frac{IB}{(m/L)g}$ or $B = \frac{(m/L)g}{I}\tan\theta = \boxed{\frac{\lambda g}{I}\tan\theta}$

P29.65 $\sum F = ma$ or $qvB\sin 90.0° = \frac{mv^2}{r}$

$\therefore$ the angular frequency for each ion is $\frac{v}{r} = \omega = \frac{qB}{m} = 2\pi f$ and

$$\Delta f = f_{12} - f_{14} = \frac{qB}{2\pi}\left(\frac{1}{m_{12}} - \frac{1}{m_{14}}\right) = \frac{\left(1.60\times10^{-19}\text{ C}\right)(2.40\text{ T})}{2\pi\left(1.66\times10^{-27}\text{ kg/u}\right)}\left(\frac{1}{12.0\text{ u}} - \frac{1}{14.0\text{ u}}\right)$$

$\Delta f = f_{12} - f_{14} = 4.38\times10^5\text{ s}^{-1} = \boxed{438\text{ kHz}}$

P29.66 Let v_x and $v_\perp$ be the components of the velocity of the positron parallel to and perpendicular to the direction of the magnetic field.

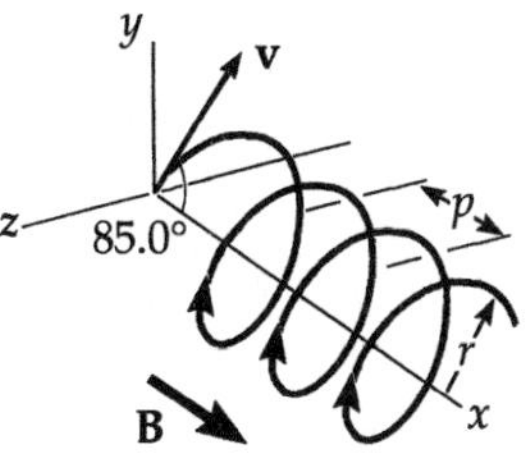

FIG. P29.66

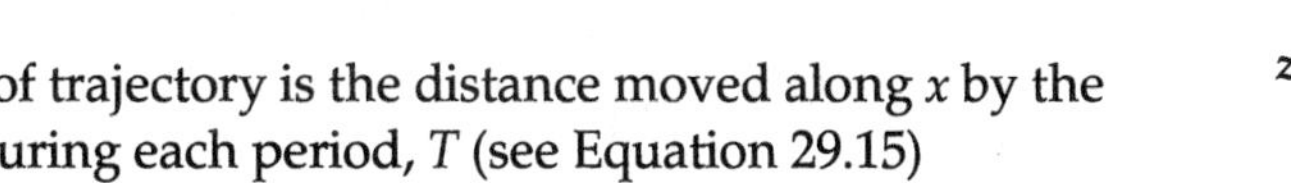

(a) The pitch of trajectory is the distance moved along x by the positron during each period, T (see Equation 29.15)

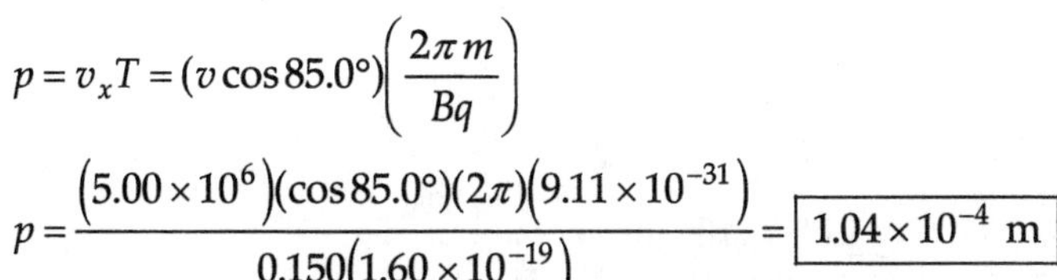

$$p = v_x T = (v\cos 85.0°)\left(\frac{2\pi m}{Bq}\right)$$

$$p = \frac{\left(5.00\times10^{6}\right)(\cos 85.0°)(2\pi)\left(9.11\times10^{-31}\right)}{0.150\left(1.60\times10^{-19}\right)} = \boxed{1.04\times10^{-4}\ \text{m}}$$

(b) From Equation 29.13, $r = \dfrac{mv_\perp}{Bq} = \dfrac{mv\sin 85.0°}{Bq}$

$$r = \frac{\left(9.11\times10^{-31}\right)\left(5.00\times10^{6}\right)(\sin 85.0°)}{(0.150)\left(1.60\times10^{-19}\right)} = \boxed{1.89\times10^{-4}\ \text{m}}$$

P29.67 $|\tau| = IAB$ where the effective current due to the orbiting electrons is $I = \dfrac{\Delta q}{\Delta t} = \dfrac{q}{T}$

and the period of the motion is $T = \dfrac{2\pi R}{v}$.

The electron's speed in its orbit is found by requiring $\dfrac{k_e q^2}{R^2} = \dfrac{mv^2}{R}$ or $v = q\sqrt{\dfrac{k_e}{mR}}$.

Substituting this expression for v into the equation for T, we find $T = 2\pi\sqrt{\dfrac{mR^3}{q^2 k_e}}$

$$T = 2\pi\sqrt{\frac{\left(9.11\times10^{-31}\right)\left(5.29\times10^{-11}\right)^3}{\left(1.60\times10^{-19}\right)^2\left(8.99\times10^{9}\right)}} = 1.52\times10^{-16}\ \text{s}.$$

Therefore, $|\tau| = \left(\dfrac{q}{T}\right)AB = \dfrac{1.60\times10^{-19}}{1.52\times10^{-16}}\pi\left(5.29\times10^{-11}\right)^2(0.400) = \boxed{3.70\times10^{-24}\ \text{N}\cdot\text{m}}$.

P29.68 Use the equation for cyclotron frequency $\omega = \dfrac{qB}{m}$ or $m = \dfrac{qB}{\omega} = \dfrac{qB}{2\pi f}$

$$m = \frac{\left(1.60\times10^{-19}\ \text{C}\right)\left(5.00\times10^{-2}\ \text{T}\right)}{(2\pi)\left(5.00\ \text{rev}/1.50\times10^{-3}\ \text{s}\right)} = \boxed{3.82\times10^{-25}\ \text{kg}}.$$

P29.69 (a) $K = \frac{1}{2}mv^2 = 6.00\text{ MeV} = \left(6.00\times10^6\text{ eV}\right)\left(1.60\times10^{-19}\text{ J/eV}\right)$

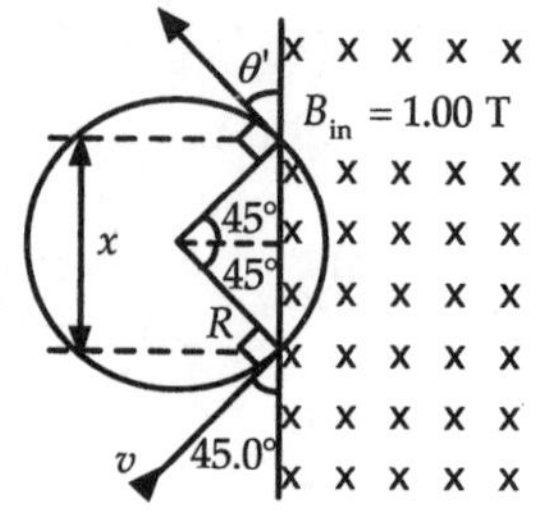

FIG. P29.69

$$K = 9.60\times10^{-13}\text{ J}$$

$$v = \sqrt{\frac{2\left(9.60\times10^{-13}\text{ J}\right)}{1.67\times10^{-27}\text{ kg}}} = 3.39\times10^7\text{ m/s}$$

$$F_B = qvB = \frac{mv^2}{R}\text{ so}$$

$$R = \frac{mv}{qB} = \frac{\left(1.67\times10^{-27}\text{ kg}\right)\left(3.39\times10^7\text{ m/s}\right)}{\left(1.60\times10^{-19}\text{ C}\right)(1.00\text{ T})} = 0.354\text{ m}$$

Then, from the diagram, $x = 2R\sin 45.0° = 2(0.354\text{ m})\sin 45.0° = \boxed{0.501\text{ m}}$

(b) From the diagram, observe that $\theta' = \boxed{45.0°}$.

P29.70 (a) See graph to the right. The Hall voltage is directly proportional to the magnetic field. A least-square fit to the data gives the equation of the best fitting line as:

$$\boxed{\Delta V_H = \left(1.00\times10^{-4}\text{ V/T}\right)B}.$$

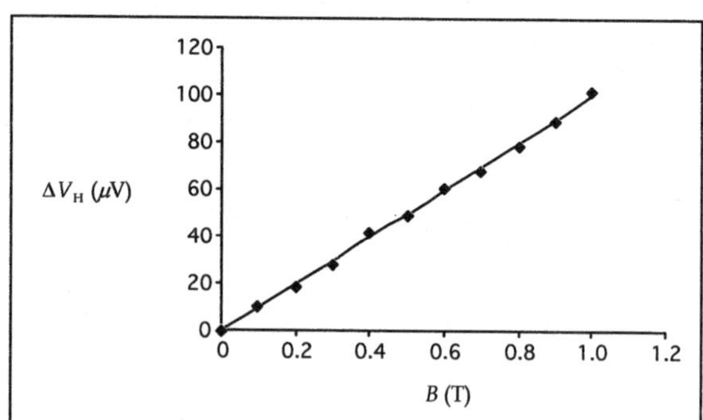

FIG. P29.70

(b) Comparing the equation of the line which fits the data best to

$$\Delta V_H = \left(\frac{1}{nqt}\right)B$$

observe that: $\frac{I}{nqt} = 1.00\times10^{-4}\text{ V/T}$, or $t = \frac{I}{nq\left(1.00\times10^{-4}\text{ V/T}\right)}$.

Then, if $I = 0.200$ A, $q = 1.60\times10^{-19}$ C, and $n = 1.00\times10^{26}\text{ m}^{-3}$, the thickness of the sample is

$$t = \frac{0.200\text{ A}}{\left(1.00\times10^{26}\text{ m}^{-3}\right)\left(1.60\times10^{-19}\text{ C}\right)\left(1.00\times10^{-4}\text{ V/T}\right)} = 1.25\times10^{-4}\text{ m} = \boxed{0.125\text{ mm}}.$$

P29.71 (a) The magnetic force acting on ions in the blood stream will deflect positive charges toward point A and negative charges toward point B. This separation of charges produces an electric field directed from A toward B. At equilibrium, the electric force caused by this field must balance the magnetic force, so

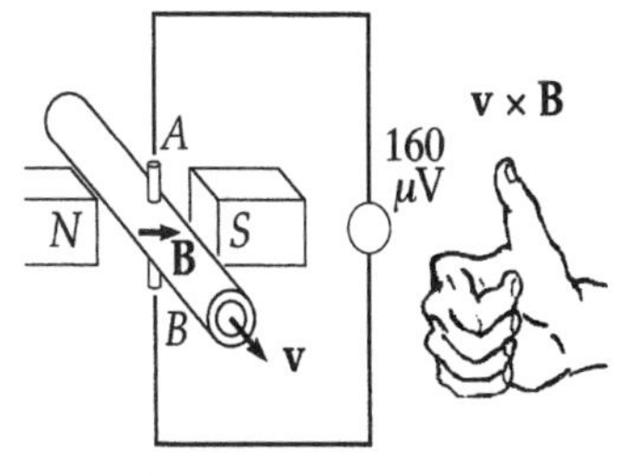

FIG. P29.71

$$qvB = qE = q\left(\frac{\Delta V}{d}\right)$$

or $$v = \frac{\Delta V}{Bd} = \frac{\left(160 \times 10^{-6}\ \text{V}\right)}{(0.040\,0\ \text{T})\left(3.00 \times 10^{-3}\ \text{m}\right)} = \boxed{1.33\ \text{m/s}}.$$

(b) $\boxed{\text{No}}$. Negative ions moving in the direction of v would be deflected toward point B, giving A a higher potential than B. Positive ions moving in the direction of v would be deflected toward A, again giving A a higher potential than B. Therefore, the sign of the potential difference does not depend on whether the ions in the blood are positively or negatively charged.

P29.72 When in the field, the particles follow a circular path according to $qvB = \frac{mv^2}{r}$, so the radius of the path is: $r = \frac{mv}{qB}$

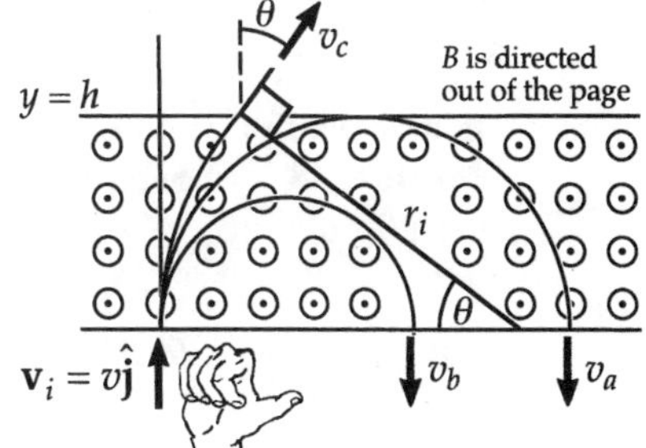

FIG. P29.72

(a) When $r = h = \frac{mv}{qB}$, that is, when $\boxed{v = \frac{qBh}{m}}$, the particle will cross the band of field. It will move in a full semicircle of radius h, leaving the field at $(2h, 0, 0)$ with velocity $\boxed{\mathbf{v}_f = -v\hat{\mathbf{j}}}$.

(b) When $v < \frac{qBh}{m}$, the particle will move in a smaller $\boxed{\text{semicircle}}$ of radius $r = \frac{mv}{qB} < h$. It will leave the field at $(2r, 0, 0)$ with velocity $\boxed{\mathbf{v}_f = -v\hat{\mathbf{j}}}$.

(c) When $v > \frac{qBh}{m}$, the particle moves in a $\boxed{\text{circular arc}}$ of radius $r = \frac{mv}{qB} > h$, centered at $(r, 0, 0)$. The arc subtends an angle given by $\theta = \sin^{-1}\left(\frac{h}{r}\right)$. It will leave the field at the point with coordinates $\left[r(1-\cos\theta), h, 0\right]$ with velocity $\boxed{\mathbf{v}_f = v\sin\theta\hat{\mathbf{i}} + v\cos\theta\hat{\mathbf{j}}}$.

ANSWERS TO EVEN PROBLEMS

P29.2 (a) west; (b) no deflection; (c) up; (d) down

P29.4 (a) 86.7 fN; (b) 51.9 Tm/s^2

P29.6 (a) 7.90 pN; (b) 0

P29.8 Gravitational force: 8.93×10^{-30} N down; Electric force: 16.0 aN up; Magnetic force: 48.0 aN down

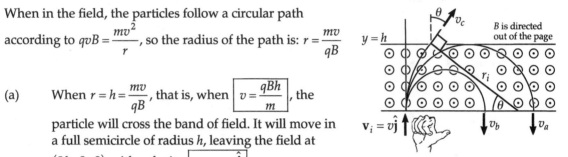

P29.10 $B_y = -2.62$ mT; $B_z = 0$; B_x may have any value

P29.12 $\left(-2.88\hat{\mathbf{j}}\right)$ N

P29.14 109 mA to the right

P29.16 $\left(\frac{4IdBL}{3m}\right)^{1/2}$

P29.18 $\mathbf{F}_{ab}=0$; $\mathbf{F}_{bc}=40.0\text{ mN}\left(-\hat{\mathbf{i}}\right)$;
$\mathbf{F}_{cd}=40.0\text{ mN}\left(-\hat{\mathbf{k}}\right)$; $\mathbf{F}_{da}=(40.0\text{ mN})\left(\hat{\mathbf{i}}+\hat{\mathbf{k}}\right)$

P29.20 (a) 5.41 $\text{mA}\cdot\text{m}^2$; (b) 4.33 $\text{mN}\cdot\text{m}$

P29.22 (a)3.97°; (b) 3.39 $\text{mN}\cdot\text{m}$

P29.24 (a) 80.1 $\text{mN}\cdot\text{m}$; (b) 104 $\text{mN}\cdot\text{m}$;
(c) 132 $\text{mN}\cdot\text{m}$;
(d) The torque on the circle.

P29.26 (a) minimum: pointing north at 48.0° below the horizontal; maximum: pointing south at 48.0° above the horizontal;
(b) 1.07 μJ

P29.28 (a) 640 $\mu\text{N}\cdot\text{m}$; (b) 241 mW; (c) 2.56 mJ;
(d) 154 mW

P29.30 1.98 cm

P29.32 65.6 mT

P29.34 (a) 5.00 cm; (b) 8.78 Mm/s

P29.36 $\frac{m'}{m}=8$

P29.38 see the solution

P29.40 244 kV/m

P29.42 278 mm

P29.44 162 mm

P29.46 3.00 T

P29.48 (a) $7.44\times10^{28}/\text{m}^3$; (b) 1.79 T

P29.50 (a) 37.7 mT; (b) $4.29\times10^{25}/\text{m}^3$

P29.52 (a) 17.9 ns; (b) 35.1 eV

P29.54 39.2 mT

P29.56 (a) B_x is indeterminate. $B_y=0$; $B_z=\frac{-F_i}{ev_i}$;
(b) $-F_i\hat{\mathbf{j}}$; (c) $-F_i\hat{\mathbf{j}}$

P29.58 128 mT north at an angle of 78.7° below the horizontal

P29.60 $\frac{3R}{4}$

P29.62 $B\sim10^{-1}$ T; $\tau\sim10^{-1}$ N·m; $I\sim1$ A;
$A\sim10^{-3}$ m^2; $N\sim10^3$

P29.64 $\frac{\lambda g\tan\theta}{I}$

P29.66 (a) 0.104 mm; (b) 0.189 mm

P29.68 3.82×10^{-25} kg

P29.70 (a) see the solution;
empirically, $\Delta V_{\text{H}}=(100\ \mu\text{V/T})B$;
(b) 0.125 mm

P29.72 (a) $v=\frac{qBh}{m}$; The particle moves in a semicircle of radius h and leaves the field with velocity $-v\hat{\mathbf{j}}$;
(b) The particle moves in a smaller semicircle of radius $\frac{mv}{qB}$, attaining final velocity $-v\hat{\mathbf{j}}$;
(c) The particle moves in a circular arc of radius $r=\frac{mv}{qB}$, leaving the field with velocity $v\sin\theta\hat{\mathbf{i}}+v\cos\theta\hat{\mathbf{j}}$ where $\theta=\sin^{-1}\left(\frac{h}{r}\right)$

30

Sources of the Magnetic Field

CHAPTER OUTLINE

ANSWERS TO QUESTIONS

Q30.1 It is not. The magnetic field created by a single loop of current resembles that of a bar magnet—strongest inside the loop, and decreasing in strength as you move away from the loop. Neither is it in a uniform direction—the magnetic field lines loop though the loop!

Q30.2 No magnetic field is created by a stationary charge, as the rate of flow is zero. A moving charge creates a magnetic field.

Q30.3 The magnetic field created by wire 1 at the position of wire 2 is into the paper. Hence, the magnetic force on wire 2 is in direction down × into the paper = to the right, away from wire 1. Now wire 2 creates a magnetic field into the page at the location of wire 1, so wire 1 feels force up ×into the paper = left, away from wire 2.

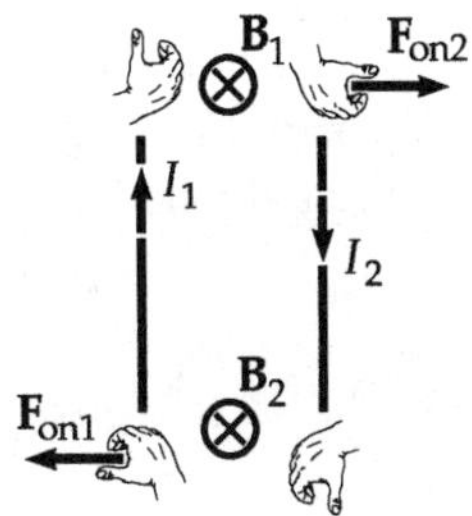

FIG. Q30.3

Q30.4 No total force, but a torque. Let wire one carry current in the y direction, toward the top of the page. Let wire two be a millimeter above the plane of the paper and carry current to the right, in the x direction. On the left-hand side of wire one, wire one creates magnetic field in the z direction, which exerts force in the $\hat{\mathbf{i}} \times \hat{\mathbf{k}} = -\hat{\mathbf{j}}$ direction on wire two. On the right-hand side, wire one produces magnetic field in the $-\hat{\mathbf{k}}$ direction and makes a $\hat{\mathbf{i}} \times (-\hat{\mathbf{k}}) = +\hat{\mathbf{j}}$ force of equal magnitude act on wire two. If wire two is free to move, its center section will twist counterclockwise and then be attracted to wire one.

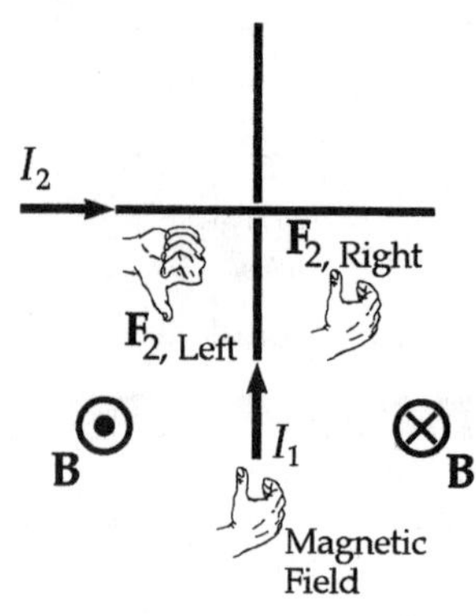

FIG. Q30.4

Q30.5 Ampère's law is valid for all closed paths surrounding a conductor, but not always convenient. There are many paths along which the integral is cumbersome to calculate, although not impossible. Consider a circular path around but *not* coaxial with a long, straight current-carrying wire.

Q30.6 The Biot-Savart law considers the contribution of each element of current in a conductor to determine the magnetic field, while for Ampère's law, one need only know the current passing through a given surface. Given situations of high degrees of symmetry, Ampère's law is more convenient to use, even though both laws are equally valid in all situations.

Q30.7 If the radius of the toroid is very large compared to its cross-sectional area, then the field is nearly uniform. If not, as in many transformers, it is not.

Q30.8 Both laws use the concept of flux—the "flow" of field lines through a surface to determine the field strength. They also both relate the integral of the field over a closed geometrical figure to a fundamental constant multiplied by the source of the appropriate field. The geometrical figure is a surface for Gauss's law and a line for Ampère's.

Q30.9 Apply Ampère's law to the circular path labeled 1 in the picture. Since there is no current inside this path, the magnetic field inside the tube must be zero. On the other hand, the current through path 2 is the current carried by the conductor. Therefore the magnetic field outside the tube is nonzero.

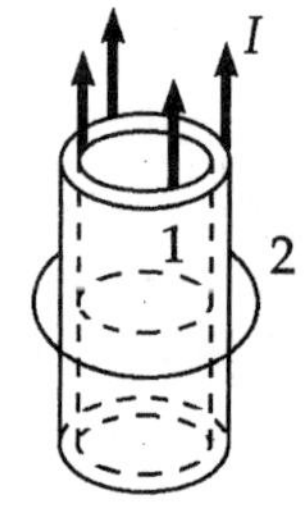

FIG. Q30.9

Q30.10 The magnetic field inside a long solenoid is given by $B = \frac{\mu_0 NI}{\ell}$.

(a) If the length ℓ is doubled, the field is cut in half.

(b) If N is doubled, the magnetic field is doubled.

Q30.11 The magnetic flux is $\Phi_B = BA\cos\theta$. Therefore the flux is maximum when **B** is perpendicular to the loop of wire. The flux is zero when there is no component of magnetic field perpendicular to the loop—that is, when the plane of the loop contains the x axis.

Q30.12 Maxwell included a term in Ampère's law to account for the contributions to the magnetic field by changing electric fields, by treating those changing electric fields as "displacement currents."

Q30.13 **M** measures the intrinsic magnetic field in the nail. Unless the nail was previously magnetized, then **M** starts out from zero. **H** is due to the current in the coil of wire around the nail. **B** is related to the sum of **M** and **H**. If the nail is aluminum or copper, **H** makes the dominant contribution to **B**, but **M** can add a little in the same or in the opposite direction. If the nail is iron, as it becomes magnetized **M** can become the dominant contributor to **B**.

Q30.14 Magnetic domain alignment creates a stronger external magnetic field. The field of one piece of iron in turn can align domains in another iron sample. A nonuniform magnetic field exerts a net force of attraction on magnetic dipoles aligned with the field.

Q30.15 The shock misaligns the domains. Heating will also decrease magnetism.

Q30.16 Magnetic levitation is illustrated in Figure Q30.31. The Earth's magnetic field is so weak that the floor of his tomb should be magnetized as well as his coffin. Alternatively, the floor of his tomb could be made of superconducting material, which exerts a force of repulsion on any magnet.

Q30.17 There is no magnetic material in a vacuum, so **M** must be zero. Therefore $\mathbf{B} = \mu_0\mathbf{H}$ in a vacuum.

Q30.18 Atoms that do not have a permanent magnetic dipole moment have electrons with spin and orbital magnetic moments that add to zero as vectors. Atoms with a permanent dipole moment have electrons with orbital and spin magnetic moments that show some net alignment.

Q30.19 The magnetic dipole moment of an atom is the sum of the dipole moments due to the electrons' orbital motions and the dipole moments due to the spin of the electrons.

Q30.20 **M** and **H** are in opposite directions. Section 30.8 argues that all atoms should be thought of as weakly diamagnetic due to the effect of an external magnetic field on the motions of atomic electrons. Paramagnetic and ferromagnetic effects dominate whenever they exist.

Q30.21 The effects of diamagnetism are significantly smaller than those of paramagnetism.

Q30.22 When the substance is above the Curie temperature, random thermal motion of the molecules prevents the formation of domains. It cannot be ferromagnetic, but only paramagnetic.

Q30.23 A ferromagnetic substance is one in which the magnetic moments of the atoms are aligned within domains, and can be aligned macroscopically. A paramagnetic substance is one in which the magnetic moments are not naturally aligned, but when placed in an external magnetic field, the molecules line their magnetic moments up with the external field. A diamagnetic material is one in which the magnetic moments are also not naturally aligned, but when placed in an external magnetic field, the molecules line up to oppose the external magnetic field.

Q30.24 (a) **B** increases slightly

(b) **B** decreases slightly

(c) **B** increases significantly

Equations 30.33 and 30.34 indicate that, when each metal is in the solenoid, the total field is $\mathbf{B} = \mu_0(1+\chi)\mathbf{H}$. Table 30.2 indicates that **B** is slightly greater than $\mu_0\mathbf{H}$ for aluminum and slightly less for copper. For iron, the field can be made thousands of times stronger, as seen in Example 30.10.

Q30.25 A "hard" ferromagnetic material requires much more energy per molecule than a "soft" ferromagnetic material to change the orientation of the magnetic dipole moments. This way, a hard ferromagnetic material is more likely to retain its magnetization than a soft ferromagnetic material.

Q30.26 The medium for any magnetic recording should be a hard ferromagnetic substance, so that thermal vibrations and stray magnetic fields will not rapidly erase the information.

Q30.27 If a soft ferromagnetic substance were used, then the magnet would not be "permanent." Any significant shock, a heating/cooling cycle, or just rotating the magnet in the Earth's magnetic field would decrease the overall magnetization by randomly aligning some of the magnetic dipole moments.

Q30.28 You can expect a magnetic tape to be weakly attracted to a magnet. Before you erase the information on the tape, the net magnetization of a macroscopic section of the tape would be nearly zero, as the different domains on the tape would have opposite magnetization, and be more or less equal in number and size. Once your external magnet aligns the magnetic moments on the tape, there would be a weak attraction, but not like that of picking up a paper clip with a magnet. A majority of the mass of the tape is non-magnetic, and so the gravitational force acting on the tape will likely be larger than the magnetic attraction.

Q30.29 To magnetize the screwdriver, stroke one pole of the magnet along the blade of the screwdriver several or many times. To demagnetize the screwdriver, drop it on a hard surface a few times, or heat it to some high temperature.

Q30.30 The north magnetic pole is near the south geographic pole. Straight up.

Q30.31 (a) The magnets repel each other with a force equal to the weight of one of them.

(b) The pencil prevents motion to the side and prevents the magnets from rotating under their mutual torques. Its constraint changes unstable equilibrium into stable.

(c) Most likely, the disks are magnetized perpendicular to their flat faces, making one face a north pole and the other a south pole. One disk has its north pole on the top side and the other has its north pole on the bottom side.

(d) Then if either were inverted they would attract each other and stick firmly together.

SOLUTIONS TO PROBLEMS

Section 30.1 The Biot-Savart Law

P30.1 $$B=\frac{\mu_0 I}{2R}=\frac{\mu_0 q(v/2\pi R)}{2R}=\boxed{12.5\text{ T}}$$

P30.2 $$B=\frac{\mu_0 I}{2\pi R}=\frac{\left(4\pi\times10^{-7}\text{ T}\cdot\text{m/A}\right)\left(1.00\times10^{4}\text{ A}\right)}{2\pi(100\text{ m})}=2.00\times10^{-5}\text{ T}=\boxed{20.0\ \mu\text{T}}$$

P30.3 (a) $B = \frac{4\mu_0 I}{4\pi a}\left(\cos\frac{\pi}{4} - \cos\frac{3\pi}{4}\right)$ where $a = \frac{\ell}{2}$

is the distance from any side to the center.

$$B = \frac{4.00\times10^{-6}}{0.200}\left(\frac{\sqrt{2}}{2} + \frac{\sqrt{2}}{2}\right) = 2\sqrt{2}\times10^{-5}\ \text{T} = \boxed{28.3\ \mu\text{T into the paper}}$$

FIG. P30.3

(b) For a single circular turn with $4\ell = 2\pi R$,

$$B = \frac{\mu_0 I}{2R} = \frac{\mu_0 \pi I}{4\ell} = \frac{\left(4\pi^2\times10^{-7}\right)(10.0)}{4(0.400)} = \boxed{24.7\ \mu\text{T into the paper}}$$

P30.4 $$B = \frac{\mu_0 I}{2\pi r} = \frac{\left(4\pi\times10^{-7}\right)(1.00\ \text{A})}{2\pi(1.00\ \text{m})} = \boxed{2.00\times10^{-7}\ \text{T}}$$

P30.5 For leg 1, $d\mathbf{s}\times\hat{\mathbf{r}} = 0$, so there is no contribution to the field from this segment. For leg 2, the wire is only semi-infinite; thus,

$$B = \frac{1}{2}\left(\frac{\mu_0 I}{2\pi x}\right) = \boxed{\frac{\mu_0 I}{4\pi x}\ \text{into the paper}}.$$

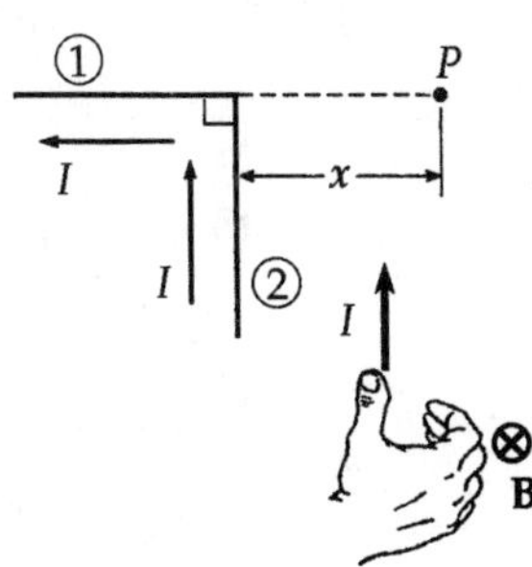

FIG. P30.5

P30.6 We can think of the total magnetic field as the superposition of the field due to the long straight wire (having magnitude $\frac{\mu_0 I}{2\pi R}$ and directed into the page) and the field due to the circular loop (having magnitude $\frac{\mu_0 I}{2R}$ and directed into the page). The resultant magnetic field is:

$$\boxed{\mathbf{B} = \left(1 + \frac{1}{\pi}\right)\frac{\mu_0 I}{2R}\ \text{(directed into the page)}}.$$

P30.7 For the straight sections $d\mathbf{s}\times\hat{\mathbf{r}} = 0$. The quarter circle makes one-fourth the field of a full loop:

$$\mathbf{B} = \frac{1}{4}\frac{\mu_0 I}{2R} = \frac{\mu_0 I}{8R}\ \text{into the paper} \qquad \mathbf{B} = \frac{\left(4\pi\times10^{-7}\ \text{T}\cdot\text{m/A}\right)(5.00\ \text{A})}{8(0.030\,0\ \text{m})} = \boxed{26.2\ \mu\text{T into the paper}}$$

P30.8 Along the axis of a circular loop of radius R,

$$B = \frac{\mu_0 I R^2}{2\left(x^2 + R^2\right)^{3/2}}$$

or

$$\frac{B}{B_0} = \left[\frac{1}{(x/R)^2 + 1}\right]^{3/2}$$

where

$$B_0 \equiv \frac{\mu_0 I}{2R}.$$

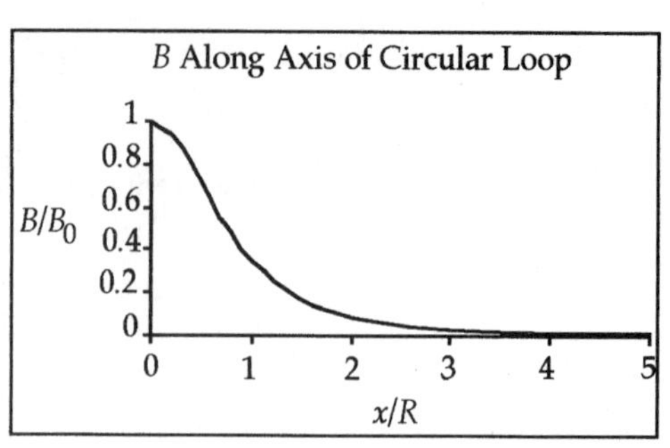

FIG. P30.8

x/R	B/B_0
0.00	1.00
1.00	0.354
2.00	0.0894
3.00	0.0316
4.00	0.0143
5.00	0.00754

***P30.9** Wire 1 creates at the origin magnetic field

$$\mathbf{B}_1 = \frac{\mu_0 I}{2\pi r} \text{ right hand rule} = \frac{\mu_0 I_1}{2\pi a} = \frac{\mu_0 I_1}{2\pi a}\hat{\mathbf{j}}$$

(a) If the total field at the origin is $\frac{2\mu_0 I_1}{2\pi a}\hat{\mathbf{j}} = \frac{\mu_0 I_1}{2\pi a}\hat{\mathbf{j}} + \mathbf{B}_2$ then the second wire must create field

according to $\mathbf{B}_2 = \frac{\mu_0 I_1}{2\pi a}\hat{\mathbf{j}} = \frac{\mu_0 I_2}{2\pi(2a)}$.

Then $I_2 = \boxed{2I_1 \text{ out of the paper}} = 2I_1\hat{\mathbf{k}}$.

(b) The other possibility is $\mathbf{B}_1 + \mathbf{B}_2 = \frac{2\mu_0 I_1}{2\pi a}\left(-\hat{\mathbf{j}}\right) = \frac{\mu_0 I_1}{2\pi a}\hat{\mathbf{j}} + \mathbf{B}_2$. Then

$$\mathbf{B}_2 = \frac{3\mu_0 I_1}{2\pi a}\left(-\hat{\mathbf{j}}\right) = \frac{\mu_0 I_2}{2\pi(2a)} \qquad I_2 = \boxed{6I_1 \text{ into the paper}} = 6I_1\left(-\hat{\mathbf{k}}\right)$$

***P30.10** Every element of current creates magnetic field in the same direction, into the page, at the center of the arc. The upper straight portion creates one-half of the field that an infinitely long straight wire would create. The curved portion creates one quarter of the field that a circular loop produces at its center. The lower straight segment also creates field $\frac{1}{2}\frac{\mu_0 I}{2\pi r}$.

The total field is

$$\mathbf{B} = \left(\frac{1}{2}\frac{\mu_0 I}{2\pi r} + \frac{1}{4}\frac{\mu_0 I}{2r} + \frac{1}{2}\frac{\mu_0 I}{2\pi r}\right) \text{into the page} = \boxed{\frac{\mu_0 I}{2r}\left(\frac{1}{\pi} + \frac{1}{4}\right) \text{into the plane of the paper}}$$

$$= \left(\frac{0.284\,15\,\mu_0 I}{r}\right) \text{into the page.}$$

***P30.11** (a) Above the pair of wires, the field out of the page of the 50 A current will be stronger than the $\left(-\hat{\mathbf{k}}\right)$ field of the 30 A current, so they cannot add to zero. Between the wires, both produce fields into the page. They can only add to zero below the wires, at coordinate $y = -|y|$. Here the total field is

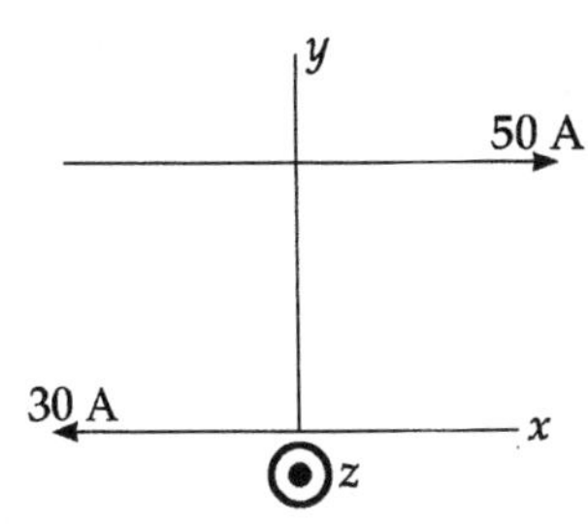

FIG. P30.11

$$\mathbf{B} = \frac{\mu_0 I}{2\pi r} \quad + \frac{\mu_0 I}{2\pi r} \quad :$$

$$0 = \frac{\mu_0}{2\pi}\left[\frac{50\text{ A}}{\left(|y| + 0.28\text{ m}\right)}\left(-\hat{\mathbf{k}}\right) + \frac{30\text{ A}}{|y|}\left(\hat{\mathbf{k}}\right)\right]$$

$$50|y| = 30\left(|y| + 0.28\text{ m}\right)$$

$$50(-y) = 30(0.28\text{ m} - y)$$

$$-20y = 30(0.28\text{ m}) \boxed{\text{at } y = -0.420\text{ m}}$$

(b) At $y = 0.1$ m the total field is $\mathbf{B} = \frac{\mu_0 I}{2\pi r} \quad + \frac{\mu_0 I}{2\pi r} \quad :$

$$\mathbf{B} = \frac{4\pi \times 10^{-7}\text{ T}\cdot\text{m/A}}{2\pi}\left(\frac{50\text{ A}}{(0.28 - 0.10)\text{ m}}\left(-\hat{\mathbf{k}}\right) + \frac{30\text{ A}}{0.10\text{ m}}\left(-\hat{\mathbf{k}}\right)\right) = 1.16 \times 10^{-4}\text{ T}\left(-\hat{\mathbf{k}}\right).$$

The force on the particle is

$$\mathbf{F} = q\mathbf{v} \times \mathbf{B} = \left(-2 \times 10^{-6}\text{ C}\right)\left(150 \times 10^{6}\text{ m/s}\right)\left(\hat{\mathbf{i}}\right) \times \left(1.16 \times 10^{-4}\text{ N}\cdot\text{s/C}\cdot\text{m}\right)\left(-\hat{\mathbf{k}}\right) = \boxed{3.47 \times 10^{-2}\text{ N}\left(-\hat{\mathbf{j}}\right)}.$$

(c) We require $\mathbf{F}_e = 3.47 \times 10^{-2}\text{ N}\left(+\hat{\mathbf{j}}\right) = q\mathbf{E} = \left(-2 \times 10^{-6}\text{ C}\right)\mathbf{E}$.

So $\mathbf{E} = \boxed{-1.73 \times 10^{4}\,\hat{\mathbf{j}}\text{ N/C}}$.

P30.12 $$dB = \frac{\mu_0 I}{4\pi}\frac{\left|d\boldsymbol{\ell} \times \hat{\mathbf{r}}\right|}{r^2}$$

$$B = \frac{\mu_0 I}{4\pi}\left(\frac{\frac{1}{6}2\pi a}{a^2} - \frac{\frac{1}{6}2\pi b}{b^2}\right)$$

$$\mathbf{B} = \boxed{\frac{\mu_0 I}{12}\left(\frac{1}{a} - \frac{1}{b}\right)\text{ directed out of the paper}}$$

***P30.13** (a) We use equation 30.4. For the distance a from the wire to the field point we have $\tan 30° = \frac{a}{L/2}$, $a = 0.288\,7L$. One wire contributes to the field at P

$$B = \frac{\mu_0 I}{4\pi a}(\cos\theta_1 - \cos\theta_2) = \frac{\mu_0 I}{4\pi(0.288\,7L)}(\cos 30° - \cos 150°)$$

$$= \frac{\mu_0 I(1.732)}{4\pi(0.288\,7L)} = \frac{1.50\mu_0 I}{\pi L}.$$

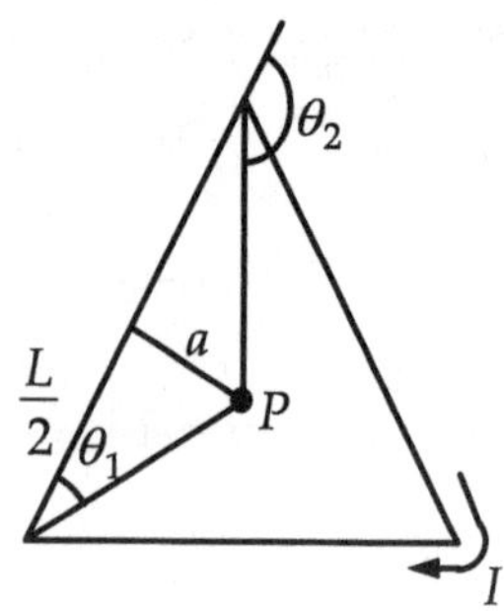

FIG. P30.13(a)

Each side contributes the same amount of field in the same direction, which is perpendicularly into the paper in the picture. So the total field is $3\left(\frac{1.50\mu_0 I}{\pi L}\right) = \boxed{\frac{4.50\mu_0 I}{\pi L}}$.

(b) As we showed in part (a), one whole side of the triangle creates field at the center $\frac{\mu_0 I(1.732)}{4\pi a}$. Now one-half of one nearby side of the triangle will be half as far away from point P_b and have a geometrically similar situation. Then it creates at P_b field $\frac{\mu_0 I(1.732)}{4\pi(a/2)} = \frac{2\mu_0 I(1.732)}{4\pi a}$. The two half-sides shown crosshatched in the picture create at P_b field $2\left(\frac{2\mu_0 I(1.732)}{4\pi a}\right) = \frac{4\mu_0 I(1.732)}{4\pi(0.288\,7L)} = \frac{6\mu_0 I}{\pi L}$. The rest of the triangle will contribute somewhat more field in the same direction, so we already have a proof that the field at P_b is $\boxed{\text{stronger}}$.

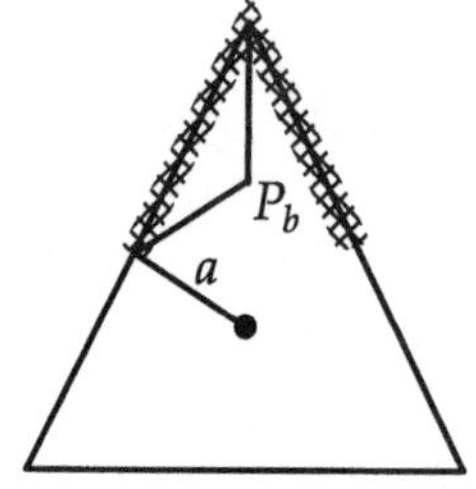

FIG. P30.13(b)

P30.14 Apply Equation 30.4 three times:

$$\mathbf{B} = \frac{\mu_0 I}{4\pi a}\left(\cos 0 - \frac{d}{\sqrt{d^2+a^2}}\right)\text{ toward you} + \frac{\mu_0 I}{4\pi d}\left(\frac{a}{\sqrt{d^2+a^2}} + \frac{a}{\sqrt{d^2+a^2}}\right)\text{ away from you}$$

$$+ \frac{\mu_0 I}{4\pi a}\left(\frac{-d}{\sqrt{d^2+a^2}} - \cos 180°\right)\text{ toward you}$$

$$\mathbf{B} = \boxed{\frac{\mu_0 I\left(a^2+d^2-d\sqrt{a^2+d^2}\right)}{2\pi a d\sqrt{a^2+d^2}}\text{ away from you}}$$

P30.15 Take the x-direction to the right and the y-direction up in the plane of the paper. Current 1 creates at P a field

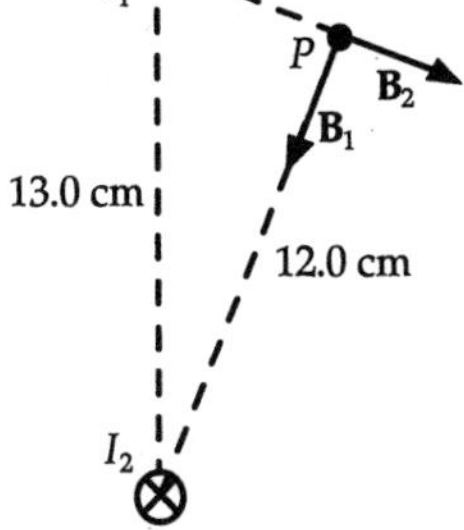

$$B_1 = \frac{\mu_0 I}{2\pi a} = \frac{\left(2.00\times10^{-7}\ \text{T}\cdot\text{m}\right)(3.00\ \text{A})}{\text{A}(0.050\,0\ \text{m})}$$

$\mathbf{B}_1 = 12.0\ \mu\text{T}$ downward and leftward, at angle 67.4° below the $-x$ axis.

Current 2 contributes

$$B_2 = \frac{\left(2.00\times10^{-7}\ \text{T}\cdot\text{m}\right)(3.00\ \text{A})}{\text{A}(0.120\ \text{m})} \text{ clockwise perpendicular to 12.0 cm}$$

FIG. P30.15

$\mathbf{B}_2 = 5.00\ \mu\text{T}$ to the right and down, at angle $-22.6°$

Then, $\mathbf{B} = \mathbf{B}_1 + \mathbf{B}_2 = (12.0\ \mu\text{T})\left(-\hat{\mathbf{i}}\cos 67.4° - \hat{\mathbf{j}}\sin 67.4°\right) + (5.00\ \mu\text{T})\left(\hat{\mathbf{i}}\cos 22.6° - \hat{\mathbf{j}}\sin 22.6°\right)$

$$\mathbf{B} = (-11.1\ \mu\text{T})\hat{\mathbf{j}} - (1.92\ \mu\text{T})\hat{\mathbf{j}} = \boxed{(-13.0\ \mu\text{T})\hat{\mathbf{j}}}$$

Section 30.2 The Magnetic Force Between Two Parallel Conductors

P30.16 Let both wires carry current in the x direction, the first at $y = 0$ and the second at $y = 10.0$ cm.

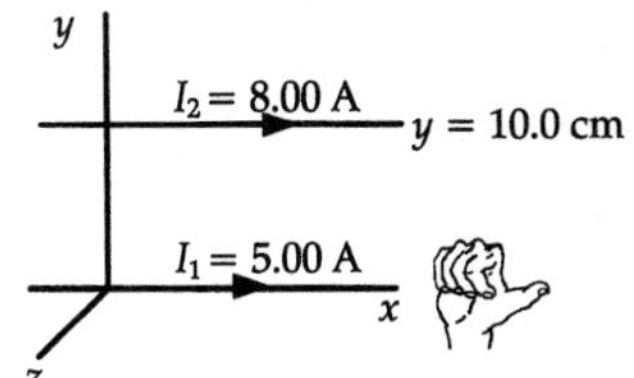

FIG. P30.16(a)

(a) $$\mathbf{B} = \frac{\mu_0 I}{2\pi r}\hat{\mathbf{k}} = \frac{\left(4\pi\times10^{-7}\ \text{T}\cdot\text{m/A}\right)(5.00\ \text{A})}{2\pi(0.100\ \text{m})}\hat{\mathbf{k}}$$

$$\mathbf{B} = \boxed{1.00\times10^{-5}\ \text{T out of the page}}$$

(b) $$\mathbf{F}_B = I_2\boldsymbol{\ell}\times\mathbf{B} = (8.00\ \text{A})\left[(1.00\ \text{m})\hat{\mathbf{i}}\times\left(1.00\times10^{-5}\ \text{T}\right)\hat{\mathbf{k}}\right] = \left(8.00\times10^{-5}\ \text{N}\right)\left(-\hat{\mathbf{j}}\right)$$

$$\boxed{\mathbf{F}_B = 8.00\times10^{-5}\ \text{N toward the first wire}}$$

(c) $$\mathbf{B} = \frac{\mu_0 I}{2\pi r}\left(-\hat{\mathbf{k}}\right) = \frac{\left(4\pi\times10^{-7}\ \text{T}\cdot\text{m/A}\right)(8.00\ \text{A})}{2\pi(0.100\ \text{m})}\left(-\hat{\mathbf{k}}\right) = \left(1.60\times10^{-5}\ \text{T}\right)\left(-\hat{\mathbf{k}}\right)$$

$$\mathbf{B} = \boxed{1.60\times10^{-5}\ \text{T into the page}}$$

(d) $$\mathbf{F}_B = I_1\boldsymbol{\ell}\times\mathbf{B} = (5.00\ \text{A})\left[(1.00\ \text{m})\hat{\mathbf{i}}\times\left(1.60\times10^{-5}\ \text{T}\right)\left(-\hat{\mathbf{k}}\right)\right] = \left(8.00\times10^{-5}\ \text{N}\right)\left(+\hat{\mathbf{j}}\right)$$

$$\mathbf{F}_B = \boxed{8.00\times10^{-5}\ \text{N towards the second wire}}$$

P30.17 By symmetry, we note that the magnetic forces on the top and bottom segments of the rectangle cancel. The net force on the vertical segments of the rectangle is (using Equation 30.11)

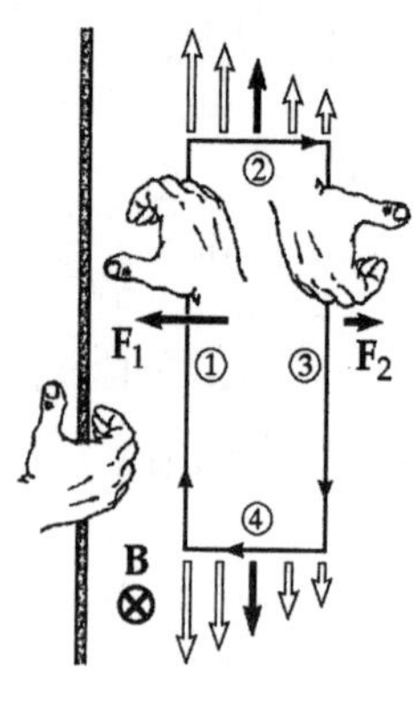

FIG. P30.17

$$\mathbf{F}=\mathbf{F}_1+\mathbf{F}_2=\frac{\mu_0 I_1 I_2 \ell}{2\pi}\left(\frac{1}{c+a}-\frac{1}{c}\right)\hat{\mathbf{i}}=\frac{\mu_0 I_1 I_2 \ell}{2\pi}\left(\frac{-a}{c(c+a)}\right)\hat{\mathbf{i}}$$

$$\mathbf{F}=\frac{\left(4\pi\times10^{-7}\ \mathrm{N/A^2}\right)(5.00\ \mathrm{A})(10.0\ \mathrm{A})(0.450\ \mathrm{m})}{2\pi}\left(\frac{-0.150\ \mathrm{m}}{(0.100\ \mathrm{m})(0.250\ \mathrm{m})}\right)\hat{\mathbf{i}}$$

$$\mathbf{F}=\left(-2.70\times10^{-5}\,\hat{\mathbf{i}}\right)\ \mathrm{N}$$

or $\mathbf{F}=\boxed{2.70\times10^{-5}\ \text{N toward the left}}$.

***P30.18** To attract, both currents must be to the right. The attraction is described by

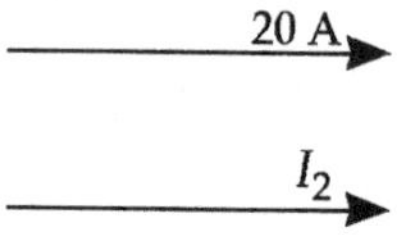

20 A

I_2

FIG. P30.18

$$F=I_2\ell B\sin 90°=I_2\ell\frac{\mu_0 I}{2\pi r}$$

So $$I_2=\frac{F}{\ell}\frac{2\pi r}{\mu_0 I_1}=\left(320\times10^{-6}\ \mathrm{N/m}\right)\left(\frac{2\pi(0.5\ \mathrm{m})}{\left(4\pi\times10^{-7}\ \mathrm{N\cdot s/C\cdot m}\right)(20\ \mathrm{A})}\right)=40.0\ \mathrm{A}$$

Let y represent the distance of the zero-field point below the upper wire.

Then $$\mathbf{B}=\frac{\mu_0 I}{2\pi r}+\frac{\mu_0 I}{2\pi r}\qquad 0=\frac{\mu_0}{2\pi}\left(\frac{20\ \mathrm{A}}{y}(\text{away})+\frac{40\ \mathrm{A}}{(0.5\ \mathrm{m}-y)}(\text{toward})\right)$$

$$20(0.5\ \mathrm{m}-y)=40y\qquad 20(0.5\ \mathrm{m})=60y$$

$y=\boxed{0.167\ \text{m below the upper wire}}$

***P30.19** Carrying oppositely directed currents, wires 1 and 2 repel each other. If wire 3 were between them, it would have to repel either 1 or 2, so the force on that wire could not be zero. If wire 3 were to the right of wire 2, it would feel a larger force exerted by 2 than that exerted by 1, so the total force on 3 could not be zero. Therefore wire 3 must be to the left of both other wires as shown. It must carry downward current so that it can attract wire 2.

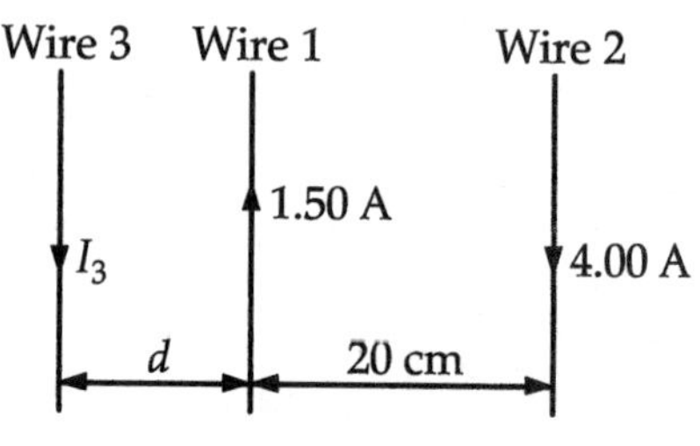

FIG. P30.19

(a) For the equilibrium of wire 3 we have

$$F_{1\text{ on }3}=F_{2\text{ on }3}\qquad \frac{\mu_0(1.50\ \mathrm{A})I_3}{2\pi d}=\frac{\mu_0(4\ \mathrm{A})I_3}{2\pi(20\ \mathrm{cm}+d)}$$

$$1.5(20\ \mathrm{cm}+d)=4d\qquad d=\frac{30\ \mathrm{cm}}{2.5}=\boxed{12.0\ \text{cm to the left of wire 1}}$$

(b) For the equilibrium of wire 1,

$$\frac{\mu_0 I_3(1.5\ \mathrm{A})}{2\pi(12\ \mathrm{cm})}=\frac{\mu_0(4\ \mathrm{A})(1.5\ \mathrm{A})}{2\pi(20\ \mathrm{cm})}\qquad I_3=\frac{12}{20}4\ \mathrm{A}=\boxed{2.40\ \text{A down}}$$

We know that wire 2 must be in equilibrium because the forces on it are equal in magnitude to the forces that it exerts on wires 1 and 3, which are equal because they both balance the equal-magnitude forces that 1 exerts on 3 and that 3 exerts on 1.

P30.20 The separation between the wires is

$$a = 2(6.00\text{ cm})\sin 8.00° = 1.67\text{ cm}.$$

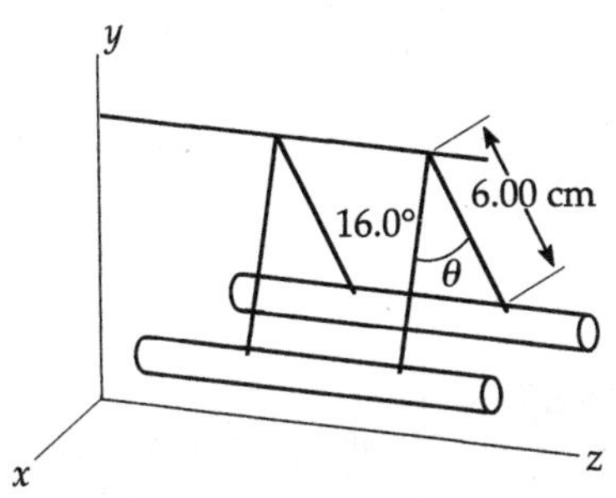

FIG. P30.20

(a) Because the wires repel, the currents are in $\boxed{\text{opposite directions}}$.

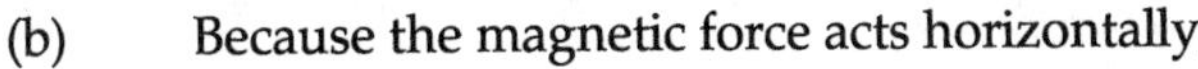

(b) Because the magnetic force acts horizontally,

$$\frac{F_B}{F_g} = \frac{\mu_0 I^2 \ell}{2\pi amg} = \tan 8.00°$$

$$I^2 = \frac{mg2\pi a}{\ell\mu_0}\tan 8.00° \text{ so } I = \boxed{67.8\text{ A}}.$$

Section 30.3 **Ampère's Law**

P30.21 Each wire is distant from P by

$$(0.200\text{ m})\cos 45.0° = 0.141\text{ m}.$$

Each wire produces a field at P of equal magnitude:

$$B_A = \frac{\mu_0 I}{2\pi a} = \frac{(2.00\times10^{-7}\text{ T}\cdot\text{m/A})(5.00\text{ A})}{(0.141\text{ m})} = 7.07\ \mu\text{T}.$$

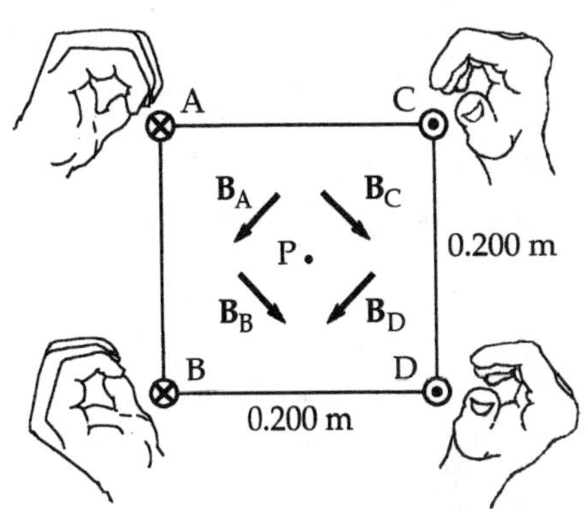

FIG. P30.21

Carrying currents into the page, A produces at P a field of 7.07 μT to the left and down at –135°, while B creates a field to the right and down at – 45°. Carrying currents toward you, C produces a field downward and to the right at – 45°, while D's contribution is downward and to the left. The total field is then

$$4(7.07\ \mu\text{T})\sin 45.0° = \boxed{20.0\ \mu\text{T}} \text{ toward the bottom of the page}$$

P30.22 Let the current I be to the right. It creates a field $B = \frac{\mu_0 I}{2\pi d}$ at the proton's location. And we have a balance between the weight of the proton and the magnetic force

$$mg(-\hat{\mathbf{j}}) + qv(-\hat{\mathbf{i}}) \times \frac{\mu_0 I}{2\pi d}(\hat{\mathbf{k}}) = 0 \text{ at a distance } d \text{ from the wire}$$

$$d = \frac{qv\mu_0 I}{2\pi mg} = \frac{(1.60\times10^{-19}\text{ C})(2.30\times10^4\text{ m/s})(4\pi\times10^{-7}\text{ T}\cdot\text{m/A})(1.20\times10^{-6}\text{ A})}{2\pi(1.67\times10^{-27}\text{ kg})(9.80\text{ m/s}^2)} = \boxed{5.40\text{ cm}}$$

P30.23 From Ampere's law, the magnetic field at point a is given by $B_a = \frac{\mu_0 I_a}{2\pi r_a}$, where I_a is the net current through the area of the circle of radius r_a. In this case, $I_a = 1.00\text{ A}$ out of the page (the current in the inner conductor), so

$$B_a = \frac{(4\pi \times 10^{-7}\text{ T}\cdot\text{m/A})(1.00\text{ A})}{2\pi(1.00 \times 10^{-3}\text{ m})} = \boxed{200\ \mu\text{T toward top of page}}.$$

Similarly at point b: $B_b = \frac{\mu_0 I_b}{2\pi r_b}$, where I_b is the net current through the area of the circle having radius r_b.

Taking out of the page as positive, $I_b = 1.00\text{ A} - 3.00\text{ A} = -2.00\text{ A}$, or $I_b = 2.00\text{ A}$ into the page. Therefore,

$$B_b = \frac{(4\pi \times 10^{-7}\text{ T}\cdot\text{m/A})(2.00\text{ A})}{2\pi(3.00 \times 10^{-3}\text{ m})} = \boxed{133\ \mu\text{T toward bottom of page}}.$$

P30.24 (a) In $B = \frac{\mu_0 I}{2\pi r}$, the field will be one-tenth as large at a ten-times larger distance: $\boxed{400\text{ cm}}$

(b) $$\mathbf{B} = \frac{\mu_0 I}{2\pi r_1}\hat{\mathbf{k}} + \frac{\mu_0 I}{2\pi r_2}(-\hat{\mathbf{k}}) \text{ so } B = \frac{4\pi \times 10^{-7}\text{ T}\cdot\text{m}(2.00\text{ A})}{2\pi\text{ A}}\left(\frac{1}{0.398\,5\text{ m}} - \frac{1}{0.401\,5\text{ m}}\right) = \boxed{7.50\text{ nT}}$$

(c) Call r the distance from cord center to field point and $2d = 3.00\text{ mm}$ the distance between conductors.

$$B = \frac{\mu_0 I}{2\pi}\left(\frac{1}{r-d} - \frac{1}{r+d}\right) = \frac{\mu_0 I}{2\pi}\frac{2d}{r^2 - d^2}$$

$$7.50 \times 10^{-10}\text{ T} = (2.00 \times 10^{-7}\text{ T}\cdot\text{m/A})(2.00\text{ A})\frac{(3.00 \times 10^{-3}\text{ m})}{r^2 - 2.25 \times 10^{-6}\text{ m}^2} \text{ so } r = \boxed{1.26\text{ m}}$$

The field of the two-conductor cord is weak to start with and falls off rapidly with distance.

(d) The cable creates $\boxed{\text{zero}}$ field at exterior points, since a loop in Ampère's law encloses zero total current. Shall we sell coaxial-cable power cords to people who worry about biological damage from weak magnetic fields?

P30.25 (a) One wire feels force due to the field of the other ninety-nine.

$$B = \frac{\mu_0 I_0 r}{2\pi R^2} = \frac{(4\pi \times 10^{-7}\text{ T}\cdot\text{m/A})(99)(2.00\text{ A})(0.200 \times 10^{-2}\text{ m})}{2\pi(0.500 \times 10^{-2}\text{ m})^2} = 3.17 \times 10^{-3}\text{ T}$$

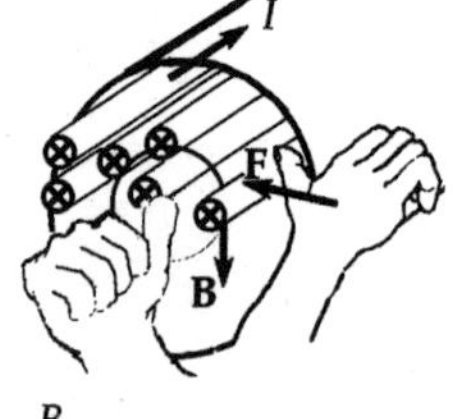

This field points tangent to a circle of radius 0.200 cm and exerts force $\mathbf{F} = I\boldsymbol{\ell} \times \mathbf{B}$ toward the center of the bundle, on the single hundredth wire:

$$\frac{F}{\ell} = IB\sin\theta = (2.00\text{ A})(3.17 \times 10^{-3}\text{ T})\sin 90° = 6.34\text{ mN/m}$$

$$\frac{F_B}{\ell} = \boxed{6.34 \times 10^{-3}\text{ N/m inward}}$$

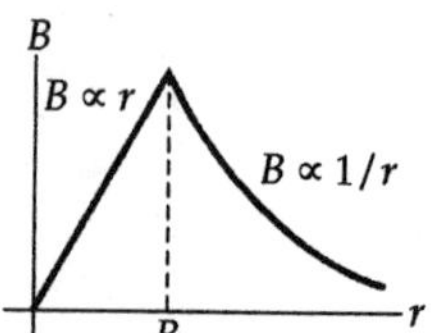

(b) $B \propto r$, so B is greatest at the outside of the bundle. Since each wire carries the same current, F is $\boxed{\text{greatest at the outer surface}}$.

FIG. P30.25

P30.26 (a) $$B_{\text{inner}}=\frac{\mu_0 NI}{2\pi r}=\frac{\left(4\pi\times10^{-7}\text{ T}\cdot\text{m/A}\right)(900)\left(14.0\times10^{3}\text{ A}\right)}{2\pi(0.700\text{ m})}=\boxed{3.60\text{ T}}$$

(b) $$B_{\text{outer}}=\frac{\mu_0 NI}{2\pi r}=\frac{\left(2\times10^{-7}\text{ T}\cdot\text{m/A}\right)(900)\left(14.0\times10^{3}\text{ A}\right)}{1.30\text{ m}}=\boxed{1.94\text{ T}}$$

***P30.27** We assume the current is vertically upward.

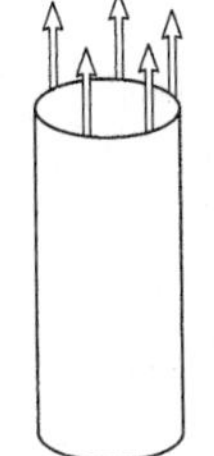

FIG. P30.27(a)

(a) Consider a circle of radius r slightly less than R. It encloses no current so from

$\oint \mathbf{B}\cdot d\mathbf{s}=\mu_0 I_{\text{inside}}$ $\qquad B(2\pi r)=0$

we conclude that the magnetic field is $\boxed{\text{zero}}$.

(b) Now let the r be barely larger than R. Ampere's law becomes $B(2\pi R)=\mu_0 I$,

so $\boxed{B=\dfrac{\mu_0 I}{2\pi R}}$.

The field's direction is $\boxed{\text{tangent to the wall of the cylinder in a counterclockwise sense}}$.

(c) Consider a strip of the wall of width dx and length ℓ. Its width is so small compared to $2\pi R$ that the field at its location would be essentially unchanged if the current in the strip were turned off.

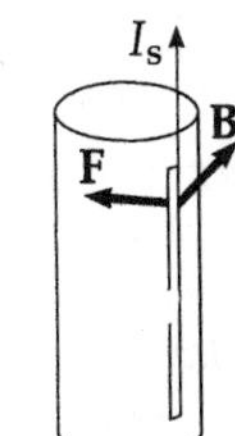

FIG. P30.27(c)

The current it carries is $I_s=\dfrac{Idx}{2\pi R}$ up.

The force on it is

$$\mathbf{F}=I_s\boldsymbol{\ell}\times\mathbf{B}=\frac{Idx}{2\pi R}\left(\ell\frac{\mu_0 I}{2\pi R}\right)\textbf{up}\times\textbf{into page}=\frac{\mu_0 I^2\ell dx}{4\pi^2R^2}\textbf{radially inward}.$$

The pressure on the strip and everywhere on the cylinder is

$$P=\frac{F}{A}=\frac{\mu_0 I^2\ell dx}{4\pi^2R^2\ell dx}=\boxed{\frac{\mu_0 I^2}{(2\pi R)^2}\text{ inward}}.$$

The pinch effect makes an effective demonstration when an aluminum can crushes itself as it carries a large current along its length.

P30.28 From $\oint \mathbf{B}\cdot d\boldsymbol{\ell}=\mu_0 I$, $\qquad I=\dfrac{2\pi rB}{\mu_0}=\dfrac{2\pi\left(1.00\times10^{-3}\right)(0.100)}{4\pi\times10^{-7}}=\boxed{500\text{ A}}$.

P30.29 Use Ampère's law, $\oint \mathbf{B}\cdot d\mathbf{s}=\mu_0 I$. For current density $\mathbf{J}$, this becomes

$\oint \mathbf{B}\cdot d\mathbf{s}=\mu_0\int \mathbf{J}\cdot d\mathbf{A}$.

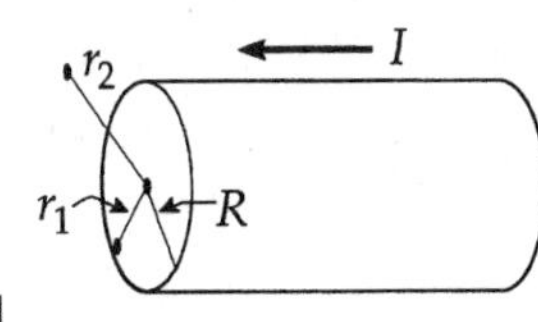

FIG. P30.29

(a) For $r_1<R$, this gives $\qquad B2\pi r_1=\mu_0\int_0^{r_1}(br)(2\pi r dr)$ and

$$B=\boxed{\frac{\mu_0 b r_1^2}{3}\text{ (for } r_1<R\text{ or inside the cylinder)}}.$$

(b) When $r_2>R$, Ampère's law yields $\qquad (2\pi r_2)B=\mu_0\int_0^{R}(br)(2\pi r dr)=\dfrac{2\pi\mu_0 bR^3}{3}$,

or $B=\boxed{\dfrac{\mu_0 bR^3}{3r_2}\text{ (for } r_2>R\text{ or outside the cylinder)}}$.

P30.30 (a) See Figure (a) to the right.

(b) At a point on the z axis, the contribution from each wire has magnitude $B = \frac{\mu_0 I}{2\pi\sqrt{a^2+z^2}}$ and is perpendicular to the line from this point to the wire as shown in Figure (b). Combining fields, the vertical components cancel while the horizontal components add, yielding

$$B_y = 2\left(\frac{\mu_0 I}{2\pi\sqrt{a^2+z^2}}\sin\theta\right) = \frac{\mu_0 I}{\pi\sqrt{a^2+z^2}}\left(\frac{z}{\sqrt{a^2+z^2}}\right) = \frac{\mu_0 I z}{\pi\left(a^2+z^2\right)}$$

The condition for a maximum is:

$$\frac{dB_y}{dz} = \frac{-\mu_0 I z(2z)}{\pi\left(a^2+z^2\right)^2} + \frac{\mu_0 I}{\pi\left(a^2+z^2\right)} = 0, \text{ or } \frac{\mu_0 I}{\pi}\frac{\left(a^2-z^2\right)}{\left(a^2+z^2\right)} = 0$$

Thus, along the z axis, the field is a maximum at $\boxed{d = a}$.

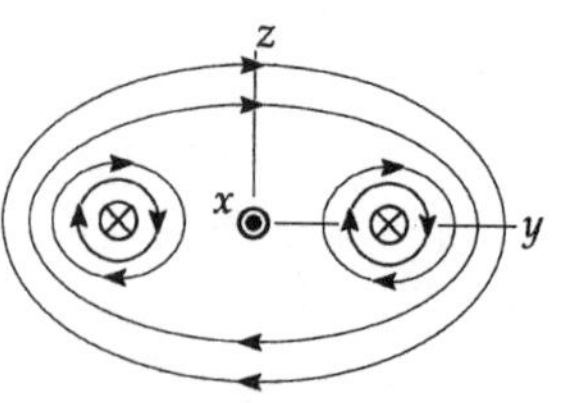

(Currents are into the paper)

Figure (a)

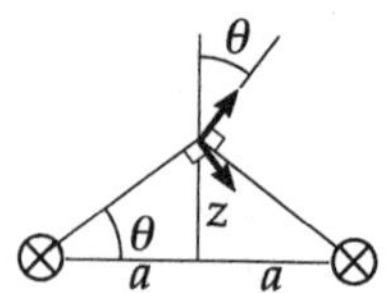

At a distance z above the plane of the conductors

Figure (b)

FIG. P30.30

Section 30.4 The Magnetic Field of a Solenoid

P30.31 $B = \mu_0 \frac{N}{\ell} I$ so $I = \frac{B}{\mu_0 n} = \frac{\left(1.00\times10^{-4}\ \text{T}\right)0.400\ \text{m}}{\left(4\pi\times10^{-7}\ \text{T}\cdot\text{m/A}\right)1\,000} = \boxed{31.8\ \text{mA}}$

***P30.32** Let the axis of the solenoid lie along the y–axis from $y = 0$ to $y = \ell$. We will determine the field at $y = a$. This point will be inside the solenoid if $0 < a < \ell$ and outside if $a < 0$ or $a > \ell$. We think of solenoid as formed of rings, each of thickness dy. Now I is the symbol for the current in each turn of wire and the number of turns per length is $\left(\frac{N}{\ell}\right)$. So the number of turns in the ring is $\left(\frac{N}{\ell}\right)dy$ and the current in the ring is $I_{\text{ring}} = I\left(\frac{N}{\ell}\right)dy$. Now we use the result of Example 30.3 for the field created by one ring:

$$B_{\text{ring}} = \frac{\mu_0 I_{\text{ring}} R^2}{2\left(x^2+R^2\right)^{3/2}}$$

where x is the name of the distance from the center of the ring, at location y, to the field point $x = a - y$. Each ring creates field in the same direction, along our y–axis, so the whole field of the solenoid is

$$B = \sum_{\text{all rings}} B_{\text{ring}} = \sum \frac{\mu_0 I_{\text{ring}} R^2}{2\left(x^2+R^2\right)^{3/2}} = \int_0^\ell \frac{\mu_0 I (N/\ell) dy R^2}{2\left((a-y)^2+R^2\right)^{3/2}} = \frac{\mu_0 I N R^2}{2\ell}\int_0^\ell \frac{dy}{2\left((a-y)^2+R^2\right)^{3/2}}.$$

To perform the integral we change variables to $u = a - y$.

$$B = \frac{\mu_0 I N R^2}{2\ell}\int_a^{a-\ell} \frac{-du}{\left(u^2+R^2\right)^{3/2}}$$

and then use the table of integrals in the appendix:

continued on next page

(a) $$B = \frac{\mu_0 INR^2}{2\ell}\frac{-u}{R^2\sqrt{u^2+R^2}}\Bigg|_a^{a-\ell} = \boxed{\frac{\mu_0 IN}{2\ell}\left[\frac{a}{\sqrt{a^2+R^2}} - \frac{a-\ell}{\sqrt{(a-\ell)^2+R^2}}\right]}$$

(b) If ℓ is much larger than R and $a = 0$,

we have $B \cong \frac{\mu_0 IN}{2\ell}\left[0 - \frac{-\ell}{\sqrt{\ell^2}}\right] = \frac{\mu_0 IN}{2\ell}$.

This is just half the magnitude of the field deep within the solenoid. We would get the same result by substituting $a = \ell$ to describe the other end.

P30.33 The field produced by the solenoid in its interior is given by

$$\mathbf{B} = \mu_0 nI(-\hat{\mathbf{i}}) = (4\pi\times10^{-7}\ \text{T}\cdot\text{m/A})\left(\frac{30.0}{10^{-2}\ \text{m}}\right)(15.0\ \text{A})(-\hat{\mathbf{i}})$$

$$\mathbf{B} = -(5.65\times10^{-2}\ \text{T})\hat{\mathbf{i}}$$

The force exerted on side AB of the square current loop is

$$(\mathbf{F}_B)_{AB} = I\mathbf{L}\times\mathbf{B} = (0.200\ \text{A})\left[(2.00\times10^{-2}\ \text{m})\hat{\mathbf{j}}\times(5.65\times10^{-2}\ \text{T})(-\hat{\mathbf{i}})\right]$$

$$(\mathbf{F}_B)_{AB} = (2.26\times10^{-4}\ \text{N})\hat{\mathbf{k}}$$

Similarly, each side of the square loop experiences a force, lying in the plane of the loop, of $\boxed{226\ \mu\text{N directed away from the center}}$. From the above result, it is seen that the net torque exerted on the square loop by the field of the solenoid should be zero. More formally, the magnetic dipole moment of the square loop is given by

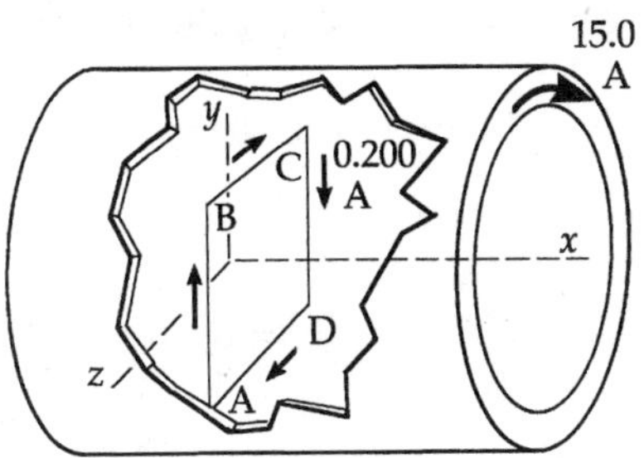

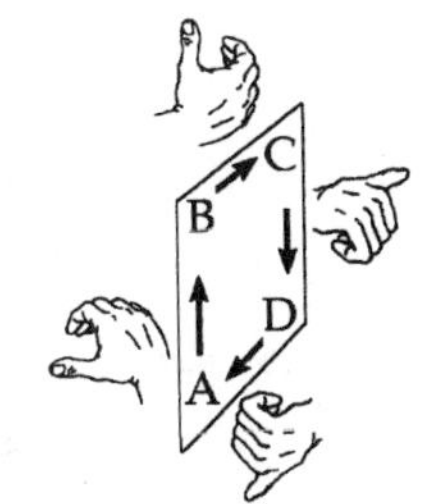

FIG. P30.33

$$\boldsymbol{\mu} = I\mathbf{A} = (0.200\ \text{A})(2.00\times10^{-2}\ \text{m})^2(-\hat{\mathbf{i}}) = -80.0\ \mu\text{A}\cdot\text{m}^2\hat{\mathbf{i}}$$

The torque exerted on the loop is then $\boldsymbol{\tau} = \boldsymbol{\mu}\times\mathbf{B} = (-80.0\ \mu\text{A}\cdot\text{m}^2\hat{\mathbf{i}})\times(-5.65\times10^{-2}\ \text{T}\hat{\mathbf{i}}) = \boxed{0}$

Section 30.5 Magnetic Flux

P30.34 (a) $(\Phi_B)_{\text{flat}} = \mathbf{B}\cdot\mathbf{A} = B\pi R^2\cos(180-\theta) = \boxed{-B\pi R^2\cos\theta}$

(b) The net flux out of the closed surface is zero: $(\Phi_B)_{\text{flat}} + (\Phi_B)_{\text{curved}} = 0$.

$(\Phi_B)_{\text{curved}} = \boxed{B\pi R^2\cos\theta}$

P30.35 (a) $\Phi_B = \int\mathbf{B}\cdot d\mathbf{A} = \mathbf{B}\cdot\mathbf{A} = (5\hat{\mathbf{i}}+4\hat{\mathbf{j}}+3\hat{\mathbf{k}})\ \text{T}\cdot(2.50\times10^{-2}\ \text{m})^2\hat{\mathbf{i}}$

$\Phi_B = 3.12\times10^{-3}\ \text{T}\cdot\text{m}^2 = 3.12\times10^{-3}\ \text{Wb} = \boxed{3.12\ \text{mWb}}$

(b) $(\Phi_B)_{\text{total}} = \oint\mathbf{B}\cdot d\mathbf{A} = \boxed{0}$ for *any* closed surface (Gauss's law for magnetism)

P30.36 (a) $\Phi_B = \mathbf{B}\cdot\mathbf{A} = BA$ where A is the cross-sectional area of the solenoid.

$$\Phi_B = \left(\frac{\mu_0 NI}{\ell}\right)\left(\pi r^2\right) = \boxed{7.40\ \mu\text{Wb}}$$

(b) $$\Phi_B = \mathbf{B}\cdot\mathbf{A} = BA = \left(\frac{\mu_0 NI}{\ell}\right)\left[\pi\left(r_2^2 - r_1^2\right)\right]$$

$$\Phi_B = \left[\frac{\left(4\pi\times10^{-7}\ \text{T}\cdot\text{m/A}\right)(300)(12.0\ \text{A})}{(0.300\ \text{m})}\right]\pi\left[(8.00)^2-(4.00)^2\right]\left(10^{-3}\ \text{m}\right)^2 = \boxed{2.27\ \mu\text{Wb}}$$

Section 30.6 Gauss's Law in Magnetism

No problems in this section

Section 30.7 Displacement Current and the General Form of Ampère's Law

P30.37 (a) $$\frac{d\Phi_E}{dt} = \frac{dQ/dt}{\epsilon_0} = \frac{I}{\epsilon_0} = \frac{(0.100\ \text{A})}{8.85\times10^{-12}\ \text{C}^2/\text{N}\cdot\text{m}^2} = \boxed{11.3\times10^9\ \text{V}\cdot\text{m/s}}$$

(b) $$I_d = \epsilon_0\frac{d\Phi_E}{dt} = I = \boxed{0.100\ \text{A}}$$

P30.38 $$\frac{d\Phi_E}{dt} = \frac{d}{dt}(EA) = \frac{dQ/dt}{\epsilon_0} = \frac{I}{\epsilon_0}$$

(a) $$\frac{dE}{dt} = \frac{I}{\epsilon_0 A} = \boxed{7.19\times10^{11}\ \text{V/m}\cdot\text{s}}$$

(b) $$\oint B\cdot ds = \epsilon_0\mu_0\frac{d\Phi_E}{dt} \text{ so } 2\pi rB = \epsilon_0\mu_0\frac{d}{dt}\left[\frac{Q}{\epsilon_0 A}\cdot\pi r^2\right]$$

$$B = \frac{\mu_0 Ir}{2A} = \frac{\mu_0(0.200)\left(5.00\times10^{-2}\right)}{2\pi(0.100)^2} = \boxed{2.00\times10^{-7}\ \text{T}}$$

Section 30.8 Magnetism in Matter

P30.39 (a) $$I = \frac{ev}{2\pi r} \qquad \mu = IA = \left(\frac{ev}{2\pi r}\right)\pi r^2 = \boxed{9.27\times10^{-24}\ \text{A}\cdot\text{m}^2}$$

The Bohr model predicts the correct magnetic moment. However, the "planetary model" is seriously deficient in other regards.

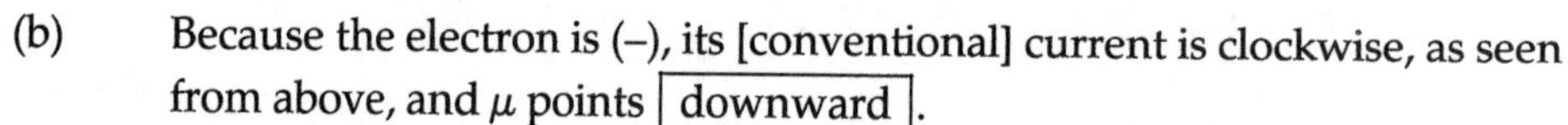

(b) Because the electron is (–), its [conventional] current is clockwise, as seen from above, and μ points $\boxed{\text{downward}}$.

FIG. P30.39

P30.40 $B = \mu n I = \mu\left(\frac{N}{2\pi r}\right)I$ so $I = \frac{(2\pi r)B}{\mu N} = \frac{2\pi(0.100\text{ m})(1.30\text{ T})}{5\,000\left(4\pi\times10^{-7}\text{ Wb/A}\cdot\text{m}\right)(470)} = \boxed{277\text{ mA}}$

P30.41 Assuming a uniform B inside the toroid is equivalent to assuming $r << R$; then $B_0 \approx \mu_0 \frac{NI}{2\pi R}$ as for a *tightly* wound solenoid.

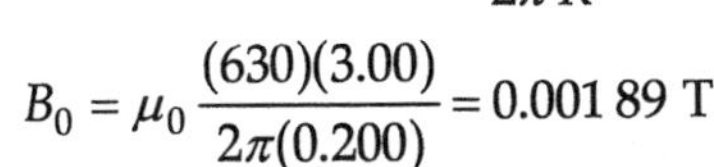

$$B_0 = \mu_0 \frac{(630)(3.00)}{2\pi(0.200)} = 0.001\,89\text{ T}$$

With the steel, $B = \kappa_m B_0 = (1+\chi)B_0 = (101)(0.001\,89\text{ T})$ $\boxed{B = 0.191\text{ T}}$

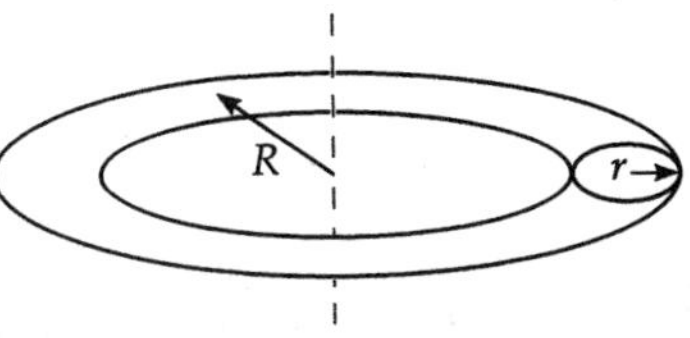

FIG. P30.41

P30.42 $C = \frac{TM}{B} = \frac{(4.00\text{ K})(10.0\%)\left(8.00\times10^{27}\text{ atoms/m}^3\right)(5.00)\left(9.27\times10^{-24}\text{ J/T}^2\right)}{5.00\text{ T}} = \boxed{2.97\times10^4\ \frac{\text{K}\cdot\text{J}}{\text{T}^2\cdot\text{m}^3}}$

P30.43 $B = \mu_0(H+M)$ so $H = \frac{B}{\mu_0} - M = \boxed{2.62\times10^6\text{ A/m}}$

P30.44 In $B = \mu_0(H+M)$ we have $2.00\text{ T} = \mu_0 M$. But also $M = xn\mu_B$. Then $B = \mu_0\mu_B xn$ where n is the number of atoms per volume and x is the number of electrons per atom contributing.

Then $$x = \frac{B}{\mu_0\mu_B n} = \frac{2.00\text{ T}}{\left(8.50\times10^{28}\text{ m}^{-3}\right)\left(9.27\times10^{-24}\text{ N}\cdot\text{m/T}\right)\left(4\pi\times10^{-7}\text{ T}\cdot\text{m/A}\right)} = \boxed{2.02}.$$

P30.45 (a) Comparing Equations 30.29 and 30.30, we see that the applied field is described by $\mathbf{B}_0 = \mu_0\mathbf{H}$. Then Eq. 30.35 becomes $M = C\frac{B_0}{T} = \frac{C}{T}\mu_0 H$, and the definition of susceptibility (Eq. 30.32) is $\boxed{\chi = \frac{M}{H} = \frac{C}{T}\mu_0}$.

(b) $C = \frac{\chi T}{\mu_0} = \frac{\left(2.70\times10^{-4}\right)(300\text{ K})}{4\pi\times10^{-7}\text{ T}\cdot\text{m/A}} = \boxed{6.45\times10^4\ \frac{\text{K}\cdot\text{A}}{\text{T}\cdot\text{m}}}$

Section 30.9 The Magnetic Field of the Earth

P30.46 (a) $B_h = B_{\text{coil}} = \frac{\mu_0 NI}{2R} = \frac{\left(4\pi\times10^{-7}\right)(5.00)(0.600)}{0.300} = \boxed{12.6\ \mu\text{T}}$

(b) $B_h = B\sin\phi \to B = \frac{B_h}{\sin\phi} = \frac{12.6\ \mu\text{T}}{\sin 13.0°} = \boxed{56.0\ \mu\text{T}}$

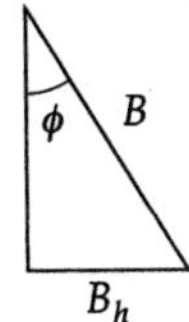

FIG. P30.46

P30.47 (a) Number of unpaired electrons $= \frac{8.00\times10^{22}\text{ A}\cdot\text{m}^2}{9.27\times10^{-24}\text{ A}\cdot\text{m}^2} = \boxed{8.63\times10^{45}}$.

Each iron atom has two unpaired electrons, so the number of iron atoms required is $\frac{1}{2}\left(8.63\times10^{45}\right)$.

(b) $\text{Mass} = \frac{\left(4.31\times10^{45}\text{ atoms}\right)\left(7\,900\text{ kg/m}^3\right)}{\left(8.50\times10^{28}\text{ atoms/m}^3\right)} = \boxed{4.01\times10^{20}\text{ kg}}$

Additional Problems

P30.48 $B = \frac{\mu_0 I R^2}{2\left(R^2 + R^2\right)^{3/2}} = \frac{\mu_0 I}{2^{5/2} R}$ $I = \frac{2^{5/2} B R}{\mu_0} = \frac{2^{5/2}\left(7.00 \times 10^{-5} \text{ T}\right)\left(6.37 \times 10^6 \text{ m}\right)}{\left(4\pi \times 10^{-7} \text{ T}\cdot\text{m/A}\right)}$

so $\boxed{I = 2.01 \times 10^9 \text{ A}}$ toward the west

P30.49 Consider a longitudinal filament of the strip of width dr as shown in the sketch. The contribution to the field at point P due to the current dI in the element dr is

$$dB = \frac{\mu_0 dI}{2\pi r}$$

where $dI = I\left(\frac{dr}{w}\right)$

$$\mathbf{B} = \int d\mathbf{B} = \int_b^{b+w} \frac{\mu_0 I dr}{2\pi w r} \hat{\mathbf{k}} = \boxed{\frac{\mu_0 I}{2\pi w} \ln\left(1 + \frac{w}{b}\right) \hat{\mathbf{k}}}.$$

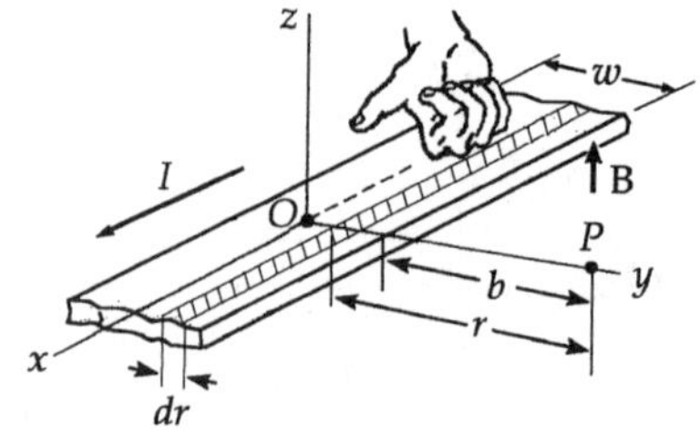

FIG. P30.49

P30.50 Suppose you have two 100-W headlights running from a 12-V battery, with the whole $\frac{200 \text{ W}}{12 \text{ V}} = 17 \text{ A}$ current going through the switch 60 cm from the compass. Suppose the dashboard contains little iron, so $\mu \approx \mu_0$. Model the current as straight. Then,

$$B = \frac{\mu_0 I}{2\pi r} = \frac{\left(4\pi \times 10^{-7}\right) 17}{2\pi (0.6)} \boxed{\sim 10^{-5} \text{ T}}.$$

If the local geomagnetic field is 5×10^{-5} T, this is $\boxed{\sim 10^{-1} \text{ times as large,}}$ enough to affect the compass noticeably.

P30.51 We find the total number of turns: $B = \frac{\mu_0 N I}{\ell}$

$$N = \frac{B\ell}{\mu_0 I} = \frac{(0.030\,0 \text{ T})(0.100 \text{ m}) \text{ A}}{\left(4\pi \times 10^{-7} \text{ T}\cdot\text{m}\right)(1.00 \text{ A})} - 2.39 \times 10^3$$

Each layer contains $\left(\frac{10.0 \text{ cm}}{0.050\,0 \text{ cm}}\right) = 200$ closely wound turns

so she needs $\left(\frac{2.39 \times 10^3}{200}\right) = \boxed{12 \text{ layers}}.$

The inner diameter of the innermost layer is 10.0 mm. The outer diameter of the outermost layer is $10.0 \text{ mm} + 2 \times 12 \times 0.500 \text{ mm} = 22.0 \text{ mm}$. The average diameter is 16.0 mm, so the total length of wire is

$$\left(2.39 \times 10^3\right)\pi\left(16.0 \times 10^{-3} \text{ m}\right) = \boxed{120 \text{ m}}.$$

***P30.52** At a point at distance x from the left end of the bar, current I_2 creates magnetic field $\mathbf{B}=\frac{\mu_0 I_2}{2\pi\sqrt{h^2+x^2}}$ to the left and above the horizontal at angle θ where $\tan\theta=\frac{x}{h}$. This field exerts force on an element of the rod of length dx

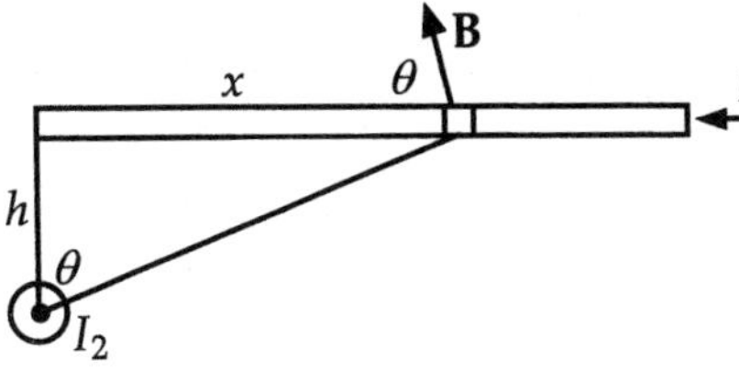

FIG. P30.52

$$d\mathbf{F}=I_1\ell\times\mathbf{B}=I_1\frac{\mu_0 I_2 dx}{2\pi\sqrt{h^2+x^2}}\underset{\text{right hand rule}}{\sin\theta}$$

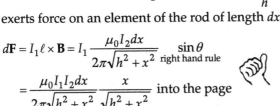

$$=\frac{\mu_0 I_1 I_2 dx}{2\pi\sqrt{h^2+x^2}}\frac{x}{\sqrt{h^2+x^2}}\text{ into the page}$$

$$d\mathbf{F}=\frac{\mu_0 I_1 I_2 x dx}{2\pi\left(h^2+x^2\right)}\left(-\hat{\mathbf{k}}\right)$$

The whole force is the sum of the forces on all of the elements of the bar:

$$\mathbf{F}=\int_{x=0}^{\ell}\frac{\mu_0 I_1 I_2 x dx}{2\pi\left(h^2+x^2\right)}\left(-\hat{\mathbf{k}}\right)=\frac{\mu_0 I_1 I_2\left(-\hat{\mathbf{k}}\right)}{4\pi}\int_0^{\ell}\frac{2x dx}{h^2+x^2}=\frac{\mu_0 I_1 I_2\left(-\hat{\mathbf{k}}\right)}{4\pi}\ln\left(h^2+x^2\right)\Big|_0^{\ell}$$

$$=\frac{\mu_0 I_1 I_2\left(-\hat{\mathbf{k}}\right)}{4\pi}\left[\ln\left(h^2+\ell^2\right)-\ln h^2\right]=\frac{10^{-7}\text{ N}(100\text{ A})(200\text{ A})\left(-\hat{\mathbf{k}}\right)}{\text{A}^2}\ln\left[\frac{(0.5\text{ cm})^2+(10\text{ cm})^2}{(0.5\text{ cm})^2}\right]$$

$$=2\times10^{-3}\text{ N}\left(-\hat{\mathbf{k}}\right)\ln 401=\boxed{1.20\times10^{-2}\text{ N}\left(-\hat{\mathbf{k}}\right)}$$

P30.53 On the axis of a current loop, the magnetic field is given by $B=\frac{\mu_0 IR^2}{2\left(x^2+R^2\right)^{3/2}}$

where in this case $I=\frac{q}{(2\pi/\omega)}$. The magnetic field is directed away from the center, with a magnitude of

$$B=\frac{\mu_0\omega R^2 q}{4\pi\left(x^2+R^2\right)^{3/2}}=\frac{\mu_0(20.0)(0.100)^2\left(10.0\times10^{-6}\right)}{4\pi\left[(0.050\,0)^2+(0.100)^2\right]^{3/2}}=\boxed{1.43\times10^{-10}\text{ T}}.$$

P30.54 On the axis of a current loop, the magnetic field is given by $B=\frac{\mu_0 IR^2}{2\left(x^2+R^2\right)^{3/2}}$

where in this case $I=\frac{q}{(2\pi/\omega)}$. Therefore, $B=\frac{\mu_0\omega R^2 q}{4\pi\left(x^2+R^2\right)^{3/2}}$

when $x=\frac{R}{2}$. then $B=\frac{\mu_0\omega R^2 q}{4\pi\left(\frac{5}{4}R^2\right)^{3/2}}=\boxed{\frac{\mu_0 q\omega}{2.5\sqrt{5}\pi R}}$.

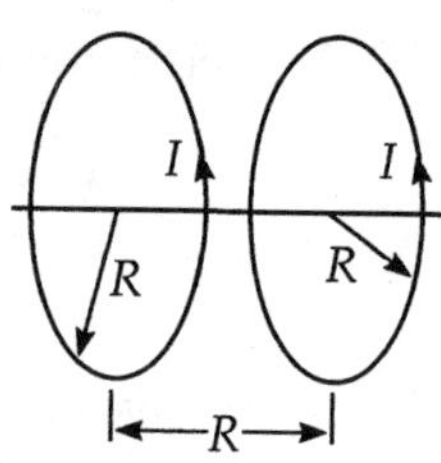

FIG. P30.55

P30.55 (a) Use equation 30.7 twice: $B_x = \frac{\mu_0 I R^2}{2\left(x^2+R^2\right)^{3/2}}$

If each coil has N turns, the field is just N times larger.

$$B = B_{x1} + B_{x2} = \frac{N\mu_0 I R^2}{2}\left[\frac{1}{\left(x^2+R^2\right)^{3/2}} + \frac{1}{\left[(R-x)^2+R^2\right]^{3/2}}\right]$$

$$\boxed{B = \frac{N\mu_0 I R^2}{2}\left[\frac{1}{\left(x^2+R^2\right)^{3/2}} + \frac{1}{\left(2R^2+x^2-2xR\right)^{3/2}}\right]}$$

(b) $$\frac{dB}{dx} = \frac{N\mu_0 I R^2}{2}\left[-\frac{3}{2}(2x)\left(x^2+R^2\right)^{-5/2} - \frac{3}{2}\left(2R^2+x^2-2xR\right)^{-5/2}(2x-2R)\right]$$

Substituting $x = \frac{R}{2}$ and canceling terms, $\boxed{\frac{dB}{dx} = 0}$.

$$\frac{d^2B}{dx^2} = \frac{-3N\mu_0 I R^2}{2}\left[\left(x^2+R^2\right)^{-5/2} - 5x^2\left(x^2+R^2\right)^{-7/2} + \left(2R^2+x^2-2xR\right)^{-5/2} - 5(x-R)^2\left(2R^2+x^2-2xR\right)^{-7/2}\right]$$

Again substituting $x = \frac{R}{2}$ and canceling terms, $\boxed{\frac{d^2B}{dx^2} = 0}$.

P30.56 "Helmholtz pair" → separation distance = radius

$$B = \frac{2\mu_0 I R^2}{2\left[(R/2)^2+R^2\right]^{3/2}} = \frac{\mu_0 I R^2}{\left[\frac{1}{4}+1\right]^{3/2} R^3} = \frac{\mu_0 I}{1.40R} \text{ for 1 turn.}$$

For N turns in each coil, $B = \frac{\mu_0 N I}{1.40R} = \frac{\left(4\pi\times10^{-7}\right)100(10.0)}{1.40(0.500)} = \boxed{1.80\times10^{-3}\text{ T}}$.

***P30.57** Consider first a solid cylindrical rod of radius R carrying current toward you, uniformly distributed over its cross-sectional area. To find the field at distance r from its center we consider a circular loop of radius r:

$$\oint \mathbf{B}\cdot d\mathbf{s} = \mu_0 I_{\text{inside}}$$

$$B2\pi r = \mu_0 \pi r^2 J \qquad B = \frac{\mu_0 J r}{2} \qquad \mathbf{B} = \frac{\mu_0 J}{2}\hat{\mathbf{k}}\times\mathbf{r}$$

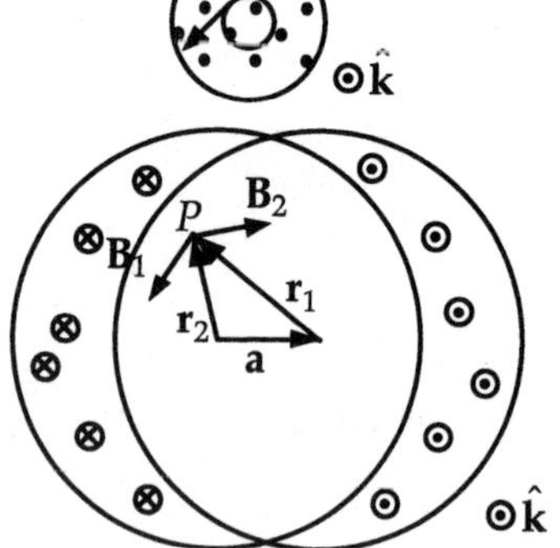

FIG. P30.57

Now the total field at P inside the saddle coils is the field due to a solid rod carrying current toward you, centered at the head of vector **a**, plus the field of a solid rod centered at the tail of vector **a** carrying current away from you.

$$\mathbf{B}_1 + \mathbf{B}_2 = \frac{\mu_0 J}{2}\hat{\mathbf{k}}\times\mathbf{r}_1 + \frac{\mu_0 J}{2}\left(-\hat{\mathbf{k}}\right)\times\mathbf{r}_2$$

Now note $\mathbf{a} + \mathbf{r}_1 = \mathbf{r}_2$

$$\mathbf{B}_1 + \mathbf{B}_2 = \frac{\mu_0 J}{2}\hat{\mathbf{k}}\times\mathbf{r}_1 - \frac{\mu_0 J}{2}\hat{\mathbf{k}}\times(\mathbf{a}+\mathbf{r}_1) = \frac{\mu_0 J}{2}\mathbf{a}\times\hat{\mathbf{k}} = \boxed{\frac{\mu_0 J a}{2}\text{ down in the diagram}}.$$

***P30.58** From example 30.6, the upper sheet creates field $\mathbf{B} = \frac{\mu_0 J_s}{2}\hat{\mathbf{k}}$ above it and $\frac{\mu_0 J_s}{2}(-\hat{\mathbf{k}})$ below it. Consider a patch of the sheet of width w parallel to the z axis and length d parallel to the x axis. The charge on it σwd passes a point in time $\frac{d}{v}$, so the current it constitutes is $\frac{q}{t} = \frac{\sigma wdv}{d}$ and the linear current density is $J_s = \frac{\sigma wv}{w} = \sigma v$. Then the magnitude of the magnetic field created by the upper sheet is $\frac{1}{2}\mu_0\sigma v$. Similarly, the lower sheet in its motion toward the right constitutes current toward the left. It creates magnetic field $\frac{1}{2}\mu_0\sigma v(-\hat{\mathbf{k}})$ above it and $\frac{1}{2}\mu_0\sigma v\hat{\mathbf{k}}$ below it.

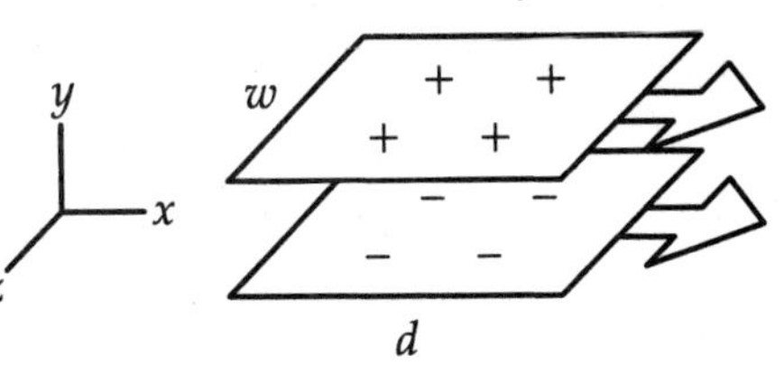

FIG. P30.58

(b) Above both sheets and below both, their equal-magnitude fields add to $\boxed{\text{zero}}$.

(a) Between the plates, their fields add to $\mu_0\sigma v(-\hat{\mathbf{k}}) = \boxed{\mu_0\sigma v \text{ away from you horizontally.}}$

(c) The upper plate exerts no force on itself. The field of the lower plate, $\frac{1}{2}\mu_0\sigma v(-\hat{\mathbf{k}})$ will exert a force on the current in the w- by d-section, given by

$$I\ell \times \mathbf{B} = \sigma wvd\hat{\mathbf{i}} \times \frac{1}{2}\mu_0\sigma v(-\hat{\mathbf{k}}) = \frac{1}{2}\mu_0\sigma^2 v^2 wd\hat{\mathbf{j}}.$$

The force per area is $\frac{1}{2}\frac{\mu_0\sigma^2 v^2 wd}{wd}\hat{\mathbf{j}} = \boxed{\frac{1}{2}\mu_0\sigma^2 v^2 \text{ up}}$.

(d) The electrical force on our section of the upper plate is $q\mathbf{E}_{\text{lower}} = \sigma\ell w\frac{\sigma}{2\epsilon_0}(-\hat{\mathbf{j}}) = \frac{\ell w\sigma^2}{2\epsilon_0}(-\hat{\mathbf{j}})$.

The electrical force per area is $\frac{\ell w\sigma^2}{2\epsilon_0 \ell w}$ down $= \frac{\sigma^2}{2\epsilon_0}$ down. To have $\frac{1}{2}\mu_0\sigma^2 v^2 = \frac{\sigma^2}{2\epsilon_0}$ we require

$$v = \frac{1}{\sqrt{\mu_0\epsilon_0}} = \frac{1}{\sqrt{4\pi\times10^{-7}(\text{Tm/A})(\text{N/TAm})8.85\times10^{-12}(\text{C}^2/\text{Nm}^2)(\text{As/C})^2}} = \boxed{3.00\times10^8 \text{ m/s}}.$$

This is the speed of light, not a possible speed for a metal plate.

P30.59 Model the two wires as straight parallel wires (!)

(a) $F_B = \frac{\mu_0 I^2 \ell}{2\pi a}$ (Equation 30.12)

$$F_B = \frac{(4\pi \times 10^{-7})(140)^2(2\pi)(0.100)}{2\pi(1.00 \times 10^{-3})}$$

$= \boxed{2.46 \text{ N}}$ upward

(b) $a_{\text{loop}} = \frac{2.46 \text{ N} - m_{\text{loop}} g}{m_{\text{loop}}} = \boxed{107 \text{ m/s}^2}$ upward

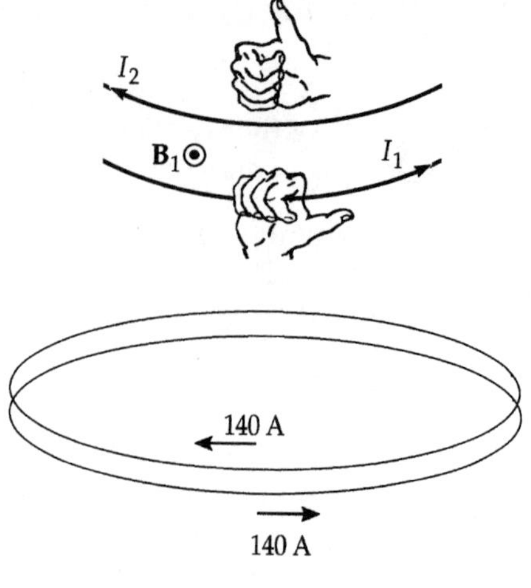

FIG. P30.59

P30.60 (a) In $d\mathbf{B} = \frac{\mu_0}{4\pi r^2} I d\mathbf{s} \times \hat{\mathbf{r}}$, the moving charge constitutes a bit of current as in $I = nqvA$. For a positive charge the direction of $d\mathbf{s}$ is the direction of $\mathbf{v}$, so $d\mathbf{B} = \frac{\mu_0}{4\pi r^2} nqA(ds)\mathbf{v} \times \hat{\mathbf{r}}$. Next, $A(ds)$ is the volume occupied by the moving charge, and $nA(ds) = 1$ for just one charge. Then,

$$\boxed{\mathbf{B} = \frac{\mu_0}{4\pi r^2} q\mathbf{v} \times \hat{\mathbf{r}}}.$$

(b) $$B = \frac{(4\pi \times 10^{-7} \text{ T}\cdot\text{m/A})(1.60 \times 10^{-19} \text{ C})(2.00 \times 10^7 \text{ m/s})}{4\pi(1.00 \times 10^{-3})^2} \sin 90.0° = \boxed{3.20 \times 10^{-13} \text{ T}}$$

(c) $F_B = q|\mathbf{v} \times \mathbf{B}| = (1.60 \times 10^{-19} \text{ C})(2.00 \times 10^7 \text{ m/s})(3.20 \times 10^{-13} \text{ T}) \sin 90.0°$

$F_B = \boxed{1.02 \times 10^{-24} \text{ N directed away from the first proton}}$

(d) $$F_e = qE = \frac{k_e q_1 q_2}{r^2} = \frac{(8.99 \times 10^9 \text{ N}\cdot\text{m}^2/\text{C}^2)(1.60 \times 10^{-19} \text{ C})^2}{(1.00 \times 10^{-3})^2}$$

$F_e = \boxed{2.30 \times 10^{-22} \text{ N directed away from the first proton}}$

Both forces act together. The electrical force is stronger by two orders of magnitude. It is productive to think about how it would look to an observer in a reference frame moving along with one proton or the other.

P30.61 (a) $$B=\frac{\mu_0 I}{2\pi r}=\frac{\left(4\pi\times10^{-7}\ \text{T}\cdot\text{m/A}\right)(24.0\ \text{A})}{2\pi(0.0175\ \text{m})}=\boxed{2.74\times10^{-4}\ \text{T}}$$

(b) At point C, conductor AB produces a field $\frac{1}{2}\left(2.74\times10^{-4}\ \text{T}\right)\left(-\hat{\mathbf{j}}\right)$, conductor DE produces a field of $\frac{1}{2}\left(2.74\times10^{-4}\ \text{T}\right)\left(-\hat{\mathbf{j}}\right)$, BD produces no field, and AE produces negligible field. The total field at C is $\boxed{2.74\times10^{-4}\ \text{T}\left(-\hat{\mathbf{j}}\right)}$.

(c) $$\mathbf{F}_B=I\boldsymbol{\ell}\times\mathbf{B}=(24.0\ \text{A})\left(0.0350\ \text{m}\hat{\mathbf{k}}\right)\times\left[5\left(2.74\times10^{-4}\ \text{T}\right)\left(-\hat{\mathbf{j}}\right)\right]=\boxed{\left(1.15\times10^{-3}\ \text{N}\right)\hat{\mathbf{i}}}$$

(d) $$\mathbf{a}=\frac{\sum\mathbf{F}}{m}=\frac{\left(1.15\times10^{-3}\ \text{N}\right)\hat{\mathbf{i}}}{3.0\times10^{-3}\ \text{kg}}=\boxed{\left(0.384\ \text{m/s}^2\right)\hat{\mathbf{i}}}$$

(e) The bar is already so far from AE that it moves through nearly constant magnetic field. The force acting on the bar is constant, and therefore the bar's $\boxed{\text{acceleration is constant}}$.

(f) $$v_f^2=v_i^2+2ax=0+2\left(0.384\ \text{m/s}^2\right)(1.30\ \text{m}),\ \text{so}\ \mathbf{v}_f=\boxed{(0.999\ \text{m/s})\hat{\mathbf{i}}}$$

***P30.62** Each turn creates field at the center $\frac{\mu_0 I}{2R}$. Together they create field

$$\frac{\mu_0 I}{2}\left(\frac{1}{R_1}+\frac{1}{R_2}+\ldots+\frac{1}{R_{50}}\right)=\frac{4\pi\times10^{-7}\ \text{Tm}I}{2\ \text{A}}\left(\frac{1}{5.05}+\frac{1}{5.15}+\ldots+\frac{1}{9.95}\right)\frac{1}{10^{-2}\ \text{m}}$$
$$=\mu_0 I(50/\text{m})6.93=\boxed{347\mu_0 I/\text{m}}$$

FIG. P30.62

P30.63 At equilibrium, $\frac{F_B}{\ell}=\frac{\mu_0 I_A I_B}{2\pi a}=\frac{mg}{\ell}$ or $I_B=\frac{2\pi a(m/\ell)g}{\mu_0 I_A}$

$$I_B=\frac{2\pi(0.0250\ \text{m})(0.0100\ \text{kg/m})\left(9.80\ \text{m/s}^2\right)}{\left(4\pi\times10^{-7}\ \text{T}\cdot\text{m/A}\right)(150\ \text{A})}=\boxed{81.7\ \text{A}}$$

P30.64 (a) The magnetic field due to an infinite sheet of current (or the magnetic field at points near a large sheet of current) is given by $B=\frac{\mu_0 J_s}{2}$. The current density $J_s=\frac{I}{\ell}$ and in this case the equivalent current of the moving charged belt is

$$I=\frac{dq}{dt}=\frac{d}{dt}(\sigma\ell x)=\sigma\ell v;\ v=\frac{dx}{dt}.$$

Therefore, $J_s=\sigma v$ and $\boxed{B=\frac{\mu_0\sigma v}{2}}$.

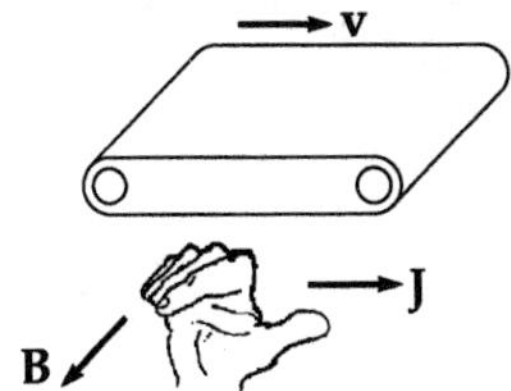

FIG. P30.64

(b) If the sheet is positively charged and moving in the direction shown, the magnetic field is $\boxed{\text{out of the page, parallel to the roller axes}}$.

P30.65 The central wire creates field $\mathbf{B} = \frac{\mu_0 I_1}{2\pi R}$ counterclockwise. The curved portions of the loop feels no force since $\boldsymbol{\ell} \times \mathbf{B} = 0$ there. The straight portions both feel $I\boldsymbol{\ell} \times \mathbf{B}$ forces to the right, amounting to

$$\mathbf{F}_B = I_2 2L \frac{\mu_0 I_1}{2\pi R} = \boxed{\frac{\mu_0 I_1 I_2 L}{\pi R} \text{ to the right}}.$$

P30.66 $I = \frac{2\pi r B}{\mu_0} = \frac{2\pi(9.00 \times 10^3)(1.50 \times 10^{-8})}{4\pi \times 10^{-7}} = \boxed{675 \text{ A}}$

Flow of $\boxed{\text{positive current is downward } or \text{ negative charge flows upward}}$.

P30.67 By symmetry of the arrangement, the magnitude of the net magnetic field at point P is $B = 8B_{0x}$ where B_0 is the contribution to the field due to current in an edge length equal to $\frac{L}{2}$. In order to calculate B_0, we use the Biot-Savart law and consider the plane of the square to be the yz-plane with point P on the x-axis. The contribution to the magnetic field at point P due to a current element of length dz and located a distance z along the axis is given by Equation 30.3.

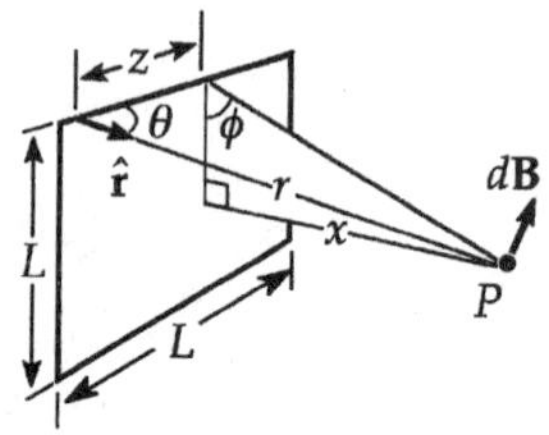

FIG. P30.67

$$\mathbf{B}_0 = \frac{\mu_0 I}{4\pi} \int \frac{d\boldsymbol{\ell} \times \hat{\mathbf{r}}}{r^2}.$$

From the figure we see that

$$r = \sqrt{x^2 + (L^2/4) + z^2} \text{ and } |d\boldsymbol{\ell} \times \hat{\mathbf{r}}| = dz \sin\theta = dz \sqrt{\frac{(L^2/4) + x^2}{(L^2/4) + x^2 + z^2}}.$$

By symmetry all components of the field $\mathbf{B}$ at P cancel except the components along x (perpendicular to the plane of the square); and

$$B_{0x} = B_0 \cos\phi \text{ where } \cos\phi = \frac{L/2}{\sqrt{(L^2/4) + x^2}}.$$

Therefore, $\mathbf{B}_{0x} = \frac{\mu_0 I}{4\pi} \int_0^{L/2} \frac{\sin\theta \cos\phi dz}{r^2}$ and $B = 8B_{0x}$.

Using the expressions given above for $\sin\theta\cos\phi$, and r, we find

$$B = \frac{\mu_0 I L^2}{2\pi\left(x^2 + (L^2/4)\right)\sqrt{x^2 + (L^2/2)}}.$$

P30.68 (a) From Equation 30.9, the magnetic field produced by one loop at the center of the second loop is given by $B = \frac{\mu_0 I R^2}{2x^3} = \frac{\mu_0 I(\pi R^2)}{2\pi x^3} = \frac{\mu_0 \mu}{2\pi x^3}$ where the magnetic moment of either loop is $\mu = I(\pi R^2)$. Therefore,

$$|F_x| = \mu \frac{dB}{dx} = \mu\left(\frac{\mu_0 \mu}{2\pi}\right)\left(\frac{3}{x^4}\right) = \frac{3\mu_0 (\pi R^2 I)^2}{2\pi x^4} = \boxed{\frac{3\pi}{2} \frac{\mu_0 I^2 R^4}{x^4}}.$$

(b) $$|F_x| = \frac{3\pi}{2} \frac{\mu_0 I^2 R^4}{x^4} = \frac{3\pi}{2} \frac{(4\pi \times 10^{-7} \text{ T}\cdot\text{m/A})(10.0 \text{ A})^2 (5.00 \times 10^{-3} \text{ m})^4}{(5.00 \times 10^{-2} \text{ m})^4} = \boxed{5.92 \times 10^{-8} \text{ N}}$$

P30.69 There is no contribution from the straight portion of the wire since $d\mathbf{s} \times \hat{\mathbf{r}} = 0$. For the field of the spiral,

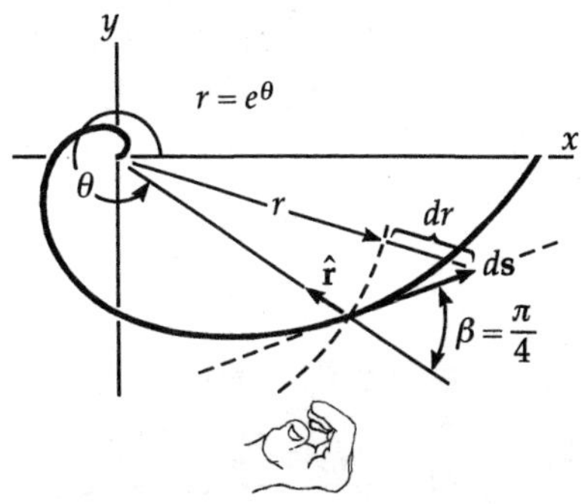

FIG. P30.69

$$d\mathbf{B} = \frac{\mu_0 I}{(4\pi)} \frac{(d\mathbf{s} \times \hat{\mathbf{r}})}{r^2}$$

$$B = \frac{\mu_0 I}{4\pi} \int_{\theta=0}^{2\pi} \frac{|d\mathbf{s}| \sin\theta |\hat{\mathbf{r}}|}{r^2} = \frac{\mu_0 I}{4\pi} \int_{\theta=0}^{2\pi} \left(\sqrt{2}dr\right) \left[\sin\left(\frac{3\pi}{4}\right)\right] \frac{1}{r^2}$$

$$B = \frac{\mu_0 I}{4\pi} \int_{\theta=0}^{2\pi} r^{-2} dr = -\frac{\mu_0 I}{4\pi} \left(r^{-1}\right)\Big|_{\theta=0}^{2\theta}$$

Substitute $r = e^\theta$: $B = -\frac{\mu_0 I}{4\pi} \left[e^{-\theta}\right]_0^{2\pi} = -\frac{\mu_0 I}{4\pi}\left[e^{-2\pi} - e^0\right] = \boxed{\frac{\mu_0 I}{4\pi}\left(1 - e^{-2\pi}\right)}$ out of the page.

P30.70 (a) $\mathbf{B} = \mathbf{B}_0 + \mu_0 \mathbf{M}$

$$\mathbf{M} = \frac{\mathbf{B} - \mathbf{B}_0}{\mu_0} \text{ and } M = \frac{|\mathbf{B} - \mathbf{B}_0|}{\mu_0}$$

Assuming that $\mathbf{B}$ and $\mathbf{B}_0$ are parallel, this becomes $M = \frac{B - B_0}{\mu_0}$.

The magnetization curve gives a plot of M versus B_0.

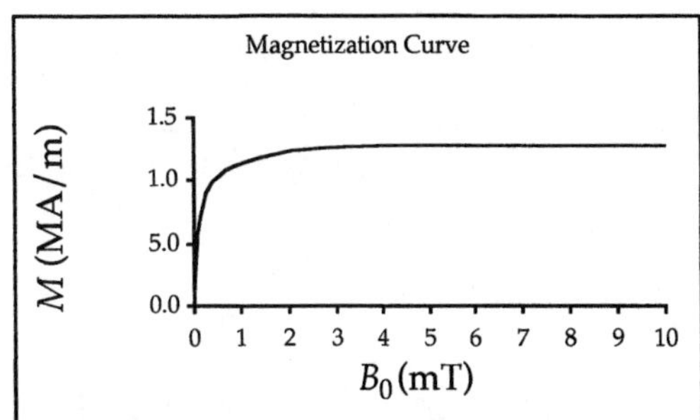

(b) The second graph is a plot of the relative permeability $\left(\frac{B}{B_0}\right)$ as a function of the applied field B_0.

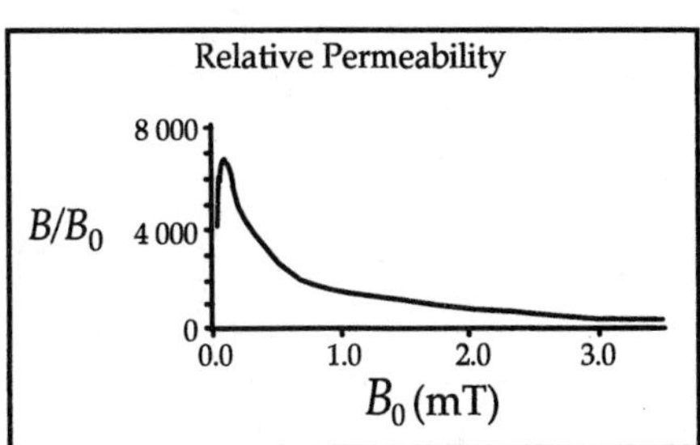

FIG. P30.70

P30.71 Consider the sphere as being built up of little rings of radius r, centered on the rotation axis. The contribution to the field from each ring is

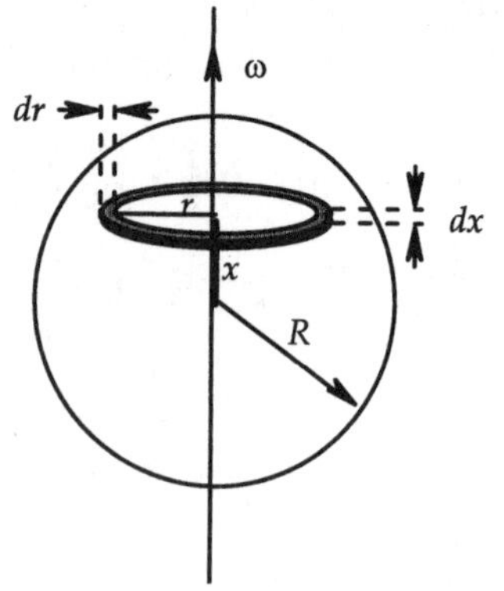

$$dB = \frac{\mu_0 r^2 dI}{2\left(x^2 + r^2\right)^{3/2}} \text{ where } dI = \frac{dQ}{t} = \frac{\omega dQ}{2\pi}$$

$$dQ = \rho dV = \rho(2\pi r dr)(dx)$$

$$dB = \frac{\mu_0 \rho \omega r^3 dr dx}{2\left(x^2 + r^2\right)^{3/2}} \text{ where } \rho = \frac{Q}{(4/3)\pi R^3}$$

$$B = \int_{x=-R}^{+R} \int_{r=0}^{\sqrt{R^2-x^2}} \frac{\mu_0 \rho \omega}{2} \frac{r^3 dr dx}{\left(x^2 + r^2\right)^{3/2}}$$

FIG. P30.71

Let $v = r^2 + x^2$, $dv = 2r dr$, and $r^2 = v - x^2$

$$B = \int_{x=-R}^{+R} \int_{v=x^2}^{R^2} \frac{\mu_0 \rho \omega}{2} \frac{\left(v - x^2\right) dv}{2v^{3/2}} dx = \frac{\mu_0 \rho \omega}{4} \int_{x=-R}^{R} \left[\int_{v=x^2}^{R^2} v^{-1/2} dv - x^2 \int_{v=x^2}^{R^2} v^{-3/2} dv \right] dx$$

$$B = \frac{\mu_0 \rho \omega}{4} \int_{x=-R}^{R} \left[2v^{1/2}\Big|_{x^2}^{R^2} + \left(2x^2\right) v^{-1/2}\Big|_{x^2}^{R^2} \right] dx = \frac{\mu_0 \rho \omega}{4} \int_{x=-R}^{R} \left[2(R - |x|) + 2x^2 \left(\frac{1}{R} - \frac{1}{|x|} \right) \right] dx$$

$$B = \frac{\mu_0 \rho \omega}{4} \int_{-R}^{R} \left[2\frac{x^2}{R} - 4|x| + 2R \right] dx = \frac{2\mu_0 \rho \omega}{4} \int_{0}^{R} \left[2\frac{x^2}{R} - 4x + 2R \right] dx$$

$$B = \frac{2\mu_0 \rho \omega}{4} \left(\frac{2R^3}{3R} - \frac{4R^2}{2} + 2R^2 \right) = \boxed{\frac{\mu_0 \rho \omega R^2}{3}}$$

P30.72 Consider the sphere as being built up of little rings of radius r, centered on the rotation axis. The current associated with each rotating ring of charge is

$$dI = \frac{dQ}{t} = \frac{\omega}{2\pi} \left[\rho(2\pi r dr)(dx) \right].$$

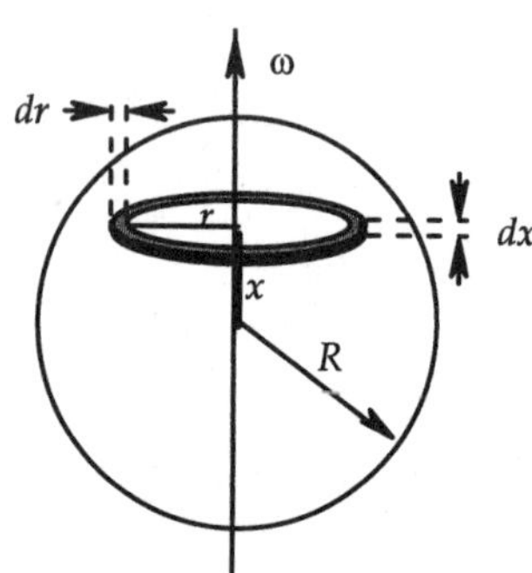

FIG. P30.72

The magnetic moment contributed by this ring is

$$d\mu = A(dI) = \pi r^2 \frac{\omega}{2\pi} \left[\rho(2\pi r dr)(dx) \right] = \pi \omega \rho r^3 dr dx$$

$$\mu = \pi \omega \rho \int_{x=-R}^{+R} \left[\int_{r=0}^{\sqrt{R^2-x^2}} r^3 dr \right] dx = \pi \omega \rho \int_{x=-R}^{+R} \frac{\left(\sqrt{R^2 - x^2}\right)^4}{4} dx = \pi \omega \rho \int_{x=-R}^{+R} \frac{\left(R^2 - x^2\right)^2}{4} dx$$

$$\mu = \frac{\pi \omega \rho}{4} \int_{x=-R}^{+R} \left(R^4 - 2R^2 x^2 + x^4 \right) dx = \frac{\pi \omega \rho}{4} \left[R^4(2R) - 2R^2 \left(\frac{2R^3}{3} \right) + \frac{2R^5}{5} \right]$$

$$\mu = \frac{\pi \omega \rho}{4} R^5 \left(2 - \frac{4}{3} + \frac{2}{5} \right) = \frac{\pi \omega \rho R^5}{4} \left(\frac{16}{15} \right) = \boxed{\frac{4\pi \omega \rho R^5}{15}} \text{ up}$$

P30.73 Note that the current I exists in the conductor with a current density $J = \frac{I}{A}$, where

$$A = \pi\left[a^2 - \frac{a^2}{4} - \frac{a^2}{4}\right] = \frac{\pi a^2}{2}.$$

Therefore, $J = \frac{2I}{\pi a^2}$.

To find the field at either point P_1 or P_2, find B_s which would exist if the conductor were solid, using Ampère's law. Next, find B_1 and B_2 that *would* be due to the conductors of radius $\frac{a}{2}$ that *could* occupy the void where the holes exist. Then use the superposition principle and subtract the field that would be due to the part of the conductor where the holes exist from the field of the solid conductor.

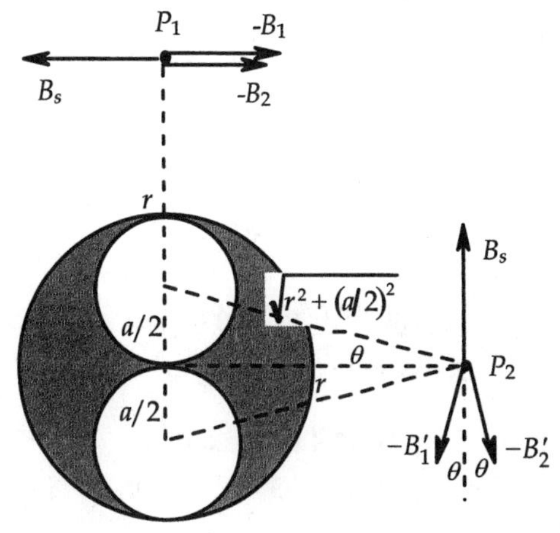

FIG. P30.73

(a) At point P_1, $B_s = \frac{\mu_0 J(\pi a^2)}{2\pi r}$, $B_1 = \frac{\mu_0 J\pi(a/2)^2}{2\pi(r-(a/2))}$, and $B_2 = \frac{\mu_0 J\pi(a/2)^2}{2\pi(r+(a/2))}$.

$$B = B_s - B_1 - B_2 = \frac{\mu J\pi a^2}{2\pi}\left[\frac{1}{r} - \frac{1}{4(r-(a/2))} - \frac{1}{4(r+(a/2))}\right]$$

$$B = \frac{\mu_0(2I)}{2\pi}\left[\frac{4r^2 - a^2 - 2r^2}{4r(r^2-(a^2/4))}\right] = \boxed{\frac{\mu_0 I}{\pi r}\left[\frac{2r^2-a^2}{4r^2-a^2}\right] \text{ directed to the left}}$$

(b) At point P_2, $B_s = \frac{\mu_0 J(\pi a^2)}{2\pi r}$ and $B_1' = B_2' = \frac{\mu_0 J\,\pi(a/2)^2}{2\pi\sqrt{r^2+(a/2)^2}}$.

The horizontal components of B_1' and B_2' cancel while their vertical components add.

$$B = B_s - B_1'\cos\theta - B_2'\cos\theta = \frac{\mu_0 J(\pi a^2)}{2\pi r} - 2\left(\frac{\mu_0 J\,\pi a^2/4}{2\pi\sqrt{r^2+(a^2/4)}}\right)\frac{r}{\sqrt{r^2+(a^2/4)}}$$

$$B = \frac{\mu_0 J(\pi a^2)}{2\pi r}\left[1 - \frac{r^2}{2(r^2+(a^2/4))}\right] = \frac{\mu_0(2I)}{2\pi r}\left[1 - \frac{2r^2}{4r^2+a^2}\right]$$

$$= \boxed{\frac{\mu_0 I}{\pi r}\left[\frac{2r^2+a^2}{4r^2+a^2}\right] \text{ directed toward the top of the page}}$$

ANSWERS TO EVEN PROBLEMS

P30.2 20.0 μT

P30.4 200 nT

P30.6 $\left(1+\frac{1}{\pi}\right)\frac{\mu_0 I}{2R}$ into the page

P30.8 see the solution

P30.10 $\left(\frac{1}{\pi}+\frac{1}{4}\right)\frac{\mu_0 I}{2r}$ into the page

P30.12 $\frac{\mu_0 I}{12}\left(\frac{1}{a}-\frac{1}{b}\right)$ out of the page

P30.14 $\frac{\mu_0 I\left(a^2+d^2-d\sqrt{a^2+d^2}\right)}{2\pi ad\sqrt{a^2+d^2}}$ into the page

P30.16 (a) 10.0 μT; (b) 80.0 μN toward wire 1; (c) 16.0 μT; (d) 80.0 μN toward wire 2

P30.18 Parallel to the wires and 0.167 m below the upper wire

P30.20 (a) opposite; (b) 67.8 A

P30.22 5.40 cm

P30.24 (a) 400 cm; (b) 7.50 nT; (c) 1.26 m; (d) zero

P30.26 (a) 3.60 T; (b) 1.94 T

P30.28 500 A

P30.30 (a) see the solution; (b) $d = a$

P30.32 (a) $\frac{\mu_0 IN}{2\ell}\left[\frac{a}{\sqrt{a^2+R^2}}-\frac{a-\ell}{\sqrt{(a-\ell)^2+R^2}}\right]$; (b) see the solution

P30.34 (a) $-B\pi R^2\cos\theta$; (b) $B\pi R^2\cos\theta$

P30.36 (a) 7.40 μWb; (b) 2.27 μWb

P30.38 (a) 7.19×10^{11} V/m·s; (b) 200 nT

P30.40 277 mA

P30.42 $2.97\times10^4\ \frac{\mathrm{K\cdot J}}{\mathrm{T^2\cdot m^3}}$

P30.44 2.02

P30.46 (a) 12.6 μT; (b) 56.0 μT

P30.48 2.01 GA west

P30.50 $\sim10^{-5}$ T, enough to affect the compass noticeably

P30.52 $12.0\ \mathrm{mN}\left(-\hat{\mathbf{k}}\right)$

P30.54 $\frac{\mu_0 q\omega}{2.5\sqrt{5}\pi R}$

P30.56 1.80 mT

P30.58 (a) $\mu_0\sigma v$ horizontally away from you; (b) 0; (c) $\frac{1}{2}\mu_0\sigma^2 v^2$ up; (d) 3.00×10^8 m/s

P30.60 (a) see the solution; (b) 3.20×10^{-13} T; (c) 1.02×10^{-24} N away from the first proton; (d) 2.30×10^{-22} N away from the first proton

P30.62 $347\mu_0 I/\mathrm{m}$ perpendicular to the coil

P30.64 (a) $\frac{1}{2}\mu_0\sigma v$; (b) out of the page, parallel to the roller axes

P30.66 675 A downward

P30.68 (a) see the solution; (b) 59.2 nN

P30.70 see the solution

P30.72 $\frac{4}{15}\pi\omega\rho R^5$ upward

31

Faraday's Law

CHAPTER OUTLINE

ANSWERS TO QUESTIONS

Q31.1 Magnetic flux measures the "flow" of the magnetic field through a given area of a loop—even though the field does not actually flow. By changing the size of the loop, or the orientation of the loop and the field, one can change the magnetic flux through the loop, but the magnetic field will not change.

Q31.2 The magnetic flux is $\Phi_B = BA\cos\theta$. Therefore the flux is maximum when **B** is perpendicular to the loop of wire and zero when there is no component of magnetic field perpendicular to the loop. The flux is zero when the loop is turned so that the field lies in the plane of its area.

Q31.3 The force on positive charges in the bar is $\mathbf{F} = q(\mathbf{v} \times \mathbf{B})$. If the bar is moving to the left, positive charge will move downward and accumulate at the bottom end of the bar, so that an electric field will be established upward.

Q31.4 No. The magnetic force acts within the bar, but has no influence on the forward motion of the bar.

Q31.5 By the magnetic force law $\mathbf{F} = q(\mathbf{v} \times \mathbf{B})$: the positive charges in the moving bar will flow downward and therefore clockwise in the circuit. If the bar is moving to the left, the positive charge in the bar will flow upward and therefore counterclockwise in the circuit.

Q31.6 We ignore mechanical friction between the bar and the rails. Moving the conducting bar through the magnetic field will force charges to move around the circuit to constitute clockwise current. The downward current in the bar feels a magnetic force to the left. Then a counterbalancing applied force to the right is required to maintain the motion.

Q31.7 A current could be set up in the bracelet by moving the bracelet through the magnetic field, or if the field rapidly changed.

Q31.8 Moving a magnet inside the hole of the doughnut-shaped toroid will not change the magnetic flux through any turn of wire in the toroid, and thus not induce any current.

Q31.9 As water falls, it gains speed and kinetic energy. It then pushes against turbine blades, transferring its energy to the rotor coils of a large AC generator. The rotor of the generator turns within a strong magnetic field. Because the rotor is spinning, the magnetic flux through its turns changes in time as $\Phi_B = BA\cos\omega t$. Generated in the rotor is an induced emf of $\varepsilon = \frac{-Nd\Phi_B}{dt}$. This induced emf is the voltage driving the current in our electric power lines.

Q31.10 Yes. Eddy currents will be induced around the circumference of the copper tube so as to fight the changing magnetic flux by the falling magnet. If a bar magnet is dropped with its north pole downwards, a ring of counterclockwise current will surround its approaching bottom end and a ring of clockwise current will surround the receding south pole at its top end. The magnetic fields created by these loops of current will exert forces on the magnet to slow the fall of the magnet quite significantly. Some of the original gravitational energy of the magnet will appear as internal energy in the walls of the tube.

Q31.11 Yes. The induced eddy currents on the surface of the aluminum will slow the descent of the aluminum. It may fall very slowly.

Q31.12 The maximum induced emf will increase, increasing the terminal voltage of the generator.

Q31.13 The increasing counterclockwise current in the solenoid coil produces an upward magnetic field that increases rapidly. The increasing upward flux of this field through the ring induces an emf to produce clockwise current in the ring. The magnetic field of the solenoid has a radially outward component at each point on the ring. This field component exerts upward force on the current in the ring there. The whole ring feels a total upward force larger than its weight.

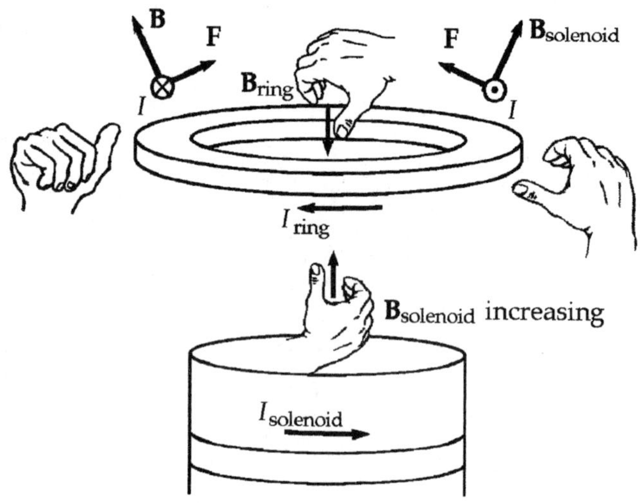

FIG. Q31.13

Q31.14 Oscillating current in the solenoid produces an always-changing magnetic field. Vertical flux through the ring, alternately increasing and decreasing, produces current in it with a direction that is alternately clockwise and counterclockwise. The current through the ring's resistance produces internal energy at the rate I^2R.

Q31.15 (a) The south pole of the magnet produces an upward magnetic field that increases as the magnet approaches. The loop opposes change by making its own downward magnetic field; it carries current clockwise, which goes to the left through the resistor.

(b) The north pole of the magnet produces an upward magnetic field. The loop sees decreasing upward flux as the magnet falls away, and tries to make an upward magnetic field of its own by carrying current counterclockwise, to the right in the resistor.

Q31.16 (a) The battery makes counterclockwise current I_1 in the primary coil, so its magnetic field $\mathbf{B}_1$ is to the right and increasing just after the switch is closed. The secondary coil will oppose the change with a leftward field $\mathbf{B}_2$, which comes from an induced clockwise current I_2 that goes to the right in the resistor.

(b) At steady state the primary magnetic field is unchanging, so no emf is induced in the secondary.

(c) The primary's field is to the right and decreasing as the switch is opened. The secondary coil opposes this decrease by making its own field to the right, carrying counterclockwise current to the left in the resistor.

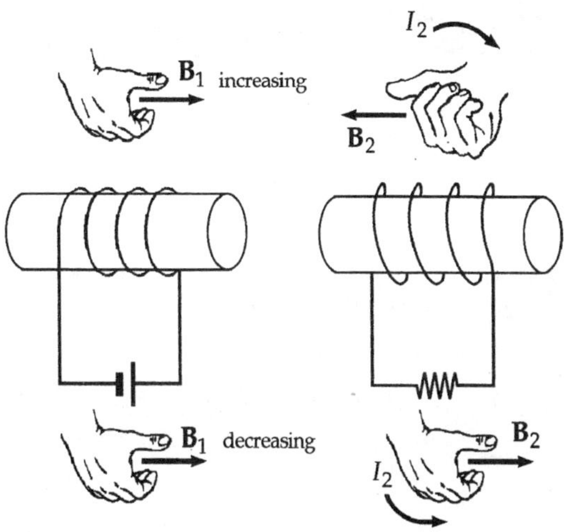

FIG. Q31.16

Q31.17 The motional emf between the wingtips cannot be used to run a light bulb. To connect the light, an extra insulated wire would have to be run out along each wing, making contact with the wing tip. The wings with the extra wires and the bulb constitute a single-loop circuit. As the plane flies through a uniform magnetic field, the magnetic flux through this loop is constant and zero emf is generated. On the other hand, if the magnetic field is not uniform, a large loop towed through it will generate pulses of positive and negative emf. This phenomenon has been demonstrated with a cable unreeled from the Space Shuttle.

Q31.18 No, they do not. Specifically, Gauss's law in magnetism prohibits magnetic monopoles. If magnetic monopoles existed, then the magnetic field lines would not have to be closed loops, but could begin or terminate on a magnetic monopole, as they can in Gauss's law in electrostatics.

Q31.19 (a) A current is induced by the changing magnetic flux through the a ring of the tube, produced by the high frequency alternating current in the coil.

(b) The higher frequency implies a greater rate of change in the magnetic field, for a larger induced voltage.

(c) The resistance of one cubic centimeter in the bulk sheet metal is low, so the I^2R rate of production of internal energy is low. At the seam, the current starts out crowded into a small area with high resistance, so the temperature rises rapidly, and the edges melt together.

(d) The edges must be in contact to allow the induced emf to create an electric current around the circumference of the tube. Additionally, (duh) the two edges must be in contact to be welded at all, just as you can't glue two pieces of paper together without putting them in contact with each other.

SOLUTIONS TO PROBLEMS

Section 31.1 Faraday's Law of Induction

Section 31.3 Lenz's Law

P31.1 $\varepsilon = \left|\frac{\Delta\Phi_B}{\Delta t}\right| = \frac{\Delta(NBA)}{\Delta t} = \boxed{500 \text{ mV}}$

P31.2 $|\varepsilon| = \left|\frac{\Delta\Phi_B}{\Delta t}\right| = \frac{\Delta(\mathbf{B}\cdot\mathbf{A})}{\Delta t} = \frac{(2.50 \text{ T} - 0.500 \text{ T})(8.00\times10^{-4} \text{ m}^2)}{1.00 \text{ s}}\left(\frac{1 \text{ N}\cdot\text{s}}{1 \text{ T}\cdot\text{C}\cdot\text{m}}\right)\left(\frac{1 \text{ V}\cdot\text{C}}{1 \text{ N}\cdot\text{m}}\right)$

$|\varepsilon| = 1.60 \text{ mV}$ and $I_{\text{loop}} = \frac{\varepsilon}{R} = \frac{1.60 \text{ mV}}{2.00 \ \Omega} = \boxed{0.800 \text{ mA}}$

P31.3 $\varepsilon = -N\frac{\Delta BA\cos\theta}{\Delta t} = -NB\pi r^2\left(\frac{\cos\theta_f - \cos\theta_i}{\Delta t}\right) = -25.0(50.0\times10^{-6} \text{ T})\left[\pi(0.500 \text{ m})^2\right]\left(\frac{\cos 180° - \cos 0°}{0.200 \text{ s}}\right)$

$\varepsilon = \boxed{+9.82 \text{ mV}}$

P31.4 (a) $\varepsilon = -\frac{d\Phi_B}{dt} = -A\frac{dB}{dt} = \boxed{\frac{AB_{\max}}{\tau}e^{-t/\tau}}$

(b) $\varepsilon = \frac{(0.160 \text{ m}^2)(0.350 \text{ T})}{2.00 \text{ s}}e^{-4.00/2.00} = \boxed{3.79 \text{ mV}}$

(c) At $t = 0$ $\varepsilon = \boxed{28.0 \text{ mV}}$

P31.5 Noting unit conversions from $\mathbf{F} = q\mathbf{v}\times\mathbf{B}$ and $U = qV$, the induced voltage is

$$\varepsilon = -N\frac{d(\mathbf{B}\cdot\mathbf{A})}{dt} = -N\left(\frac{0 - B_iA\cos\theta}{\Delta t}\right) = \frac{+200(1.60 \text{ T})(0.200 \text{ m}^2)\cos 0°}{20.0\times10^{-3} \text{ s}}\left(\frac{1 \text{ N}\cdot\text{s}}{1 \text{ T}\cdot\text{C}\cdot\text{m}}\right)\left(\frac{1 \text{ V}\cdot\text{C}}{\text{N}\cdot\text{m}}\right) = 3\,200 \text{ V}$$

$I = \frac{\varepsilon}{R} = \frac{3\,200 \text{ V}}{20.0 \ \Omega} = \boxed{160 \text{ A}}$

P31.6 $\varepsilon = -N\frac{d\Phi_B}{dt} = -\frac{N(BA - 0)}{\Delta t}$

$\Delta t = \frac{NBA}{|\varepsilon|} = \frac{NB(\pi r^2)}{\varepsilon} = \frac{500(0.200)\pi(5.00\times10^{-2})^2}{10.0\times10^3} = \boxed{7.85\times10^{-5} \text{ s}}$

P31.7 $|\varepsilon| = \frac{d(BA)}{dt} = 0.500\mu_0 nA\frac{dI}{dt} = 0.480 \times 10^{-3}\text{ V}$

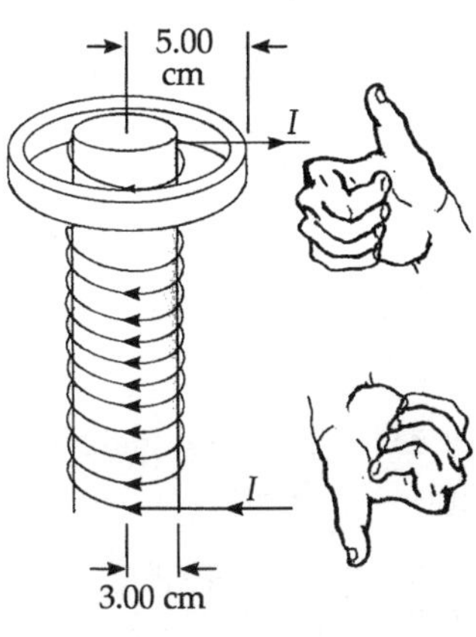

FIG. P31.7

(a) $I_{\text{ring}} = \frac{\varepsilon}{R} = \frac{4.80 \times 10^{-4}}{3.00 \times 10^{-4}} = \boxed{1.60\text{ A}}$

(b) $B_{\text{ring}} = \frac{\mu_0 I}{2r_{\text{ring}}} = \boxed{20.1\ \mu\text{T}}$

(c) Coil's field points downward, and is increasing, so $\boxed{B_{\text{ring}}\text{ points upward}}$.

P31.8 $|\varepsilon| = \frac{d(BA)}{dt} = 0.500\mu_0 nA\frac{dI}{dt} = 0.500\mu_0 n\pi r_2^2\frac{\Delta I}{\Delta t}$

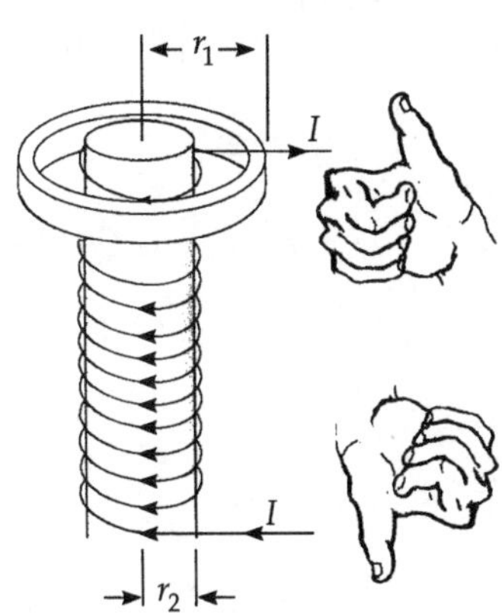

FIG. P31.8

(a) $I_{\text{ring}} = \frac{\varepsilon}{R} = \boxed{\frac{\mu_0 n\pi r_2^2}{2R}\frac{\Delta I}{\Delta t}}$

(b) $B = \frac{\mu_0 I}{2r_1} = \boxed{\frac{\mu_0^2 n\pi r_2^2}{4r_1 R}\frac{\Delta I}{\Delta t}}$

(c) The coil's field points downward, and is increasing, so $\boxed{B_{\text{ring}}\text{ points upward}}$.

P31.9 (a) $d\Phi_B = \mathbf{B}\cdot d\mathbf{A} = \frac{\mu_0 I}{2\pi x}L\,dx$: $\Phi_B = \int_h^{h+w}\frac{\mu_0 IL}{2\pi}\frac{dx}{x} = \boxed{\frac{\mu_0 IL}{2\pi}\ln\left(\frac{h+w}{h}\right)}$

(b) $\varepsilon = -\frac{d\Phi_B}{dt} = -\frac{d}{dt}\left[\frac{\mu_0 IL}{2\pi}\ln\left(\frac{h+w}{h}\right)\right] = -\left[\frac{\mu_0 L}{2\pi}\ln\left(\frac{h+w}{h}\right)\right]\frac{dI}{dt}$

$$\varepsilon = -\frac{(4\pi \times 10^{-7}\text{ T}\cdot\text{m/A})(1.00\text{ m})}{2\pi}\ln\left(\frac{1.00+10.0}{1.00}\right)(10.0\text{ A/s}) = \boxed{-4.80\ \mu\text{V}}$$

The long wire produces magnetic flux into the page through the rectangle, shown by the first hand in the figure to the right.

As the magnetic flux increases, the rectangle produces its own magnetic field out of the page, which it does by carrying $\boxed{\text{counterclockwise}}$ current (second hand in the figure).

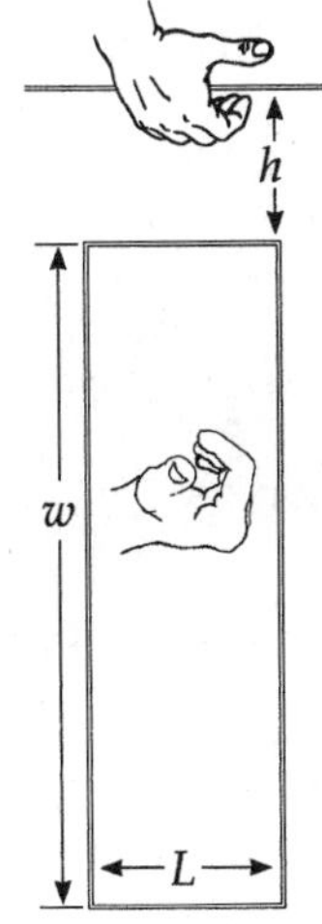

FIG. P31.9

P31.10 $\Phi_B = (\mu_0 n I) A_{\text{solenoid}}$

$$\varepsilon = -N\frac{d\Phi_B}{dt} = -N\mu_0 n\left(\pi r_{\text{solenoid}}^2\right)\frac{dI}{dt}$$

$$\varepsilon = -15.0\left(4\pi\times10^{-7}\ \text{T}\cdot\text{m/A}\right)\left(1.00\times10^{3}\ \text{m}^{-1}\right)\pi(0.020\,0\ \text{m})^2(600\ \text{A/s})\cos(120t)$$

$$\boxed{\varepsilon = -14.2\cos(120t)\ \text{mV}}$$

P31.11 For a counterclockwise trip around the left-hand loop, with $B = At$

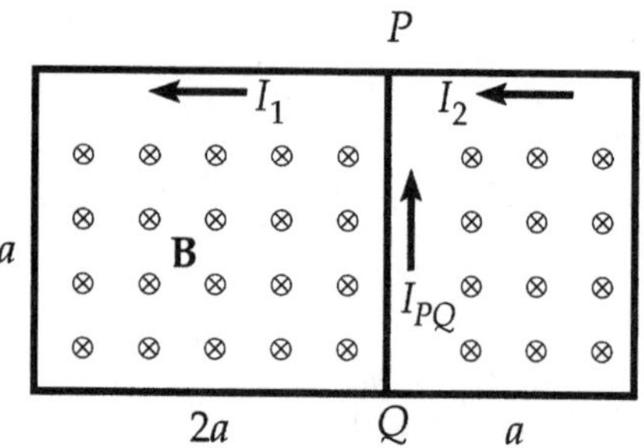

FIG. P31.11

$$\frac{d}{dt}\left[At\left(2a^2\right)\cos 0°\right] - I_1(5R) - I_{PQ}R = 0$$

and for the right-hand loop,

$$\frac{d}{dt}\left[Ata^2\right] + I_{PQ}R - I_2(3R) = 0$$

where $I_{PQ} = I_1 - I_2$ is the upward current in QP.

Thus, $\quad 2Aa^2 - 5R\left(I_{PQ} + I_2\right) - I_{PQ}R = 0$

and $\quad Aa^2 + I_{PQ}R = I_2(3R)$

$$2Aa^2 - 6RI_{PQ} - \frac{5}{3}\left(Aa^2 + I_{PQ}R\right) = 0$$

$$I_{PQ} = \frac{Aa^2}{23R}$$ upward, and since $R = (0.100\ \Omega/\text{m})(0.650\ \text{m}) = 0.065\,0\ \Omega$

$$I_{PQ} = \frac{\left(1.00\times10^{-3}\ \text{T/s}\right)(0.650\ \text{m})^2}{23(0.065\,0\ \Omega)} = \boxed{283\ \mu\text{A upward}}.$$

P31.12 $|\varepsilon| = \left|\frac{\Delta\Phi_B}{\Delta t}\right| = N\left(\frac{dB}{dt}\right)A = N(0.010\,0 + 0.080\,0t)A$

At $t = 5.00$ s, $|\varepsilon| = 30.0(0.410\ \text{T/s})\left[\pi(0.040\,0\ \text{m})^2\right] = \boxed{61.8\ \text{mV}}$

P31.13 $B = \mu_0 n I = \mu_0 n(30.0\ \text{A})\left(1 - e^{-1.60t}\right)$

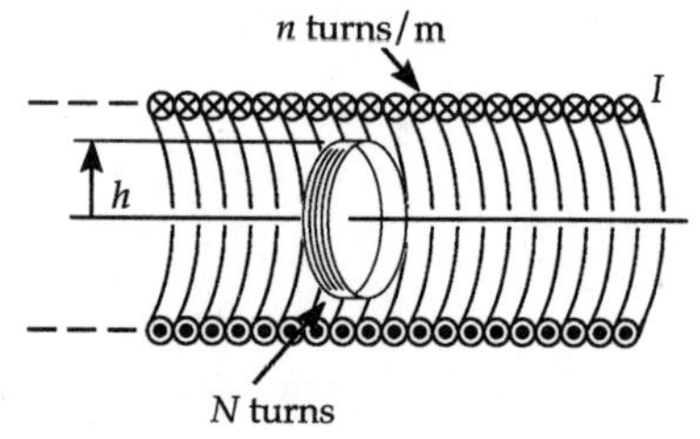

FIG. P31.13

$$\Phi_B = \int B\,dA = \mu_0 n(30.0\ \text{A})\left(1 - e^{-1.60t}\right)\int dA$$

$$\Phi_B = \mu_0 n(30.0\ \text{A})\left(1 - e^{-1.60t}\right)\pi R^2$$

$$\varepsilon = -N\frac{d\Phi_B}{dt} = -N\mu_0 n(30.0\ \text{A})\pi R^2(1.60)e^{-1.60t}$$

$$\varepsilon = -(250)\left(4\pi\times10^{-7}\ \text{N/A}^2\right)\left(400\ \text{m}^{-1}\right)(30.0\ \text{A})\left[\pi(0.060\,0\ \text{m})^2\right]1.60\ \text{s}^{-1}e^{-1.60t}$$

$$\varepsilon = \boxed{(68.2\ \text{mV})e^{-1.60t}\ \text{counterclockwise}}$$

***P31.14** (a) Each coil has a pulse of voltage tending to produce counterclockwise current as the projectile approaches, and then a pulse of clockwise voltage as the projectile recedes.

(b) 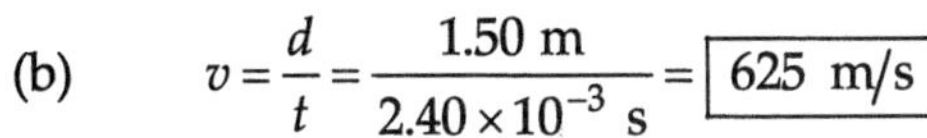

$$v=\frac{d}{t}=\frac{1.50\text{ m}}{2.40\times 10^{-3}\text{ s}}=\boxed{625\text{ m/s}}$$

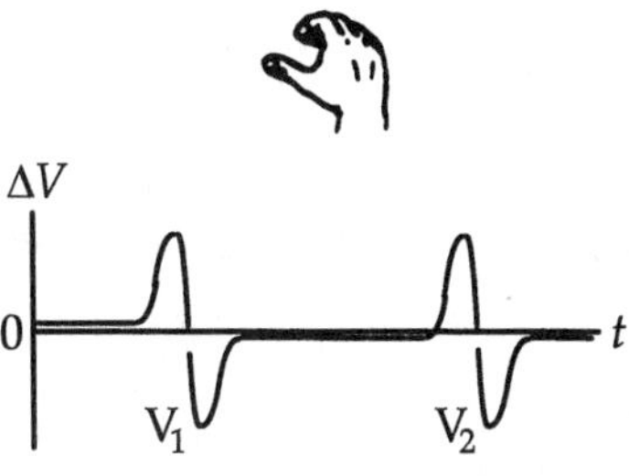

FIG. P31.14

P31.15 $$\varepsilon=\frac{d}{dt}\left(NB\ell^2\cos\theta\right)=\frac{N\ell^2\Delta B\cos\theta}{\Delta t}$$

$$\ell=\sqrt{\frac{\varepsilon\Delta t}{N\Delta B\cos\theta}}=\sqrt{\frac{\left(80.0\times 10^{-3}\text{ V}\right)(0.400\text{ s})}{(50)\left(600\times 10^{-6}\text{ T}-200\times 10^{-6}\text{ T}\right)\cos(30.0°)}}=1.36\text{ m}$$

$$\text{Length}=4\ell N=4(1.36\text{ m})(50)=\boxed{272\text{ m}}$$

***P31.16** (a) Suppose, first, that the central wire is long and straight. The enclosed current of unknown amplitude creates a circular magnetic field around it, with the magnitude of the field given by Ampere's Law.

$$\oint\mathbf{B}\cdot d\mathbf{s}=\mu_0 I:\quad B=\frac{\mu_0 I_{\max}\sin\omega t}{2\pi R}$$

at the location of the Rogowski coil, which we assume is centered on the wire. This field passes perpendicularly through each turn of the toroid, producing flux

$$\mathbf{B}\cdot\mathbf{A}=\frac{\mu_0 I_{\max}A\sin\omega t}{2\pi R}.$$

The toroid has $2\pi Rn$ turns. As the magnetic field varies, the emf induced in it is

$$\varepsilon=-N\frac{d}{dt}\mathbf{B}\cdot\mathbf{A}=-2\pi Rn\frac{\mu_0 I_{\max}A}{2\pi R}\frac{d}{dt}\sin\omega t=-\mu_0 I_{\max}nA\omega\cos\omega t.$$

This is an alternating voltage with amplitude $\varepsilon_{\max}=\mu_0 nA\omega I_{\max}$. Measuring the amplitude determines the size $I_{\max}$ of the central current. Our assumptions that the central wire is long and straight and passes perpendicularly through the center of the Rogowski coil are all unnecessary.

(b) If the wire is not centered, the coil will respond to stronger magnetic fields on one side, but to correspondingly weaker fields on the opposite side. The emf induced in the coil is proportional to the line integral of the magnetic field around the circular axis of the toroid. Ampere's Law says that this line integral depends only on the amount of current the coil encloses. It does not depend on the shape or location of the current within the coil, or on any currents outside the coil.

P31.17 In a toroid, all the flux is confined to the inside of the toroid.

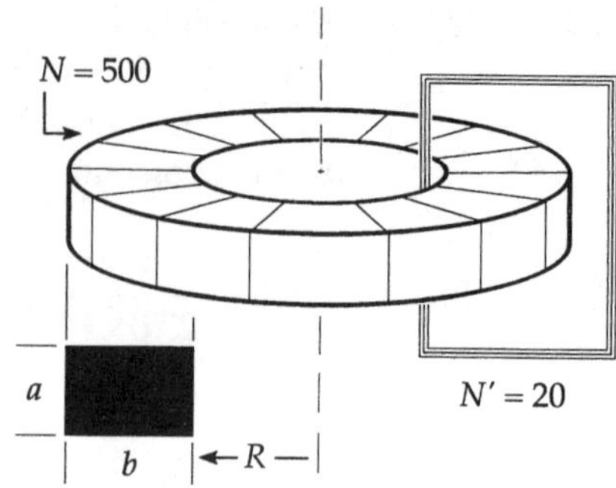

FIG. P31.17

$$B=\frac{\mu_0 NI}{2\pi r}=\frac{500\mu_0 I}{2\pi r}$$

$$\Phi_B=\int BdA=\frac{500\mu_0 I_{\max}}{2\pi}\sin\omega t\int\frac{adr}{r}$$

$$\Phi_B=\frac{500\mu_0 I_{\max}}{2\pi}a\sin\omega t\ln\left(\frac{b+R}{R}\right)$$

$$\varepsilon=N'\frac{d\Phi_B}{dt}=20\left(\frac{500\mu_0 I_{\max}}{2\pi}\right)\omega a\ln\left(\frac{b+R}{R}\right)\cos\omega t$$

$$\varepsilon=\frac{10^4}{2\pi}\left(4\pi\times10^{-7}\ \text{N/A}^2\right)(50.0\ \text{A})(377\ \text{rad/s})(0.020\,0\ \text{m})\ln\left(\frac{(3.00+4.00)\ \text{cm}}{4.00\ \text{cm}}\right)\cos\omega t$$

$$=\boxed{(0.422\ \text{V})\cos\omega t}$$

***P31.18** The upper loop has area $\pi(0.05\ \text{m})^2=7.85\times10^{-3}\ \text{m}^2$. The induced emf in it is

$$\varepsilon=-N\frac{d}{dt}BA\cos\theta=-1A\cos0°\frac{dB}{dt}=-7.85\times10^{-3}\ \text{m}^2(2\ \text{T/s})=-1.57\times10^{-2}\ \text{V}.$$

The minus sign indicates that it tends to produce counterclockwise current, to make its own magnetic field out of the page. Similarly, the induced emf in the lower loop is

$$\varepsilon=-NA\cos\theta\frac{dB}{dt}=-\pi(0.09\ \text{m})^2 2\ \text{T/s}=-5.09\times10^{-2}\ \text{V}=+5.09\times10^{-2}\ \text{V}\ \text{to produce}$$

$\boxed{\text{counterclockwise current in the lower loop, which becomes clockwise current in the upper loop}}$.

The net emf for current in this sense around the figure 8 is

$5.09\times10^{-2}\ \text{V}-1.57\times10^{-2}\ \text{V}=3.52\times10^{-2}\ \text{V}$.

It pushes current in this sense through series resistance $\left[2\pi(0.05\ \text{m})+2\pi(0.09\ \text{m})\right]3\ \Omega/\text{m}=2.64\ \Omega$.

The current is $I=\frac{\varepsilon}{R}=\frac{3.52\times10^{-2}\ \text{V}}{2.64\ \Omega}=\boxed{13.3\ \text{mA}}$.

Section 31.2 Motional emf

Section 31.3 Lenz's Law

P31.19 (a) For maximum induced emf, with positive charge at the top of the antenna, $\mathbf{F}_+=q_+(\mathbf{v}\times\mathbf{B})$, so the auto must move $\boxed{\textit{east}}$.

(b) $$\varepsilon=B\ell v=\left(5.00\times10^{-5}\ \text{T}\right)(1.20\ \text{m})\left(\frac{65.0\times10^3\ \text{m}}{3\,600\ \text{s}}\right)\cos65.0°=\boxed{4.58\times10^{-4}\ \text{V}}$$

P31.20 $I = \frac{\varepsilon}{R} = \frac{B\ell v}{R}$

$\boxed{v = 1.00\ \text{m/s}}$

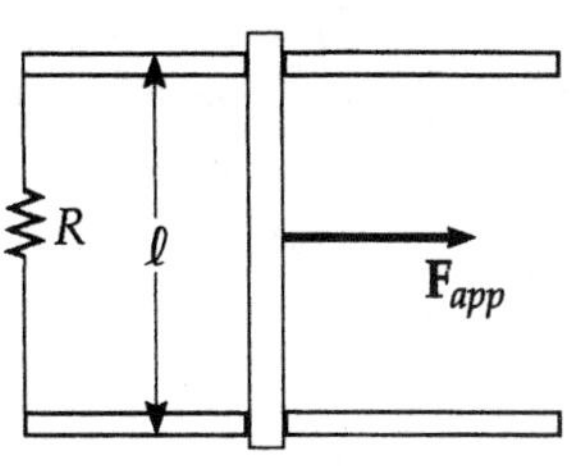

FIG. P31.20

P31.21 (a) $|\mathbf{F}_B| = I|\boldsymbol{\ell} \times \mathbf{B}| = I\ell B$

When $I = \frac{\varepsilon}{R}$

and $\varepsilon = B\ell v$

we get $F_B = \frac{B\ell v}{R}(\ell B) = \frac{B^2\ell^2 v}{R} = \frac{(2.50)^2(1.20)^2(2.00)}{6.00} = 3.00\ \text{N}$.

The applied force is $\boxed{\text{3.00 N to the right}}$.

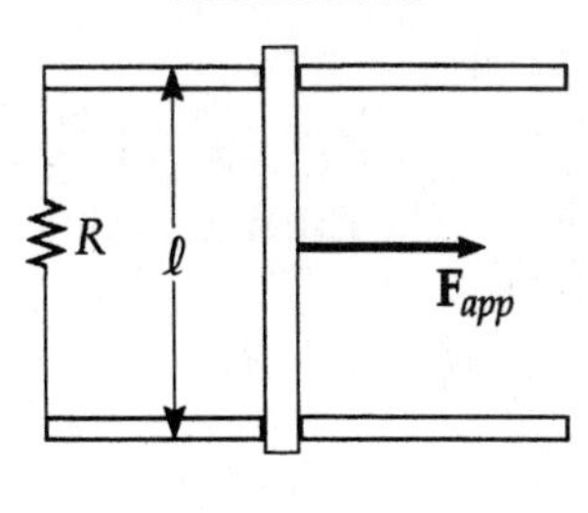

FIG. P31.21

(b) $\mathcal{P} = I^2 R = \frac{B^2\ell^2 v^2}{R} = 6.00\ \text{W}$ or $\mathcal{P} = Fv = \boxed{6.00\ \text{W}}$

P31.22 $F_B = I\ell B$ and $\varepsilon = B\ell v$

$I = \frac{\varepsilon}{R} = \frac{B\ell v}{R}$ so $B = \frac{IR}{\ell v}$

(a) $F_B = \frac{I^2 \ell R}{\ell v}$ and $I = \sqrt{\frac{F_B v}{R}} = \boxed{0.500\ \text{A}}$

(b) $I^2 R = \boxed{2.00\ \text{W}}$

(c) For constant force, $\mathcal{P} = \mathbf{F} \cdot \mathbf{v} = (1.00\ \text{N})(2.00\ \text{m/s}) = \boxed{2.00\ \text{W}}$.

***P31.23** Model the magnetic flux inside the metallic tube as constant as it shrinks form radius R to radius r:

$2.50\ \text{T}\left(\pi R^2\right) = B_f \pi r^2$

$B_f = 2.50\ \text{T}\left(\frac{R}{r}\right)^2 = 2.50\ \text{T}(12)^2 = \boxed{360\ \text{T}}$

***P31.24** Observe that the homopolar generator has no commutator and produces a voltage constant in time: DC with no ripple. In time dt, the disk turns by angle $d\theta = \omega dt$. The outer brush slides over distance $rd\theta$. The radial line to the outer brush sweeps over area

$$dA = \frac{1}{2}rrd\theta = \frac{1}{2}r^2\omega dt.$$

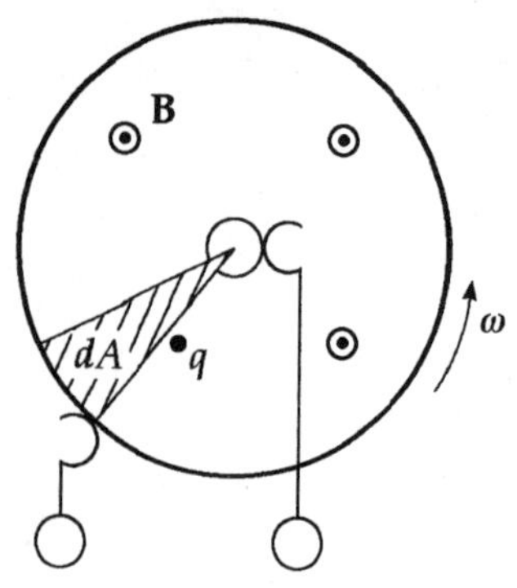

FIG. P31.24

The emf generated is $\quad \varepsilon = -N\frac{d}{dt}\mathbf{B}\cdot\mathbf{A}$

$$\varepsilon = -(1)B\cos 0°\frac{dA}{dt} = -B\left(\frac{1}{2}r^2\omega\right)$$

(We could think of this as following from the result of Example 31.4.)
The magnitude of the emf is

$$|\varepsilon| = B\left(\frac{1}{2}r^2\omega\right) = (0.9\ \text{N}\cdot\text{s/C}\cdot\text{m})\left[\frac{1}{2}(0.4\ \text{m})^2(3\ 200\ \text{rev/min})\right]\left(\frac{2\pi\ \text{rad/rev}}{60\ \text{s/min}}\right)$$

$$|\varepsilon| = \boxed{24.1\ \text{V}}$$

A free positive charge q shown, turning with the disk, feels a magnetic force $q\mathbf{v}\times\mathbf{B}$ radially outward. Thus the $\boxed{\text{outer contact is positive}}$.

***P31.25** The speed of waves on the wire is

$$v = \sqrt{\frac{T}{\mu}} = \sqrt{\frac{267\ \text{N}\cdot\text{m}}{3\times 10^{-3}\ \text{kg}}} = 298\ \text{m/s}.$$

In the simplest standing-wave vibration state,

$$d_{NN} = 0.64\ \text{m} = \frac{\lambda}{2} \qquad \lambda = 1.28\ \text{m}$$

and $f = \dfrac{v}{\lambda} = \dfrac{298\ \text{m/s}}{1.28\ \text{m}} = 233\ \text{Hz}.$

(a) The changing flux of magnetic field through the circuit containing the wire will drive current to the left in the wire as it moves up and to the right as it moves down. The emf will have this same frequency of $\boxed{233\ \text{Hz}}$.

(b) The vertical coordinate of the center of the wire is described by

$$x = A\cos\omega t = (1.5\ \text{cm})\cos(2\pi 233\, t/\text{s}).$$

Its velocity is $v = \dfrac{dx}{dt} = -(1.5\ \text{cm})(2\pi\, 233/\text{s})\sin(2\pi 233\ t/\text{s})$.

Its maximum speed is $1.5\ \text{cm}(2\pi)233/\text{s} = 22.0\ \text{m/s}$.

The induced emf is $\varepsilon = -B\ell v$, with amplitude

$$\varepsilon_{\max} = B\ell v_{\max} = 4.50\times 10^{-3}\ \text{T}(0.02\ \text{m})22\ \text{m/s} = \boxed{1.98\times 10^{-3}\ \text{V}}.$$

P31.26 $\varepsilon = -N\frac{d}{dt}BA\cos\theta = -NB\cos\theta\left(\frac{\Delta A}{\Delta t}\right)$

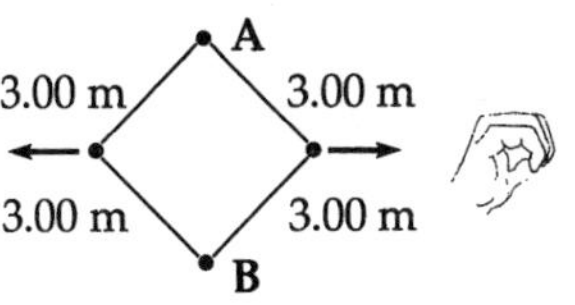

FIG. P31.26

$$\varepsilon = -1(0.100\ \text{T})\cos 0°\frac{(3.00\ \text{m}\times 3.00\ \text{m}\sin 60.0°)-(3.00\ \text{m})^2}{0.100\ \text{s}} = 1.21\ \text{V}$$

$$I = \frac{1.21\ \text{V}}{10.0\ \Omega} = \boxed{0.121\ \text{A}}$$

The flux is into the page and decreasing. The loop makes its own magnetic field into the page by carrying $\boxed{\text{clockwise}}$ current.

P31.27 $\omega = (2.00\ \text{rev/s})(2\pi\ \text{rad/rev}) = 4.00\pi\ \text{rad/s}$

$$\varepsilon = \frac{1}{2}B\omega\ell^2 = \boxed{2.83\ \text{mV}}$$

P31.28 (a) $\mathbf{B}_{ext} = B_{ext}\hat{\mathbf{i}}$ and B_{ext} decreases; therefore, the induced field is $\mathbf{B}_0 = B_0\hat{\mathbf{i}}$ (to the right) and the current in the resistor is directed $\boxed{\text{to the right}}$.

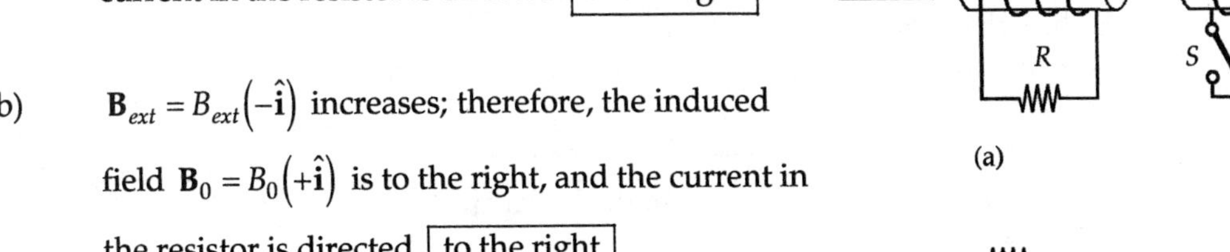

(b) $\mathbf{B}_{ext} = B_{ext}\left(-\hat{\mathbf{i}}\right)$ increases; therefore, the induced field $\mathbf{B}_0 = B_0\left(+\hat{\mathbf{i}}\right)$ is to the right, and the current in the resistor is directed $\boxed{\text{to the right}}$.

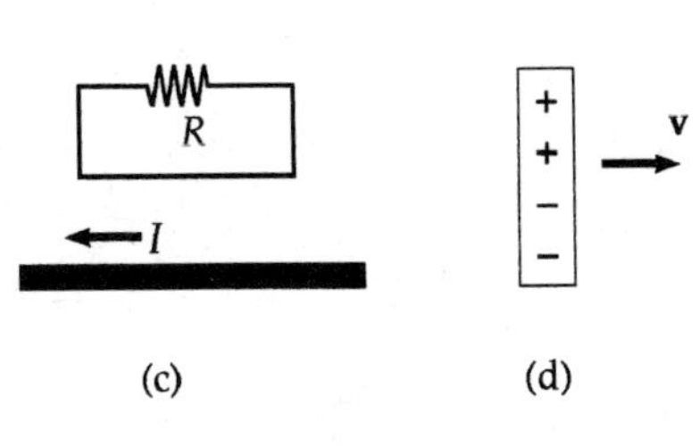

(c) $\mathbf{B}_{ext} = B_{ext}\left(-\hat{\mathbf{k}}\right)$ into the paper and B_{ext} decreases; therefore, the induced field is $\mathbf{B}_0 = B_0\left(-\hat{\mathbf{k}}\right)$ into the paper, and the current in the resistor is directed $\boxed{\text{to the right}}$.

FIG. P31.28

(d) By the magnetic force law, $F_B = q(\mathbf{v}\times\mathbf{B})$. Therefore, a positive charge will move to the top of the bar if **B** is $\boxed{\text{into the paper}}$.

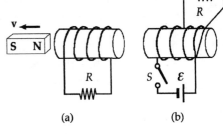

P31.29 (a) The force on the side of the coil entering the field (consisting of N wires) is

$$F = N(ILB) = N(IwB).$$

The induced emf in the coil is

$$|\varepsilon| = N\frac{d\Phi_B}{dt} = N\frac{d(Bwx)}{dt} = NBwv.$$

so the current is $I = \frac{|\varepsilon|}{R} = \frac{NBwv}{R}$ counterclockwise.

The force on the leading side of the coil is then:

$$F = N\left(\frac{NBwv}{R}\right)wB = \boxed{\frac{N^2B^2w^2v}{R} \text{ to the left}}.$$

(b) 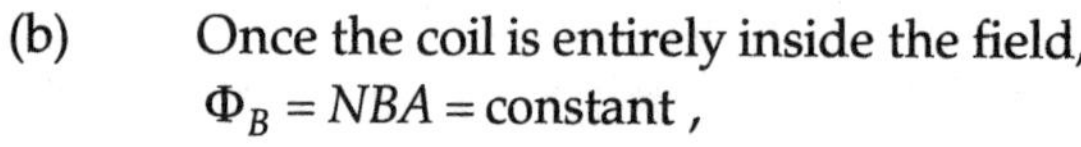Once the coil is entirely inside the field, $\Phi_B = NBA = \text{constant}$,

so $\varepsilon = 0$, $I = 0$, and $F = \boxed{0}$.

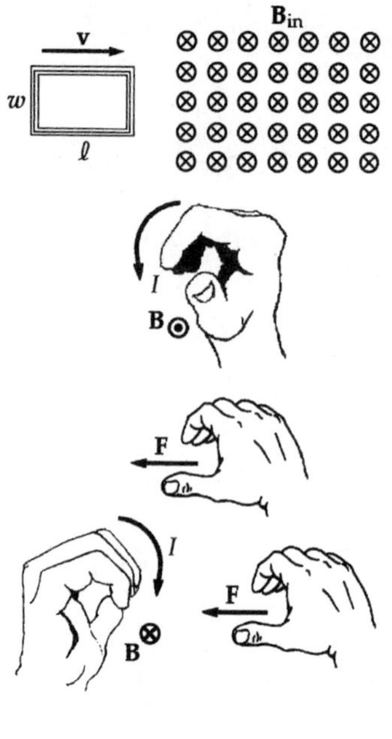

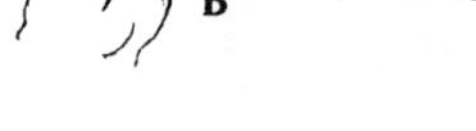

FIG. P31.29

(c) As the coil starts to leave the field, the flux *decreases* at the rate Bwv, so the magnitude of the current is the same as in part (a), but now the current is clockwise. Thus, the force exerted on the trailing side of the coil is:

$$F = \boxed{\frac{N^2B^2w^2v}{R} \text{ to the left again}}.$$

P31.30 Look in the direction of *ba*. The bar magnet creates a field into the page, and the field increases. The loop will create a field out of the page by carrying a counterclockwise current. Therefore, current must flow from b to a through the resistor. Hence, $V_a - V_b$ will be $\boxed{\text{negative}}$.

P31.31 Name the currents as shown in the diagram:

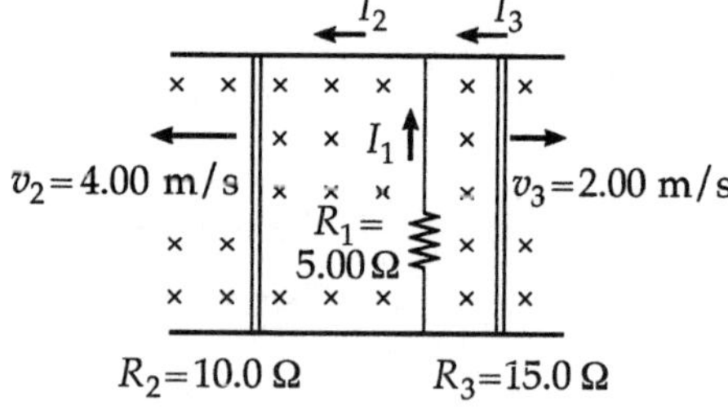

FIG. P31.31

Left loop: $+Bdv_2 - I_2R_2 - I_1R_1 = 0$

Right loop: $+Bdv_3 - I_3R_3 + I_1R_1 = 0$

At the junction: $I_2 = I_1 + I_3$

Then, $Bdv_2 - I_1R_2 - I_3R_2 - I_1R_1 = 0$

$$I_3 = \frac{Bdv_3}{R_3} + \frac{I_1R_1}{R_3}.$$

So, $$Bdv_2 - I_1(R_1 + R_2) - \frac{Bdv_3R_2}{R_3} - \frac{I_1R_1R_2}{R_3} = 0$$

$$I_1 = Bd\left(\frac{v_2R_3 - v_3R_2}{R_1R_2 + R_1R_3 + R_2R_3}\right) \text{ upward}$$

$$I_1 = (0.010\,0\text{ T})(0.100\text{ m})\left[\frac{(4.00\text{ m/s})(15.0\ \Omega) - (2.00\text{ m/s})(10.0\ \Omega)}{(5.00\ \Omega)(10.0\ \Omega) + (5.00\ \Omega)(15.0\ \Omega) + (10.0\ \Omega)(15.0\ \Omega)}\right] = \boxed{145\ \mu\text{A}} \text{ upward.}$$

Section 31.4 **Induced emf and Electric Fields**

P31.32 (a) $\frac{dB}{dt} = 6.00t^2 - 8.00t$ $\quad |\varepsilon| = \frac{d\Phi_B}{dt}$

At $t = 2.00$ s, $\quad E = \frac{\pi R^2 (dB/dt)}{2\pi r_2} = \frac{8.00\pi(0.025\,0)^2}{2\pi(0.050\,0)}$

$$F = qE = \boxed{8.00 \times 10^{-21} \text{ N}}$$

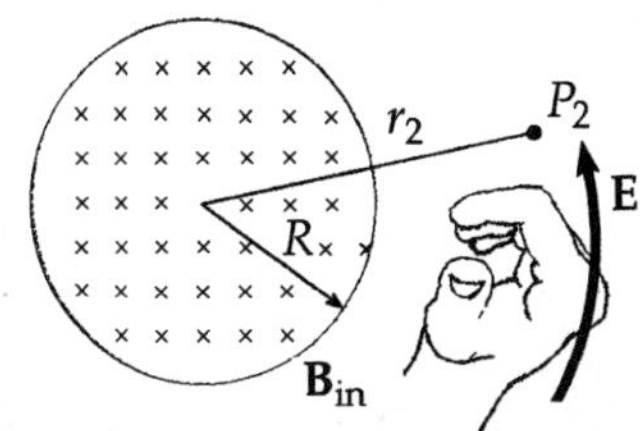

FIG. P31.32

(b) When $6.00t^2 - 8.00t = 0$, $\quad t = \boxed{1.33 \text{ s}}$

P31.33 $\frac{dB}{dt} = 0.060\,0t$ $\quad |\varepsilon| = \frac{d\Phi_B}{dt} = \pi r_1^2 \frac{dB}{dt} = 2\pi r_1 E$

At $t = 3.00$ s,

$$E = \left(\frac{\pi r_1^2}{2\pi r_1}\right)\frac{dB}{dt} = \frac{0.020\,0 \text{ m}}{2}\left(0.060\,0 \text{ T/s}^2\right)(3.00 \text{ s})\left(\frac{1 \text{ N}\cdot\text{s}}{1 \text{ T}\cdot\text{C}\cdot\text{m}}\right)$$

$$\mathbf{E} = \boxed{1.80 \times 10^{-3} \text{ N/C perpendicular to } r_1 \text{ and counterclockwise}}$$

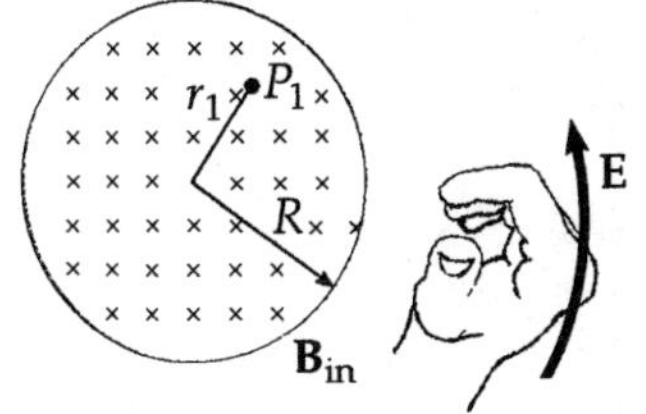

FIG. P31.33

P31.34 (a) $\oint \mathbf{E} \cdot d\ell = \left|\frac{d\Phi_B}{dt}\right|$

$2\pi r E = \left(\pi r^2\right)\frac{dB}{dt}$ so $\quad E = \boxed{(9.87 \text{ mV/m})\cos(100\pi t)}$

(b) The E field is always opposite to increasing B. $\therefore$ $\boxed{\text{clockwise}}$.

Section 31.5 **Generators and Motors**

P31.35 (a) $\varepsilon_{max} = NAB\omega = (1\,000)(0.100)(0.200)(120\pi) = \boxed{7.54 \text{ kV}}$

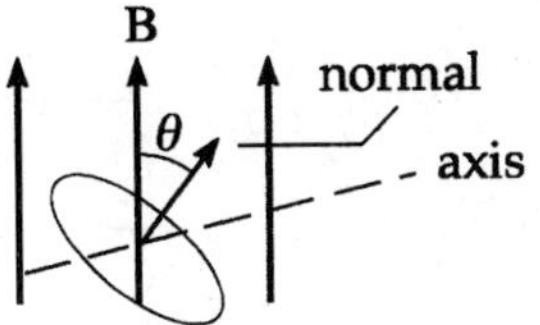

FIG. P31.35

(b) $\varepsilon(t) = NBA\omega \sin\omega t = NBA\omega \sin\theta$

$|\varepsilon|$ is maximal when $|\sin\theta| = 1$

or $\theta = \pm\frac{\pi}{2}$

so the $\boxed{\text{plane of coil is parallel to } \mathbf{B}}$.

P31.36 For the alternator, $\omega = (3\,000 \text{ rev/min})\left(\frac{2\pi \text{ rad}}{1 \text{ rev}}\right)\left(\frac{1 \text{ min}}{60 \text{ s}}\right) = 314 \text{ rad/s}$

$$\varepsilon = -N\frac{d\Phi_B}{dt} = -250\frac{d}{dt}\left[\left(2.50\times10^{-4}\text{ T}\cdot\text{m}^2\right)\cos(314t/\text{s})\right] = +250\left(2.50\times10^{-4}\text{ T}\cdot\text{m}^2\right)(314/\text{s})\sin(314t)$$

(a) $\boxed{\varepsilon = (19.6\text{ V})\sin(314t)}$

(b) $\boxed{\varepsilon_{\max} = 19.6\text{ V}}$

P31.37 $B = \mu_0 nI = \left(4\pi\times10^{-7}\text{ T}\cdot\text{m/A}\right)\left(200\text{ m}^{-1}\right)(15.0\text{ A}) = 3.77\times10^{-3}\text{ T}$

For the small coil, $\Phi_B = N\mathbf{B}\cdot\mathbf{A} = NBA\cos\omega t = NB\left(\pi r^2\right)\cos\omega t$.

Thus, $\varepsilon = -\frac{d\Phi_B}{dt} = NB\pi r^2\omega\sin\omega t$

$$\varepsilon = (30.0)\left(3.77\times10^{-3}\text{ T}\right)\pi(0.080\,0\text{ m})^2\left(4.00\pi\text{ s}^{-1}\right)\sin(4.00\pi t) = \boxed{(28.6\text{ mV})\sin(4.00\pi t)}.$$

P31.38 As the magnet rotates, the flux through the coil varies sinusoidally in time with $\Phi_B = 0$ at $t = 0$. Choosing the flux as positive when the field passes from left to right through the area of the coil, the flux at any time may be written as $\Phi_B = -\Phi_{\max}\sin\omega t$ so the induced emf is given by

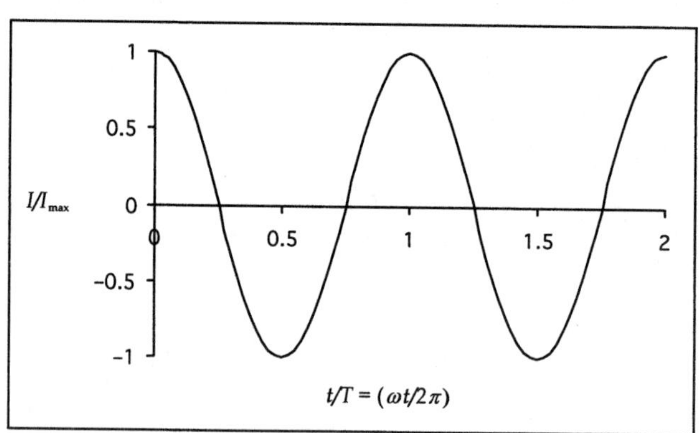

FIG. P31.38

$$\varepsilon = -\frac{d\Phi_B}{dt} = \omega\Phi_{\max}\cos\omega t.$$

The current in the coil is then $I = \frac{\varepsilon}{R} = \frac{\omega\Phi_{\max}}{R}\cos\omega t = \boxed{I_{\max}\cos\omega t}$.

***P31.39**

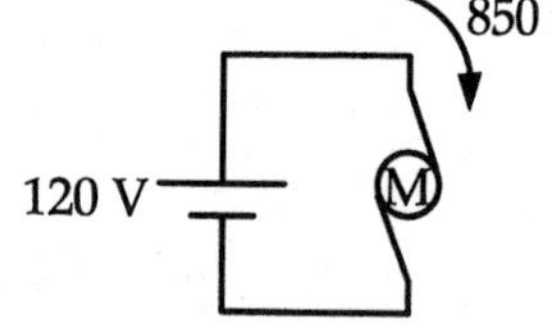

To analyze the actual circuit, we model it as

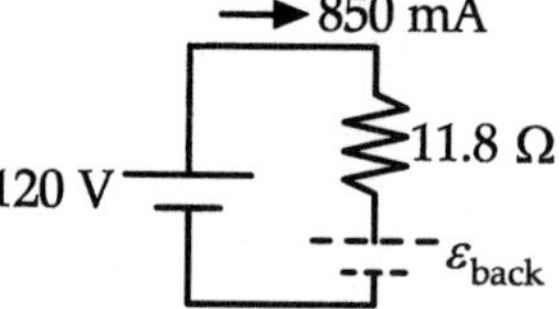

(a) The loop rule gives $+120\text{ V} - 0.85\text{ A}(11.8\ \Omega) - \varepsilon_{\text{back}} = 0$ $\quad \varepsilon_{\text{back}} = \boxed{110\text{ V}}$.

(b) The resistor is the device changing electrical work input into internal energy: $\mathcal{P} = I^2R = (0.85\text{ A})^2(11.8\ \Omega) = \boxed{8.53\text{ W}}$.

(c) With no motion, the motor does not function as a generator, and $\varepsilon_{\text{back}} = 0$. Then

$120\text{ V} - I_c(11.8\ \Omega) = 0 \qquad I_c = 10.2\text{ A}$

$\mathcal{P}_c = I_c^2R = (10.2\text{ A})^2(11.8\ \Omega) = \boxed{1.22\text{ kW}}$

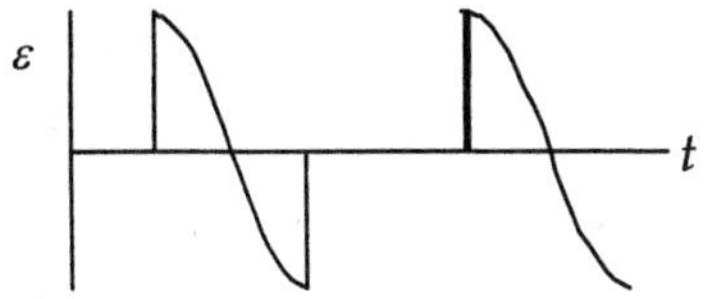

P31.40 (a) $\mathcal{E}_{max} = BA\omega = B\left(\frac{1}{2}\pi R^2\right)\omega$

$\mathcal{E}_{max} = (1.30\text{ T})\frac{\pi}{2}(0.250\text{ m})^2(4.00\pi\text{ rad/s})$

$\mathcal{E}_{max} = \boxed{1.60\text{ V}}$

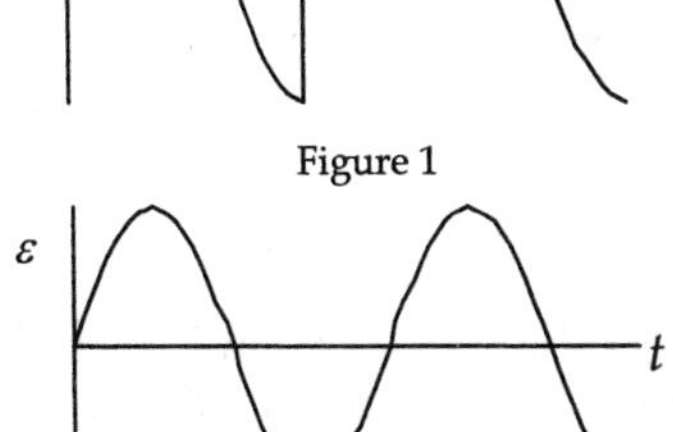

Figure 1

(b) $\bar{\mathcal{E}} = \int_0^{2\pi} \frac{\mathcal{E}}{2\pi} d\theta = \frac{BA\omega}{2\pi}\int_0^{2\pi} \sin\theta d\theta = \boxed{0}$

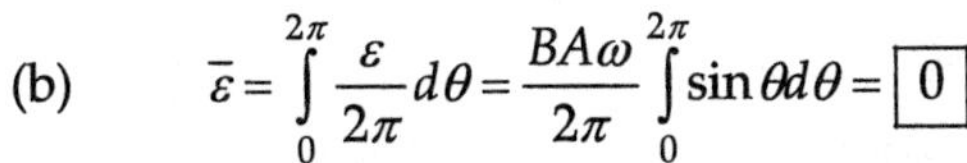

Figure 2

FIG. P31.40

(c) The maximum and average $\mathcal{E}$ would remain unchanged.

(d) See Figure 1 at the right.

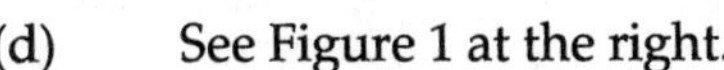

(e) See Figure 2 at the right.

P31.41 (a) $\Phi_B = BA\cos\theta = BA\cos\omega t = (0.800\text{ T})\left(0.010\,0\text{ m}^2\right)\cos 2\pi(60.0)t = \boxed{\left(8.00\text{ mT}\cdot\text{m}^2\right)\cos(377t)}$

(b) $\mathcal{E} = -\frac{d\Phi_B}{dt} = \boxed{(3.02\text{ V})\sin(377t)}$

(c) $I = \frac{\mathcal{E}}{R} = \boxed{(3.02\text{ A})\sin(377t)}$

(d) $\mathcal{P} = I^2R = \boxed{(9.10\text{ W})\sin^2(377t)}$

(e) $\mathcal{P} = Fv = \tau\omega$ so $\tau = \frac{\mathcal{P}}{\omega} = \boxed{(24.1\text{ mN}\cdot\text{m})\sin^2(377t)}$

Section 31.6 **Eddy Currents**

P31.42 The current in the magnet creates an  upward magnetic field, so the N and S poles on the solenoid core are shown correctly. On the rail in front of the brake, the upward flux of **B** increases as the coil approaches, so a current is induced here to create a downward magnetic field. This is  clockwise current, so the S pole on the rail is shown correctly. On the rail behind the brake, the upward magnetic flux is decreasing. The induced current in the rail will produce upward magnetic field by being  counterclockwise as the picture correctly shows.

P31.43 (a) At terminal speed,

$$Mg = F_B = IwB = \left(\frac{\varepsilon}{R}\right)wB = \left(\frac{Bwv_T}{R}\right)wB = \frac{B^2w^2v_T}{R}$$

or $\boxed{v_T = \dfrac{MgR}{B^2\omega^2}}$.

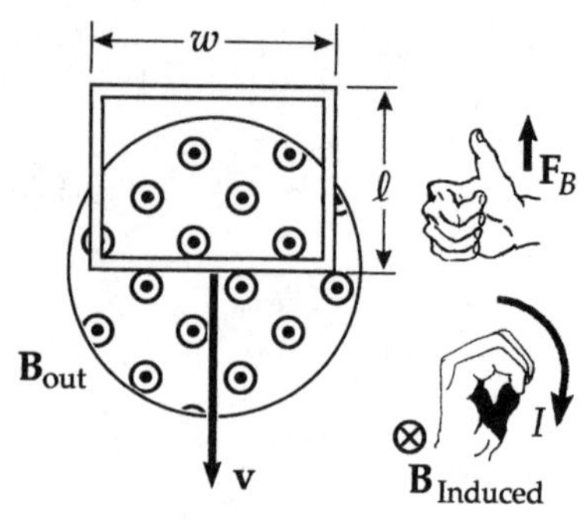

FIG. P31.43

(b) The emf is directly proportional to v_T, but the current is inversely proportional to R. A large R means a small current at a given speed, so the loop must travel faster to get $F_B = mg$.

(c) At a given speed, the current is directly proportional to the magnetic field. But the force is proportional to the product of the current and the field. For a small B, the speed must increase to compensate for both the small B and also the current, so $v_T \propto B^2$.

Section 31.7 Maxwell's Equations

P31.44 $\mathbf{F} = m\mathbf{a} = q\mathbf{E} + q\mathbf{v}\times\mathbf{B}$ so $\mathbf{a} = \dfrac{-e}{m}[\mathbf{E} + \mathbf{v}\times\mathbf{B}]$ where $\mathbf{v}\times\mathbf{B} = \begin{vmatrix} \hat{\mathbf{i}} & \hat{\mathbf{j}} & \hat{\mathbf{k}} \\ 10.0 & 0 & 0 \\ 0 & 0 & 0.400 \end{vmatrix} = -4.00\hat{\mathbf{j}}$

$$\mathbf{a} = \frac{(-1.60\times10^{-19})}{9.11\times10^{-31}}\left[2.50\hat{\mathbf{i}} + 5.00\hat{\mathbf{j}} - 4.00\hat{\mathbf{j}}\right] = (-1.76\times10^{11})\left[2.50\hat{\mathbf{i}} + 1.00\hat{\mathbf{j}}\right]$$

$$\mathbf{a} = \boxed{\left(-4.39\times10^{11}\hat{\mathbf{i}} - 1.76\times10^{11}\hat{\mathbf{j}}\right)\ \text{m/s}^2}$$

P31.45 $\mathbf{F} = m\mathbf{a} = q\mathbf{E} + q\mathbf{v}\times\mathbf{B}$

$$\mathbf{a} = \frac{e}{m}[\mathbf{E} + \mathbf{v}\times\mathbf{B}] \text{ where } \mathbf{v}\times\mathbf{B} = \begin{vmatrix} \hat{\mathbf{i}} & \hat{\mathbf{j}} & \hat{\mathbf{k}} \\ 200 & 0 & 0 \\ 0.200 & 0.300 & 0.400 \end{vmatrix} = -200(0.400)\hat{\mathbf{j}} + 200(0.300)\hat{\mathbf{k}}$$

$$\mathbf{a} = \frac{1.60\times10^{-19}}{1.67\times10^{-27}}\left[50.0\hat{\mathbf{j}} - 80.0\hat{\mathbf{j}} + 60.0\hat{\mathbf{k}}\right] = 9.58\times10^{7}\left[-30.0\hat{\mathbf{j}} + 60.0\hat{\mathbf{k}}\right]$$

$$\mathbf{a} = 2.87\times10^{9}\left[-\hat{\mathbf{j}} + 2\hat{\mathbf{k}}\right]\ \text{m/s}^2 = \boxed{\left(-2.87\times10^{9}\hat{\mathbf{j}} + 5.75\times10^{9}\hat{\mathbf{k}}\right)\ \text{m/s}^2}$$

Additional Problems

P31.46 $\varepsilon = -N\dfrac{d}{dt}(BA\cos\theta) = -N(\pi r^2)\cos 0°\left(\dfrac{dB}{dt}\right)$

$$\varepsilon = -(30.0)\left[\pi(2.70\times10^{-3}\ \text{m})^2\right](1)\frac{d}{dt}\left[50.0\ \text{mT} + (3.20\ \text{mT})\sin\left(2\pi\left[523t\ \text{s}^{-1}\right]\right)\right]$$

$$\varepsilon = -(30.0)\left[\pi(2.70\times10^{-3}\ \text{m})^2\right](3.20\times10^{-3}\ \text{T})\left[2\pi(523\ \text{s}^{-1})\cos\left(2\pi\left[523t\ \text{s}^{-1}\right]\right)\right]$$

$$\varepsilon = \boxed{-(7.22\times10^{-3}\ \text{V})\cos\left[2\pi(523t\ \text{s}^{-1})\right]}$$

P31.47 (a) Doubling the number of turns.

Amplitude doubles: period unchanged

(b) Doubling the angular velocity.

doubles the amplitude: cuts the period in half

(c) Doubling the angular velocity while reducing the number of turns to one half the original value.

Amplitude unchanged: cuts the period in half

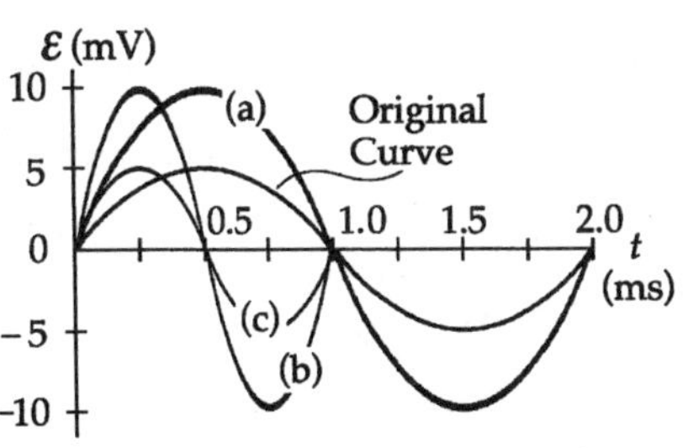

FIG. P31.47

P31.48 $$\varepsilon = -N\frac{\Delta}{\Delta t}(BA\cos\theta) = -N\left(\pi r^2\right)\cos 0°\frac{\Delta B}{\Delta t} = -1\left(0.005\,00\text{ m}^2\right)(1)\left(\frac{1.50\text{ T} - 5.00\text{ T}}{20.0\times 10^{-3}\text{ s}}\right) = 0.875\text{ V}$$

(a) $$I = \frac{\varepsilon}{R} = \frac{0.875\text{ V}}{0.020\,0\ \Omega} = \boxed{43.8\text{ A}}$$

(b) $$\mathcal{P} = \varepsilon I = (0.875\text{ V})(43.8\text{ A}) = \boxed{38.3\text{ W}}$$

P31.49 In the loop on the left, the induced emf is

$$|\varepsilon| = \frac{d\Phi_B}{dt} = A\frac{dB}{dt} = \pi(0.100\text{ m})^2(100\text{ T/s}) = \pi\text{ V}$$

and it attempts to produce a counterclockwise current in this loop.

In the loop on the right, the induced emf is

$$|\varepsilon| = \frac{d\Phi_B}{dt} = \pi(0.150\text{ m})^2(100\text{ T/s}) = 2.25\pi\text{ V}$$

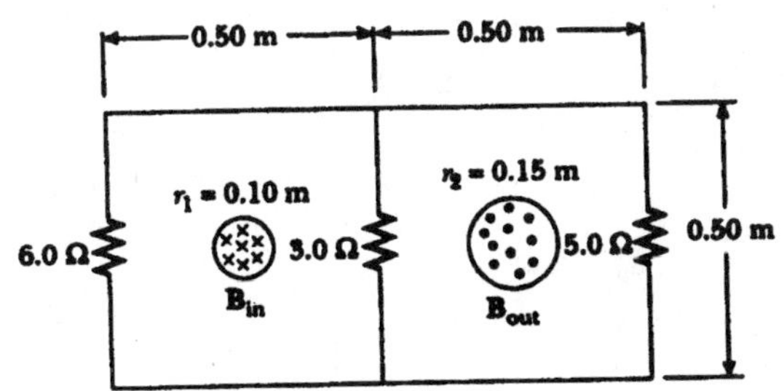

FIG. P31.49

and it attempts to produce a clockwise current. Assume that I_1 flows down through the 6.00-Ω resistor, I_2 flows down through the 5.00-Ω resistor, and that I_3 flows up through the 3.00-Ω resistor.

From Kirchhoff's junction rule: $I_3 = I_1 + I_2$ (1)

Using the loop rule on the left loop: $6.00I_1 + 3.00I_3 = \pi$ (2)

Using the loop rule on the right loop: $5.00I_2 + 3.00I_3 = 2.25\pi$ (3)

Solving these three equations simultaneously,

$I_1 = \boxed{0.062\,3\text{ A}}$, $I_2 = \boxed{0.860\text{ A}}$, and $I_3 = \boxed{0.923\text{ A}}$.

P31.50 The emf induced between the ends of the moving bar is

$$\varepsilon = B\ell v = (2.50\text{ T})(0.350\text{ m})(8.00\text{ m/s}) = 7.00\text{ V}.$$

The left-hand loop contains decreasing flux away from you, so the induced current in it will be clockwise, to produce its own field directed away from you. Let I_1 represent the current flowing upward through the 2.00-Ω resistor. The right-hand loop will carry counterclockwise current. Let I_3 be the upward current in the 5.00-Ω resistor.

(a) Kirchhoff's loop rule then gives: $+7.00\text{ V} - I_1(2.00\ \Omega) = 0$ $\quad I_1 = \boxed{3.50\text{ A}}$

and $+7.00\text{ V} - I_3(5.00\ \Omega) = 0$ $\quad I_3 = \boxed{1.40\text{ A}}$.

(b) The total power dissipated in the resistors of the circuit is

$$P = \varepsilon I_1 + \varepsilon I_3 = \varepsilon(I_1 + I_3) = (7.00\text{ V})(3.50\text{ A} + 1.40\text{ A}) = \boxed{34.3\text{ W}}.$$

(c) *Method 1*: The current in the sliding conductor is downward with value $I_2 = 3.50\text{ A} + 1.40\text{ A} = 4.90\text{ A}$. The magnetic field exerts a force of $F_m = I\ell B = (4.90\text{ A})(0.350\text{ m})(2.50\text{ T}) = 4.29\text{ N}$ directed toward the right on this conductor. An outside agent must then exert a force of $\boxed{4.29\text{ N}}$ to the left to keep the bar moving.

Method 2: The agent moving the bar must supply the power according to $\mathcal{P} = \mathbf{F}\cdot\mathbf{v} = Fv\cos 0°$. The force required is then:

$$F = \frac{\mathcal{P}}{v} = \frac{34.3\text{ W}}{8.00\text{ m/s}} = \boxed{4.29\text{ N}}.$$

P31.51 Suppose we wrap twenty turns of wire into a flat compact circular coil of diameter 3 cm. Suppose we use a bar magnet to produce field 10^{-3} T through the coil in one direction along its axis. Suppose we then flip the magnet to reverse the flux in 10^{-1} s. The average induced emf is then

$$\bar{\varepsilon} = -N\frac{\Delta\Phi_B}{\Delta t} = -N\frac{\Delta[BA\cos\theta]}{\Delta t} = -NB(\pi r^2)\left(\frac{\cos 180° - \cos 0°}{\Delta t}\right)$$

$$\bar{\varepsilon} = -(20)(10^{-3}\text{ T})\pi(0.015\,0\text{ m})^2\left(\frac{-2}{10^{-1}\text{ s}}\right)\boxed{\sim 10^{-4}\text{ V}}$$

P31.52 $I = \frac{\varepsilon + \varepsilon_{\text{induced}}}{R}$ and $\varepsilon_{\text{induced}} = -\frac{d}{dt}(BA)$

$$F = m\frac{dv}{dt} = IBd$$

$$\frac{dv}{dt} = \frac{IBd}{m} = \frac{Bd}{mR}(\varepsilon + \varepsilon_{\text{induced}})$$

$$\frac{dv}{dt} = \frac{Bd}{mR}(\varepsilon - Bvd)$$

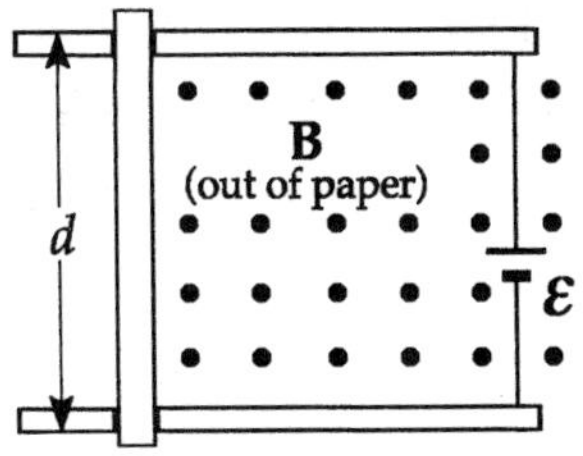

B (out of paper)

FIG. P31.52

To solve the differential equation, let $u = \varepsilon - Bvd$

$$\frac{du}{dt} = -Bd\frac{dv}{dt}$$

$$-\frac{1}{Bd}\frac{du}{dt} = \frac{Bd}{mR}u$$

so $$\int_{u_0}^{u}\frac{du}{u} = -\int_{0}^{t}\frac{(Bd)^2}{mR}dt.$$

Integrating from $t = 0$ to $t = t$, $$\ln\frac{u}{u_0} = -\frac{(Bd)^2}{mR}t$$

or $$\frac{u}{u_0} = e^{-B^2d^2t/mR}.$$

Since $v = 0$ when $t = 0$, $u_0 = \varepsilon$

and $u = \varepsilon - Bvd$

$$\varepsilon - Bvd = \varepsilon e^{-B^2d^2t/mR}.$$

Therefore, $$\boxed{v = \frac{\varepsilon}{Bd}\left(1 - e^{-B^2d^2t/mR}\right)}.$$

***P31.53** The enclosed flux is $\Phi_B = BA = B\pi r^2$.

The particle moves according to $\sum \mathbf{F} = m\mathbf{a}$: $qvB\sin 90° = \frac{mv^2}{r}$

$$r = \frac{mv}{qB}.$$

Then $$\Phi_B = \frac{B\pi m^2v^2}{q^2B^2}.$$

(a) $$v = \sqrt{\frac{\Phi_B q^2 B}{\pi m^2}} = \sqrt{\frac{(15\times10^{-6}\ \text{T}\cdot\text{m}^2)(30\times10^{-9}\ \text{C})^2(0.6\ \text{T})}{\pi(2\times10^{-16}\ \text{kg})^2}} = \boxed{2.54\times10^5\ \text{m/s}}$$

(b) Energy for the particle-electric field system is conserved in the firing process:

$U_i = K_f$: $q\Delta V = \frac{1}{2}mv^2$

$$\Delta V = \frac{mv^2}{2q} = \frac{(2\times10^{-16}\ \text{kg})(2.54\times10^5\ \text{m/s})^2}{2(30\times10^{-9}\ \text{C})} = \boxed{215\ \text{V}}.$$

***P31.54** (a) Consider an annulus of radius r, width dr, height b, and resistivity ρ. Around its circumference, a voltage is induced according to

$$\varepsilon = -N\frac{d}{dt}\mathbf{B}\cdot\mathbf{A} = -1\frac{d}{dt}B_{\text{max}}(\cos\omega t)\pi r^2 = +B_{\text{max}}\pi r^2\omega\sin\omega t.$$

The resistance around the loop is $\frac{\rho\ell}{A_x} = \frac{\rho(2\pi r)}{bdr}$.

The eddy current in the ring is $dI = \frac{\varepsilon}{\text{resistance}} = \frac{B_{\text{max}}\pi r^2\omega(\sin\omega t)bdr}{\rho(2\pi r)} = \frac{B_{\text{max}}rb\omega dr\sin\omega t}{2\rho}$.

The instantaneous power is $d\mathcal{P}_i = \varepsilon\, dI = \frac{B_{\text{max}}^2\pi r^3 b\omega^2 dr\sin^2\omega t}{2\rho}$.

The time average of the function $\sin^2\omega t = \frac{1}{2} - \frac{1}{2}\cos 2\omega t$ is $\frac{1}{2} - 0 = \frac{1}{2}$

so the time-averaged power delivered to the annulus is

$$d\mathcal{P} = \frac{B_{\text{max}}^2\pi r^3 b\omega^2 dr}{4\rho}.$$

The power delivered to the disk is $\mathcal{P} = \int d\mathcal{P} = \int_0^R \frac{B_{\text{max}}^2\pi b\omega^2}{4\rho} r^3 dr$

$$\mathcal{P} = \frac{B_{\text{max}}^2\pi b\omega^2}{4\rho}\left(\frac{R^4}{4} - 0\right) = \boxed{\frac{\pi B_{\text{max}}^2 R^4 b\omega^2}{16\rho}}.$$

(b) When B_{max} gets two times larger, B_{max}^2 and $\mathcal{P}$ get $\boxed{4}$ times larger.

(c) When f and $\omega = 2\pi f$ double, ω^2 and $\mathcal{P}$ get $\boxed{4}$ times larger.

(d) When R doubles, R^4 and $\mathcal{P}$ become $2^4 = \boxed{16}$ times larger.

P31.55 $I = \frac{\varepsilon}{R} = \frac{B|A|}{R\,\Delta t}$

so $q = I\Delta t = \frac{(15.0\ \mu\text{T})(0.200\ \text{m})^2}{0.500\ \Omega} = \boxed{1.20\ \mu\text{C}}$

P31.56 (a) $I = \frac{dq}{dt} = \frac{\varepsilon}{R}$ where $\varepsilon = -N\frac{d\Phi_B}{dt}$ so $\int dq = \frac{N}{R}\int_{\Phi_1}^{\Phi_2} d\Phi_B$

and the charge through the circuit will be $|Q| = \frac{N}{R}(\Phi_2 - \Phi_1)$.

(b) $Q = \frac{N}{R}\left[BA\cos 0 - BA\cos\left(\frac{\pi}{2}\right)\right] = \frac{BAN}{R}$

so $B = \frac{RQ}{NA} = \frac{(200\ \Omega)(5.00\times10^{-4}\ \text{C})}{(100)(40.0\times10^{-4}\ \text{m}^2)} = \boxed{0.250\ \text{T}}$.

P31.57 (a) $\varepsilon = B\ell v = 0.360 \text{ V}$ $\quad I = \frac{\varepsilon}{R} = \boxed{0.900 \text{ A}}$

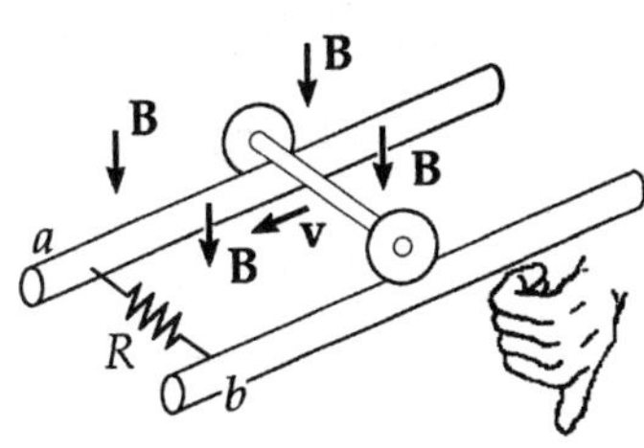

FIG. P31.57

(b) $F_B = I\ell B = \boxed{0.108 \text{ N}}$

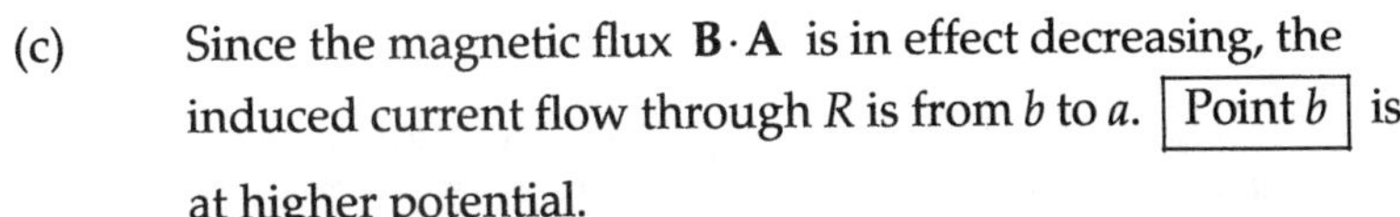

(c) Since the magnetic flux $\mathbf{B} \cdot \mathbf{A}$ is in effect decreasing, the induced current flow through R is from b to a. $\boxed{\text{Point } b}$ is at higher potential.

(d) $\boxed{\text{No}}$. Magnetic flux will increase through a loop to the left of ab. Here counterclockwise current will flow to produce upward magnetic field. The current in R is still from b to a.

P31.58 $\varepsilon = B\ell v$ at a distance r from wire

$$|\varepsilon| = \left(\frac{\mu_0 I}{2\pi r}\right)\ell v$$

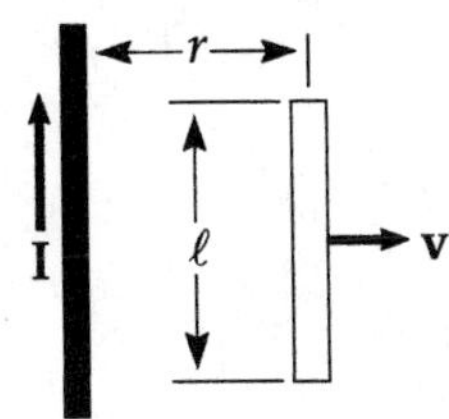

FIG. P31.58

P31.59 (a) At time t, the flux through the loop is $\Phi_B = BA\cos\theta = (a+bt)\left(\pi r^2\right)\cos 0° = \pi(a+bt)r^2$.

At $t = 0$, $\Phi_B = \boxed{\pi a r^2}$.

(b) $$\varepsilon = -\frac{d\Phi_B}{dt} = -\pi r^2 \frac{d(a+bt)}{dt} = \boxed{-\pi b r^2}$$

(c) $$I = \frac{\varepsilon}{R} = \boxed{-\frac{\pi b r^2}{R}}$$

(d) $$\mathcal{P} = \varepsilon I = \left(-\frac{\pi b r^2}{R}\right)\left(-\pi b r^2\right) = \boxed{\frac{\pi^2 b^2 r^4}{R}}$$

P31.60 $$\varepsilon = -\frac{d}{dt}(NBA) = -1\left(\frac{dB}{dt}\right)\pi a^2 = \pi a^2 K$$

(a) $Q = C\varepsilon = \boxed{C\pi a^2 K}$

(b) **B** into the paper is decreasing; therefore, current will attempt to counteract this. Positive charge will go to $\boxed{\text{upper plate}}$.

(c) The changing magnetic field through the enclosed area $\boxed{\text{induces an electric field}}$, surrounding the **B**-field, and this pushes on charges in the wire.

P31.61 The flux through the coil is $\Phi_B = \mathbf{B}\cdot\mathbf{A} = BA\cos\theta = BA\cos\omega t$. The induced emf is

$$\varepsilon = -N\frac{d\Phi_B}{dt} = -NBA\frac{d(\cos\omega t)}{dt} = NBA\omega\sin\omega t.$$

(a) $\varepsilon_{\max} = NBA\omega = 60.0(1.00\text{ T})(0.100\times 0.200\text{ m}^2)(30.0\text{ rad/s}) = \boxed{36.0\text{ V}}$

(b) $\dfrac{d\Phi_B}{dt} = \dfrac{\varepsilon}{N}$, thus $\left|\dfrac{d\Phi_B}{dt}\right|_{\max} = \dfrac{\varepsilon_{\max}}{N} = \dfrac{36.0\text{ V}}{60.0} = 0.600\text{ V} = \boxed{0.600\text{ Wb/s}}$

(c) At $t = 0.050\,0\text{ s}$, $\omega t = 1.50\text{ rad}$ and
$\varepsilon = \varepsilon_{\max}\sin(1.50\text{ rad}) = (36.0\text{ V})\sin(1.50\text{ rad}) = \boxed{35.9\text{ V}}$.

(d) The torque on the coil at any time is
$\tau = |\mu\times\mathbf{B}| = |NI\mathbf{A}\times\mathbf{B}| = (NAB)I|\sin\omega t| = \left(\dfrac{\varepsilon_{\max}}{\omega}\right)\left(\dfrac{\varepsilon}{R}\right)|\sin\omega t|$.

When $\varepsilon = \varepsilon_{\max}$, $\sin\omega t = 1.00$ and $\tau = \dfrac{\varepsilon_{\max}^2}{\omega R} = \dfrac{(36.0\text{ V})^2}{(30.0\text{ rad/s})(10.0\ \Omega)} = \boxed{4.32\text{ N}\cdot\text{m}}$.

P31.62 (a) We use $\varepsilon = -N\dfrac{\Delta\Phi_B}{\Delta t}$, with $N = 1$.

Taking $a = 5.00\times 10^{-3}$ m to be the radius of the washer, and $h = 0.500$ m,

$$\Delta\Phi_B = B_2A - B_1A = A(B_2 - B_1) = \pi a^2\left(\frac{\mu_0 I}{2\pi(h+a)} - \frac{\mu_0 I}{2\pi a}\right) = \frac{a^2\mu_0 I}{2}\left(\frac{1}{h+a} - \frac{1}{a}\right) = \frac{-\mu_0 a h I}{2(h+a)}.$$

The time for the washer to drop a distance h (from rest) is: $\Delta t = \sqrt{\dfrac{2h}{g}}$.

Therefore, $\varepsilon = \dfrac{\mu_0 a h I}{2(h+a)\Delta t} = \dfrac{\mu_0 a h I}{2(h+a)}\sqrt{\dfrac{g}{2h}} = \dfrac{\mu_0 a I}{2(h+a)}\sqrt{\dfrac{gh}{2}}$

and $\varepsilon = \dfrac{(4\pi\times 10^{-7}\text{ T}\cdot\text{m/A})(5.00\times 10^{-3}\text{ m})(10.0\text{ A})}{2(0.500\text{ m} + 0.005\,00\text{ m})}\sqrt{\dfrac{(9.80\text{ m/s}^2)(0.500\text{ m})}{2}} = \boxed{97.4\text{ nV}}$.

(b) Since the magnetic flux going through the washer (into the plane of the paper) is decreasing in time, a current will form in the washer so as to oppose that decrease. Therefore, the current will flow in a $\boxed{\text{clockwise direction}}$.

P31.63 Find an expression for the flux through a rectangular area "swept out" by the bar in time t. The magnetic field at a distance x from wire is

$B = \dfrac{\mu_0 I}{2\pi x}$ and $\Phi_B = \int B\,dA$. Therefore,

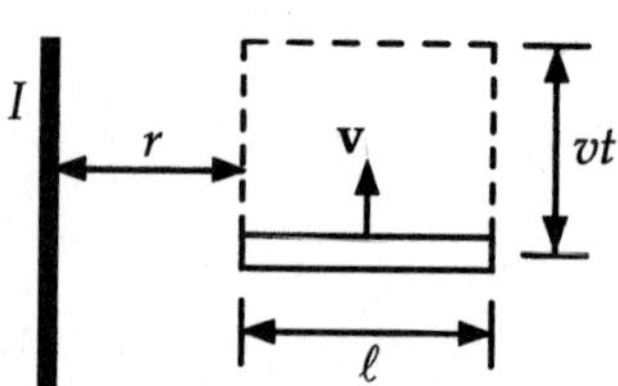

FIG. P31.63

$\Phi_B = \dfrac{\mu_0 I v t}{2\pi}\displaystyle\int_r^{r+\ell}\frac{dx}{x}$ where vt is the distance the bar has moved in time t.

Then, $|\varepsilon| = \dfrac{d\Phi_B}{dt} = \boxed{\dfrac{\mu_0 I v}{2\pi}\ln\left(1 + \dfrac{\ell}{r}\right)}$.

P31.64 The magnetic field at a distance x from a long wire is $B=\frac{\mu_0 I}{2\pi x}$. Find an expression for the flux through the loop.

$$d\Phi_B=\frac{\mu_0 I}{2\pi x}(\ell dx) \text{ so } \Phi_B=\frac{\mu_0 I\ell}{2\pi}\int_r^{r+w}\frac{dx}{x}=\frac{\mu_0 I\ell}{2\pi}\ln\left(1+\frac{w}{r}\right)$$

Therefore,
$$\varepsilon=-\frac{d\Phi_B}{dt}=\frac{\mu_0 I\ell v}{2\pi r}\frac{w}{(r+w)} \text{ and } I=\frac{\varepsilon}{R}=\boxed{\frac{\mu_0 I\ell v}{2\pi Rr}\frac{w}{(r+w)}}.$$

P31.65 We are given
$$\Phi_B=\left(6.00t^3-18.0t^2\right)\text{ T}\cdot\text{m}^2$$

and
$$\varepsilon=-\frac{d\Phi_B}{dt}=-18.0t^2+36.0t.$$

Maximum E occurs when
$$\frac{d\varepsilon}{dt}=-36.0t+36.0=0$$

which gives
$$t=1.00\text{ s}.$$

Therefore, the maximum current (at $t=1.00$ s) is
$$I=\frac{\varepsilon}{R}=\frac{(-18.0+36.0)\text{ V}}{3.00\ \Omega}=\boxed{6.00\text{ A}}.$$

P31.66 For the suspended mass, M: $\sum F=Mg-T=Ma$.

For the sliding bar, m: $\sum F=T-I\ell B=ma$, where
$$I=\frac{\varepsilon}{R}=\frac{B\ell v}{R}$$

$$Mg-\frac{B^2\ell^2 v}{R}=(m+M)a \text{ or } a=\frac{dv}{dt}=\frac{Mg}{m+M}-\frac{B^2\ell^2 v}{R(M+m)}$$

$$\int_0^v\frac{dv}{(\alpha-\beta v)}=\int_0^t dt \text{ where } \alpha=\frac{Mg}{M+m} \text{ and } \beta=\frac{B^2\ell^2}{R(M+m)}.$$

Therefore, the velocity varies with time as
$$v=\frac{\alpha}{\beta}\left(1-e^{-\beta t}\right)=\boxed{\frac{MgR}{B^2\ell^2}\left[1-e^{-B^2\ell^2 t/R(M+m)}\right]}.$$

P31.67 (a)
$$\varepsilon=-N\frac{d\Phi_B}{dt}=-NA\frac{dB}{dt}=-NA\frac{d}{dt}(\mu_0 nI) \text{ where } A=\text{area of coil}$$

$N=$ number of turns in coil

and $n=$ number of turns per unit length in solenoid.

Therefore,
$$|\varepsilon|=N\mu_0 An\frac{d}{dt}\left[4\sin(120\pi t)\right]=N\mu_0 An(480\pi)\cos(120\pi t)$$
$$|\varepsilon|=40\left(4\pi\times10^{-7}\right)\left[\pi(0.050\,0\text{ m})^2\right]\left(2.00\times10^3\right)(480\pi)\cos(120\pi t)$$
$$|\varepsilon|=\boxed{(1.19\text{ V})\cos(120\pi t)}$$

(b)
$$I=\frac{\Delta V}{R} \text{ and } \mathcal{P}=\Delta VI=\frac{(1.19\text{ V})^2\cos^2(120\pi t)}{8.00\ \Omega}$$

From
$$\cos^2\theta=\frac{1}{2}+\frac{1}{2}\cos 2\theta$$

the average value of $\cos^2\theta$ is $\frac{1}{2}$, so
$$\bar{\mathcal{P}}=\frac{1}{2}\frac{(1.19\text{ V})^2}{(8.00\ \Omega)}=\boxed{88.5\text{ mW}}.$$

***P31.68** (a) $\varepsilon = -N\frac{d}{dt}BA\cos\theta = -1\frac{d}{dt}B\frac{\theta a^2}{2}\cos 0° = -\frac{Ba^2}{2}\frac{d\theta}{dt} = -\frac{1}{2}Ba^2\omega = -\frac{1}{2}(0.5\text{ T})(0.5\text{ m})^2 2\text{ rad/s}$

$= -0.125\text{ V} = \boxed{0.125\text{ V clockwise}}$

The – sign indicates that the induced emf produces clockwise current, to make its own magnetic field into the page.

(b) At this instant $\theta = \omega t = 2\text{ rad/s}(0.25\text{ s}) = 0.5\text{ rad}$. The arc PQ has length $r\theta == (0.5\text{ rad})(0.5\text{ m}) = 0.25\text{ m}$. The length of the circuit is $0.5\text{ m} + 0.5\text{ m} + 0.25\text{ m} = 1.25\text{ m}$ its resistance is $1.25\text{ m}(5\ \Omega/\text{m}) = 6.25\ \Omega$. The current is $\frac{0.125\text{ V}}{6.25\ \Omega} = \boxed{0.020\,0\text{ A clockwise}}$.

***P31.69** Suppose the field is vertically down. When an electron is moving away from you the force on it is in the direction given by

$q\mathbf{v}\times\mathbf{B}_c$ as $-(\text{away})\times\text{down} = -$ $= -\text{left} = \text{right}$.

Therefore, the electrons circulate clockwise.

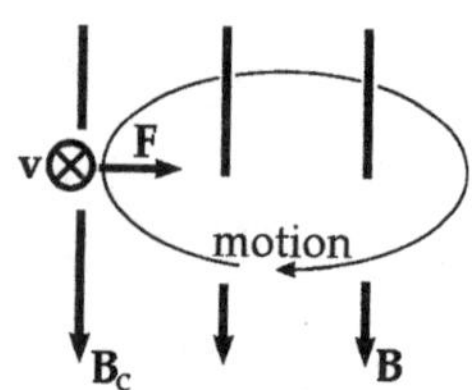

FIG. P31.69

(a) As the downward field increases, an emf is induced to produce some current that in turn produces an upward field. This current is directed counterclockwise, carried by negative electrons moving clockwise. Therefore the original electron motion speeds up.

(b) At the circumference, we have $\sum F_c = ma_c$: $\quad |q|vB_c\sin 90° = \frac{mv^2}{r}$

$mv = |q|rB_c$.

The increasing magnetic field $\mathbf{B}_{av}$ in the area enclosed by the orbit produces a tangential electric field according to

$\left|\oint \mathbf{E}\cdot d\mathbf{s}\right| = \left|-\frac{d}{dt}\mathbf{B}_{av}\cdot\mathbf{A}\right| \qquad E(2\pi r) = \pi r^2\frac{dB_{av}}{dt} \qquad E = \frac{r}{2}\frac{dB_{av}}{dt}$.

An electron feels a tangential force according to $\sum F_t = ma_t$: $\quad |q|E = m\frac{dv}{dt}$.

Then $\quad |q|\frac{r}{2}\frac{dB_{av}}{dt} = m\frac{dv}{dt} \qquad |q|\frac{r}{2}B_{av} = mv = |q|rB_c$

and $\quad B_{av} = 2B_c$.

P31.70 The induced emf is $\varepsilon = B\ell v$ where $B = \frac{\mu_0 I}{2\pi y}$, $v_f = v_i + gt = (9.80\text{ m/s}^2)t$, and

$y_f = y_i - \frac{1}{2}gt^2 = 0.800\text{ m} - (4.90\text{ m/s}^2)t^2$.

$$\varepsilon = \frac{(4\pi\times10^{-7}\text{ T}\cdot\text{m/A})(200\text{ A})}{2\pi[0.800\text{ m} - (4.90\text{ m/s}^2)t^2]}(0.300\text{ m})(9.80\text{ m/s}^2)t = \boxed{\frac{(1.18\times10^{-4})t}{[0.800 - 4.90t^2]}\text{ V}}$$

At $t = 0.300\text{ s}$, $\varepsilon = \frac{(1.18\times10^{-4})(0.300)}{[0.800 - 4.90(0.300)^2]}\text{ V} = \boxed{98.3\ \mu\text{V}}$.

P31.71 The magnetic field produced by the current in the straight wire is perpendicular to the plane of the coil at all points within the coil. The magnitude of the field is $B = \frac{\mu_0 I}{2\pi r}$. Thus, the flux linkage is

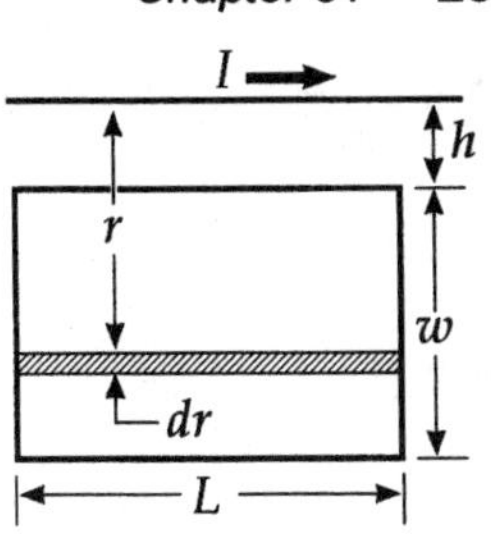

FIG. P31.71

$$N\Phi_B = \frac{\mu_0 NIL}{2\pi}\int_h^{h+w}\frac{dr}{r} = \frac{\mu_0 NI_{\max}L}{2\pi}\ln\left(\frac{h+w}{h}\right)\sin(\omega t+\phi).$$

Finally, the induced emf is

$$\varepsilon = -\frac{\mu_0 NI_{\max}L\omega}{2\pi}\ln\left(1+\frac{w}{h}\right)\cos(\omega t+\phi)$$

$$\varepsilon = -\frac{\left(4\pi\times 10^{-7}\right)(100)(50.0)(0.200\text{ m})\left(200\pi\text{ s}^{-1}\right)}{2\pi}\ln\left(1+\frac{5.00\text{ cm}}{5.00\text{ cm}}\right)\cos(\omega t+\phi)$$

$$\varepsilon = \boxed{-(87.1\text{ mV})\cos(200\pi t+\phi)}$$

The term $\sin(\omega t+\phi)$ in the expression for the current in the straight wire does not change appreciably when ωt changes by 0.10 rad or less. Thus, the current does not change appreciably during a time interval

$$\Delta t < \frac{0.10}{\left(200\pi\text{ s}^{-1}\right)} = 1.6\times 10^{-4}\text{ s}.$$

We define a critical length, $c\Delta t = \left(3.00\times 10^{8}\text{ m/s}\right)\left(1.6\times 10^{-4}\text{ s}\right) = 4.8\times 10^{4}\text{ m}$ equal to the distance to which field changes could be propagated during an interval of 1.6×10^{-4} s. This length is so much larger than any dimension of the coil or its distance from the wire that, although we consider the straight wire to be infinitely long, we can also safely ignore the field propagation effects in the vicinity of the coil. Moreover, the phase angle can be considered to be constant along the wire in the vicinity of the coil.

If the frequency w were much larger, say, $200\pi\times 10^{5}\text{ s}^{-1}$, the corresponding critical length would be only 48 cm. In this situation propagation effects would be important and the above expression for ε would require modification. As a "rule of thumb" we can consider field propagation effects for circuits of laboratory size to be negligible for frequencies, $f = \frac{\omega}{2\pi}$, that are less than about 10^{6} Hz.

P31.72 $\Phi_B = BA\cos\theta$ $\frac{d\Phi_B}{dt} = -\omega BA\sin\theta$;

$I \propto -\sin\theta$

$\tau \propto IB\sin\theta$ $\boxed{\propto -\sin^2\theta}$

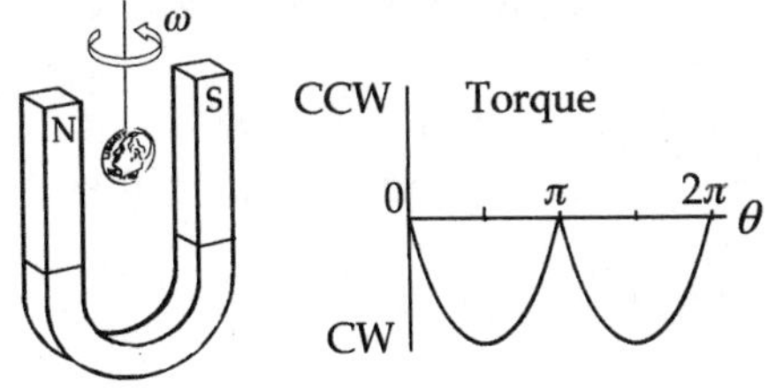

FIG. P31.72

ANSWERS TO EVEN PROBLEMS

P31.2 0.800 mA

P31.4 (a) see the solution; (b) 3.79 mV; (c) 28.0 mV

P31.6 78.5 μs

P31.8 (a) $\frac{\mu_0 n\pi r_2^2}{2R}\frac{\Delta I}{\Delta t}$ counterclockwise; (b) $\frac{\mu_0^2 n\pi r_2^2}{4r_1 R}\frac{\Delta I}{\Delta t}$; (c) upward

P31.10 $-14.2\text{ mV}\cos(120t)$

P31.12 61.8 mV

P31.14 (a) see the solution; (b) 625 m/s

P31.16 see the solution

P31.18 13.3 mA counterclockwise in the lower loop and clockwise in the upper loop.

P31.20 1.00 m/s

P31.22 (a) 500 mA; (b) 2.00 W; (c) 2.00 W

P31.24 24.1 V with the outer contact positive

P31.26 121 mA clockwise

P31.28 (a) to the right; (b) to the right; (c) to the right; (d) into the paper

P31.30 negative; see the solution

P31.32 (a) 8.00×10^{-21} N downward perpendicular to r_1; (b) 1.33 s

P31.34 (a) $(9.87\text{ mV/m})\cos(100\pi t)$; (b) clockwise

P31.36 (a) $(19.6\text{ V})\sin(314t)$; (b) 19.6 V

P31.38 see the solution

P31.40 (a) 1.60 V; (b) 0; (c) no change; (d) and (e) see the solution

P31.42 both are correct; see the solution

P31.44 $(-4.39\hat{\mathbf{i}}-1.76\hat{\mathbf{j}})10^{11}\text{ m/s}^2$

P31.46 $-(7.22\text{ mV})\cos(2\pi 523\,t/\text{s})$

P31.48 (a) 43.8 A; (b) 38.3 W

P31.50 (a) 3.50 A up in 2 Ω and 1.40 A up in 5 Ω; (b) 34.3 W; (c) 4.29 N

P31.52 see the solution

P31.54 (a) $\frac{\pi B_{max}^2 R^4 b\omega^2}{16\rho}$; (b) 4 times larger; (c) 4 times larger; (d) 16 times larger

P31.56 (a) see the solution; (b) 0.250 T

P31.58 see the solution

P31.60 (a) $C\pi a^2 K$; (b) the upper plate; (c) see the solution

P31.62 (a) 97.4 nV; (b) clockwise

P31.64 $\frac{\mu_0 I\ell v}{2\pi Rr}\frac{w}{(r+w)}$

P31.66 $\frac{MgR}{B^2\ell^2}\left[1-e^{-B^2\ell^2 t/R(M+m)}\right]$

P31.68 (a) 0.125 V to produce clockwise current; (b) 20.0 mA clockwise

P31.70 $\frac{1.18\times10^{-4}}{0.800-4.90t^2}$; 98.3 μV

P31.72 see the solution

32

Inductance

CHAPTER OUTLINE

ANSWERS TO QUESTIONS

Q32.1 The emf induced in an inductor is opposite to the direction of the changing current. For example, in a simple *RL* circuit with current flowing clockwise, if the current in the circuit increases, the inductor will generate an emf to oppose the increasing current.

Q32.2 The coil has an inductance regardless of the nature of the current in the circuit. Inductance depends only on the coil geometry and its construction. Since the current is constant, the self-induced emf in the coil is zero, and the coil does not affect the steady-state current. (We assume the resistance of the coil is negligible.)

Q32.3 The inductance of a coil is determined by (a) the geometry of the coil and (b) the "contents" of the coil. This is similar to the parameters that determine the capacitance of a capacitor and the resistance of a resistor. With an inductor, the most important factor in the geometry is the number of turns of wire, or turns per unit length. By the "contents" we refer to the material in which the inductor establishes a magnetic field, notably the magnetic properties of the core around which the wire is wrapped.

Q32.4 If the first set of turns is wrapped clockwise around a spool, wrap the second set counter-clockwise, so that the coil produces negligible magnetic field. Then the inductance of each set of turns effectively negates the inductive effects of the other set.

Q32.5 After the switch is closed, the back emf will not exceed that of the battery. If this were the case, then the current in the circuit would change direction to counterclockwise. Just after the switch is opened, the back emf can be much larger than the battery emf, to temporarily maintain the clockwise current in a spark.

Q32.6 The current decreases not instantaneously but over some span of time. The faster the decrease in the current, the larger will be the emf generated in the inductor. A spark can appear at the switch as it is opened because the self-induced voltage is a maximum at this instant. The voltage can therefore briefly cause dielectric breakdown of the air between the contacts.

Q32.7 When it is being opened. When the switch is initially standing open, there is no current in the circuit. Just after the switch is then closed, the inductor tends to maintain the zero-current condition, and there is very little chance of sparking. When the switch is standing closed, there is current in the circuit. When the switch is then opened, the current rapidly decreases. The induced emf is created in the inductor, and this emf tends to maintain the original current. Sparking occurs as the current bridges the air gap between the contacts of the switch.

Q32.8 A physicist's list of constituents of the universe in 1829 might include matter, light, heat, the stuff of stars, charge, momentum, and several other entries. Our list today might include the quarks, electrons, muons, tauons, and neutrinos of matter; gravitons of gravitational fields; photons of electric and magnetic fields; W and Z particles; gluons; energy; momentum; angular momentum; charge; baryon number; three different lepton numbers; upness; downness; strangeness; charm; topness; and bottomness. Alternatively, the relativistic interconvertability of mass and energy, and of electric and magnetic fields, can be used to make the list look shorter. Some might think of the conserved quantities energy, momentum, ... bottomness as properties of matter, rather than as things with their own existence. The idea of a field is not due to Henry, but rather to Faraday, to whom Henry personally demonstrated self-induction. Still the thesis stated in the question has an important germ of truth. Henry precipitated a basic change if he did not cause it. The biggest difference between the two lists is that the 1829 list does not include fields and today's list does.

Q32.9 The energy stored in the magnetic field of an inductor is proportional to the square of the current. Doubling I makes $U = \frac{1}{2}LI^2$ get four times larger.

Q32.10 The energy stored in a capacitor is proportional to the square of the electric field, and the energy stored in an induction coil is proportional to the square of the magnetic field. The capacitor's energy is proportional to its capacitance, which depends on its geometry and the dielectric material inside. The coil's energy is proportional to its inductance, which depends on its geometry and the core material. On the other hand, we can think of Henry's discovery of self-inductance as fundamentally new. Before a certain school vacation at the Albany Academy about 1830, one could visualize the universe as consisting of only one thing, matter. All the forms of energy then known (kinetic, gravitational, elastic, internal, electrical) belonged to chunks of matter. But the energy that temporarily maintains a current in a coil after the battery is removed is not energy that belongs to any bit of matter. This energy is vastly larger than the kinetic energy of the drifting electrons in the wires. This energy belongs to the magnetic field around the coil. Beginning in 1830, Nature has forced us to admit that the universe consists of matter and also of fields, massless and invisible, known only by their effects.

Q32.11 The inductance of the series combination of inductor L_1 and inductor L_2 is $L_1 + L_2 + M_{12}$, where M_{12} is the mutual inductance of the two coils. It can be defined as the emf induced in coil two when the current in coil one changes at one ampere per second, due to the magnetic field of coil one producing flux through coil two. The coils can be arranged to have large mutual inductance, as by winding them onto the same core. The coils can be arranged to have negligible mutual inductance, as separate toroids do.

Q32.12 The mutual inductance of two loops in free space—that is, ignoring the use of cores—is a maximum if the loops are coaxial. In this way, the maximum flux of the primary loop will pass through the secondary loop, generating the largest possible emf given the changing magnetic field due to the first. The mutual inductance is a minimum if the magnetic field of the first coil lies in the plane of the second coil, producing no flux through the area the second coil encloses.

Q32.13 The answer depends on the orientation of the solenoids. If they are coaxial, such as two solenoids end-to-end, then there certainty will be mutual induction. If, however, they are oriented in such a way that the magnetic field of one coil does not go through turns of the second coil, then there will be no mutual induction. Consider the case of two solenoids physically arranged in a "T" formation, but still connected electrically in series. The magnetic field lines of the first coil will not produce any net flux in the second coil, and thus no mutual induction will be present.

Q32.14 When the capacitor is fully discharged, the current in the circuit is a maximum. The inductance of the coil is making the current continue to flow. At this time the magnetic field of the coil contains all the energy that was originally stored in the charged capacitor. The current has just finished discharging the capacitor and is proceeding to charge it up again with the opposite polarity.

Q32.15 The oscillations would eventually decrease, but perhaps with very small damping. The original potential energy would be converted to internal energy within the wires. Such a situation constitutes an *RLC* circuit. Remember that a real battery generally contains an internal resistance.

Q32.16 If $R > \sqrt{\frac{4L}{C}}$, then the oscillator is overdamped—it will not oscillate. If $R < \sqrt{\frac{4L}{C}}$, then the oscillator is underdamped and can go through several cycles of oscillation before the radiated signal falls below background noise.

Q32.17 The condition for critical damping must be investigated to design a circuit for a particular purpose. For example, in building a radio receiver, one would want to construct the receiving circuit so that it is underdamped. Then it can oscillate in resonance and detect the desired signal. Conversely, when designing a probe to measure a changing signal, such free oscillations are undesirable. An electrical vibration in the probe would constitute "ringing" of the system, where the probe would measure an additional signal—that of the probe itself! In this case, one would want to design a probe that is critically damped or overdamped, so that the only signal measured is the one under study. Critical damping represents the threshold between underdamping and overdamping. One must know the condition for it to meet the design criteria for a project.

Q32.18 An object cannot exert a net force on itself. An object cannot create momentum out of nothing. A coil can induce an emf in itself. When it does so, the actual forces acting on charges in different parts of the loop add as vectors to zero. The term electromotive force does not refer to a force, but to a voltage.

SOLUTIONS TO PROBLEMS

Section 32.1 **Self-Inductance**

P32.1 $$|\varepsilon| = L\frac{\Delta I}{\Delta t} = \left(3.00\times10^{-3}\text{ H}\right)\left(\frac{1.50\text{ A}-0.200\text{ A}}{0.200\text{ s}}\right) = 1.95\times10^{-2}\text{ V} = \boxed{19.5\text{ mV}}$$

P32.2 Treating the telephone cord as a solenoid, we have:

$$L = \frac{\mu_0 N^2 A}{\ell} = \frac{\left(4\pi\times10^{-7}\text{ T}\cdot\text{m/A}\right)(70.0)^2\,\pi\left(6.50\times10^{-3}\text{ m}\right)^2}{0.600\text{ m}} = \boxed{1.36\ \mu\text{H}}.$$

P32.3 $$\bar{\varepsilon} = -L\frac{\Delta I}{\Delta t} = (-2.00\text{ H})\left(\frac{0-0.500\text{ A}}{0.010\,0\text{ s}}\right)\left(\frac{1\text{ V}\cdot\text{s}}{1\text{ H}\cdot\text{A}}\right) = \boxed{100\text{ V}}$$

P32.4 $$L = \frac{N\Phi_B}{I} \to \Phi_B = \frac{LI}{N} = \boxed{240\text{ nT}\cdot\text{m}^2}\text{ through each turn}$$

P32.5 $$\varepsilon_{\text{back}} = -\varepsilon = L\frac{dI}{dt} = L\frac{d}{dt}\left(I_{\max}\sin\omega t\right) = L\omega I_{\max}\cos\omega t = \left(10.0\times10^{-3}\right)(120\pi)(5.00)\cos\omega t$$

$$\varepsilon_{\text{back}} = (6.00\pi)\cos(120\pi t) = \boxed{(18.8\text{ V})\cos(377t)}$$

P32.6 From $|\varepsilon| = L\left(\frac{\Delta I}{\Delta t}\right)$, we have $L = \frac{\varepsilon}{(\Delta I/\Delta t)} = \frac{24.0 \times 10^{-3}\ \text{V}}{10.0\ \text{A/s}} = 2.40 \times 10^{-3}\ \text{H}$.

From $L = \frac{N\Phi_B}{I}$, we have $\Phi_B = \frac{LI}{N} = \frac{(2.40 \times 10^{-3}\ \text{H})(4.00\ \text{A})}{500} = \boxed{19.2\ \mu\text{T}\cdot\text{m}^2}$.

P32.7 $L = \frac{\mu_0 N^2 A}{\ell} = \frac{\mu_0 (420)^2 (3.00 \times 10^{-4})}{0.160} = 4.16 \times 10^{-4}\ \text{H}$

$\varepsilon = -L\frac{dI}{dt} \rightarrow \frac{dI}{dt} = \frac{-\varepsilon}{L} = \frac{-175 \times 10^{-6}\ \text{V}}{4.16 \times 10^{-4}\ \text{H}} = \boxed{-0.421\ \text{A/s}}$

P32.8 $|\varepsilon| = L\frac{dI}{dt} = (90.0 \times 10^{-3})\frac{d}{dt}(t^2 - 6t)\ \text{V}$

(a) At $t = 1.00$ s, $\varepsilon = \boxed{360\ \text{mV}}$

(b) At $t = 4.00$ s, $\varepsilon = \boxed{180\ \text{mV}}$

(c) $\varepsilon = (90.0 \times 10^{-3})(2t - 6) = 0$

when $\boxed{t = 3.00\ \text{s}}$.

P32.9 (a) $B = \mu_0 nI = \mu_0\left(\frac{450}{0.120}\right)(0.040\,0\ \text{A}) = \boxed{188\ \mu\text{T}}$

(b) $\Phi_B = BA = \boxed{3.33 \times 10^{-8}\ \text{T}\cdot\text{m}^2}$

(c) $L = \frac{N\Phi_B}{I} = \boxed{0.375\ \text{mH}}$

(d) $\boxed{B \text{ and } \Phi_B \text{ are proportional to current; } L \text{ is independent of current}}$

P32.10 (a) $L = \frac{\mu_0 N^2 A}{\ell} = \frac{\mu_0 (120)^2 \pi (5.00 \times 10^{-3})^2}{0.090\,0} = \boxed{15.8\ \mu\text{H}}$

(b) $\Phi_B' = \frac{\mu_m}{\mu_0}\Phi_B \rightarrow L = \frac{\mu_m N^2 A}{\ell} = 800(1.58 \times 10^{-5}\ \text{H}) = \boxed{12.6\ \text{mH}}$

***P32.11** We can directly find the self inductance of the solenoid:

$\varepsilon = -L\frac{dI}{dt}$ $\quad +0.08\ \text{V} = -L\frac{0 - 1.8\ \text{A}}{0.12\ \text{s}}$ $\quad L = 5.33 \times 10^{-3}\ \text{Vs/A} = \frac{\mu_0 N^2 A}{\ell}$.

Here $A = \pi r^2$, $200\ \text{m} = N2\pi r$, and $\ell = N(10^{-3}\ \text{m})$. Eliminating extra unknowns step by step, we have

$$5.33 \times 10^{-3}\ \text{Vs/A} = \frac{\mu_0 N^2 \pi r^2}{\ell} = \frac{\mu_0 N^2 \pi}{\ell}\left(\frac{200\ \text{m}}{2\pi N}\right)^2 = \frac{\mu_0\, 40\,000\ \text{m}^2}{4\pi \ell} = \frac{10^{-7}(40\,000\ \text{m}^2)\text{Tm}}{\ell \quad \text{A}}$$

$\ell = \frac{4 \times 10^{-3}\ \text{WbmA}}{5.33 \times 10^{-3}\ \text{AVs}} = \boxed{0.750\ \text{m}}$

P32.12 $L = \frac{N\Phi_B}{I} = \frac{NBA}{I} \approx \frac{NA}{I} \cdot \frac{\mu_0 NI}{2\pi R} = \boxed{\frac{\mu_0 N^2 A}{2\pi R}}$

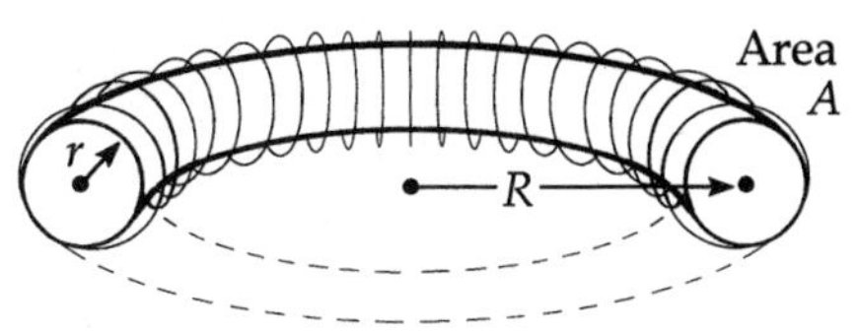

FIG. P32.12

P32.13 $\varepsilon = \varepsilon_0 e^{-kt} = -L\frac{dI}{dt}$

$$dI = -\frac{\varepsilon_0}{L}e^{-kt}dt$$

If we require $I \to 0$ as $t \to \infty$, the solution is $I = \frac{\varepsilon_0}{kL}e^{-kt} = \frac{dq}{dt}$

$$Q = \int I dt = \int_0^{\infty} \frac{\varepsilon_0}{kL}e^{-kt}dt = -\frac{\varepsilon_0}{k^2 L} \qquad \boxed{|Q| = \frac{\varepsilon_0}{k^2 L}}.$$

Section 32.2 *RL* Circuits

P32.14 $I = \frac{\varepsilon}{R}\left(1 - e^{-Rt/L}\right)$: $\quad 0.900\frac{\varepsilon}{R} = \frac{\varepsilon}{R}\left[1 - e^{-R(3.00\text{ s})/2.50\text{ H}}\right]$

$$\exp\left(-\frac{R(3.00\text{ s})}{2.50\text{ H}}\right) = 0.100$$

$$R = \frac{2.50\text{ H}}{3.00\text{ s}}\ln 10.0 = \boxed{1.92\ \Omega}$$

P32.15 (a) At time t, $\quad I(t) = \frac{\varepsilon\left(1 - e^{-t/\tau}\right)}{R}$

where $\quad \tau = \frac{L}{R} = 0.200\text{ s}$.

After a long time, $\quad I_{max} = \frac{\varepsilon\left(1 - e^{-\infty}\right)}{R} = \frac{\varepsilon}{R}$.

At $I(t) = 0.500 I_{max}$ $\quad (0.500)\frac{\varepsilon}{R} = \frac{\varepsilon\left(1 - e^{-t/0.200\text{ s}}\right)}{R}$

so $\quad 0.500 = 1 - e^{-t/0.200\text{ s}}$.

Isolating the constants on the right, $\quad \ln\left(e^{-t/0.200\text{ s}}\right) = \ln(0.500)$

and solving for t, $\quad -\frac{t}{0.200\text{ s}} = -0.693$

or $\quad t = \boxed{0.139\text{ s}}$.

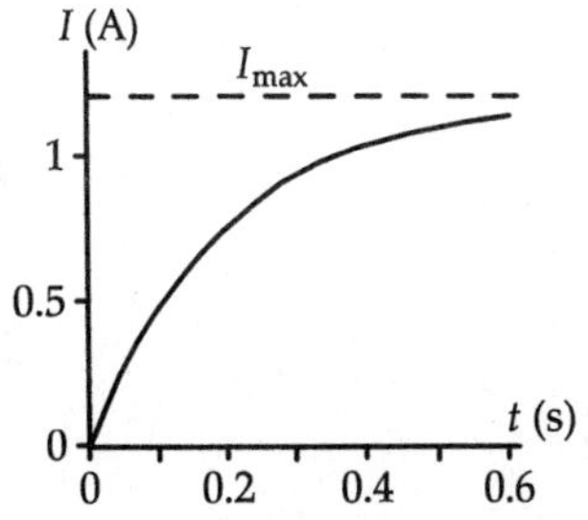

FIG. P32.15

(b) Similarly, to reach 90% of I_{max}, $\quad 0.900 = 1 - e^{-t/\tau}$

and $\quad t = -\tau\ln(1 - 0.900)$.

Thus, $\quad t = -(0.200\text{ s})\ln(0.100) = \boxed{0.461\text{ s}}$.

P32.16 Taking $\tau = \frac{L}{R}$, $\quad I = I_0 e^{-t/\tau}$: $\quad \frac{dI}{dt} = I_0 e^{-t/\tau}\left(-\frac{1}{\tau}\right)$

$IR + L\frac{dI}{dt} = 0$ will be true if $\quad I_0 R e^{-t/\tau} + L\left(I_0 e^{-t/\tau}\right)\left(-\frac{1}{\tau}\right) = 0$.

Because $\tau = \frac{L}{R}$, we have agreement with $0 = 0$.

P32.17 (a) $\tau = \frac{L}{R} = 2.00 \times 10^{-3}\text{ s} = \boxed{2.00\text{ ms}}$

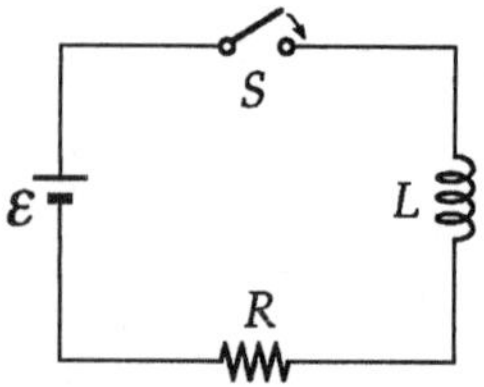

FIG. P32.17

(b) $I = I_{\max}\left(1 - e^{-t/\tau}\right) = \left(\frac{6.00\text{ V}}{4.00\ \Omega}\right)\left(1 - e^{-0.250/2.00}\right) = \boxed{0.176\text{ A}}$

(c) $I_{\max} = \frac{\varepsilon}{R} = \frac{6.00\text{ V}}{4.00\ \Omega} = \boxed{1.50\text{ A}}$

(d) $0.800 = 1 - e^{-t/2.00\text{ ms}} \rightarrow t = -(2.00\text{ ms})\ln(0.200) = \boxed{3.22\text{ ms}}$

P32.18 $I = \frac{\varepsilon}{R}\left(1 - e^{-t/\tau}\right) = \frac{120}{9.00}\left(1 - e^{-1.80/7.00}\right) = 3.02\text{ A}$

$\Delta V_R = IR = (3.02)(9.00) = 27.2\text{ V}$

$\Delta V_L = \varepsilon - \Delta V_R = 120 - 27.2 = \boxed{92.8\text{ V}}$

P32.19 *Note*: It may not be correct to call the voltage or emf across a coil a "potential difference." Electric potential can only be defined for a conservative electric field, and not for the electric field around an inductor.

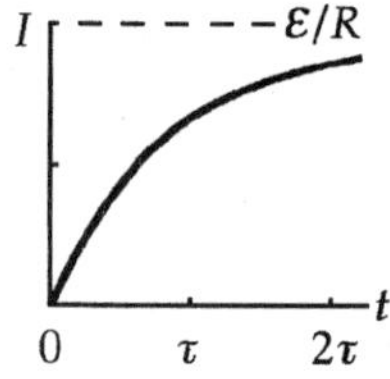

FIG. P32.19

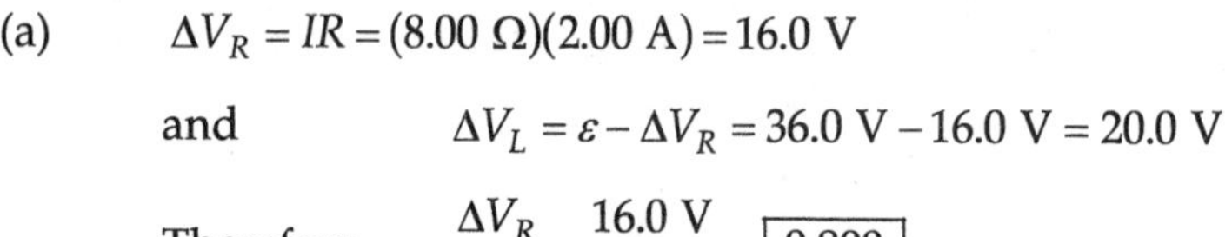

(a) $\Delta V_R = IR = (8.00\ \Omega)(2.00\text{ A}) = 16.0\text{ V}$

and $\quad \Delta V_L = \varepsilon - \Delta V_R = 36.0\text{ V} - 16.0\text{ V} = 20.0\text{ V}$.

Therefore, $\quad \frac{\Delta V_R}{\Delta V_L} = \frac{16.0\text{ V}}{20.0\text{ V}} = \boxed{0.800}$.

(b) $\Delta V_R = IR = (4.50\text{ A})(8.00\ \Omega) = 36.0\text{ V}$

$\Delta V_L = \varepsilon - \Delta V_R = \boxed{0}$

P32.20 After a long time, $12.0\text{ V} = (0.200\text{ A})R$. Thus, $R = 60.0\ \Omega$. Now, $\tau = \frac{L}{R}$ gives

$L = \tau R = \left(5.00 \times 10^{-4}\text{ s}\right)(60.0\text{ V/A}) = \boxed{30.0\text{ mH}}$.

P32.21 $I = I_{\max}\left(1 - e^{-t/\tau}\right)$: $\quad \frac{dI}{dt} = -I_{\max}\left(e^{-t/\tau}\right)\left(-\frac{1}{\tau}\right)$

$\tau = \frac{L}{R} = \frac{15.0\text{ H}}{30.0\ \Omega} = 0.500\text{ s}$: $\quad \frac{dI}{dt} = \frac{R}{L} I_{\max} e^{-t/\tau}$ and $I_{\max} = \frac{\varepsilon}{R}$

(a) $t = 0$: $\frac{dI}{dt} = \frac{R}{L} I_{\max} e^0 = \frac{\varepsilon}{L} = \frac{100\text{ V}}{15.0\text{ H}} = \boxed{6.67\text{ A/s}}$

(b) $t = 1.50\text{ s}$: $\frac{dI}{dt} = \frac{\varepsilon}{L} e^{-t/\tau} = (6.67\text{ A/s})e^{-1.50/(0.500)} = (6.67\text{ A/s})e^{-3.00} = \boxed{0.332\text{ A/s}}$

P32.22 $I = I_{max}\left(1 - e^{-t/\tau}\right)$: $\quad 0.980 = 1 - e^{-3.00\times10^{-3}/\tau}$

$$0.020\,0 = e^{-3.00\times10^{-3}/\tau}$$

$$\tau = -\frac{3.00\times10^{-3}}{\ln(0.020\,0)} = 7.67\times10^{-4}\text{ s}$$

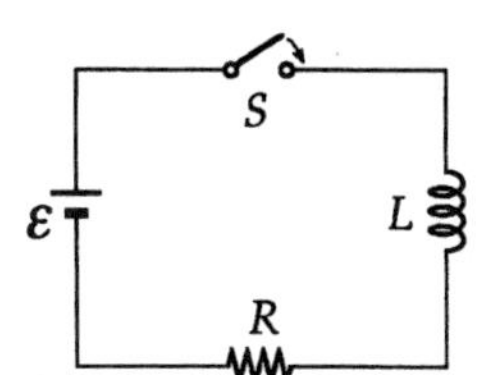

FIG. P32.22

$\tau = \frac{L}{R}$, so $\quad L = \tau R = \left(7.67\times10^{-4}\right)(10.0) = \boxed{7.67\text{ mH}}$

P32.23 Name the currents as shown. By Kirchhoff's laws:

$$I_1 = I_2 + I_3 \qquad (1)$$

$$+10.0\text{ V} - 4.00I_1 - 4.00I_2 = 0 \qquad (2)$$

$$+10.0\text{ V} - 4.00I_1 - 8.00I_3 - (1.00)\frac{dI_3}{dt} = 0 \qquad (3)$$

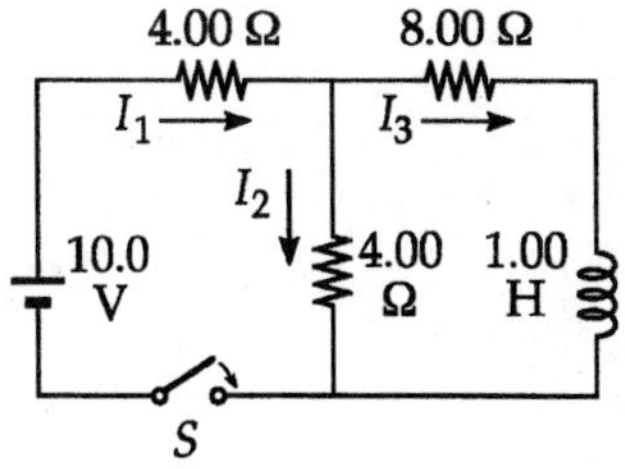

FIG. P32.23

From (1) and (2), $\quad +10.0 - 4.00I_1 - 4.00I_1 + 4.00I_3 = 0$

and $\quad I_1 = 0.500I_3 + 1.25\text{ A}$.

Then (3) becomes $\quad 10.0\text{ V} - 4.00(0.500I_3 + 1.25\text{ A}) - 8.00I_3 - (1.00)\frac{dI_3}{dt} = 0$

$$(1.00\text{ H})\left(\frac{dI_3}{dt}\right) + (10.0\ \Omega)I_3 = 5.00\text{ V}.$$

We solve the differential equation using Equations 32.6 and 32.7:

$$I_3(t) = \left(\frac{5.00\text{ V}}{10.0\ \Omega}\right)\left[1 - e^{-(10.0\ \Omega)t/1.00\text{ H}}\right] = \boxed{(0.500\text{ A})\left[1 - e^{-10t/\text{s}}\right]}$$

$$I_1 = 1.25 + 0.500I_3 = \boxed{1.50\text{ A} - (0.250\text{ A})e^{-10t/\text{s}}}$$

P32.24 (a) Using $\tau = RC = \frac{L}{R}$, we get $R = \sqrt{\frac{L}{C}} = \sqrt{\frac{3.00\text{ H}}{3.00\times10^{-6}\text{ F}}} = 1.00\times10^3\ \Omega = \boxed{1.00\text{ k}\Omega}$.

(b) $\tau = RC = \left(1.00\times10^3\ \Omega\right)\left(3.00\times10^{-6}\text{ F}\right) = 3.00\times10^{-3}\text{ s} = \boxed{3.00\text{ ms}}$

P32.25 For $t \le 0$, the current in the inductor is $\boxed{\text{zero}}$. At $t = 0$, it starts to grow from zero toward 10.0 A with time constant

$$\tau = \frac{L}{R} = \frac{(10.0\text{ mH})}{(100\ \Omega)} = 1.00\times10^{-4}\text{ s}.$$

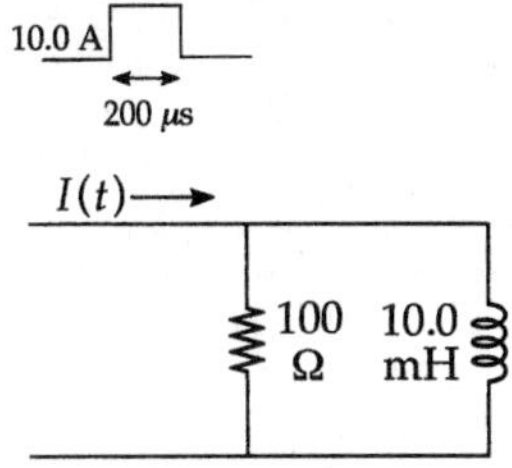

FIG. P32.25

For $0 \le t \le 200\ \mu\text{s}$, $I = I_{max}\left(1 - e^{-t/\tau}\right) = \boxed{(10.0\text{ A})\left(1 - e^{-10\,000t/\text{s}}\right)}$.

At $t = 200\ \mu\text{s}$, $I = (10.00\text{ A})\left(1 - e^{-2.00}\right) = 8.65\text{ A}$.

Thereafter, it decays exponentially as $I = I_0e^{-t'/\tau}$, so for $t \ge 200\ \mu\text{s}$,

$$I = (8.65\text{ A})e^{-10\,000(t - 200\ \mu\text{s})/\text{s}} = (8.65\text{ A})e^{-10\,000t/\text{s} + 2.00} = \left(8.65e^{2.00}\text{ A}\right)e^{-10\,000t/\text{s}} = \boxed{(63.9\text{ A})e^{-10\,000t/\text{s}}}.$$

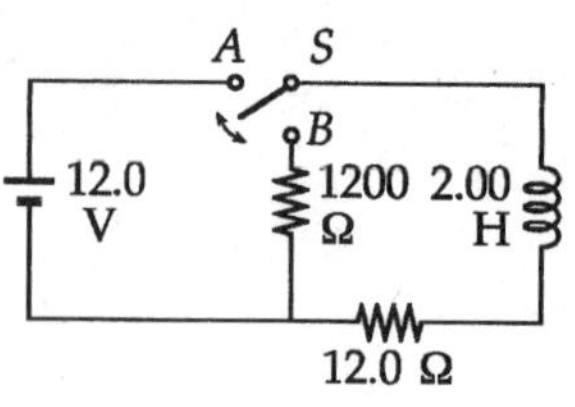

FIG. P32.26

P32.26 (a) $I = \frac{\varepsilon}{R} = \frac{12.0\text{ V}}{12.0\ \Omega} = \boxed{1.00\text{ A}}$

(b) Initial current is 1.00 A: $\Delta V_{12} = (1.00\text{ A})(12.00\ \Omega) = \boxed{12.0\text{ V}}$

$$\Delta V_{1\,200} = (1.00\text{ A})(1\,200\ \Omega) = \boxed{1.20\text{ kV}}$$

$$\Delta V_L = \boxed{1.21\text{ kV}}.$$

(c) $I = I_{\max} e^{-Rt/L}$: $\quad \frac{dI}{dt} = -I_{\max}\frac{R}{L}e^{-Rt/L}$

and $\quad -L\frac{dI}{dt} = \Delta V_L = I_{\max} R e^{-Rt/L}$.

Solving $\quad 12.0\text{ V} = (1\,212\text{ V})e^{-1\,212t/2.00}$

so $\quad 9.90 \times 10^{-3} = e^{-606t}$.

Thus, $\quad \boxed{t = 7.62\text{ ms}}$.

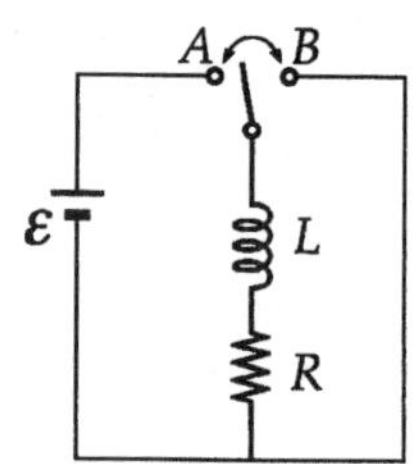

FIG. P32.27

P32.27 $\tau = \frac{L}{R} = \frac{0.140}{4.90} = 28.6\text{ ms}$

$I_{\max} = \frac{\varepsilon}{R} = \frac{6.00\text{ V}}{4.90\ \Omega} = 1.22\text{ A}$

(a) $I = I_{\max}\left(1 - e^{-t/\tau}\right)$ so $0.220 = 1.22\left(1 - e^{-t/\tau}\right)$

$e^{-t/\tau} = 0.820$: $\quad t = -\tau \ln(0.820) = \boxed{5.66\text{ ms}}$

(b) $I = I_{\max}\left(1 - e^{-10.0/0.028\,6}\right) = (1.22\text{ A})\left(1 - e^{-350}\right) = \boxed{1.22\text{ A}}$

(c) $I = I_{\max} e^{-t/\tau}$ and $0.160 = 1.22 e^{-t/\tau}$

so $\quad t = -\tau \ln(0.131) = \boxed{58.1\text{ ms}}$.

P32.28 (a) For a series connection, both inductors carry equal currents at every instant, so $\frac{dI}{dt}$ is the same for both. The voltage across the pair is

$L_{eq}\frac{dI}{dt} = L_1\frac{dI}{dt} + L_2\frac{dI}{dt}$ so $\boxed{L_{eq} = L_1 + L_2}$.

(b) $L_{eq}\frac{dI}{dt} = L_1\frac{dI_1}{dt} = L_2\frac{dI_2}{dt} = \Delta V_L$ where $I = I_1 + I_2$ and $\frac{dI}{dt} = \frac{dI_1}{dt} + \frac{dI_2}{dt}$.

Thus, $\frac{\Delta V_L}{L_{eq}} = \frac{\Delta V_L}{L_1} + \frac{\Delta V_L}{L_2}$ and $\boxed{\frac{1}{L_{eq}} = \frac{1}{L_1} + \frac{1}{L_2}}$.

(c) $L_{eq}\frac{dI}{dt} + R_{eq}I = L_1\frac{dI}{dt} + IR_1 + L_2\frac{dI}{dt} + IR_2$

Now I and $\frac{dI}{dt}$ are separate quantities under our control, so functional equality requires

both $\boxed{L_{eq} = L_1 + L_2 \quad \text{and} \quad R_{eq} = R_1 + R_2}$.

continued on next page

(d) $$\Delta V = L_{\text{eq}}\frac{dI}{dt} + R_{\text{eq}}I = L_1\frac{dI_1}{dt} + R_1 I_1 = L_2\frac{dI_2}{dt} + R_2 I_2 \text{ where } I = I_1 + I_2 \text{ and } \frac{dI}{dt} = \frac{dI_1}{dt} + \frac{dI_2}{dt}.$$

We may choose to keep the currents constant in time. Then, $\frac{1}{R_{\text{eq}}} = \frac{1}{R_1} + \frac{1}{R_2}$.

We may choose to make the current swing through 0. Then, $\frac{1}{L_{\text{eq}}} = \frac{1}{L_1} + \frac{1}{L_2}$.

This equivalent coil with resistance will be equivalent to the pair of real inductors for all other currents as well.

Section 32.3 Energy in a Magnetic Field

P32.29 $$L = \frac{N\Phi_B}{I} = \frac{200\left(3.70\times10^{-4}\right)}{1.75} = 42.3 \text{ mH so } U = \frac{1}{2}LI^2 = \frac{1}{2}(0.423 \text{ H})(1.75 \text{ A})^2 = \boxed{0.064\,8 \text{ J}}.$$

P32.30 (a) The magnetic energy density is given by

$$\mu = \frac{B^2}{2\mu_0} = \frac{(4.50 \text{ T})^2}{2\left(1.26\times10^{-6} \text{ T}\cdot\text{m/A}\right)} = \boxed{8.06\times10^6 \text{ J/m}^3}.$$

(b) The magnetic energy stored in the field equals u times the volume of the solenoid (the volume in which B is non-zero).

$$U = uV = \left(8.06\times10^6 \text{ J/m}^3\right)\left[(0.260 \text{ m})\pi(0.031\,0 \text{ m})^2\right] = \boxed{6.32 \text{ kJ}}$$

P32.31 $$L = \mu_0\frac{N^2A}{\ell} = \mu_0\frac{(68.0)^2\left[\pi\left(0.600\times10^{-2}\right)^2\right]}{0.080\,0} = 8.21\ \mu\text{H}$$

$$U = \frac{1}{2}LI^2 = \frac{1}{2}\left(8.21\times10^{-6} \text{ H}\right)(0.770 \text{ A})^2 = \boxed{2.44\ \mu\text{J}}$$

P32.32 (a) $$U = \frac{1}{2}LI^2 = \frac{1}{2}L\left(\frac{\varepsilon}{2R}\right)^2 = \frac{L\varepsilon^2}{8R^2} = \frac{(0.800)(500)^2}{8(30.0)^2} = \boxed{27.8 \text{ J}}$$

(b) $$I = \left(\frac{\varepsilon}{R}\right)\left[1 - e^{-(R/L)t}\right] \quad \text{so} \quad \frac{\varepsilon}{2R} = \left(\frac{\varepsilon}{R}\right)\left[1 - e^{-(R/L)t}\right] \rightarrow e^{-(R/L)t} = \frac{1}{2}$$

$$\frac{R}{L}t = \ln 2 \quad \text{so} \quad t = \frac{L}{R}\ln 2 = \frac{0.800}{30.0}\ln 2 = \boxed{18.5 \text{ ms}}$$

P32.33 $$u = \epsilon_0\frac{E^2}{2} = \boxed{44.2 \text{ nJ/m}^3} \qquad u = \frac{B^2}{2\mu_0} = \boxed{995\ \mu\text{J/m}^3}$$

***P32.34** $$\int_0^\infty e^{-2Rt/L}dt = -\frac{L}{2R}\int_0^\infty e^{-2Rt/L}\left(\frac{-2Rdt}{L}\right) = -\frac{L}{2R}e^{-2Rt/L}\Big|_0^\infty = -\frac{L}{2R}\left(e^{-\infty} - e^0\right) = \frac{L}{2R}(0-1) = \boxed{\frac{L}{2R}}$$

P32.35 (a) $U = \frac{1}{2}LI^2 = \frac{1}{2}(4.00\text{ H})(0.500\text{ A})^2 \quad U = \boxed{0.500\text{ J}}$

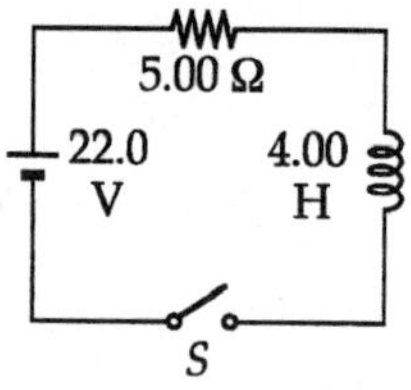

(b) When the current is 1.00 A,
Kirchhoff's loop rule reads $+22.0\text{ V} - (1.00\text{ A})(5.00\ \Omega) - \Delta V_L = 0$.
Then $\Delta V_L = 17.0\text{ V}$.
The power being stored in the inductor is

$$I\Delta V_L = (1.00\text{ A})(17.0\text{ V}) = \boxed{17.0\text{ W}}.$$

5.00 Ω
22.0 V
4.00 H
S

FIG. P32.35

(c) $\mathcal{P} = I\Delta V = (0.500\text{ A})(22.0\text{ V}) \quad \mathcal{P} = \boxed{11.0\text{ W}}$

P32.36 From Equation 32.7, $I = \frac{\mathcal{E}}{R}\left(1 - e^{-Rt/L}\right)$.

(a) The maximum current, after a long time t, is $I = \frac{\mathcal{E}}{R} = 2.00\text{ A}$.

At that time, the inductor is fully energized and $\mathcal{P} = I(\Delta V) = (2.00\text{ A})(10.0\text{ V}) = \boxed{20.0\text{ W}}$.

(b) $\mathcal{P}_{\text{lost}} = I^2R = (2.00\text{ A})^2(5.00\ \Omega) = \boxed{20.0\text{ W}}$

(c) $\mathcal{P}_{\text{inductor}} = I\left(\Delta V_{\text{drop}}\right) = \boxed{0}$

(d) $U = \frac{LI^2}{2} = \frac{(10.0\text{ H})(2.00\text{ A})^2}{2} = \boxed{20.0\text{ J}}$

P32.37 We have $u = \epsilon_0 \frac{E^2}{2}$ and $u = \frac{B^2}{2\mu_0}$.

Therefore $\epsilon_0 \frac{E^2}{2} = \frac{B^2}{2\mu_0}$ so $B^2 = \epsilon_0 \mu_0 E^2$

$$B = E\sqrt{\epsilon_0 \mu_0} = \frac{6.80 \times 10^5\text{ V/m}}{3.00 \times 10^8\text{ m/s}} = \boxed{2.27 \times 10^{-3}\text{ T}}.$$

P32.38 The total magnetic energy is the volume integral of the energy density, $u = \frac{B^2}{2\mu_0}$.

Because B changes with position, u is not constant. For $B = B_0\left(\frac{R}{r}\right)^2$, $u = \left(\frac{B_0^2}{2\mu_0}\right)\left(\frac{R}{r}\right)^4$.

Next, we set up an expression for the magnetic energy in a spherical shell of radius r and thickness dr. Such a shell has a volume $4\pi r^2 dr$, so the energy stored in it is

$$dU = u\left(4\pi r^2 dr\right) = \left(\frac{2\pi B_0^2 R^4}{\mu_0}\right)\frac{dr}{r^2}.$$

We integrate this expression for $r = R$ to $r = \infty$ to obtain the total magnetic energy outside the sphere. This gives

$$U = \boxed{\frac{2\pi B_0^2 R^3}{\mu_0}} = \frac{2\pi\left(5.00 \times 10^{-5}\text{ T}\right)^2\left(6.00 \times 10^6\text{ m}\right)^3}{\left(1.26 \times 10^{-6}\text{ T}\cdot\text{m/A}\right)} = \boxed{2.70 \times 10^{18}\text{ J}}.$$

Section 32.4 **Mutual Inductance**

P32.39 $I_1(t) = I_{max}e^{-\alpha t}\sin\omega t$ with $I_{max} = 5.00\text{ A}$, $\alpha = 0.025\,0\text{ s}^{-1}$, and $\omega = 377\text{ rad/s}$

$$\frac{dI_1}{dt} = I_{max}e^{-\alpha t}(-\alpha\sin\omega t + \omega\cos\omega t).$$

At $t = 0.800\text{ s}$,

$$\frac{dI_1}{dt} = (5.00\text{ A/s})e^{-0.020\,0}\left[-(0.025\,0)\sin(0.800(377)) + 377\cos(0.800(377))\right]$$

$$\frac{dI_1}{dt} = 1.85\times10^{3}\text{ A/s}.$$

Thus, $\varepsilon_2 = -M\dfrac{dI_1}{dt}$: $\quad M = \dfrac{-\varepsilon_2}{dI_1/dt} = \dfrac{+3.20\text{ V}}{1.85\times10^{3}\text{ A/s}} = \boxed{1.73\text{ mH}}$.

P32.40 $\varepsilon_2 = -M\dfrac{dI_1}{dt} = -(1.00\times10^{-4}\text{ H})(1.00\times10^{4}\text{ A/s})\cos(1\,000t)$

$(\varepsilon_2)_{max} = \boxed{1.00\text{ V}}$

P32.41 $M = \left|\dfrac{\varepsilon_2}{dI_1/dt}\right| = \dfrac{96.0\text{ mV}}{1.20\text{ A/s}} = \boxed{80.0\text{ mH}}$

P32.42 Assume the long wire carries current I. Then the magnitude of the magnetic field it generates at distance x from the wire is $B = \dfrac{\mu_0 I}{2\pi x}$, and this field passes perpendicularly through the plane of the loop. The flux through the loop is

$$\Phi_B = \int \mathbf{B}\cdot d\mathbf{A} = \int B\,dA = \int B(\ell\,dx) = \frac{\mu_0 I\ell}{2\pi}\int_{0.400\text{ mm}}^{1.70\text{ mm}}\frac{dx}{x} = \frac{\mu_0 I\ell}{2\pi}\ln\left(\frac{1.70}{0.400}\right).$$

The mutual inductance between the wire and the loop is then

$$M = \frac{N_2\Phi_{12}}{I_1} = \frac{N_2\mu_0 I\ell}{2\pi I}\ln\left(\frac{1.70}{0.400}\right) = \frac{N_2\mu_0\ell}{2\pi}(1.45) = \frac{1(4\pi\times10^{-7}\text{ T}\cdot\text{m/A})(2.70\times10^{-3}\text{ m})}{2\pi}(1.45)$$

$M = 7.81\times10^{-10}\text{ H} = \boxed{781\text{ pH}}$

P32.43 (a) $M = \dfrac{N_B\Phi_{BA}}{I_A} = \dfrac{700(90.0\times10^{-6})}{3.50} = \boxed{18.0\text{ mH}}$

(b) $L_A = \dfrac{\Phi_A}{I_A} = \dfrac{400(300\times10^{-6})}{3.50} = \boxed{34.3\text{ mH}}$

(c) $\varepsilon_B = -M\dfrac{dI_A}{dt} = -(18.0\text{ mH})(0.500\text{ A/s}) = \boxed{-9.00\text{ mV}}$

***P32.44** The large coil produces this field at the center of the small coil: $\frac{N_1\mu_0 I_1 R_1^2}{2\left(x^2+R_1^2\right)^{3/2}}$. The field is normal to the area of the small coil and nearly uniform over this area, so it produces flux

$\Phi_{12} = \frac{N_1\mu_0 I_1 R_1^2}{2\left(x^2+R_1^2\right)^{3/2}}\pi R_2^2$ through the face area of the small coil. When current I_1 varies, this is the emf induced in the small coil:

$$\varepsilon_2 = -N_2\frac{d}{dt}\frac{N_1\mu_0 R_1^2\pi R_2^2}{2\left(x^2+R_1^2\right)^{3/2}}I_1 = -\frac{N_1N_2\pi\mu_0 R_1^2R_2^2}{2\left(x^2+R_1^2\right)^{3/2}}\frac{dI_1}{dt} = -M\frac{dI_1}{dt} \text{ so } \boxed{M = \frac{N_1N_2\pi\mu_0R_1^2R_2^2}{2\left(x^2+R_1^2\right)^{3/2}}}.$$

P32.45 With $I = I_1 + I_2$, the voltage across the pair is:

$$\Delta V = -L_1\frac{dI_1}{dt} - M\frac{dI_2}{dt} = -L_2\frac{dI_2}{dt} - M\frac{dI_1}{dt} = -L_{eq}\frac{dI}{dt}.$$

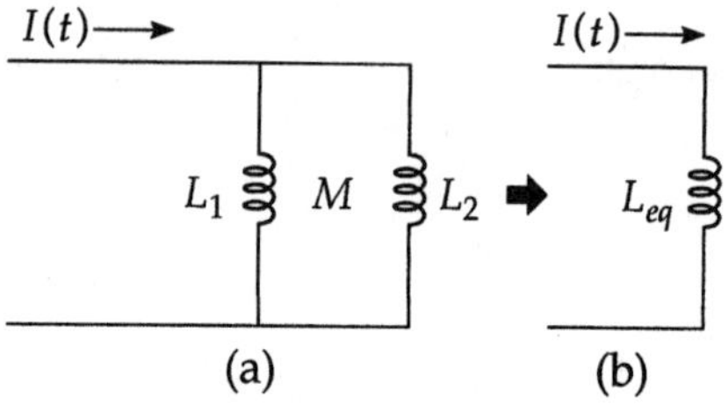

So, $$-\frac{dI_1}{dt} = \frac{\Delta V}{L_1} + \frac{M}{L_1}\frac{dI_2}{dt}$$

and $$-L_2\frac{dI_2}{dt} + \frac{M(\Delta V)}{L_1} + \frac{M^2}{L_1}\frac{dI_2}{dt} = \Delta V$$

$$\left(-L_1L_2 + M^2\right)\frac{dI_2}{dt} = \Delta V\left(L_1 - M\right). \quad [1]$$

By substitution, $$-\frac{dI_2}{dt} = \frac{\Delta V}{L_2} + \frac{M}{L_2}\frac{dI_1}{dt}$$

leads to $$\left(-L_1L_2 + M^2\right)\frac{dI_1}{dt} = \Delta V\left(L_2 - M\right). \quad [2]$$

Adding [1] to [2], $$\left(-L_1L_2 + M^2\right)\frac{dI}{dt} = \Delta V\left(L_1 + L_2 - 2M\right).$$

So, $$L_{eq} = -\frac{\Delta V}{dI/dt} = \boxed{\frac{L_1L_2 - M^2}{L_1 + L_2 - 2M}}.$$

I(t)→ ; L_1 M L_2 ➡ L_{eq} ; I(t)→
(a) (b)

FIG. P32.45

Section 32.5 **Oscillations in an LC Circuit**

P32.46 At different times, $(U_C)_{max} = (U_L)_{max}$ so $\left[\frac{1}{2}C(\Delta V)^2\right]_{max} = \left(\frac{1}{2}LI^2\right)_{max}$

$$I_{max} = \sqrt{\frac{C}{L}}(\Delta V)_{max} = \sqrt{\frac{1.00\times10^{-6}\text{ F}}{10.0\times10^{-3}\text{ H}}}(40.0\text{ V}) = \boxed{0.400\text{ A}}.$$

P32.47 $\left[\frac{1}{2}C(\Delta V)^2\right]_{\max} = \left(\frac{1}{2}LI^2\right)_{\max}$ so $(\Delta V_C)_{\max} = \sqrt{\frac{L}{C}}I_{\max} = \sqrt{\frac{20.0\times10^{-3}\text{ H}}{0.500\times10^{-6}\text{ F}}}(0.100\text{ A}) = \boxed{20.0\text{ V}}$

P32.48 When the switch has been closed for a long time, battery, resistor, and coil carry constant current $I_{\max} = \frac{\varepsilon}{R}$. When the switch is opened, current in battery and resistor drops to zero, but the coil carries this same current for a moment as oscillations begin in the LC loop.

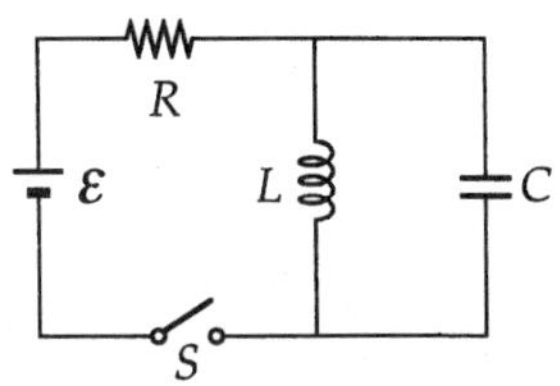

FIG. P32.50

We interpret the problem to mean that the voltage amplitude of these oscillations is ΔV, in $\frac{1}{2}C(\Delta V)^2 = \frac{1}{2}LI_{\max}^2$.

Then, $L = \frac{C(\Delta V)^2}{I_{\max}^2} = \frac{C(\Delta V)^2R^2}{\varepsilon^2} = \frac{(0.500\times10^{-6}\text{ F})(150\text{ V})^2(250\ \Omega)^2}{(50.0\text{ V})^2} = \boxed{0.281\text{ H}}$.

P32.49 This radio is a radiotelephone on a ship, according to frequency assignments made by international treaties, laws, and decisions of the National Telecommunications and Information Administration.

The resonance frequency is $f_0 = \frac{1}{2\pi\sqrt{LC}}$.

Thus, $C = \frac{1}{(2\pi f_0)^2 L} = \frac{1}{\left[2\pi(6.30\times10^6\text{ Hz})\right]^2(1.05\times10^{-6}\text{ H})} = \boxed{608\text{ pF}}$.

P32.50 $f = \frac{1}{2\pi\sqrt{LC}}$: $L = \frac{1}{(2\pi f)^2 C} = \frac{1}{[2\pi(120)]^2(8.00\times10^{-6})} = \boxed{0.220\text{ H}}$

P32.51 (a) $f = \frac{1}{2\pi\sqrt{LC}} = \frac{1}{2\pi\sqrt{(0.082\,0\text{ H})(17.0\times10^{-6}\text{ F})}} = \boxed{135\text{ Hz}}$

(b) $Q = Q_{\max}\cos\omega t = (180\ \mu\text{C})\cos(847\times0.001\,00) = \boxed{119\ \mu\text{C}}$

(c) $I = \frac{dQ}{dt} = -\omega Q_{\max}\sin\omega t = -(847)(180)\sin(0.847) = \boxed{-114\text{ mA}}$

P32.52 (a) $f = \frac{1}{2\pi\sqrt{LC}} = \frac{1}{2\pi\sqrt{(0.100\text{ H})(1.00\times10^{-6}\text{ F})}} = \boxed{503\text{ Hz}}$

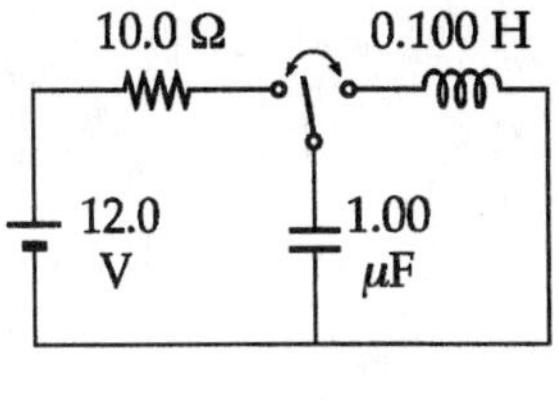

(b) $Q = C\varepsilon = (1.00\times10^{-6}\text{ F})(12.0\text{ V}) = \boxed{12.0\ \mu\text{C}}$

(c) $\frac{1}{2}C\varepsilon^2 = \frac{1}{2}LI_{\max}^2$

$I_{\max} = \varepsilon\sqrt{\frac{C}{L}} = 12\text{ V}\sqrt{\frac{1.00\times10^{-6}\text{ F}}{0.100\text{ H}}} = \boxed{37.9\text{ mA}}$

FIG. P32.52

(d) At all times $U = \frac{1}{2}C\varepsilon^2 = \frac{1}{2}(1.00\times10^{-6}\text{ F})(12.0\text{ V})^2 = \boxed{72.0\ \mu\text{J}}$.

P32.53 $$\omega = \frac{1}{\sqrt{LC}} = \frac{1}{\sqrt{(3.30\text{ H})(840\times10^{-12}\text{ F})}} = 1.899\times10^{4}\text{ rad/s}$$

$$Q = Q_{\max}\cos\omega t,\ I = \frac{dQ}{dt} = -\omega Q_{\max}\sin\omega t$$

(a) $$U_C = \frac{Q^2}{2C} = \frac{\left(\left[105\times10^{-6}\right]\cos\left[\left(1.899\times10^{4}\text{ rad/s}\right)\left(2.00\times10^{-3}\text{ s}\right)\right]\right)^2}{2\left(840\times10^{-12}\right)} = \boxed{6.03\text{ J}}$$

(b) $$U_L = \frac{1}{2}LI^2 = \frac{1}{2}L\omega^2Q_{\max}^2\sin^2(\omega t) = \frac{Q_{\max}^2\sin^2(\omega t)}{2C}$$

$$U_L = \frac{\left(105\times10^{-6}\text{ C}\right)^2\sin^2\left[\left(1.899\times10^{4}\text{ rad/s}\right)\left(2.00\times10^{-3}\text{ s}\right)\right]}{2\left(840\times10^{-12}\text{ F}\right)} = \boxed{0.529\text{ J}}$$

(c) $$U_{\text{total}} = U_C + U_L = \boxed{6.56\text{ J}}$$

Section 32.6 The *RLC* Circuit

P32.54 (a) $$\omega_d = \sqrt{\frac{1}{LC} - \left(\frac{R}{2L}\right)^2} = \sqrt{\frac{1}{\left(2.20\times10^{-3}\right)\left(1.80\times10^{-6}\right)} - \left(\frac{7.60}{2\left(2.20\times10^{-3}\right)}\right)^2} = 1.58\times10^{4}\text{ rad/s}$$

Therefore, $f_d = \frac{\omega_d}{2\pi} = \boxed{2.51\text{ kHz}}$.

(b) $$R_c = \sqrt{\frac{4L}{C}} = \boxed{69.9\ \Omega}$$

P32.55 (a) $$\omega_0 = \frac{1}{\sqrt{LC}} = \frac{1}{\sqrt{(0.500)\left(0.100\times10^{-6}\right)}} = \boxed{4.47\text{ krad/s}}$$

(b) $$\omega_d = \sqrt{\frac{1}{LC} - \left(\frac{R}{2L}\right)^2} = \boxed{4.36\text{ krad/s}}$$

(c) $$\frac{\Delta\omega}{\omega_0} = \boxed{2.53\%\text{ lower}}$$

P32.56 Choose to call positive current clockwise in Figure 32.21. It drains charge from the capacitor according to $I = -\frac{dQ}{dt}$. A clockwise trip around the circuit then gives

$$+\frac{Q}{C} - IR - L\frac{dI}{dt} = 0$$

$+\frac{Q}{C} + \frac{dQ}{dt}R + L\frac{d}{dt}\frac{dQ}{dt} = 0$, identical with Equation 32.28.

***P32.57** The period of damped oscillation is $T = \frac{2\pi}{\omega_d}$. After one oscillation the charge returning to the capacitor is $Q = Q_{max}e^{-RT/2L} = Q_{max}e^{-2\pi R/2L\omega_d}$. The energy is proportional to the charge squared, so after one oscillation it is $U = U_0 e^{-2\pi R/L\omega_d} = 0.99U_0$. Then

$$e^{2\pi R/L\omega_d} = \frac{1}{0.99}$$

$$\frac{2\pi 2\ \Omega}{L\omega_d} = \ln(1.010\,1) = 0.001\,005$$

$$L\omega_d = \frac{2\pi 2\ \Omega}{0.001\,005} = 1\,250\ \Omega = L\left(\frac{1}{LC} - \frac{R^2}{4L^2}\right)^{1/2}$$

$$1.563 \times 10^6\ \Omega^2 = \frac{L}{C} - \frac{(2\ \Omega)^2}{4}$$

$$\frac{L}{C} = 1.563 \times 10^6\ \Omega^2$$

We are also given

$$\omega = 2\pi \times 10^3/\text{s} = \frac{1}{\sqrt{LC}}$$

$$LC = \frac{1}{(2\pi \times 10^3/\text{s})^2} = 2.533 \times 10^{-8}\ \text{s}^2$$

Solving simultaneously,

$$C = 2.533 \times 10^{-8}\ \text{s}^2/L$$

$$\frac{L^2}{2.533 \times 10^{-8}\ \text{s}^2} = 1.563 \times 10^6\ \Omega^2 \quad \boxed{L = 0.199\ \text{H}}$$

$$C = \frac{2.533 \times 10^{-8}\ \text{s}^2}{0.199\ \text{H}} = \boxed{127\ \text{nF} = C}$$

P32.58 (a) $Q = Q_{max}e^{-Rt/2L}\cos\omega_d t$ so $I_{max} \propto e^{-Rt/2L}$

$0.500 = e^{-Rt/2L}$ and $\frac{Rt}{2L} = -\ln(0.500)$

$$t = -\frac{2L}{R}\ln(0.500) = \boxed{0.693\left(\frac{2L}{R}\right)}$$

(b) $U_0 \propto Q_{max}^2$ and $U = 0.500U_0$ so $Q = \sqrt{0.500}Q_{max} = 0.707Q_{max}$

$$t = -\frac{2L}{R}\ln(0.707) = \boxed{0.347\left(\frac{2L}{R}\right)} \text{ (half as long)}$$

Additional Problems

***P32.59** (a) Let Q represent the magnitude of the opposite charges on the plates of a parallel plate capacitor, the two plates having area A and separation d. The negative plate creates electric field $\mathbf{E} = \frac{Q}{2\epsilon_0 A}$ toward itself. It exerts on the positive plate force $\mathbf{F} = \frac{Q^2}{2\epsilon_0 A}$ toward the negative plate. The total field between the plates is $\frac{Q}{\epsilon_0 A}$. The energy density is $u_E = \frac{1}{2}\epsilon_0 E^2 = \frac{1}{2}\epsilon_0 \frac{Q^2}{\epsilon_0^2 A^2} = \frac{Q^2}{2\epsilon_0 A^2}$. Modeling this as a negative or inward pressure, we have for the force on one plate $F = PA = \frac{Q^2}{2\epsilon_0 A^2}$, in agreement with our first analysis.

(b) The lower of the two current sheets shown creates above it magnetic field $\mathbf{B} = \frac{\mu_0 J_s}{2}\left(-\hat{\mathbf{k}}\right)$. Let ℓ and w represent the length and width of each sheet. The upper sheet carries current $J_s w$ and feels force

$$\mathbf{F} = I\boldsymbol{\ell} \times \mathbf{B} = J_s w\ell \frac{\mu_0 J_s}{2}\hat{\mathbf{i}} \times \left(-\hat{\mathbf{k}}\right) = \frac{\mu_0 w\ell J_s^2}{2}\hat{\mathbf{j}}.$$

The force per area is $P = \frac{F}{\ell w} = \boxed{\frac{\mu_0 J_s^2}{2}}$.

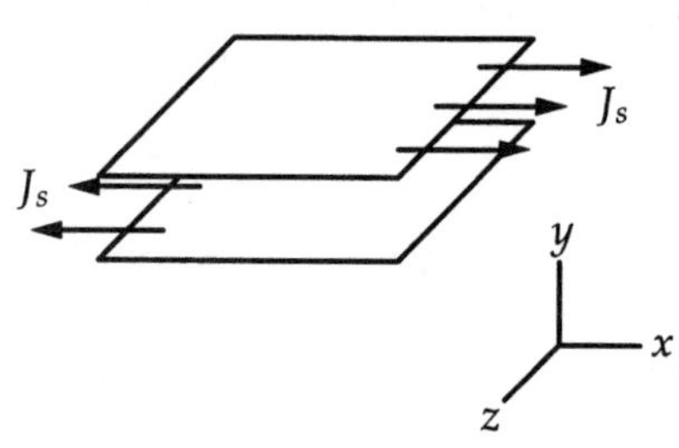

FIG. P32.59(b)

(c) Between the two sheets the total magnetic field is $\frac{\mu_0 J_s}{2}\left(-\hat{\mathbf{k}}\right) + \frac{\mu_0 J_s}{2}\left(-\hat{\mathbf{k}}\right) = \mu_0 J_s \hat{\mathbf{k}}$, with magnitude $\boxed{B = \mu_0 J_s}$. Outside the space they enclose, the fields of the separate sheets are in opposite directions and add to $\boxed{\text{zero}}$.

(d) $$u_B = \frac{1}{2\mu_0}B^2 = \frac{\mu_0^2 J_s^2}{2\mu_0} = \boxed{\frac{\mu_0 J_s^2}{2}}$$

(e) This energy density agrees with the magnetic pressure found in part (b).

P32.60 With $Q = Q_{max}$ at $t = 0$, the charge on the capacitor at any time is $Q = Q_{max}\cos\omega t$ where $\omega = \frac{1}{\sqrt{LC}}$.

The energy stored in the capacitor at time t is then

$$U = \frac{Q^2}{2C} = \frac{Q_{max}^2}{2C}\cos^2\omega t = U_0\cos^2\omega t.$$

When $U = \frac{1}{4}U_0$, $\quad \cos\omega t = \frac{1}{2}$ $\quad$ and $\quad \omega t = \frac{1}{3}\pi\,\text{rad}$.

Therefore, $\quad \frac{t}{\sqrt{LC}} = \frac{\pi}{3}$ $\quad$ or $\quad \frac{t^2}{LC} = \frac{\pi^2}{9}$.

The inductance is then: $\quad L = \boxed{\frac{9t^2}{\pi^2 C}}$.

P32.61 (a) $\varepsilon_L = -L\dfrac{dI}{dt} = -(1.00\text{ mH})\dfrac{d(20.0t)}{dt} = \boxed{-20.0\text{ mV}}$

(b) $Q = \int_0^t I dt = \int_0^t (20.0t)dt = 10.0t^2$

$$\Delta V_C = \frac{-Q}{C} = \frac{-10.0t^2}{1.00\times10^{-6}\text{ F}} = \boxed{-\left(10.0\text{ MV/s}^2\right)t^2}$$

(c) When $\dfrac{Q^2}{2C} \ge \dfrac{1}{2}LI^2$, or $\dfrac{\left(-10.0t^2\right)^2}{2\left(1.00\times10^{-6}\right)} \ge \dfrac{1}{2}\left(1.00\times10^{-3}\right)(20.0t)^2$,

then $100t^4 \ge \left(400\times10^{-9}\right)t^2$. The earliest time this is true is at $t = \sqrt{4.00\times10^{-9}}\text{ s} = \boxed{63.2\ \mu\text{s}}$.

P32.62 (a) $\varepsilon_L = -L\dfrac{dI}{dt} = -L\dfrac{d}{dt}(Kt) = \boxed{-LK}$

(b) $I = \dfrac{dQ}{dt}$, so $Q = \int_0^t I dt = \int_0^t Kt dt = \dfrac{1}{2}Kt^2$

and $\Delta V_C = \dfrac{-Q}{C} = \boxed{-\dfrac{Kt^2}{2C}}$

(c) When $\dfrac{1}{2}C(\Delta V_C)^2 = \dfrac{1}{2}LI^2$, $\dfrac{1}{2}C\left(\dfrac{K^2t^4}{4C^2}\right) = \dfrac{1}{2}L\left(K^2t^2\right)$

Thus $t = \boxed{2\sqrt{LC}}$

P32.63 $\dfrac{1}{2}\dfrac{Q^2}{C} = \dfrac{1}{2C}\left(\dfrac{Q}{2}\right)^2 + \dfrac{1}{2}LI^2$ so $I = \sqrt{\dfrac{3Q^2}{4CL}}$.

The flux through each turn of the coil is $\Phi_B = \dfrac{LI}{N} = \boxed{\dfrac{Q}{2N}\sqrt{\dfrac{3L}{C}}}$

where N is the number of turns.

P32.64 $B = \dfrac{\mu_0 NI}{2\pi r}$

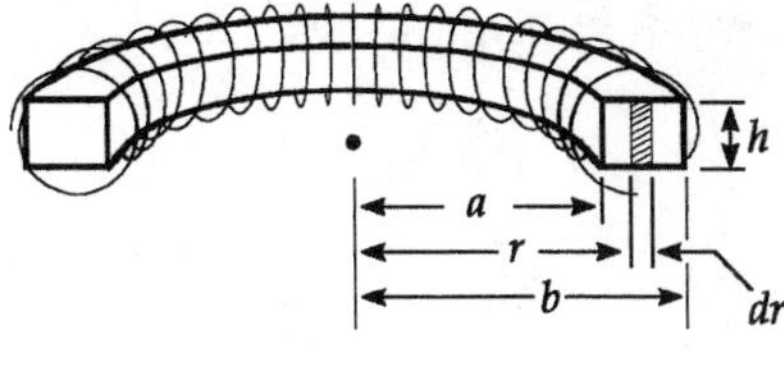

FIG. P32.64

(a) $\Phi_B = \int B dA = \int_a^b \dfrac{\mu_0 NI}{2\pi r}h dr = \dfrac{\mu_0 NIh}{2\pi}\int_a^b \dfrac{dr}{r} = \dfrac{\mu_0 NIh}{2\pi}\ln\left(\dfrac{b}{a}\right)$

$$L = \frac{N\Phi_B}{I} = \boxed{\frac{\mu_0 N^2 h}{2\pi}\ln\left(\frac{b}{a}\right)}$$

(b) $L = \dfrac{\mu_0(500)^2(0.010\,0)}{2\pi}\ln\left(\dfrac{12.0}{10.0}\right) = \boxed{91.2\ \mu\text{H}}$

(c) $L_{\text{appx}} = \dfrac{\mu_0 N^2}{2\pi}\left(\dfrac{A}{R}\right) = \dfrac{\mu_0(500)^2}{2\pi}\left(\dfrac{2.00\times10^{-4}\text{ m}^2}{0.110}\right) = \boxed{90.9\ \mu\text{H}}$, only 0.3% different.

P32.65 (a) At the center, $B = \frac{N\mu_0 IR^2}{2(R^2+0^2)^{3/2}} = \frac{N\mu_0 I}{2R}$.

So the coil creates flux through itself $\Phi_B = BA\cos\theta = \frac{N\mu_0 I}{2R}\pi R^2 \cos 0° = \frac{\pi}{2}N\mu_0 IR$.

When the current it carries changes, $\mathcal{E}_L = -N\frac{d\Phi_B}{dt} \approx -N\left(\frac{\pi}{2}\right)N\mu_0 R\frac{dI}{dt} = -L\frac{dI}{dt}$

so $\boxed{L \approx \frac{\pi}{2}N^2\mu_0 R}$.

(b) $2\pi r = 3(0.3 \text{ m})$ so $r \approx 0.14 \text{ m}$

$$L \approx \frac{\pi}{2}(1^2)(4\pi\times10^{-7} \text{ T}\cdot\text{m/A})(0.14 \text{ m}) = 2.8\times10^{-7} \text{ H}$$

$\boxed{L \sim 100 \text{ nH}}$

(c) $\frac{L}{R} = \frac{2.8\times10^{-7} \text{ V}\cdot\text{s/A}}{270 \text{ V/A}} = 1.0\times10^{-9} \text{ s}$ $\boxed{\frac{L}{R} \sim 1 \text{ ns}}$

P32.66 (a) If unrolled, the wire forms the diagonal of a 0.100 m (10.0 cm) rectangle as shown. The length of this rectangle is

$$L' = \sqrt{(9.80 \text{ m})^2 - (0.100 \text{ m})^2}.$$

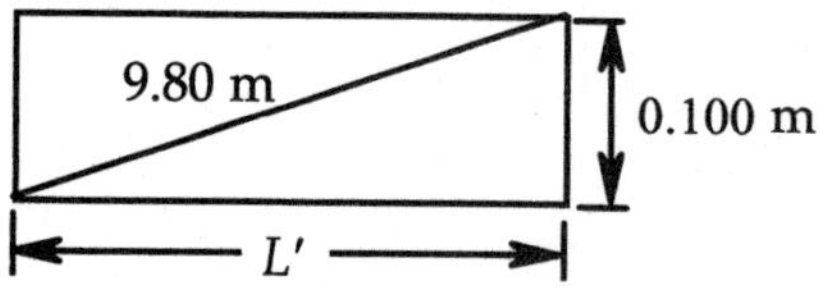

FIG. P32.66(a)

The mean circumference of each turn is $C = 2\pi r'$, where $r' = \frac{24.0+0.644}{2}$ mm is the mean radius of each turn. The number of turns is then:

$$N = \frac{L'}{C} = \frac{\sqrt{(9.80 \text{ m})^2 - (0.100 \text{ m})^2}}{2\pi[(24.0+0.644)/2]\times10^{-3} \text{ m}} = \boxed{127}.$$

(b) $$R = \frac{\rho\ell}{A} = \frac{(1.70\times10^{-8} \ \Omega\cdot\text{m})(10.0 \text{ m})}{\pi(0.322\times10^{-3} \text{ m})^2} = \boxed{0.522 \ \Omega}$$

(c) $$L = \frac{\mu N^2 A}{\ell'} = \frac{800\mu_0}{\ell'}\left(\frac{L'}{C}\right)^2 \pi(r')^2$$

$$L = \frac{800(4\pi\times10^{-7})}{0.100 \text{ m}}\left(\frac{\sqrt{(9.80 \text{ m})^2 - (0.100 \text{ m})^2}}{\pi(24.0+0.644)\times10^{-3} \text{ m}}\right)^2 \pi\left[\left(\frac{24.0+0.644}{2}\right)\times10^{-3} \text{ m}\right]^2$$

$L = 7.68\times10^{-2} \text{ H} = \boxed{76.8 \text{ mH}}$

P32.67 From Ampere's law, the magnetic field at distance $r \le R$ is found as:

$$B(2\pi r) = \mu_0 J\left(\pi r^2\right) = \mu_0\left(\frac{I}{\pi R^2}\right)\left(\pi r^2\right), \text{ or } B = \frac{\mu_0 I r}{2\pi R^2}.$$

The magnetic energy per unit length within the wire is then

$$\frac{U}{\ell} = \int_0^R \frac{B^2}{2\mu_0}(2\pi r\,dr) = \frac{\mu_0 I^2}{4\pi R^4}\int_0^R r^3\,dr = \frac{\mu_0 I^2}{4\pi R^4}\left(\frac{R^4}{4}\right) = \boxed{\frac{\mu_0 I^2}{16\pi}}.$$

This is independent of the radius of the wire.

P32.68 The primary circuit (containing the battery and solenoid) is an *RL* circuit with $R = 14.0\ \Omega$, and

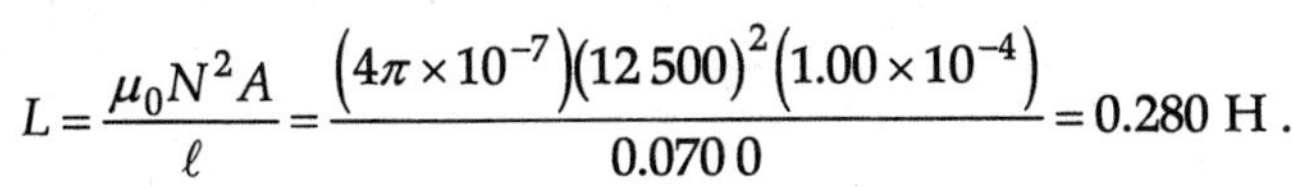

$$L = \frac{\mu_0 N^2 A}{\ell} = \frac{\left(4\pi\times10^{-7}\right)(12\,500)^2\left(1.00\times10^{-4}\right)}{0.070\,0} = 0.280\ \text{H}.$$

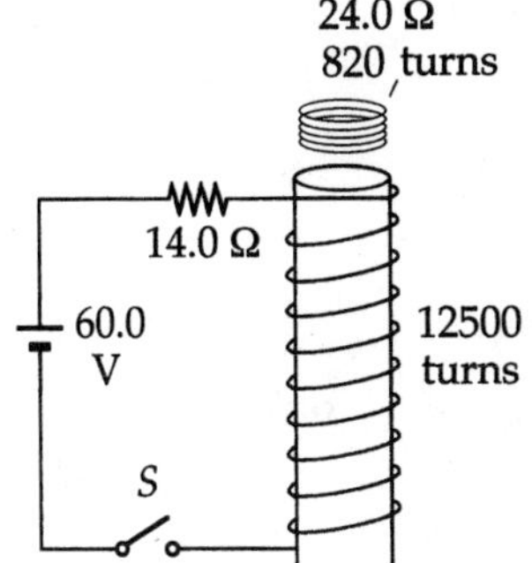

FIG. P32.68

(a) The time for the current to reach 63.2% of the maximum value is the time constant of the circuit:

$$\tau = \frac{L}{R} = \frac{0.280\ \text{H}}{14.0\ \Omega} = 0.020\,0\ \text{s} = \boxed{20.0\ \text{ms}}.$$

(b) The solenoid's average back emf is $\left|\bar{\varepsilon}_L\right| = L\left(\frac{\Delta I}{\Delta t}\right) = L\left(\frac{I_f - 0}{\Delta t}\right)$

where $I_f = 0.632 I_{\max} = 0.632\left(\frac{\Delta V}{R}\right) = 0.632\left(\frac{60.0\ \text{V}}{14.0\ \Omega}\right) = 2.71\ \text{A}.$

Thus, $\left|\bar{\varepsilon}_L\right| = (0.280\ \text{H})\left(\frac{2.71\ \text{A}}{0.020\,0\ \text{s}}\right) = \boxed{37.9\ \text{V}}.$

(c) The average rate of change of flux through each turn of the overwrapped concentric coil is the same as that through a turn on the solenoid:

$$\frac{\Delta\Phi_B}{\Delta t} = \frac{\mu_0 n(\Delta I)A}{\Delta t} = \frac{\left(4\pi\times10^{-7}\ \text{T}\cdot\text{m/A}\right)(12\,500/0.070\,0\ \text{m})(2.71\ \text{A})\left(1.00\times10^{-4}\ \text{m}^2\right)}{0.020\,0\ \text{s}}$$

$$= \boxed{3.04\ \text{mV}}$$

(d) The magnitude of the average induced emf in the coil is $\left|\varepsilon_L\right| = N\left(\frac{\Delta\Phi_B}{\Delta t}\right)$ and magnitude of the average induced current is

$$I = \frac{\left|\varepsilon_L\right|}{R} = \frac{N}{R}\left(\frac{\Delta\Phi_B}{\Delta t}\right) = \frac{820}{24.0\ \Omega}\left(3.04\times10^{-3}\ \text{V}\right) = 0.104\ \text{A} = \boxed{104\ \text{mA}}.$$

P32.69 Left-hand loop: $\varepsilon-(I+I_2)R_1-I_2R_2=0$.

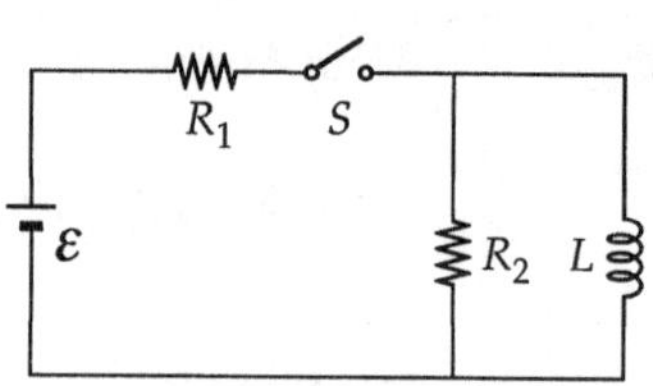

FIG. P32.69

Outside loop: $\varepsilon-(I+I_2)R_1-L\dfrac{dI}{dt}=0$.

Eliminating I_2 gives $\varepsilon'-IR'-L\dfrac{dI}{dt}=0$.

This is of the same form as Equation 32.6, so its solution is of the same form as Equation 32.7:

$$I(t)=\frac{\varepsilon'}{R'}\left(1-e^{-R't/L}\right).$$

But $R'=\dfrac{R_1R_2}{R_1+R_2}$ and $\varepsilon'=\dfrac{R_2\varepsilon}{R_1+R_2}$, so $\dfrac{\varepsilon'}{R'}=\dfrac{\varepsilon R_2/(R_1+R_2)}{R_1R_2/(R_1+R_2)}=\dfrac{\varepsilon}{R_1}$.

Thus $$I(t)=\frac{\varepsilon}{R_1}\left(1-e^{-R't/L}\right).$$

P32.70 When switch is closed, steady current $I_0=1.20\text{ A}$. When the switch is opened after being closed a long time, the current in the right loop is

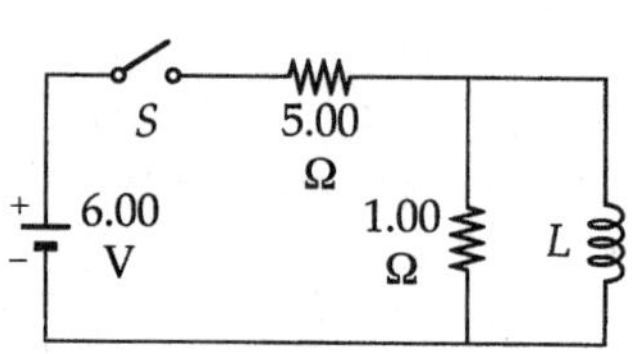

FIG. P32.70

$$I=I_0e^{-R_2t/L}$$

so $e^{Rt/L}=\dfrac{I_0}{I}$ and $\dfrac{Rt}{L}=\ln\left(\dfrac{I_0}{I}\right)$.

Therefore, $$L=\frac{R_2t}{\ln(I_0/I)}=\frac{(1.00\ \Omega)(0.150\text{ s})}{\ln(1.20\text{ A}/0.250\text{ A})}=0.095\,6\text{ H}=\boxed{95.6\text{ mH}}.$$

P32.71 (a) While steady-state conditions exist, a 9.00 mA flows clockwise around the right loop of the circuit. Immediately after the switch is opened, a 9.00 mA current will flow around the outer loop of the circuit. Applying Kirchhoff's loop rule to this loop gives:

$$+\varepsilon_0-\left[(2.00+6.00)\times10^3\ \Omega\right]\left(9.00\times10^{-3}\text{ A}\right)=0$$

$$+\varepsilon_0=\boxed{72.0\text{ V with end } b \text{ at the higher potential}}$$

(b)

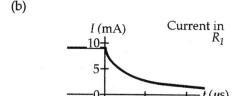

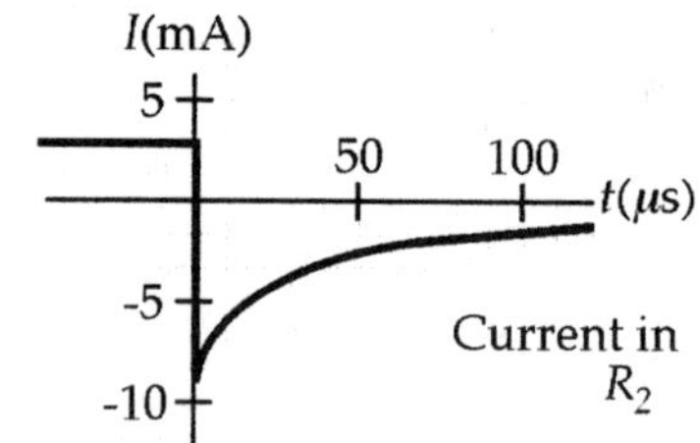

FIG. P32.71(b)

(c) After the switch is opened, the current around the outer loop decays as

$I=I_{max}e^{-Rt/L}$ with $I_{max}=9.00\text{ mA}$, $R=8.00\text{ k}\Omega$, and $L=0.400\text{ H}$.

Thus, when the current has reached a value $I=2.00\text{ mA}$, the elapsed time is:

$$t=\left(\frac{L}{R}\right)\ln\left(\frac{I_{max}}{I}\right)=\left(\frac{0.400\text{ H}}{8.00\times10^3\ \Omega}\right)\ln\left(\frac{9.00}{2.00}\right)=7.52\times10^{-5}\text{ s}=\boxed{75.2\ \mu\text{s}}.$$

P32.72 (a) The instant after the switch is closed, the situation is as shown in the circuit diagram of Figure (a). The requested quantities are:

$$\boxed{I_L = 0,\ I_C = \frac{\varepsilon_0}{R},\ I_R = \frac{\varepsilon_0}{R}}$$

$$\boxed{\Delta V_L = \varepsilon_0,\ \Delta V_C = 0,\ \Delta V_R = \varepsilon_0}$$

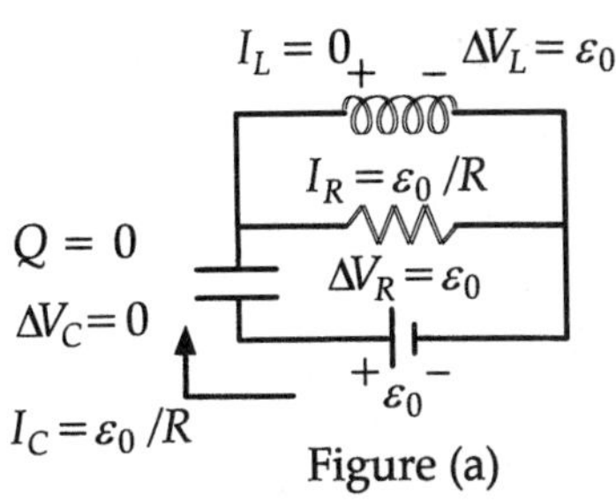

Figure (a)

(b) After the switch has been closed a long time, the steady-state conditions shown in Figure (b) will exist. The currents and voltages are:

$$\boxed{I_L = 0,\ I_C = 0,\ I_R = 0}$$

$$\boxed{\Delta V_L = 0,\ \Delta V_C = \varepsilon_0,\ \Delta V_R = 0}$$

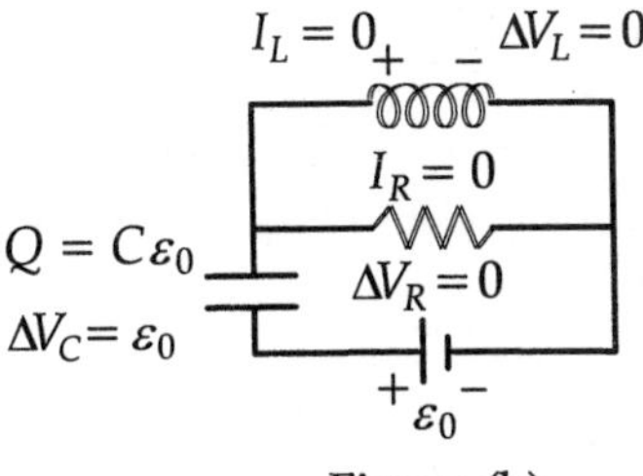

Figure (b)

FIG. P32.72

P32.73 When the switch is closed, as shown in figure (a), the current in the inductor is I:

$12.0 - 7.50I - 10.0 = 0 \rightarrow I = 0.267\ \text{A}$.

When the switch is opened, the initial current in the inductor remains at 0.267 A.

$IR = \Delta V$: $\quad (0.267\ \text{A})R \le 80.0\ \text{V}$

$$\boxed{R \le 300\ \Omega}$$

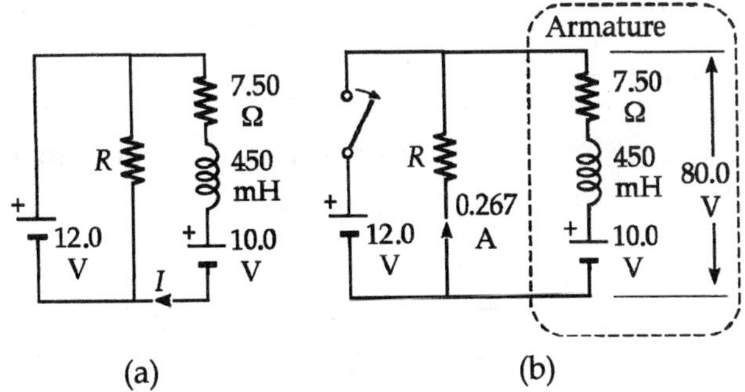

FIG. P32.73

P32.74 (a)
$$L_1 = \frac{\mu_0 N_1^2 A}{\ell_1} = \frac{(4\pi \times 10^{-7}\ \text{T}\cdot\text{m/A})(1\,000)^2(1.00 \times 10^{-4}\ \text{m}^2)}{0.500\ \text{m}} = 2.51 \times 10^{-4}\ \text{H} = \boxed{251\ \mu\text{H}}$$

(b)
$$M = \frac{N_2\Phi_2}{I_1} = \frac{N_2\Phi_1}{I_1} = \frac{N_2 BA}{I_1} = \frac{N_2[\mu_0(N_1/\ell_1)I_1]A}{I_1} = \frac{\mu_0 N_1 N_2 A}{\ell_1}$$

$$M = \frac{(4\pi \times 10^{-7}\ \text{T}\cdot\text{m/A})(1\,000)(100)(1.00 \times 10^{-4}\ \text{m}^2)}{0.500\ \text{m}} = 2.51 \times 10^{-5}\ \text{H} = \boxed{25.1\ \mu\text{H}}$$

(c)
$$\varepsilon_1 = -M\frac{dI_2}{dt},\ \text{or}\ I_1R_1 = -M\frac{dI_2}{dt}\ \text{and}\ I_1 = \frac{dQ_1}{dt} = -\frac{M}{R_1}\frac{dI_2}{dt}$$

$$Q_1 = -\frac{M}{R_1}\int_0^{t_f} dI_2 = -\frac{M}{R_1}(I_{2f} - I_{2i}) = -\frac{M}{R_1}(0 - I_{2i}) = \frac{MI_{2i}}{R_1}$$

$$Q_1 = \frac{(2.51 \times 10^{-5}\ \text{H})(1.00\ \text{A})}{1\,000\Omega} = 2.51 \times 10^{-8}\ \text{C} = \boxed{25.1\ \text{nC}}$$

P32.75 (a) It has a magnetic field, and it stores energy, so $L = \frac{2U}{I^2}$ is non-zero.

(b) Every field line goes through the rectangle between the conductors.

(c) $\Phi = LI$ so $L = \frac{\Phi}{I} = \frac{1}{I}\int_{y=a}^{w-a} B\,dA$

$$L = \frac{1}{I}\int_{a}^{w-a} x\,dy\left(\frac{\mu_0 I}{2\pi y} + \frac{\mu_0 I}{2\pi(w-y)}\right) = \frac{2}{I}\int \frac{\mu_0 I x}{2\pi y}\,dy = \frac{2\mu_0 x}{2\pi}\ln y\Big|_{a}^{w-a}.$$

Thus $L = \frac{\mu_0 x}{\pi}\ln\left(\frac{w-a}{a}\right).$

P32.76 For an *RL* circuit,

$I(t) = I_{max}e^{-(R/L)t}$: $\frac{I(t)}{I_{max}} = 1 - 10^{-9} = e^{-(R/L)t} \cong 1 - \frac{R}{L}t$

$\frac{R}{L}t = 10^{-9}$ so $R_{max} = \frac{(3.14\times10^{-8})(10^{-9})}{(2.50\text{ yr})(3.16\times10^{7}\text{ s/yr})} = \boxed{3.97\times10^{-25}\ \Omega}.$

(If the ring were of purest copper, of diameter 1 cm, and cross-sectional area 1 mm^2, its resistance would be at least $10^{-6}\ \Omega$).

P32.77 (a) $U_B = \frac{1}{2}LI^2 = \frac{1}{2}(50.0\text{ H})(50.0\times10^{3}\text{ A})^2 = \boxed{6.25\times10^{10}\text{ J}}$

(b) Two adjacent turns are parallel wires carrying current in the same direction. Since the loops have such large radius, a one-meter section can be regarded as straight.

Then one wire creates a field of $B = \frac{\mu_0 I}{2\pi r}.$

This causes a force on the next wire of $F = I\ell B\sin\theta$

giving $F = I\ell\frac{\mu_0 I}{2\pi r}\sin 90° = \frac{\mu_0 \ell I^2}{2\pi r}.$

Evaluating the force, $F = \left(4\pi\times10^{-7}\text{ N/A}^2\right)\frac{(1.00\text{ m})(50.0\times10^{3}\text{ A})^2}{2\pi(0.250\text{ m})} = \boxed{2\,000\text{ N}}.$

P32.78 $\mathcal{P} = I\Delta V$ $\qquad I = \dfrac{\mathcal{P}}{\Delta V} = \dfrac{1.00 \times 10^9 \text{ W}}{200 \times 10^3 \text{ V}} = 5.00 \times 10^3 \text{ A}$

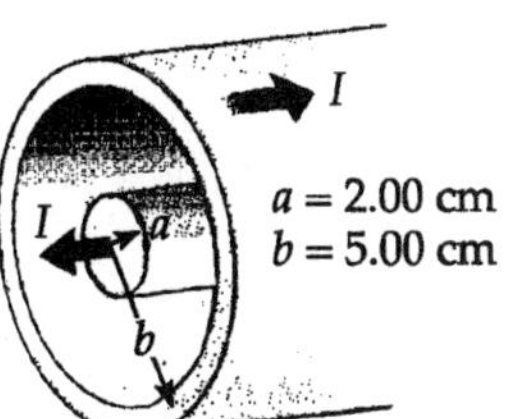

FIG. P32.73

From Ampere's law, $B(2\pi r) = \mu_0 I_{\text{enclosed}}$ or $B = \dfrac{\mu_0 I_{\text{enclosed}}}{2\pi r}$.

(a) At $r = a = 0.020\,0 \text{ m}$, $I_{\text{enclosed}} = 5.00 \times 10^3 \text{ A}$

and $$B = \frac{(4\pi \times 10^{-7} \text{ T}\cdot\text{m/A})(5.00 \times 10^3 \text{ A})}{2\pi(0.020\,0 \text{ m})} = 0.050\,0 \text{ T} = \boxed{50.0 \text{ mT}}.$$

(b) At $r = b = 0.050\,0 \text{ m}$, $I_{\text{enclosed}} = I = 5.00 \times 10^3 \text{ A}$

and $$B = \frac{(4\pi \times 10^{-7} \text{ T}\cdot\text{m/A})(5.00 \times 10^3 \text{ A})}{2\pi(0.050\,0 \text{ m})} = 0.020\,0 \text{ T} = \boxed{20.0 \text{ mT}}.$$

(c) $$U = \int u\,dV = \int_a^b \frac{[B(r)]^2 (2\pi r\ell\,dr)}{2\mu_0} = \frac{\mu_0 I^2 \ell}{4\pi}\int_a^b \frac{dr}{r} = \frac{\mu_0 I^2 \ell}{4\pi}\ln\left(\frac{b}{a}\right)$$

$$U = \frac{(4\pi \times 10^{-7} \text{ T}\cdot\text{m/A})(5.00 \times 10^3 \text{ A})^2 (1\,000 \times 10^3 \text{ m})}{4\pi}\ln\left(\frac{5.00 \text{ cm}}{2.00 \text{ cm}}\right) = 2.29 \times 10^6 \text{ J} = \boxed{2.29 \text{ MJ}}$$

(d) The magnetic field created by the inner conductor exerts a force of repulsion on the current in the outer sheath. The strength of this field, from part (b), is 20.0 mT. Consider a small rectangular section of the outer cylinder of length ℓ and width w.

It carries a current of $$(5.00 \times 10^3 \text{ A})\left(\frac{w}{2\pi(0.050\,0 \text{ m})}\right)$$

and experiences an outward force
$$F = I\ell B\sin\theta = \frac{(5.00 \times 10^3 \text{ A})w}{2\pi(0.050\,0 \text{ m})}\ell(20.0 \times 10^{-3} \text{ T})\sin 90.0°.$$

The pressure on it is $$P = \frac{F}{A} = \frac{F}{w\ell} = \frac{(5.00 \times 10^3 \text{ A})(20.0 \times 10^{-3} \text{ T})}{2\pi(0.050\,0 \text{ m})} = \boxed{318 \text{ Pa}}.$$

P32.79 (a) $B=\frac{\mu_0 NI}{\ell}=\frac{(4\pi\times10^{-7}\ \text{T}\cdot\text{m/A})(1\,400)(2.00\ \text{A})}{1.20\ \text{m}}=\boxed{2.93\times10^{-3}\ \text{T (upward)}}$

(b) $u=\frac{B^2}{2\mu_0}=\frac{(2.93\times10^{-3}\ \text{T})^2}{2(4\pi\times10^{-7}\ \text{T}\cdot\text{m/A})}=(3.42\ \text{J/m}^3)\left(\frac{1\ \text{N}\cdot\text{m}}{1\ \text{J}}\right)=3.42\ \text{N/m}^2=\boxed{3.42\ \text{Pa}}$

(c) To produce a downward magnetic field, the surface of the superconductor must carry a $\boxed{\text{clockwise}}$ current.

(d) The vertical component of the field of the solenoid exerts an inward force on the superconductor. The total horizontal force is zero. Over the top end of the solenoid, its field diverges and has a radially outward horizontal component. This component exerts upward force on the clockwise superconductor current. The total force on the core is $\boxed{\text{upward}}$. You can think of it as a force of repulsion between the solenoid with its north end pointing up, and the core, with its north end pointing down.

(e) $F=PA=(3.42\ \text{Pa})\left[\pi(1.10\times10^{-2}\ \text{m})^2\right]=\boxed{1.30\times10^{-3}\ \text{N}}$

Note that we have not proven that energy density is pressure. In fact, it is not in some cases; Equation 21.2 shows that the pressure is two-thirds of the translational energy density in an ideal gas.

ANSWERS TO EVEN PROBLEMS

P32.2 1.36 μH

P32.4 240 nWb

P32.6 19.2 μWb

P32.8 (a) 360 mV; (b) 180 mV; (c) $t=3.00$ s

P32.10 (a) 15.8 μH; (b) 12.6 mH

P32.12 see the solution

P32.14 1.92 Ω

P32.16 see the solution

P32.18 92.8 V

P32.20 30.0 mH

P32.22 7.67 mH

P32.24 (a) 1.00 kΩ; (b) 3.00 ms

P32.26 (a) 1.00 A; (b) $\Delta V_{12}=12.0\ \text{V}$, $\Delta V_{1\,200}=1.20\ \text{kV}$, $\Delta V_L=1.21\ \text{kV}$; (c) 7.62 ms

P32.28 (a), (b), and (c) see the solution; (d) yes; see the solution

P32.30 (a) 8.06 MJ/m^3; (b) 6.32 kJ

P32.32 (a) 27.8 J; (b) 18.5 ms

P32.34 see the solution

P32.36 (a) 20.0 W; (b) 20.0 W; (c) 0;(d) 20.0 J

P32.38 $\frac{2\pi B_0^2 R^3}{\mu_0}=2.70\times10^{18}\ \text{J}$

P32.40 1.00 V

P32.42 781 pH

P32.44 $M=\frac{N_1 N_2 \pi\mu_0 R_1^2 R_2^2}{2(x^2+R_1^2)^{3/2}}$

P32.46 400 mA

P32.48 281 mH

P32.50 220 mH

P32.52 (a) 503 Hz; (b) 12.0 μC; (c) 37.9 mA; (d) 72.0 μJ

P32.54 (a) 2.51 kHz; (b) 69.9 Ω

P32.56 see the solution

P32.58 (a) $0.693\left(\frac{2L}{R}\right)$; (b) $0.347\left(\frac{2L}{R}\right)$

P32.60 $\frac{9t^2}{\pi^2 C}$

P32.62 (a) $\varepsilon_L = -LK$; (b) $\Delta V_c = \frac{-Kt^2}{2C}$; (c) $t = 2\sqrt{LC}$

P32.64 (a) see the solution; (b) 91.2 μH; (c) 90.9 μH, 0.3% smaller

P32.66 (a) 127; (b) 0.522 Ω; (c) 76.8 mH

P32.68 (a) 20.0 ms; (b) 37.9 V; (c) 3.04 mV; (d) 104 mA

P32.70 95.6 mH

P32.72 (a) $I_L = 0$, $I_C = \frac{\varepsilon_0}{R}$, $I_R = \frac{\varepsilon_0}{R}$, $\Delta V_L = \varepsilon_0$, $\Delta V_C = 0$, $\Delta V_R = \varepsilon_0$; (b) $I_L = 0$, $I_C = 0$, $I_R = 0$, $\Delta V_L = 0$, $\Delta V_C = \varepsilon_0$, $\Delta V_R = 0$

P32.74 (a) 251 μH; (b) 25.1 μH; (c) 25.1 nC

P32.76 $3.97 \times 10^{-25}\ \Omega$

P32.78 (a) 50.0 mT; (b) 20.0 mT; (c) 2.29 MJ; (d) 318 Pa

33

Alternating Current Circuits

CHAPTER OUTLINE

ANSWERS TO QUESTIONS

Q33.1 If the current is positive half the time and negative half the time, the average current can be zero. The rms current is not zero. By squaring all of the values of the current, they all become positive. The average (mean) of these positive values is also positive, as is the square root of the average.

Q33.2 $\Delta V_{avg} = \frac{\Delta V_{max}}{2}$, $\Delta V_{rms} = \frac{\Delta V_{max}}{\sqrt{2}}$

Q33.3 AC ammeters and voltmeters read rms values. With an oscilloscope you can read a maximum voltage, or test whether the average is zero.

Q33.4 Suppose the voltage across an inductor varies sinusoidally. Then the current in the inductor will have its instantaneous peak positive value $\frac{1}{4}$ cycle *after* the voltage peaks. The voltage is zero and going positive $\frac{1}{4}$ cycle (90°) before the current is zero and going positive.

Q33.5 If it is run directly from the electric line, a fluorescent light tube can dim considerably twice in every cycle of the AC current that drives it. Looking at one sinusoidal cycle, the voltage passes through zero twice. We don't notice the flickering due to a phenomenon called retinal imaging. We do not notice that the lights turn on and off since our retinas continue to send information to our brains after the light has turned off. For example, most TV screens refresh at between 60 to 75 times per second, yet we do not see the evening news flickering. Home video cameras record information at frequencies as low as 30 frames per second, yet we still see them as continuous action. A vivid display of retinal imaging is that persistent purple spot you see after someone has taken a picture of you with a flash camera.

Q33.6 The capacitive reactance is proportional to the inverse of the frequency. At higher and higher frequencies, the capacitive reactance approaches zero, making a capacitor behave like a wire. As the frequency goes to zero, the capacitive reactance approaches infinity—the resistance of an open circuit.

Q33.7 The second letter in each word stands for the circuit element. For an inductor L, the emf ε leads the current I—thus ELI. For a capacitor C, the current leads the voltage across the device. In a circuit in which the capacitive reactance is larger than the inductive reactance, the current leads the source emf—thus ICE.

Q33.8 The voltages are not added in a scalar form, but in a vector form, as shown in the phasor diagrams throughout the chapter. Kirchhoff's loop rule is true at any instant, but the voltages across different circuit elements are not simultaneously at their maximum values. Do not forget that an inductor can induce an emf in itself and that the voltage across it is 90° *ahead* of the current in the circuit in phase.

Q33.9 In an RLC series circuit, the phase angle depends on the source frequency. At very low frequency the capacitor dominates the impedance and the phase angle is near –90°. The phase angle is zero at the resonance frequency, where the inductive and capacitive reactances are equal. At very high frequencies ϕ approaches +90°.

Q33.10 $-90° \le \phi \le 90°$. The extremes are reached when there is no significant resistance in the circuit.

Q33.11 The resistance remains unchanged, the inductive resistance doubles, and the capacitive reactance is reduced by one half.

Q33.12 The power factor, as seen in equation 33.29, is the cosine of the phase angle between the current and applied voltage. Maximum power will be delivered if ΔV and I are in phase. If ΔV and I are 90° out of phase, the source voltage drives a net current of zero in each cycle and the average power is zero.

Q33.13 The person is doing work at a rate of $\mathcal{P} = Fv\cos\theta$. One can consider the emf as the "force" that moves the charges through the circuit, and the current as the "speed" of the moving charges. The $\cos\theta$ factor measures the effectiveness of the cause in producing the effect. Theta is an angle in real space for the vacuum cleaner and phi is the analogous angle of phase difference between the emf and the current in the circuit.

Q33.14 As mentioned in Question 33.5, lights that are powered by alternating current flicker or get slightly brighter and dimmer at twice the frequency of the AC power source. Even if you tried using two banks of lights, one driven by AC 180° of phase from the other, you would not have a stable light source, but one that exhibits a "ripple" in intensity.

Q33.15 In 1881, an assassin shot President James Garfield. The bullet was lost in his body. Alexander Graham Bell invented the metal detector in an effort to save the President's life. The coil is preserved in the Smithsonian Institution. The detector was thrown off by metal springs in Garfield's mattress, a new invention itself. Surgeons went hunting for the bullet in the wrong place and Garfield died.

Q33.16 As seen in Example 33.8, it is far more economical to transmit at high voltage than at low voltage, as the I^2R loss on the transmission line is significantly lower. Transmitting power at high voltage permits the use of step-down transformers to make "low" voltages and high currents available to the end user.

Q33.17 Insulation and safety limit the voltage of a transmission line. For an underground cable, the thickness and dielectric strength of the insulation between the conductors determines the maximum voltage that can be applied, just as with a capacitor. For an overhead line on towers, the designer must consider electrical breakdown of the surrounding air, possible accidents, sparking across the insulating supports, ozone production, and inducing voltages in cars, fences, and the roof gutters of nearby houses. Nuisance effects include noise, electrical noise, and a prankster lighting a hand-held fluorescent tube under the line.

Q33.18 No. A voltage is only induced in the secondary coil if the flux through the core changes in time.

Q33.19 This person needs to consider the difference between the power delivered by a power plant and I^2R losses in transmission lines. At lower voltages, transmission lines must carry higher currents to transmit the same power, as seen in Example 33.8. The high transmitted current at low voltage actually results in more internal energy production than a lower current at high voltage. In his formula $\frac{(\Delta V)^2}{R}$, the ΔV does not represent the line voltage but the potential difference between the ends of one conductor. This is very small when the current is small.

Q33.20 The Q factor determines the selectivity of the radio receiver. For example, a receiver with a very low Q factor will respond to a wide range of frequencies and might pick up several adjacent radio stations at the same time. To discriminate between 102.5 MHz and 102.7 MHz requires a high-Q circuit. Typically, lowering the resistance in the circuit is the way to get a higher quality resonance.

Q33.21 Both coils are wrapped around the same core so that nearly all of the magnetic flux created by the primary passes through the secondary coil, and thus induces current in the secondary when the current in the primary changes.

Q33.22 The frequency of a DC signal is zero, making the capacitive reactance at DC infinite. The capacitor then acts as an open switch. An AC signal has a non-zero frequency, and thus the capacitive reactance is finite, allowing a signal to pass from Circuit A to Circuit B.

SOLUTIONS TO PROBLEMS

Section 33.1 AC Sources

Section 33.2 Resistors in an AC Circuit

P33.1 $\Delta v(t) = \Delta V_{max}\sin(\omega t) = \sqrt{2}\Delta V_{rms}\sin(\omega t) = 200\sqrt{2}\sin[2\pi(100t)] = \boxed{(283\text{ V})\sin(628t)}$

P33.2 $\Delta V_{rms} = \frac{170\text{ V}}{\sqrt{2}} = 120\text{ V}$

(a) $\mathcal{P} = \frac{(\Delta V_{rms})^2}{R} \rightarrow R = \frac{(120\text{ V})^2}{75.0\text{ W}} = \boxed{193\ \Omega}$

(b) $R = \frac{(120\text{ V})^2}{100\text{ W}} = \boxed{144\ \Omega}$

P33.3 Each meter reads the rms value.

$\Delta V_{rms} = \frac{100\text{ V}}{\sqrt{2}} = \boxed{70.7\text{ V}}$

$I_{rms} = \frac{\Delta V_{rms}}{R} = \frac{70.7\text{ V}}{24.0\ \Omega} = \boxed{2.95\text{ A}}$

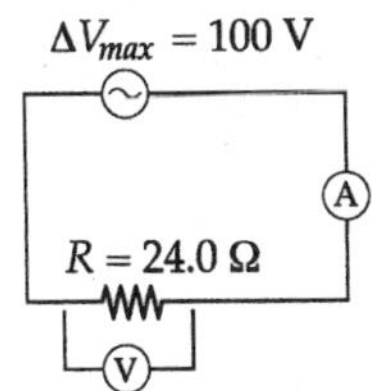

FIG. P33.3

P33.4 (a) $\Delta v_R = \Delta V_{max} \sin \omega t$

$\Delta v_R = 0.250(\Delta V_{max})$, so $\sin \omega t = 0.250$, or $\omega t = \sin^{-1}(0.250)$.

The smallest angle for which this is true is $\omega t = 0.253$ rad Thus, if $t = 0.010\,0$ s,

$$\omega = \frac{0.253 \text{ rad}}{0.010\,0 \text{ s}} = \boxed{25.3 \text{ rad/s}}.$$

(b) The second time when $\Delta v_R = 0.250(\Delta V_{max})$, $\omega t = \sin^{-1}(0.250)$ again. For this occurrence, $\omega t = \pi - 0.253 \text{ rad} = 2.89$ rad (to understand why this is true, recall the identity $\sin(\pi - \theta) = \sin\theta$ from trigonometry). Thus,

$$t = \frac{2.89 \text{ rad}}{25.3 \text{ rad/s}} = \boxed{0.114 \text{ s}}.$$

P33.5 $i_R = I_{max} \sin \omega t$ becomes $0.600 = \sin(\omega\, 0.007\,00)$.

Thus, $(0.007\,00)\omega = \sin^{-1}(0.600) = 0.644$

and $\omega = 91.9 \text{ rad/s} = 2\pi f$ so $\boxed{f = 14.6 \text{ Hz}}$.

P33.6 $\mathscr{P} = I_{rms}(\Delta V_{rms})$ and $\Delta V_{rms} = 120$ V for each bulb (parallel circuit), so:

$$I_1 = I_2 = \frac{\mathscr{P}_1}{\Delta V_{rms}} = \frac{150 \text{ W}}{120 \text{ V}} = \boxed{1.25 \text{ A}}, \text{ and } R_1 = \frac{\Delta V_{rms}}{I_1} = \frac{120 \text{ V}}{1.25 \text{ A}} = \boxed{96.0\ \Omega} = R_2$$

$$I_3 = \frac{\mathscr{P}_3}{\Delta V_{rms}} = \frac{100 \text{ W}}{120 \text{ V}} = \boxed{0.833 \text{ A}}, \text{ and } R_3 = \frac{\Delta V_{rms}}{I_3} = \frac{120 \text{ V}}{0.833 \text{ A}} = \boxed{144\ \Omega}.$$

P33.7 $\Delta V_{max} = 15.0$ V and $R_{total} = 8.20\ \Omega + 10.4\ \Omega = 18.6\ \Omega$

$$I_{max} = \frac{\Delta V_{max}}{R_{total}} = \frac{15.0 \text{ V}}{18.6\ \Omega} = 0.806 \text{ A} = \sqrt{2} I_{rms}$$

$$\mathscr{P}_{speaker} = I_{rms}^2 R_{speaker} = \left(\frac{0.806 \text{ A}}{\sqrt{2}}\right)^2 (10.4\ \Omega) = \boxed{3.38 \text{ W}}$$

Section 33.3 Inductors in an AC Circuit

P33.8 For $I_{max} = 80.0$ mA, $I_{rms} = \dfrac{80.0 \text{ mA}}{\sqrt{2}} = 56.6$ mA

$$(X_L)_{min} = \frac{V_{rms}}{I_{rms}} = \frac{50.0 \text{ V}}{0.056\,6 \text{ A}} = 884\ \Omega$$

$$X_L = 2\pi fL \to L = \frac{X_L}{2\pi f} \ge \frac{884\ \Omega}{2\pi(20.0)} \ge \boxed{7.03 \text{ H}}$$

P33.9 (a) $X_L = \frac{\Delta V_{max}}{I_{max}} = \frac{100}{7.50} = 13.3\ \Omega$

$$L = \frac{X_L}{\omega} = \frac{13.3}{2\pi(50.0)} = 0.042\,4\text{ H} = \boxed{42.4\text{ mH}}$$

(b) $X_L = \frac{\Delta V_{max}}{I_{max}} = \frac{100}{2.50} = 40.0\ \Omega$

$$\omega = \frac{X_L}{L} = \frac{40.0}{42.4\times 10^{-3}} = \boxed{942\text{ rad/s}}$$

P33.10 At 50.0 Hz, $X_L = 2\pi(50.0\text{ Hz})L = 2\pi(50.0\text{ Hz})\left(\frac{X_L|_{60.0\text{ Hz}}}{2\pi(60.0\text{ Hz})}\right) = \frac{50.0}{60.0}(54.0\ \Omega) = 45.0\ \Omega$

$$I_{max} = \frac{\Delta V_{max}}{X_L} = \frac{\sqrt{2}(\Delta V_{rms})}{X_L} = \frac{\sqrt{2}(100\text{ V})}{45.0\ \Omega} = \boxed{3.14\text{ A}}.$$

P33.11 $i_L(t) = \frac{\Delta V_{max}}{\omega L}\sin\left(\omega t - \frac{\pi}{2}\right) = \frac{(80.0\text{ V})\sin\left[(65.0\pi)(0.015\,5) - \pi/2\right]}{(65.0\pi\text{ rad/s})(70.0\times 10^{-3}\text{ H})}$

$$i_L(t) = (5.60\text{ A})\sin(1.59\text{ rad}) = \boxed{5.60\text{ A}}$$

P33.12 $\omega = 2\pi f = 2\pi(60.0/\text{s}) = 377\text{ rad/s}$

$$X_L = \omega L = (377/\text{s})(0.020\,0\text{ V}\cdot\text{s/A}) = 7.54\ \Omega$$

$$I_{rms} = \frac{\Delta V_{rms}}{X_L} = \frac{120\text{ V}}{7.54\ \Omega} = 15.9\text{ A}$$

$$I_{max} = \sqrt{2}I_{rms} = \sqrt{2}(15.9\text{ A}) = 22.5\text{ A}$$

$$i(t) = I_{max}\sin\omega t = (22.5\text{ A})\sin\left(\frac{2\pi(60.0)}{\text{s}}\cdot\frac{1\text{ s}}{180}\right) = (22.5\text{ A})\sin 120° = 19.5\text{ A}$$

$$U = \frac{1}{2}Li^2 = \frac{1}{2}(0.020\,0\text{ V}\cdot\text{s/A})(19.5\text{ A})^2 = \boxed{3.80\text{ J}}$$

P33.13 $L = \frac{N\Phi_B}{I}$ where Φ_B is the flux through each turn. $N\Phi_{B,\,max} = LI_{max} = \frac{X_L}{\omega}\frac{(\Delta V_{L,\,max})}{X_L}$

$$N\Phi_{B,\,max} = \frac{\sqrt{2}(\Delta V_{L,\,rms})}{2\pi f} = \frac{120\text{ V}\cdot\text{s}}{\sqrt{2}\pi(60.0)}\left(\frac{\text{T}\cdot\text{C}\cdot\text{m}}{\text{N}\cdot\text{s}}\right)\left(\frac{\text{N}\cdot\text{m}}{\text{J}}\right)\left(\frac{\text{J}}{\text{V}\cdot\text{C}}\right) = \boxed{0.450\text{ T}\cdot\text{m}^2}.$$

Section 33.4 Capacitors in an AC Circuit

P33.14 (a) $X_C = \frac{1}{2\pi f C}: \frac{1}{2\pi f\left(22.0\times10^{-6}\right)} < 175\ \Omega$

$$\frac{1}{2\pi\left(22.0\times10^{-6}\right)(175)} < f \qquad \boxed{f > 41.3\text{ Hz}}$$

(b) $X_C \propto \frac{1}{C}$, so $X(44) = \frac{1}{2}X(22)$: $\boxed{X_C < 87.5\ \Omega}$

P33.15 $I_{max} = \sqrt{2}I_{rms} = \frac{\sqrt{2}(\Delta V_{rms})}{X_C} = \sqrt{2}(\Delta V_{rms})2\pi f C$

(a) $I_{max} = \sqrt{2}(120\text{ V})2\pi(60.0/\text{s})\left(2.20\times10^{-6}\ \text{C/V}\right) = \boxed{141\text{ mA}}$

(b) $I_{max} = \sqrt{2}(240\text{ V})2\pi(50.0/\text{s})\left(2.20\times10^{-6}\ \text{F}\right) = \boxed{235\text{ mA}}$

P33.16 $Q_{max} = C(\Delta V_{max}) = C\left[\sqrt{2}(\Delta V_{rms})\right] = \boxed{\sqrt{2}C(\Delta V_{rms})}$

P33.17 $I_{max} = (\Delta V_{max})\omega C = (48.0\text{ V})(2\pi)\left(90.0\text{ s}^{-1}\right)\left(3.70\times10^{-6}\ \text{F}\right) = \boxed{100\text{ mA}}$

P33.18 $X_C = \frac{1}{\omega C} = \frac{1}{2\pi(60.0/\text{s})\left(1.00\times10^{-3}\ \text{C/V}\right)} = 2.65\ \Omega$

$v_C(t) = \Delta V_{max}\sin\omega t$, to be zero at $t = 0$

$$i_C = \frac{\Delta V_{max}}{X_C}\sin(\omega t+\phi) = \frac{\sqrt{2}(120\text{ V})}{2.65\ \Omega}\sin\left[2\pi\frac{60\text{ s}^{-1}}{180\text{ s}^{-1}} + 90.0°\right] = (64.0\text{ A})\sin(120°+90.0°) = \boxed{-32.0\text{ A}}$$

Section 33.5 The RLC Series Circuit

P33.19 (a) $X_L = \omega L = 2\pi(50.0)\left(400\times10^{-3}\right) = 126\ \Omega$

$$X_C = \frac{1}{\omega C} = \frac{1}{2\pi(50.0)\left(4.43\times10^{-6}\right)} = 719\ \Omega$$

$$Z = \sqrt{R^2 + (X_L - X_C)^2} = \sqrt{500^2 + (126-719)^2} = 776\ \Omega$$

$$\Delta V_{max} = I_{max}Z = \left(250\times10^{-3}\right)(776) = \boxed{194\text{ V}}$$

400 mH
50.0 Hz
4.43 μF
500 Ω

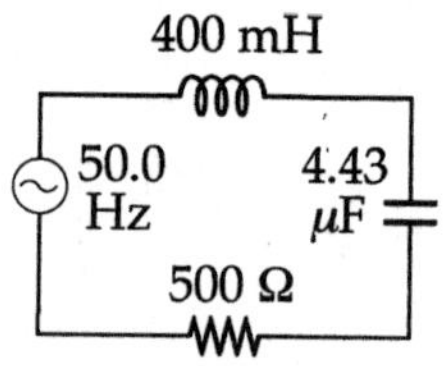

FIG. P33.19

(b) $\phi = \tan^{-1}\left(\frac{X_L - X_C}{R}\right) = \tan^{-1}\left(\frac{126-719}{500}\right) = \boxed{-49.9°}$. Thus, the $\boxed{\text{Current leads the voltage.}}$

P33.20 $\omega L = \frac{1}{\omega C} \rightarrow \omega = \frac{1}{\sqrt{LC}} = \frac{1}{\sqrt{\left(57.0\times10^{-6}\right)\left(57.0\times10^{-6}\right)}} = 1.75\times10^{4}\ \text{rad/s}$

$$f = \frac{\omega}{2\pi} = \boxed{2.79\text{ kHz}}$$

P33.21 (a) $X_L = \omega L = 2\pi\left(50.0\ \text{s}^{-1}\right)\left(250\times10^{-3}\ \text{H}\right) = \boxed{78.5\ \Omega}$

(b) $X_C = \dfrac{1}{\omega C} = \left[2\pi\left(50.0\ \text{s}^{-1}\right)\left(2.00\times10^{-6}\ \text{F}\right)\right]^{-1} = \boxed{1.59\ \text{k}\Omega}$

(c) $Z = \sqrt{R^2 + (X_L - X_C)^2} = \boxed{1.52\ \text{k}\Omega}$

(d) $I_{\text{max}} = \dfrac{\Delta V_{\text{max}}}{Z} = \dfrac{210\ \text{V}}{1.52\times10^3\ \Omega} = \boxed{138\ \text{mA}}$

(e) $\phi = \tan^{-1}\left[\dfrac{X_L - X_C}{R}\right] = \tan^{-1}(-10.1) = \boxed{-84.3°}$

P33.22 (a) $Z = \sqrt{R^2 + (X_L - X_C)^2} = \sqrt{68.0^2 + (16.0 - 101)^2} = \boxed{109\ \Omega}$

$X_L = \omega L = (100)(0.160) = 16.0\ \Omega$

$X_C = \dfrac{1}{\omega C} = \dfrac{1}{(100)\left(99.0\times10^{-6}\right)} = 101\ \Omega$

(b) $I_{\text{max}} = \dfrac{\Delta V_{\text{max}}}{Z} = \dfrac{40.0\ \text{V}}{109\ \Omega} = \boxed{0.367\ \text{A}}$

(c) $\tan\phi = \dfrac{X_L - X_C}{R} = \dfrac{16.0 - 101}{68.0} = -1.25$:

$\phi = -0.896\ \text{rad} = -51.3°$

$\boxed{I_{\text{max}} = 0.367\ \text{A}}$ $\boxed{\omega = 100\ \text{rad/s}}$ $\boxed{\phi = -0.896\ \text{rad} = -51.3°}$

P33.23 $X_L = 2\pi f L = 2\pi(60.0)(0.460) = 173\ \Omega$

$X_C = \dfrac{1}{2\pi f C} = \dfrac{1}{2\pi(60.0)\left(21.0\times10^{-6}\right)} = 126\ \Omega$

(a) $\tan\phi = \dfrac{X_L - X_C}{R} = \dfrac{173\ \Omega - 126\ \Omega}{150\ \Omega} = 0.314$

$\phi = 0.304\ \text{rad} = \boxed{17.4°}$

(b) Since $X_L > X_C$, ϕ is positive; so $\boxed{\text{voltage leads the current}}$.

***P33.24** For the source-capacitor circuit, the rms source voltage is $\Delta V_s = (25.1\ \text{mA})X_C$. For the circuit with resistor, $\Delta V_s = (15.7\ \text{mA})\sqrt{R^2 + X_C^2} = (25.1\ \text{mA})X_C$. This gives $R = 1.247X_C$. For the circuit with ideal inductor, $\Delta V_s = (68.2\ \text{mA})|X_L - X_C| = (25.1\ \text{mA})X_C$. So $|X_L - X_C| = 0.368\,0X_C$. Now for the full circuit

$\Delta V_s = I\sqrt{R^2 + (X_L - X_C)^2}$

$(25.1\ \text{mA})X_C = I\sqrt{(1.247X_C)^2 + (0.368X_C)^2}$

$\boxed{I = 19.3\ \text{mA}}$

P33.25 $X_C = \dfrac{1}{2\pi f C} = \dfrac{1}{2\pi(60.0\text{ Hz})(20.0\times10^{-12}\text{ F})} = 1.33\times10^{8}\ \Omega$

$$Z = \sqrt{(50.0\times10^{3}\ \Omega)^2 + (1.33\times10^{8}\ \Omega)^2} \approx 1.33\times10^{8}\ \Omega$$

$$I_{\text{rms}} = \frac{\Delta V_{\text{rms}}}{Z} = \frac{5\,000\text{ V}}{1.33\times10^{8}\ \Omega} = 3.77\times10^{-5}\text{ A}$$

$$(\Delta V_{\text{rms}})_{\text{body}} = I_{\text{rms}} R_{\text{body}} = (3.77\times10^{-5}\text{ A})(50.0\times10^{3}\ \Omega) = \boxed{1.88\text{ V}}$$

P33.26 $X_C = \dfrac{1}{\omega C} = \dfrac{1}{2\pi(50.0)(65.0\times10^{-6})} = 49.0\ \Omega$

$$X_L = \omega L = 2\pi(50.0)(185\times10^{-3}) = 58.1\ \Omega$$

$$Z = \sqrt{R^2 + (X_L - X_C)^2} = \sqrt{(40.0)^2 + (58.1-49.0)^2} = 41.0\ \Omega$$

$$I_{\max} = \frac{\Delta V_{\max}}{Z} = \frac{150}{41.0} = 3.66\text{ A}$$

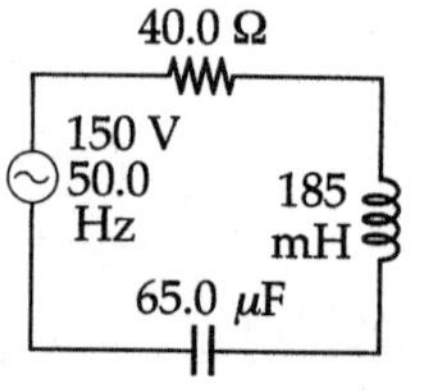

FIG. P33.26

(a) $\Delta V_R = I_{\max} R = (3.66)(40) = \boxed{146\text{ V}}$

(b) $\Delta V_L = I_{\max} X_L = (3.66)(58.1) = 212.5 = \boxed{212\text{ V}}$

(c) $\Delta V_C = I_{\max} X_C = (3.66)(49.0) = 179.1\text{ V} = \boxed{179\text{ V}}$

(d) $\Delta V_L - \Delta V_C = 212.5 - 179.1 = \boxed{33.4\text{ V}}$

P33.27 $R = 300\ \Omega$

$$X_L = \omega L = 2\pi\left(\frac{500}{\pi}\text{ s}^{-1}\right)(0.200\text{ H}) = 200\ \Omega$$

$$X_C = \frac{1}{\omega C} = \left[2\pi\left(\frac{500}{\pi}\text{ s}^{-1}\right)(11.0\times10^{-6}\text{ F})\right]^{-1} = 90.9\ \Omega$$

$Z = \sqrt{R^2 + (X_L - X_C)^2} = 319\ \Omega$ and

$$\phi = \tan^{-1}\left(\frac{X_L - X_C}{R}\right) = 20.0°$$

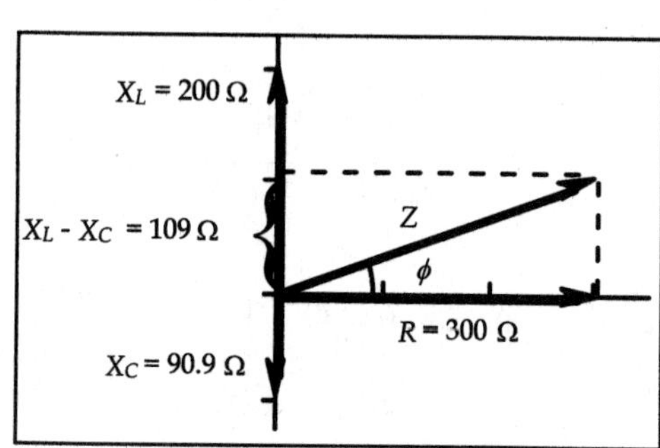

FIG. P33.27

***P33.28** Let X_c represent the initial capacitive reactance. Moving the plates to half their original separation doubles the capacitance and cuts $X_C = \dfrac{1}{\omega C}$ in half. For the current to double, the total impedance must be cut in half: $Z_i = 2Z_f$, $\sqrt{R^2 + (X_L - X_C)^2} = 2\sqrt{R^2 + \left(X_L - \dfrac{X_C}{2}\right)^2}$,

$$R^2 + (R - X_C)^2 = 4\left(R^2 + \left(R - \frac{X_C}{2}\right)^2\right)$$

$$2R^2 - 2RX_C + X_C^2 = 8R^2 - 4RX_C + X_C^2$$

$$\boxed{X_C = 3R}$$

P33.29 (a) $X_L = 2\pi(100\text{ Hz})(20.5\text{ H}) = 1.29\times10^4\ \Omega$

$$Z = \frac{\Delta V_{\text{rms}}}{I_{\text{rms}}} = \frac{200\text{ V}}{4.00\text{ A}} = 50.0\ \Omega$$

$$(X_L - X_C)^2 = Z^2 - R^2 = (50.0\ \Omega)^2 - (35.0\ \Omega)^2$$

$$X_L - X_C = 1.29\times10^4\ \Omega - \frac{1}{2\pi(100\text{ Hz})C} = \pm35.7\ \Omega \quad \boxed{C = 123\text{ nF or }124\text{ nF}}$$

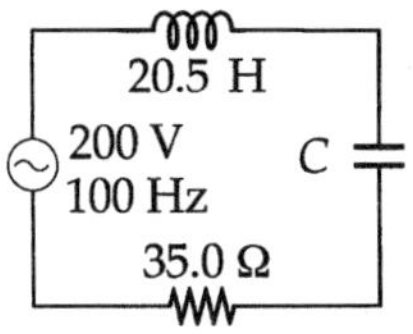

FIG. P33.29

(b) $\Delta V_{L,\text{rms}} = I_{\text{rms}}X_L = (4.00\text{ A})(1.29\times10^4\ \Omega) = \boxed{51.5\text{ kV}}$

Notice that this is a very large voltage!

Section 33.6 **Power in an AC Circuit**

P33.30 $X_L = \omega L = [(1\,000/\text{s})(0.050\,0\text{ H})] = 50.0\ \Omega$

$$X_C = \frac{1}{\omega C} = \left[(1\,000/\text{s})(50.0\times10^{-6}\text{ F})\right]^{-1} = 20.0\ \Omega$$

$$Z = \sqrt{R^2 + (X_L - X_C)^2}$$

$$Z = \sqrt{(40.0)^2 + (50.0 - 20.0)^2} = 50.0\ \Omega$$

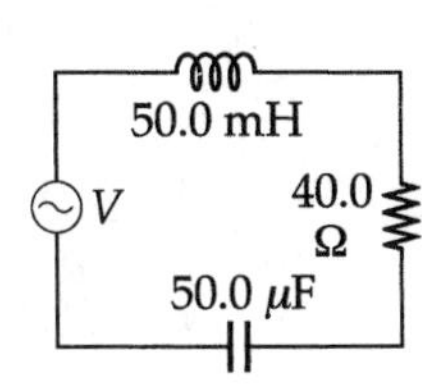

FIG. P33.30

(a) $I_{\text{rms}} = \dfrac{(\Delta V_{\text{rms}})}{Z} = \dfrac{100\text{ V}}{50.0\ \Omega}$

$I_{\text{rms}} = \boxed{2.00\text{ A}}$

$$\phi = \arctan\left(\frac{X_L - X_C}{R}\right)$$

$$\phi = \arctan\frac{30.0\ \Omega}{40.0\ \Omega} = 36.9°$$

(b) $\mathscr{P} = (\Delta V_{\text{rms}})I_{\text{rms}}\cos\phi = 100\text{ V}(2.00\text{ A})\cos 36.9° = \boxed{160\text{ W}}$

(c) $\mathscr{P}_R = I_{\text{rms}}^2 R = (2.00\text{ A})^2\,40.0\ \Omega = \boxed{160\text{ W}}$

P33.31 $\omega = 1\,000\text{ rad/s}$, $R = 400\ \Omega$, $C = 5.00\times10^{-6}\text{ F}$, $L = 0.500\text{ H}$

$\Delta V_{\max} = 100\text{ V}$, $\omega L = 500\ \Omega$, $\left(\dfrac{1}{\omega C}\right) = 200\ \Omega$

$$Z = \sqrt{R^2 + \left(\omega L - \frac{1}{\omega C}\right)^2} = \sqrt{400^2 + 300^2} = 500\ \Omega$$

$$I_{\max} = \frac{\Delta V_{\max}}{Z} = \frac{100}{500} = 0.200\text{ A}$$

The average power dissipated in the circuit is $\mathscr{P} = I_{\text{rms}}^2 R = \left(\dfrac{I_{\max}^2}{2}\right)R$.

$$\mathscr{P} = \frac{(0.200\text{ A})^2}{2}(400\ \Omega) = \boxed{8.00\text{ W}}$$

P33.32 $Z=\sqrt{R^2+(X_L-X_C)^2}$ or $(X_L-X_C)=\sqrt{Z^2-R^2}$

$$(X_L-X_C)=\sqrt{(75.0\ \Omega)^2-(45.0\ \Omega)^2}=60.0\ \Omega$$

$$\phi=\tan^{-1}\left(\frac{X_L-X_C}{R}\right)=\tan^{-1}\left(\frac{60.0\ \Omega}{45.0\ \Omega}\right)=53.1°$$

$$I_{\text{rms}}=\frac{\Delta V_{\text{rms}}}{Z}=\frac{210\ \text{V}}{75.0\ \Omega}=2.80\ \text{A}$$

$$\mathcal{P}=(\Delta V_{\text{rms}})I_{\text{rms}}\cos\phi=(210\ \text{V})(2.80\ \text{A})\cos(53.1°)=\boxed{353\ \text{W}}$$

P33.33 (a) $\mathcal{P}=I_{\text{rms}}(\Delta V_{\text{rms}})\cos\phi=(9.00)180\cos(-37.0°)=1.29\times10^3\ \text{W}$

$\mathcal{P}=I_{\text{rms}}^2R$ so $1.29\times10^3=(9.00)^2R$ and $R=\boxed{16.0\ \Omega}$.

(b) $\tan\phi=\dfrac{X_L-X_C}{R}$ becomes $\tan(-37.0°)=\dfrac{X_L-X_C}{16}$: so $X_L-X_C=\boxed{-12.0\ \Omega}$.

P33.34 $X_L=\omega L=2\pi(60.0/\text{s})(0.025\,0\ \text{H})=9.42\ \Omega$

$$Z=\sqrt{R^2+(X_L-X_C)^2}=\sqrt{(20.0)^2+(9.42)^2}\ \Omega=22.1\ \Omega$$

(a) $I_{\text{rms}}=\dfrac{\Delta V_{\text{rms}}}{Z}=\dfrac{120\ \text{V}}{22.1\ \Omega}=\boxed{5.43\ \text{A}}$

(b) $\phi=\tan^{-1}\left(\dfrac{9.42}{20.0}\right)=25.2°$ so power factor $=\cos\phi=\boxed{0.905}$.

(c) We require $\phi=0$. Thus, $X_L=X_C$: $9.42\ \Omega=\dfrac{1}{2\pi\left(60.0\ \text{s}^{-1}\right)C}$

and $C=\boxed{281\ \mu\text{F}}$.

(d) $\mathcal{P}_b=\mathcal{P}_d$ or $(\Delta V_{\text{rms}})_b(I_{\text{rms}})_b\cos\phi_b=\dfrac{(\Delta V_{\text{rms}})_d^2}{R}$

$$(\Delta V_{\text{rms}})_d=\sqrt{R(\Delta V_{\text{rms}})_b(I_{\text{rms}})_b\cos\phi_b}=\sqrt{(20.0\ \Omega)(120\ \text{V})(5.43\ \text{A})(0.905)}=\boxed{109\ \text{V}}$$

P33.35 Consider a two-wire transmission line:

$I_{\text{rms}}=\dfrac{\mathcal{P}}{\Delta V_{\text{rms}}}$ and power loss $=I_{\text{rms}}^2R_{\text{line}}=\dfrac{\mathcal{P}}{100}$.

Thus, $\left(\dfrac{\mathcal{P}}{\Delta V_{\text{rms}}}\right)^2(2R_1)=\dfrac{\mathcal{P}}{100}$ or $R_1=\dfrac{(\Delta V_{\text{rms}})^2}{200\mathcal{P}}$

$R_1=\dfrac{\rho d}{A}=\dfrac{(\Delta V_{\text{rms}})^2}{200\mathcal{P}}$ or $A=\dfrac{\pi(2r)^2}{4}=\dfrac{200\rho\mathcal{P}d}{(\Delta V_{\text{rms}})^2}$

and the diameter is $2r=\boxed{\sqrt{\dfrac{800\rho\mathcal{P}d}{\pi(\Delta V)^2}}}$.

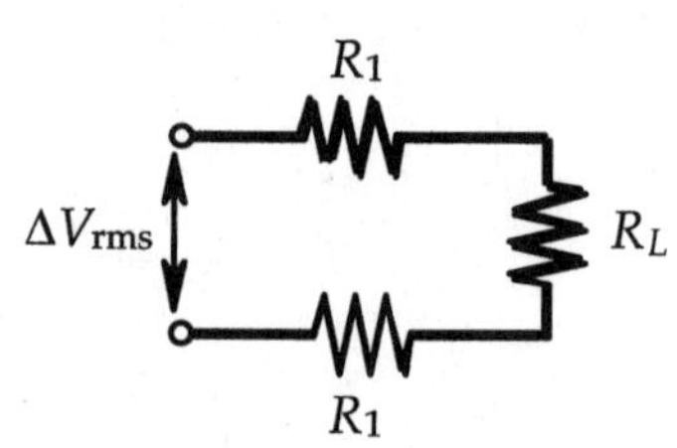

FIG. P33.35

P33.36 One-half the time, the left side of the generator is positive, the top diode conducts, and the bottom diode switches off. The power supply sees resistance

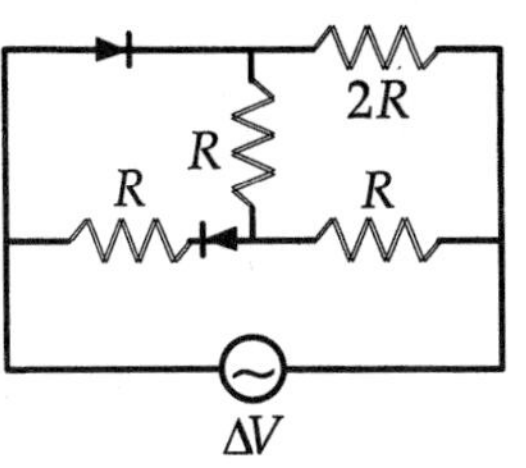

FIG. P33.36

$$\left[\frac{1}{2R}+\frac{1}{2R}\right]^{-1}=R \text{ and the power is } \frac{(\Delta V_{\text{rms}})^2}{R}.$$

The other half of the time the right side of the generator is positive, the upper diode is an open circuit, and the lower diode has zero resistance. The equivalent resistance is then

$$R_{\text{eq}}=R+\left[\frac{1}{3R}+\frac{1}{R}\right]^{-1}=\frac{7R}{4} \quad \text{and} \quad \mathscr{P}=\frac{(\Delta V_{\text{rms}})^2}{R_{\text{eq}}}=\frac{4(\Delta V_{\text{rms}})^2}{7R}.$$

The overall time average power is: $\dfrac{\left[(\Delta V_{\text{rms}})^2/R\right]+\left[4(\Delta V_{\text{rms}})^2/7R\right]}{2}=\boxed{\dfrac{11(\Delta V_{\text{rms}})^2}{14R}}$.

Section 33.7 Resonance in a Series RLC Circuit

P33.37 $\omega_0=2\pi\left(99.7\times10^6\right)=6.26\times10^8 \text{ rad/s}=\dfrac{1}{\sqrt{LC}}$

$$C=\frac{1}{\omega_0^2L}=\frac{1}{\left(6.26\times10^8\right)^2\left(1.40\times10^{-6}\right)}=\boxed{1.82 \text{ pF}}$$

P33.38 At resonance, $\dfrac{1}{2\pi fC}=2\pi fL$ and $\dfrac{1}{(2\pi f)^2L}=C$.

The range of values for C is $\boxed{46.5 \text{ pF to } 419 \text{ pF}}$.

***P33.39** (a) $f=\dfrac{1}{2\pi\sqrt{LC}}$

$$C=\frac{1}{4\pi^2f^2L}=\frac{1}{4\pi^2\left(10^{10}/\text{s}\right)^2 400\times10^{-12} \text{ Vs}}\frac{\text{A}}{}\left(\frac{\text{C}}{\text{As}}\right)=\boxed{6.33\times10^{-13} \text{ F}}$$

(b) $C=\dfrac{\kappa \in_0 A}{d}=\dfrac{\kappa \in_0 \ell^2}{d}$

$$\ell=\left(\frac{Cd}{\kappa\in_0}\right)^{1/2}=\left(\frac{6.33\times10^{-13} \text{ F}\times10^{-3} \text{ mm}}{1\times8.85\times10^{-12} \text{ F}}\right)^{1/2}=\boxed{8.46\times10^{-3} \text{ m}}$$

(c) $X_L=2\pi fL=2\pi\times10^{10}/\text{s}\times400\times10^{-12} \text{ Vs/A}=\boxed{25.1 \ \Omega}$

P33.40 $L = 20.0\text{ mH}$, $C = 1.00 \times 10^{-7}$, $R = 20.0\ \Omega$, $\Delta V_{\max} = 100\text{ V}$

(a) The resonant frequency for a series $-RLC$ circuit is $f = \frac{1}{2\pi}\sqrt{\frac{1}{LC}} = \boxed{3.56\text{ kHz}}$.

(b) At resonance, $I_{\max} = \frac{\Delta V_{\max}}{R} = \boxed{5.00\text{ A}}$.

(c) From Equation 33.38, $Q = \frac{\omega_0 L}{R} = \boxed{22.4}$.

(d) $\Delta V_{L,\max} = X_L I_{\max} = \omega_0 L I_{\max} = \boxed{2.24\text{ kV}}$

P33.41 The resonance frequency is $\omega_0 = \frac{1}{\sqrt{LC}}$. Thus, if $\omega = 2\omega_0$,

$$X_L = \omega L = \left(\frac{2}{\sqrt{LC}}\right)L = 2\sqrt{\frac{L}{C}} \quad \text{and} \quad X_C = \frac{1}{\omega C} = \frac{\sqrt{LC}}{2C} = \frac{1}{2}\sqrt{\frac{L}{C}}$$

$$Z = \sqrt{R^2 + (X_L - X_C)^2} = \sqrt{R^2 + 2.25\left(\frac{L}{C}\right)} \quad \text{so} \quad I_{\text{rms}} = \frac{\Delta V_{\text{rms}}}{Z} = \frac{\Delta V_{\text{rms}}}{\sqrt{R^2 + 2.25(L/C)}}$$

and the energy delivered in one period is $E = \mathcal{P}\Delta t$:

$$E = \frac{(\Delta V_{\text{rms}})^2 R}{R^2 + 2.25(L/C)}\left(\frac{2\pi}{\omega}\right) = \frac{(\Delta V_{\text{rms}})^2 RC}{R^2 C + 2.25L}\left(\pi\sqrt{LC}\right) = \frac{4\pi(\Delta V_{\text{rms}})^2 RC\sqrt{LC}}{4R^2 C + 9.00L}.$$

With the values specified for this circuit, this gives:

$$E = \frac{4\pi(50.0\text{ V})^2(10.0\ \Omega)\left(100\times10^{-6}\text{ F}\right)^{3/2}\left(10.0\times10^{-3}\text{ H}\right)^{1/2}}{4(10.0\ \Omega)^2\left(100\times10^{-6}\text{ F}\right) + 9.00\left(10.0\times10^{-3}\text{ H}\right)} = \boxed{242\text{ mJ}}.$$

P33.42 The resonance frequency is $\omega_0 = \frac{1}{\sqrt{LC}}$. Thus, if $\omega = 2\omega_0$,

$$X_L = \omega L = \left(\frac{2}{\sqrt{LC}}\right)L = 2\sqrt{\frac{L}{C}} \quad \text{and} \quad X_C = \frac{1}{\omega C} = \frac{\sqrt{LC}}{2C} = \frac{1}{2}\sqrt{\frac{L}{C}}.$$

Then $Z = \sqrt{R^2 + (X_L - X_C)^2} = \sqrt{R^2 + 2.25\left(\frac{L}{C}\right)}$ so $I_{\text{rms}} = \frac{\Delta V_{\text{rms}}}{Z} = \frac{\Delta V_{\text{rms}}}{\sqrt{R^2 + 2.25(L/C)}}$

and the energy delivered in one period is

$$E = \mathcal{P}\Delta t = \frac{(\Delta V_{\text{rms}})^2 R}{R^2 + 2.25(L/C)}\left(\frac{2\pi}{\omega}\right) = \frac{(\Delta V_{\text{rms}})^2 RC}{R^2 C + 2.25L}\left(\pi\sqrt{LC}\right) = \boxed{\frac{4\pi(\Delta V_{\text{rms}})^2 RC\sqrt{LC}}{4R^2 C + 9.00L}}.$$

P33.43 For the circuit of Problem 22, $\omega_0 = \frac{1}{\sqrt{LC}} = \frac{1}{\sqrt{(160 \times 10^{-3}\text{ H})(99.0 \times 10^{-6}\text{ F})}} = 251\text{ rad/s}$

$$Q = \frac{\omega_0 L}{R} = \frac{(251\text{ rad/s})(160 \times 10^{-3}\text{ H})}{68.0\ \Omega} = \boxed{0.591}.$$

For the circuit of Problem 23, $Q = \frac{\omega_0 L}{R} = \frac{L}{R\sqrt{LC}} = \frac{1}{R}\sqrt{\frac{L}{C}} = \frac{1}{150\ \Omega}\sqrt{\frac{460 \times 10^{-3}\text{ H}}{21.0 \times 10^{-6}\text{ F}}} = \boxed{0.987}.$

The $\boxed{\text{circuit of Problem 23}}$ has a sharper resonance.

Section 33.8 The Transformer and Power Transmission

P33.44 (a) $\Delta V_{2,\text{ rms}} = \frac{1}{13}(120\text{ V}) = \boxed{9.23\text{ V}}$

(b) $\Delta V_{1,\text{ rms}} I_{1,\text{ rms}} = \Delta V_{2,\text{ rms}} I_{2,\text{ rms}}$

$(120\text{ V})(0.350\text{ A}) = (9.23\text{ V}) I_{2,\text{ rms}}$

$I_{2,\text{ rms}} = \frac{42.0\text{ W}}{9.23\text{ V}} = \boxed{4.55\text{ A}}$ for a transformer with no energy loss.

(c) $\mathcal{P} = \boxed{42.0\text{ W}}$ from part (b).

P33.45 $(\Delta V_{\text{out}})_{\max} = \frac{N_2}{N_1}(\Delta V_{\text{in}})_{\max} = \left(\frac{2\,000}{350}\right)(170\text{ V}) = 971\text{ V}$

$(\Delta V_{\text{out}})_{\text{rms}} = \frac{(971\text{ V})}{\sqrt{2}} = \boxed{687\text{ V}}$

P33.46 (a) $(\Delta V_{2,\text{ rms}}) = \frac{N_2}{N_1}(\Delta V_{1,\text{ rms}})$ $\quad N_2 = \frac{(2\,200)(80)}{110} = \boxed{1\,600\text{ windings}}$

(b) $I_{1,\text{ rms}}(\Delta V_{1,\text{ rms}}) = I_{2,\text{ rms}}(\Delta V_{2,\text{ rms}})$ $\quad I_{1,\text{ rms}} = \frac{(1.50)(2\,200)}{110} = \boxed{30.0\text{ A}}$

(c) $0.950 I_{1,\text{ rms}}(\Delta V_{1,\text{ rms}}) = I_{2,\text{ rms}}(\Delta V_{2,\text{ rms}})$ $\quad I_{1,\text{ rms}} = \frac{(1.20)(2\,200)}{110(0.950)} = \boxed{25.3\text{ A}}$

P33.47 The rms voltage across the transformer primary is

$$\frac{N_1}{N_2}\left(\Delta V_{2,\text{ rms}}\right)$$

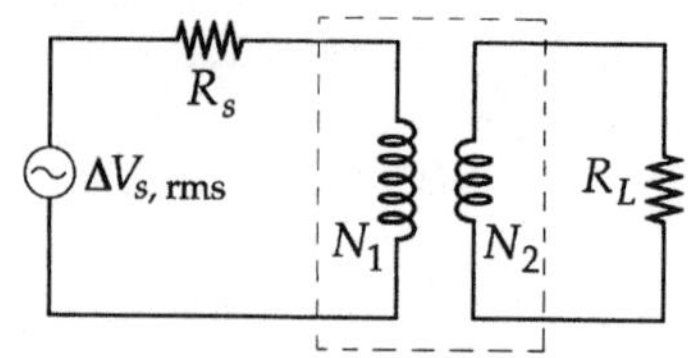

FIG. P33.47

so the source voltage is $\Delta V_{s,\text{ rms}} = I_{1,\text{ rms}}R_s + \frac{N_1}{N_2}\left(\Delta V_{2,\text{ rms}}\right)$.

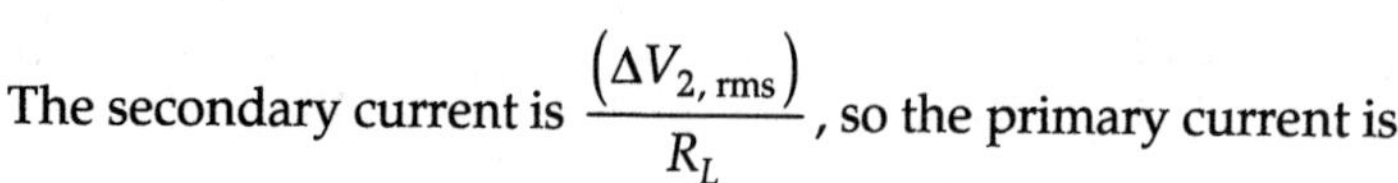

The secondary current is $\frac{\left(\Delta V_{2,\text{ rms}}\right)}{R_L}$, so the primary current is

$$\frac{N_2}{N_1}\frac{\left(\Delta V_{2,\text{ rms}}\right)}{R_L} = I_{1,\text{ rms}}.$$

Then $\Delta V_{s,\text{ rms}} = \frac{N_2\left(\Delta V_{2,\text{ rms}}\right)R_s}{N_1 R_L} + \frac{N_1\left(\Delta V_{2,\text{ rms}}\right)}{N_2}$

and $R_s = \frac{N_1 R_L}{N_2\left(\Delta V_{2,\text{ rms}}\right)}\left(\Delta V_{s,\text{ rms}} - \frac{N_1\left(\Delta V_{2,\text{ rms}}\right)}{N_2}\right) = \frac{5(50.0\ \Omega)}{2(25.0\ \text{V})}\left(80.0\ \text{V} - \frac{5(25.0\ \text{V})}{2}\right) = \boxed{87.5\ \Omega}$.

P33.48 (a) $\Delta V_{2,\text{ rms}} = \frac{N_2}{N_1}\left(\Delta V_{1,\text{ rms}}\right)$ $\qquad \frac{N_2}{N_1} = \frac{\Delta V_{2,\text{ rms}}}{\Delta V_{1,\text{ rms}}} = \frac{10.0\times10^3\ \text{V}}{120\ \text{V}} = \boxed{83.3}$

(b) $I_{2,\text{ rms}}\left(\Delta V_{2,\text{ rms}}\right) = 0.900 I_{1,\text{ rms}}\left(\Delta V_{1,\text{ rms}}\right)$

$I_{2,\text{ rms}}\left(10.0\times10^3\ \text{V}\right) = 0.900\left(\frac{120\ \text{V}}{24.0\ \Omega}\right)(120\ \text{V}) \qquad I_{2,\text{ rms}} = \boxed{54.0\ \text{mA}}$

(c) $Z_2 = \frac{\Delta V_{2,\text{ rms}}}{I_{2,\text{ rms}}} = \frac{10.0\times10^3\ \text{V}}{0.054\ \text{A}} = \boxed{185\ \text{k}\Omega}$

P33.49 (a) $R = \left(4.50\times10^{-4}\ \Omega/\text{M}\right)\left(6.44\times10^5\ \text{m}\right) = 290\ \Omega$ and $I_{\text{rms}} = \frac{\mathcal{P}}{\Delta V_{\text{rms}}} = \frac{5.00\times10^6\ \text{W}}{5.00\times10^5\ \text{V}} = 10.0\ \text{A}$

$\mathcal{P}_{\text{loss}} = I_{\text{rms}}^2 R = (10.0\ \text{A})^2(290\ \Omega) = \boxed{29.0\ \text{kW}}$

(b) $\frac{\mathcal{P}_{\text{loss}}}{\mathcal{P}} = \frac{2.90\times10^4}{5.00\times10^6} = \boxed{5.80\times10^{-3}}$

(c) It is impossible to transmit so much power at such low voltage. Maximum power transfer occurs when load resistance equals the line resistance of $290\ \Omega$, and is

$\frac{\left(4.50\times10^3\ \text{V}\right)^2}{2\cdot2(290\ \Omega)} = 17.5\ \text{kW}$ far below the required 5 000 kW.

Section 33.9 **Rectifiers and Filters**

***P33.50** (a) Input power $= 8\text{ W}$

Useful output power $= I\Delta V = 0.3\text{ A}(9\text{ V}) = 2.7\text{ W}$

$$\text{efficiency} = \frac{\text{useful output}}{\text{total input}} = \frac{2.7\text{ W}}{8\text{ W}} = \boxed{0.34} = 34\%$$

(b) Total input power = Total output power

$8\text{ W} = 2.7\text{ W} + \text{wasted power}$

$\text{wasted power} = \boxed{5.3\text{ W}}$

(c) $$E = \mathcal{P}\Delta t = 8\text{ W}(6)(31\text{ d})\left(\frac{86\,400\text{ s}}{1\text{ d}}\right)\left(\frac{1\text{ J}}{1\text{ Ws}}\right) = 1.29\times10^{8}\text{ J}\left(\frac{\$0.135}{3.6\times10^{6}\text{ J}}\right) = \boxed{\$4.8}$$

***P33.51** (a) The input voltage is $\Delta V_{\text{in}} = IZ = I\sqrt{R^2 + X_C^2} = I\sqrt{R^2 + \left(\frac{1}{\omega C}\right)^2}$. The output voltage is $\Delta V_{\text{out}} = IR$. The gain ratio is $\frac{\Delta V_{\text{out}}}{\Delta V_{\text{in}}} = \frac{IR}{I\sqrt{R^2 + (1/\omega C)^2}} = \frac{R}{\sqrt{R^2 + (1/\omega C)^2}}$.

(b) As $\omega \to 0$, $\frac{1}{\omega C} \to \infty$ and $\frac{\Delta V_{\text{out}}}{\Delta V_{\text{in}}} \to \boxed{0}$

As $\omega \to \infty$, $\frac{1}{\omega C} \to 0$ and $\frac{\Delta V_{\text{out}}}{\Delta V_{\text{in}}} \to \frac{R}{R} = \boxed{1}$

(c) $$\frac{1}{2} = \frac{R}{\sqrt{R^2 + (1/\omega C)^2}}$$

$$R^2 + \frac{1}{\omega^2 C^2} = 4R^2 \qquad \omega^2 C^2 = \frac{1}{3R^2} \qquad \omega = 2\pi f = \frac{1}{\sqrt{3}RC} \qquad \boxed{f = \frac{1}{2\pi\sqrt{3}RC}}$$

P33.52 (a) The input voltage is $\Delta V_{\text{in}} = IZ = I\sqrt{R^2 + X_C^2} = I\sqrt{R^2 + (1/\omega C)^2}$. The output voltage is $\Delta V_{\text{out}} = IX_C = \frac{I}{\omega C}$. The gain ratio is $\frac{\Delta V_{\text{out}}}{\Delta V_{\text{in}}} = \frac{I/\omega C}{I\sqrt{R^2 + (1/\omega C)^2}} = \frac{1/\omega C}{\sqrt{R^2 + (1/\omega C)^2}}$.

(b) As $\omega \to 0$, $\frac{1}{\omega C} \to \infty$ and R becomes negligible in comparison. Then $\frac{\Delta V_{\text{out}}}{\Delta V_{\text{in}}} \to \frac{1/\omega C}{1/\omega C} = \boxed{1}$. As $\omega \to \infty$, $\frac{1}{\omega C} \to 0$ and $\frac{\Delta V_{\text{out}}}{\Delta V_{\text{in}}} \to \boxed{0}$.

(c) $$\frac{1}{2} = \frac{1/\omega C}{\sqrt{R^2 + (1/\omega C)^2}} \qquad R^2 + \left(\frac{1}{\omega C}\right)^2 = \frac{4}{\omega^2 C^2} \qquad R^2\omega^2 C^2 = 3 \qquad \omega = 2\pi f = \frac{\sqrt{3}}{RC}$$

$$\boxed{f = \frac{\sqrt{3}}{2\pi RC}}$$

P33.53 For this RC high-pass filter, $\frac{\Delta V_{out}}{\Delta V_{in}} = \frac{R}{\sqrt{R^2 + X_C^2}}$.

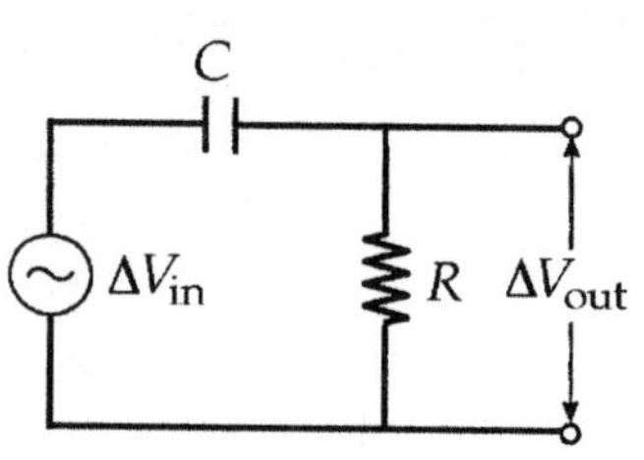

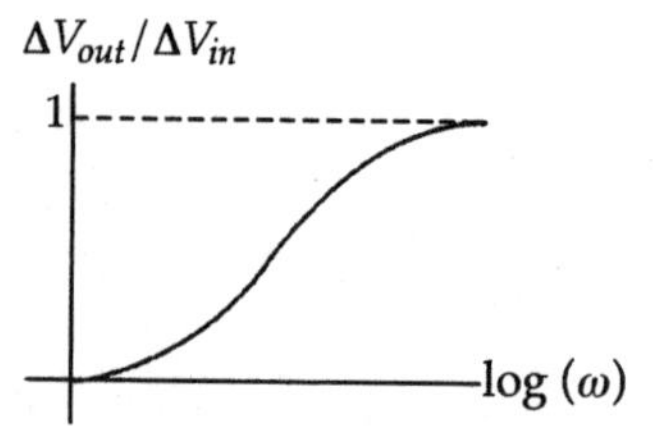

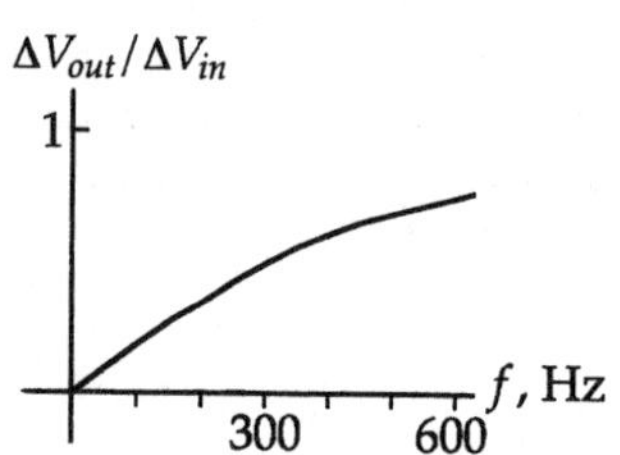

FIG. P33.53

(a) When $\frac{\Delta V_{out}}{\Delta V_{in}} = 0.500$,

then $\frac{0.500\ \Omega}{\sqrt{(0.500\ \Omega)^2 + X_C^2}} = 0.500$ or $X_C = 0.866\ \Omega$.

If this occurs at $f = 300$ Hz, the capacitance is

$$C = \frac{1}{2\pi f X_C} = \frac{1}{2\pi(300\text{ Hz})(0.866\ \Omega)} = 6.13\times10^{-4}\text{ F} = \boxed{613\ \mu\text{F}}.$$

(b) With this capacitance and a frequency of 600 Hz,

$$X_C = \frac{1}{2\pi(600\text{ Hz})(6.13\times10^{-4}\text{ F})} = 0.433\ \Omega$$

$$\frac{\Delta V_{out}}{\Delta V_{in}} = \frac{R}{\sqrt{R^2 + X_C^2}} = \frac{0.500\ \Omega}{\sqrt{(0.500\ \Omega)^2 + (0.433\ \Omega)^2}} = \boxed{0.756}.$$

P33.54 For the filter circuit, $\frac{\Delta V_{out}}{\Delta V_{in}} = \frac{X_C}{\sqrt{R^2 + X_C^2}}$.

(a) At $f = 600$ Hz, $X_C = \frac{1}{2\pi f C} = \frac{1}{2\pi(600\text{ Hz})(8.00\times10^{-9}\text{ F})} = 3.32\times10^4\ \Omega$

and $\frac{\Delta V_{out}}{\Delta V_{in}} = \frac{3.32\times10^4\ \Omega}{\sqrt{(90.0\ \Omega)^2 + (3.32\times10^4\ \Omega)^2}} \approx \boxed{1.00}$.

(b) At $f = 600$ kHz, $X_C = \frac{1}{2\pi f C} = \frac{1}{2\pi(600\times10^3\text{ Hz})(8.00\times10^{-9}\text{ F})} = 33.2\ \Omega$

and $\frac{\Delta V_{out}}{\Delta V_{in}} = \frac{33.2\ \Omega}{\sqrt{(90.0\ \Omega)^2 + (33.2\ \Omega)^2}} = \boxed{0.346}$.

P33.55 $\dfrac{\Delta V_{out}}{\Delta V_{in}} = \dfrac{R}{\sqrt{R^2 + (X_L - X_C)^2}}$

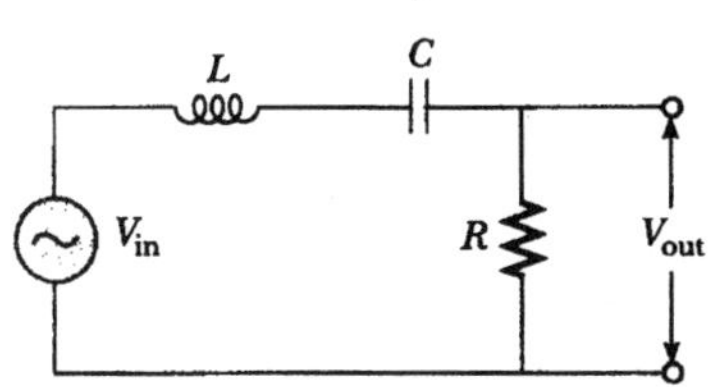

FIG. P33.55(a)

(a) At 200 Hz: $\dfrac{1}{4} = \dfrac{(8.00\ \Omega)^2}{(8.00\ \Omega)^2 + [400\pi L - 1/400\pi C]^2}$.

At 4 000 Hz: $(8.00\ \Omega)^2 + \left[8\,000\pi L - \dfrac{1}{8\,000\pi C}\right]^2 = 4(8.00\ \Omega)^2$.

At the low frequency, $X_L - X_C < 0$. This reduces to $400\pi L - \dfrac{1}{400\pi C} = -13.9\ \Omega$. [1]

For the high frequency half-voltage point, $8\,000\pi L - \dfrac{1}{8\,000\pi C} = +13.9\ \Omega$. [2]

Solving Equations (1) and (2) simultaneously gives $C = \boxed{54.6\ \mu\text{F}}$ and $L = \boxed{580\ \mu\text{H}}$.

(b) When $X_L = X_C$, $\dfrac{\Delta V_{out}}{\Delta V_{in}} = \left(\dfrac{\Delta V_{out}}{\Delta V_{in}}\right)_{max} = \boxed{1.00}$.

(c) $X_L = X_C$ requires $f_0 = \dfrac{1}{2\pi\sqrt{LC}} = \dfrac{1}{2\pi\sqrt{(5.80\times10^{-4}\ \text{H})(5.46\times10^{-5}\ \text{F})}} = \boxed{894\ \text{Hz}}$.

(d) At 200 Hz, $\dfrac{\Delta V_{out}}{\Delta V_{in}} = \dfrac{R}{Z} = \dfrac{1}{2}$ and $X_C > X_L$,

so the phasor diagram is as shown:

or

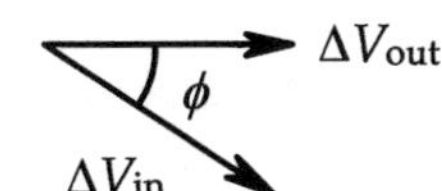

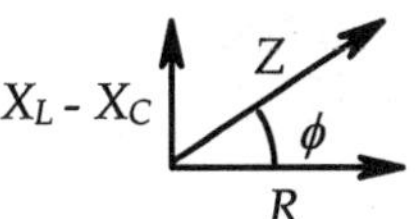

or

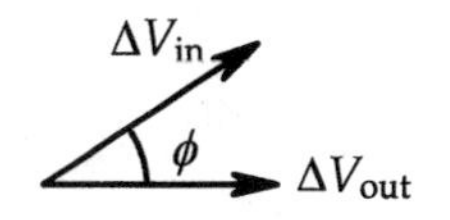

FIG. P33.55(d)

$\phi = -\cos^{-1}\left(\dfrac{R}{Z}\right) = -\cos^{-1}\left(\dfrac{1}{2}\right)$ so

$\boxed{\Delta V_{out} \text{ leads } \Delta V_{in} \text{ by } 60.0°}$.

At f_0, $X_L = X_C$ so

$\boxed{\Delta V_{out} \text{ and } \Delta V_{in} \text{ have a phase difference of } 0°}$.

At 4 000 Hz, $\dfrac{\Delta V_{out}}{\Delta V_{in}} = \dfrac{R}{Z} = \dfrac{1}{2}$ and $X_L - X_C > 0$.

Thus, $\phi = \cos^{-1}\left(\dfrac{1}{2}\right) = 60.0°$

or $\boxed{\Delta V_{out} \text{ lags } \Delta V_{in} \text{ by } 60.0°}$.

(e) At 200 Hz and at 4 kHz,

$$\mathscr{P} = \frac{(\Delta V_{out,\,rms})^2}{R} = \frac{((1/2)\Delta V_{in,\,rms})^2}{R} = \frac{(1/2)[(1/2)\Delta V_{in,\,max}]^2}{R} = \frac{(10.0\ \text{V})^2}{8(8.00\ \Omega)} = \boxed{1.56\ \text{W}}.$$

At f_0, $\mathscr{P} = \dfrac{(\Delta V_{out,\,rms})^2}{R} = \dfrac{(\Delta V_{in,\,rms})^2}{R} = \dfrac{(1/2)[\Delta V_{in,\,max}]^2}{R} = \dfrac{(10.0\ \text{V})^2}{2(8.00\ \Omega)} = \boxed{6.25\ \text{W}}$.

(f) We take: $Q = \dfrac{\omega_0 L}{R} = \dfrac{2\pi f_0 L}{R} = \dfrac{2\pi(894\ \text{Hz})(5.80\times10^{-4}\ \text{H})}{8.00\ \Omega} = \boxed{0.408}$.

Additional Problems

P33.56 The equation for $\Delta v(t)$ during the first period (using $y = mx + b$) is:

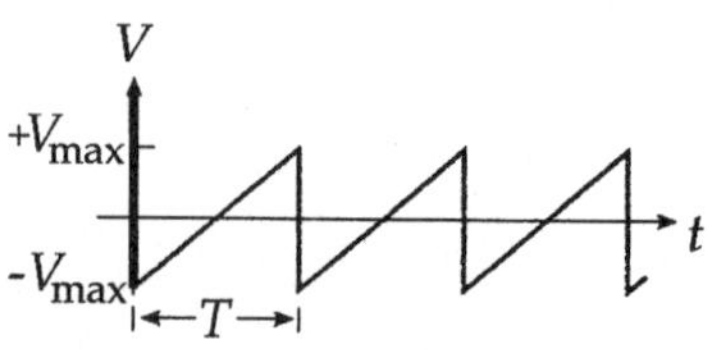

FIG. P33.56

$$\Delta v(t) = \frac{2(\Delta V_{max})t}{T} - \Delta V_{max}$$

$$\left[(\Delta v)^2\right]_{ave} = \frac{1}{T}\int_0^T [\Delta v(t)]^2\,dt = \frac{(\Delta V_{max})^2}{T}\int_0^T \left[\frac{2}{T}t - 1\right]^2 dt$$

$$\left[(\Delta v)^2\right]_{ave} = \frac{(\Delta V_{max})^2}{T}\left(\frac{T}{2}\right)\frac{[2t/T-1]^3}{3}\Bigg|_{t=0}^{t=T} = \frac{(\Delta V_{max})^2}{6}\left[(+1)^3 - (-1)^3\right] = \frac{(\Delta V_{max})^2}{3}$$

$$\Delta V_{rms} = \sqrt{\left[(\Delta v)^2\right]_{ave}} = \sqrt{\frac{(\Delta V_{max})^2}{3}} = \boxed{\frac{\Delta V_{max}}{\sqrt{3}}}$$

P33.57 $\omega_0 = \dfrac{1}{\sqrt{LC}} = \dfrac{1}{\sqrt{(0.050\,0\text{ H})(5.00\times10^{-6}\text{ F})}} = 2\,000\text{ s}^{-1}$

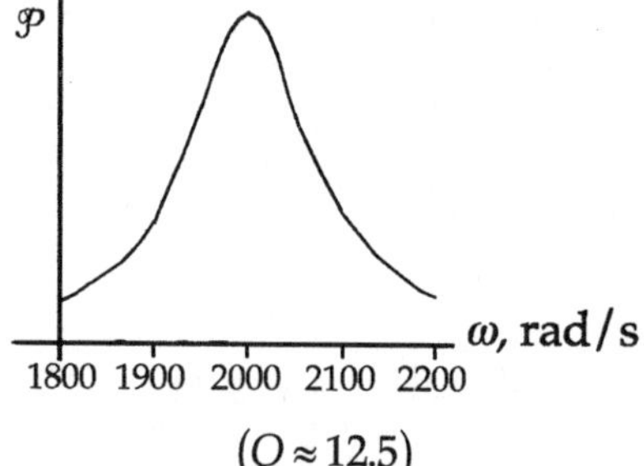

$(Q \approx 12.5)$

FIG. P33.57

so the operating angular frequency of the circuit is

$\omega = \dfrac{\omega_0}{2} = 1\,000\text{ s}^{-1}$.

Using Equation 33.37, $\mathcal{P} = \dfrac{(\Delta V_{rms})^2 R\omega^2}{R^2\omega^2 + L^2(\omega^2 - \omega_0^2)^2}$

$$P = \frac{(400)^2(8.00)(1\,000)^2}{(8.00)^2(1\,000)^2 + (0.050\,0)^2\left[(1.00-4.00)\times10^6\right]^2} = \boxed{56.7\text{ W}}.$$

***P33.58** The angular frequency is $\omega = 2\pi 60/\text{s} = 377/\text{s}$. When S is open, R, L, and C are in series with the source:

$$R^2 + (X_L - X_C)^2 = \left(\frac{\Delta V_s}{I}\right)^2 = \left(\frac{20\text{ V}}{0.183\text{ A}}\right)^2 = 1.194\times10^4\ \Omega^2. \tag{1}$$

When S is in position 1, a parallel combination of two R's presents equivalent resistance $\dfrac{R}{2}$, in series with L and C:

$$\left(\frac{R}{2}\right)^2 + (X_L - X_C)^2 = \left(\frac{20\text{ V}}{0.298\text{ A}}\right)^2 = 4.504\times10^3\ \Omega^2. \tag{2}$$

When S is in position 2, the current by passes the inductor. R and C are in series with the source:

$$R^2 + X_C^2 = \left(\frac{20\text{ V}}{0.137\text{ A}}\right)^2 = 2.131\times10^4\ \Omega^2. \tag{3}$$

Take equation (1) minus equation (2):

$\dfrac{3}{4}R^2 = 7.440\times10^3\ \Omega^2$ $\boxed{R = 99.6\ \Omega}$

continued on next page

(only the positive root is physical.) Now equation (3) gives

$$X_C = \left[2.131\times10^4 - (99.6)^2\right]^{1/2}\ \Omega = 106.7\ \Omega = \frac{1}{\omega C}\ \text{(only the positive root is physical.)}$$

$$C = (\omega X_C)^{-1} = \left[(377/\text{s})106.7\ \Omega\right]^{-1} = \boxed{2.49\times10^{-5}\ \text{F} = C}.$$

Now equation (1) gives

$$X_L - X_C = \pm\left[1.194\times10^4 - (99.6)^2\right]^{1/2}\ \Omega = \pm 44.99\ \Omega$$

$$X_L = 106.7\ \Omega + 44.99\ \Omega = 61.74\ \Omega \text{ or } 151.7\ \Omega = \omega L$$

$$L = \frac{X_L}{\omega} = \boxed{0.164\ \text{H or } 0.402\ \text{H} = L}$$

P33.59 The resistance of the circuit is $R = \frac{\Delta V}{I} = \frac{12.0\ \text{V}}{0.630\ \text{A}} = 19.0\ \Omega$.

The impedance of the circuit is $Z = \frac{\Delta V_{\text{rms}}}{I_{\text{rms}}} = \frac{24.0\ \text{V}}{0.570\ \text{A}} = 42.1\ \Omega$.

$$Z^2 = R^2 + \omega^2 L^2$$

$$L = \frac{1}{\omega}\sqrt{Z^2 - R^2} = \frac{1}{377}\sqrt{(42.1)^2 - (19.0)^2} = \boxed{99.6\ \text{mH}}$$

***P33.60** The lowest-frequency standing-wave state is NAN. The distance between the clamps we represent as $L = d_{\text{NN}} = \frac{\lambda}{2}$. The speed of transverse waves on the string is $v = f\lambda = \sqrt{\frac{T}{\mu}} = f2L$. The magnetic force on the wire oscillates at 60 Hz, so the wire will oscillate in resonance at 60 Hz.

$$\frac{T}{0.019\ \text{kg/m}} = (60/\text{s})^2 4L^2 \qquad \boxed{T = \left(274\ \text{kg/ms}^2\right)L^2}$$

Any values of T and L related according to this expression will work, including $\boxed{\text{if } L = 0.200\ \text{m} \quad T = 10.9\ \text{N}}$. We did not need to use the value of the current and magnetic field. If we assume the subsection of wire in the field is 2 cm wide, we can find the rms value of the magnetic force:

$$F_B = I\ell B\sin\theta = (9\ \text{A})(0.02\ \text{m})(0.015\,3T)\sin 90° = 2.75\ \text{mN}.$$

So a small force can produce an oscillation of noticeable amplitude if internal friction is small.

P33.61 (a) When ωL is very large, the bottom branch carries negligible current. Also, $\frac{1}{\omega C}$ will be negligible compared to $200\ \Omega$ and $\frac{45.0\ \text{V}}{200\ \Omega} = \boxed{225\ \text{mA}}$ flows in the power supply and the top branch.

(b) Now $\frac{1}{\omega C} \to \infty$ and $\omega L \to 0$ so the generator and bottom branch carry $\boxed{450\ \text{mA}}$.

P33.62 (a) With both switches closed, the current goes only through generator and resistor.

$$\boxed{i(t)=\frac{\Delta V_{max}}{R}\cos\omega t}$$

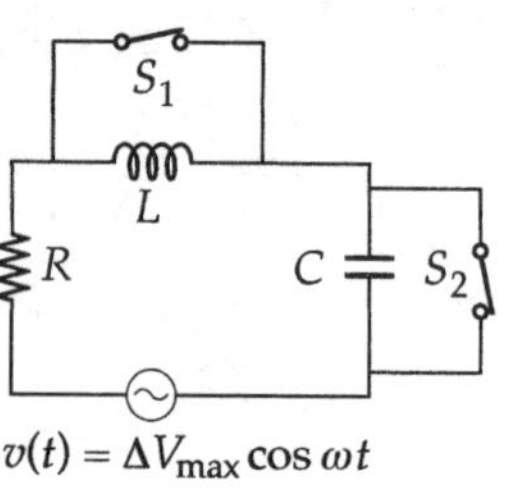

FIG. P33.62

(b) 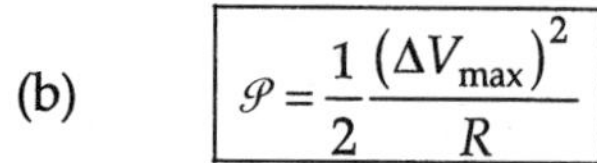

$$\boxed{\mathscr{P}=\frac{1}{2}\frac{(\Delta V_{max})^2}{R}}$$

(c) $$\boxed{i(t)=\frac{\Delta V_{max}}{\sqrt{R^2+\omega^2L^2}}\cos\left[\omega t+\arctan\left(\frac{\omega L}{R}\right)\right]}$$

(d) For $$0=\phi=\arctan\left(\frac{\omega_0L-(1/\omega_0C)}{R}\right).$$

We require $\omega_0L=\frac{1}{\omega_0C}$, so $\boxed{C=\frac{1}{\omega_0^2L}}$.

(e) At this resonance frequency, $Z=\boxed{R}$.

(f) $$U=\frac{1}{2}C(\Delta V_C)^2=\frac{1}{2}CI^2X_C^2$$

$$U_{max}=\frac{1}{2}CI_{max}^2X_C^2=\frac{1}{2}C\frac{(\Delta V_{max})^2}{R^2}\frac{1}{\omega_0^2C^2}=\boxed{\frac{(\Delta V_{max})^2L}{2R^2}}$$

(g) $$U_{max}=\frac{1}{2}LI_{max}^2=\boxed{\frac{1}{2}L\frac{(\Delta V_{max})^2}{R^2}}$$

(h) Now $\omega=2\omega_0=\frac{2}{\sqrt{LC}}$.

So $\phi=\arctan\left(\frac{\omega L-(1/\omega C)}{R}\right)=\arctan\left(\frac{2\sqrt{L/C}-(1/2)\sqrt{L/C}}{R}\right)=\boxed{\arctan\left(\frac{3}{2R}\sqrt{\frac{L}{C}}\right)}$.

(i) Now $\omega L=\frac{1}{2}\frac{1}{\omega C}$ $\quad\omega=\boxed{\frac{1}{\sqrt{2LC}}}=\frac{\omega_0}{\sqrt{2}}$.

P33.63 (a) $$I_{R,\,rms}=\frac{\Delta V_{rms}}{R}=\frac{100\text{ V}}{80.0\ \Omega}=\boxed{1.25\text{ A}}$$

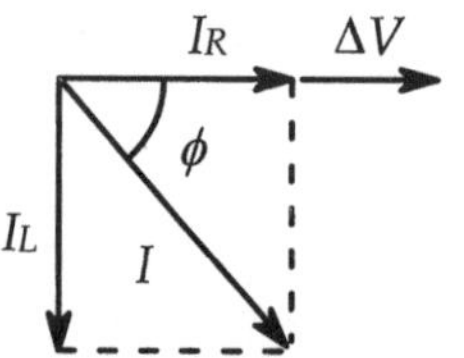

FIG. P33.63

(b) The total current will $\boxed{\text{lag}}$ the applied voltage as seen in the phasor diagram at the right.

$$I_{L,\,rms}=\frac{\Delta V_{rms}}{X_L}=\frac{100\text{ V}}{2\pi(60.0\text{ s}^{-1})(0.200\text{ H})}=1.33\text{ A}$$

Thus, the phase angle is: $\phi=\tan^{-1}\left(\frac{I_{L,\,rms}}{I_{R,\,rms}}\right)=\tan^{-1}\left(\frac{1.33\text{ A}}{1.25\text{ A}}\right)=\boxed{46.7°}$.

P33.64 Suppose each of the 20 000 people uses an average power of 500 W. (This means 12 kWh per day, or \$36 per 30 days at 10¢ per kWh). Suppose the transmission line is at 20 kV. Then

$$I_{rms} = \frac{\mathcal{P}}{\Delta V_{rms}} = \frac{(20\,000)(500 \text{ W})}{20\,000 \text{ V}} \boxed{\sim 10^3 \text{ A}}.$$

If the transmission line had been at 200 kV, the current would be only $\boxed{\sim 10^2 \text{ A}}$.

P33.65 $R = 200\ \Omega$, $L = 663$ mH, $C = 26.5\ \mu\text{F}$, $\omega = 377\ \text{s}^{-1}$, $\Delta V_{max} = 50.0$ V

$$\omega L = 250\ \Omega,\ \left(\frac{1}{\omega C}\right) = 100\ \Omega,\ Z = \sqrt{R^2 + (X_L - X_C)^2} = 250\ \Omega$$

(a) $$I_{max} = \frac{\Delta V_{max}}{Z} = \frac{50.0 \text{ V}}{250\ \Omega} = \boxed{0.200 \text{ A}}$$

$$\phi = \tan^{-1}\left(\frac{X_L - X_C}{R}\right) = \boxed{36.8°}\ (\Delta V \text{ leads } I)$$

(b) $$\Delta V_{R,\,max} = I_{max}R = \boxed{40.0 \text{ V}} \text{ at } \boxed{\phi = 0°}$$

(c) $$\Delta V_{C,\,max} = \frac{I_{max}}{\omega C} = \boxed{20.0 \text{ V}} \text{ at } \boxed{\phi = -90.0°}\ (I \text{ leads } \Delta V)$$

(d) $$\Delta V_{L,\,max} = I_{max}\omega L = \boxed{50.0 \text{ V}} \text{ at } \boxed{\phi = +90.0°}\ (\Delta V \text{ leads } I)$$

P33.66 $L = 2.00$ H, $C = 10.0 \times 10^{-6}$ F, $R = 10.0\ \Omega$, $\Delta v(t) = (100 \sin \omega t)$

(a) The resonant frequency ω_0 produces the maximum current and thus the maximum power delivery to the resistor.

$$\omega_0 = \frac{1}{\sqrt{LC}} = \frac{1}{\sqrt{(2.00)(10.0 \times 10^{-6})}} = \boxed{224 \text{ rad/s}}$$

(b) $$\mathcal{P} = \frac{(\Delta V_{max})^2}{2R} = \frac{(100)^2}{2(10.0)} = \boxed{500 \text{ W}}$$

(c) $$I_{rms} = \frac{\Delta V_{rms}}{Z} = \frac{\Delta V_{rms}}{\sqrt{R^2 + (\omega L - (1/\omega C))^2}} \quad \text{and} \quad (I_{rms})_{max} = \frac{\Delta V_{rms}}{R}$$

$$I_{rms}^2 R = \frac{1}{2}\left(I_{rms}^2\right)_{max} R \quad \text{or} \quad \frac{(\Delta V_{rms})^2}{Z^2}R = \frac{1}{2}\frac{(\Delta V_{rms})^2}{R^2}R.$$

This occurs where $Z^2 = 2R^2$: $$R^2 + \left(\omega L - \frac{1}{\omega C}\right)^2 = 2R^2$$

$$\omega^4 L^2 C^2 - 2L\omega^2 C - R^2\omega^2 C^2 + 1 = 0 \quad \text{or} \quad L^2C^2\omega^4 - \left(2LC + R^2C^2\right)\omega^2 + 1 = 0$$

$$\left[(2.00)^2\left(10.0 \times 10^{-6}\right)^2\right]\omega^4 - \left[2(2.00)\left(10.0 \times 10^{-6}\right) + (10.0)^2\left(10.0 \times 10^{-6}\right)^2\right]\omega^2 + 1 = 0.$$

Solving this quadratic equation, we find that $\omega^2 = 51\,130$, or $48\,894$

$$\omega_1 = \sqrt{48\,894} = \boxed{221 \text{ rad/s}} \quad \text{and} \quad \omega_2 = \sqrt{51\,130} = \boxed{226 \text{ rad/s}}.$$

P33.67 (a) From Equation 33.41, $\frac{N_1}{N_2} = \frac{\Delta V_1}{\Delta V_2}$.

Let input impedance $Z_1 = \frac{\Delta V_1}{I_1}$ and the output impedance $Z_2 = \frac{\Delta V_2}{I_2}$

so that $\frac{N_1}{N_2} = \frac{Z_1 I_1}{Z_2 I_2}$. But from Eq. 33.42, $\frac{I_1}{I_2} = \frac{\Delta V_2}{\Delta V_1} = \frac{N_2}{N_1}$.

So, combining with the previous result we have $\boxed{\frac{N_1}{N_2} = \sqrt{\frac{Z_1}{Z_2}}}$.

(b) $\frac{N_1}{N_2} = \sqrt{\frac{Z_1}{Z_2}} = \sqrt{\frac{8\,000}{8.00}} = \boxed{31.6}$

P33.68 $P = I_{\text{rms}}^2 R = \left(\frac{\Delta V_{\text{rms}}}{Z}\right)^2 R$, so $250 \text{ W} = \frac{(120 \text{ V})^2}{Z^2}(40.0\ \Omega)$: $Z = \sqrt{R^2 + \left(\omega L - \frac{1}{\omega C}\right)^2}$

$$250 = \frac{(120)^2(40.0)}{(40.0)^2 + \left[2\pi f(0.185) - \left[1/2\pi f\left(65.0\times10^{-6}\right)\right]\right]^2}$$ and $$250 = \frac{576\,000 f^2}{1\,600 f^2 + \left(1.162\,4 f^2 - 2\,448.5\right)^2}$$

$$1 = \frac{2\,304 f^2}{1\,600 f^2 + 1.351\,1 f^4 - 5\,692.3 f^2 + 5\,995\,300}$$ so $$1.351\,1 f^4 - 6\,396.3 f^2 + 5\,995\,300 = 0$$

$$f^2 = \frac{6\,396.3 \pm \sqrt{(6\,396.3)^2 - 4(1.351\,1)(5\,995\,300)}}{2(1.351\,1)} = 3\,446.5 \text{ or } 1\,287.4$$

$f = \boxed{58.7 \text{ Hz or } 35.9 \text{ Hz}}$

P33.69 $I_R = \frac{\Delta V_{\text{rms}}}{R}$; $I_L = \frac{\Delta V_{\text{rms}}}{\omega L}$; $I_C = \frac{\Delta V_{\text{rms}}}{(\omega C)^{-1}}$

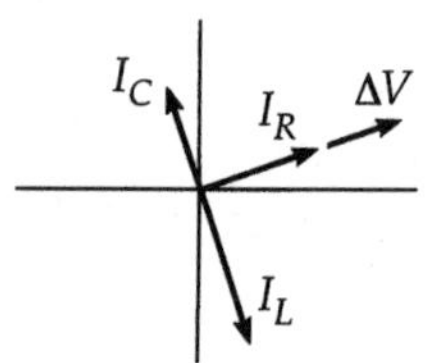

FIG. P33.69

(a) $I_{\text{rms}} = \sqrt{I_R^2 + (I_C - I_L)^2} = \boxed{\Delta V_{\text{rms}}\sqrt{\left(\frac{1}{R^2}\right) + \left(\omega C - \frac{1}{\omega L}\right)^2}}$

(b) $\tan\phi = \frac{I_C - I_L}{I_R} = \Delta V_{\text{rms}}\left[\frac{1}{X_C} - \frac{1}{X_L}\right]\left(\frac{1}{\Delta V_{\text{rms}}/R}\right)$

$\boxed{\tan\phi = R\left[\frac{1}{X_C} - \frac{1}{X_L}\right]}$

P33.70 (a) $I_{\text{rms}} = \Delta V_{\text{rms}} \sqrt{\dfrac{1}{R^2} + \left(\omega C - \dfrac{1}{\omega L}\right)^2}$

$\Delta V_{\text{rms}} \to (\Delta V_{\text{rms}})_{\text{max}}$ when $\omega C = \dfrac{1}{\omega L}$

$$f = \frac{1}{2\pi\sqrt{LC}} = \frac{1}{2\pi\sqrt{200 \times 10^{-3}\ \text{H}\left(0.150 \times 10^{-6}\ \text{F}\right)}} = \boxed{919\ \text{Hz}}$$

(b) $I_R = \dfrac{\Delta V_{\text{rms}}}{R} = \dfrac{120\ \text{V}}{80.0\ \Omega} = \boxed{1.50\ \text{A}}$

$I_L = \dfrac{\Delta V_{\text{rms}}}{\omega L} = \dfrac{120\ \text{V}}{\left(374\ \text{s}^{-1}\right)(0.200\ \text{H})} = \boxed{1.60\ \text{A}}$

$I_C = \Delta V_{\text{rms}}(\omega C) = (120\ \text{V})\left(374\ \text{s}^{-1}\right)\left(0.150 \times 10^{-6}\ \text{F}\right) = \boxed{6.73\ \text{mA}}$

(c) $I_{\text{rms}} = \sqrt{I_R^2 + (I_C - I_L)^2} = \sqrt{(1.50)^2 + (0.006\,73 - 1.60)^2} = \boxed{2.19\ \text{A}}$

(d) $\phi = \tan^{-1}\left[\dfrac{I_C - I_L}{I_R}\right] = \tan^{-1}\left[\dfrac{0.006\,73 - 1.60}{1.50}\right] = \boxed{-46.7°}$

The $\boxed{\text{current is lagging the voltage}}$.

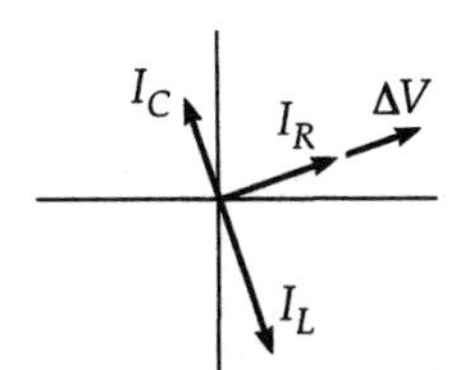

FIG. P33.70

P33.71 (a) $X_L = X_C = 1\,884\ \Omega$ when $f = 2\,000$ Hz

$L = \dfrac{X_L}{2\pi f} = \dfrac{1\,884\ \Omega}{4\,000\pi\ \text{rad/s}} = 0.150\ \text{H}$ and

$C = \dfrac{1}{(2\pi f)X_C} = \dfrac{1}{(4\,000\pi\ \text{rad/s})(1\,884\ \Omega)} = 42.2\ \text{nF}$

$X_L = 2\pi f(0.150\ \text{H}) \qquad X_C = \dfrac{1}{(2\pi f)\left(4.22 \times 10^{-8}\ \text{F}\right)}$

$Z = \sqrt{(40.0\ \Omega)^2 + (X_L - X_C)^2}$

f (Hz)	X_L (Ω)	X_C (Ω)	Z (Ω)
300	283	12 600	1 2300
600	565	6 280	5 720
800	754	4 710	3 960
1 000	942	3 770	2 830
1 500	1 410	2 510	1 100
2 000	1 880	1 880	40
3 000	2 830	1 260	1 570
4 000	3 770	942	2 830
6 000	5 650	628	5 020
10 000	9 420	377	9 040

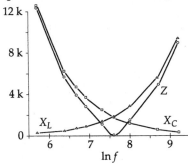

(b) Impedence, Ω

12 k
8 k
4 k
0
6 7 8 9
ln f
X_L Z X_C

FIG. P33.71(b)

P33.72 $\omega_0 = \frac{1}{\sqrt{LC}} = 1.00 \times 10^6$ rad/s

For each angular frequency, we find

$$Z = \sqrt{R^2 + (\omega L - 1/\omega C)^2}$$

then $I = \frac{1.00 \text{ V}}{Z}$

and $\mathscr{P} = I^2(1.00\ \Omega)$.

The full width at half maximum is:

$$\Delta f = \frac{\Delta\omega}{2\pi} = \frac{(1.0005 - 0.9995)\omega_0}{2\pi}$$

$$\Delta f = \frac{1.00 \times 10^3 \text{ s}^{-1}}{2\pi} = 159 \text{ Hz}$$

while

$$\frac{R}{2\pi L} = \frac{1.00\ \Omega}{2\pi\left(1.00 \times 10^{-3} \text{ H}\right)} = 159 \text{ Hz}.$$

$\frac{\omega}{\omega_0}$	ωL (Ω)	$\frac{1}{\omega C}$ (Ω)	Z (Ω)	$P = I^2R$ (W)
0.9990	999.0	1001.0	2.24	0.19984
0.9991	999.1	1000.9	2.06	0.23569
0.9993	999.3	1000.7	1.72	0.33768
0.9995	999.5	1000.5	1.41	0.49987
0.9997	999.7	1000.3	1.17	0.73524
0.9999	999.9	1000.1	1.02	0.96153
1.0000	1000	1000.0	1.00	1.00000
1.0001	1000.1	999.9	1.02	0.96154
1.0003	1000.3	999.7	1.17	0.73535
1.0005	1000.5	999.5	1.41	0.50012
1.0007	1000.7	999.3	1.72	0.33799
1.0009	1000.9	999.1	2.06	0.23601
1.0010	1001	999.0	2.24	0.20016

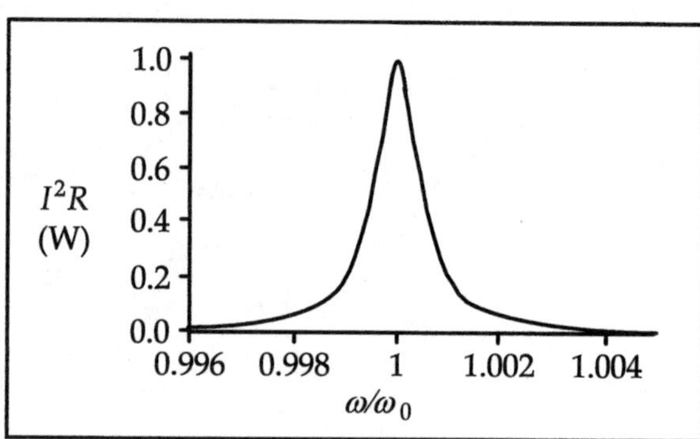

FIG. P33.72

P33.73 $\frac{\Delta V_{out}}{\Delta V_{in}} = \frac{R}{\sqrt{R^2 + (1/\omega C)^2}} = \frac{R}{\sqrt{R^2 + (1/2\pi f C)^2}}$

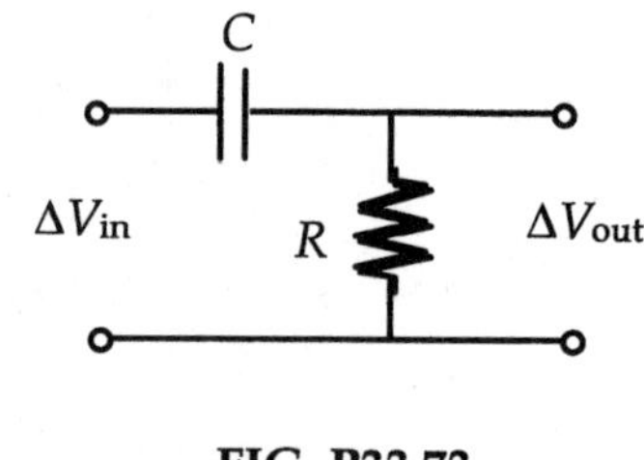

FIG. P33.73

(a) $\frac{\Delta V_{out}}{\Delta V_{in}} = \frac{1}{2}$ when $\frac{1}{\omega C} = R\sqrt{3}$.

Hence, $f = \frac{\omega}{2\pi} = \frac{1}{2\pi RC\sqrt{3}} = \boxed{1.84 \text{ kHz}}$.

continued on next page

(b)

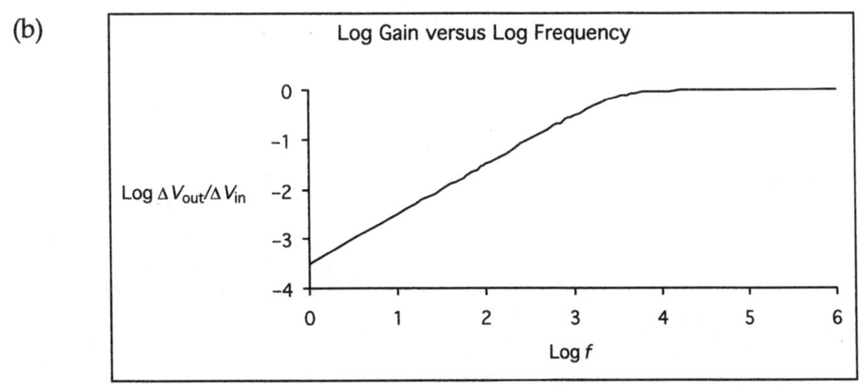

FIG. P33.73(b)

ANSWERS TO EVEN PROBLEMS

P33.2	(a) 193 Ω; (b) 144 Ω
P33.4	(a) 25.3 rad/s; (b) 0.114 s
P33.6	1.25 A and 96.0 Ω for bulbs 1 and 2; 0.833 A and 144 Ω for bulb 3
P33.8	7.03 H or more
P33.10	3.14 A
P33.12	3.80 J
P33.14	(a) greater than 41.3 Hz; (b) less than 87.5 Ω
P33.16	$\sqrt{2}C(\Delta V_{rms})$
P33.18	–32.0 A
P33.20	2.79 kHz
P33.22	(a) 109 Ω; (b) 0.367 A; (c) $I_{max} = 0.367$ A, $\omega = 100$ rad/s, $\phi = -0.896$ rad
P33.24	19.3 mA
P33.26	(a) 146 V; (b) 212 V; (c) 179 V; (d) 33.4 V
P33.28	$X_C = 3R$
P33.30	(a) 2.00 A; (b) 160 W; (c) see the solution
P33.32	353 W
P33.34	(a) 5.43 A; (b) 0.905; (c) 281 μF; (d) 109 V
P33.36	$\dfrac{11(\Delta V_{rms})^2}{14R}$
P33.38	46.5 pF to 419 pF
P33.40	(a) 3.56 kHz; (b) 5.00 A; (c) 22.4; (d) 2.24 kV
P33.42	$\dfrac{4\pi(\Delta V_{rms})^2 RC\sqrt{LC}}{4R^2C+9L}$
P33.44	(a) 9.23 V; (b) 4.55 A; (c) 42.0 W
P33.46	(a) 1 600 turns; (b) 30.0 A; (c) 25.3 A
P33.48	(a) 83.3; (b) 54.0 mA; (c) 185 kΩ
P33.50	(a) 0.34; (b) 5.3 W; (c) $4.8
P33.52	(a) see the solution; (b) 1; 0; (c) $\dfrac{\sqrt{3}}{2\pi RC}$
P33.54	(a) 1.00; (b) 0.346
P33.56	see the solution
P33.58	$R = 99.6\ \Omega$, $C = 24.9\ \mu$F, $L = 164$ mH or 402 mH

P33.60 $L = 0.200$ m and $T = 10.9$ N, or any values related by $T = \left(274\ \text{kg/ms}^2\right)L^2$

P33.62 (a) $i(t) = \dfrac{\Delta V_{\max}}{R}\cos\omega t$; (b) $\mathscr{P} = \dfrac{(\Delta V_{\max})^2}{2R}$;

(c) $i(t) = \dfrac{\Delta V_{\max}}{\sqrt{R^2 + \omega^2 L^2}}\cos\left[\omega t + \tan^{-1}\left(\dfrac{\omega L}{R}\right)\right]$;

(d) $C = \dfrac{1}{\omega_0^2 L}$; (e) $Z = R$; (f) $\dfrac{(\Delta V_{\max})^2 L}{2R^2}$;

(g) $\dfrac{(\Delta V_{\max})^2 L}{2R^2}$; (h) $\tan^{-1}\left(\dfrac{3}{2R}\sqrt{\dfrac{L}{C}}\right)$;

(i) $\dfrac{1}{\sqrt{2LC}}$

P33.64 $\sim 10^3$ A

P33.66 (a) 224 rad/s; (b) 500 W;
(c) 221 rad/s and 226 rad/s

P33.68 either 58.7 Hz or 35.9 Hz

P33.70 (a) 919 Hz;
(b) $I_R = 1.50$ A, $I_L = 1.60$ A, $I_C = 6.73$ mA;
(c) 2.19 A; (d) –46.7°; current lagging

P33.72 see the solution

34

Electromagnetic Waves

CHAPTER OUTLINE

ANSWERS TO QUESTIONS

Q34.1 Radio waves move at the speed of light. They can travel around the curved surface of the Earth, bouncing between the ground and the ionosphere, which has an altitude that is small when compared to the radius of the Earth. The distance across the lower forty-eight states is approximately 5 000 km, requiring a transit time of $\frac{5\times10^6 \text{ m}}{3\times10^8 \text{ m/s}} \sim 10^{-2}$ s. To go halfway around the Earth takes only 0.07 s. In other words, a speech can be heard on the other side of the world before it is heard at the back of a large room.

Q34.2 The Sun's angular speed in our sky is our rate of rotation, $\frac{360°}{24 \text{ h}} = 15°/\text{h}$. In 8.3 minutes it moves west by $\theta = \omega t = (15°/\text{h})\left(\frac{1 \text{ h}}{60 \text{ min}}\right)(8.3 \text{ min}) = 2.1°$. This is about four times the angular diameter of the Sun.

Q34.3 Energy moves. No matter moves. You could say that electric and magnetic fields move, but it is nicer to say that the fields at one point stay at that point and oscillate. The fields vary in time, like sports fans in the grandstand when the crowd does the wave. The fields constitute the medium for the wave, and energy moves.

Q34.4 No. If a single wire carries DC current, it does not emit electromagnetic waves. In this case, there is a constant magnetic field around the wire. Alternately, if the cable is a coaxial cable, it ideally does not emit electromagnetic waves even while carrying AC current.

Q34.5 Acceleration of electric charge.

Q34.6 The changing magnetic field of the solenoid induces eddy currents in the conducting core. This is accompanied by I^2R conversion of electrically-transmitted energy into internal energy in the conductor.

Q34.7 A wire connected to the terminals of a battery does not radiate electromagnetic waves. The battery establishes an electric field, which produces current in the wire. The current in the wire creates a magnetic field. Both fields are constant in time, so no electromagnetic induction or "magneto-electric induction" happens. Neither field creates a new cycle of the other field. No wave propagation occurs.

Q34.8 No. Static electricity is just that: static. Without acceleration of the charge, there can be no electromagnetic wave.

Q34.9

Sound	*Light*
The world of sound extends to the top of the atmosphere and stops there; sound requires a material medium. Sound propagates by a chain reaction of density and pressure disturbances recreating each other. Sound in air moves at hundreds of meters per second. Audible sound has frequencies over a range of three decades (ten octaves) from 20 Hz to 20 kHz. Audible sound has wavelengths of ordinary size (1.7 cm to 17 m). Sound waves are longitudinal.	The universe of light fills the whole universe. Light moves through materials, but faster in a vacuum. Light propagates by a chain reaction of electric and magnetic fields recreating each other. Light in air moves at hundreds of millions of meters per second. Visible light has frequencies over a range of less than one octave, from 430 to 750 **Tera**hertz. Visible light has wavelengths of very small size (400 nm to 700 nm). Light waves are transverse.

Sound and light can both be reflected, refracted, or absorbed to produce internal energy. Both have amplitude and frequency set by the source, speed set by the medium, and wavelength set by both source and medium. Sound and light both exhibit the Doppler effect, standing waves, beats, interference, diffraction, and resonance. Both can be focused to make images. Both are described by wave functions satisfying wave equations. **Both carry energy**. If the source is small, their intensities both follow an inverse-square law. Both are waves.

Q34.10 The Poynting vector **S** describes the energy flow associated with an electromagnetic wave. The direction of **S** is along the direction of propagation and the magnitude of **S** is the rate at which electromagnetic energy crosses a unit surface area perpendicular to the direction of **S**.

Q34.11 Photons carry momentum. Recalling what we learned in Chapter 9, the impulse imparted to a particle that bounces elastically is twice that imparted to an object that sticks to a massive wall. Similarly, the impulse, and hence the pressure exerted by a photon reflecting from a surface must be twice that exerted by a photon that is absorbed.

Q34.12 Different stations have transmitting antennas at different locations. For best reception align your rabbit ears perpendicular to the straight-line path from your TV to the transmitting antenna. The transmitted signals are also polarized. The polarization direction of the wave can be changed by reflection from surfaces—including the atmosphere—and through Kerr rotation—a change in polarization axis when passing through an organic substance. In your home, the plane of polarization is determined by your surroundings, so antennas need to be adjusted to align with the polarization of the wave.

Q34.13 You become part of the receiving antenna! You are a big sack of salt water. Your contribution usually increases the gain of the antenna by a few tenths of a dB, enough to noticeably improve reception.

Q34.14 On the TV set, each side of the dipole antenna is a 1/4 of the wavelength of the VHF radio wave. The electric field of the wave moves free charges in the antenna in electrical resonance, giving maximum current in the center of the antenna, where the cable connects it to the receiver.

Q34.15 The loop antenna is essentially a solenoid. As the UHF radio wave varies the magnetic field inside the loop, an AC emf is induced in the loop as described by Faraday's and Lenz's laws. This signal is then carried down a cable to the UHF receiving circuit in the TV. An excellent reference for antennas and all things radio is the *ARRL Handbook*.

Q34.16 The voltage induced in the loop antenna is proportional to the rate of change of the magnetic field in the wave. A wave of higher frequency induces a larger emf in direct proportion. The instantaneous voltage between the ends of a dipole antenna is the distance between the ends multiplied by the electric field of the wave. It does not depend on the frequency of the wave.

Q34.17 The radiation resistance of a broadcast antenna is the equivalent resistance that would take the same power that the antenna radiates, and convert it into internal energy.

Q34.18 Consider a typical metal rod antenna for a car radio. The rod detects the electric field portion of the carrier wave. Variations in the amplitude of the incoming radio wave cause the electrons in the rod to vibrate with amplitudes emulating those of the carrier wave. Likewise, for frequency modulation, the variations of the frequency of the carrier wave cause constant-amplitude vibrations of the electrons in the rod but at frequencies that imitate those of the carrier.

Q34.19 The frequency of EM waves in a microwave oven, typically 2.45 GHz, is chosen to be in a band of frequencies absorbed by water molecules. The plastic and the glass contain no water molecules. Plastic and glass have very different absorption frequencies from water, so they may not absorb any significant microwave energy and remain cool to the touch.

Q34.20 People of all the world's races have skin the same color in the infrared. When you blush or exercise or get excited, you stand out like a beacon in an infrared group picture. The brightest portions of your face show where you radiate the most. Your nostrils and the openings of your ear canals are bright; brighter still are just the pupils of your eyes.

Q34.21 Light bulbs and the toaster shine brightly in the infrared. Somewhat fainter are the back of the refrigerator and the back of the television set, while the TV screen is dark. The pipes under the sink show the same weak sheen as the walls until you turn on the faucets. Then the pipe on the right turns very black while that on the left develops a rich glow that quickly runs up along its length. The food on your plate shines; so does human skin, the same color for all races. Clothing is dark as a rule, but your bottom glows like a monkey's rump when you get up from a chair, and you leave behind a patch of the same blush on the chair seat. Your face shows you are lit from within, like a jack-o-lantern: your nostrils and the openings of your ear canals are bright; brighter still are just the pupils of your eyes.

Q34.22 Welding produces ultraviolet light, along with high intensity visible and infrared.

Q34.23 12.2 cm waves have a frequency of 2.46 GHz. If the Q value of the phone is low (namely if it is cheap), and your microwave oven is not well shielded (namely, if it is also cheap), the phone can likely pick up interference from the oven. If the phone is well constructed and has a high Q value, then there should be no interference at all.

SOLUTIONS TO PROBLEMS

Section 34.1 Maxwell's Equations and Hertz's Discoveries

***P34.1** (a) The rod creates the same electric field that it would if stationary. We apply Gauss's law to a cylinder of radius $r = 20$ cm and length ℓ:

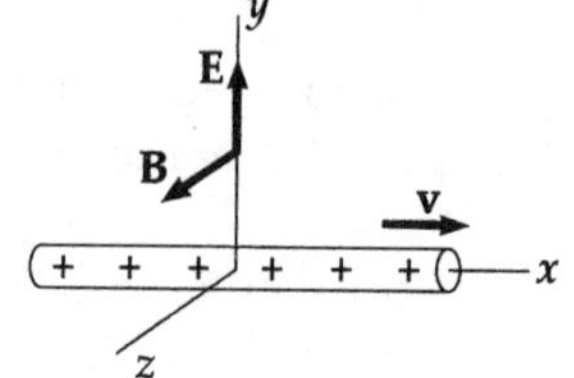

FIG. P34.1

$$\oint \mathbf{E}\cdot d\mathbf{A} = \frac{q_{\text{inside}}}{\epsilon_0}$$

$$E(2\pi rl)\cos 0° = \frac{\lambda l}{\epsilon_0}$$

$$\mathbf{E} = \frac{\lambda}{2\pi\epsilon_0 r}\text{ radially outward} = \frac{\left(35\times10^{-9}\text{ C/m}\right)\text{N}\cdot\text{m}^2}{2\pi\left(8.85\times10^{-12}\text{ C}^2\right)(0.2\text{ m})}\hat{\mathbf{j}} = \boxed{3.15\times10^3\,\hat{\mathbf{j}}\text{ N/C}}.$$

(b) The charge in motion constitutes a current of $\left(35\times10^{-9}\text{ C/m}\right)\left(15\times10^6\text{ m/s}\right) = 0.525$ A. This current creates a magnetic field.

$$\mathbf{B} = \frac{\mu_0 I}{2\pi r} = \frac{\left(4\pi\times10^{-7}\text{ T}\cdot\text{m/A}\right)(0.525\text{ A})}{2\pi(0.2\text{ m})}\hat{\mathbf{k}} = \boxed{5.25\times10^{-7}\,\hat{\mathbf{k}}\text{ T}}$$

(c) The Lorentz force on the electron is $F = q\mathbf{E} + q\mathbf{v}\times\mathbf{B}$

$$F = \left(-1.6\times10^{-19}\text{ C}\right)\left(3.15\times10^3\,\hat{\mathbf{j}}\text{ N/C}\right) + \left(-1.6\times10^{-19}\text{ C}\right)\left(240\times10^6\,\hat{\mathbf{i}}\text{ m/s}\right)\times\left(5.25\times10^{-7}\,\hat{\mathbf{k}}\,\frac{\text{N}\cdot\text{s}}{\text{C}\cdot\text{m}}\right)$$

$$F = 5.04\times10^{-16}\left(-\hat{\mathbf{j}}\right)\text{N} + 2.02\times10^{-17}\left(+\hat{\mathbf{j}}\right)\text{N} = \boxed{4.83\times10^{-16}\left(-\hat{\mathbf{j}}\right)\text{N}}$$

Section 34.2 Plane Electromagnetic Waves

P34.2 (a) Since the light from this star travels at 3.00×10^8 m/s

the last bit of light will hit the Earth in $\dfrac{6.44\times10^{18}\text{ m}}{3.00\times10^8\text{ m/s}} = 2.15\times10^{10}\text{ s} = 680$ years.

Therefore, it will disappear from the sky in the year $2\,004 + 680 = \boxed{2.68\times10^3\text{ C.E.}}$.

The star is 680 light-years away.

(b) $$\Delta t = \frac{\Delta x}{v} = \frac{1.496\times10^{11}\text{ m}}{3\times10^8\text{ m/s}} = \boxed{499\text{ s}} = 8.31\text{ min}$$

(c) $$\Delta t = \frac{\Delta x}{v} = \frac{2\left(3.84\times10^8\text{ m}\right)}{3\times10^8\text{ m/s}} = \boxed{2.56\text{ s}}$$

(d) $$\Delta t = \frac{\Delta x}{v} = \frac{2\pi\left(6.37\times10^6\text{ m}\right)}{3\times10^8\text{ m/s}} = \boxed{0.133\text{ s}}$$

(e) $$\Delta t = \frac{\Delta x}{v} = \frac{10\times10^3\text{ m}}{3\times10^8\text{ m/s}} = \boxed{3.33\times10^{-5}\text{ s}}$$

P34.3 $v = \dfrac{1}{\sqrt{\kappa \mu_0 \in_0}} = \dfrac{1}{\sqrt{1.78}}c = 0.750c = \boxed{2.25 \times 10^8 \text{ m/s}}$

P34.4 $\dfrac{E}{B} = c$

or $\dfrac{220}{B} = 3.00 \times 10^8$

so $B = 7.33 \times 10^{-7}\text{ T} = \boxed{733 \text{ nT}}$.

P34.5 (a) $f\lambda = c$

or $f(50.0 \text{ m}) = 3.00 \times 10^8 \text{ m/s}$

so $\boxed{f = 6.00 \times 10^6 \text{ Hz} = 6.00 \text{ MHz}}$.

(b) $\dfrac{E}{B} = c$

or $\dfrac{22.0}{B_{max}} = 3.00 \times 10^8$

so $\mathbf{B}_{max} = \boxed{-73.3\hat{\mathbf{k}} \text{ nT}}$.

(c) $k = \dfrac{2\pi}{\lambda} = \dfrac{2\pi}{50.0} = 0.126 \text{ m}^{-1}$

and $\omega = 2\pi f = 2\pi\left(6.00 \times 10^6 \text{ s}^{-1}\right) = 3.77 \times 10^7 \text{ rad/s}$

$\mathbf{B} = \mathbf{B}_{max}\cos(kx - \omega t) = \boxed{-73.3\cos\left(0.126x - 3.77 \times 10^7 t\right)\hat{\mathbf{k}} \text{ nT}}$.

P34.6 $\omega = 2\pi f = 6.00\pi \times 10^9 \text{ s}^{-1} = 1.88 \times 10^{10} \text{ s}^{-1}$

$k = \dfrac{2\pi}{\lambda} = \dfrac{\omega}{c} = \dfrac{6.00\pi \times 10^9 \text{ s}^{-1}}{3.00 \times 10^8 \text{ m/s}} = 20.0\pi = 62.8 \text{ m}^{-1}$ $\quad B_{max} = \dfrac{E}{c} = \dfrac{300 \text{ V/m}}{3.00 \times 10^8 \text{ m/s}} = 1.00\ \mu\text{T}$

$\boxed{E = (300 \text{ V/m})\cos\left(62.8x - 1.88 \times 10^{10} t\right)}$ $\quad \boxed{B = (1.00\ \mu\text{T})\cos\left(62.8x - 1.88 \times 10^{10} t\right)}$

P34.7 (a) $B = \dfrac{E}{c} = \dfrac{100 \text{ V/m}}{3.00 \times 10^8 \text{ m/s}} = 3.33 \times 10^{-7} \text{ T} = \boxed{0.333\ \mu\text{T}}$

(b) $\lambda = \dfrac{2\pi}{k} = \dfrac{2\pi}{1.00 \times 10^7 \text{ m}^{-1}} = \boxed{0.628\ \mu\text{m}}$

(c) $f = \dfrac{c}{\lambda} = \dfrac{3.00 \times 10^8 \text{ m/s}}{6.28 \times 10^{-7} \text{ m}} = \boxed{4.77 \times 10^{14} \text{ Hz}}$

P34.8 $E = E_{max}\cos(kx - \omega t)$

$$\frac{\partial E}{\partial x} = -E_{max}\sin(kx-\omega t)(k)$$

$$\frac{\partial E}{\partial t} = -E_{max}\sin(kx-\omega t)(-\omega)$$

$$\frac{\partial^2 E}{\partial x^2} = -E_{max}\cos(kx-\omega t)(k^2)$$

$$\frac{\partial^2 E}{\partial t^2} = -E_{max}\cos(kx-\omega t)(-\omega)^2$$

We must show: $\frac{\partial E}{\partial x^2} = \mu_0 \in_0 \frac{\partial^2 E}{\partial t^2}$.

That is, $-(k^2)E_{max}\cos(kx-\omega t) = -\mu_0 \in_0 (-\omega)^2 E_{max}\cos(kx-\omega t)$.

But this is true, because $\frac{k^2}{\omega^2} = \left(\frac{1}{f\lambda}\right)^2 = \frac{1}{c^2} = \mu_0 \in_0$.

The proof for the wave of magnetic field follows precisely the same steps.

P34.9 In the fundamental mode, there is a single loop in the standing wave between the plates. Therefore, the distance between the plates is equal to half a wavelength.

$$\lambda = 2L = 2(2.00\text{ m}) = 4.00\text{ m}$$

Thus, $f = \frac{c}{\lambda} = \frac{3.00\times10^8\text{ m/s}}{4.00\text{ m}} = 7.50\times10^7\text{ Hz} = \boxed{75.0\text{ MHz}}$.

P34.10 $d_{\text{A to A}} = 6\text{ cm}\pm5\% = \frac{\lambda}{2}$

$\lambda = 12\text{ cm}\pm5\%$

$v = \lambda f = (0.12\text{ m}\pm5\%)(2.45\times10^9\text{ s}^{-1}) = \boxed{2.9\times10^8\text{ m/s}\pm5\%}$

Section 34.3 Energy Carried by Electromagnetic Waves

P34.11 $S = I = \frac{U}{At} = \frac{Uc}{V} = uc$ $\quad\frac{\text{Energy}}{\text{Unit Volume}} = u = \frac{I}{c} = \frac{1\,000\text{ W/m}^2}{3.00\times10^8\text{ m/s}} = \boxed{3.33\ \mu\text{J/m}^3}$

P34.12 $S_{av} = \frac{\mathscr{P}}{4\pi r^2} = \frac{4.00\times10^3\text{ W}}{4\pi(4.00\times1\,609\text{ m})^2} = 7.68\ \mu\text{W/m}^2$

$E_{max} = \sqrt{2\mu_0 c S_{av}} = 0.076\,1\text{ V/m}$

$\Delta V_{max} = E_{max}L = (76.1\text{ mV/m})(0.650\text{ m}) = \boxed{49.5\text{ mV (amplitude)}}$ or 35.0 mV (rms)

P34.13 $r = (5.00 \text{ mi})(1\,609 \text{ m/mi}) = 8.04 \times 10^3 \text{ m}$

$$S = \frac{\overline{\mathcal{P}}}{4\pi r^2} = \frac{250 \times 10^3 \text{ W}}{4\pi\left(8.04 \times 10^3 \text{ W}\right)^2} = \boxed{307 \ \mu\text{W/m}^2}$$

P34.14 $I = \dfrac{100 \text{ W}}{4\pi(1.00 \text{ m})^2} = 7.96 \text{ W/m}^2$

$$u = \frac{I}{c} = 2.65 \times 10^{-8} \text{ J/m}^3 = 26.5 \text{ nJ/m}^3$$

(a) $u_E = \dfrac{1}{2}u = \boxed{13.3 \text{ nJ/m}^3}$

(b) $u_B = \dfrac{1}{2}u = \boxed{13.3 \text{ nJ/m}^3}$

(c) $I = \boxed{7.96 \text{ W/m}^2}$

P34.15 Power output = (power input)(efficiency).

Thus, $\text{Power input} = \dfrac{\text{Power out}}{\text{eff}} = \dfrac{1.00 \times 10^6 \text{ W}}{0.300} = 3.33 \times 10^6 \text{ W}$

and $A = \dfrac{\mathcal{P}}{I} = \dfrac{3.33 \times 10^6 \text{ W}}{1.00 \times 10^3 \text{ W/m}^2} = \boxed{3.33 \times 10^3 \text{ m}^2}$.

P34.16 $I = \dfrac{B_{\max}^2 c}{2\mu_0} = \dfrac{\mathcal{P}}{4\pi r^2}$

$$B_{\max} = \sqrt{\left(\frac{\mathcal{P}}{4\pi r^2}\right)\left(\frac{2\mu_0}{c}\right)} = \sqrt{\frac{\left(10.0 \times 10^3\right)(2)\left(4\pi \times 10^{-7}\right)}{4\pi\left(5.00 \times 10^3\right)^2\left(3.00 \times 10^8\right)}} = \boxed{5.16 \times 10^{-10} \text{ T}}$$

Since the magnetic field of the Earth is approximately 5×10^{-5} T, the Earth's field is some 100 000 times stronger.

P34.17 (a) $\mathcal{P} = I^2 R = 150 \text{ W}$

$$A = 2\pi r L = 2\pi\left(0.900 \times 10^{-3} \text{ m}\right)(0.080\,0 \text{ m}) = 4.52 \times 10^{-4} \text{ m}^2$$

$$S = \frac{\mathcal{P}}{A} = \boxed{332 \text{ kW/m}^2} \text{ (points radially inward)}$$

(b) $B = \dfrac{\mu_0 I}{2\pi r} = \dfrac{\mu_0(1.00)}{2\pi\left(0.900 \times 10^{-3}\right)} = \boxed{222 \ \mu\text{T}}$

$$E = \frac{\Delta V}{\Delta x} = \frac{IR}{L} = \frac{150 \text{ V}}{0.080\,0 \text{ m}} = \boxed{1.88 \text{ kV/m}}$$

Note: $S = \dfrac{EB}{\mu_0} = 332 \text{ kW/m}^2$

***P34.18** (a) $$I=\frac{E_{max}^2}{2\mu_0 c}=\frac{\left(3\times10^6\text{ V/m}\right)^2}{2\left(4\pi\times10^{-7}\text{ T}\cdot\text{m/A}\right)\left(3\times10^8\text{ m/s}\right)}\left(\frac{\text{J}}{\text{V}\cdot\text{C}}\right)^2\left(\frac{\text{C}}{\text{A}\cdot\text{s}}\right)\left(\frac{\text{T}\cdot\text{C}\cdot\text{m}}{\text{N}\cdot\text{s}}\right)\left(\frac{\text{N}\cdot\text{m}}{\text{J}}\right)$$

$$I=\boxed{1.19\times10^{10}\text{ W/m}^2}$$

(b) $$\mathcal{P}=IA=\left(1.19\times10^{10}\text{ W/m}^2\right)\pi\left(\frac{5\times10^{-3}\text{ m}}{2}\right)^2=\boxed{2.34\times10^5\text{ W}}$$

P34.19 (a) $$\mathbf{E}\cdot\mathbf{B}=\left(80.0\hat{\mathbf{i}}+32.0\hat{\mathbf{j}}-64.0\hat{\mathbf{k}}\right)(\text{N/C})\cdot\left(0.200\hat{\mathbf{i}}+0.080\,0\hat{\mathbf{j}}+0.290\hat{\mathbf{k}}\right)\mu\text{T}$$

$$\mathbf{E}\cdot\mathbf{B}=(16.0+2.56-18.56)\text{ N}^2\cdot\text{s/C}^2\cdot\text{m}=\boxed{0}$$

(b) $$\mathbf{S}=\frac{1}{\mu_0}\mathbf{E}\times\mathbf{B}=\frac{\left[\left(80.0\hat{\mathbf{i}}+32.0\hat{\mathbf{j}}-64.0\hat{\mathbf{k}}\right)\text{ N/C}\right]\times\left[\left(0.200\hat{\mathbf{i}}+0.080\,0\hat{\mathbf{j}}+0.290\hat{\mathbf{k}}\right)\mu\text{T}\right]}{4\pi\times10^{-7}\text{ T}\cdot\text{m/A}}$$

$$\mathbf{S}=\frac{\left(6.40\hat{\mathbf{k}}-23.2\hat{\mathbf{j}}-6.40\hat{\mathbf{k}}+9.28\hat{\mathbf{i}}-12.8\hat{\mathbf{j}}+5.12\hat{\mathbf{i}}\right)\times10^{-6}\text{ W/m}^2}{4\pi\times10^{-7}}$$

$$\mathbf{S}=\boxed{\left(11.5\hat{\mathbf{i}}-28.6\hat{\mathbf{j}}\right)\text{ W/m}^2}=30.9\text{ W/m}^2\text{ at }-68.2°\text{ from the }+x\text{ axis.}$$

***P34.20** The energy put into the water in each container by electromagnetic radiation can be written as $e\mathcal{P}\Delta t=eIA\Delta t$ where e is the percentage absorption efficiency. This energy has the same effect as heat in raising the temperature of the water:

$eIA\Delta t=mc\Delta T=\rho Vc\Delta T$

$$\Delta T=\frac{eI\ell^2\Delta t}{\rho\ell^3 c}=\frac{eI\Delta t}{\rho\ell c}$$

where ℓ is the edge dimension of the container and c the specific heat of water. For the small container,

$$\Delta T=\frac{0.7\left(25\times10^3\text{ W/m}^2\right)480\text{ s}}{\left(10^3\text{ kg/m}^3\right)(0.06\text{ m})4\,186\text{ J/kg}\cdot°\text{C}}=\boxed{33.4°\text{C}}.$$

For the larger,

$$\Delta T=\frac{0.91\left(25\text{ J/s}\cdot\text{m}^2\right)480\text{ s}}{\left(0.12/\text{m}^2\right)4\,186\text{ J/°C}}=\boxed{21.7°\text{C}}.$$

P34.21 We call the current I_{rms} and the intensity I. The power radiated at this frequency is

$$\mathcal{P}=(0.010\,0)(\Delta V_{rms})I_{rms}=\frac{0.010\,0(\Delta V_{rms})^2}{R}=1.31\text{ W}.$$

If it is isotropic, the intensity one meter away is

$$I=\frac{\mathcal{P}}{A}=\frac{1.31\text{ W}}{4\pi(1.00\text{ m})^2}=0.104\text{ W/m}^2=S_{av}=\frac{c}{2\mu_0}B_{max}^2$$

$$B_{max}=\sqrt{\frac{2\mu_0 I}{c}}=\sqrt{\frac{2\left(4\pi\times10^{-7}\text{ T}\cdot\text{m/A}\right)\left(0.104\text{ W/m}^2\right)}{3.00\times10^8\text{ m/s}}}=\boxed{29.5\text{ nT}}$$

P34.22 (a) $$\text{efficiency} = \frac{\text{useful power output}}{\text{total power input}} \times 100\% = \left(\frac{700 \text{ W}}{1\,400 \text{ W}}\right) \times 100\% = \boxed{50.0\%}$$

(b) $$S_{av} = \frac{\mathcal{P}}{A} = \frac{700 \text{ W}}{(0.068\,3 \text{ m})(0.038\,1 \text{ m})} = 2.69 \times 10^5 \text{ W/m}^2$$

$$\mathbf{S}_{av} = \boxed{269 \text{ kW/m}^2 \text{ toward the oven chamber}}$$

(c) $$S_{av} = \frac{E_{max}^2}{2\mu_0 c}$$

$$E_{max} = \sqrt{2\left(4\pi \times 10^{-7} \text{ T}\cdot\text{m/A}\right)\left(3.00 \times 10^8 \text{ m/s}\right)\left(2.69 \times 10^5 \text{ W/m}^2\right)} = 1.42 \times 10^4 \text{ V/m}$$

$$= \boxed{14.2 \text{ kV/m}}$$

P34.23 (a) $$B_{max} = \frac{E_{max}}{c}: \qquad B_{max} = \frac{7.00 \times 10^5 \text{ N/C}}{3.00 \times 10^8 \text{ m/s}} = \boxed{2.33 \text{ mT}}$$

(b) $$I = \frac{E_{max}^2}{2\mu_0 c}: \qquad I = \frac{\left(7.00 \times 10^5\right)^2}{2\left(4\pi \times 10^{-7}\right)\left(3.00 \times 10^8\right)} = \boxed{650 \text{ MW/m}^2}$$

(c) $$I = \frac{\mathcal{P}}{A}: \qquad \mathcal{P} = IA = \left(6.50 \times 10^8 \text{ W/m}^2\right)\left[\frac{\pi}{4}\left(1.00 \times 10^{-3} \text{ m}\right)^2\right] = \boxed{510 \text{ W}}$$

P34.24 (a) $$I = \frac{\left(10.0 \times 10^{-3}\right) \text{ W}}{\pi\left(0.800 \times 10^{-3} \text{ m}\right)^2} = \boxed{4.97 \text{ kW/m}^2}$$

(b) $$u_{av} = \frac{I}{c} = \frac{4.97 \times 10^3 \text{ J/m}^2\cdot\text{s}}{3.00 \times 10^8 \text{ m/s}} = \boxed{16.6 \ \mu\text{J/m}^3}$$

P34.25 (a) $$E = cB = \left(3.00 \times 10^8 \text{ m/s}\right)\left(1.80 \times 10^{-6} \text{ T}\right) = \boxed{540 \text{ V/m}}$$

(b) $$u_{av} = \frac{B^2}{\mu_0} = \frac{\left(1.80 \times 10^{-6}\right)^2}{4\pi \times 10^{-7}} = \boxed{2.58 \ \mu\text{J/m}^3}$$

(c) $$S_{av} = cu_{av} = \left(3.00 \times 10^8\right)\left(2.58 \times 10^{-6}\right) = \boxed{773 \text{ W/m}^2}$$

(d) This is $\boxed{\text{77.3\% of the intensity in Example 34.5}}$. It may be cloudy, or the Sun may be setting.

Section 34.4 **Momentum and Radiation Pressure**

P34.26 The pressure P upon the mirror is $P = \frac{2S_{av}}{c}$

where A is the cross-sectional area of the beam and $S_{av} = \frac{\mathcal{P}}{A}$.

The force on the mirror is then $F = PA = \frac{2}{c}\left(\frac{\mathcal{P}}{A}\right)A = \frac{2\mathcal{P}}{c}$.

Therefore, $F = \frac{2(100 \times 10^{-3})}{(3 \times 10^{8})} = \boxed{6.67 \times 10^{-10}\ \text{N}}$.

P34.27 For complete absorption, $P = \frac{S}{c} = \frac{25.0}{3.00 \times 10^{8}} = \boxed{83.3\ \text{nPa}}$.

P34.28 (a) The radiation pressure is $\frac{2(1\,340\ \text{W/m}^2)}{3.00 \times 10^{8}\ \text{m/s}^2} = 8.93 \times 10^{-6}\ \text{N/m}^2$.

Multiplying by the total area, $A = 6.00 \times 10^{5}\ \text{m}^2$ gives: $F = \boxed{5.36\ \text{N}}$.

(b) The acceleration is: $a = \frac{F}{m} = \frac{5.36\ \text{N}}{6\,000\ \text{kg}} = \boxed{8.93 \times 10^{-4}\ \text{m/s}^2}$.

(c) It will arrive at time t where $d = \frac{1}{2}at^2$

or $t = \sqrt{\frac{2d}{a}} = \sqrt{\frac{2(3.84 \times 10^{8}\ \text{m})}{(8.93 \times 10^{-4}\ \text{m/s}^2)}} = 9.27 \times 10^{5}\ \text{s} = \boxed{10.7\ \text{days}}$.

P34.29 $I = \frac{\mathcal{P}}{\pi r^2} = \frac{E_{max}^2}{2\mu_0 c}$

(a) $E_{max} = \sqrt{\frac{\mathcal{P}(2\mu_0 c)}{\pi r^2}} = \boxed{1.90\ \text{kN/C}}$

(b) $\frac{15 \times 10^{-3}\ \text{J/s}}{3.00 \times 10^{8}\ \text{m/s}}(1.00\ \text{m}) = \boxed{50.0\ \text{pJ}}$

(c) $p = \frac{U}{c} = \frac{5 \times 10^{-11}}{3.00 \times 10^{8}} = \boxed{1.67 \times 10^{-19}\ \text{kg} \cdot \text{m/s}}$

P34.30 (a) If $\mathscr{P}_S$ is the total power radiated by the Sun, and r_E and r_M are the radii of the orbits of the planets Earth and Mars, then the intensities of the solar radiation at these planets are:

$$I_E = \frac{\mathscr{P}_S}{4\pi r_E^2}$$

and

$$I_M = \frac{\mathscr{P}_S}{4\pi r_M^2}.$$

Thus,

$$I_M = I_E\left(\frac{r_E}{r_M}\right)^2 = \left(1\,340\ \text{W/m}^2\right)\left(\frac{1.496\times10^{11}\ \text{m}}{2.28\times10^{11}\ \text{m}}\right)^2 = \boxed{577\ \text{W/m}^2}.$$

(b) Mars intercepts the power falling on its circular face:

$$\mathscr{P}_M = I_M\left(\pi R_M^2\right) = \left(577\ \text{W/m}^2\right)\left[\pi\left(3.37\times10^6\ \text{m}\right)^2\right] = \boxed{2.06\times10^{16}\ \text{W}}.$$

(c) If Mars behaves as a perfect absorber, it feels pressure $P = \frac{S_M}{c} = \frac{I_M}{c}$

and force

$$F = PA = \frac{I_M}{c}\left(\pi R_M^2\right) = \frac{\mathscr{P}_M}{c} = \frac{2.06\times10^{16}\ \text{W}}{3.00\times10^8\ \text{m/s}} = \boxed{6.87\times10^7\ \text{N}}.$$

(d) The attractive gravitational force exerted on Mars by the Sun is

$$F_g = \frac{GM_SM_M}{r_M^2} = \frac{\left(6.67\times10^{-11}\ \text{N}\cdot\text{m}^2/\text{kg}^2\right)\left(1.991\times10^{30}\ \text{kg}\right)\left(6.42\times10^{23}\ \text{kg}\right)}{\left(2.28\times10^{11}\ \text{m}\right)^2} = 1.64\times10^{21}\ \text{N}$$

which is $\boxed{\sim10^{13}\ \text{times stronger}}$ than the repulsive force of part (c).

P34.31 (a) The total energy absorbed by the surface is

$$U = \left(\frac{1}{2}I\right)At = \left[\frac{1}{2}\left(750\ \text{W/m}^2\right)\right]\left(0.500\times1.00\ \text{m}^2\right)(60.0\ \text{s}) = \boxed{11.3\ \text{kJ}}.$$

(b) The total energy incident on the surface in this time is $2U = 22.5$ kJ, with $U = 11.3$ kJ being absorbed and $U = 11.3$ kJ being reflected. The total momentum transferred to the surface is

$$p = (\text{momentum from absorption}) + (\text{momentum from reflection})$$

$$p = \left(\frac{U}{c}\right) + \left(\frac{2U}{c}\right) = \frac{3U}{c} = \frac{3\left(11.3\times10^3\ \text{J}\right)}{3.00\times10^8\ \text{m/s}} = \boxed{1.13\times10^{-4}\ \text{kg}\cdot\text{m/s}}$$

***P34.32** The radiation pressure on the disk is $P=\frac{S}{c}=\frac{I}{c}=\frac{F}{A}=\frac{F}{\pi r^2}$.

Then $F=\frac{\pi r^2 I}{c}$.

Take torques about the hinge: $\sum \tau = 0$

$$H_x(0)+H_y(0)-mgr\sin\theta+\frac{\pi r^2 Ir}{c}=0$$

$$\theta=\sin^{-1}\frac{\pi r^2 I}{mgc}=\sin^{-1}\frac{\pi(0.4\text{ m})^2 10^7\text{ W s}^2\text{ s}}{(0.024\text{ kg})\text{ m}^2(9.8\text{ m})\left(3\times10^8\text{ m}\right)}\left(\frac{1\text{ kg m}^2}{1\text{ W s}^3}\right)$$

$$=\sin^{-1}0.0712=\boxed{4.09°}$$

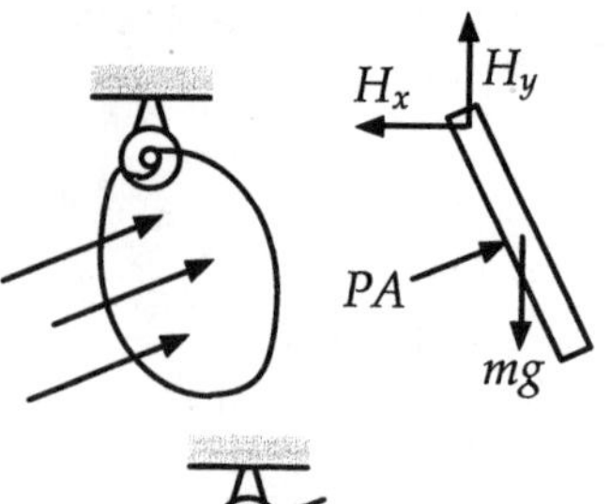

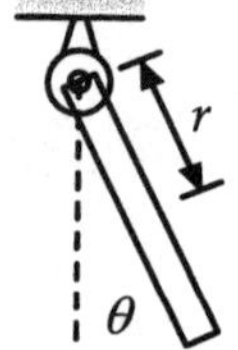

FIG. P34.32

Section 34.5 Production of Electromagnetic Waves by an Antenna

P34.33 $\lambda=\frac{c}{f}=536\text{ m}$ so $h=\frac{\lambda}{4}=\boxed{134\text{ m}}$

$\lambda=\frac{c}{f}=188\text{ m}$ so $h=\frac{\lambda}{4}=\boxed{46.9\text{ m}}$

P34.34 $\mathscr{P}=\frac{(\Delta V)^2}{R}$ or $\mathscr{P}\propto(\Delta V)^2$

$\Delta V=(-)E_y\cdot\Delta y=E_y\cdot\ell\cos\theta$

$\Delta V\propto\cos\theta$ so $\mathscr{P}\propto\cos^2\theta$

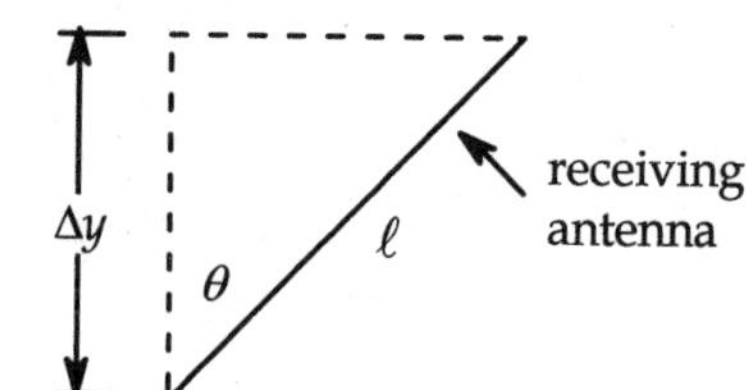

FIG. P34.34

(a) $\theta=15.0°:\ \mathscr{P}=\mathscr{P}_{max}\cos^2(15.0°)=0.933\mathscr{P}_{max}=\boxed{93.3\%}$

(b) $\theta=45.0°:\ \mathscr{P}=\mathscr{P}_{max}\cos^2(45.0°)=0.500\mathscr{P}_{max}=\boxed{50.0\%}$

(c) $\theta=90.0°:\ \mathscr{P}=\mathscr{P}_{max}\cos^2(90.0°)=\boxed{0}$

P34.35 (a) Constructive interference occurs when $d\cos\theta = n\lambda$ for some integer n.

$$\cos\theta = n\frac{\lambda}{d} = n\left(\frac{\lambda}{\lambda/2}\right) = 2n$$

$$n = 0, \pm1, \pm2, \ldots$$

$\therefore$ $\boxed{\text{strong signal @ } \theta = \cos^{-1} 0 = 90°, 270°}$

(b) Destructive interference occurs when

$$d\cos\theta = \left(\frac{2n+1}{2}\right)\lambda: \qquad \cos\theta = 2n+1$$

$\therefore$ $\boxed{\text{weak signal @ } \theta = \cos^{-1}(\pm1) = 0°, 180°}$

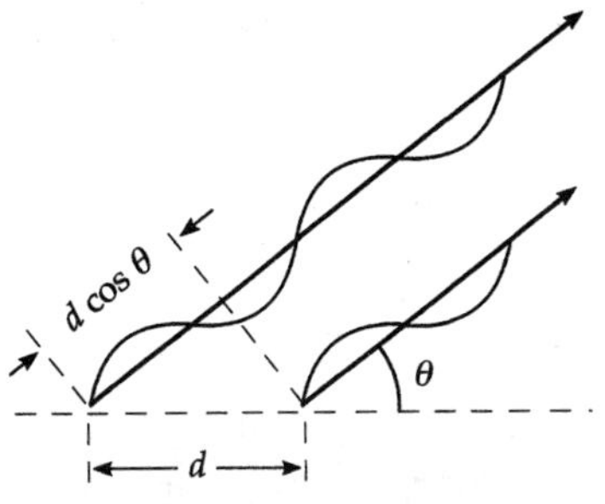

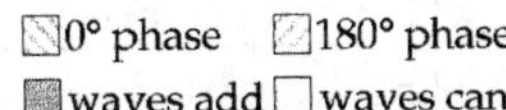

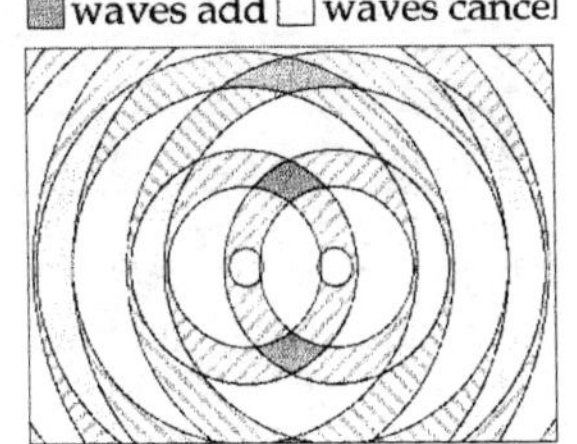

FIG. P34.35

P34.36 For the proton, $\sum F = ma$ yields $\qquad qvB\sin 90.0° = \dfrac{mv^2}{R}$.

The period of the proton's circular motion is therefore: $\qquad T = \dfrac{2\pi R}{v} = \dfrac{2\pi m}{qB}$.

The frequency of the proton's motion is $\qquad f = \dfrac{1}{T}$.

The charge will radiate electromagnetic waves at this frequency, with $\qquad \lambda = \dfrac{c}{f} = cT = \boxed{\dfrac{2\pi mc}{qB}}$.

***P34.37** (a) The magnetic field $\mathbf{B} = \frac{1}{2}\mu_0 J_{max}\cos(kx - \omega t)\hat{\mathbf{k}}$ applies for $x > 0$, since it describes a wave moving in the $\hat{\mathbf{i}}$ direction. The electric field direction must satisfy $\mathbf{S} = \frac{1}{\mu_0}\mathbf{E}\times\mathbf{B}$ as $\hat{\mathbf{i}} = \hat{\mathbf{j}}\times\hat{\mathbf{k}}$ so the direction of the electric field is $\hat{\mathbf{j}}$ when the cosine is positive. For its magnitude we have $E = cB$, so altogether we have $\boxed{\mathbf{E} = \frac{1}{2}\mu_0 cJ_{max}\cos(kx - \omega t)\hat{\mathbf{j}}}$.

(b) $$\mathbf{S} = \frac{1}{\mu_0}\mathbf{E}\times\mathbf{B} = \frac{1}{\mu_0}\frac{1}{4}\mu_0^2 cJ_{max}^2\cos^2(kx - \omega t)\hat{\mathbf{i}}$$

$$\boxed{\mathbf{S} = \frac{1}{4}\mu_0 cJ_{max}^2\cos^2(kx - \omega t)\hat{\mathbf{i}}}$$

(c) The intensity is the magnitude of the Poynting vector averaged over one or more cycles. The average of the cosine-squared function is $\frac{1}{2}$, so $\boxed{I = \frac{1}{8}\mu_0 cJ_{max}^2}$.

(d) $$J_{max} = \sqrt{\frac{8I}{\mu_0 c}} = \sqrt{\frac{8(570\ \text{W/m}^2)}{4\pi\times10^{-7}(\text{Tm/A})3\times10^8\ \text{m/s}}} = \boxed{3.48\ \text{A/m}}$$

Section 34.6 The Spectrum of Electromagnetic Waves

P34.38 From the electromagnetic spectrum chart and accompanying text discussion, the following identifications are made:

Frequency, f	Wavelength, $\lambda = \frac{c}{f}$	Classification
$2\text{ Hz} = 2\times10^{0}\text{ Hz}$	150 Mm	Radio
$2\text{ kHz} = 2\times10^{3}\text{ Hz}$	150 km	Radio
$2\text{ MHz} = 2\times10^{6}\text{ Hz}$	150 m	Radio
$2\text{ GHz} = 2\times10^{9}\text{ Hz}$	15 cm	Microwave
$2\text{ THz} = 2\times10^{12}\text{ Hz}$	150 μm	Infrared
$2\text{ PHz} = 2\times10^{15}\text{ Hz}$	150 nm	Ultraviolet
$2\text{ EHz} = 2\times10^{18}\text{ Hz}$	150 pm	X-ray
$2\text{ ZHz} = 2\times10^{21}\text{ Hz}$	150 fm	Gamma ray
$2\text{ YHz} = 2\times10^{24}\text{ Hz}$	150 am	Gamma ray

Wavelength, λ	Frequency, $f = \frac{c}{\lambda}$	Classification
$2\text{ km} = 2\times10^{3}\text{ m}$	$1.5\times10^{5}\text{ Hz}$	Radio
$2\text{ m} = 2\times10^{0}\text{ m}$	$1.5\times10^{8}\text{ Hz}$	Radio
$2\text{ mm} = 2\times10^{-3}\text{ m}$	$1.5\times10^{11}\text{ Hz}$	Microwave
$2\ \mu\text{m} = 2\times10^{-6}\text{ m}$	$1.5\times10^{14}\text{ Hz}$	Infrared
$2\text{ nm} = 2\times10^{-9}\text{ m}$	$1.5\times10^{17}\text{ Hz}$	Ultraviolet/X-ray
$2\text{ pm} = 2\times10^{-12}\text{ m}$	$1.5\times10^{20}\text{ Hz}$	X-ray/Gamma ray
$2\text{ fm} = 2\times10^{-15}\text{ m}$	$1.5\times10^{23}\text{ Hz}$	Gamma ray
$2\text{ am} = 2\times10^{-18}\text{ m}$	$1.5\times10^{26}\text{ Hz}$	Gamma ray

P34.39 $f = \frac{c}{\lambda} = \frac{3.00\times10^{8}\text{ m/s}}{5.50\times10^{-7}\text{ m}} = \boxed{5.45\times10^{14}\text{ Hz}}$

P34.40 (a) $f = \frac{c}{\lambda} = \frac{3\times10^{8}\text{ m/s}}{1.7\text{ m}}\ \boxed{\sim10^{8}\text{ Hz}}\ \boxed{\text{radio wave}}$

(b) 1 000 pages, 500 sheets, is about 3 cm thick so one sheet is about $6\times10^{-5}\text{ m}$ thick.

$$f = \frac{3.00\times10^{8}\text{ m/s}}{6\times10^{-5}\text{ m}}\ \boxed{\sim10^{13}\text{ Hz}}\ \boxed{\text{infrared}}$$

P34.41 (a) $f\lambda = c$ gives $(5.00\times10^{19}\text{ Hz})\lambda = 3.00\times10^{8}\text{ m/s}$: $\boxed{\lambda = 6.00\times10^{-12}\text{ m} = 6.00\text{ pm}}$

(b) $f\lambda = c$ gives $(4.00\times10^{9}\text{ Hz})\lambda = 3.00\times10^{8}\text{ m/s}$: $\boxed{\lambda = 0.075\text{ m} = 7.50\text{ cm}}$

P34.42 (a) $\lambda = \frac{c}{f} = \frac{3.00 \times 10^8 \text{ m/s}}{1\,150 \times 10^3 \text{ s}^{-1}} = 261 \text{ m}$ so $\frac{180 \text{ m}}{261 \text{ m}} = \boxed{0.690 \text{ wavelengths}}$

(b) $\lambda = \frac{c}{f} = \frac{3.00 \times 10^8 \text{ m/s}}{98.1 \times 10^6 \text{ s}^{-1}} = 3.06 \text{ m}$ so $\frac{180 \text{ m}}{3.06 \text{ m}} = \boxed{58.9 \text{ wavelengths}}$

P34.43 Time to reach object $= \frac{1}{2}(\text{total time of flight}) = \frac{1}{2}\left(4.00 \times 10^{-4} \text{ s}\right) = 2.00 \times 10^{-4} \text{ s}$.

Thus, $d = vt = \left(3.00 \times 10^8 \text{ m/s}\right)\left(2.00 \times 10^{-4} \text{ s}\right) = 6.00 \times 10^4 \text{ m} = \boxed{60.0 \text{ km}}$.

P34.44 The time for the radio signal to travel 100 km is: $\Delta t_r = \frac{100 \times 10^3 \text{ m}}{3.00 \times 10^8 \text{ m/s}} = 3.33 \times 10^{-4} \text{ s}$.

The sound wave travels 3.00 m across the room in: $\Delta t_s = \frac{3.00 \text{ m}}{343 \text{ m/s}} = 8.75 \times 10^{-3} \text{ s}$.

Therefore, $\boxed{\text{listeners 100 km away}}$ will receive the news before the people in the news room by a total time difference of

$\Delta t = 8.75 \times 10^{-3} \text{ s} - 3.33 \times 10^{-4} \text{ s} = 8.41 \times 10^{-3} \text{ s}$.

P34.45 The wavelength of an ELF wave of frequency 75.0 Hz is $\lambda = \frac{c}{f} = \frac{3.00 \times 10^8 \text{ m/s}}{75.0 \text{ Hz}} = 4.00 \times 10^6 \text{ m}$.

The length of a quarter-wavelength antenna would be $L = 1.00 \times 10^6 \text{ m} = \boxed{1.00 \times 10^3 \text{ km}}$

or $L = (1\,000 \text{ km})\left(\frac{0.621 \text{ mi}}{1.00 \text{ km}}\right) = \boxed{621 \text{ mi}}$.

Thus, while the project may be theoretically possible, it is not very practical.

P34.46 (a) For the AM band, $\lambda_{\max} = \frac{c}{f_{\min}} = \frac{3.00 \times 10^8 \text{ m/s}}{540 \times 10^3 \text{ Hz}} = \boxed{556 \text{ m}}$

$$\lambda_{\min} = \frac{c}{f_{\max}} = \frac{3.00 \times 10^8 \text{ m/s}}{1\,600 \times 10^3 \text{ Hz}} = \boxed{187 \text{ m}}.$$

(b) For the FM band, $\lambda_{\max} = \frac{c}{f_{\min}} = \frac{3.00 \times 10^8 \text{ m/s}}{88.0 \times 10^6 \text{ Hz}} = \boxed{3.41 \text{ m}}$

$$\lambda_{\min} = \frac{c}{f_{\max}} = \frac{3.00 \times 10^8 \text{ m/s}}{108 \times 10^6 \text{ Hz}} = \boxed{2.78 \text{ m}}.$$

Additional Problems

P34.47 (a) $\mathcal{P} = SA$: $\mathcal{P} = \left(1\,340\ \text{W/m}^2\right)\left[4\pi\left(1.496\times10^{11}\ \text{m}\right)^2\right] = \boxed{3.77\times10^{26}\ \text{W}}$

(b) $S = \dfrac{cB_{max}^2}{2\mu_0}$ so $B_{max} = \sqrt{\dfrac{2\mu_0 S}{c}} = \sqrt{\dfrac{2\left(4\pi\times10^{-7}\ \text{N/A}^2\right)\left(1\,340\ \text{W/m}^2\right)}{3.00\times10^8\ \text{m/s}}} = \boxed{3.35\ \mu\text{T}}$

$S = \dfrac{E_{max}^2}{2\mu_0 c}$ so $E_{max} = \sqrt{2\mu_0 cS} = \sqrt{2\left(4\pi\times10^{-7}\right)\left(3.00\times10^8\right)\left(1\,340\right)} = \boxed{1.01\ \text{kV/m}}$

P34.48 Suppose you cover a 1.7 m-by-0.3 m section of beach blanket. Suppose the elevation angle of the Sun is 60°. Then the target area you fill in the Sun's field of view is

$$(1.7\ \text{m})(0.3\ \text{m})\cos 30° = 0.4\ \text{m}^2.$$

Now $I = \dfrac{\mathcal{P}}{A} = \dfrac{U}{At}$ $U = IAt = \left(1\,340\ \text{W/m}^2\right)\left[(0.6)(0.5)\left(0.4\ \text{m}^2\right)\right](3\,600\ \text{s})\boxed{\sim10^6\ \text{J}}$.

P34.49 (a) $\varepsilon = -\dfrac{d\Phi_B}{dt} = -\dfrac{d}{dt}(BA\cos\theta)$ $\varepsilon = -A\dfrac{d}{dt}(B_{max}\cos\omega t\cos\theta) = AB_{max}\omega(\sin\omega t\cos\theta)$

$\varepsilon(t) = 2\pi fB_{max}A\sin 2\pi ft\cos\theta$ $\varepsilon(t) = 2\pi^2r^2fB_{max}\cos\theta\sin 2\pi ft$

Thus, $\boxed{\varepsilon_{max} = 2\pi^2r^2fB_{max}\cos\theta}$

where θ is the angle between the magnetic field and the normal to the loop.

(b) If **E** is vertical, **B** is horizontal, so $\boxed{\text{the plane of the loop should be vertical}}$

and $\boxed{\text{the plane should contain the line of sight of the transmitter}}$.

P34.50 (a) $F_{grav} = \dfrac{GM_Sm}{R^2} = \left(\dfrac{GM_S}{R^2}\right)\left[\rho\left(\dfrac{4}{3}\pi r^3\right)\right]$

where M_S = mass of Sun, r = radius of particle and R = distance from Sun to particle.

Since $F_{rad} = \dfrac{S\pi r^2}{c}$,

$$\frac{F_{rad}}{F_{grav}} = \left(\frac{1}{r}\right)\left(\frac{3SR^2}{4cGM_S\rho}\right) \propto \frac{1}{r}.$$

(b) From the result found in part (a), when $F_{grav} = F_{rad}$,

we have $r = \dfrac{3SR^2}{4cGM_S\rho}$

$$r = \frac{3\left(214\ \text{W/m}^2\right)\left(3.75\times10^{11}\ \text{m}\right)^2}{4\left(6.67\times10^{-11}\ \text{N}\cdot\text{m}^2/\text{kg}^2\right)\left(1.991\times10^{30}\ \text{kg}\right)\left(1\,500\ \text{kg/m}^3\right)\left(3.00\times10^8\ \text{m/s}\right)}$$

$= \boxed{3.78\times10^{-7}\ \text{m}}$

P34.51 (a) $B_{max} = \dfrac{E_{max}}{c} = \boxed{6.67 \times 10^{-16}\ \text{T}}$

(b) $S_{av} = \dfrac{E_{max}^2}{2\mu_0 c} = \boxed{5.31 \times 10^{-17}\ \text{W/m}^2}$

(c) $\mathcal{P} = S_{av} A = \boxed{1.67 \times 10^{-14}\ \text{W}}$

(d) $F = PA = \left(\dfrac{S_{av}}{c}\right) A = \boxed{5.56 \times 10^{-23}\ \text{N}}$ (≅ the weight of 3 000 H atoms!)

FIG. P34.51

P34.52 (a) The power incident on the mirror is: $\mathcal{P}_I = IA = \left(1\,340\ \text{W/m}^2\right)\left[\pi(100\ \text{m})^2\right] = 4.21 \times 10^7\ \text{W}$.

The power reflected through the atmosphere is $\mathcal{P}_R = 0.746\left(4.21 \times 10^7\ \text{W}\right) = \boxed{3.14 \times 10^7\ \text{W}}$.

(b) $S = \dfrac{\mathcal{P}_R}{A} = \dfrac{3.14 \times 10^7\ \text{W}}{\pi\left(4.00 \times 10^3\ \text{m}\right)^2} = \boxed{0.625\ \text{W/m}^2}$

(c) Noon sunshine in Saint Petersburg produces this power-per-area on a horizontal surface:

$\dfrac{\mathcal{P}_N}{A} = 0.746\left(1\,340\ \text{W/m}^2\right)\sin 7.00° = 122\ \text{W/m}^2$.

The radiation intensity received from the mirror is

$\left(\dfrac{0.625\ \text{W/m}^2}{122\ \text{W/m}^2}\right)100\% = \boxed{0.513\%}$ of that from the noon Sun in January.

P34.53 $u = \dfrac{1}{2} \epsilon_0 E_{max}^2$ $\qquad E_{max} = \sqrt{\dfrac{2u}{\epsilon_0}} = \boxed{95.1\ \text{mV/m}}$

P34.54 The area over which we model the antenna as radiating is the lateral surface of a cylinder,

$$A = 2\pi r\ell = 2\pi\left(4.00 \times 10^{-2}\ \text{m}\right)(0.100\ \text{m}) = 2.51 \times 10^{-2}\ \text{m}^2.$$

(a) The intensity is then: $S = \dfrac{\mathcal{P}}{A} = \dfrac{0.600\ \text{W}}{2.51 \times 10^{-2}\ \text{m}^2} = \boxed{23.9\ \text{W/m}^2}$.

(b) The standard is:

$0.570\ \text{mW/cm}^2 = 0.570\left(\text{mW/cm}^2\right)\left(\dfrac{1.00 \times 10^{-3}\ \text{W}}{1.00\ \text{mW}}\right)\left(\dfrac{1.00 \times 10^4\ \text{cm}^2}{1.00\ \text{m}^2}\right) = 5.70\ \text{W/m}^2$.

While it is on, the telephone is over the standard by $\dfrac{23.9\ \text{W/m}^2}{5.70\ \text{W/m}^2} = \boxed{4.19\ \text{times}}$.

P34.55 (a) $B_{max} = \frac{E_{max}}{c} = \frac{175 \text{ V/m}}{3.00 \times 10^8 \text{ m/s}} = \boxed{5.83 \times 10^{-7} \text{ T}}$

$k = \frac{2\pi}{\lambda} = \frac{2\pi}{0.0150 \text{ m}} = \boxed{419 \text{ rad/m}}$ $\qquad \omega = kc = \boxed{1.26 \times 10^{11} \text{ rad/s}}$

Since **S** is along x, and **E** is along y, **B** must be in $\boxed{\text{the } z \text{ direction}}$. (That is $\mathbf{S} \propto \mathbf{E} \times \mathbf{B}$.)

(b) $S_{av} = \frac{E_{max}B_{max}}{2\mu_0} = 40.6 \text{ W/m}^2$ $\qquad \mathbf{S}_{av} = \boxed{\left(40.6 \text{ W/m}^2\right)\hat{\mathbf{i}}}$

(c) $P_r = \frac{2S}{c} = \boxed{2.71 \times 10^{-7} \text{ N/m}^2}$

(d) $a = \frac{\sum F}{m} = \frac{PA}{m} = \frac{\left(2.71 \times 10^{-7} \text{ N/m}^2\right)\left(0.750 \text{ m}^2\right)}{0.500 \text{ kg}} = 4.06 \times 10^{-7} \text{ m/s}^2$ $\qquad \mathbf{a} = \boxed{\left(406 \text{ nm/s}^2\right)\hat{\mathbf{i}}}$

P34.56 Of the intensity $\qquad S = 1\,340 \text{ W/m}^2$

the 38.0% that is reflected exerts a pressure $\qquad P_1 = \frac{2S_r}{c} = \frac{2(0.380)S}{c}$.

The absorbed light exerts pressure $\qquad P_2 = \frac{S_a}{c} = \frac{0.620S}{c}$.

Altogether the pressure at the subsolar point on Earth is

(a) $P_{total} = P_1 + P_2 = \frac{1.38S}{c} = \frac{1.38\left(1\,340 \text{ W/m}^2\right)}{3.00 \times 10^8 \text{ m/s}} = \boxed{6.16 \times 10^{-6} \text{ Pa}}$

(b) $\frac{P_a}{P_{total}} = \frac{1.01 \times 10^5 \text{ N/m}^2}{6.16 \times 10^{-6} \text{ N/m}^2} = \boxed{1.64 \times 10^{10} \text{ times smaller than atmospheric pressure}}$

P34.57 (a) $P = \frac{F}{A} = \frac{I}{c}$ $\qquad F = \frac{IA}{c} = \frac{\mathscr{P}}{c} = \frac{100 \text{ J/s}}{3.00 \times 10^8 \text{ m/s}} = 3.33 \times 10^{-7} \text{ N} = (110 \text{ kg})a$

$a = 3.03 \times 10^{-9} \text{ m/s}^2$ and $\qquad x = \frac{1}{2}at^2$

$t = \sqrt{\frac{2x}{a}} = 8.12 \times 10^4 \text{ s} = \boxed{22.6 \text{ h}}$

(b) $0 = (107 \text{ kg})v - (3.00 \text{ kg})(12.0 \text{ m/s} - v) = (107 \text{ kg})v - 36.0 \text{ kg}\cdot\text{m/s} + (3.00 \text{ kg})v$

$v = \frac{36.0}{110} = 0.327 \text{ m/s}$ $\qquad t = \boxed{30.6 \text{ s}}$

P34.58 The mirror intercepts power $\mathscr{P} = I_1 A_1 = \left(1.00 \times 10^3 \text{ W/m}^2\right)\left[\pi(0.500 \text{ m})^2\right] = 785 \text{ W}$.

In the image,

(a) $I_2 = \dfrac{\mathscr{P}}{A_2}$: $\quad I_2 = \dfrac{785 \text{ W}}{\pi(0.020\,0 \text{ m})^2} = \boxed{625 \text{ kW/m}^2}$

(b) $I_2 = \dfrac{E_{max}^2}{2\mu_0 c}$ so $\quad E_{max} = \sqrt{2\mu_0 c I_2} = \sqrt{2\left(4\pi \times 10^{-7}\right)\left(3.00 \times 10^8\right)\left(6.25 \times 10^5\right)} = \boxed{21.7 \text{ kN/C}}$

$$B_{max} = \frac{E_{max}}{c} = \boxed{72.4\ \mu\text{T}}$$

(c) $0.400\mathscr{P}\Delta t = mc\Delta T$

$$0.400(785 \text{ W})\Delta t = (1.00 \text{ kg})(4\,186 \text{ J/kg}\cdot{}^\circ\text{C})(100^\circ\text{C} - 20.0^\circ\text{C})$$

$$\Delta t = \frac{3.35 \times 10^5 \text{ J}}{314 \text{ W}} = 1.07 \times 10^3 \text{ s} = \boxed{17.8 \text{ min}}$$

P34.59 Think of light going up and being absorbed by the bead which presents a face area πr_b^2.

The light pressure is $P = \dfrac{S}{c} = \dfrac{I}{c}$.

(a) $F_\ell = \dfrac{I\pi r_b^2}{c} = mg = \rho\dfrac{4}{3}\pi r_b^3 g$ and $\quad I = \dfrac{4\rho g c}{3}\left(\dfrac{3m}{4\pi\rho}\right)^{1/3} = \boxed{8.32 \times 10^7 \text{ W/m}^2}$

(b) $\mathscr{P} = IA = \left(8.32 \times 10^7 \text{ W/m}^2\right)\pi\left(2.00 \times 10^{-3} \text{ m}\right)^2 = \boxed{1.05 \text{ kW}}$

P34.60 Think of light going up and being absorbed by the bead, which presents face area πr_b^2.

If we take the bead to be perfectly absorbing, the light pressure is $P = \dfrac{S_{av}}{c} = \dfrac{I}{c} = \dfrac{F_\ell}{A}$.

(a) $F_\ell = F_g$

so $$I = \frac{F_\ell c}{A} = \frac{F_g c}{A} = \frac{mgc}{\pi r_b^2}.$$

From the definition of density, $\rho = \dfrac{m}{V} = \dfrac{m}{(4/3)\pi r_b^3}$

so $$\frac{1}{r_b} = \left(\frac{(4/3)\pi\rho}{m}\right)^{1/3}.$$

Substituting for r_b, $$I = \frac{mgc}{\pi}\left(\frac{4\pi\rho}{3m}\right)^{2/3} = gc\left(\frac{4\rho}{3}\right)^{2/3}\left(\frac{m}{\pi}\right)^{1/3} = \boxed{\frac{4\rho gc}{3}\left(\frac{3m}{4\pi\rho}\right)^{1/3}}$$

(b) $\mathscr{P} = IA$ $$\mathscr{P} = \boxed{\frac{4\pi r^2 \rho gc}{3}\left(\frac{3m}{4\pi\rho}\right)^{1/3}}$$

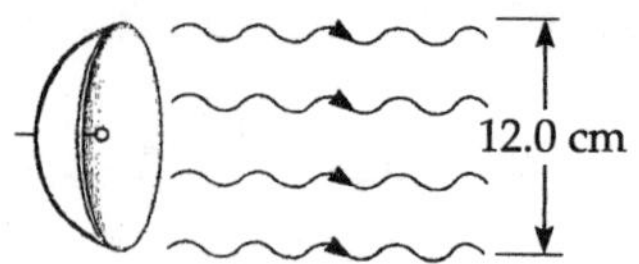

FIG. P34.61

P34.61 (a) $\lambda = \frac{c}{f} = \frac{3.00 \times 10^8 \text{ m/s}}{20.0 \times 10^9 \text{ s}^{-1}} = \boxed{1.50 \text{ cm}}$

(b) $U = \mathcal{P}(\Delta t) = (25.0 \times 10^3 \text{ J/s})(1.00 \times 10^{-9} \text{ s}) = 25.0 \times 10^{-6} \text{ J}$

$= \boxed{25.0 \ \mu\text{J}}$

(c) $$u_{av} = \frac{U}{V} = \frac{U}{(\pi r^2)\ell} = \frac{U}{(\pi r^2)c(\Delta t)} = \frac{25.0 \times 10^{-6} \text{ J}}{\pi (0.060\,0 \text{ m})^2 (3.00 \times 10^8 \text{ m/s})(1.00 \times 10^{-9} \text{ s})}$$

$u_{av} = 7.37 \times 10^{-3} \text{ J/m}^3 = \boxed{7.37 \text{ mJ/m}^3}$

(d) $$E_{max} = \sqrt{\frac{2u_{av}}{\epsilon_0}} = \sqrt{\frac{2(7.37 \times 10^{-3} \text{ J/m}^3)}{8.85 \times 10^{-12} \text{ C}^2/\text{N}\cdot\text{m}^2}} = 4.08 \times 10^4 \text{ V/m} = \boxed{40.8 \text{ kV/m}}$$

$$B_{max} = \frac{E_{max}}{c} = \frac{4.08 \times 10^4 \text{ V/m}}{3.00 \times 10^8 \text{ m/s}} = 1.36 \times 10^{-4} \text{ T} = \boxed{136 \ \mu\text{T}}$$

(e) $F = PA = \left(\frac{S}{c}\right)A = u_{av}A = (7.37 \times 10^{-3} \text{ J/m}^3)\pi(0.060\,0 \text{ m})^2 = 8.33 \times 10^{-5} \text{ N} = \boxed{83.3 \ \mu\text{N}}$

P34.62 (a) On the right side of the equation, $\frac{\text{C}^2(\text{m/s}^2)^2}{(\text{C}^2/\text{N}\cdot\text{m}^2)(\text{m/s})^3} = \frac{\text{N}\cdot\text{m}^2\cdot\text{C}^2\cdot\text{m}^2\cdot\text{s}^3}{\text{C}^2\cdot\text{s}^4\cdot\text{m}^3} = \frac{\text{N}\cdot\text{m}}{\text{s}} = \frac{\text{J}}{\text{s}} = \text{W}$.

(b) $F = ma = qE$ or $a = \frac{qE}{m} = \frac{(1.60 \times 10^{-19} \text{ C})(100 \text{ N/C})}{9.11 \times 10^{-31} \text{ kg}} = \boxed{1.76 \times 10^{13} \text{ m/s}^2}$.

The radiated power is then: $\mathcal{P} = \frac{q^2a^2}{6\pi \epsilon_0 c^3} = \frac{(1.60 \times 10^{-19})^2 (1.76 \times 10^{13})^2}{6\pi(8.85 \times 10^{-12})(3.00 \times 10^8)^3} = \boxed{1.75 \times 10^{-27} \text{ W}}$.

(c) $F = ma_c = m\left(\frac{v^2}{r}\right) = qvB$ so $v = \frac{qBr}{m}$.

The proton accelerates at $a = \frac{v^2}{r} = \frac{q^2B^2r}{m^2} = \frac{(1.60 \times 10^{-19})^2 (0.350)^2 (0.500)}{(1.67 \times 10^{-27})^2} = 5.62 \times 10^{14} \text{ m/s}^2$.

The proton then radiates $P = \frac{q^2a^2}{6\pi \epsilon_0 c^3} = \frac{(1.60 \times 10^{-19})^2 (5.62 \times 10^{14})^2}{6\pi(8.85 \times 10^{-12})(3.00 \times 10^8)^3} = \boxed{1.80 \times 10^{-24} \text{ W}}$.

P34.63 $P = \frac{S}{c} = \frac{\text{Power}}{Ac} = \frac{\mathcal{P}}{2\pi r\ell c} = \frac{60.0 \text{ W}}{2\pi(0.050\,0 \text{ m})(1.00 \text{ m})(3.00 \times 10^8 \text{ m/s})} = \boxed{6.37 \times 10^{-7} \text{ Pa}}$

P34.64 $F = PA = \frac{SA}{c} = \frac{(\mathcal{P}/A)A}{c} = \frac{\mathcal{P}}{c}$, $\tau = F\left(\frac{\ell}{2}\right) = \frac{\mathcal{P}\ell}{2c}$, and $\tau = \kappa\theta$.

Therefore, $\theta = \frac{\mathcal{P}\ell}{2c\kappa} = \frac{(3.00\times10^{-3})(0.060\,0)}{2(3.00\times10^{8})(1.00\times10^{-11})} = \boxed{3.00\times10^{-2}\text{ deg}}$.

P34.65 The light intensity is $I = S_{av} = \frac{E^2}{2\mu_0 c}$.

The light pressure is $P = \frac{S}{c} = \frac{E^2}{2\mu_0 c^2} = \frac{1}{2}\epsilon_0 E^2$.

For the asteroid, $PA = ma$ and $a = \boxed{\frac{\epsilon_0 E^2 A}{2m}}$.

P34.66 $f = 90.0\text{ MHz}$, $E_{max} = 2.00\times10^{-3}\text{ V/m} = 200\text{ mV/m}$

(a) $\lambda = \frac{c}{f} = \boxed{3.33\text{ m}}$

$T = \frac{1}{f} = 1.11\times10^{-8}\text{ s} = \boxed{11.1\text{ ns}}$

$B_{max} = \frac{E_{max}}{c} = 6.67\times10^{-12}\text{ T} = \boxed{6.67\text{ pT}}$

(b) $\boxed{\mathbf{E} = (2.00\text{ mV/m})\cos 2\pi\left(\frac{x}{3.33\text{ m}} - \frac{t}{11.1\text{ ns}}\right)\hat{\mathbf{j}}}$ $\boxed{\mathbf{B} = (6.67\text{ pT})\hat{\mathbf{k}}\cos 2\pi\left(\frac{x}{3.33\text{ m}} - \frac{t}{11.1\text{ ns}}\right)}$

(c) $I = \frac{E_{max}^2}{2\mu_0 c} = \frac{(2.00\times10^{-3})^2}{2(4\pi\times10^{-7})(3.00\times10^{8})} = \boxed{5.31\times10^{-9}\text{ W/m}^2}$

(d) $I = cu_{av}$ so $u_{av} = \boxed{1.77\times10^{-17}\text{ J/m}^3}$

(e) $P = \frac{2I}{c} = \frac{(2)(5.31\times10^{-9})}{3.00\times10^{8}} = \boxed{3.54\times10^{-17}\text{ Pa}}$

***P34.67** (a) $m = \rho V = \rho \frac{1}{2}\frac{4}{3}\pi r^3$

$$r = \left(\frac{6m}{\rho 4\pi}\right)^{1/3} = \left(\frac{6(8.7\text{ kg})}{(990\text{ kg/m}^3)4\pi}\right)^{1/3} = \boxed{0.161\text{ m}}$$

(b) $A = \frac{1}{2}4\pi r^2 = 2\pi(0.161\text{ m})^2 = \boxed{0.163\text{ m}^2}$

(c) $I = e\sigma T^4 = 0.970(5.67\times10^{-8}\text{ W/m}^2\cdot\text{K}^4)(304\text{ K})^4 = \boxed{470\text{ W/m}^2}$

(d) $\mathcal{P} = IA = (470\text{ W/m}^2)0.163\text{ m}^2 = \boxed{76.8\text{ W}}$

(e) $I = \frac{E_{\text{max}}^2}{2\mu_0 c}$

$$E_{\text{max}} = (2\mu_0 cI)^{1/2} = \left[(8\pi\times10^{-7}\text{ Tm/A})(3\times10^8\text{ m/s})(470\text{ W/m}^2)\right]^{1/2} = \boxed{595\text{ N/C}}$$

(f) $E_{\text{max}} = cB_{\text{max}}$

$$B_{\text{max}} = \frac{595\text{ N/C}}{3\times10^8\text{ m/s}} = \boxed{1.98\ \mu\text{T}}$$

(g) The sleeping cats are uncharged and nonmagnetic. They carry no macroscopic current. They are a source of infrared radiation. They glow not by visible-light emission but by infrared emission.

(h) Each kitten has radius $r_k = \left(\frac{6(0.8)}{990\times4\pi}\right)^{1/3} = 0.072\,8\text{ m}$ and radiating area $2\pi(0.072\,8\text{ m})^2 = 0.033\,3\text{ m}^2$. Eliza has area $2\pi\left(\frac{6(5.5)}{990\times4\pi}\right)^{2/3} = 0.120\text{ m}^2$. The total glowing area is $0.120\text{ m}^2 + 4(0.033\,3\text{ m}^2) = 0.254\text{ m}^2$ and has power output $\mathcal{P} = IA = (470\text{ W/m}^2)0.254\text{ m}^2 = \boxed{119\text{ W}}$.

P34.68 (a) At steady state, $\mathcal{P}_{\text{in}} = \mathcal{P}_{\text{out}}$ and the power radiated out is $\mathcal{P}_{\text{out}} = e\sigma AT^4$.

Thus, $0.900(1\,000\text{ W/m}^2)A = 0.700(5.67\times10^{-8}\text{ W/m}^2\cdot\text{K}^4)AT^4$

or $$T = \left[\frac{900\text{ W/m}^2}{0.700(5.67\times10^{-8}\text{ W/m}^2\cdot\text{K}^4)}\right]^{1/4} = \boxed{388\text{ K}} = 115°\text{C}.$$

(b) The box of horizontal area A, presents projected area $A\sin 50.0°$ perpendicular to the sunlight. Then by the same reasoning,

$$0.900(1\,000\text{ W/m}^2)A\sin 50.0° = 0.700(5.67\times10^{-8}\text{ W/m}^2\cdot\text{K}^4)AT^4$$

or $$T = \left[\frac{(900\text{ W/m}^2)\sin 50.0°}{0.700(5.67\times10^{-8}\text{ W/m}^2\cdot\text{K}^4)}\right]^{1/4} = \boxed{363\text{ K}} = 90.0°\text{C}.$$

P34.69 We take R to be the planet's distance from its star. The planet, of radius r, presents a $\boxed{\text{projected area } \pi r^2}$ perpendicular to the starlight. $\boxed{\text{It radiates over area } 4\pi r^2.}$

At steady-state, $\mathscr{P}_{\text{in}} = \mathscr{P}_{\text{out}}$: $\quad eI_{\text{in}}\left(\pi r^2\right) = e\sigma\left(4\pi r^2\right)T^4$

$$e\left(\frac{6.00\times 10^{23}\text{ W}}{4\pi R^2}\right)\left(\pi r^2\right) = e\sigma\left(4\pi r^2\right)T^4 \text{ so that } 6.00\times 10^{23}\text{ W} = 16\pi\sigma R^2 T^4$$

$$R = \sqrt{\frac{6.00\times 10^{23}\text{ W}}{16\pi\sigma T^4}} = \sqrt{\frac{6.00\times 10^{23}\text{ W}}{16\pi\left(5.67\times 10^{-8}\text{ W/m}^2\cdot\text{K}^4\right)(310\text{ K})^4}} = \boxed{4.77\times 10^9\text{ m} = 4.77\text{ Gm}}.$$

ANSWERS TO EVEN PROBLEMS

P34.2 (a) 2.68×10^3 AD; (b) 8.31 min; (c) 2.56 s; (d) 0.133 s; (e) 33.3 μs

P34.4 733 nT

P34.6 $E = (300\text{ V/m})\cos\left(62.8x - 1.88\times 10^{10}t\right)$; $B = (1.00\ \mu\text{T})\cos\left(62.8x - 1.88\times 10^{10}t\right)$

P34.8 see the solution

P34.10 2.9×10^8 m/s $\pm 5\%$

P34.12 49.5 mV

P34.14 (a) 13.3 nJ/m^3; (b) 13.3 nJ/m^3; (c) 7.96 W/m^2

P34.16 516 pT, $\sim 10^5$ times stronger than the Earth's field

P34.18 (a) 11.9 GW/m^2; (b) 234 kW

P34.20 33.4°C for the smaller container and 21.7°C for the larger

P34.22 (a) 50.0%; (b) 269 kW/m^2 toward the oven chamber; (c) 14.2 kV/m

P34.24 (a) 4.97 kW/m^2; (b) 16.6 μJ/m^3

P34.26 667 pN

P34.28 (a) 5.36 N; (b) 893 μm/s^2; (c) 10.7 days

P34.30 (a) 577 W/m^2; (b) 2.06×10^{16} W; (c) 68.7 MN; (d) The gravitational force is $\sim 10^{13}$ times stronger and in the opposite direction.

P34.32 4.09°

P34.34 (a) 93.3%; (b) 50.0%; (c) 0

P34.36 $\dfrac{2\pi m_p c}{eB}$

P34.38 see the solution

P34.40 (a) $\sim 10^8$ Hz radio wave; (b) $\sim 10^{13}$ Hz infrared light

P34.42 (a) 0.690 wavelengths; (b) 58.9 wavelengths

P34.44 The radio audience gets the news 8.41 ms sooner.

P34.46 (a) 187 m to 556 m; (b) 2.78 m to 3.41 m

P34.48 $\sim 10^6$ J

P34.50 (a) see the solution; (b) 378 nm

P34.52 (a) 31.4 MW; (b) 0.625 W/m^2; (c) 0.513%

P34.54 (a) 23.9 W/m^2; (b) 4.19 times the standard

P34.56 (a) 6.16 μPa; (b) 1.64×10^{10} times less than atmospheric pressure

P34.58 (a) 625 kW/m^2;
(b) 21.7 kN/C and 72.4 μT; (c) 17.8 min

P34.60 (a) $\left(\dfrac{16m\rho^2}{9\pi}\right)^{1/3} gc$; (b) $\left(\dfrac{16\pi^2 m\rho^2}{9}\right)^{1/3} r^2 gc$

P34.62 (a) see the solution;
(b) 17.6 Tm/s^2, 1.75×10^{-27} W;
(c) 1.80×10^{-24} W

P34.64 3.00×10^{-2} deg

P34.66 (a) 3.33 m, 11.1 ns, 6.67 pT;
(b) $\mathbf{E}=(2.00\text{ mV/m})\cos 2\pi\left(\dfrac{x}{3.33\text{ m}}-\dfrac{t}{11.1\text{ ns}}\right)\hat{\mathbf{j}}$;
$\mathbf{B}=(6.67\text{ pT})\hat{\mathbf{k}}\cos 2\pi\left(\dfrac{x}{3.33\text{ m}}-\dfrac{t}{11.1\text{ ns}}\right)$;
(c) 5.31 nW/m^2; (d) 1.77×10^{-17} J/m^3;
(e) 3.54×10^{-17} Pa

P34.68 (a) 388 K; (b) 363 K

35

The Nature of Light and the Laws of Geometric Optics

CHAPTER OUTLINE

ANSWERS TO QUESTIONS

Q35.1 The ray approximation, predicting sharp shadows, is valid for $\lambda << d$. For $\lambda \sim d$ diffraction effects become important, and the light waves will spread out noticeably beyond the slit.

Q35.2 Light travels through a vacuum at a speed of 300 000 km per second. Thus, an image we see from a distant star or galaxy must have been generated some time ago. For example, the star Altair is 16 light-years away; if we look at an image of Altair today, we know only what was happening 16 years ago. This may not initially seem significant, but astronomers who look at other galaxies can gain an idea of what galaxies looked like when they were significantly younger. Thus, it actually makes sense to speak of "looking backward in time."

Q35.3

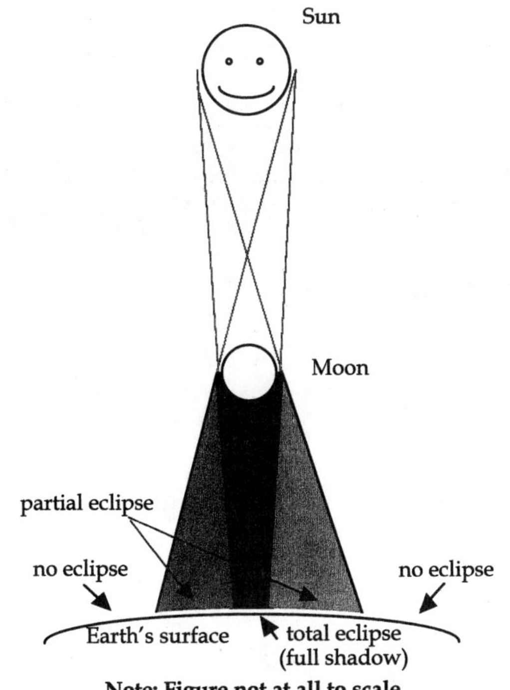

FIG. Q35.3

Q35.4 With a vertical shop window, streetlights and his own reflection can impede the window shopper's clear view of the display. The tilted shop window can put these reflections out of the way. Windows of airport control towers are also tilted like this, as are automobile windshields.

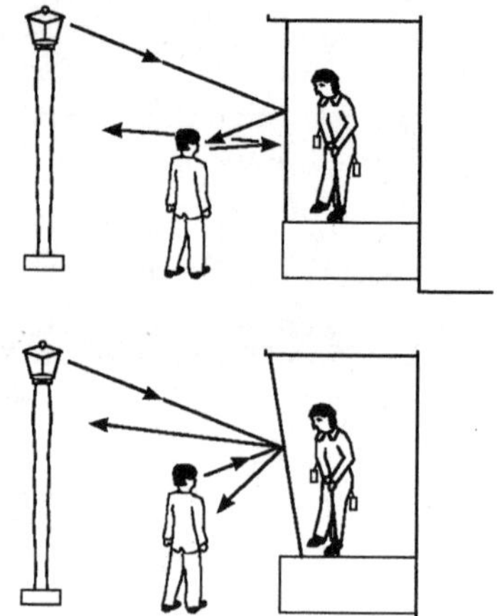

FIG. Q35.4

Q35.5 We assume that you and the child are always standing close together. For a flat wall to make an echo of a sound that you make, you must be standing along a normal to the wall. You must be on the order of 100 m away, to make the transit time sufficiently long that you can hear the echo separately from the original sound. Your sound must be loud enough so that you can hear it even at this considerable range. In the picture, the dashed rectangle represents an area in which you can be standing. The arrows represent rays of sound.

Now suppose two vertical perpendicular walls form an inside corner that you can see. Some of the sound you radiate horizontally will be headed generally toward the corner. It will reflect from both walls with high efficiency to reverse in direction and come back to you. You can stand anywhere reasonably far away to hear a retroreflected echo of sound you produce.

If the two walls are not perpendicular, the inside corner will not produce retroreflection. You will generally hear no echo of your shout or clap.

If two perpendicular walls have a reasonably narrow gap between them at the corner, you can still hear a clear echo. It is not the corner line itself that retroreflects the sound, but the perpendicular walls on both sides of the corner. Diagram (b) applies also in this case.

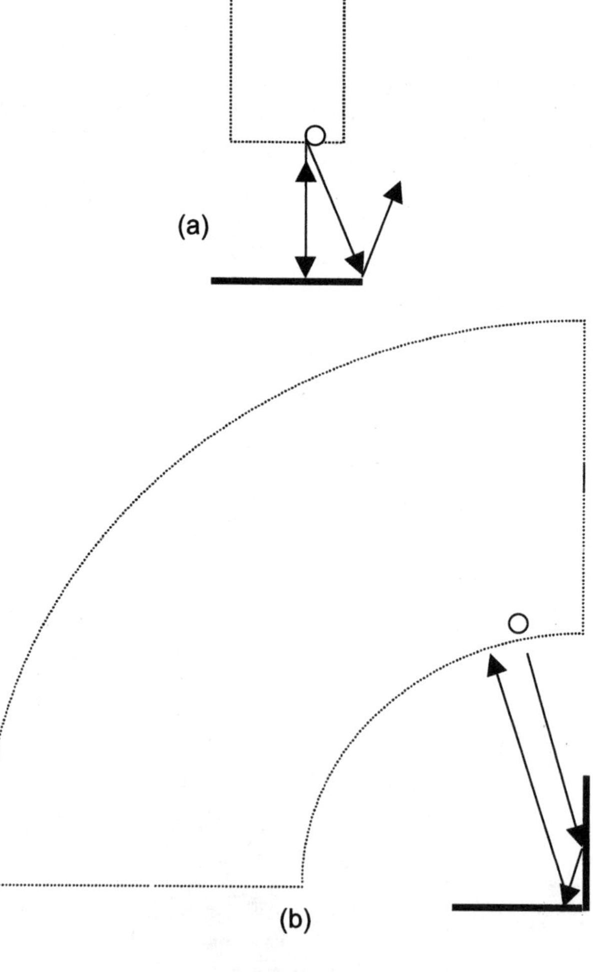

FIG. Q35.4

Q35.6 The stealth fighter is designed so that adjacent panels are not joined at right angles, to prevent any retroreflection of radar signals. This means that radar signals directed at the fighter will not be channeled back toward the detector by reflection. Just as with sound, radar signals can be treated as *diverging* rays, so that any ray that is by chance reflected back to the detector will be too weak in intensity to distinguish from background noise. This author is still waiting for the automotive industry to utilize this technology.

Q35.7 An echo is an example of the reflection of sound. Hearing the noise of a distant highway on a cold morning, when you cannot hear it after the ground warms up, is an example of acoustical refraction. You can use a rubber inner tube inflated with helium as an acoustical lens to concentrate sound in the way a lens can focus light. At your next party, see if you can experimentally find the approximate focal point!

Q35.8 No. If the incidence angle is zero, then the ray does not change direction. Also, if the ray travels from a medium of relatively high index of refraction to one of lower index of refraction, it will bend away from the normal.

Q35.9 Suppose the light moves into a medium of higher refractive index. Then its wavelength decreases. The frequency remains constant. The speed diminishes by a factor equal to the index of refraction.

Q35.10 If a laser beam enters a sugar solution with a concentration gradient (density and index of refraction increasing with depth) then the laser beam will be progressively bent downward (toward the normal) as it passes into regions of greater index of refraction.

Q35.11 As measured from the diagram, the incidence angle is 60°, and the refraction angle is 35°. Using equation 35.3, $\frac{\sin\theta_2}{\sin\theta_1} = \frac{v_2}{v_1}$, then $\frac{\sin 35°}{\sin 60°} = \frac{v_2}{c}$ and the speed of light in Lucite is 2.0×10^8 m/s.

The frequency of the light does not change upon refraction. Knowing the wavelength in a vacuum, we can use the speed of light in a vacuum to determine the frequency: $c = f\lambda$, thus $3.00 \times 10^8 = f\left(632.8 \times 10^{-9}\right)$, so the frequency is 474.1 THz. To find the wavelength of light in Lucite, we use the same wave speed relation, $v = f\lambda$, so $2.0 \times 10^8 = \left(4.741 \times 10^{14}\right)\lambda$, so $\lambda_{\text{Lucite}} = 420$ nm.

Q35.12 Blue light would be refracted at a smaller angle from the normal, since the index of refraction for blue light—a smaller wavelength than red light—is larger.

Q35.13 The index of refraction of water is 1.33, quite different from 1.00 for air. Babies learn that the refraction of light going through the water indicates the water is there. On the other hand, the index of refraction of liquid helium is close to that of air, so it gives little visible evidence of its presence.

Q35.14 The outgoing beam would be a rainbow, with the different colors of light traveling parallel to each other. The white light would undergo dispersion upon refraction into the slab, with blue light bending towards the normal more than the red light. Upon refraction out of the block, all rays of light would exit the slab at the same angle at which they entered the slab, but offset from each other.

Q35.15 Diamond has higher index of refraction than glass and consequently a smaller critical angle for total internal reflection. A brilliant-cut diamond is shaped to admit light from above, reflect it totally at the converging facets on the underside of the jewel, and let the light escape only at the top. Glass will have less light internally reflected.

Q35.16 Light coming up from underwater is bent away from the normal. Therefore the part of the oar that is submerged appears bent upward.

Q35.17 Highly silvered mirrors reflect about 98% of the incident light. With a 2-mirror periscope, that results in approximately a 4% decrease in intensity of light as the light passes through the periscope. This may not seem like much, but in low-light conditions, that lost light may mean the difference between being able to distinguish an enemy armada or an iceberg from the sky beyond. Using prisms results in total internal reflection, meaning that 100% of the incident light is reflected through the periscope. That is the "total" in total internal reflection.

Q35.18 Sound travels faster in the warmer air, and thus the sound traveling through the warm air aloft will refract much like the light refracting through the nonuniform sugar-water solution in Question 35.10. Sound that would normally travel up over the tree-tops can be refracted back towards the ground.

Q35.19 The light with the greater change in speed will have the larger deviation. If the glass has a higher index than the surrounding medium, X travels slower in the glass.

Q35.20 Immediately around the dark shadow of my head, I see a halo brighter than the rest of the dewy grass. It is called the *heiligenschein*. Cellini believed that it was a miraculous sign of divine favor pertaining to him alone. Apparently none of the people to whom he showed it told him that they could see halos around their own shadows but not around Cellini's. Thoreau knew that each person had his own halo. He did not draw any ray diagrams but assumed that it was entirely natural. Between Cellini's time and Thoreau's, the Enlightenment and Newton's explanation of the rainbow had happened. Today the effect is easy to see, whenever your shadow falls on a retroreflecting traffic sign, license plate, or road stripe. When a bicyclist's shadow falls on a paint stripe marking the edge of the road, her halo races along with her. It is a shame that few people are sufficiently curious observers of the natural world to have noticed the phenomenon.

Q35.21 Suppose the Sun is low in the sky and an observer faces away from the Sun toward a large uniform rain shower. A ray of light passing overhead strikes a drop of water. The light is refracted first at the front surface of the drop, with the violet light deviating the most and the red light the least. At the back of the drop the light is reflected and it returns to the front surface where it again undergoes refraction with additional dispersion as it moves from water into air. The rays leave the drop so that the angle between the incident white light and the most intense returning violet light is 40°, and the angle between the white light and the most intense returning red light is 42°. The observer can see a ring of raindrops shining violet, a ring with angular radius 40° around her shadow. From the locus of directions at 42° away from the antisolar direction, the observer receives red light. The other spectral colors make up the rainbow in between. An observer of a rainbow sees violet light at 40° angular separation from the direction opposite the Sun, then the other spectral colors, and then red light on the outside the rainbow, with angular radius 42°.

Q35.22 At the altitude of the plane the surface of the Earth need not block off the lower half of the rainbow. Thus, the full circle can be seen. You can see such a rainbow by climbing on a stepladder above a garden sprinkler in the middle of a sunny day. Set the sprinkler for fine mist. Do not let the slippery children fall from the ladder.

Q35.23 Total internal reflection occurs only when light moving originally in a medium of high index of refraction falls on an interface with a medium of lower index of refraction. Thus, light moving from air ($n = 1$) to water ($n = 1.33$) cannot undergo total internal reflection.

Q35.24 A mirage occurs when light changes direction as it moves between batches of air having different indices of refraction because they have different densities at different temperatures. When the sun makes a blacktop road hot, an apparent wet spot is bright due to refraction of light from the bright sky. The light, originally headed a little below the horizontal, always bends up as it first enters and then leaves sequentially hotter, lower-density, lower-index layers of air closer to the road surface.

SOLUTIONS TO PROBLEMS

Section 35.1 **The Nature of Light**

Section 35.2 **Measurements of the Speed of Light**

P35.1 The Moon's radius is 1.74×10^{6} m and the Earth's radius is 6.37×10^{6} m. The total distance traveled by the light is:

$$d = 2\left(3.84\times10^{8}\text{ m} - 1.74\times10^{6}\text{ m} - 6.37\times10^{6}\text{ m}\right) = 7.52\times10^{8}\text{ m}.$$

This takes 2.51 s, so $v = \dfrac{7.52\times10^{8}\text{ m}}{2.51\text{ s}} = 2.995\times10^{8}\text{ m/s} = \boxed{299.5\text{ Mm/s}}$.

P35.2 $\Delta x = ct$; $\quad c = \dfrac{\Delta x}{t} = \dfrac{2\left(1.50\times10^{8}\text{ km}\right)(1\,000\text{ m/km})}{(22.0\text{ min})(60.0\text{ s/min})} = 2.27\times10^{8}\text{ m/s} = \boxed{227\text{ Mm/s}}$

P35.3 The experiment is most convincing if the wheel turns fast enough to pass outgoing light through one notch and returning light through the next: $t = \dfrac{2\ell}{c}$

$$\theta = \omega t = \omega\left(\frac{2\ell}{c}\right) \quad \text{so} \quad \omega = \frac{c\theta}{2\ell} = \frac{\left(2.998\times10^{8}\right)\left[2\pi/(720)\right]}{2\left(11.45\times10^{3}\right)} = \boxed{114\text{ rad/s}}.$$

The returning light would be blocked by a tooth at one-half the angular speed, giving another data point.

P35.4 (a) For the light beam to make it through both slots, the time for the light to travel the distance d must equal the time for the disk to rotate through the angle θ, if c is the speed of light,

$$\frac{d}{c} = \frac{\theta}{\omega}, \text{ so } \boxed{c = \frac{d\omega}{\theta}}.$$

(b) We are given that

$$d = 2.50\text{ m},\ \theta = \frac{1.00°}{60.0}\left(\frac{\pi\text{ rad}}{180°}\right) = 2.91\times10^{-4}\text{ rad},\ \omega = 5\,555\text{ rev/s}\left(\frac{2\pi\text{ rad}}{1.00\text{ rev}}\right) = 3.49\times10^{4}\text{ rad/s}$$

$$c = \frac{d\omega}{\theta} = \frac{(2.50\text{ m})\left(3.49\times10^{4}\text{ rad/s}\right)}{2.91\times10^{-4}\text{ rad}} = 3.00\times10^{8}\text{ m/s} = \boxed{300\text{ Mm/s}}$$

Section 35.3 The Ray Approximation in Geometric Optics

Section 35.4 Reflection

Section 35.5 Refraction

***P35.5** (a) Let AB be the originally horizontal ceiling, BC its originally vertical normal, AD the new ceiling and DE its normal. Then angle $BAD = \phi$. By definition DE is perpendicular to AD and BC is perpendicular to AB. Then the angle between DE extended and BC is ϕ because angles are equal when their sides are perpendicular, right side to right side and left side to left side.

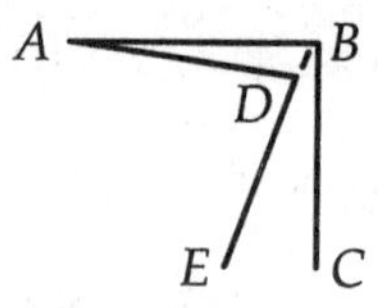

FIG. P35.5(a)

(b) Now $CBE = \phi$ is the angle of incidence of the vertical light beam. Its angle of reflection is also ϕ. The angle between the vertical incident beam and the reflected beam is 2ϕ.

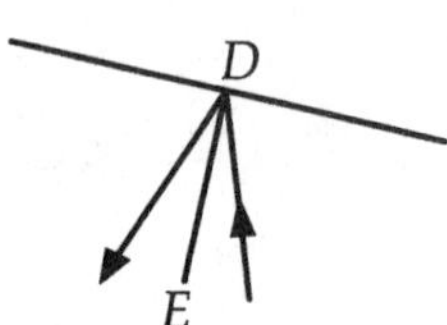

FIG. P35.5(b)

(c) $\tan 2\phi = \dfrac{1.40 \text{ cm}}{720 \text{ cm}} = 0.001\,94$ $\boxed{\phi = 0.055\,7°}$

P35.6 (a) From geometry, $1.25 \text{ m} = d \sin 40.0°$

so $d = \boxed{1.94 \text{ m}}$.

(b) $\boxed{50.0° \text{ above the horizontal}}$

or parallel to the incident ray.

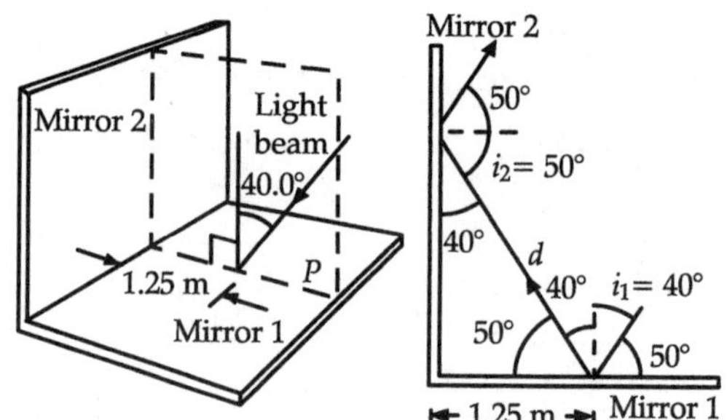

FIG. P35.6

***P35.7** (a) **Method One:**

The incident ray makes angle $\alpha = 90° - \theta_1$ with the first mirror. In the picture, the law of reflection implies that

$$\theta_1 = \theta_1' .$$

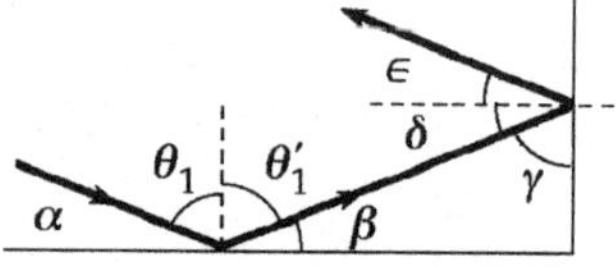

FIG. P35.7

Then $$\beta = 90° - \theta_1' = 90 - \theta_1 = \alpha .$$

In the triangle made by the mirrors and the ray passing between them,

$$\beta + 90° + \gamma = 180°$$

$$\gamma = 90° - \beta$$

Further, $$\delta = 90° - \gamma = \beta = \alpha$$

and $$\epsilon = \delta = \alpha .$$

Thus the final ray makes the same angle with the first mirror as did the incident ray. Its direction is opposite to the incident ray.

continued on next page

Method Two:
The vector velocity of the incident light has a component v_y perpendicular to the first mirror and a component v_x perpendicular to the second. The v_y component is reversed upon the first reflection, which leaves v_x unchanged. The second reflection reverses v_x and leaves v_y unchanged. The doubly reflected ray then has velocity opposite to the incident ray.

(b) The incident ray has velocity $v_x\hat{\mathbf{i}}+v_y\hat{\mathbf{j}}+v_z\hat{\mathbf{k}}$. Each reflection reverses one component and leaves the other two unchanged. After all the reflections, the light has velocity $-v_x\hat{\mathbf{i}}-v_y\hat{\mathbf{j}}-v_z\hat{\mathbf{k}}$, opposite to the incident ray.

P35.8 The incident light reaches the left-hand mirror at distance

$(1.00\text{ m})\tan 5.00° = 0.087\,5\text{ m}$

above its bottom edge. The reflected light first reaches the right-hand mirror at height

$2(0.087\,5\text{ m}) = 0.175\text{ m}$.

It bounces between the mirrors with this distance between points of contact with either.

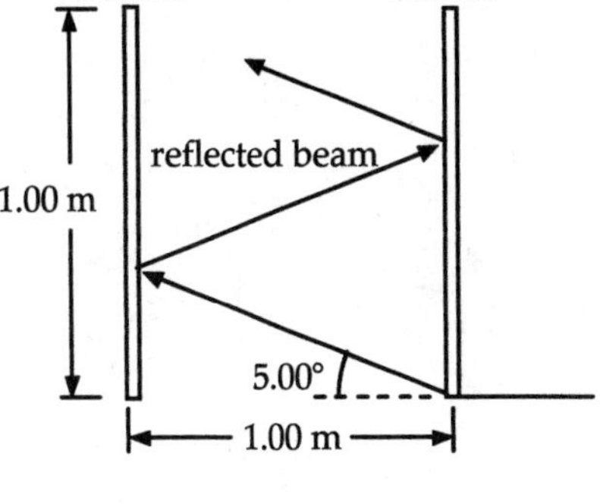

FIG. P35.8

Since $\dfrac{1.00\text{ m}}{0.175\text{ m}} = 5.72$

the light reflects $\boxed{\text{five times from the right-hand mirror and six times from the left}}$.

***P35.9** Let d represent the perpendicular distance from the person to the mirror. The distance between lamp and peson measured parallel to the mirror can be written in two ways: $2d\tan\theta + d\tan\theta = d\tan\phi$. The condition on the distance traveled by the light is $\dfrac{2d}{\cos\phi} = \dfrac{2d}{\cos\theta} + \dfrac{d}{\cos\theta}$. We have the two equations $3\tan\theta = \tan\phi$ and $2\cos\theta = 3\cos\phi$. To eliminate ϕ we write

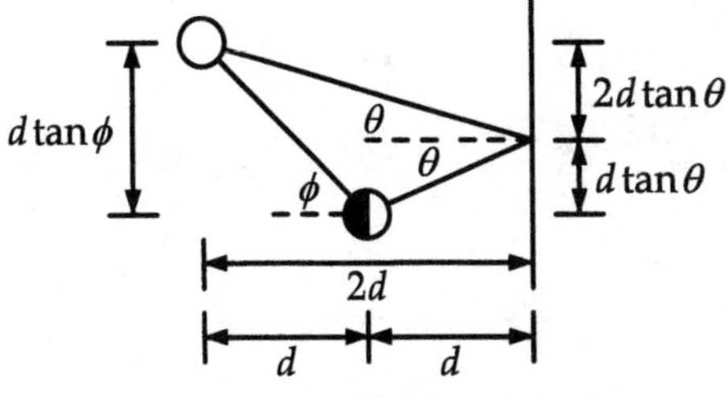

FIG. P35.9

$$\frac{9\sin^2\theta}{\cos^2\theta} = \frac{\sin^2\phi}{\cos^2\phi} \qquad 4\cos^2\theta = 9\cos^2\phi$$

$$9\cos^2\phi\sin^2\theta = \cos^2\theta\left(1-\cos^2\phi\right)$$

$$4\cos^2\theta\sin^2\theta = \cos^2\theta\left(1-\frac{4}{9}\cos^2\theta\right)$$

$$4\sin^2\theta = 1-\frac{4}{9}\left(1-\sin^2\theta\right) \qquad 36\sin^2\theta = 9-4+4\sin^2\theta$$

$$\sin^2\theta = \frac{5}{32} \qquad \theta = \boxed{23.3°}$$

P35.10 Using Snell's law, $\sin\theta_2 = \frac{n_1}{n_2}\sin\theta_1$

$$\theta_2 = \boxed{25.5°}$$

$$\lambda_2 = \frac{\lambda_1}{n_1} = \boxed{442\text{ nm}}.$$

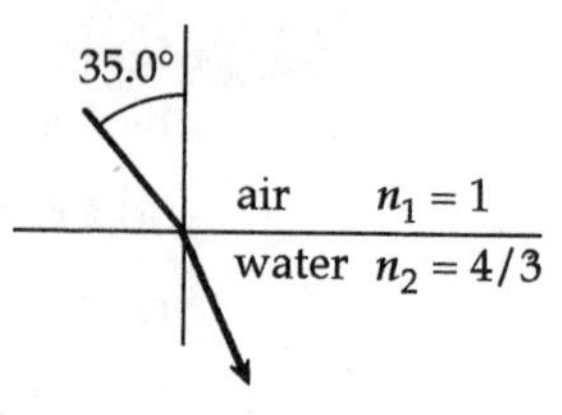

FIG. P35.10

***P35.11** The law of refraction $n_1\sin\theta_1 = n_2\sin\theta_2$ can be put into the more general form

$$\frac{c}{v_1}\sin\theta_1 = \frac{c}{v_2}\sin\theta_2$$

$$\frac{\sin\theta_1}{v_1} = \frac{\sin\theta_2}{v_2}$$

In this form it applies to all kinds of waves that move through space.

$$\frac{\sin 3.5°}{343\text{ m/s}} = \frac{\sin\theta_2}{1\,493\text{ m/s}}$$

$$\sin\theta_2 = 0.266$$

$$\theta_2 = \boxed{15.4°}$$

The wave keeps constant frequency in

$$f = \frac{v_1}{\lambda_1} = \frac{v_2}{\lambda_2}$$

$$\lambda_2 = \frac{v_2\lambda_1}{v_1} = \frac{1\,493\text{ m/s}(0.589\text{ m})}{343\text{ m/s}} = \boxed{2.56\text{ m}}$$

P35.12 (a) $f = \frac{c}{\lambda} = \frac{3.00\times10^8\text{ m/s}}{6.328\times10^{-7}\text{ m}} = \boxed{4.74\times10^{14}\text{ Hz}}$

(b) $\lambda_{glass} = \frac{\lambda_{air}}{n} = \frac{632.8\text{ nm}}{1.50} = \boxed{422\text{ nm}}$

(c) $v_{glass} = \frac{c_{air}}{n} = \frac{3.00\times10^8\text{ m/s}}{1.50} = 2.00\times10^8\text{ m/s} = \boxed{200\text{ Mm/s}}$

P35.13 $n_1\sin\theta_1 = n_2\sin\theta_2$

$$\sin\theta_1 = 1.333\sin 45°$$

$$\sin\theta_1 = (1.33)(0.707) = 0.943$$

$$\theta_1 = 70.5° \rightarrow \boxed{19.5°\text{ above the horizon}}$$

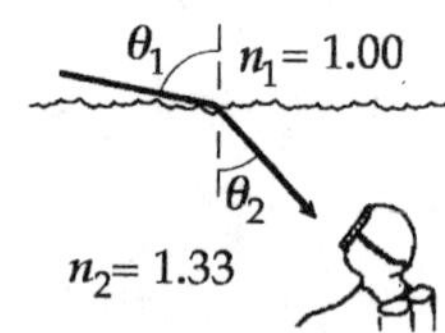

FIG. P35.13

***P35.14** We find the angle of incidence:

$$n_1\sin\theta_1 = n_2\sin\theta_2$$

$$1.333\sin\theta_1 = 1.52\sin 19.6°$$

$$\theta_1 = 22.5°$$

The angle of reflection of the beam in water is then also $\boxed{22.5°}$.

P35.15 (a) $n_1 \sin\theta_1 = n_2 \sin\theta_2$

$1.00 \sin 30.0° = n \sin 19.24°$

$n = \boxed{1.52}$

(c) $f = \frac{c}{\lambda} = \frac{3.00\times10^8 \text{ m/s}}{6.328\times10^{-7} \text{ m}} = \boxed{4.74\times10^{14} \text{ Hz}}$ in air and in syrup.

(d) $v = \frac{c}{n} = \frac{3.00\times10^8 \text{ m/s}}{1.52} = 1.98\times10^8 \text{ m/s} = \boxed{198 \text{ Mm/s}}$

(b) $\lambda = \frac{v}{f} = \frac{1.98\times10^8 \text{ m/s}}{4.74\times10^{14}/\text{s}} = \boxed{417 \text{ nm}}$

P35.16 (a) Flint Glass: $v = \frac{c}{n} = \frac{3.00\times10^8 \text{ m/s}}{1.66} = 1.81\times10^8 \text{ m/s} = \boxed{181 \text{ Mm/s}}$

(b) Water: $v = \frac{c}{n} = \frac{3.00\times10^8 \text{ m/s}}{1.333} = 2.25\times10^8 \text{ m/s} = \boxed{225 \text{ Mm/s}}$

(c) Cubic Zirconia: $v = \frac{c}{n} = \frac{3.00\times10^8 \text{ m/s}}{2.20} = 1.36\times10^8 \text{ m/s} = \boxed{136 \text{ Mm/s}}$

P35.17 $n_1 \sin\theta_1 = n_2 \sin\theta_2$: $1.333 \sin 37.0° = n_2 \sin 25.0°$

$n_2 = 1.90 = \frac{c}{v}$: $v = \frac{c}{1.90} = 1.58\times10^8 \text{ m/s} = \boxed{158 \text{ Mm/s}}$

P35.18 $\sin\theta_1 = n_w \sin\theta_2$

$\sin\theta_2 = \frac{1}{1.333}\sin\theta_1 = \frac{1}{1.333}\sin(90.0°-28.0°) = 0.662$

$\theta_2 = \sin^{-1}(0.662) = 41.5°$

$h = \frac{d}{\tan\theta_2} = \frac{3.00 \text{ m}}{\tan 41.5°} = \boxed{3.39 \text{ m}}$

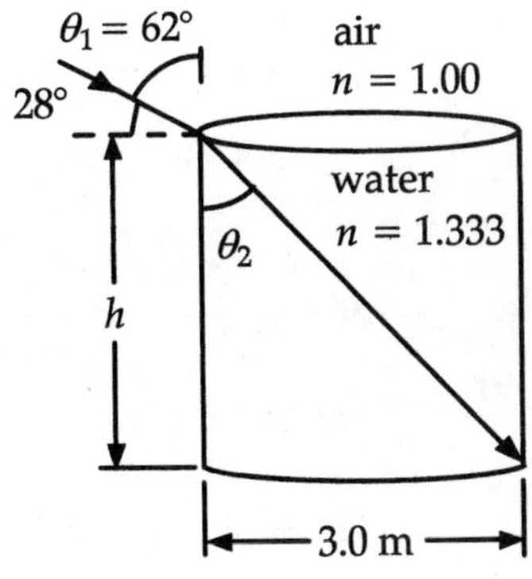

FIG. P35.18

P35.19 $n_1 \sin\theta_1 = n_2 \sin\theta_2$: $\theta_2 = \sin^{-1}\left(\frac{n_1 \sin\theta_1}{n_2}\right)$

$$\theta_2 = \sin^{-1}\left\{\frac{1.00 \sin 30°}{1.50}\right\} = \boxed{19.5°}$$

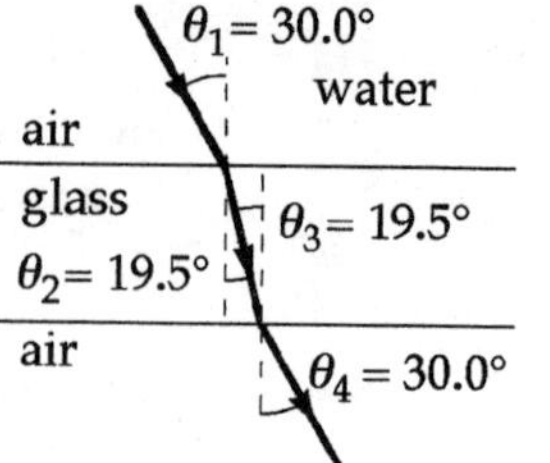

FIG. P35.19

θ_2 and θ_3 are alternate interior angles formed by the ray cutting parallel normals.

So,

$$\theta_3 = \theta_2 = \boxed{19.5°}$$
$$1.50 \sin\theta_3 = 1.00 \sin\theta_4$$
$$\theta_4 = \boxed{30.0°}$$

***P35.20** For $\alpha + \beta = 90°$

with $\theta_1' + \alpha + \beta + \theta_2 = 180°$

we have $\theta_1' + \theta_2 = 90°$.

Also, $\theta_1' = \theta_1$

and $1 \sin\theta_1 = n \sin\theta_2$.

Then, $\sin\theta_1 = n \sin(90 - \theta_1) = n \cos\theta_1$

$$\frac{\sin\theta_1}{\cos\theta_1} = n = \tan\theta_1 \qquad \boxed{\theta_1 = \tan^{-1} n}.$$

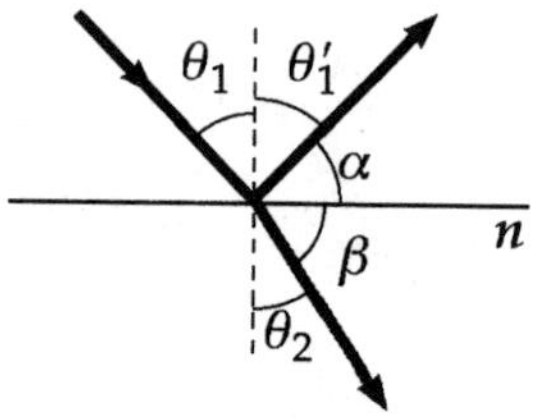

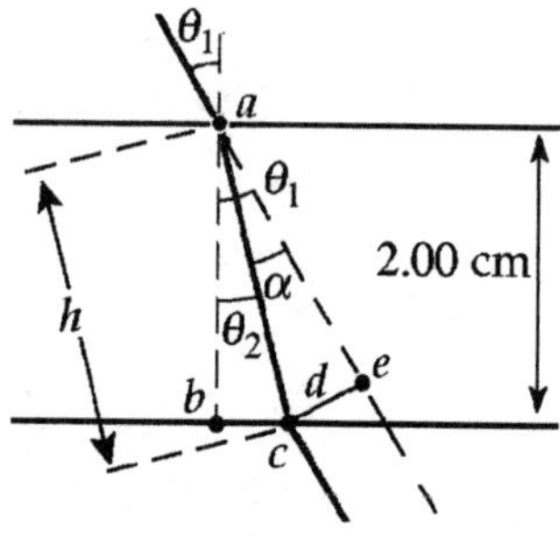

FIG. P35.20

P35.21 At entry, $n_1 \sin\theta_1 = n_2 \sin\theta_2$

or $1.00 \sin 30.0° = 1.50 \sin\theta_2$

$\theta_2 = 19.5°$.

The distance h the light travels in the medium is given by

$$\cos\theta_2 = \frac{2.00 \text{ cm}}{h}$$

or $h = \frac{2.00 \text{ cm}}{\cos 19.5°} = 2.12 \text{ cm}$.

FIG. P35.21

The angle of deviation upon entry is $\alpha = \theta_1 - \theta_2 = 30.0° - 19.5° = 10.5°$.

The offset distance comes from $\sin\alpha = \frac{d}{h}$: $d = (2.21 \text{ cm}) \sin 10.5° = \boxed{0.388 \text{ cm}}$.

P35.22 The distance, h, traveled by the light is $h = \frac{2.00 \text{ cm}}{\cos 19.5°} = 2.12 \text{ cm}$

The speed of light in the material is $v = \frac{c}{h} = \frac{3.00 \times 10^8 \text{ m/s}}{1.50} = 2.00 \times 10^8 \text{ m/s}$

Therefore, $t = \frac{h}{v} = \frac{2.12 \times 10^{-2} \text{ m}}{2.00 \times 10^8 \text{ m/s}} = 1.06 \times 10^{-10} \text{ s} = \boxed{106 \text{ ps}}$.

P35.23 Applying Snell's law at the air-oil interface,

$$n_{\text{air}} \sin\theta = n_{\text{oil}} \sin 20.0°$$

yields $\boxed{\theta = 30.4°}$.

Applying Snell's law at the oil-water interface

$$n_w \sin\theta' = n_{\text{oil}} \sin 20.0°$$

yields $\boxed{\theta' = 22.3°}$.

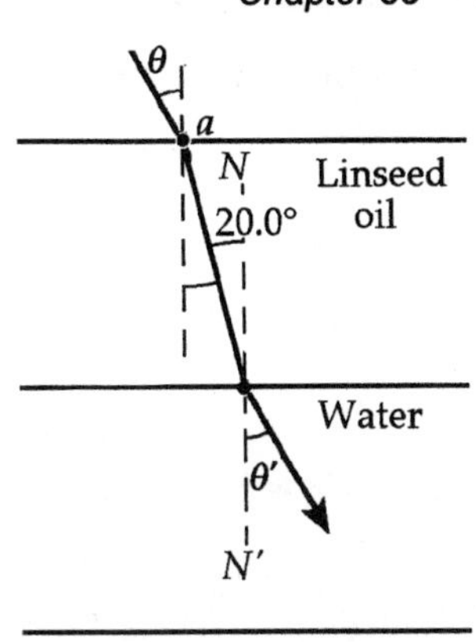

FIG. P35.23

***P35.24** For sheets 1 and 2 as described,

$n_1 \sin 26.5° = n_2 \sin 31.7°$
$0.849n_1 = n_2$

For the trial with sheets 3 and 2,

$n_3 \sin 26.5° = n_2 \sin 36.7°$
$0.747n_3 = n_2$

Now

$0.747n_3 = 0.849n_1$
$n_3 = 1.14n_1$

For the third trial,

$n_1 \sin 26.5° = n_3 \sin\theta_3 = 1.14n_1 \sin\theta_3$
$\theta_3 = \boxed{23.1°}$

P35.25 Consider glass with an index of refraction of 1.5, which is 3 mm thick. The speed of light in the glass is

$$\frac{3\times10^8 \text{ m/s}}{1.5} = 2\times10^8 \text{ m/s}.$$

The extra travel time is $\dfrac{3\times10^{-3}\text{ m}}{2\times10^8\text{ m/s}} - \dfrac{3\times10^{-3}\text{ m}}{3\times10^8\text{ m/s}} \boxed{\sim10^{-11}\text{ s}}$.

For light of wavelength 600 nm in vacuum and wavelength $\dfrac{600\text{ nm}}{1.5} = 400$ nm in glass,

the extra optical path, in wavelengths, is $\dfrac{3\times10^{-3}\text{ m}}{4\times10^{-7}\text{ m}} - \dfrac{3\times10^{-3}\text{ m}}{6\times10^{-7}\text{ m}} \boxed{\sim10^3\text{ wavelengths}}$.

P35.26 Refraction proceeds according to $(1.00)\sin\theta_1 = (1.66)\sin\theta_2$. (1)

(a) For the normal component of velocity to be constant, $v_1 \cos\theta_1 = v_2 \cos\theta_2$

or $(c)\cos\theta_1 = \left(\dfrac{c}{1.66}\right)\cos\theta_2$. (2)

We multiply Equations (1) and (2), obtaining: $\sin\theta_1 \cos\theta_1 = \sin\theta_2 \cos\theta_2$

or $\sin 2\theta_1 = \sin 2\theta_2$.

The solution $\theta_1 = \theta_2 = 0$ does not satisfy Equation (2) and must be rejected. The physical solution is $2\theta_1 = 180° - 2\theta_2$ or $\theta_2 = 90.0° - \theta_1$. Then Equation (1) becomes:

$\sin\theta_1 = 1.66\cos\theta_1$, or $\tan\theta_1 = 1.66$

which yields $\theta_1 = \boxed{58.9°}$.

(b) Light entering the glass slows down and makes a smaller angle with the normal. Both effects reduce the velocity component parallel to the surface of the glass, so that component cannot remain constant, or will remain constant only in the trivial case $\boxed{\theta_1 = \theta_2 = 0}$.

P35.27 See the sketch showing the path of the light ray. α and γ are angles of incidence at mirrors 1 and 2.

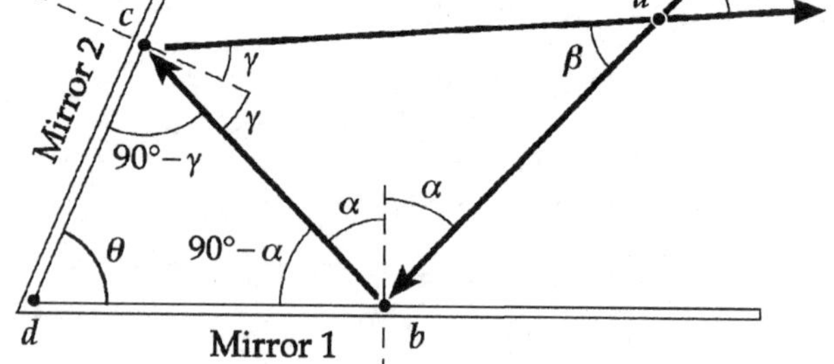

FIG. P35.27

For triangle *abca*,

$$2\alpha + 2\gamma + \beta = 180°$$

or $\beta = 180° - 2(\alpha + \gamma)$. (1)

Now for triangle *bcdb*,

$$(90.0° - \alpha) + (90.0° - \gamma) + \theta = 180°$$

or $\theta = \alpha + \gamma$. (2)

Substituting Equation (2) into Equation (1) gives $\boxed{\beta = 180° - 2\theta}$.

Note: From Equation (2), $\gamma = \theta - \alpha$. Thus, the ray will follow a path like that shown only if $\alpha < 0$. For $\alpha > 0$, γ is negative and multiple reflections from each mirror will occur before the incident and reflected rays intersect.

Section 35.6 Huygen's Principle

***P35.28** (a) For the diagrams of contour lines and wave fronts and rays, see Figures (a) and (b) below. As the waves move to shallower water, the wave fronts bend to become more nearly parallel to the contour lines.

(b) For the diagrams of contour lines and wave fronts and rays, see Figures (c) and (d) below. We suppose that the headlands are steep underwater, as they are above water. The rays are everywhere perpendicular to the wave fronts of the incoming refracting waves. As shown, the rays bend toward the headlands and deliver more energy per length at the headlands.

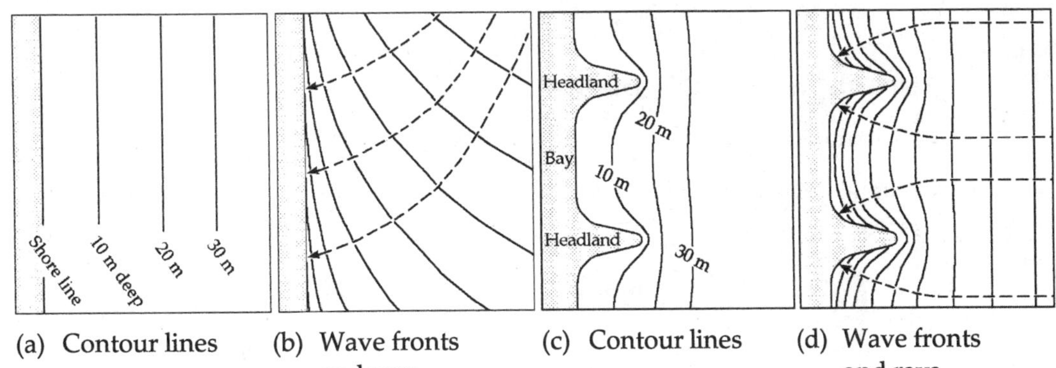

(a) Contour lines (b) Wave fronts and rays (c) Contour lines (d) Wave fronts and rays

FIG. P35.28

Section 35.7 Dispersion and Prisms

P35.29 From Fig 35.21 $n_v = 1.470$ at 400 nm and $n_r = 1.458$ at 700 nm.

Then $1.00 \sin\theta = 1.470 \sin\theta_v$ and $1.00 \sin\theta = 1.458 \sin\theta_r$

$$\delta_r - \delta_v = \theta_r - \theta_v = \sin^{-1}\left(\frac{\sin\theta}{1.458}\right) - \sin^{-1}\left(\frac{\sin\theta}{1.470}\right)$$

$$\Delta\delta = \sin^{-1}\left(\frac{\sin 30.0°}{1.458}\right) - \sin^{-1}\left(\frac{\sin 30.0°}{1.470}\right) = \boxed{0.171°}$$

P35.30 $n(700 \text{ nm}) = 1.458$

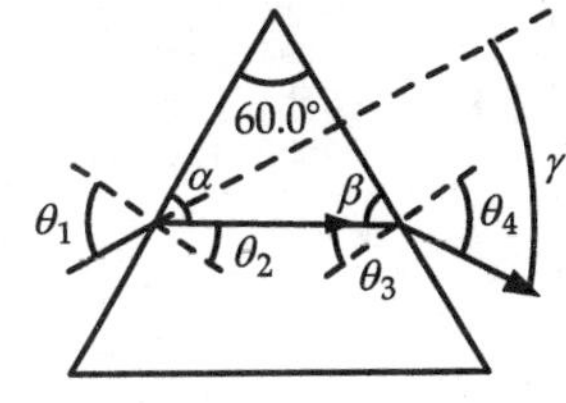

FIG. P35.30

(a) $(1.00)\sin 75.0° = 1.458 \sin\theta_2$; $\theta_2 = \boxed{41.5°}$

(b) Let $\theta_3 + \beta = 90.0°$, $\theta_2 + \alpha = 90.0°$ then $\alpha + \beta + 60.0° = 180°$.

So $60.0° - \theta_2 - \theta_3 = 0 \Rightarrow 60.0° - 41.5° = \theta_3 = \boxed{18.5°}$.

(c) $1.458 \sin 18.5° = 1.00 \sin\theta_4$ $\theta_4 = \boxed{27.6°}$

(d) $\gamma = (\theta_1 - \theta_2) + [\beta - (90.0° - \theta_4)]$

$\gamma = 75.0° - 41.5° + (90.0° - 18.5°) - (90.0° - 27.6°) = \boxed{42.6°}$

P35.31 Taking Φ to be the apex angle and $\delta_{\min}$ to be the angle of minimum deviation, from Equation 35.9, the index of refraction of the prism material is

$$n = \frac{\sin\left[(\Phi + \delta_{\min})/2\right]}{\sin(\Phi/2)}$$

Solving for $\delta_{\min}$, $\quad \delta_{\min} = 2\sin^{-1}\left(n \sin\frac{\Phi}{2}\right) - \Phi = 2\sin^{-1}\left[(2.20)\sin(25.0°)\right] - 50.0° = \boxed{86.8°}$.

P35.32 Note for use in every part: $\quad \Phi + (90.0° - \theta_2) + (90.0° - \theta_3) = 180°$

so $\quad \theta_3 = \Phi - \theta_2$.

At the first surface the deviation is $\quad \alpha = \theta_1 - \theta_2$.

At exit, the deviation is $\quad \beta = \theta_4 - \theta_3$.

The total deviation is therefore $\quad \delta = \alpha + \beta = \theta_1 + \theta_4 - \theta_2 - \theta_3 = \theta_1 + \theta_4 - \Phi$.

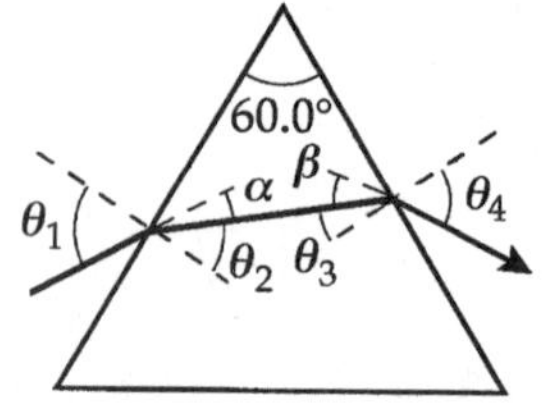

FIG. P35.32

(a) At entry: $\quad n_1 \sin\theta_1 = n_2 \sin\theta_2 \quad$ or $\quad \theta_2 = \sin^{-1}\left(\frac{\sin 48.6°}{1.50}\right) = 30.0°$.

Thus, $\quad \theta_3 = 60.0° - 30.0° = 30.0°$.

At exit: $\quad 1.50 \sin 30.0° = 1.00 \sin\theta_4 \quad$ or $\quad \theta_4 = \sin^{-1}\left[1.50\sin(30.0°)\right] = 48.6°$

so the path through the prism is symmetric when $\theta_1 = 48.6°$.

(b) $\delta = 48.6° + 48.6° - 60.0° = \boxed{37.2°}$

(c) At entry: $\quad \sin\theta_2 = \frac{\sin 45.6°}{1.50} \Rightarrow \theta_2 = 28.4° \quad\quad \theta_3 = 60.0° - 28.4° = 31.6°$.

At exit: $\quad \sin\theta_4 = 1.50\sin(31.6°) \Rightarrow \theta_4 = 51.7° \quad\quad \delta = 45.6° + 51.7° - 60.0° = \boxed{37.3°}$.

(d) At entry: $\quad \sin\theta_2 = \frac{\sin 51.6°}{1.50} \Rightarrow \theta_2 = 31.5° \quad\quad \theta_3 = 60.0° - 31.5° = 28.5°$.

At exit: $\quad \sin\theta_4 = 1.50\sin(28.5°) \Rightarrow \theta_4 = 45.7° \quad\quad \delta = 51.6° + 45.7° - 60.0° = \boxed{37.3°}$.

P35.33 At the first refraction, $\quad 1.00\sin\theta_1 = n\sin\theta_2$.

The critical angle at the second surface is given by $n\sin\theta_3 = 1.00$:

or $\quad \theta_3 = \sin^{-1}\left(\frac{1.00}{1.50}\right) = 41.8°$.

But, $\quad \theta_2 = 60.0° - \theta_3$.

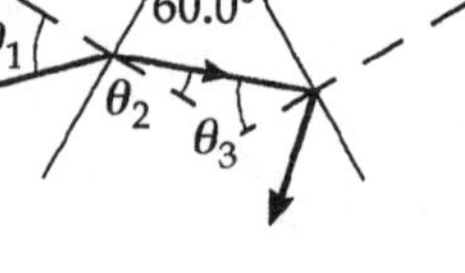

FIG. P35.33

Thus, to avoid total internal reflection at the second surface (i.e., have $\theta_3 < 41.8°$)

it is necessary that $\quad \theta_2 > 18.2°$.

Since $\sin\theta_1 = n\sin\theta_2$, this becomes $\quad \sin\theta_1 > 1.50\sin 18.2° = 0.468$

or $\quad \theta_1 > \boxed{27.9°}$.

P35.34 At the first refraction, $1.00\sin\theta_1 = n\sin\theta_2$.

The critical angle at the second surface is given by

$n\sin\theta_3 = 1.00$, or $\theta_3 = \sin^{-1}\left(\frac{1.00}{n}\right)$.

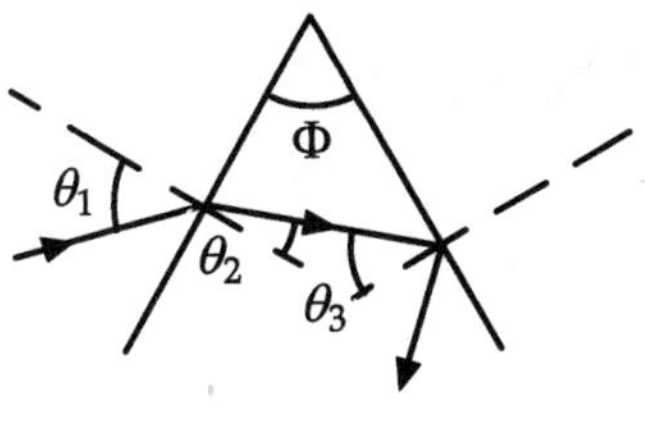

But $(90.0°-\theta_2)+(90.0°-\theta_3)+\Phi = 180°$

which gives $\theta_2 = \Phi - \theta_3$.

FIG. P35.34

Thus, to have $\theta_3 < \sin^{-1}\left(\frac{1.00}{n}\right)$ and avoid total internal reflection at the second surface,

it is necessary that $\theta_2 > \Phi - \sin^{-1}\left(\frac{1.00}{n}\right)$.

Since $\sin\theta_1 = n\sin\theta_2$, this requirement becomes $\sin\theta_1 > n\sin\left[\Phi - \sin^{-1}\left(\frac{1.00}{n}\right)\right]$

or $\theta_1 > \boxed{\sin^{-1}\left(n\sin\left[\Phi - \sin^{-1}\left(\frac{1.00}{n}\right)\right]\right)}$.

Through the application of trigonometric identities, $\theta_1 > \boxed{\sin^{-1}\left(\sqrt{n^2-1}\sin\Phi - \cos\Phi\right)}$.

P35.35 For the incoming ray, $\sin\theta_2 = \frac{\sin\theta_1}{n}$.

Using the figure to the right, $(\theta_2)_{violet} = \sin^{-1}\left(\frac{\sin 50.0°}{1.66}\right) = 27.48°$

$(\theta_2)_{red} = \sin^{-1}\left(\frac{\sin 50.0°}{1.62}\right) = 28.22°$.

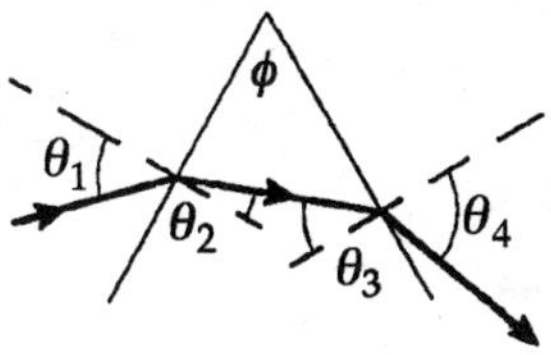

FIG. P35.35

For the outgoing ray, $\theta_3 = 60.0° - \theta_2$

and $\sin\theta_4 = n\sin\theta_3$: $(\theta_4)_{violet} = \sin^{-1}[1.66\sin 32.52°] = 63.17°$

$(\theta_4)_{red} = \sin^{-1}[1.62\sin 31.78°] = 58.56°$.

The angular dispersion is the difference $\Delta\theta_4 = (\theta_4)_{violet} - (\theta_4)_{red} = 63.17° - 58.56° = \boxed{4.61°}$.

Section 35.8 Total Internal Reflection

P35.36 $n\sin\theta = 1$. From Table 35.1,

(a) $\theta = \sin^{-1}\left(\frac{1}{2.419}\right) = \boxed{24.4°}$

(b) $\theta = \sin^{-1}\left(\frac{1}{1.66}\right) = \boxed{37.0°}$

(c) $\theta = \sin^{-1}\left(\frac{1}{1.309}\right) = \boxed{49.8°}$

P35.37 $\sin\theta_c = \frac{n_2}{n_1}$: $\theta_c = \sin^{-1}\left(\frac{n_2}{n_1}\right)$

(a) Diamond: $\theta_c = \sin^{-1}\left(\frac{1.333}{2.419}\right) = \boxed{33.4°}$

(b) Flint glass: $\theta_c = \sin^{-1}\left(\frac{1.333}{1.66}\right) = \boxed{53.4°}$

(c) Ice: Since $n_2 > n_1$, $\boxed{\text{there is no critical angle}}$.

P35.38 $\sin\theta_c = \frac{n_{\text{air}}}{n_{\text{pipe}}} = \frac{1.00}{1.36} = 0.735$ $\theta_c = 47.3°$

Geometry shows that the angle of refraction at the end is

$\phi = 90.0° - \theta_c = 90.0° - 47.3° = 42.7°$.

Then, Snell's law at the end, $1.00\sin\theta = 1.36\sin 42.7°$

gives $\boxed{\theta = 67.2°}$.

The 2-μm diameter is unnecessary information.

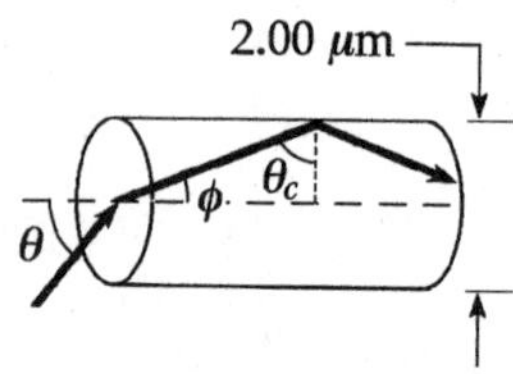

FIG. P35.38

P35.39 $\sin\theta_c = \frac{n_2}{n_1}$

$n_2 = n_1 \sin 88.8° = (1.000\,3)(0.999\,8) = \boxed{1.000\,08}$

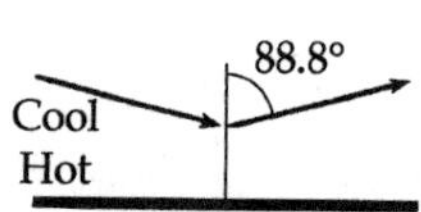

FIG. P35.39

***P35.40** (a) A ray along the inner edge will escape if any ray escapes. Its angle of incidence is described by $\sin\theta = \frac{R-d}{R}$ and by $n\sin\theta > 1\sin 90°$. Then

$\frac{n(R-d)}{R} > 1$ $nR - nd > R$ $nR - R > nd$ $R > \boxed{\frac{nd}{n-1}}$.

(b) As $d \to 0$, $R_{\min} \to 0$. This is reasonable.
As n increases, $R_{\min}$ decreases. This is reasonable.
As n decreases toward 1, $R_{\min}$ increases. This is reasonable.

(c) $R_{\min} = \frac{1.40(100 \times 10^{-6}\text{ m})}{0.40} = \boxed{350 \times 10^{-6}\text{ m}}$

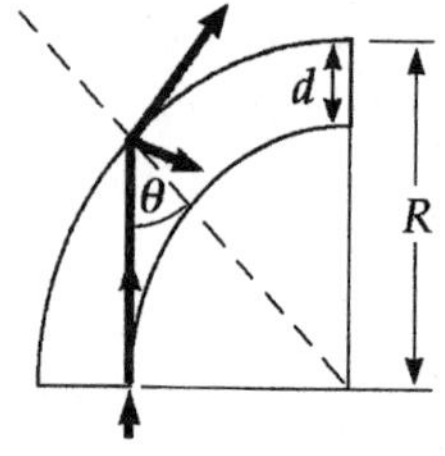

FIG. P35.40

P35.41 From Snell's law, $n_1 \sin\theta_1 = n_2 \sin\theta_2$.

At the extreme angle of viewing, $\theta_2 = 90.0°$

$(1.59)(\sin\theta_1) = (1.00)\sin 90.0°$.

So $\theta_1 = 39.0°$.

Therefore, the depth of the air bubble is

$\frac{r_d}{\tan\theta_1} < d < \frac{r_p}{\tan\theta_1}$

or $\boxed{1.08\text{ cm} < d < 1.17\text{ cm}}$.

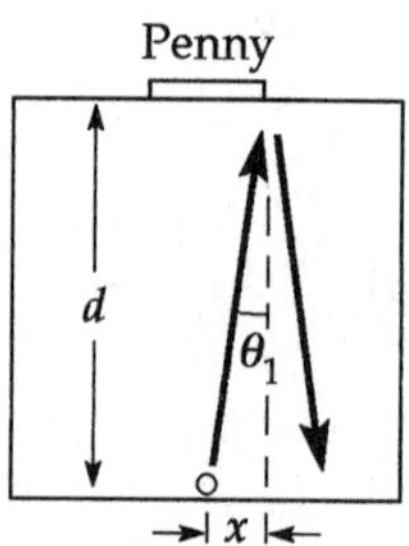

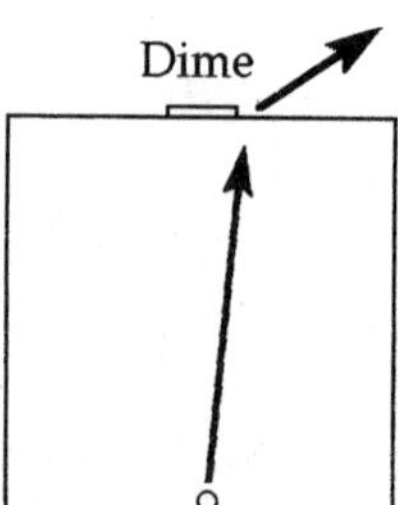

FIG. P35.41

P35.42 (a) $\frac{\sin\theta_2}{\sin\theta_1} = \frac{v_2}{v_1}$

and $\theta_2 = 90.0°$ at the critical angle

$$\frac{\sin 90.0°}{\sin\theta_c} = \frac{1\,850 \text{ m/s}}{343 \text{ m/s}}$$

so $\theta_c = \sin^{-1}(0.185) = \boxed{10.7°}$.

(b) Sound can be totally reflected if it is traveling in the medium where it travels slower: $\boxed{\text{air}}$.

(c) $\boxed{\text{Sound in air falling on the wall from most directions is 100\% reflected}}$, so the wall is a good mirror.

P35.43 For plastic with index of refraction $\boxed{n \ge 1.42}$ surrounded by air, the critical angle for total internal reflection is given by

$$\theta_c = \sin^{-1}\left(\frac{1}{n}\right) \le \sin^{-1}\left(\frac{1}{1.42}\right) = 44.8°.$$

In the gasoline gauge, skylight from above travels down the plastic. The rays close to the vertical are totally reflected from the sides of the slab and from both facets at the lower end of the plastic, where it is not immersed in gasoline. This light returns up inside the plastic and makes it look bright. Where the plastic is immersed in gasoline, with index of refraction about 1.50, total internal reflection should not happen. The light passes out of the lower end of the plastic with little reflected, making this part of the gauge look dark. To frustrate total internal reflection in the gasoline, the index of refraction of the plastic should be $\boxed{n < 2.12}$.

since $\theta_c = \sin^{-1}\left(\frac{1.50}{2.12}\right) = 45.0°$.

Section 35.9 **Fermat's Principle**

P35.44 Assume the lifeguard's initial path makes angle θ_1 with the north-south normal to the shoreline, and angle θ_2 with this normal in the water. By Fermat's principle, his path should follow the law of refraction:

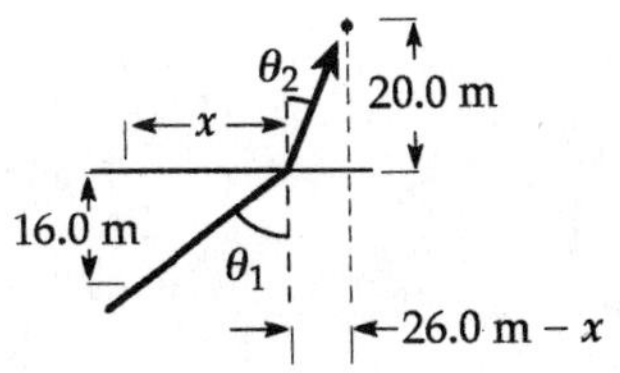

$$\frac{\sin\theta_1}{\sin\theta_2} = \frac{v_1}{v_2} = \frac{7.00 \text{ m/s}}{1.40 \text{ m/s}} = 5.00 \text{ or } \theta_2 = \sin^{-1}\left(\frac{\sin\theta_1}{5}\right).$$

FIG. P35.44

The lifeguard on land travels eastward a distance $x = (16.0 \text{ m})\tan\theta_1$. Then in the water, he travels $26.0 \text{ m} - x = (20.0 \text{ m})\tan\theta_2$ further east. Thus, $26.0 \text{ m} = (16.0 \text{ m})\tan\theta_1 + (20.0 \text{ m})\tan\theta_2$

or $26.0 \text{ m} = (16.0 \text{ m})\tan\theta_1 + (20.0 \text{ m})\tan\left[\sin^{-1}\left(\frac{\sin\theta_1}{5}\right)\right]$.

We home in on the solution as follows:

θ_1 (deg)	50.0	60.0	54.0	54.8	54.81
right-hand side	22.2 m	31.2 m	25.3 m	25.99 m	26.003 m

The lifeguard should start running at $\boxed{54.8° \text{ east of north}}$.

Additional Problems

***P35.45** Scattered light leaves the center of the photograph (a) in all horizontal directions between $\theta_1 = 0°$ and 90° from the normal. When it immediately enters the water (b), it is gathered into a fan between 0° and $\theta_{2\ max}$ given by

$$n_1 \sin\theta_1 = n_2 \sin\theta_2$$
$$1.00 \sin 90 = 1.333 \sin\theta_{2\ max}$$
$$\theta_{2\ max} = 48.6°$$

The light leaves the cylinder without deviation, so the viewer only receives light from the center of the photograph when he has turned by an angle less than 48.6°. When the paperweight is turned farther, light at the back surface undergoes total internal reflection (c). The viewer sees things outside the globe on the far side.

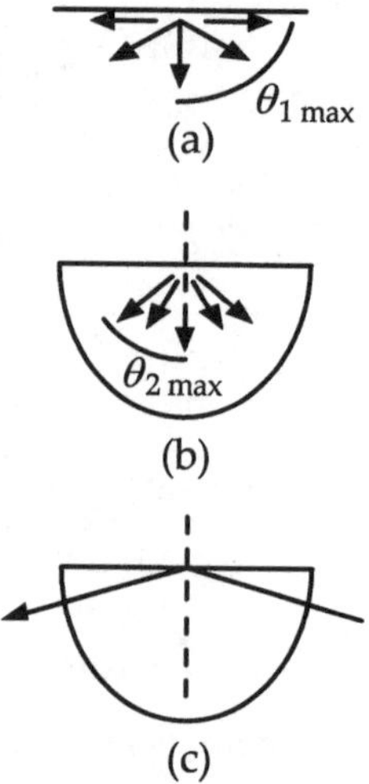

FIG. P35.45

P35.46 Let $n(x)$ be the index of refraction at distance x below the top of the atmosphere and $n(x = h) = n$ be its value at the planet surface.

Then, $$n(x) = 1.000 + \left(\frac{n - 1.000}{h}\right)x.$$

(a) The total time interval required to traverse the atmosphere is

$$\Delta t = \int_0^h \frac{dx}{v} = \int_0^h \frac{n(x)}{c}dx: \qquad \Delta t = \frac{1}{c}\int_0^h \left[1.000 + \left(\frac{n - 1.000}{h}\right)x\right]dx$$

$$\Delta t = \frac{h}{c} + \frac{(n - 1.000)}{ch}\left(\frac{h^2}{2}\right) = \boxed{\frac{h}{c}\left(\frac{n + 1.000}{2}\right)}.$$

(b) The travel time in the absence of an atmosphere would be $\frac{h}{c}$.

Thus, the time in the presence of an atmosphere is $\boxed{\left(\frac{n + 1.000}{2}\right) \text{ times larger}}$.

P35.47 Let the air and glass be medium 1 and 2, respectively. By Snell's law, $n_2 \sin\theta_2 = n_1 \sin\theta_1$

or $1.56 \sin\theta_2 = \sin\theta_1$.

But the conditions of the problem are such that $\theta_1 = 2\theta_2$. $1.56 \sin\theta_2 = \sin 2\theta_2$.

We now use the double-angle trig identity suggested. $1.56 \sin\theta_2 = 2 \sin\theta_2 \cos\theta_2$

or $\cos\theta_2 = \frac{1.56}{2} = 0.780$.

Thus, $\theta_2 = 38.7°$ and $\theta_1 = 2\theta_2 = \boxed{77.5°}$.

P35.48 (a) $\theta_1' = \theta_1 = \boxed{30.0°}$ $n_1 \sin\theta_1 = n_2 \sin\theta_2$

$$1.00 \sin 30.0° = 1.55 \sin\theta_2$$

$$\theta_2 = \boxed{18.8°}$$

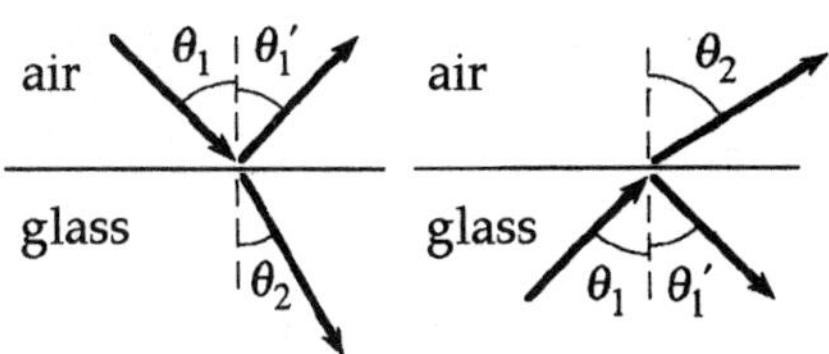

FIG. P35.48

(b) $\theta_1' = \theta_1 = \boxed{30.0°}$ $\theta_2 = \sin^{-1}\left(\frac{n_1 \sin\theta_1}{n_2}\right)$

$$= \sin^{-1}\left(\frac{1.55 \sin 30.0°}{1}\right) = \boxed{50.8°}$$

(c), (d) The other entries are computed similarly, and are shown in the table below.

(c) air into glass, angles in degrees			(d) glass into air, angles in degrees		
incidence	reflection	refraction	incidence	reflection	refraction
0	0	0	0	0	0
10.0	10.0	6.43	10.0	10.0	15.6
20.0	20.0	12.7	20.0	20.0	32.0
30.0	30.0	18.8	30.0	30.0	50.8
40.0	40.0	24.5	40.0	40.0	85.1
50.0	50.0	29.6	50.0	50.0	none*
60.0	60.0	34.0	60.0	60.0	none*
70.0	70.0	37.3	70.0	70.0	none*
80.0	80.0	39.4	80.0	80.0	none*
90.0	90.0	40.2	90.0	90.0	none*

*total internal reflection

P35.49 For water, $\sin\theta_c = \frac{1}{4/3} = \frac{3}{4}$.

Thus $\theta_c = \sin^{-1}(0.750) = 48.6°$

and $d = 2[(1.00 \text{ m})\tan\theta_c]$

$$d = (2.00 \text{ m})\tan 48.6° = \boxed{2.27 \text{ m}}.$$

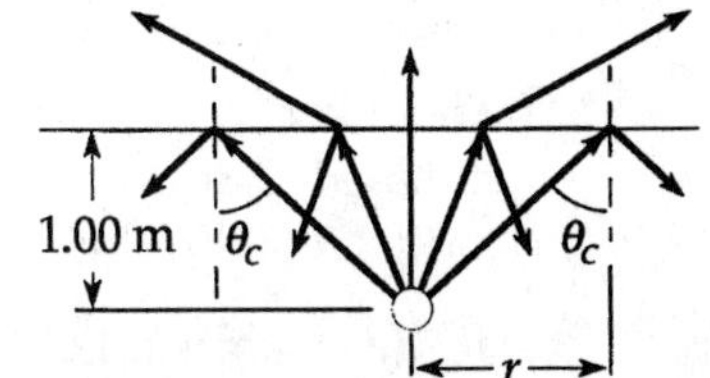

FIG. P35.49

P35.50 Call θ_1 the angle of incidence and of reflection on the left face and θ_2 those angles on the right face. Let α represent the complement of θ_1 and β be the complement of θ_2. Now $\alpha = \gamma$ and $\beta = \delta$ because they are pairs of alternate interior angles. We have

$$A = \gamma + \delta = \alpha + \beta$$

and $B = \alpha + A + \beta = \alpha + \beta + A = \boxed{2A}$.

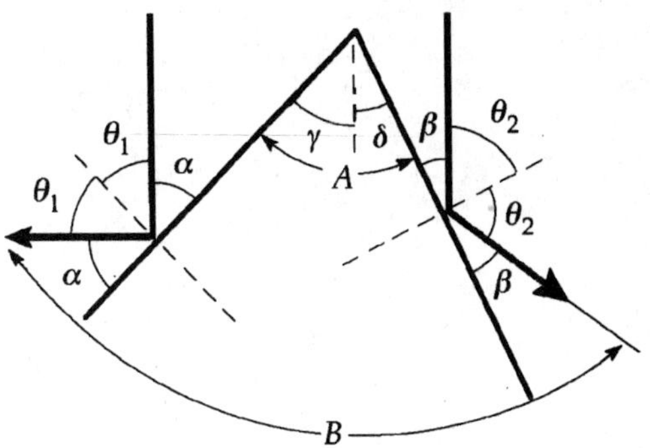

FIG. P35.50

P35.51 (a) We see the Sun moving from east to west across the sky. Its angular speed is

$$\omega = \frac{\Delta\theta}{\Delta t} = \frac{2\pi\text{ rad}}{86\,400\text{ s}} = 7.27\times10^{-5}\text{ rad/s}.$$

The direction of sunlight crossing the cell from the window changes at this rate, moving on the opposite wall at speed

$$v = r\omega = (2.37\text{ m})\left(7.27\times10^{-5}\text{ rad/s}\right) = 1.72\times10^{-4}\text{ m/s} = \boxed{0.172\text{ mm/s}}.$$

(b) The mirror folds into the cell the motion that would occur in a room twice as wide:

$$v = r\omega = 2(0.174\text{ mm/s}) = \boxed{0.345\text{ mm/s}}.$$

(c), (d) As the Sun moves southward and upward at 50.0°, we may regard the corner of the window as fixed, and both patches of light move $\boxed{\text{northward and downward at }50.0°}$.

***P35.52** (a) $\boxed{45.0°}$ as shown in the first figure to the right.

(b) 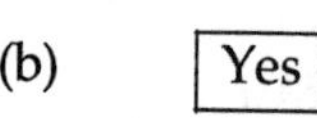

Yes

If grazing angle is halved, the number of reflections from the side faces is doubled.

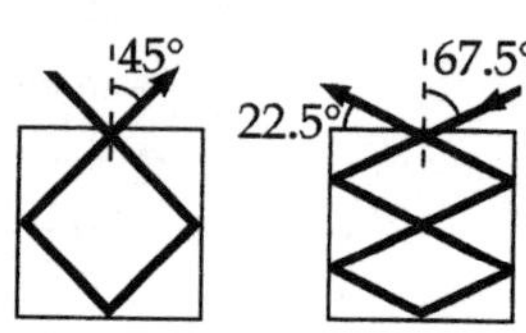

FIG. P35.52

P35.53 Horizontal light rays from the setting Sun pass above the hiker. The light rays are twice refracted and once reflected, as in Figure (b). The most intense light reaching the hiker, that which represents the visible rainbow, is located between angles of 40° and 42° from the hiker's shadow.

The hiker sees a greater percentage of the violet inner edge, so we consider the red outer edge. The radius R of the circle of droplets is

$$R = (8.00\text{ km})\sin 42.0° = 5.35\text{ km}.$$

Then the angle ϕ, between the vertical and the radius where the bow touches the ground, is given by

$$\cos\phi = \frac{2.00\text{ km}}{R} = \frac{2.00\text{ km}}{5.35\text{ km}} = 0.374$$

or $\phi = 68.1°$.

The angle filled by the visible bow is $360° - (2\times 68.1°) = 224°$

so the visible bow is $\frac{224°}{360°} = \boxed{62.2\%\text{ of a circle}}$.

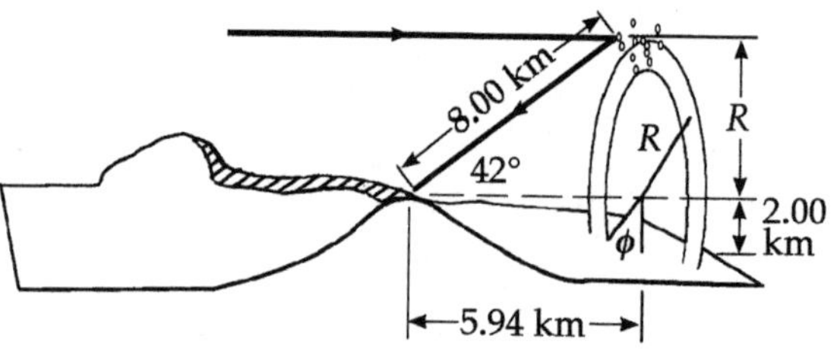

Figure (a)

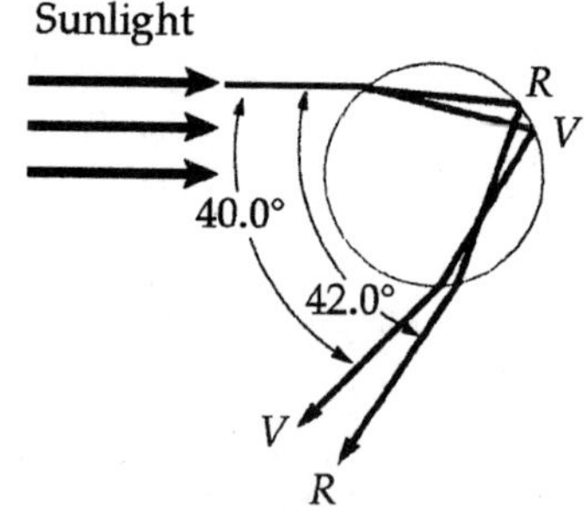

Figure (b)

FIG. P35.53

P35.54 Light passing the top of the pole makes an angle of incidence $\phi_1 = 90.0° - \theta$. It falls on the water surface at distance from the pole

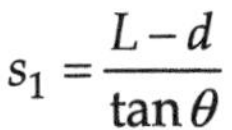

$$s_1 = \frac{L-d}{\tan\theta}$$

and has an angle of refraction ϕ_2 from $1.00\sin\phi_1 = n\sin\phi_2$.

Then $s_2 = d\tan\phi_2$

and the whole shadow length is

$$s_1 + s_2 = \frac{L-d}{\tan\theta} + d\tan\left(\sin^{-1}\left(\frac{\sin\phi_1}{n}\right)\right)$$

$$s_1 + s_2 = \frac{L-d}{\tan\theta} + d\tan\left(\sin^{-1}\left(\frac{\cos\theta}{n}\right)\right)$$

$$= \frac{2.00\text{ m}}{\tan 40.0°} + (2.00\text{ m})\tan\left(\sin^{-1}\left(\frac{\cos 40.0°}{1.33}\right)\right) = \boxed{3.79\text{ m}}$$

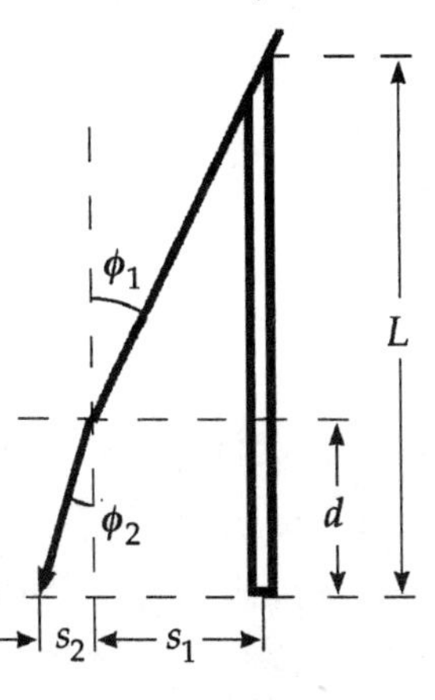

FIG. P35.54

P35.55 As the beam enters the slab,

$$1.00\sin 50.0° = 1.48\sin\theta_2$$

giving $\theta_2 = 31.2°$.

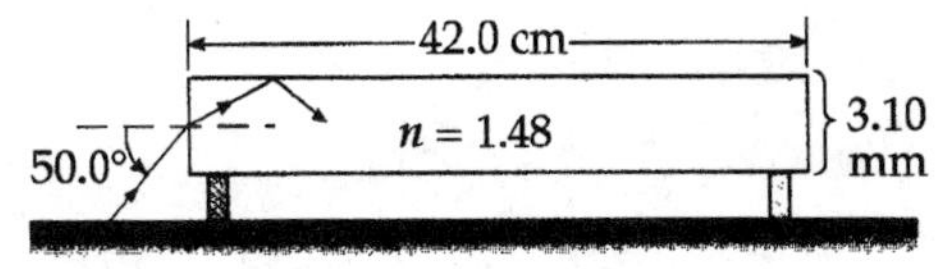

FIG. P35.55

The beam then strikes the top of the slab at $x_1 = \dfrac{1.55\text{ mm}}{\tan 31.2°}$ from the left end. Thereafter, the beam strikes a face each time it has traveled a distance of $2x_1$ along the length of the slab. Since the slab is 420 mm long, the beam has an additional $420\text{ mm} - x_1$ to travel after the first reflection. The number of additional reflections is

$$\frac{420\text{ mm} - x_1}{2x_1} = \frac{420\text{ mm} - 1.55\text{ mm}/\tan 31.2°}{3.10\text{ mm}/\tan 31.2°} = 81.5 \qquad \text{or 81 reflections}$$

since the answer must be an integer. The total number of reflections made in the slab is then $\boxed{82}$.

P35.56 (a) $$\frac{S_1'}{S_1} = \left[\frac{n_2 - n_1}{n_2 + n_1}\right]^2 = \left[\frac{1.52 - 1.00}{1.52 + 1.00}\right]^2 = \boxed{0.042\,6}$$

(b) If medium 1 is glass and medium 2 is air, $\dfrac{S_1'}{S_1} = \left[\dfrac{n_2 - n_1}{n_2 + n_1}\right]^2 = \left[\dfrac{1.00 - 1.52}{1.00 + 1.52}\right]^2 = 0.042\,6$.

There is $\boxed{\text{no difference}}$.

P35.57 (a) With $n_1 = 1$

and $n_2 = n$

the reflected fractional intensity is $\dfrac{S_1'}{S_1} = \left(\dfrac{n-1}{n+1}\right)^2$.

The remaining intensity must be transmitted:

$$\frac{S_2}{S_1} = 1 - \left(\frac{n-1}{n+1}\right)^2 = \frac{(n+1)^2 - (n-1)^2}{(n+1)^2} = \frac{n^2 + 2n + 1 - n^2 + 2n - 1}{(n+1)^2} = \boxed{\frac{4n}{(n+1)^2}}.$$

continued on next page

(b) At entry, $\frac{S_2}{S_1} = 1 - \left(\frac{n-1}{n+1}\right)^2 = \frac{4(2.419)}{(2.419+1)^2} = 0.828$.

At exit, $\frac{S_3}{S_2} = 0.828$.

Overall, $\frac{S_3}{S_1} = \left(\frac{S_3}{S_2}\right)\left(\frac{S_2}{S_1}\right) = (0.828)^2 = 0.685$

or $\boxed{68.5\%}$.

P35.58 Define $T = \frac{4n}{(n+1)^2}$ as the transmission coefficient for one encounter with an interface. For diamond and air, it is 0.828, as in Problem 57.

As shown in the figure, the total amount transmitted is

$T^2 + T^2(1-T)^2 + T^2(1-T)^4 + T^2(1-T)^6$
$+ \ldots + T^2(1-T)^{2n} + \ldots$

We have $1 - T = 1 - 0.828 = 0.172$ so the total transmission is

$(0.828)^2\left[1 + (0.172)^2 + (0.172)^4 + (0.172)^6 + \ldots\right]$.

To sum this series, define $F = 1 + (0.172)^2 + (0.172)^4 + (0.172)^6 + \ldots$.

Note that $(0.172)^2 F = (0.172)^2 + (0.172)^4 + (0.172)^6 + \ldots$, and

$1 + (0.172)^2 F = 1 + (0.172)^2 + (0.172)^4 + (0.172)^6 + \ldots = F$.

Then, $1 = F - (0.172)^2 F$ or $F = \frac{1}{1-(0.172)^2}$.

The overall transmission is then $\frac{(0.828)^2}{1-(0.172)^2} = 0.706$ or $\boxed{70.6\%}$.

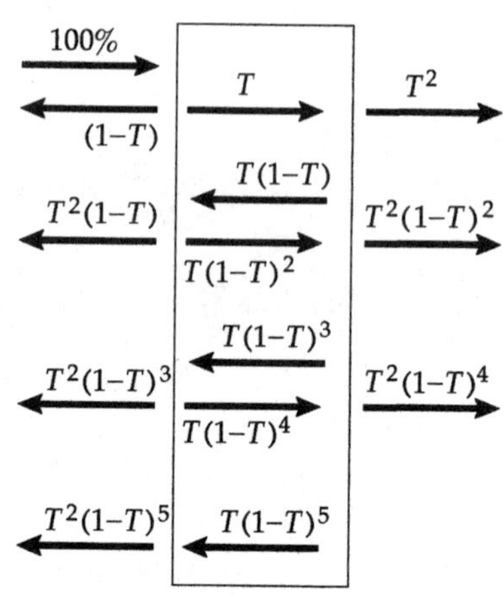

FIG. P35.58

P35.59 Define n_1 to be the index of refraction of the surrounding medium and n_2 to be that for the prism material. We can use the critical angle of 42.0° to find the ratio $\frac{n_2}{n_1}$:

$$n_2 \sin 42.0° = n_1 \sin 90.0°.$$

So, $$\frac{n_2}{n_1} = \frac{1}{\sin 42.0°} = 1.49.$$

Call the angle of refraction θ_2 at the surface 1. The ray inside the prism forms a triangle with surfaces 1 and 2, so the sum of the interior angles of this triangle must be 180°.

Thus, $(90.0° - \theta_2) + 60.0° + (90.0° - 42.0°) = 180°$.

Therefore, $\theta_2 = 18.0°$.

Applying Snell's law at surface 1, $n_1 \sin\theta_1 = n_2 \sin 18.0°$

$\sin\theta_1 = \left(\frac{n_2}{n_1}\right)\sin\theta_2 = 1.49 \sin 18.0°$ $\boxed{\theta_1 = 27.5°}$.

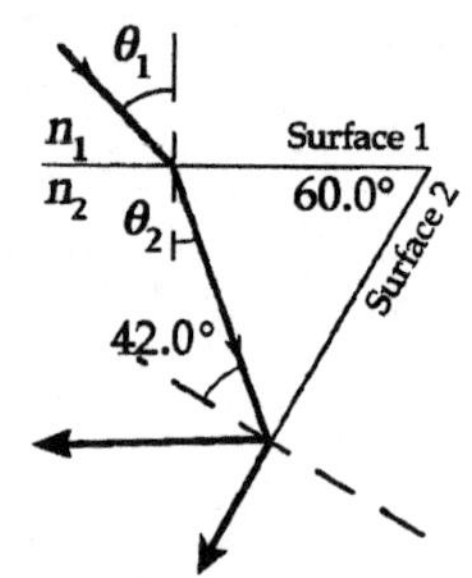

FIG. P35.59

***P35.60** (a) As the mirror turns through angle θ, the angle of incidence increases by θ and so does the angle of reflection. The incident ray is stationary, so the reflected ray turns through angle 2θ. The angular speed of the reflected ray is $2\omega_m$. The speed of the dot of light on the circular wall is $\boxed{2\omega_m R}$.

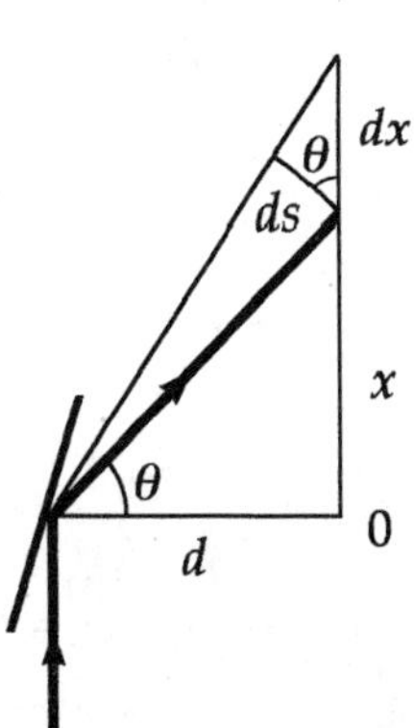

FIG. P35.60

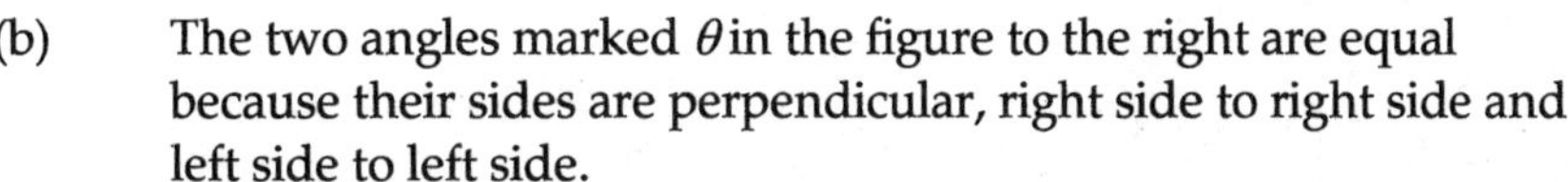
(b) The two angles marked θ in the figure to the right are equal because their sides are perpendicular, right side to right side and left side to left side.

We have $$\cos\theta = \frac{d}{\sqrt{x^2+d^2}} = \frac{ds}{dx}$$

and $$\frac{ds}{dt} = 2\omega_m\sqrt{x^2+d^2}.$$

So $$\frac{dx}{dt} = \frac{ds}{dt}\frac{\sqrt{x^2+d^2}}{d} = \boxed{2\omega_m\frac{x^2+d^2}{d}}.$$

P35.61 (a) For polystyrene *surrounded by air*, internal reflection requires

$$\theta_3 = \sin^{-1}\left(\frac{1.00}{1.49}\right) = 42.2°.$$

Then from geometry, $\theta_2 = 90.0° - \theta_3 = 47.8°$.

From Snell's law, $\sin\theta_1 = 1.49\sin 47.8° = 1.10$.

This has no solution.

Therefore, total internal reflection $\boxed{\text{always happens}}$.

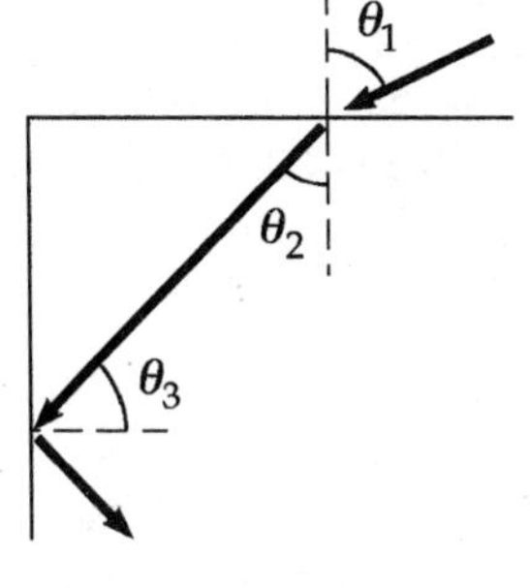

FIG. P35.61

(b) For polystyrene *surrounded by water*, $\theta_3 = \sin^{-1}\left(\frac{1.33}{1.49}\right) = 63.2°$

and $\theta_2 = 26.8°$.

From Snell's law, $\theta_1 = \boxed{30.3°}$.

(c) $\boxed{\text{No internal refraction is possible}}$

since the beam is initially traveling in a medium of lower index of refraction.

***P35.62** The picture illustrates optical sunrise. At the center of the earth,

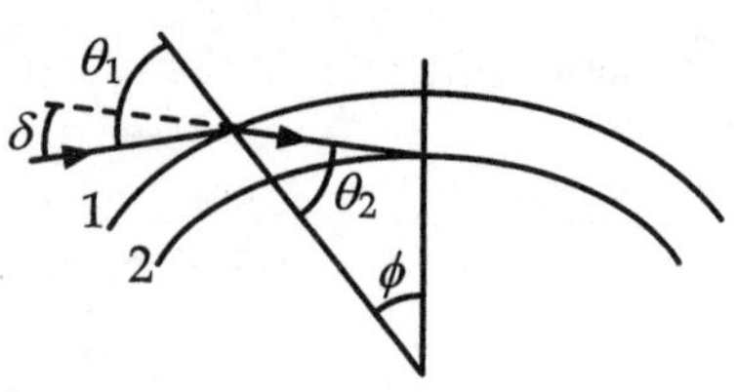

FIG. P35.62

$$\cos\phi = \frac{6.37\times10^6 \text{ m}}{6.37\times10^6 \text{ m} + 8\,614}$$

$$\phi = 2.98°$$

$$\theta_2 = 90 - 2.98° = 87.0°$$

At the top of the atmosphere

$$n_1 \sin\theta_1 = n_2 \sin\theta_2$$

$$1\sin\theta_1 = 1.000\,293 \sin 87.0°$$

$$\theta_1 = 87.4°$$

Deviation upon entry is

$$\delta = |\theta_1 - \theta_2|$$

$$\delta = 87.364° - 87.022° = 0.342°$$

Sunrise of the optical day is before geometric sunrise by $0.342°\left(\frac{86\,400 \text{ s}}{360°}\right) = 82.2 \text{ s}$. Optical sunset occurs later too, so the optical day is longer by $\boxed{164 \text{ s}}$.

P35.63 $\tan\theta_1 = \frac{4.00 \text{ cm}}{h}$

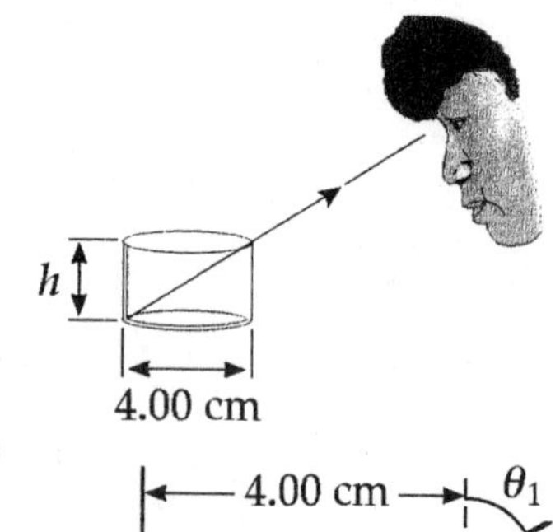

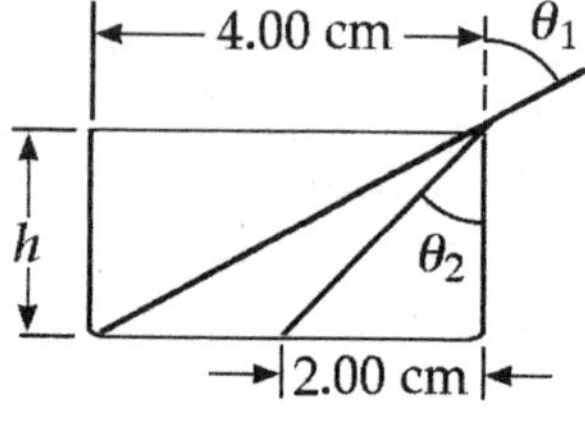

FIG. P35.63

and $\tan\theta_2 = \frac{2.00 \text{ cm}}{h}$

$$\tan^2\theta_1 = (2.00\tan\theta_2)^2 = 4.00\tan^2\theta_2$$

$$\frac{\sin^2\theta_1}{1-\sin^2\theta_1} = 4.00\left(\frac{\sin^2\theta_2}{1-\sin^2\theta_2}\right). \quad (1)$$

Snell's law in this case is: $n_1\sin\theta_1 = n_2\sin\theta_2$

$$\sin\theta_1 = 1.333\sin\theta_2.$$

Squaring both sides, $\sin^2\theta_1 = 1.777\sin^2\theta_2. \quad (2)$

Substituting (2) into (1), $\frac{1.777\sin^2\theta_2}{1-1.777\sin^2\theta_2} = 4.00\left(\frac{\sin^2\theta_2}{1-\sin^2\theta_2}\right).$

Defining $x = \sin^2\theta$, $\frac{0.444}{1-1.777x} = \frac{1}{1-x}.$

Solving for x, $0.444 - 0.444x = 1 - 1.777x$ and $x = 0.417$.

From x we can solve for θ_2: $\theta_2 = \sin^{-1}\sqrt{0.417} = 40.2°$.

Thus, the height is $h = \frac{2.00 \text{ cm}}{\tan\theta_2} = \frac{2.00 \text{ cm}}{\tan 40.2°} = \boxed{2.36 \text{ cm}}$.

P35.64 $\delta = \theta_1 - \theta_2 = 10.0°$ and $n_1 \sin\theta_1 = n_2 \sin\theta_2$

with $n_1 = 1,\ n_2 = \frac{4}{3}$.

Thus, $\theta_1 = \sin^{-1}(n_2 \sin\theta_2) = \sin^{-1}[n_2 \sin(\theta_1 - 10.0°)]$.

(You can use a calculator to home in on an approximate solution to this equation, testing different values of θ_1 until you find that $\theta_1 = \boxed{36.5°}$. Alternatively, you can solve for θ_1 exactly, as shown below.)

We are given that $\sin\theta_1 = \frac{4}{3}\sin(\theta_1 - 10.0°)$.

This is the sine of a difference, so $\frac{3}{4}\sin\theta_1 = \sin\theta_1 \cos 10.0° - \cos\theta_1 \sin 10.0°$.

Rearranging, $\sin 10.0° \cos\theta_1 = \left(\cos 10.0° - \frac{3}{4}\right)\sin\theta_1$

$\frac{\sin 10.0°}{\cos 10.0° - 0.750} = \tan\theta_1$ and $\theta_1 = \tan^{-1}(0.740) = \boxed{36.5°}$.

P35.65 To derive the law of *reflection*, locate point O so that the time of travel from point A to point B will be minimum.

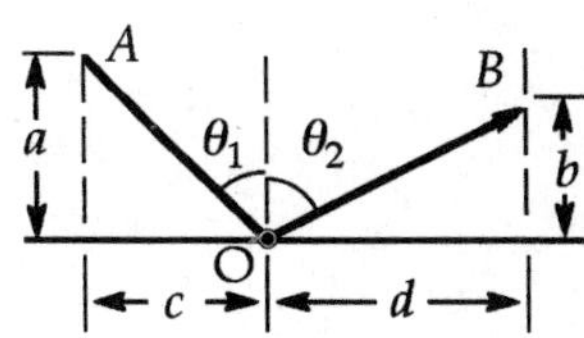

FIG. P35.65

The *total* light path is $L = a\sec\theta_1 + b\sec\theta_2$.

The time of travel is $t = \left(\frac{1}{v}\right)(a\sec\theta_1 + b\sec\theta_2)$.

If point O is displaced by dx, then

$$dt = \left(\frac{1}{v}\right)(a\sec\theta_1 \tan\theta_1 d\theta_1 + b\sec\theta_2 \tan\theta_2 d\theta_2) = 0 \qquad (1)$$

(since for minimum time $dt = 0$).

Also, $c + d = a\tan\theta_1 + b\tan\theta_2 = \text{constant}$

so, $$a\sec^2\theta_1 d\theta_1 + b\sec^2\theta_2 d\theta_2 = 0. \qquad (2)$$

Divide equations (1) and (2) to find $\boxed{\theta_1 = \theta_2}$.

P35.66 Observe in the sketch that the angle of incidence at point P is γ, and using triangle OPQ:

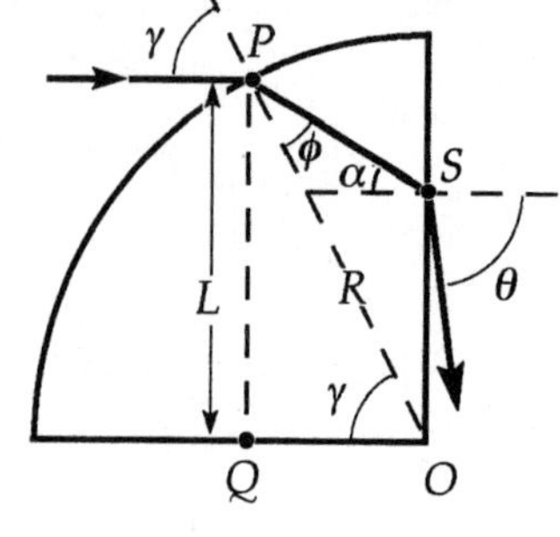

FIG. P35.66

$$\sin\gamma = \frac{L}{R}.$$

Also, $$\cos\gamma = \sqrt{1-\sin^2\gamma} = \frac{\sqrt{R^2-L^2}}{R}.$$

Applying Snell's law at point P, $1.00\sin\gamma = n\sin\phi$.

Thus, $$\sin\phi = \frac{\sin\gamma}{n} = \frac{L}{nR}$$

and $$\cos\phi = \sqrt{1-\sin^2\phi} = \frac{\sqrt{n^2R^2-L^2}}{nR}.$$

From triangle OPS, $\phi + (\alpha + 90.0°) + (90.0° - \gamma) = 180°$ or the angle of incidence at point S is $\alpha = \gamma - \phi$. Then, applying Snell's law at point S

gives $$1.00\sin\theta = n\sin\alpha = n\sin(\gamma - \phi)$$

or $$\sin\theta = n[\sin\gamma\cos\phi - \cos\gamma\sin\phi] = n\left[\left(\frac{L}{R}\right)\frac{\sqrt{n^2R^2-L^2}}{nR} - \frac{\sqrt{R^2-L^2}}{R}\left(\frac{L}{nR}\right)\right]$$

$$\sin\theta = \frac{L}{R^2}\left(\sqrt{n^2R^2-L^2} - \sqrt{R^2-L^2}\right)$$

and $$\theta = \boxed{\sin^{-1}\left[\frac{L}{R^2}\left(\sqrt{n^2R^2-L^2} - \sqrt{R^2-L^2}\right)\right]}.$$

P35.67 As shown in the sketch, the angle of incidence at point A is:

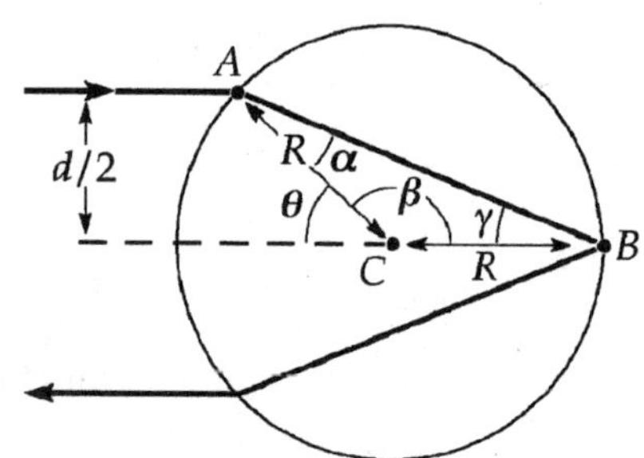

FIG. P35.67

$$\theta = \sin^{-1}\left(\frac{d/2}{R}\right) = \sin^{-1}\left(\frac{1.00\text{ m}}{2.00\text{ m}}\right) = 30.0°.$$

If the emerging ray is to be parallel to the incident ray, the path must be symmetric about the centerline CB of the cylinder. In the isosceles triangle ABC,

$$\gamma = \alpha \quad \text{and} \quad \beta = 180° - \theta.$$

Therefore, $$\alpha + \beta + \gamma = 180°$$

becomes $$2\alpha + 180° - \theta = 180°$$

or $$\alpha = \frac{\theta}{2} = 15.0°.$$

Then, applying Snell's law at point A,

$$n\sin\alpha = 1.00\sin\theta$$

or $$n = \frac{\sin\theta}{\sin\alpha} = \frac{\sin 30.0°}{\sin 15.0°} = \boxed{1.93}.$$

***P35.68** (a) The apparent radius of the glowing sphere is R_3 as shown. For it

$$\sin\theta_1 = \frac{R_1}{R_2}$$

$$\sin\theta_2 = \frac{R_3}{R_2}$$

$$n\sin\theta_1 = 1\sin\theta_2$$

$$n\frac{R_1}{R_2} = \frac{R_3}{R_2} \qquad \boxed{R_3 = nR_1}$$

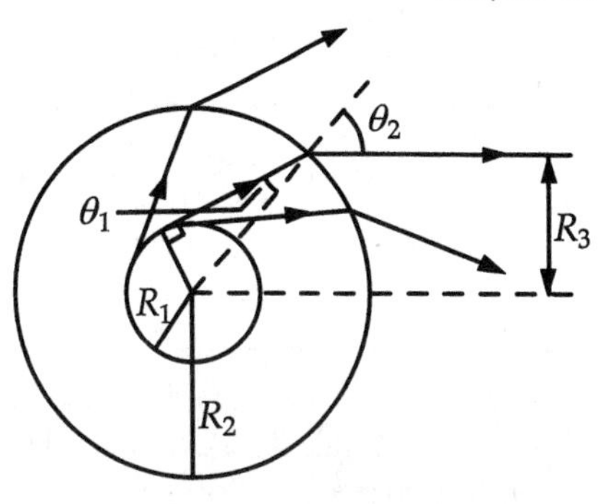

FIG. P35.68(a)

(b) If $nR_1 > R_2$, then $\sin\theta_2$ cannot be equal to $\frac{nR_1}{R_2}$. The ray considered in part (a) undergoes total internal reflection. In this case a ray escaping the atmosphere as shown here is responsible for the apparent radius of the glowing sphere and

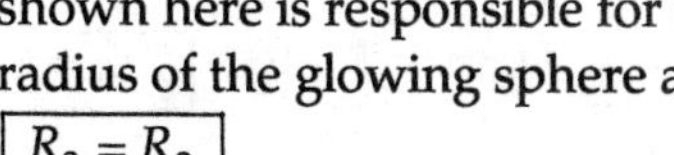

$\boxed{R_3 = R_2}$.

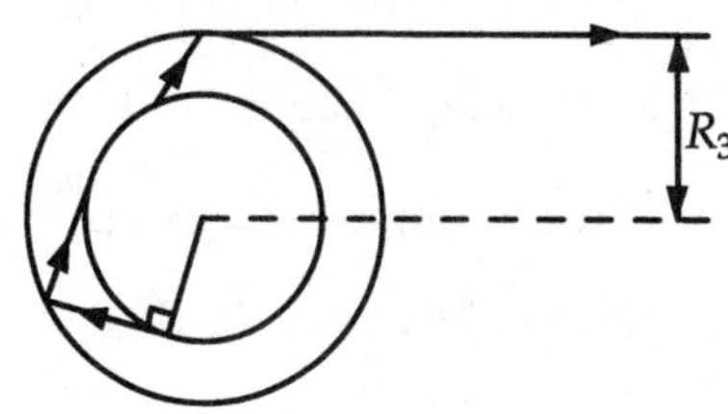

FIG. P35.68(b)

P35.69 (a) At the boundary of the air and glass, the critical angle is given by

$$\sin\theta_c = \frac{1}{n}.$$

Consider the critical ray PBB': $\tan\theta_c = \frac{d/4}{t}$ or $\frac{\sin\theta_c}{\cos\theta_c} = \frac{d}{4t}$.

Squaring the last equation gives: $\frac{\sin^2\theta_c}{\cos^2\theta_c} = \frac{\sin^2\theta_c}{1-\sin^2\theta_c} = \left(\frac{d}{4t}\right)^2$.

Since $\sin\theta_c = \frac{1}{n}$, this becomes $\frac{1}{n^2-1} = \left(\frac{d}{4t}\right)^2$ or $\boxed{n = \sqrt{1+\left(\frac{4t}{d}\right)^2}}$.

FIG. P35.69

(b) Solving for d, $d = \frac{4t}{\sqrt{n^2-1}}$.

Thus, if $n = 1.52$ and $t = 0.600\text{ cm}$, $d = \frac{4(0.600\text{ cm})}{\sqrt{(1.52)^2-1}} = \boxed{2.10\text{ cm}}$.

(c) Since violet light has a larger index of refraction, it will lead to a smaller critical angle and the inner edge of the white halo will be tinged with $\boxed{\text{violet}}$ light.

P35.70 From the sketch, observe that the angle of incidence at point A is the same as the prism angle θ at point O. Given that $\theta = 60.0°$, application of Snell's law at point A gives

$$1.50 \sin\beta = 1.00 \sin 60.0° \text{ or } \beta = 35.3°.$$

From triangle AOB, we calculate the angle of incidence (and reflection) at point B.

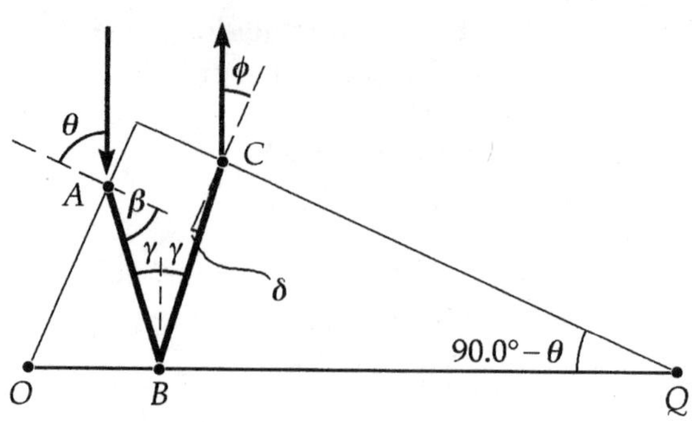

FIG. P35.70

$\theta = (90.0° - \beta) + (90.0° - \gamma) = 180°$ so $\quad \gamma = \theta - \beta = 60.0° - 35.3° = 24.7°$.

Now, using triangle BCQ: $\quad (90.0° - \gamma) + (90.0° - \delta) + (90.0° - \theta) = 180°$.

Thus the angle of incidence at point C is $\quad \delta = (90.0° - \theta) - \gamma = 30.0° - 24.7° = 5.30°$.

Finally, Snell's law applied at point C gives $\quad 1.00 \sin\phi = 1.50 \sin 5.30°$

or $\quad \phi = \sin^{-1}(1.50 \sin 5.30°) = \boxed{7.96°}$.

P35.71 (a) Given that $\theta_1 = 45.0°$ and $\theta_2 = 76.0°$.

Snell's law at the first surface gives

$$n \sin\alpha = 1.00 \sin 45.0° \qquad (1)$$

Observe that the angle of incidence at the second surface is

$$\beta = 90.0° - \alpha.$$

Thus, Snell's law at the second surface yields

$$n \sin\beta = n \sin(90.0° - \alpha) = 1.00 \sin 76.0°$$

or $\quad n \cos\alpha = \sin 76.0°. \qquad (2)$

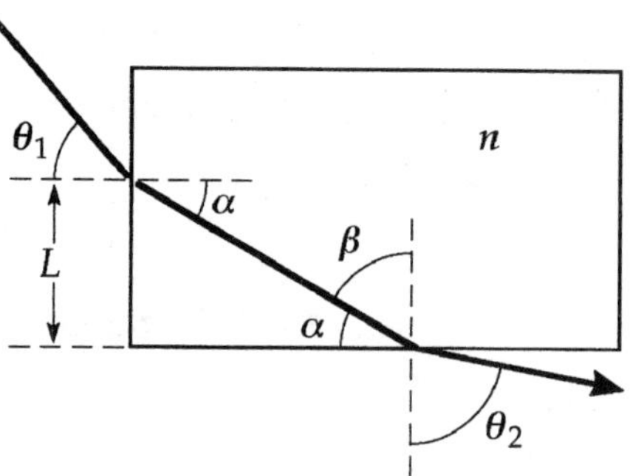

FIG. P35.71

Dividing Equation (1) by Equation (2), $\quad \tan\alpha = \dfrac{\sin 45.0°}{\sin 76.0°} = 0.729$

or $\quad \alpha = 36.1°$.

Then, from Equation (1), $\quad n = \dfrac{\sin 45.0°}{\sin\alpha} = \dfrac{\sin 45.0°}{\sin 36.1°} = \boxed{1.20}$.

(b) From the sketch, observe that the distance the light travels in the plastic is $d = \dfrac{L}{\sin\alpha}$. Also, the speed of light in the plastic is $v = \dfrac{c}{n}$, so the time required to travel through the plastic is

$$\Delta t = \frac{d}{v} = \frac{nL}{c \sin\alpha} = \frac{1.20(0.500 \text{ m})}{(3.00 \times 10^8 \text{ m/s}) \sin 36.1°} = 3.40 \times 10^{-9} \text{ s} = \boxed{3.40 \text{ ns}}.$$

P35.72

$\sin\theta_1$	$\sin\theta_2$	$\dfrac{\sin\theta_1}{\sin\theta_2}$
0.174	0.131	1.330 4
0.342	0.261	1.312 9
0.500	0.379	1.317 7
0.643	0.480	1.338 5
0.766	0.576	1.328 9
0.866	0.647	1.339 0
0.940	0.711	1.322 0
0.985	0.740	1.331 5

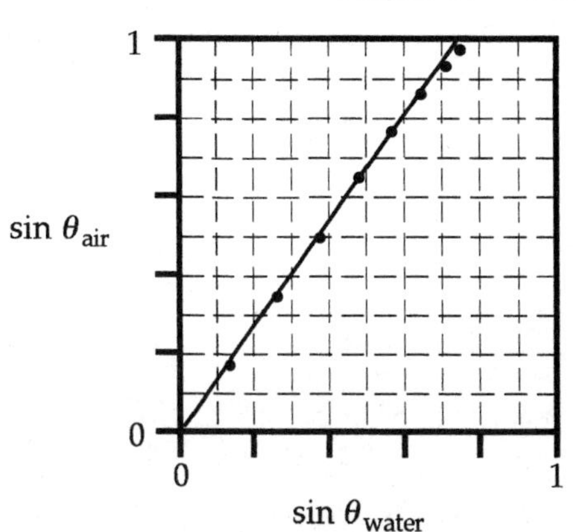

FIG. P35.72

The straightness of the graph line demonstrates Snell's proportionality.

The slope of the line is $\bar{n} = 1.327\,6 \pm 0.01$

and $n = \boxed{1.328 \pm 0.8\%}$.

ANSWERS TO EVEN PROBLEMS

P35.2 227 Mm/s

P35.4 (a) see the solution; (b) 300 Mm/s

P35.6 (a) 1.94 m; (b) 50.0° above the horizontal: antiparallel to the incident ray

P35.8 five times by the right-hand mirror and six times by the left-hand mirror

P35.10 25.5°; 442 nm

P35.12 (a) 474 THz; (b) 422 nm; (c) 200 Mm/s

P35.14 22.5°

P35.16 (a) 181 Mm/s; (b) 225 Mm/s; (c) 136 Mm/s

P35.18 3.39 m

P35.20 $\theta_1 = \tan^{-1} n$

P35.22 106 ps

P35.24 23.1°

P35.26 (a) 58.9°; (b) Only if $\theta_1 = \theta_2 = 0$

P35.28 see the solution

P35.30 (a) 41.5°; (b) 18.5°; (c) 27.6°; (d) 42.6°

P35.32 (a) see the solution; (b) 37.2°; (c) 37.3°; (d) 37.3°

P35.34 $\sin^{-1}\left(\sqrt{n^2-1}\sin\Phi - \cos\Phi\right)$

P35.36 (a) 24.4°; (b) 37.0°; (c) 49.8°

P35.38 67.2

P35.40 (a) $\dfrac{nd}{n-1}$; (b) yes; (c) 350 μm

P35.42 (a) 10.7°; (b) air; (c) Sound falling on the wall from most directions is 100% reflected.

P35.44 54.8° east of north

P35.46 (a) $\dfrac{h}{c}\left(\dfrac{n+1}{2}\right)$; (b) larger by $\dfrac{n+1}{2}$ times

P35.48 see the solution

P35.50 see the solution

P35.52 (a) 45.0°; (b) yes; see the solution

P35.54 3.79 m

P35.56 (a) 0.0426; (b) no difference

P35.58 0.706

P35.60 (a) $2\omega_m R$; (b) $2\omega_m \dfrac{x^2+d^2}{d}$

P35.62 164 s

P35.64 36.5°

P35.66 $\theta = \sin^{-1}\left[\dfrac{L}{R^2}\left(\sqrt{n^2R^2-L^2}-\sqrt{R^2-L^2}\right)\right]$

P35.68 (a) nR_1; (b) R_2

P35.70 7.96°

P35.72 see the solution; $n = 1.328 \pm 0.8\%$

36

Image Formation

CHAPTER OUTLINE

ANSWERS TO QUESTIONS

Q36.1 The mirror shown in the textbook picture produces an inverted image. It actually reverses top and bottom. It is not true in the same sense that "Most mirrors reverse left and right." Mirrors don't actually flip images side to side—we just assign the labels "left" and "right" to images as if they were real people mimicking us. If you stand face to face with a real person and raise your left hand, then he or she would have to raise his or her *right* hand to "mirror" your movement. Try this while facing a mirror. For sake of argument, let's assume you are facing north and wear a watch on your left hand, which is on the western side. If you raise your left hand, you might say that your image raises its right hand, based on the labels we assign to other people. But your image raises its western-side hand, which is the hand with the watch.

Q36.2 With a concave spherical mirror, for objects beyond the focal length the image will be real and inverted. For objects inside the focal length, the image will be virtual, upright, and magnified. Try a shaving or makeup mirror as an example.

Q36.3 With a convex spherical mirror, all images of real objects are upright, virtual and smaller than the object. As seen in Question 36.2, you only get a change of orientation when you pass the focal point—but the focal point of a convex mirror is on the non-reflecting side!

Q36.4 The mirror equation and the magnification equation apply to plane mirrors. A curved mirror is made flat by increasing its radius of curvature without bound, so that its focal length goes to infinity. From $\frac{1}{p}+\frac{1}{q}=\frac{1}{f}=0$ we have $\frac{1}{p}=-\frac{1}{q}$; therefore, $p=-q$. The virtual image is as far behind the mirror as the object is in front. The magnification is $M=-\frac{q}{p}=\frac{p}{p}=1$. The image is right side up and actual size.

Q36.5 Stones at the bottom of a clear stream always appears closer to the surface because light is refracted away from the normal at the surface. Example 36.8 in the textbook shows that its apparent depth is three quarters of its actual depth.

Q36.6 For definiteness, we consider real objects ($p>0$).

(a) For $M=-\frac{q}{p}$ to be negative, q must be positive. This will happen in $\frac{1}{q}=\frac{1}{f}-\frac{1}{p}$ if $p>f$, if the object is farther than the focal point.

(b) For $M=-\frac{q}{p}$ to be positive, q must be negative.
From $\frac{1}{q}=\frac{1}{f}-\frac{1}{p}$ we need $p<f$.

(c) For a real image, q must be positive.
As in part (a), it is sufficient for p to be larger than f.

(d) For $q<0$ we need $p<f$.

(e) For $|M|>1$, we consider separately $M<-1$ and $M>1$.

If $M=-\frac{q}{p}<-1$, we need $\frac{q}{p}>1$ or $q>p$

or $\frac{1}{q}<\frac{1}{p}$

From $\frac{1}{p}+\frac{1}{q}=\frac{1}{f}$, $\frac{1}{p}+\frac{1}{p}>\frac{1}{f}$ or $\frac{2}{p}>\frac{1}{f}$

or $\frac{p}{2}<f$ or $p<2f$.

Now if $-\frac{q}{p}>1$ or $-q>p$ or $q<-p$

we may require $q<0$, since then $\frac{1}{p}=\frac{1}{f}-\frac{1}{q}$ with $\frac{1}{f}>0$

gives $\frac{1}{p}>-\frac{1}{q}$ as required or $-p>q$.

For $q<0$ in $\frac{1}{q}=\frac{1}{f}-\frac{1}{p}$ we need $p<f$.

Thus the overall condition for an enlarged image is simply $p<2f$.

(f) For $|M|<1$, we have the reverse of part (e), requiring $p>2f$.

Q36.7 Using the same analysis as in Question 36.6 except $f<0$.

(a) Never.

(b) Always.

(c) Never, for light rays passing through the lens will always diverge.

(d) Always.

(e) Never.

(f) Always.

Q36.8 We assume the lens has a refractive index higher than its surroundings. For the biconvex lens in Figure 36.27(a), $R_1 > 0$ and $R_2 < 0$. Then all terms in $(n-1)\left(\frac{1}{R_1}-\frac{1}{R_2}\right)$ are positive and $f > 0$. For the other two lenses in part (a) of the figure, R_1 and R_2 are both positive but R_1 is less than R_2. Then $\frac{1}{R_1} > \frac{1}{R_2}$ and the focal length is again positive.

For the biconcave lens and the plano-concave lens in Figure 36.27(b), $R_1 < 0$ and $R_2 > 0$. Then both terms are negative in $\frac{1}{R_1}-\frac{1}{R_2}$ and the focal length is negative. For the middle lens in part (b) of the figure, R_1 and R_2 are both positive but R_1 is greater than R_2. Then $\frac{1}{R_1} < \frac{1}{R_2}$ and the focal length is again negative.

Q36.9 Both words are inverted. However OXIDE has up-down symmetry whereas LEAD does not.

Q36.10 An infinite number. In general, an infinite number of rays leave each point of any object and travel in all directions. Note that the three principal rays that we use for imaging are just a subset of the infinite number of rays. All three principal rays can be drawn in a ray diagram, provided that we extend the plane of the lens as shown in Figure Q36.10.

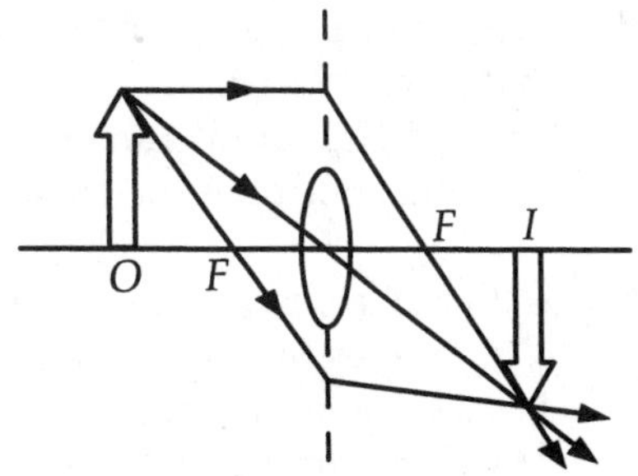

FIG. Q36.10

Q36.11 In this case, the index of refraction of the lens material is less than that of the surrounding medium. Under these conditions, a biconvex lens will be diverging.

Q36.12 Chromatic aberration arises because a material medium's refractive index can be frequency dependent. A mirror changes the direction of light by reflection, not refraction. Light of all wavelengths follows the same path according to the law of reflection, so no chromatic aberration happens.

Q36.13 This is a convex mirror. The mirror gives the driver a wide field of view and an upright image with the possible disadvantage of having objects appear diminished. Your brain can then interpret them as farther away than the objects really are.

Q36.14 As pointed out in Question 36.11, if the converging lens is immersed in a liquid with an index of refraction significantly greater than that of the lens itself, it will make light from a distant source diverge. This is not the case with a converging (concave) mirror, as the law of reflection has nothing to do with the indices of refraction.

Q36.15 As in the diagram, let the center of curvature C of the fishbowl and the bottom of the fish define the optical axis, intersecting the fishbowl at vertex V. A ray from the top of the fish that reaches the bowl surface along a radial line through C has angle of incidence zero and angle of refraction zero. This ray exits from the bowl unchanged in direction. A ray from the top of the fish to V is refracted to bend away from the normal. Its extension back inside the fishbowl determines the location of the image and the characteristics of the image. The image is upright, virtual, and enlarged.

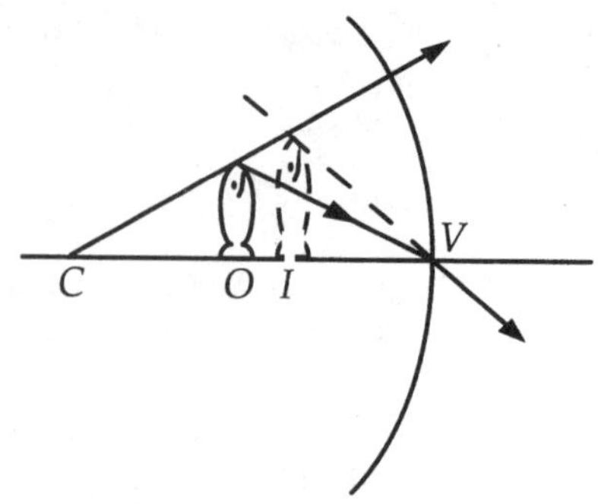

FIG. Q36.15

Q36.16 Because when you look at the ƎƆИA⅃UᙠMA in your rear view mirror, the apparent left-right inversion clearly displays the name of the AMBULANCE behind you. Do not jam on your brakes when a MIAMI city bus is right behind you.

Q36.17 The entire image is visible, but only at half the intensity. Each point on the object is a source of rays that travel in all directions. Thus, light from all parts of the object goes through all unblocked parts of the lens and forms an image. If you block part of the lens, you are blocking some of the rays, but the remaining ones still come from all parts of the object.

Q36.18 With the meniscus design, when you direct your gaze near the outer circumference of the lens you receive a ray that has passed through glass with more nearly parallel surfaces of entry and exit. Thus, the lens minimally distorts the direction to the object you are looking at. If you wear glasses, turn them around and look through them the wrong way to maximize this distortion.

Q36.19 The eyeglasses on the left are diverging lenses that correct for nearsightedness. If you look carefully at the edge of the person's face through the lens, you will see that everything viewed through these glasses is reduced in size. The eyeglasses on the right are converging lenses, which correct for farsightedness. These lenses make everything that is viewed through them look larger.

Q36.20 The eyeglass wearer's eye is at an object distance from the lens that is quite small—the eye is on the order of 10^{-2} meter from the lens. The focal length of an eyeglass lens is several decimeters, positive or negative. Therefore the image distance will be similar in magnitude to the object distance. The onlooker sees a sharp image of the eye behind the lens. Look closely at the left side of Figure Q36.19 and notice that the wearer's eyes seem not only to be smaller, but also positioned a bit behind the plane of his face—namely where they would be if he was not wearing glasses. Similarly, in the right half of Figure Q36.19, his eyes seem to be in front of the plane of his face and magnified. We as observers take this light information coming from the object through the lens and perceive or photograph the image as if it were an object.

Q36.21 In the diagram, only two of the three principal rays have been used to locate images to reduce the amount of visual clutter. The upright shaded arrows are the objects, and the correspondingly numbered inverted arrows are the images. As you can see, object 2 is closer to the focal point than object 1, and image 2 is farther to the left than image 1.

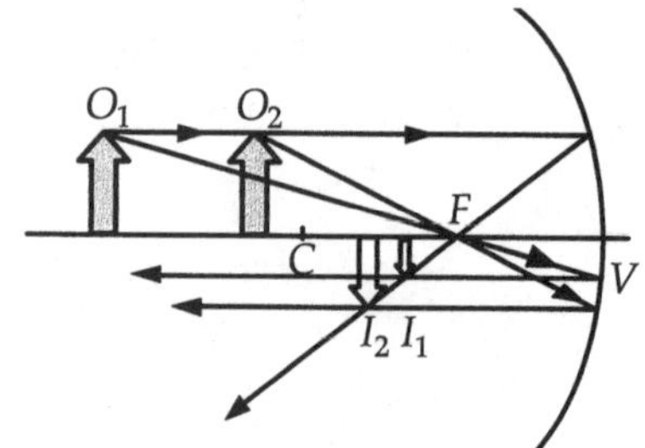

FIG. Q36.21

Q36.22 Absolutely. Only absorbed light, not transmitted light, contributes internal energy to a transparent object. A clear lens can stay ice-cold and solid as megajoules of light energy pass through it.

Q36.23 One can change the *f* number either by changing the focal length (if using a "zoom" lens) or by changing the aperture of the camera lens. As the *f* number increases, the exposure time required increases also, as both increasing the focal length or decreasing the aperture decreases the light intensity reaching the film.

Q36.24 Make the mirror an efficient reflector (shiny). Make it reflect to the image even rays far from the axis, by giving it a parabolic shape. Most important, make it large in diameter to intercept a lot of solar power. And you get higher temperature if the image is smaller, as you get with shorter focal length; and if the furnace enclosure is an efficient absorber (black).

Q36.25 For the explanation, we ignore the lens and consider two objects. Hold your two thumbs parallel and extended upward in front of you, at different distances from your nose. Alternately close your left eye and your right eye. You see both thumbs jump back and forth against the background of more distant objects. Parallax by definition is this apparent motion of a stationary object (one thumb) caused by motion of the observer (jumping from right eye to left eye). Your nearer thumb jumps by a larger angle against the background than your farther thumb does. They will jump by the same amount only if they are equally distant from your face. The method of parallax for adjusting one object so that it is the same distance away from you as another object will work even if one 'object' is an image.

Q36.26 The artist's statements are accurate, perceptive, and eloquent. The image you see is "almost one's whole surroundings," including things behind you and things farther in front of you than the globe is, but nothing eclipsed by the opaque globe or by your head. For example, we cannot see Escher's index and middle fingers or their reflections in the globe.

The point halfway between your eyes is indeed the focus in a figurative sense, but it is not an optical focus. The principal axis will always lie in a line that runs through the center of the sphere and the bridge of your nose. Outside the globe, you are at the center of your observable universe. If you wink at the ball, the center of the looking-glass world hops over to the location of the image of your open eye.

Q36.27 The three mirrors, two of which are shown as M and N in the figure to the right, reflect any incident ray back parallel to its original direction. When you look into the corner you see image I_3 of yourself.

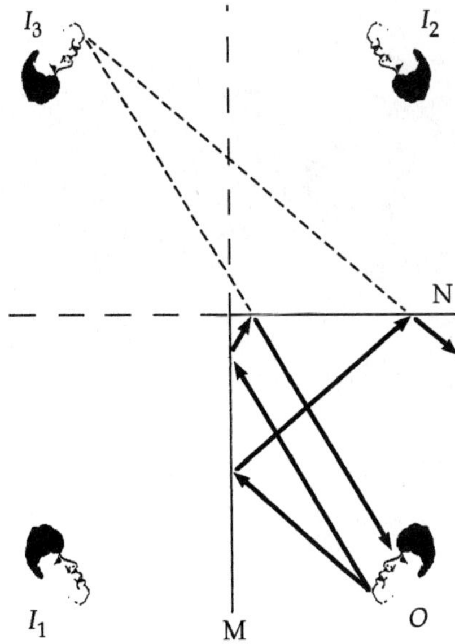

FIG. Q36.21

Q36.28 You have likely seen a Fresnel mirror for sound. The diagram represents first a side view of a band shell. It is a concave mirror for sound, designed to channel sound into a beam toward the audience in front of the band shell. Sections of its surface can be kept at the right orientations as they are pushed around inside a rectangular box to form an auditorium with good diffusion of sound from stage to audience, with a floor plan suggested by the second part of the diagram.

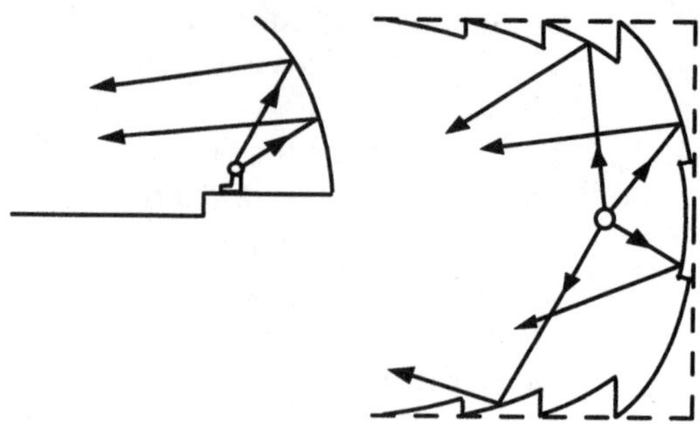

FIG. Q36.28

SOLUTIONS TO PROBLEMS

Section 36.1 **Images Formed by Flat Mirrors**

P36.1 I stand 40 cm from my bathroom mirror. I scatter light, which travels to the mirror and back to me in time

$$\frac{0.8\text{ m}}{3\times10^{8}\text{ m/s}}\boxed{\sim10^{-9}\text{ s}}$$

showing me a view of myself as I was at that look-back time. I'm no Dorian Gray!

P36.2 The virtual image is as far behind the mirror as the choir is in front of the mirror. Thus, the image is 5.30 m behind the mirror. The image of the choir is $0.800\text{ m}+5.30\text{ m}=6.10\text{ m}$ from the organist. Using similar triangles:

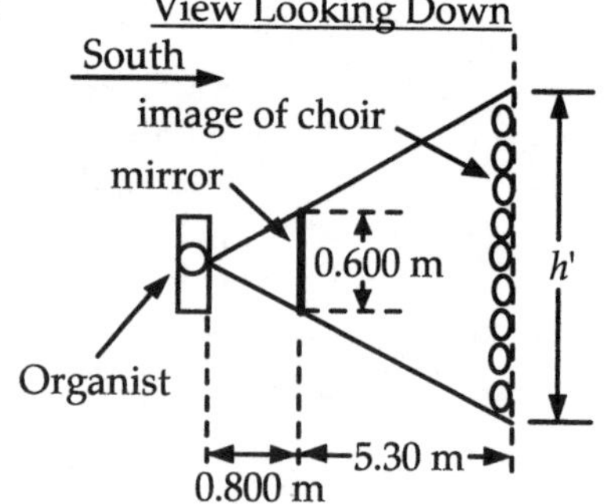

FIG. P36.2

$$\frac{h'}{0.600\text{ m}}=\frac{6.10\text{ m}}{0.800\text{ m}}$$

or

$$h'=(0.600\text{ m})\left(\frac{6.10\text{ m}}{0.800\text{ m}}\right)=\boxed{4.58\text{ m}}.$$

P36.3 The flatness of the mirror is described

by $R = \infty$, $f = \infty$

and $\frac{1}{f} = 0$.

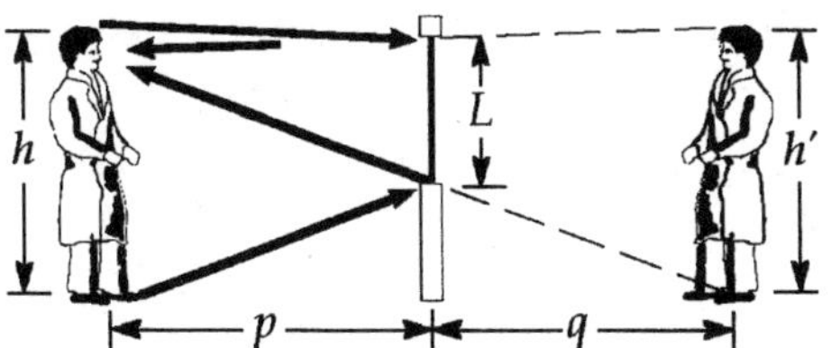

FIG. P36.3

By our general mirror equation,

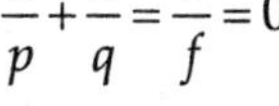

$$\frac{1}{p} + \frac{1}{q} = \frac{1}{f} = 0$$

or $q = -p$.

Thus, the image is as far behind the mirror as the person is in front. The magnification is then

$$M = \frac{-q}{p} = 1 = \frac{h'}{h}$$

so $h' = h = 70.0$ inches.

The required height of the mirror is defined by the triangle from the person's eyes to the top and bottom of his image, as shown. From the geometry of the triangle, we see that the mirror height must be:

$$h'\left(\frac{p}{p-q}\right) = h'\left(\frac{p}{2p}\right) = \frac{h'}{2}.$$

Thus, the mirror must be $\boxed{\text{at least 35.0 inches high}}$.

P36.4 A graphical construction produces 5 images, with images I_1 and I_2 directly into the mirrors from the object O,

and (O, I_3, I_4)

and (I_2, I_1, I_5)

forming the vertices of equilateral triangles.

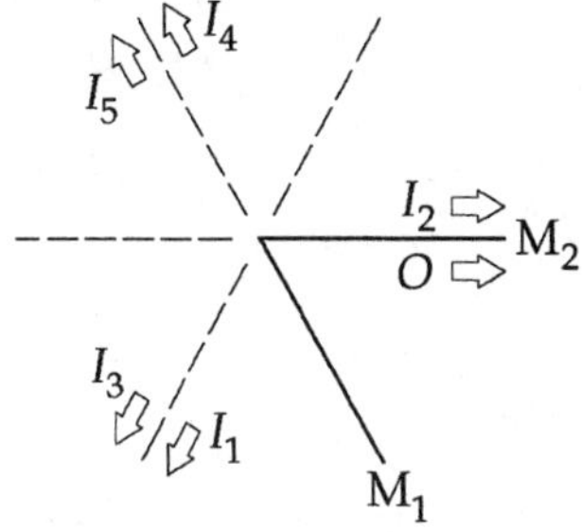

FIG. P36.4

P36.5 (1) The first image in the left mirror is 5.00 ft behind the mirror, or $\boxed{10.0\text{ ft}}$ from the position of the person.

(2) The first image in the right mirror is located 10.0 ft behind the right mirror, but this location is 25.0 ft from the left mirror. Thus, the second image in the left mirror is 25.0 ft behind the mirror, or $\boxed{30.0\text{ ft}}$ from the person.

(3) The first image in the left mirror forms an image in the right mirror. This first image is 20.0 ft from the right mirror, and, thus, an image 20.0 ft behind the right mirror is formed. This image in the right mirror also forms an image in the left mirror. The distance from this image in the right mirror to the left mirror is 35.0 ft. The third image in the left mirror is, thus, 35.0 ft behind the mirror, or $\boxed{40.0\text{ ft}}$ from the person.

***P36.6** (a) The flat mirrors have

$$R \to \infty$$

and $f \to \infty$.

The upper mirror M_1 produces a virtual, actual sized image I_1 according to

$$\frac{1}{p_1} + \frac{1}{q_1} = \frac{1}{f} = \frac{1}{\infty} = 0$$

$$q_1 = -p_1$$

with $M_1 = -\frac{q_1}{p_1} = +1$.

As shown, this image is above the upper mirror. It is the object for mirror M_2, at object distance

$$p_2 = p_1 + h.$$

The lower mirror produces a virtual, actual-size, right-side-up image according to

$$\frac{1}{p_2} + \frac{1}{q_2} = 0$$

$$q_2 = -p_2 = -(p_1 + h)$$

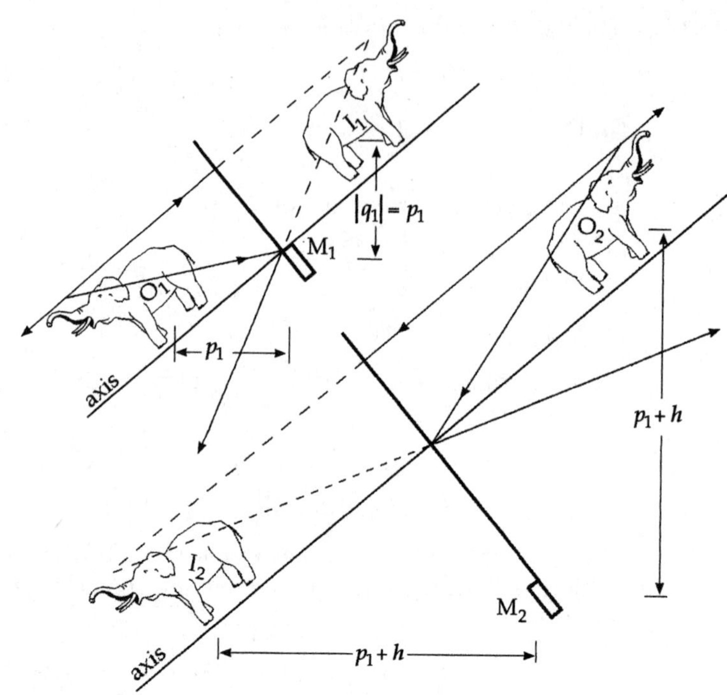

FIG. P36.6

with $M_2 = -\frac{q_2}{p_2} = +1$ and $M_{\text{overall}} = M_1 M_2 = 1$.

Thus the final image is at distance $\boxed{p_1 + h}$ behind the lower mirror.

(b) It is $\boxed{\text{virtual}}$.

(c) $\boxed{\text{Upright}}$

(d) With magnification $\boxed{+1}$.

(e) It $\boxed{\text{does not appear to be reversed}}$ left and right. In a top view of the periscope, parallel rays from the right and left sides of the object stay parallel and on the right and left.

Section 36.2 **Images Formed by Spherical Mirrors**

P36.7 For a concave mirror, both R and f are positive.

We also know that $$f=\frac{R}{2}=10.0\text{ cm}.$$

(a) $$\frac{1}{q}=\frac{1}{f}-\frac{1}{p}=\frac{1}{10.0\text{ cm}}-\frac{1}{40.0\text{ cm}}=\frac{3}{40.0\text{ cm}}$$

and $$\boxed{q=13.3\text{ cm}}$$

$$M=\frac{q}{p}=-\frac{13.3\text{ cm}}{40.0\text{ cm}}=\boxed{-0.333}.$$

The image is 13.3 cm in front of the mirror, $\boxed{\text{real, and inverted}}$.

(b) $$\frac{1}{q}=\frac{1}{f}-\frac{1}{p}=\frac{1}{10.0\text{ cm}}-\frac{1}{20.0\text{ cm}}=\frac{1}{20.0\text{ cm}}$$

and $$\boxed{q=20.0\text{ cm}}$$

$$M=\frac{q}{p}=-\frac{20.0\text{ cm}}{20.0\text{ cm}}=\boxed{-1.00}.$$

The image is 20.0 cm in front of the mirror, $\boxed{\text{real, and inverted}}$.

(c) $$\frac{1}{q}=\frac{1}{f}-\frac{1}{p}=\frac{1}{10.0\text{ cm}}-\frac{1}{10.0\text{ cm}}=0$$

Thus, q = infinity.

$\boxed{\text{No image is formed}}$. The rays are reflected parallel to each other.

P36.8 $$\frac{1}{q}=\frac{1}{f}-\frac{1}{p}=-\frac{1}{0.275\text{ m}}-\frac{1}{10.0\text{ m}}$$ gives $\boxed{q=-0.267\text{ m}}$.

Thus, the image is $\boxed{\text{virtual}}$.

$$M=\frac{-q}{p}=-\frac{-0.267}{10.0\text{ m}}=\boxed{0.0267}$$

Thus, the image is $\boxed{\text{upright}}$ $(+M)$ and $\boxed{\text{diminished}}$ $(|M|<1)$.

P36.9 (a) $\frac{1}{p}+\frac{1}{q}=\frac{2}{R}$ gives $\frac{1}{30.0\text{ cm}}+\frac{1}{q}=\frac{2}{(-40.0\text{ cm})}$

$\frac{1}{q}=-\frac{2}{40.0\text{ cm}}-\frac{1}{30.0\text{ cm}}=-0.083\,3\text{ cm}^{-1}$ so $q=\boxed{-12.0\text{ cm}}$

$$M=\frac{-q}{p}=-\frac{(-12.0\text{ cm})}{30.0\text{ cm}}=\boxed{0.400}.$$

(b) $\frac{1}{p}+\frac{1}{q}=\frac{2}{R}$ gives $\frac{1}{60.0\text{ cm}}+\frac{1}{q}=\frac{2}{(-40.0\text{ cm})}$

$\frac{1}{q}=-\frac{2}{40.0\text{ cm}}-\frac{1}{60.0\text{ cm}}=-0.066\,6\text{ cm}^{-1}$ so $q=\boxed{-15.0\text{ cm}}$

$$M=\frac{-q}{p}=-\frac{(-15.0\text{ cm})}{60.0\text{ cm}}=\boxed{0.250}.$$

(c) Since $M>0$, the images are $\boxed{\text{upright}}$.

P36.10 With radius 2.50 m, the cylindrical wall is a highly efficient mirror for sound, with focal length

$$f=\frac{R}{2}=1.25\text{ m}.$$

In a vertical plane the sound disperses as usual, but that radiated in a horizontal plane is concentrated in a sound image at distance q from the back of the niche, where

$\frac{1}{p}+\frac{1}{q}=\frac{1}{f}$ so $\frac{1}{2.00\text{ m}}+\frac{1}{q}=\frac{1}{1.25\text{ m}}$

$$q=\boxed{3.33\text{ m}}.$$

P36.11 (a) $\frac{1}{p}+\frac{1}{q}=\frac{2}{R}$ becomes $\frac{1}{q}=\frac{2}{60.0\text{ cm}}-\frac{1}{90.0\text{ cm}}$

$q=\boxed{45.0\text{ cm}}$ and $M=\frac{-q}{p}=-\frac{45.0\text{ cm}}{90.0\text{ cm}}=\boxed{-0.500}$.

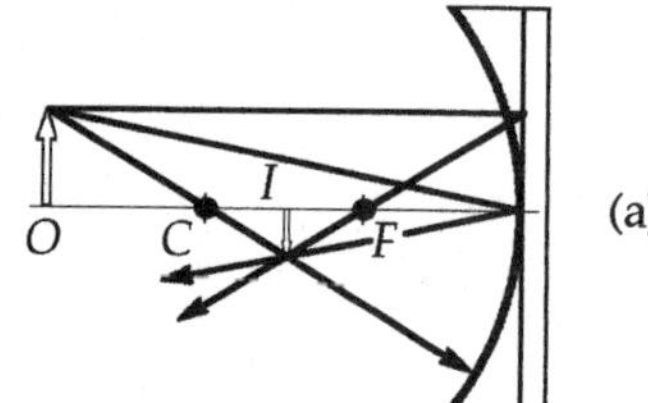

(b) $\frac{1}{p}+\frac{1}{q}=\frac{2}{R}$ becomes $\frac{1}{q}=\frac{2}{60.0\text{ cm}}-\frac{1}{20.0\text{ cm}}$

$q=\boxed{-60.0\text{ cm}}$ and $M=\frac{-q}{p}=-\frac{(-60.0\text{ cm})}{(20.0\text{ cm})}=\boxed{3.00}$.

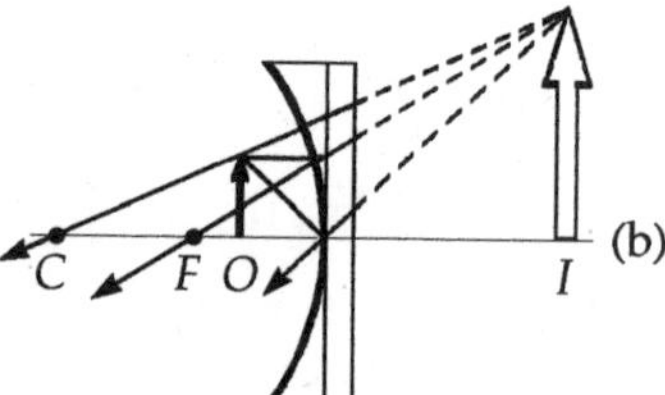

FIG. P36.11

(c) The image (a) is real, inverted and diminished. That of (b) is virtual, upright, and enlarged. The ray diagrams are similar to Figure 36.15(a) and 36.15(b) in the text, respectively.

P36.12 For a concave mirror, R and f are positive. Also, for an erect image, M is positive. Therefore,

$$M = -\frac{q}{p} = 4 \text{ and } q = -4p.$$

$$\frac{1}{f} = \frac{1}{p} + \frac{1}{q} \text{ becomes } \frac{1}{40.0 \text{ cm}} = \frac{1}{p} - \frac{1}{4p} = \frac{3}{4p}; \text{ from which, } p = \boxed{30.0 \text{ cm}}.$$

***P36.13** The ball is a convex mirror with $R = -4.25$ cm and

$f = \frac{R}{2} = -2.125$ cm. We have

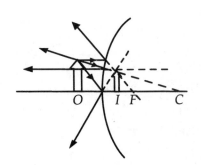

$$M = \frac{3}{4} = -\frac{q}{p}$$

$$q = -\frac{3}{4}p$$

$$\frac{1}{p} + \frac{1}{q} = \frac{1}{f}$$

$$\frac{1}{p} + \frac{1}{-(3/4)p} = \frac{1}{-2.125 \text{ cm}}$$

$$\frac{3}{3p} - \frac{4}{3p} = \frac{1}{-2.125 \text{ cm}}$$

$$3p = 2.125 \text{ cm}$$

$\boxed{p = 0.708 \text{ cm}}$ in front of the sphere.

The image is upright, virtual, and diminished.

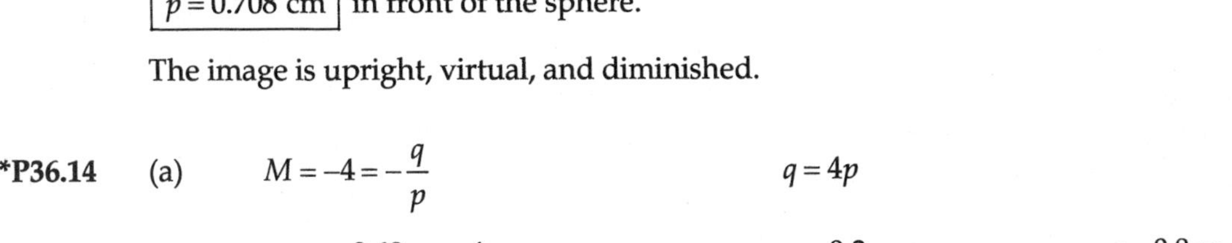

FIG. P36.13

***P36.14** (a)

$$M = -4 = -\frac{q}{p} \qquad q = 4p$$

$$q - p = 0.60 \text{ m} = 4p - p \qquad p = 0.2 \text{ m} \qquad q = 0.8 \text{ m}$$

$$\frac{1}{f} = \frac{1}{p} + \frac{1}{q} = \frac{1}{0.2 \text{ m}} + \frac{1}{0.8 \text{ m}} \qquad f = \boxed{160 \text{ mm}}$$

(b)

$$M = +\frac{1}{2} = -\frac{q}{p} \qquad p = -2q$$

$$|q| + p = 0.20 \text{ m} = -q + p = -q - 2q$$

$$q = -66.7 \text{ mm} \qquad p = 133 \text{ mm}$$

$$\frac{1}{p} + \frac{1}{q} = \frac{2}{R} = \frac{1}{0.133 \text{ m}} + \frac{1}{-0.0667 \text{ m}} \qquad R = \boxed{-267 \text{ mm}}$$

***P36.15** $M = -\dfrac{q}{p}$

$$q = -Mp = -0.013(30\text{ cm}) = -0.39\text{ cm}$$

$$\frac{1}{p}+\frac{1}{q}=\frac{1}{f}=\frac{2}{R}:$$

$$\frac{1}{30\text{ cm}}+\frac{1}{-0.39\text{ cm}}=\frac{2}{R}$$

$$R=\frac{2}{-2.53\text{ m}^{-1}}=-0.790\text{ cm}$$

The cornea is convex, with radius of curvature $\boxed{0.790\text{ cm}}$.

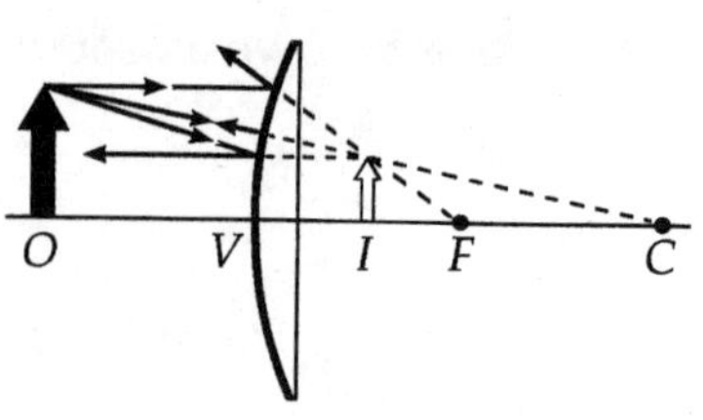

FIG. P36.15

***P36.16** With

$$M=\frac{h'}{h}=\frac{+4.00\text{ cm}}{10.0\text{ cm}}=+0.400=-\frac{q}{p}$$

$$q=-0.400p$$

the image must be virtual.

(a) It is a $\boxed{\text{convex}}$ mirror that produces a diminished upright virtual image.

(b) We must have

$$p+|q|=42.0\text{ cm}=p-q$$

$$p=42.0\text{ cm}+q$$

$$p=42.0\text{ cm}-0.400p$$

$$p=\frac{42.0\text{ cm}}{1.40}=30.0\text{ cm}$$

The mirror is $\boxed{\text{at the 30.0 cm mark}}$.

(c) $\dfrac{1}{p}+\dfrac{1}{q}=\dfrac{1}{f}=\dfrac{1}{30\text{ cm}}+\dfrac{1}{-0.4(30\text{ cm})}=\dfrac{1}{f}=-0.050\,0/\text{cm}$ $\boxed{f=-20.0\text{ cm}}$

The ray diagram looks like Figure 36.15(c) in the text.

P36.17 (a) $q=(p+5.00\text{ m})$ and, since the image must be real,

$$M=-\frac{q}{p}=-5 \qquad \text{or} \qquad q=5p.$$

Therefore, $p+5.00\text{ m}=5p$

or $p=1.25\text{ m}$ and $q=6.25\text{ m}$.

From $\dfrac{1}{p}+\dfrac{1}{q}=\dfrac{2}{R}$, $R=\dfrac{2pq}{p+q}=\dfrac{2(1.25)(6.25)}{1.25+6.25}$

$$=\boxed{2.08\text{ m(concave)}}$$

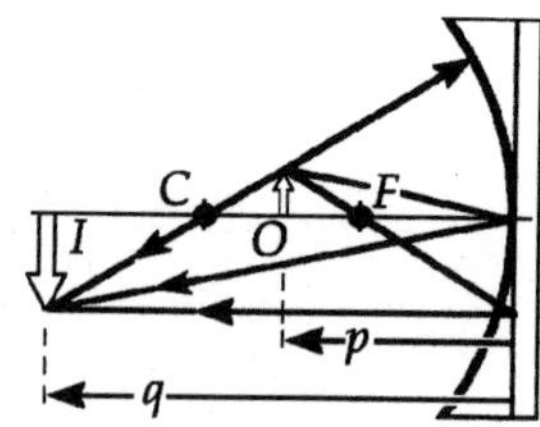

FIG. P36.17

(b) From part (a), $p=1.25\text{ m}$; the mirror should be $\boxed{1.25\text{ m}}$ in front of the object.

P36.18 Assume that the object distance is the same in both cases (i.e., her face is the same distance from the hubcap regardless of which way it is turned). Also realize that the near image ($q=-10.0\text{ cm}$) occurs when using the convex side of the hubcap. Applying the mirror equation to both cases gives:

(concave side: $R=|R|$, $q=-30.0\text{ cm}$)

$$\frac{1}{p}-\frac{1}{30.0}=\frac{2}{|R|}$$

or
$$\frac{2}{|R|}=\frac{30.0\text{ cm}-p}{(30.0\text{ cm})p} \qquad (1)$$

(convex side: $R=-|R|$, $q=-10.0\text{ cm}$)

$$\frac{1}{p}-\frac{1}{10.0}=-\frac{2}{|R|}$$

or
$$\frac{2}{|R|}=\frac{p-10.0\text{ cm}}{(10.0\text{ cm})p}. \qquad (2)$$

(a) Equating Equations (1) and (2) gives:

$$\frac{30.0\text{ cm}-p}{3.00}=p-10.0\text{ cm}$$

or
$$p=15.0\text{ cm}.$$

Thus, her face is $\boxed{15.0\text{ cm}}$ from the hubcap.

(b) Using the above result ($p=15.0\text{ cm}$) in Equation (1) gives:

$$\frac{2}{|R|}=\frac{30.0\text{ cm}-15.0\text{ cm}}{(30.0\text{ cm})(15.0\text{ cm})}$$

or
$$\frac{2}{|R|}=\frac{1}{30.0\text{ cm}}$$

and
$$|R|=60.0\text{ cm}.$$

The radius of the hubcap is $\boxed{60.0\text{ cm}}$.

***P36.19** (a) The flat mirror produces an image according to

$$\frac{1}{p}+\frac{1}{q}=\frac{1}{f}=\frac{2}{R} \qquad \frac{1}{24\text{ cm}}+\frac{1}{q}=\frac{1}{\infty}=0 \qquad q=-24.0\text{ m}.$$

The image is 24.0 m behind the mirror, distant from your eyes by

$$1.55\text{ m}+24.0\text{ m}=\boxed{25.6\text{ m}}.$$

(b) The image is the same size as the object, so $\theta=\frac{h}{d}=\frac{1.50\text{ m}}{25.6\text{ m}}=\boxed{0.0587\text{ rad}}$.

(c)
$$\frac{1}{p}+\frac{1}{q}=\frac{2}{R} \qquad \frac{1}{24\text{ m}}+\frac{1}{q}=\frac{2}{(-2\text{ m})} \qquad q=\frac{1}{-(1/1\text{ m})-(1/24\text{ m})}=-0.960\text{ m}$$

This image is distant from your eyes by $1.55\text{ m}+0.960\text{ m}=\boxed{2.51\text{ m}}$.

continued on next page

(d) The image size is given by $M = \frac{h'}{h} = -\frac{q}{p}$ $h' = -h\frac{q}{p} = -1.50\text{ m}\left(\frac{-0.960\text{ m}}{24\text{ m}}\right) = 0.060\,0\text{ m}$.

So its angular size at your eye is $\theta' = \frac{h'}{d} = \frac{0.06\text{ m}}{2.51\text{ m}} = \boxed{0.023\,9\text{ rad}}$.

(e) Your brain assumes that the car is 1.50 m high and calculate its distance as

$$d' = \frac{h}{\theta'} = \frac{1.50\text{ m}}{0.023\,9} = \boxed{62.8\text{ m}}.$$

P36.20 (a) The image starts from a point whose height above the mirror vertex is given by

$$\frac{1}{p} + \frac{1}{q} = \frac{1}{f} = \frac{2}{R} \qquad \frac{1}{3.00\text{ m}} + \frac{1}{q} = \frac{1}{0.500\text{ m}}. \qquad \text{Therefore,} \qquad q = 0.600\text{ m}.$$

As the ball falls, p decreases and q increases. Ball and image pass when $q_1 = p_1$. When this is true,

$$\frac{1}{p_1} + \frac{1}{p_1} = \frac{1}{0.500\text{ m}} = \frac{2}{p_1} \qquad \text{or} \qquad p_1 = 1.00\text{ m}.$$

As the ball passes the focal point, the image switches from infinitely far above the mirror to infinitely far below the mirror. As the ball approaches the mirror from above, the virtual image approaches the mirror from below, reaching it together when $p_2 = q_2 = 0$.

(b) The falling ball passes its real image when it has fallen

$$3.00\text{ m} - 1.00\text{ m} = 2.00\text{ m} = \frac{1}{2}gt^2, \text{ or when } t = \sqrt{\frac{2(2.00\text{ m})}{9.80\text{ m/s}^2}} = \boxed{0.639\text{ s}}.$$

The ball reaches its virtual image when it has traversed

$$3.00\text{ m} - 0 = 3.00\text{ m} = \frac{1}{2}gt^2, \text{ or at } t = \sqrt{\frac{2(3.00\text{ m})}{9.80\text{ m/s}^2}} = \boxed{0.782\text{ s}}.$$

Section 36.3 **Images Formed by Refraction**

P36.21 $\frac{n_1}{p} + \frac{n_2}{q} = \frac{n_2 - n_1}{R} = 0$ and $R \to \infty$

$$q = -\frac{n_2}{n_1}p = -\frac{1}{1.309}(50.0\text{ cm}) = -38.2\text{ cm}$$

Thus, the virtual image of the dust speck is $\boxed{\text{38.2 cm below the top surface}}$ of the ice.

P36.22 When $R \to \infty$, the equation describing image formation at a single refracting surface becomes $q = -p\left(\frac{n_2}{n_1}\right)$. We use this to locate the final images of the two surfaces of the glass plate. First, find the image the glass forms of the *bottom* of the plate.

$$q_{B1} = -\left(\frac{1.33}{1.66}\right)(8.00 \text{ cm}) = -6.41 \text{ cm}$$

This virtual image is 6.41 cm below the top surface of the glass of 18.41 cm below the water surface. Next, use this image as an object and locate the image the water forms of the bottom of the plate.

$$q_{B2} = -\left(\frac{1.00}{1.33}\right)(18.41 \text{ cm}) = -13.84 \text{ cm} \qquad \text{or} \qquad 13.84 \text{ cm below the water surface.}$$

Now find image the water forms of the *top* surface of the glass.

$$q_3 = -\left(\frac{1}{1.33}\right)(12.0 \text{ cm}) = -9.02 \text{ cm} \qquad \text{or} \qquad 9.02 \text{ cm below the water surface.}$$

Therefore, the apparent thickness of the glass is $\Delta t = 13.84 \text{ cm} - 9.02 \text{ cm} = \boxed{4.82 \text{ cm}}$.

P36.23 From Equation 36.8 $\qquad \frac{n_1}{p} + \frac{n_2}{q} = \frac{n_2 - n_1}{R}$.

Solve for q to find $\qquad q = \frac{n_2 R p}{p(n_2 - n_1) - n_1 R}$.

In this case, $\qquad n_1 = 1.50$, $n_2 = 1.00$, $R = -15.0$ cm

and $\qquad p = 10.0$ cm.

So $\qquad q = \frac{(1.00)(-15.0 \text{ cm})(10.0 \text{ cm})}{(10.0 \text{ cm})(1.00 - 1.50) - (1.50)(-15.0 \text{ cm})} = -8.57 \text{ cm}$.

Therefore, the $\qquad \boxed{\text{apparent depth is 8.57 cm}}$.

P36.24 $\frac{n_1}{p} + \frac{n_2}{q} = \frac{n_2 - n_1}{R}$ $\qquad$ so $\qquad \frac{1.00}{\infty} + \frac{1.40}{21.0 \text{ mm}} = \frac{1.40 - 1.00}{6.00 \text{ mm}}$

and $\qquad 0.0667 = 0.0667$.

They agree. $\qquad \boxed{\text{The image is inverted, real and diminished.}}$

P36.25 $\frac{n_1}{p} + \frac{n_2}{q} = \frac{n_2 - n_1}{R}$ $\qquad$ becomes $\qquad \frac{1.00}{p} + \frac{1.50}{q} = \frac{1.50 - 1.00}{6.00 \text{ cm}} = \frac{1}{12.0 \text{ cm}}$

(a) $\qquad \frac{1.00}{20.0 \text{ cm}} + \frac{1.50}{q} = \frac{1}{12.0 \text{ cm}}$ $\qquad$ or $\qquad q = \frac{1.50}{\left[(1.00/12.0 \text{ cm}) - (1.00/20.0 \text{ cm})\right]} = \boxed{45.0 \text{ cm}}$

(b) $\qquad \frac{1.00}{10.0 \text{ cm}} + \frac{1.50}{q} = \frac{1}{12.0 \text{ cm}}$ $\qquad$ or $\qquad q = \frac{1.50}{\left[(1.00/12.0 \text{ cm}) - (1.00/10.0 \text{ cm})\right]} = \boxed{-90.0 \text{ cm}}$

(c) $\qquad \frac{1.00}{3.0 \text{ cm}} + \frac{1.50}{q} = \frac{1}{12.0 \text{ cm}}$ $\qquad$ or $\qquad q = \frac{1.50}{\left[(1.00/12.0 \text{ cm}) - (1.00/3.0 \text{ cm})\right]} = \boxed{-6.00 \text{ cm}}$

P36.26 $p = \infty$ and $q = +2R$

$$\frac{1.00}{p} + \frac{n_2}{q} = \frac{n_2 - 1.00}{R}$$

$$0 + \frac{n_2}{2R} = \frac{n_2 - 1.00}{R} \qquad \text{so} \qquad \boxed{n_2 = 2.00}$$

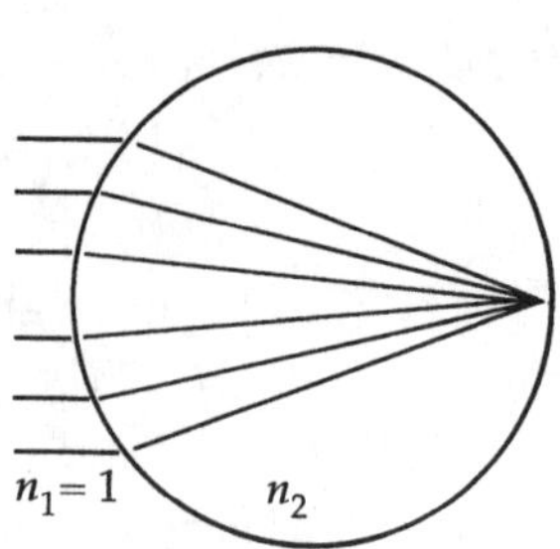

FIG. P36.26

P36.27 For a plane surface, $\dfrac{n_1}{p} + \dfrac{n_2}{q} = \dfrac{n_2 - n_1}{R}$ becomes $q = -\dfrac{n_2 p}{n_1}$.

Thus, the magnitudes of the rate of change in the image and object positions are related by

$$\left|\frac{dq}{dt}\right| = \frac{n_2}{n_1}\left|\frac{dp}{dt}\right|.$$

If the fish swims toward the wall with a speed of 2.00 cm/s, the speed of the image is given by

$$v_{\text{image}} = \left|\frac{dq}{dt}\right| = \frac{1.00}{1.33}(2.00\ \text{cm/s}) = \boxed{1.50\ \text{cm/s}}.$$

Section 36.4 Thin Lenses

P36.28 Let R_1 = outer radius and R_2 = inner radius

$$\frac{1}{f} = (n-1)\left[\frac{1}{R_1} - \frac{1}{R_2}\right] = (1.50 - 1)\left[\frac{1}{2.00\ \text{m}} - \frac{1}{2.50\ \text{cm}}\right] = 0.050\,0\ \text{cm}^{-1}$$

so $f = \boxed{20.0\ \text{cm}}$.

P36.29 (a)

$$\frac{1}{f} = (n-1)\left[\frac{1}{R_1} - \frac{1}{R_2}\right] = (0.440)\left[\frac{1}{12.0\ \text{cm}} - \frac{1}{(-18.0\ \text{cm})}\right]$$

$$f = \boxed{16.4\ \text{cm}}$$

(b)

$$\frac{1}{f} = (0.440)\left[\frac{1}{18.0\ \text{cm}} - \frac{1}{(-12.0\ \text{cm})}\right]$$

$$f = \boxed{16.4\ \text{cm}}$$

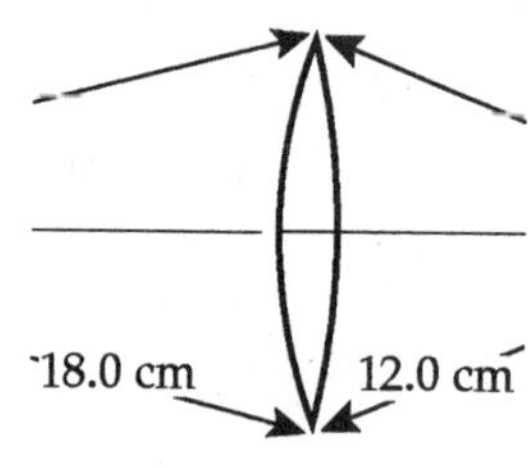

FIG. P36.29

P36.30 For a converging lens, f is positive. We use $\frac{1}{p}+\frac{1}{q}=\frac{1}{f}$.

(a) $\frac{1}{q}=\frac{1}{f}-\frac{1}{p}=\frac{1}{20.0\text{ cm}}-\frac{1}{40.0\text{ cm}}=\frac{1}{40.0\text{ cm}}$ $\boxed{q=40.0\text{ cm}}$

$M=-\frac{q}{p}=-\frac{40.0}{40.0}=\boxed{-1.00}$

The image is $\boxed{\text{real, inverted}}$, and located 40.0 cm past the lens.

(b) $\frac{1}{q}=\frac{1}{f}-\frac{1}{p}=\frac{1}{20.0\text{ cm}}-\frac{1}{20.0\text{ cm}}=0$ $\boxed{q=\text{infinity}}$

$\boxed{\text{No image}}$ is formed. The rays emerging from the lens are parallel to each other.

(c) $\frac{1}{q}=\frac{1}{f}-\frac{1}{p}=\frac{1}{20.0\text{ cm}}-\frac{1}{10.0\text{ cm}}=-\frac{1}{20.0\text{ cm}}$ $\boxed{q=-20.0\text{ cm}}$

$M=-\frac{q}{p}=-\frac{(-20.0)}{10.0}=\boxed{2.00}$

The image is $\boxed{\text{upright, virtual}}$ and 20.0 cm in front of the lens.

P36.31 (a) $\frac{1}{q}=\frac{1}{f}-\frac{1}{p}=\frac{1}{25.0\text{ cm}}-\frac{1}{26.0\text{ cm}}$ $\boxed{q=650\text{ cm}}$

The image is $\boxed{\text{real, inverted, and enlarged}}$.

(b) $\frac{1}{q}=\frac{1}{f}-\frac{1}{p}=\frac{1}{25.0\text{ cm}}-\frac{1}{24.0\text{ cm}}$ $\boxed{q=-600\text{ cm}}$

The image is $\boxed{\text{virtual, upright, and enlarged}}$.

P36.32 (a) $\frac{1}{p}+\frac{1}{q}=\frac{1}{f}$: $\frac{1}{32.0\text{ cm}}+\frac{1}{8.00\text{ cm}}=\frac{1}{f}$

so $\boxed{f=6.40\text{ cm}}$

(b) $M=-\frac{q}{p}=-\frac{8.00\text{ cm}}{32.0\text{ cm}}=\boxed{-0.250}$

(c) Since $f>0$, the lens is $\boxed{\text{converging}}$.

P36.33 We are looking at an enlarged, upright, virtual image:

$$M=\frac{h'}{h}=2=-\frac{q}{p} \qquad \text{so} \qquad p=-\frac{q}{2}=-\frac{(-2.84\text{ cm})}{2}=+1.42\text{ cm}$$

$$\frac{1}{p}+\frac{1}{q}=\frac{1}{f} \qquad \text{gives} \qquad \frac{1}{1.42\text{ cm}}+\frac{1}{(-2.84\text{ cm})}=\frac{1}{f}$$

$\boxed{f=2.84\text{ cm}}$.

FIG. P36.33

P36.34 (a) $\frac{1}{p}+\frac{1}{q}=\frac{1}{f}$: $\frac{1}{p}+\frac{1}{-30.0\text{ cm}}=\frac{1}{12.5\text{ cm}}$

$p=8.82\text{ cm}$ $\quad M=-\frac{q}{p}=-\frac{(-30.0)}{8.82}=\boxed{3.40,\text{ upright}}$

(b) See the figure to the right.

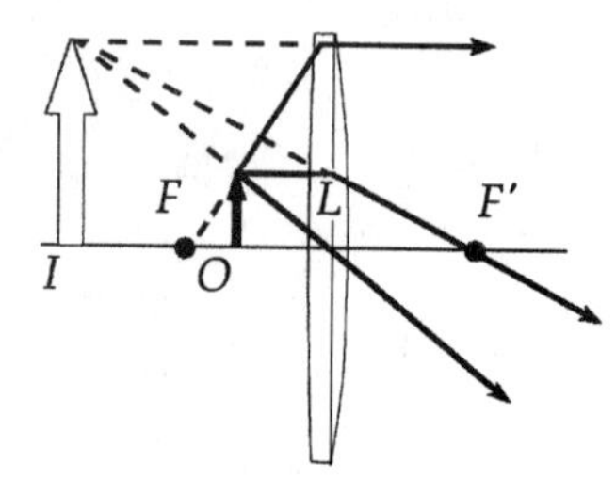

FIG. P36.34(b)

P36.35 $\frac{1}{p}+\frac{1}{q}=\frac{1}{f}$: $\qquad p^{-1}+q^{-1}=\text{constant}$

We may differentiate through with respect to p: $\qquad -1p^{-2}-1q^{-2}\frac{dq}{dp}=0$

$$\frac{dq}{dp}=-\frac{q^2}{p^2}=-M^2.$$

P36.36 The image is inverted: $\qquad M=\frac{h'}{h}=\frac{-1.80\text{ m}}{0.0240\text{ m}}=-75.0=\frac{-q}{p}$ $\qquad q=75.0p$.

(b) $q+p=3.00\text{ m}=75.0p+p$ $\qquad p=\boxed{39.5\text{ mm}}$

(a) $q=2.96\text{ m}$ $\qquad \frac{1}{f}=\frac{1}{p}+\frac{1}{q}=\frac{1}{0.0395\text{ m}}+\frac{1}{2.96\text{ m}}$ $\qquad f=\boxed{39.0\text{ mm}}$

P36.37 (a) $\frac{1}{p}+\frac{1}{q}=\frac{1}{f}$ $\qquad \frac{1}{20.0\text{ cm}}+\frac{1}{q}=\frac{1}{(-32.0\text{ cm})}$

so $\qquad q=-\left(\frac{1}{20.0}+\frac{1}{32.0}\right)^{-1}=\boxed{-12.3\text{ cm}}$

The image is 12.3 cm to the left of the lens.

(b) $M=-\frac{q}{p}=-\frac{(-12.3\text{ cm})}{20.0\text{ cm}}=\boxed{0.615}$

(c) See the ray diagram to the right.

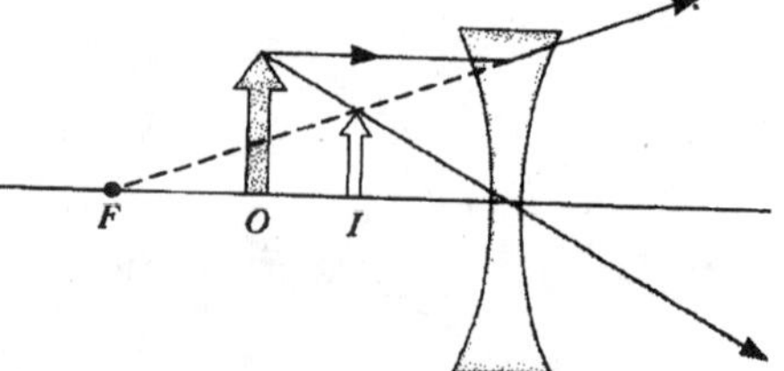

FIG. P36.37

***P36.38** In

$$\frac{1}{p}+\frac{1}{q}=\frac{1}{f}$$

$p^{-1}+q^{-1}=\text{constant},$

we differentiate with respect to time

$$-1\left(p^{-2}\right)\frac{dp}{dt}-1\left(q^{-2}\right)\frac{dq}{dt}=0$$

$$\frac{dq}{dt}=\frac{-q^2}{p^2}\frac{dp}{dt}.$$

We must find the momentary image location q:

$$\frac{1}{20\text{ m}}+\frac{1}{q}=\frac{1}{0.3\text{ m}}$$

$q=0.305\text{ m}.$

Now $\frac{dq}{dt}=-\frac{(0.305\text{ m})^2}{(20\text{ m})^2}5\text{ m/s}=-0.001\,16\text{ m/s}=\boxed{1.16\text{ mm/s toward the lens}}.$

***P36.39** (a) $\frac{1}{p}+\frac{1}{q}=\frac{1}{f}$ $\quad \frac{1}{480\text{ cm}}+\frac{1}{q}=\frac{1}{7.00\text{ cm}}$ $\quad q=\boxed{7.10\text{ cm}}$

(b) $M=\frac{h'}{h}=-\frac{q}{p}$ $\quad h'=\frac{-hq}{p}=\frac{-(5.00\text{ mm})(7.10\text{ cm})}{480\text{ cm}}=-0.074\,0\text{ mm}$

diameter of illuminated spot $=\boxed{74.0\ \mu\text{m}}$

(c) $I=\frac{\mathcal{P}}{A}=\frac{\mathcal{P}4}{\pi d^2}=\frac{0.100\text{ W}(4)}{\pi\left(74.0\times10^{-6}\text{ m}\right)^2}=\boxed{2.33\times10^7\text{ W/m}^2}$

P36.40 (a) $\frac{1}{f}=(n-1)\left[\frac{1}{R_1}-\frac{1}{R_2}\right]=(1.50-1)\left[\frac{1}{15.0\text{ cm}}-\frac{1}{(-12.0\text{ cm})}\right]$ or $\boxed{f=13.3\text{ cm}}$

(b)

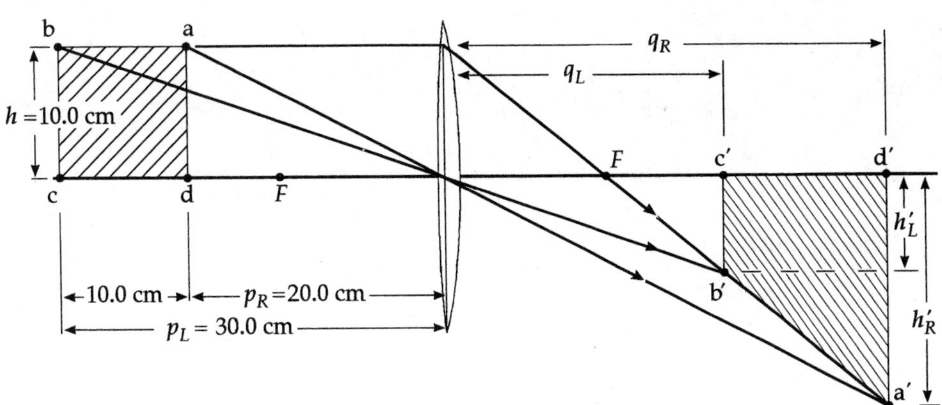

The square is imaged as a trapezoid.

FIG. P36.40(b)

continued on next page

(c) To find the area, first find q_R and q_L, along with the heights h'_R and h'_L, using the thin lens equation.

$$\frac{1}{p_R}+\frac{1}{q_R}=\frac{1}{f} \quad \text{becomes} \quad \frac{1}{20.0\text{ cm}}+\frac{1}{q_R}=\frac{1}{13.3\text{ cm}} \quad \text{or} \quad q_R=40.0\text{ cm}$$

$$h'_R=hM_R=h\left(\frac{-q_R}{p_R}\right)=(10.0\text{ cm})(-2.00)=-20.0\text{ cm}$$

$$\frac{1}{30.0\text{ cm}}+\frac{1}{q_L}=\frac{1}{13.3\text{ cm}} \quad \text{or} \quad q_L=24.0\text{ cm}$$

$$h'_L=hM_L=(10.0\text{ cm})(-0.800)=-8.00\text{ cm}$$

Thus, the area of the image is: $\text{Area}=|q_R-q_L||h'_L|+\frac{1}{2}|q_R-q_L||h'_R-h'_L|=\boxed{224\text{ cm}^2}$.

P36.41 (a) The image distance is: $q=d-p$.

Thus, $\frac{1}{p}+\frac{1}{q}=\frac{1}{f}$ becomes $\frac{1}{p}+\frac{1}{d-p}=\frac{1}{f}$.

This reduces to a quadratic equation: $p^2+(-d)p+fd=0$

which yields: $\boxed{p=\frac{d\pm\sqrt{d^2-4fd}}{2}=\frac{d}{2}\pm\sqrt{\frac{d^2}{4}-fd}}$.

Since $f<\frac{d}{4}$, both solutions are meaningful and the two solutions are not equal to each other. Thus, there are two distinct lens positions that form an image on the screen.

(b) The smaller solution for p gives a larger value for q, with a $\boxed{\text{real, enlarged, inverted image}}$.

The larger solution for p describes a $\boxed{\text{real, diminished, inverted image}}$.

P36.42 To properly focus the image of a distant object, the lens must be at a distance equal to the focal length from the film ($q_1=65.0$ mm). For the closer object:

$$\frac{1}{p_2}+\frac{1}{q_2}=\frac{1}{f}$$

becomes $$\frac{1}{2\,000\text{ mm}}+\frac{1}{q_2}=\frac{1}{65.0\text{ mm}}$$

and $$q_2=(65.0\text{ mm})\left(\frac{2\,000}{2\,000-65.0}\right).$$

The lens must be moved $\boxed{\text{away from the film}}$ by a distance

$$D=q_2-q_1=(65.0\text{ mm})\left(\frac{2\,000}{2\,000-65.0}\right)-65.0\text{ mm}=\boxed{2.18\text{ mm}}.$$

***P36.43** In the first arrangement the lens is used as a magnifying glass, producing an upright, virtual enlarged image:

$$M=\frac{h'}{h}=\frac{120\text{ cm}}{3.6\text{ cm}}=33.3=-\frac{q}{p}$$

$$q=-33.3p=-33.3(20\text{ cm})=-667\text{ cm}$$

For the lens,

$$\frac{1}{p}+\frac{1}{q}=\frac{1}{f}=\frac{1}{20\text{ cm}}+\frac{1}{-667\text{ cm}}=\frac{1}{f}$$

$$f=20.62\text{ cm}$$

In the second arrangement the lens us used as a projection lens to produce a real inverted enlarged image:

$$-\frac{120\text{ cm}}{3.6\text{ cm}}=-33.3=-\frac{q_2}{p_2}\qquad q_2=33.3p_2$$

$$\frac{1}{p_2}+\frac{1}{33.3p_2}=\frac{1}{20.62\text{ cm}}\qquad \frac{34.3}{33.3p_2}=\frac{1}{20.62\text{ cm}}\qquad p_2=21.24\text{ cm}$$

The lens was moved $21.24\text{ cm}-20.0\text{ cm}=\boxed{1.24\text{ cm}}$.

Section 36.5 Lens Aberrations

P36.44 (a) The focal length of the lens is given by

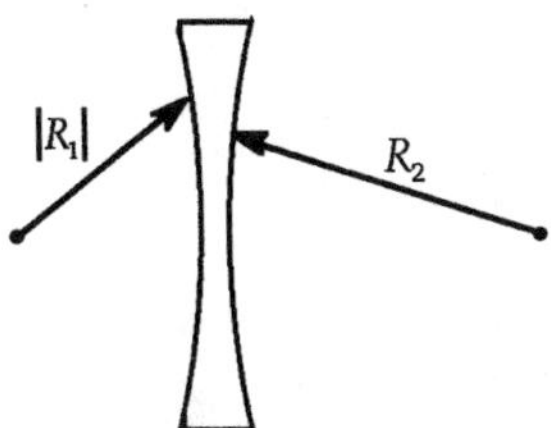

$$\frac{1}{f}=(n-1)\left(\frac{1}{R_1}-\frac{1}{R_2}\right)=(1.53-1.00)\left(\frac{1}{-32.5\text{ cm}}-\frac{1}{42.5\text{ cm}}\right)$$

$$f=-34.7\text{ cm}$$

Note that R_1 is negative because the center of curvature of the first surface is on the virtual image side.

When $p=\infty$

the thin lens equation gives $q=f$.

Thus, the violet image of a very distant object is formed

at $\boxed{q=-34.7\text{ cm}}$.

The image is $\boxed{\text{virtual, upright and diminshed}}$.

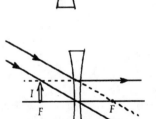

FIG. P36.44

(b) The same ray diagram and image characteristics apply for red light.

Again, $q=f$

and now $$\frac{1}{f}=(1.51-1.00)\left(\frac{1}{-32.5\text{ cm}}-\frac{1}{42.5\text{ cm}}\right)$$

giving $f=\boxed{-36.1\text{ cm}}$.

P36.45 Ray h_1 is undeviated at the plane surface and strikes the second surface at angle of incidence given by

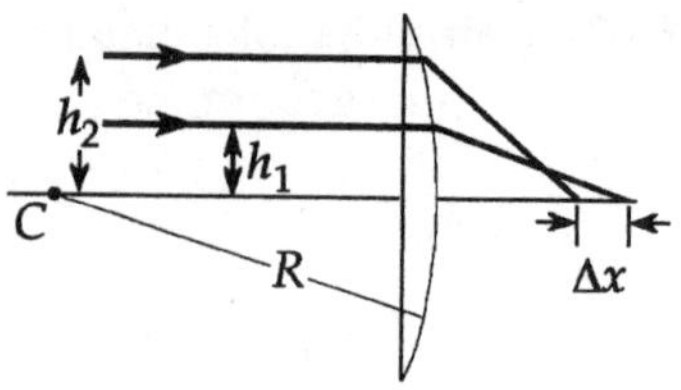

$$\theta_1 = \sin^{-1}\left(\frac{h_1}{R}\right) = \sin^{-1}\left(\frac{0.500 \text{ cm}}{20.0 \text{ cm}}\right) = 1.43° .$$

FIG. P36.45

Then, $$1.00 \sin\theta_2 = 1.60 \sin\theta_1 = (1.60)\left(\frac{0.500}{20.0 \text{ cm}}\right)$$

so $$\theta_2 = 2.29° .$$

The angle this emerging ray makes with the horizontal is $\theta_2 - \theta_1 = 0.860°$.

It crosses the axis at a point farther out by f_1

where $$f_1 = \frac{h_1}{\tan(\theta_2 - \theta_1)} = \frac{0.500 \text{ cm}}{\tan(0.860°)} = 33.3 \text{ cm} .$$

The point of exit for this ray is distant axially from the lens vertex by

$$20.0 \text{ cm} - \sqrt{(20.0 \text{ cm})^2 - (0.500 \text{ cm})^2} = 0.006\ 25 \text{ cm}$$

so ray h_1 crosses the axis at this distance from the vertex:

$$x_1 = 33.3 \text{ cm} - 0.006\ 25 \text{ cm} = 33.3 \text{ cm} .$$

Now we repeat this calculation for ray h_2:

$$\theta = \sin^{-1}\left(\frac{12.0 \text{ cm}}{20.0 \text{ cm}}\right) = 36.9°$$

$$1.00 \sin\theta_2 = 1.60 \sin\theta_1 = (1.60)\left(\frac{12.00}{20.0}\right) \qquad \theta_2 = 73.7°$$

$$f_2 = \frac{h_2}{\tan(\theta_1 - \theta_2)} = \frac{12.0 \text{ cm}}{\tan 36.8°} = 16.0 \text{ cm}$$

$$x_2 = (16.0 \text{ cm})\left(20.0 \text{ cm} - \sqrt{(20.0 \text{ cm})^2 - (12.0 \text{ cm})^2}\right) = 12.0 \text{ cm} .$$

Now $$\Delta x = 33.3 \text{ cm} - 12.0 \text{ cm} = \boxed{21.3 \text{ cm}} .$$

Section 36.6 **The Camera**

***P36.46** The same light intensity is received from the subject, and the same light energy on the film is required:

$$IA_1\Delta t_1 = IA_2\Delta t_2$$

$$\frac{\pi d_1^2}{4}\Delta t_1 = \frac{\pi d_2^2}{4}\Delta t_2$$

$$\left(\frac{f}{4}\right)^2\left(\frac{1}{16} \text{ s}\right) = d_2^2\left(\frac{1}{128} \text{ s}\right)$$

$$d_2 = \sqrt{\frac{128}{16}}\frac{f}{4} = \boxed{\frac{f}{1.41}}$$

Section 36.7 **The Eye**

P36.47 $P=\frac{1}{f}=\frac{1}{p}+\frac{1}{q}=\frac{1}{\infty}-\frac{1}{0.250\text{ m}}=-4.00\text{ diopters}=\boxed{-4.00\text{ diopters, a diverging lens}}$

P36.48 For starlight going through Nick's glasses, $\frac{1}{p}+\frac{1}{q}=\frac{1}{f}$

$$\frac{1}{\infty}+\frac{1}{(-0.800\text{ m})}=\frac{1}{f}=-1.25\text{ diopters}.$$

For a nearby object, $\frac{1}{p}+\frac{1}{(-0.180\text{ m})}=-1.25\text{ m}^{-1}$, so $p=\boxed{23.2\text{ cm}}$.

P36.49 Consider an object at infinity, imaged at the person's far point:

$$\frac{1}{p}+\frac{1}{q}=\frac{1}{f} \qquad \frac{1}{\infty}+\frac{1}{q}=-4.00\text{ m}^{-1} \qquad q=-25.0\text{ cm}.$$

The person's far point is $25.0\text{ cm}+2.00\text{ cm}=27.0\text{ cm}$ from his eyes. For the contact lenses we want

$$\frac{1}{\infty}+\frac{1}{(-0.270\text{ m})}=\frac{1}{f}=\boxed{-3.70\text{ diopters}}.$$

Section 36.8 **The Simple Magnifier**

Section 36.9 **The Compound Microscope**

Section 36.10 **The Telescope**

P36.50 (a) From the thin lens equation: $\frac{1}{p}+\frac{1}{(-25.0\text{ cm})}=\frac{1}{5.00\text{ cm}}$ or $p=\boxed{4.17\text{ cm}}$.

(b) $M=-\frac{q}{p}=1+\frac{25.0\text{ cm}}{f}=1+\frac{25.0\text{ cm}}{5.00\text{ cm}}=\boxed{6.00}$

P36.51 Using Equation 36.24, $M\approx-\left(\frac{L}{f_o}\right)\left(\frac{25.0\text{ cm}}{f_e}\right)=-\left(\frac{23.0\text{ cm}}{0.400\text{ cm}}\right)\left(\frac{25.0\text{ cm}}{2.50\text{ cm}}\right)=\boxed{-575}$.

P36.52 $M=M_om_e=M_o\left(\frac{25.0\text{ cm}}{f_e}\right)\Rightarrow f_e=\left(\frac{M_o}{M}\right)(25.0\text{ cm})=\left(\frac{-12.0}{-140}\right)(25.0\text{ cm})=\boxed{2.14\text{ cm}}$

P36.53 $f_o=20.0\text{ m}$ $\qquad f_e=0.025\,0\text{ m}$

(a) The angular magnification produced by this telescope is: $m=-\frac{f_o}{f_e}=\boxed{-800}$.

(b) Since $m<0$, the image is $\boxed{\text{inverted}}$.

P36.54 (a) The lensmaker's equation $\frac{1}{p}+\frac{1}{q}=\frac{1}{f}$

gives $q=\frac{1}{1/f-1/p}=\frac{1}{(p-f)/fp}=\frac{fp}{p-f}$.

Then, $M=\frac{h'}{h}=-\frac{q}{p}=-\frac{f}{p-f}$

gives $\boxed{h'=\frac{hf}{f-p}}$.

(b) For $p>>f$, $f-p\approx -p$. Then, $h'=\boxed{-\frac{hf}{p}}$.

(c) Suppose the telescope observes the space station at the zenith:

$$h'=-\frac{hf}{p}=-\frac{(108.6\text{ m})(4.00\text{ m})}{407\times 10^3\text{ m}}=\boxed{-1.07\text{ mm}}.$$

P36.55 (b) Call the focal length of the objective f_o and that of the eyepiece $-|f_e|$. The distance between the lenses is $f_o-|f_e|$. The objective forms a real diminished inverted image of a very distant object at $q_1=f_o$. This image is a virtual object for the eyepiece at $p_2=-|f_e|$.

For it $\frac{1}{p}+\frac{1}{q}=\frac{1}{f}$ becomes $\frac{1}{-|f_e|}+\frac{1}{q}=\frac{1}{-|f_e|}$, $\frac{1}{q_2}=0$

and $\boxed{q_2=\infty}$.

(a) The user views the image as $\boxed{\text{virtual}}$. Letting h' represent the height of the first image, $\theta_o=\frac{h'}{f_o}$ and $\theta=\frac{h'}{|f_e|}$. The angular magnification is

$$m=\frac{\theta}{\theta_o}=\frac{h'/|f_e|}{h'/f_o}=\frac{f_o}{|f_e|}.$$

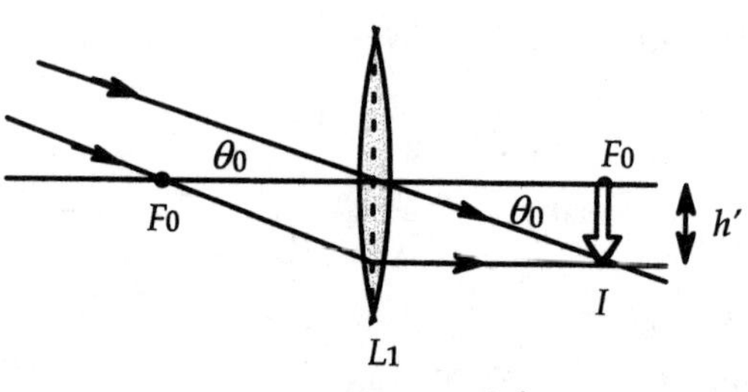

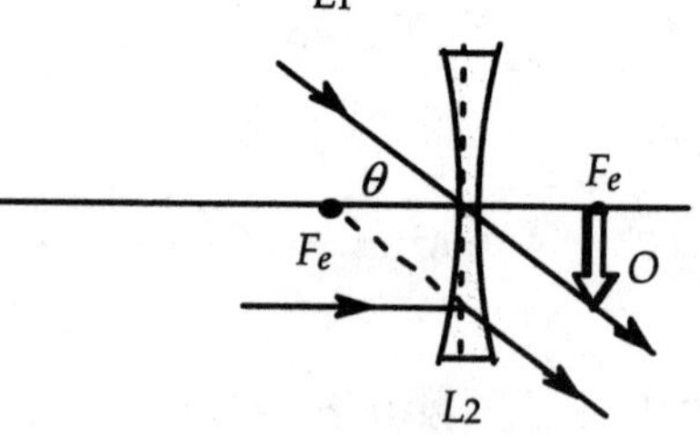

FIG. P36.55

(c) Here, $f_o-|f_e|=10.0\text{ cm}$ and $\frac{f_o}{|f_e|}=3.00$.

Thus, $|f_e|=\frac{f_o}{3.00}$ and $\frac{2}{3}f_o=10.0\text{ cm}$.

$f_o=\boxed{15.0\text{ cm}}$

$|f_e|=5.00\text{ cm}$ and $f_e=\boxed{-5.00\text{ cm}}$

P36.56 Let I_0 represent the intensity of the light from the nebula and θ_0 its angular diameter. With the first telescope, the image diameter h' on the film is given by $\theta_o = -\dfrac{h'}{f_o}$ as $h' = -\theta_o(2\,000\text{ mm})$.

The light power captured by the telescope aperture is $\mathscr{P}_1 = I_0 A_1 = I_0\left[\dfrac{\pi(200\text{ mm})^2}{4}\right]$, and the light energy focused on the film during the exposure is $E_1 = \mathscr{P}_1\Delta t_1 = I_0\left[\dfrac{\pi(200\text{ mm})^2}{4}\right](1.50\text{ min})$.

Likewise, the light power captured by the aperture of the second telescope is $\mathscr{P}_2 = I_0 A_2 = I_0\left[\dfrac{\pi(60.0\text{ mm})^2}{4}\right]$ and the light energy is $E_2 = I_0\left[\dfrac{\pi(60.0\text{ mm})^2}{4}\right]\Delta t_2$. Therefore, to have the same light energy per unit area, it is necessary that

$$\frac{I_0\left[\pi(60.0\text{ mm})^2/4\right]\Delta t_2}{\pi\left[\theta_o(900\text{ mm})^2/4\right]} = \frac{I_0\left[\pi(200\text{ mm})^2/4\right](1.50\text{ min})}{\pi\left[\theta_o(2\,000\text{ mm})^2/4\right]}.$$

The required exposure time with the second telescope is

$$\Delta t_2 = \frac{(200\text{ mm})^2(900\text{ mm})^2}{(60.0\text{ mm})^2(2\,000\text{ mm})^2}(1.50\text{ min}) = \boxed{3.38\text{ min}}.$$

Additional Problems

P36.57 Only a diverging lens gives an upright diminished image. The image is virtual and

$d = p - |q| = p + q$: $\qquad M = -\dfrac{q}{p}$ so $q = -Mp$ and $d = p - Mp$

$p = \dfrac{d}{1-M}$: $\qquad \dfrac{1}{p} + \dfrac{1}{q} = \dfrac{1}{f} = \dfrac{1}{p} + \dfrac{1}{-Mp} = \dfrac{-M+1}{-Mp} = \dfrac{(1-M)^2}{-Md}$

$$f = \frac{-Md}{(1-M)^2} = \frac{-(0.500)(20.0\text{ cm})}{(1-0.500)^2} = \boxed{-40.0\text{ cm}}.$$

P36.58 If $M < 1$, the lens is diverging and the image is virtual. $\qquad d = p - |q| = p + q$

$M = -\dfrac{q}{p}$ $\qquad$ so $\qquad q = -Mp$ $\qquad$ and $\qquad d = p - Mp$

$p = \dfrac{d}{1-M}$: $\qquad \dfrac{1}{p} + \dfrac{1}{q} = \dfrac{1}{f} = \dfrac{1}{p} + \dfrac{1}{(-Mp)} = \dfrac{(-M+1)}{-Mp} = \dfrac{(1-M)^2}{-Md}$ $\qquad \boxed{f = \dfrac{-Md}{(1-M)^2}}.$

If $M > 1$, the lens is converging and the image is still virtual.

Now $\qquad d = -q - p$.

We obtain in this case $\qquad \boxed{f = \dfrac{Md}{(M-1)^2}}.$

P36.59 (a) $\frac{1}{f}=(n-1)\left(\frac{1}{R_1}-\frac{1}{R_2}\right)$

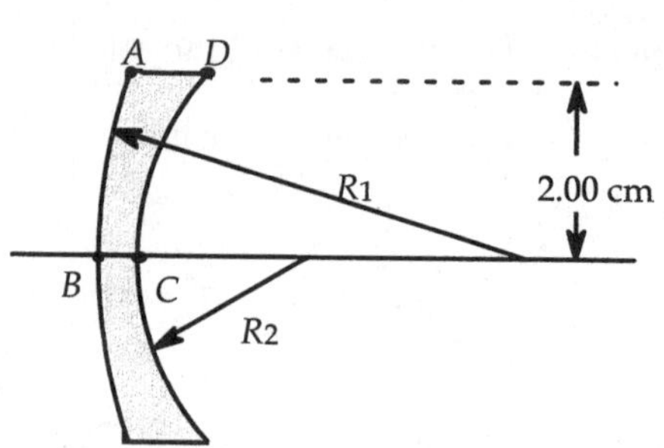

FIG. P36.59

$$\frac{1}{-65.0\text{ cm}}=(1.66-1)\left(\frac{1}{50.0\text{ cm}}-\frac{1}{R_2}\right)$$

$$\frac{1}{R_2}=\frac{1}{50.0\text{ cm}}+\frac{1}{42.9\text{ cm}}\qquad\text{so}\qquad R_2=\boxed{23.1\text{ cm}}$$

(b) The distance along the axis from B to A is

$$R_1-\sqrt{R_1^2-(2.00\text{ cm})^2}=50.0\text{ cm}-\sqrt{(50.0\text{ cm})^2-(2.00\text{ cm})^2}=0.040\,0\text{ cm}.$$

Similarly, the axial distance from C to D is

$$23.1\text{ cm}-\sqrt{(23.1\text{ cm})^2-(2.00\text{ cm})^2}=0.086\,8\text{ cm}.$$

Then, $AD=0.100\text{ cm}-0.040\,0\text{ cm}+0.086\,8\text{ cm}=\boxed{0.147\text{ cm}}$.

***P36.60** We consider light entering the rod. The surface of entry is convex to the object rays, so $R_1=+4.50$ cm

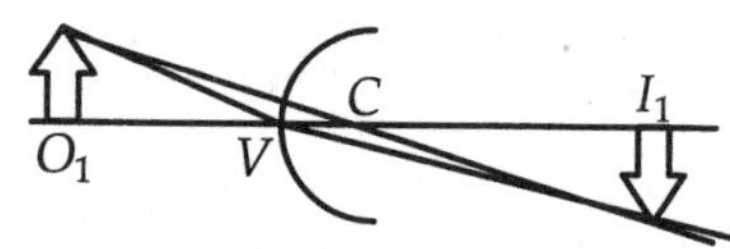

FIG. P36.60

$$\frac{n_1}{p_1}+\frac{n_2}{q_1}=\frac{n_2-n_1}{R_1}\qquad\frac{1.33}{100\text{ cm}}+\frac{1.50}{q_1}=\frac{1.50-1.33}{4.50\text{ cm}}$$

$$\frac{1.50}{q_1}=0.037\,8/\text{cm}-0.013\,3/\text{cm}=0.024\,5/\text{cm}\qquad q_1=61.3\text{ cm}$$

The first image is real, inverted and diminished. To find its magnification we can use two similar triangles in the ray diagram with their vertices meeting at the center of curvature:

$$\frac{h_1}{100\text{ cm}+4.5\text{ cm}}=\frac{|h_1'|}{61.3\text{ cm}-4.5\text{ cm}}\qquad\frac{h_1'}{h_1}=-0.543.$$

Now the first image is a real object for the second surface at object distance from its vertex

$$75.0\text{ cm}+4.50\text{ cm}+4.50\text{ cm}-61.3\text{ cm}=22.7\text{ cm}$$

$$\frac{1.50}{22.7\text{ cm}}+\frac{1.33}{q_2}=\frac{1.33-1.50}{-4.50\text{ cm}}$$

$$\frac{1.33}{q_2}=0.037\,8/\text{cm}-0.066\,0/\text{cm}=-0.028\,2/\text{cm}$$

$$q_2=-47.1\text{ cm}$$

(a) The final image is $\boxed{\text{inside the rod, 47.1 cm from the second surface}}$.

(b) It is $\boxed{\text{virtual, inverted, and enlarged}}$. Again by similar triangles meeting at C we have

$$\frac{h_2}{22.7\text{ cm}-4.5\text{ cm}}=\frac{h_2'}{47.1\text{ cm}-4.5\text{ cm}}\qquad\frac{h_2'}{h_2}=2.34.$$

Since $h_2=h_1'$, the overall magnification is $M_1M_2=\frac{h_1'}{h_1}\frac{h_2'}{h_2}=\frac{h_2'}{h_1}=(-0.543)(2.34)=-1.27$.

***P36.61** (a) $\frac{1}{q_1} = \frac{1}{f_1} - \frac{1}{p_1} = \frac{1}{5 \text{ cm}} - \frac{1}{7.5 \text{ cm}}$ $\therefore q_1 = 15 \text{ cm}$

$M_1 = -\frac{q_1}{p_1} = -\frac{15 \text{ cm}}{7.5 \text{ cm}} = -2$

$M = M_1 M_2$ $\therefore 1 = (-2)M_2$

$\therefore M_2 = -\frac{1}{2} = -\frac{q_2}{p_2}$ $\therefore p_2 = 2q_2$

$\frac{1}{p_2} + \frac{1}{q_2} = \frac{1}{f_2}$ $\therefore \frac{1}{2q_2} + \frac{1}{q_2} = \frac{1}{10 \text{ cm}}$ $\therefore q_2 = 15 \text{ cm},\ p_2 = 30 \text{ cm}$

$p_1 + q_1 + p_2 + q_2 = 7.5 \text{ cm} + 15 \text{ cm} + 30 \text{ cm} + 15 \text{ cm} = \boxed{67.5 \text{ cm}}$

(b) $\frac{1}{p_1'} + \frac{1}{q_1'} = \frac{1}{f_1} = \frac{1}{5 \text{ cm}}$

Solve for q_1' in terms of p_1': $q_1' = \frac{5p_1'}{p_1' - 5}$ (1)

$M_1' = -\frac{q_1'}{p_1'} = -\frac{5}{p_1' - 5}$, using (1).

$M' = M_1' M_2'$ $\therefore M_2' = \frac{M'}{M_1'} = -\frac{3}{5}(p_1' - 5) = -\frac{q_2'}{p_2'}$

$\therefore q_2' = \frac{3}{5} p_2' (p_1' - 5)$ (2)

Substitute (2) into the lens equation $\frac{1}{p_2'} + \frac{1}{q_2'} = \frac{1}{f_2} = \frac{1}{10 \text{ cm}}$ and obtain p_2' in terms of p_1':

$p_2' = \frac{10(3p_1' - 10)}{3(p_1' - 5)}$. (3)

Substituting (3) in (2), obtain q_2' in terms of p_1':

$q_2' = 2(3p_1' - 10)$. (4)

Now, $p_1' + q_1' + p_2' + q_2' =$ a constant.

Using (1), (3) and (4), and the value obtained in (a):

$p_1' + \frac{5p_1'}{p_1' - 5} + \frac{10(3p_1' - 10)}{3(p' - 5)} + 2(3p_1' - 10) = 67.5$.

This reduces to the quadratic equation

$21p_1'^2 - 322.5p_1' + 1\,212.5 = 0$,

which has solutions $p_1' = 8.784$ cm and 6.573 cm.

Case 1: $p_1' = 8.784 \text{ cm}$

$\therefore p_1' - p_1 = 8.784 \text{ cm} - 7.5 \text{ cm} = 1.28 \text{ cm}$.

From (4): $q_2' = 32.7 \text{ cm}$

$\therefore q_2' - q_2 = 32.7 \text{ cm} - 15 \text{ cm} = 17.7 \text{ cm}$.

Case 2: $p_1' = 6.573 \text{ cm}$

$\therefore p_1' - p_1 = 6.573 \text{ cm} - 7.5 \text{ cm} = -0.927 \text{ cm}$.

From (4): $q_2' = 19.44 \text{ cm}$

$\therefore q_2' = q_2 = 19.44 \text{ cm} - 15 \text{ cm} = 4.44 \text{ cm}$.

From these results it is concluded that:

The lenses can be displaced in two ways. The first lens can be moved 1.28 cm farther from the object and the second lens 17.7 cm toward the object. Alternatively, the first lens can be moved 0.927 cm toward the object and the second lens 4.44 cm toward the object.

P36.62 $$\frac{1}{q_1}=\frac{1}{f_1}-\frac{1}{p_1}=\frac{1}{10.0\text{ cm}}-\frac{1}{12.5\text{ cm}}$$

so $$q_1=50.0\text{ cm (to left of mirror).}$$

This serves as an object for the lens (a virtual object), so

$$\frac{1}{q_2}=\frac{1}{f_2}-\frac{1}{p_2}=\frac{1}{(-16.7\text{ cm})}-\frac{1}{(-25.0\text{ cm})}\text{ and } q_2=-50.3\text{ cm},$$

meaning 50.3 cm to the right of the lens. Thus, the final image is located $\boxed{\text{25.3 cm to right of mirror}}$.

$$M_1=-\frac{q_1}{p_1}=-\frac{50.0\text{ cm}}{12.5\text{ cm}}=-4.00$$

$$M_2=-\frac{q_2}{p_2}=-\frac{(-50.3\text{ cm})}{(-25.0\text{ cm})}=-2.01$$

$$M=M_1M_2=\boxed{8.05}$$

Thus, the final image is $\boxed{\text{virtual, upright}}$, 8.05 times the size of object, and 25.3 cm to right of the mirror.

P36.63 We first find the focal length of the mirror.

$$\frac{1}{f}=\frac{1}{p}+\frac{1}{q}=\frac{1}{10.0\text{ cm}}+\frac{1}{8.00\text{ cm}}=\frac{9}{40.0\text{ cm}}\quad\text{and}\quad f=4.44\text{ cm}.$$

Hence, if $p=20.0\text{ cm}$, $$\frac{1}{q}=\frac{1}{f}-\frac{1}{p}=\frac{1}{4.44\text{ cm}}-\frac{1}{20.0\text{ cm}}=\frac{15.56}{88.8\text{ cm}}.$$

Thus, $$q=\boxed{5.71\text{ cm}}\text{, real.}$$

***P36.64** A telescope with an eyepiece decreases the diameter of a beam of parallel rays. When light is sent through the same device in the opposite direction, the beam expands. Send the light first through the diverging lens. It will then be diverging from a virtual image found like this:

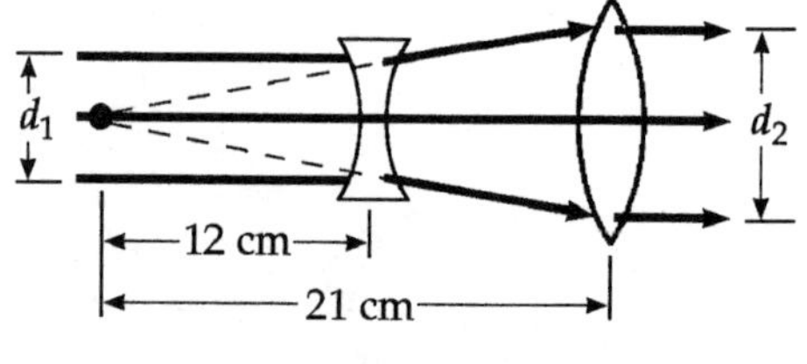

FIG. P36.64

$$\frac{1}{p}+\frac{1}{q}=\frac{1}{f}\qquad \frac{1}{\infty}+\frac{1}{q}=\frac{1}{-12\text{ cm}}$$

$$q=-12\text{ cm}.$$

Use this image as a real object for the converging lens, placing it at the focal point on the object side of the lens, at $p=21\text{ cm}$. Then

$$\frac{1}{p}+\frac{1}{q}=\frac{1}{f}\qquad \frac{1}{21\text{ cm}}+\frac{1}{q}=\frac{1}{21\text{ cm}}$$

$$q=\infty.$$

The exiting rays will be parallel. The lenses must be $21.0\text{ cm}-12.0\text{ cm}=9.00\text{ cm}$ apart.

By similar triangles, $$\frac{d_2}{d_1}=\frac{21\text{ cm}}{12\text{ cm}}=\boxed{1.75\text{ times}}.$$

P36.65 A hemisphere is too thick to be described as a thin lens. The light is undeviated on entry into the flat face. We next consider the light's exit from the second surface, for which $R = -6.00\text{ cm}$.

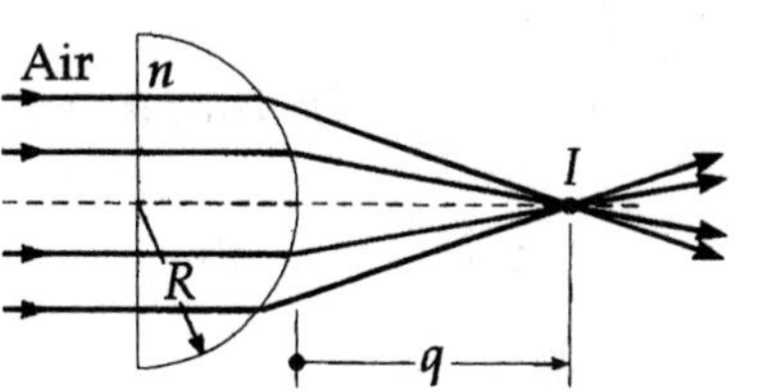

FIG. P36.65

The incident rays are parallel, so $p = \infty$.

Then, $$\frac{n_1}{p} + \frac{n_2}{q} = \frac{n_2 - n_1}{R}$$

becomes $$0 + \frac{1}{q} = \frac{1.00 - 1.56}{-6.00\text{ cm}}$$

and $$\boxed{q = 10.7\text{ cm}}.$$

P36.66 (a) $$I = \frac{\mathscr{P}}{4\pi r^2} = \frac{4.50\text{ W}}{4\pi\left(1.60 \times 10^{-2}\text{ m}\right)^2} = \boxed{1.40\text{ kW/m}^2}$$

(b) $$I = \frac{\mathscr{P}}{4\pi r^2} = \frac{4.50\text{ W}}{4\pi(7.20\text{ m})^2} = \boxed{6.91\text{ mW/m}^2}$$

(c) $\frac{1}{p} + \frac{1}{q} = \frac{1}{f}$: $$\frac{1}{7.20\text{ m}} + \frac{1}{q} = \frac{1}{0.350\text{ m}}$$

so $$q = 0.368\text{ m}$$

and $$M = \frac{h'}{3.20\text{ cm}} = -\frac{q}{p} = -\frac{0.368\text{ m}}{7.20\text{ m}}$$

$$h' = \boxed{0.164\text{ cm}}$$

(d) The lens intercepts power given by $$\mathscr{P} = IA = \left(6.91 \times 10^{-3}\text{ W/m}^2\right)\left[\frac{\pi}{4}(0.150\text{ m})^2\right]$$

and puts it all onto the image where $$I = \frac{\mathscr{P}}{A} = \frac{\left(6.91 \times 10^{-3}\text{ W/m}^2\right)\left[\pi(15.0\text{ cm})^2/4\right]}{\pi(0.164\text{ cm})^2/4}$$

$$I = \boxed{58.1\text{ W/m}^2}.$$

P36.67 From the thin lens equation, $q_1 = \frac{f_1 p_1}{p_1 - f_1} = \frac{(-6.00\text{ cm})(12.0\text{ cm})}{12.0\text{ cm} - (-6.00\text{ cm})} = -4.00\text{ cm}$.

When we require that $q_2 \to \infty$, the thin lens equation becomes $p_2 = f_2$.

In this case, $p_2 = d - (-4.00\text{ cm})$.

Therefore, $d + 4.00\text{ cm} = f_2 = 12.0\text{ cm}$ and $d = \boxed{8.00\text{ cm}}$.

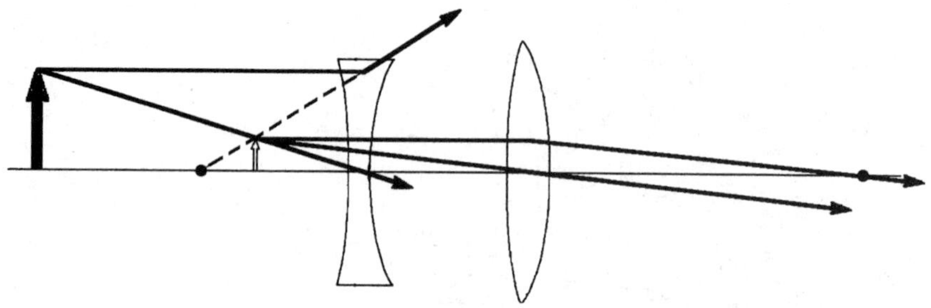

FIG. P36.67

***P36.68** The inverted real image is formed by the lens operating on light directly from the object, on light that has not reflected from the mirror.

For this we have $M = -1.50 = -\frac{q}{p}$ $\quad q = 1.50p$

$$\frac{1}{p} + \frac{1}{q} = \frac{1}{f} \qquad \frac{1}{p} + \frac{1}{1.50p} = \frac{1}{10\text{ cm}} = \frac{2.50}{1.50p} \qquad p = 10\text{ cm}\left(\frac{2.5}{1.5}\right) = 16.7\text{ cm}$$

Then the object is distant from the mirror by $40.0\text{ cm} - 16.7\text{ cm} = 23.3\text{ cm}$.

The second image seen by the person is formed by light that first reflects from the mirror and then goes through the lens. For it to be in the same position as the inverted image, the lens must be receiving light from an image formed by the mirror at the same location as the physical object. The formation of this image is described by

$$\frac{1}{p} + \frac{1}{q} = \frac{1}{f} \qquad \frac{1}{23.3\text{ cm}} + \frac{1}{23.3\text{ cm}} = \frac{1}{f} \qquad f = \boxed{11.7\text{ cm}}.$$

P36.69 For the mirror, $f = \frac{R}{2} = +1.50\text{ m}$. In addition, because the distance to the Sun is so much larger than any other distances, we can take $p = \infty$.

The mirror equation, $\frac{1}{p} + \frac{1}{q} = \frac{1}{f}$, then gives $q = f = \boxed{1.50\text{ m}}$.

Now, in $M = -\frac{q}{p} = \frac{h'}{h}$

the magnification is nearly zero, but we can be more precise: $\frac{h}{p}$ is the angular diameter of the object.

Thus, the image diameter is

$$h' = -\frac{hq}{p} = (-0.533°)\left(\frac{\pi\text{ rad}}{180°}\right)(1.50\text{ m}) = -0.014\,0\text{ m} = \boxed{-1.40\text{ cm}}.$$

P36.70 (a) For the light the mirror intercepts,

$$\mathcal{P} = I_0 A = I_0 \pi R_a^2$$

$$350\text{ W} = \left(1\,000\text{ W/m}^2\right)\pi R_a^2$$

and $R_a = \boxed{0.334\text{ m or larger}}$.

(b) In $\dfrac{1}{p} + \dfrac{1}{q} = \dfrac{1}{f} = \dfrac{2}{R}$

we have $p \to \infty$

so $q = \dfrac{R}{2}$

$$M = \frac{h'}{h} = -\frac{q}{p}$$

so $h' = -q\left(\dfrac{h}{p}\right) = -\left(\dfrac{R}{2}\right)\left[0.533°\left(\dfrac{\pi\text{ rad}}{180°}\right)\right] = -\left(\dfrac{R}{2}\right)(9.30\text{ m rad})$

where $\dfrac{h}{p}$ is the angle the Sun subtends. The intensity at the image is

then $I = \dfrac{\mathcal{P}}{\pi h'^2/4} = \dfrac{4 I_0 \pi R_a^2}{\pi h'^2} = \dfrac{4 I_0 R_a^2}{(R/2)^2\left(9.30 \times 10^{-3}\text{ rad}\right)^2}$

$$120 \times 10^3\text{ W/m}^2 = \frac{16\left(1\,000\text{ W/m}^2\right)R_a^2}{R^2\left(9.30 \times 10^{-3}\text{ rad}\right)^2}$$

so $\boxed{\dfrac{R_a}{R} = 0.025\,5\text{ or larger}}$.

P36.71 In the original situation, $p_1 + q_1 = 1.50\text{ m}$.

In the final situation, $p_2 = p_1 + 0.900\text{ m}$

and $q_2 = q_1 - 0.900\text{ m} = 0.600\text{ m} - p_1$.

Our lens equation is $\dfrac{1}{p_1} + \dfrac{1}{q_1} = \dfrac{1}{f} = \dfrac{1}{p_2} + \dfrac{1}{q_2}$.

Substituting, we have $\dfrac{1}{p_1} + \dfrac{1}{1.50\text{ m} - p_1} = \dfrac{1}{p_1 + 0.900} + \dfrac{1}{0.600 - p_1}$.

Adding the fractions, $\dfrac{1.50\text{ m} - p_1 + p_1}{p_1(1.50\text{ m} - p_1)} = \dfrac{0.600 - p_1 + p_1 + 0.900}{(p_1 + 0.900)(0.600 - p_1)}$.

Simplified, this becomes $p_1(1.50\text{ m} - p_1) = (p_1 + 0.900)(0.600 - p_1)$.

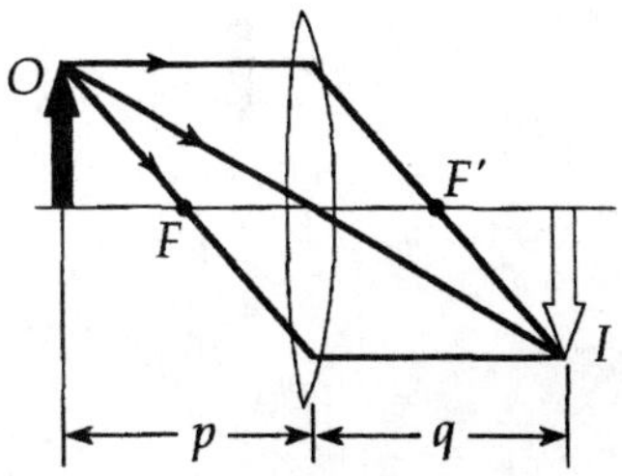

FIG. P36.71

(a) Thus, $p_1 = \dfrac{0.540}{1.80}\text{ m} = \boxed{0.300\text{ m}}$ $\qquad p_2 = p_1 + 0.900 = \boxed{1.20\text{ m}}$

(b) $\dfrac{1}{f} = \dfrac{1}{0.300\text{ m}} + \dfrac{1}{1.50\text{ m} - 0.300\text{ m}}$ and $f = \boxed{0.240\text{ m}}$

(c) The second image is $\boxed{\text{real, inverted, and diminished}}$

with $M = -\dfrac{q_2}{p_2} = \boxed{-0.250}$.

P36.72 (a) The lens makers' equation, $\frac{1}{f}=(n-1)\left(\frac{1}{R_1}+\frac{1}{R_2}\right)$

becomes: $\frac{1}{5.00\text{ cm}}=(n-1)\left[\frac{1}{9.00\text{ cm}}-\frac{1}{(-11.0\text{ cm})}\right]$ giving $n=\boxed{1.99}$.

(b) As the light passes through the lens for the first time, the thin lens equation

$$\frac{1}{p_1}+\frac{1}{q_1}=\frac{1}{f}$$

becomes: $$\frac{1}{8.00\text{ cm}}+\frac{1}{q_1}=\frac{1}{5.00\text{ cm}}$$

or $q_1=13.3\text{ cm}$, and $M_1=-\frac{q_1}{p_1}=-\frac{13.3\text{ cm}}{8.00\text{ cm}}=-1.67$.

This image becomes the object for the concave mirror with:

$$p_m=20.0\text{ cm}-q_1=20.0\text{ cm}-13.3\text{ cm}=6.67\text{ cm}$$

and $$f=\frac{R}{2}=+4.00\text{ cm}.$$

The mirror equation becomes: $$\frac{1}{6.67\text{ cm}}+\frac{1}{q_m}=\frac{1}{4.00\text{ cm}}$$

giving $$q_m=10.0\text{ cm}$$

and $$M_2=-\frac{q_m}{p_m}=-\frac{10.0\text{ cm}}{6.67\text{ cm}}=-1.50.$$

The image formed by the mirror serves as a real object for the lens on the second pass of the light through the lens with:

$$p_3=20.0\text{ cm}-q_m=+10.0\text{ cm}.$$

The thin lens equation yields: $$\frac{1}{10.0\text{ cm}}+\frac{1}{q_3}=\frac{1}{5.00\text{ cm}}$$

or $$q_3=10.0\text{ cm}$$

and $$M_3=-\frac{q_3}{p_3}=-\frac{10.0\text{ cm}}{10.0\text{ cm}}=-1.00.$$

The final image is a real image located $\boxed{\text{10.0 cm to the left of the lens}}$.

The overall magnification is $M_{\text{total}}=M_1M_2M_3=\boxed{-2.50}$.

(c) Since the total magnification is negative, this final image is $\boxed{\text{inverted}}$.

P36.73 For the objective: $\frac{1}{p}+\frac{1}{q}=\frac{1}{f}$ becomes $\frac{1}{3.40\text{ mm}}+\frac{1}{q}=\frac{1}{3.00\text{ mm}}$ so $q=25.5\text{ mm}$.

The objective produces magnification $M_1=-\frac{q}{p}=-\frac{25.5\text{ mm}}{3.40\text{ mm}}=-7.50$.

For the eyepiece as a simple magnifier, $m_e=\frac{25.0\text{ cm}}{f}=\frac{25.0\text{ cm}}{2.50\text{ cm}}=10.0$

and overall $M=M_1m_e=\boxed{-75.0}$.

P36.74 (a) Start with the second lens: This lens must form a virtual image located 19.0 cm to the left of it (i.e., $q_2 = -19.0\text{ cm}$). The required object distance for this lens is then

$$p_2 = \frac{q_2 f_2}{q_2 - f_2} = \frac{(-19.0\text{ cm})(20.0\text{ cm})}{-19.0\text{ cm} - 20.0\text{ cm}} = \frac{380\text{ cm}}{39.0}.$$

The image formed by the first lens serves as the object for the second lens. Therefore, the image distance for the first lens is

$$q_1 = 50.0\text{ cm} - p_2 = 50.0\text{ cm} - \frac{380\text{ cm}}{39.0} = \frac{1\,570\text{ cm}}{39.0}.$$

The distance the original object must be located to the left of the first lens is then given by

$$\frac{1}{p_1} = \frac{1}{f_1} - \frac{1}{q_1} = \frac{1}{10.0\text{ cm}} - \frac{39.0}{1\,570\text{ cm}} = \frac{157 - 39.0}{1\,570\text{ cm}} = \frac{118}{1\,570\text{ cm}} \quad \text{or} \quad p_1 = \frac{1\,570\text{ cm}}{118} = \boxed{13.3\text{ cm}}.$$

(b) $$M = M_1 M_2 = \left(-\frac{q_1}{p_1}\right)\left(-\frac{q_2}{p_2}\right) = \left[\left(\frac{1\,570\text{ cm}}{39.0}\right)\left(\frac{118}{1\,570\text{ cm}}\right)\right]\left[\frac{(-19.0\text{ cm})(39.0)}{380\text{ cm}}\right] = \boxed{-5.90}$$

(c) Since $M < 0$, the final image is $\boxed{\text{inverted}}$.

P36.75 (a) $$P = \frac{1}{f} = \frac{1}{p} + \frac{1}{q} = \frac{1}{(0.022\,4\text{ m})} + \frac{1}{\infty} = \boxed{44.6\text{ diopters}}$$

(b) $$P = \frac{1}{f} = \frac{1}{p} + \frac{1}{q} = \frac{1}{(0.330\text{ m})} + \frac{1}{\infty} = \boxed{3.03\text{ diopters}}$$

P36.76 The object is located at the focal point of the upper mirror. Thus, the upper mirror creates an image at infinity (i.e., parallel rays leave this mirror).

The lower mirror focuses these parallel rays at its focal point, located at the hole in the upper mirror.

Thus, the $\boxed{\text{image is real, inverted, and actual size}}$.

For the upper mirror:

$$\frac{1}{p} + \frac{1}{q} = \frac{1}{f}: \qquad \frac{1}{7.50\text{ cm}} + \frac{1}{q_1} = \frac{1}{7.50\text{ cm}} \qquad q_1 = \infty.$$

For the lower mirror:

$$\frac{1}{\infty} + \frac{1}{q_2} = \frac{1}{7.50\text{ cm}} \qquad q_2 = 7.50\text{ cm}.$$

Light directed into the hole in the upper mirror reflects as shown, to behave as if it were reflecting from the hole.

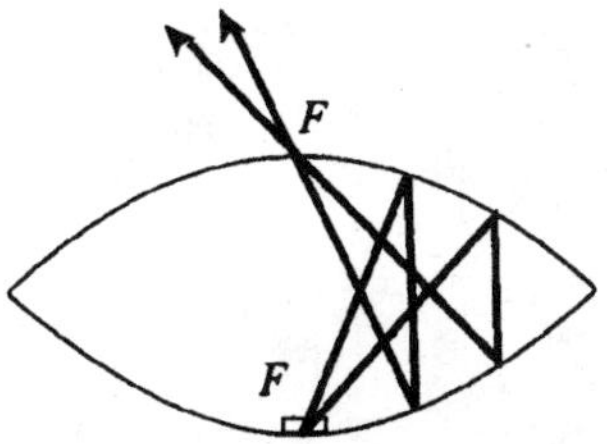

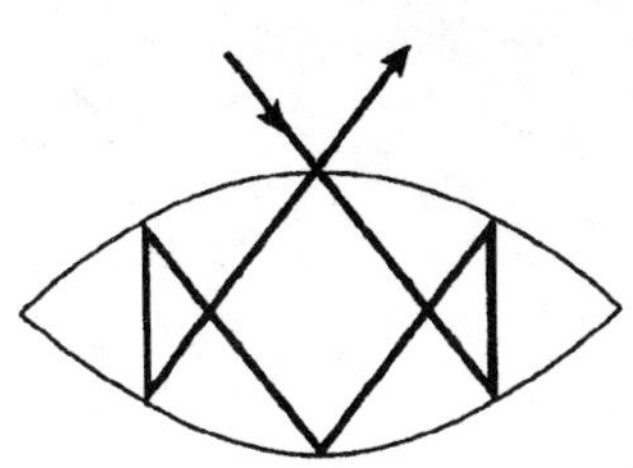

FIG. P36.76

P36.77 (a) For lens one, as shown in the first figure,

$$\frac{1}{40.0\text{ cm}}+\frac{1}{q_1}=\frac{1}{30.0\text{ cm}}$$

$$q_1=120\text{ cm}$$

$$M_1=-\frac{q_1}{p_1}=-\frac{120\text{ cm}}{40.0\text{ cm}}=-3.00$$

This real image $I_1=O_2$ is a virtual object for the second lens. That is, it is *behind* the lens, as shown in the second figure. The object distance is

$$p_2=110\text{ cm}-120\text{ cm}=-10.0\text{ cm}$$

$$\frac{1}{-10.0\text{ cm}}+\frac{1}{q_2}=\frac{1}{-20.0\text{ cm}}:$$

$$q_2=\boxed{20.0\text{ cm}}$$

$$M_2=-\frac{q_2}{p_2}=-\frac{20.0\text{ cm}}{(-10.0\text{ cm})}=+2.00$$

$$M_{\text{overall}}=M_1M_2=\boxed{-6.00}$$

(b) $M_{\text{overall}}<0$, so final image is $\boxed{\text{inverted}}$.

(c) If lens two is a converging lens (third figure):

$$\frac{1}{-10.0\text{ cm}}+\frac{1}{q_2}=\frac{1}{20.0\text{ cm}}$$

$$q_2=\boxed{6.67\text{ cm}}$$

$$M_2=-\frac{6.67\text{ cm}}{(-10.0\text{ cm})}=+0.667$$

$$M_{\text{overall}}=M_1M_2=\boxed{-2.00}$$

Again, $M_{\text{overall}}<0$ and the final image is $\boxed{\text{inverted}}$.

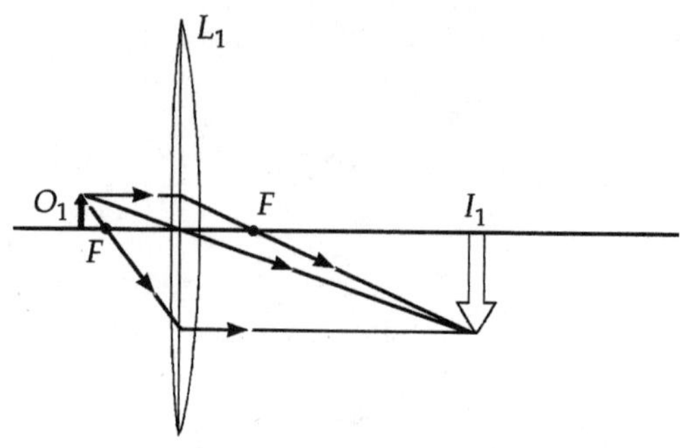

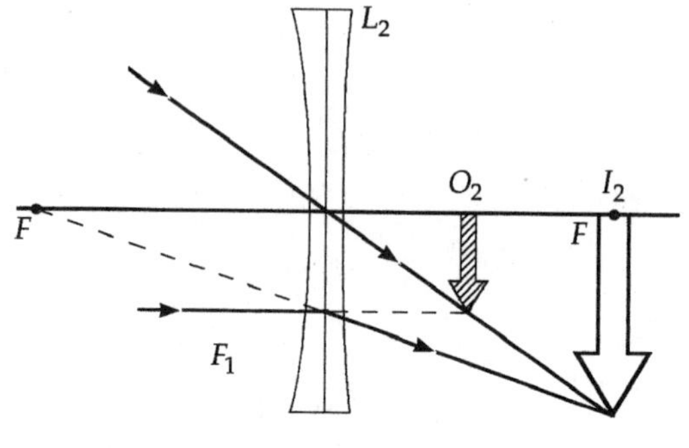

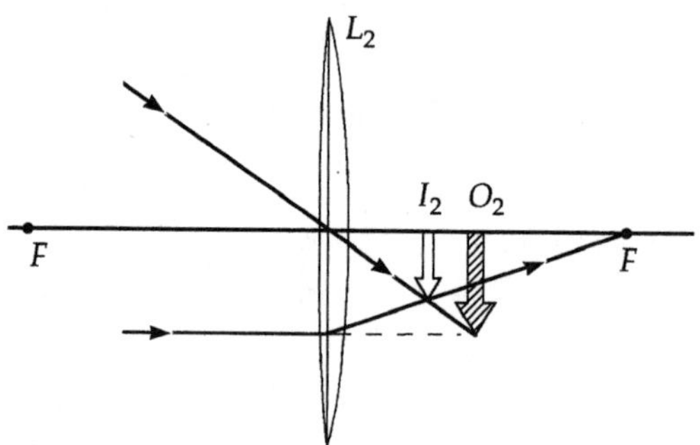

FIG. P36.77

***P36.78** The first lens has focal length described by

$$\frac{1}{f_1}=(n_1-1)\left(\frac{1}{R_{11}}-\frac{1}{R_{12}}\right)=(n_1-1)\left(\frac{1}{\infty}-\frac{1}{R}\right)=-\frac{n_1-1}{R}.$$

For the second lens

$$\frac{1}{f_2}=(n_2-1)\left(\frac{1}{R_{21}}-\frac{1}{R_{22}}\right)=(n_2-1)\left(\frac{1}{+R}-\frac{1}{-R}\right)=+\frac{2(n_2-1)}{R}.$$

Let an object be placed at any distance p_1 large compared to the thickness of the doublet. The first lens forms an image according to

$$\frac{1}{p_1}+\frac{1}{q_1}=\frac{1}{f_1}$$

$$\frac{1}{q_1}=\frac{-n_1+1}{R}-\frac{1}{p_1}.$$

This virtual $(q_1<0)$ image is a real object for the second lens at distance $p_2=-q_1$. For the second lens

$$\frac{1}{p_2}+\frac{1}{q_2}=\frac{1}{f_2}$$

$$\frac{1}{q_2}=\frac{2n_2-2}{R}-\frac{1}{p_2}=\frac{2n_2-2}{R}+\frac{1}{q_1}=\frac{2n_2-2}{R}+\frac{-n_1+1}{R}-\frac{1}{p_1}=\frac{2n_2-n_1-1}{R}-\frac{1}{p_1}.$$

Then $\frac{1}{p_1}+\frac{1}{q_2}=\frac{2n_2-n_1-1}{R}$ so the doublet behaves like a single lens with $\frac{1}{f}=\frac{2n_2-n_1-1}{R}$.

ANSWERS TO EVEN PROBLEMS

P36.2 4.58 m

P36.4 see the solution

P36.6 (a) p_1+h; (b) virtual; (c) upright; (d) $+1$; (e) No

P36.8 at $q=-0.267$ m virtual upright and diminished with $M=0.0267$

P36.10 at 3.33 m from the deepest point of the niche

P36.12 30.0 cm

P36.14 (a) 160 mm; (b) $R=-267$ mm

P36.16 (a) convex; (b) At the 30.0 cm mark; (c) –20.0 cm

P36.18 (a) 15.0 cm; (b) 60.0 cm

P36.20 (a) see the solution; (b) at 0.639 s and at 0.782 s

P36.22 4.82 cm

P36.24 see the solution; real, inverted, diminished

P36.26 2.00

P36.28 20.0 cm

P36.30 (a) $q=40.0$ cm real, inverted, actual size $M=-1.00$; (b) $q=\infty$, $M=\infty$, no image is formed; (c) $q=-20.0$ cm upright, virtual, enlarged $M=+2.00$

P36.32 (a) 6.40 cm; (b) –0.250; (c) converging

P36.34 (a) 3.40, upright; (b) see the solution

P36.36 (a) 39.0 mm; (b) 39.5 mm

P36.38 1.16 mm/s toward the lens

P36.40 (a) 13.3 cm;
(b) see the solution; a trapezoid;
(c) 224 cm^2

P36.42 2.18 mm away from the film

P36.44 (a) at $q = -34.7$ cm
virtual, upright and diminshed;
(b) at $q = -36.1$ cm
virtual, upright and diminshed

P36.46 $\dfrac{f}{1.41}$

P36.48 23.2 cm

P36.50 (a) at 4.17 cm; (b) 6.00

P36.52 2.14 cm

P36.54 (a) see the solution; (b) $h' = -\dfrac{hf}{p}$;
(c) −1.07 mm

P36.56 3.38 min

P36.58 if $M < 1$, $f = \dfrac{-Md}{(1-M)^2}$,
if $M > 1$, $f = \dfrac{Md}{(M-1)^2}$

P36.60 (a) inside the rod, 47.1 cm from the second surface;
(b) virtual, inverted, and enlarged

P36.62 25.3 cm to right of mirror,
virtual, upright, enlarged 8.05 times

P36.64 place the lenses 9.00 cm apart and let light pass through the diverging lens first.
1.75 times

P36.66 (a) 1.40 kW/m^2; (b) 6.91 mW/m^2;
(c) 0.164 cm; (d) 58.1 W/m^2

P36.68 11.7 cm

P36.70 (a) 0.334 m or larger;
(b) $\dfrac{R_a}{R} = 0.025\,5$ or larger

P36.72 (a) 1.99;
(b) 10.0 cm to the left of the lens; −2.50;
(c) inverted

P36.74 (a) 13.3 cm; (b) −5.90; (c) inverted

P36.76 see the solution;
real, inverted, and actual size

P36.78 see the solution

37

Interference of Light Waves

CHAPTER OUTLINE

ANSWERS TO QUESTIONS

Q37.1 (a) Two waves interfere constructively if their path difference is zero, or an integral multiple of the wavelength, according to $\delta = m\lambda$, with $m = 0, 1, 2, 3, \ldots$.

(b) Two waves interfere destructively if their path difference is a half wavelength, or an odd multiple of $\frac{\lambda}{2}$, described by $\delta = \left(m + \frac{1}{2}\right)\lambda$, with $m = 0, 1, 2, 3, \ldots$.

Q37.2 The light from the flashlights consists of many different wavelengths (that's why it's white) with random time differences between the light waves. There is no *coherence* between the two sources. The light from the two flashlights does not maintain a constant phase relationship over time. These three equivalent statements mean no possibility of an interference pattern.

Q37.3 Underwater, the wavelength of the light would decrease, $\lambda_{\text{water}} = \frac{\lambda_{\text{air}}}{n_{\text{water}}}$. Since the positions of light and dark bands are proportional to λ, (according to Equations 37.2 and 37.3), the underwater fringe separations will decrease.

Q37.4 Every color produces its own pattern, with a spacing between the maxima that is characteristic of the wavelength. With several colors, the patterns are superimposed and it can be difficult to pick out a single maximum. Using monochromatic light can eliminate this problem.

Q37.5 The threads that are woven together to make the cloth have small meshes between them. These bits of space act as pinholes through which the light diffracts. Since the cloth is a grid of such pinholes, an interference pattern is formed, as when you look through a diffraction grating.

Q37.6 If the oil film is brightest where it is thinnest, then $n_{\text{air}} < n_{\text{oil}} < n_{\text{water}}$. With this condition, light reflecting from both the top and the bottom surface of the oil film will undergo phase reversal. Then these two beams will be in phase with each other where the film is very thin. This is the condition for constructive interference as the thickness of the oil film decreases toward zero.

Q37.7 As water evaporates from the 'soap' bubble, the thickness of the bubble wall approaches zero. Since light reflecting from the front of the water surface is phase-shifted 180° and light reflecting from the back of the soap film is phase-shifted 0°, the reflected light meets the conditions for a minimum. Thus the soap film appears black, as in the illustration accompanying textbook Example 37.5, "Interference in a Wedge-Shaped Film."

Q37.8 If the film is more than a few wavelengths thick, the interference fringes are so close together that you cannot resolve them.

Q37.9 If R is large, light reflecting from the lower surface of the lens can interfere with light reflecting from the upper surface of the flat. The latter undergoes phase reversal on reflection while the former does not. Where there is negligible distance between the surfaces, at the center of the pattern you will see a dark spot because of the destructive interference associated with the 180° phase shift. Colored rings surround the dark spot. If the lens is a perfect sphere the rings are perfect circles. Distorted rings reveal bumps or hollows on the fine scale of the wavelength of visible light.

Q37.10 A camera lens will have more than one element, to correct (at least) for chromatic aberration. It will have several surfaces, each of which would reflect some fraction of the incident light. To maximize light throughput the surfaces need antireflective coatings. The coating thickness is chosen to produce destructive interference for reflected light of some wavelength.

Q37.11 To do Young's double-slit interference experiment with light from an ordinary source, you must first pass the light through a prism or diffraction grating to disperse different colors into different directions. With a single narrow slit you select a single color and make that light diffract to cover both of the slits for the interference experiment. Thus you may have trouble lining things up and you will generally have low light power reaching the screen. The laser light is already monochromatic and coherent across the width of the beam.

Q37.12 Suppose the coating is intermediate in index of refraction between vacuum and the glass. When the coating is very thin, light reflected from its top and bottom surfaces will interfere constructively, so you see the surface white and brighter. As the thickness reaches one quarter of the wavelength of violet light in the coating, destructive interference for violet will make the surface look red or perhaps orange. Next to interfere destructively are blue, green, yellow, orange, and red, making the surface look red, purple, and then blue. As the coating gets still thicker, we can get constructive interference for violet and then for other colors in spectral order. Still thicker coating will give constructive and destructive interference for several visible wavelengths, so the reflected light will start to look white again.

Q37.13 Assume the film is higher in refractive index than the medium on both sides of it. The condition for destructive interference of the two transmitted beams is that the waves be out of phase by $\frac{\lambda}{2}$. The ray that reflects through the film undergoes phase reversal both at the bottom and at the top surface. Then this ray should also travel an extra distance of $\frac{\lambda}{2}$. Since this ray passes through two extra thicknesses of film, the thickness should be $\frac{\lambda}{4}$. This is different from the condition for destructive interference of light reflected from the film, but it is the same as the condition for constructive interference of reflected light. The energy of the extra reflected light is energy diverted from light otherwise transmitted.

Q37.14 The metal body of the airplane is reflecting radio waves broadcast by the television station. The reflected wave that your antenna receives has traveled an extra distance compared to the stronger signal that came straight from the transmitter tower. You receive it with a short time delay. On the television screen you see a faint image offset to the side.

SOLUTIONS TO PROBLEMS

Section 37.1 Conditions for Interference

Section 37.2 Young's Double-Slit Experiment

P37.1 $\Delta y_{\text{bright}} = \dfrac{\lambda L}{d} = \dfrac{(632.8 \times 10^{-9})(5.00)}{2.00 \times 10^{-4}}\ \text{m} = \boxed{1.58\ \text{cm}}$

P37.2 $y_{\text{bright}} = \dfrac{\lambda L}{d} m$

For $m = 1$, $\lambda = \dfrac{yd}{L} = \dfrac{(3.40 \times 10^{-3}\ \text{m})(5.00 \times 10^{-4}\ \text{m})}{3.30\ \text{m}} = \boxed{515\ \text{nm}}$

P37.3 Note, with the conditions given, the small angle approximation **does not work well**. That is, $\sin\theta$, $\tan\theta$, and θ are significantly different. We treat the interference as a Fraunhofer pattern.

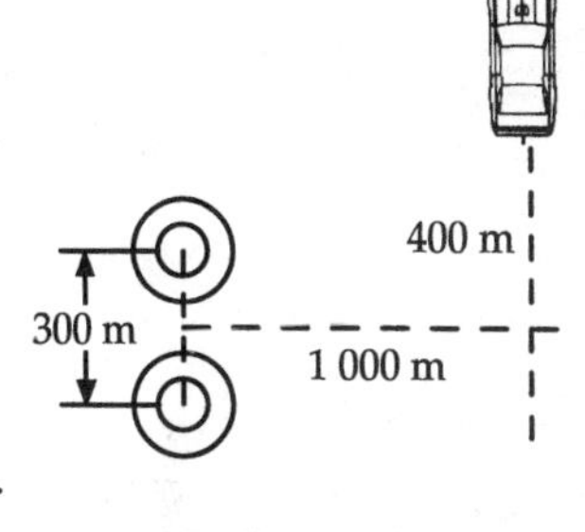

FIG. P37.3

(a) At the $m = 2$ maximum, $\tan\theta = \dfrac{400\ \text{m}}{1\,000\ \text{m}} = 0.400$

$\theta = 21.8°$

so $\lambda = \dfrac{d\sin\theta}{m} = \dfrac{(300\ \text{m})\sin 21.8°}{2} = \boxed{55.7\ \text{m}}$.

(b) The next minimum encountered is the $m = 2$ minimum;

and at that point, $d\sin\theta = \left(m + \dfrac{1}{2}\right)\lambda$

which becomes $d\sin\theta = \dfrac{5}{2}\lambda$

or $\sin\theta = \dfrac{5}{2}\dfrac{\lambda}{d} = \dfrac{5}{2}\left(\dfrac{55.7\ \text{m}}{300\ \text{m}}\right) = 0.464$

and $\theta = 27.7°$

so $y = (1\,000\ \text{m})\tan 27.7° = 524\ \text{m}$.

Therefore, the car must travel an additional $\boxed{124\ \text{m}}$.

If we considered Fresnel interference, we would more precisely find (a) $\lambda = \dfrac{1}{2}\left(\sqrt{550^2 + 1\,000^2} - \sqrt{250^2 + 1\,000^2}\right) = 55.2\ \text{m}$ and (b) 123 m.

P37.4 $\lambda = \frac{v}{f} = \frac{354 \text{ m/s}}{2\,000 \text{ s}^{-1}} = 0.177 \text{ m}$

(a) $d\sin\theta = m\lambda$ so $(0.300 \text{ m})\sin\theta = 1(0.177 \text{ m})$ and $\theta = \boxed{36.2°}$

(b) $d\sin\theta = m\lambda$ so $d\sin 36.2° = 1(0.030\,0 \text{ m})$ and $d = \boxed{5.08 \text{ cm}}$

(c) $\left(1.00\times10^{-6} \text{ m}\right)\sin 36.2° = (1)\lambda$ so $\lambda = 590 \text{ nm}$

$$f = \frac{c}{\lambda} = \frac{3.00\times10^{8} \text{ m/s}}{5.90\times10^{-7} \text{ m}} = \boxed{508 \text{ THz}}$$

P37.5 In the equation $d\sin\theta = \left(m + \frac{1}{2}\right)\lambda$.

The first minimum is described by $m = 0$

and the tenth by $m = 9$: $\sin\theta = \frac{\lambda}{d}\left(9 + \frac{1}{2}\right)$.

Also, $\tan\theta = \frac{y}{L}$

but for small θ, $\sin\theta \approx \tan\theta$.

Thus, $d = \frac{9.5\lambda}{\sin\theta} = \frac{9.5\lambda L}{y}$

$$d = \frac{9.5\left(5\,890\times10^{-10} \text{ m}\right)(2.00 \text{ m})}{7.26\times10^{-3} \text{ m}} = 1.54\times10^{-3} \text{ m} = \boxed{1.54 \text{ mm}}.$$

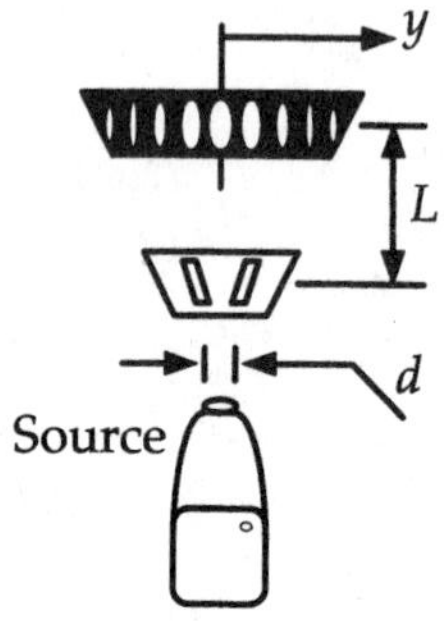

FIG. P37.5

P37.6 $\lambda = \frac{340 \text{ m/s}}{2\,000 \text{ Hz}} = 0.170 \text{ m}$

Maxima are at $d\sin\theta = m\lambda$:

$m = 0$ gives $\theta = 0°$

$m = 1$ gives $\sin\theta = \frac{\lambda}{d} = \frac{0.170 \text{ m}}{0.350 \text{ m}}$ $\theta = 29.1°$

$m = 2$ gives $\sin\theta = \frac{2\lambda}{d} = 0.971$ $\theta = 76.3°$

$m = 3$ gives $\sin\theta = 1.46$ No solution.

Minima are at $d\sin\theta = \left(m + \frac{1}{2}\right)\lambda$:

$m = 0$ gives $\sin\theta = \frac{\lambda}{2d} = 0.243$ $\theta = 14.1°$

$m = 1$ gives $\sin\theta = \frac{3\lambda}{2d} = 0.729$ $\theta = 46.8°$

$m = 2$ gives $\sin\theta = 1.21$ No solution.

$\boxed{\text{So we have maxima at } 0°,\ 29.1°, \text{ and } 76.3°; \text{ minima at } 14.1° \text{ and } 46.8°}$.

P37.7 (a) For the bright fringe,

$$y_{\text{bright}} = \frac{m\lambda L}{d} \text{ where } m = 1$$

$$y = \frac{(546.1\times10^{-9}\text{ m})(1.20\text{ m})}{0.250\times10^{-3}\text{ m}} = 2.62\times10^{-3}\text{ m} = \boxed{2.62\text{ mm}}.$$

(b) For the dark bands, $y_{\text{dark}} = \frac{\lambda L}{d}\left(m+\frac{1}{2}\right);\ m = 0, 1, 2, 3, \ldots$

$$y_2 - y_1 = \frac{\lambda L}{d}\left[\left(1+\frac{1}{2}\right)-\left(0+\frac{1}{2}\right)\right] = \frac{\lambda L}{d}(1)$$

$$= \frac{(546.1\times10^{-9}\text{ m})(1.20\text{ m})}{0.250\times10^{-3}\text{ m}}$$

$$\Delta y = \boxed{2.62\text{ mm}}.$$

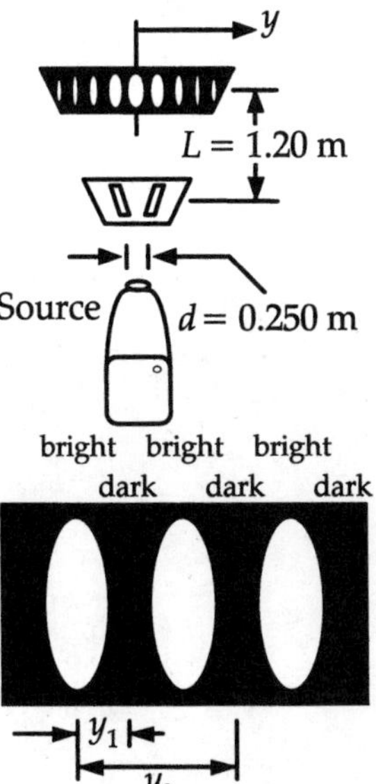

FIG. P37.7

P37.8 Taking $m = 0$ and $y = 0.200$ mm in Equation 37.6 gives

$$L \approx \frac{2dy}{\lambda} = \frac{2(0.400\times10^{-3}\text{ m})(0.200\times10^{-3}\text{ m})}{442\times10^{-9}\text{ m}} = 0.362\text{ m}$$

$$L \approx \boxed{36.2\text{ cm}}$$

Geometric optics incorrectly predicts bright regions opposite the slits and darkness in between. But, as this example shows, interference can produce just the opposite.

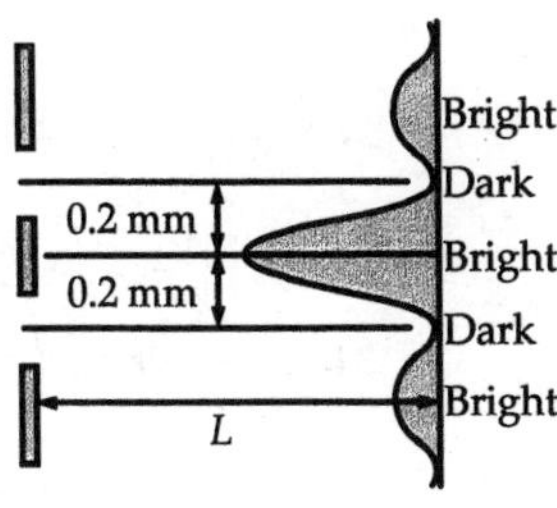

FIG. P37.7

P37.9 Location of A = central maximum,

Location of B = first minimum.

So, $$\Delta y = [y_{\min} - y_{\max}] = \frac{\lambda L}{d}\left(0+\frac{1}{2}\right) - 0 = \frac{1}{2}\frac{\lambda L}{d} = 20.0\text{ m}.$$

Thus, $$d = \frac{\lambda L}{2(20.0\text{ m})} = \frac{(3.00\text{ m})(150\text{ m})}{40.0\text{ m}} = \boxed{11.3\text{ m}}.$$

P37.10 At $30.0°$, $d\sin\theta = m\lambda$

$(3.20\times10^{-4}\text{ m})\sin 30.0° = m(500\times10^{-9}\text{ m})$ so $m = 320$

There are 320 maxima to the right, 320 to the left, and one for $m = 0$ straight ahead.

There are $\boxed{641\text{ maxima}}$.

***P37.11** Observe that the pilot must not only home in on the airport, but must be headed in the right direction when she arrives at the end of the runway.

(a) $$\lambda = \frac{c}{f} = \frac{3\times 10^8\ \text{m/s}}{30\times 10^6\ \text{s}^{-1}} = \boxed{10.0\ \text{m}}$$

(b) The first side maximum is at an angle given by $d\sin\theta = (1)\lambda$.

$(40\ \text{m})\sin\theta = 10\ \text{m}$ $\qquad\theta = 14.5°$ $\qquad\tan\theta = \frac{y}{L}$

$$y = L\tan\theta = (2\,000\ \text{m})\tan 14.5° = \boxed{516\ \text{m}}$$

(c) The signal of 10-m wavelength in parts (a) and (b) would show maxima at 0°, 14.5°, 30.0°, 48.6°, and 90°. A signal of wavelength 11.23-m would show maxima at 0°, 16.3°, 34.2°, and 57.3°. The only value in common is 0°. If λ_1 and λ_2 were related by a ratio of small integers (a just musical consonance!) in $\frac{\lambda_1}{\lambda_2} = \frac{n_1}{n_2}$, then the equations $d\sin\theta = n_2\lambda_1$ and $d\sin\theta = n_1\lambda_2$ would both be satisfied for the same nonzero angle. The pilot could come flying in with that inappropriate bearing, and run off the runway immediately after touchdown.

***P37.12** In $d\sin\theta = m\lambda$ $\qquad d\frac{y}{L} = m\lambda$ $\qquad y = \frac{m\lambda L}{d}$

$$\frac{dy}{dt} = \frac{m\lambda}{d}\frac{dL}{dt} = \frac{1(633\times 10^{-9}\ \text{m})}{(0.3\times 10^{-3}\ \text{m})}3\ \text{m/s} = \boxed{6.33\ \text{mm/s}}$$

P37.13 $$\phi = \frac{2\pi}{\lambda}d\sin\theta = \frac{2\pi}{\lambda}d\left(\frac{y}{L}\right)$$

(a) $$\phi = \frac{2\pi}{(5.00\times 10^{-7}\ \text{m})}(1.20\times 10^{-4}\ \text{m})\sin(0.500°) = \boxed{13.2\ \text{rad}}$$

(b) $$\phi = \frac{2\pi}{(5.00\times 10^{-7}\ \text{m})}(1.20\times 10^{-4}\ \text{m})\left(\frac{5.00\times 10^{-3}\ \text{m}}{1.20\ \text{m}}\right) = \boxed{6.28\ \text{rad}}$$

(c) If $\phi = 0.333\ \text{rad} = \frac{2\pi d\sin\theta}{\lambda}$ $\qquad \theta = \sin^{-1}\left(\frac{\lambda\phi}{2\pi d}\right) = \sin^{-1}\left[\frac{(5.00\times 10^{-7}\ \text{m})(0.333\ \text{rad})}{2\pi(1.20\times 10^{-4}\ \text{m})}\right]$

$$\theta = \boxed{1.27\times 10^{-2}\ \text{deg}}.$$

(d) If $d\sin\theta = \frac{\lambda}{4}$ $\qquad \theta = \sin^{-1}\left(\frac{\lambda}{4d}\right) = \sin^{-1}\left[\frac{5\times 10^{-7}\ \text{m}}{4(1.20\times 10^{-4}\ \text{m})}\right]$

$$\theta = \boxed{5.97\times 10^{-2}\ \text{deg}}.$$

P37.14 The path difference between rays 1 and 2 is: $\delta = d\sin\theta_1 - d\sin\theta_2$.

For constructive interference, this path difference must be equal to an integral number of wavelengths: $d\sin\theta_1 - d\sin\theta_2 = m\lambda$, or

$$\boxed{d(\sin\theta_1 - \sin\theta_2) = m\lambda}.$$

P37.15 (a) The path difference $\delta = d\sin\theta$ and when $L >> y$

$$\delta = \frac{yd}{L} = \frac{(1.80\times10^{-2}\text{ m})(1.50\times10^{-4}\text{ m})}{1.40\text{ m}} = 1.93\times10^{-6}\text{ m} = \boxed{1.93\ \mu\text{m}}.$$

(b) $$\frac{\delta}{\lambda} = \frac{1.93\times10^{-6}\text{ m}}{6.43\times10^{-7}\text{ m}} = 3.00\text{, or } \boxed{\delta = 3.00\lambda}$$

(c) Point P will be a $\boxed{\text{maximum}}$ since the path difference is an integer multiple of the wavelength.

Section 37.3 Intensity Distribution of the Double-Slit Interference Pattern

P37.16 (a) $$\frac{I}{I_{\max}} = \cos^2\left(\frac{\phi}{2}\right) \qquad \text{(Equation 37.11)}$$

Therefore, $$\phi = 2\cos^{-1}\sqrt{\frac{I}{I_{\max}}} = 2\cos^{-1}\sqrt{0.640} = \boxed{1.29\text{ rad}}.$$

(b) $$\delta = \frac{\lambda\phi}{2\pi} = \frac{(486\text{ nm})(1.29\text{ rad})}{2\pi} = \boxed{99.8\text{ nm}}$$

P37.17 $$I_{av} = I_{\max}\cos^2\left(\frac{\pi d\sin\theta}{\lambda}\right)$$

For small θ, $\sin\theta = \dfrac{y}{L}$

and $I_{av} = 0.750 I_{\max}$

$$y = \frac{\lambda L}{\pi d}\cos^{-1}\sqrt{\frac{I_{av}}{I_{\max}}}$$

$$y = \frac{(6.00\times10^{-7})(1.20\text{ m})}{\pi(2.50\times10^{-3}\text{ m})}\cos^{-1}\sqrt{\frac{0.750 I_{\max}}{I_{\max}}} = \boxed{48.0\ \mu\text{m}}$$

P37.18 $$I = I_{\max}\cos^2\left(\frac{\pi yd}{\lambda L}\right)$$

$$\frac{I}{I_{\max}} = \cos^2\left[\frac{\pi(6.00\times10^{-3}\text{ m})(1.80\times10^{-4}\text{ m})}{(656.3\times10^{-9}\text{ m})(0.800\text{ m})}\right] = \boxed{0.968}$$

P37.19 (a) From Equation 37.8,

$$\phi = \frac{2\pi d}{\lambda}\sin\theta = \frac{2\pi d}{\lambda}\cdot\frac{y}{\sqrt{y^2 + D^2}}$$

$$\phi \approx \frac{2\pi yd}{\lambda D} = \frac{2\pi\left(0.850\times10^{-3}\text{ m}\right)\left(2.50\times10^{-3}\text{ m}\right)}{\left(600\times10^{-9}\text{ m}\right)(2.80\text{ m})} = \boxed{7.95\text{ rad}}$$

(b) $$\frac{I}{I_{max}} = \frac{\cos^2\left[(\pi d/\lambda)\sin\theta\right]}{\cos^2\left[(\pi d/\lambda)\sin\theta_{max}\right]} = \frac{\cos^2(\phi/2)}{\cos^2 m\pi}$$

$$\frac{I}{I_{max}} = \cos^2\frac{\phi}{2} = \cos^2\left(\frac{7.95\text{ rad}}{2}\right) = \boxed{0.453}$$

P37.20 (a) The resultant amplitude is

$$E_r = E_0\sin\omega t + E_0\sin(\omega t+\phi) + E_0(\omega t + 2\phi), \qquad \text{where} \qquad \phi = \frac{2\pi}{\lambda}d\sin\theta.$$

$$E_r = E_0(\sin\omega t + \sin\omega t\cos\phi + \cos\omega t\sin\phi + \sin\omega t\cos 2\phi + \cos\omega t\sin 2\phi)$$

$$E_r = E_0(\sin\omega t)\left(1+\cos\phi + 2\cos^2\phi - 1\right) + E_0(\cos\omega t)(\sin\phi + 2\sin\phi\cos\phi)$$

$$E_r = E_0(1+2\cos\phi)(\sin\omega t\cos\phi + \cos\omega t\sin\phi) = E_0(1+2\cos\phi)\sin(\omega t+\phi)$$

Then the intensity is $I \propto E_r^2 = E_0^2(1+2\cos\phi)^2\left(\frac{1}{2}\right)$

where the time average of $\sin^2(\omega t+\phi)$ is $\frac{1}{2}$.

From one slit alone we would get intensity $I_{max} \propto E_0^2\left(\frac{1}{2}\right)$ so

$$\boxed{I = I_{max}\left[1 + 2\cos\left(\frac{2\pi d\sin\theta}{\lambda}\right)\right]^2}.$$

(b) Look at the $N=3$ graph in Figure 37.14. Minimum intensity is zero, attained where $\cos\phi = -\frac{1}{2}$. One relative maximum occurs at $\cos\phi = -1.00$, where $I = I_{max}$.

The larger local maximum happens where $\cos\phi = +1.00$, giving $I = 9.00 I_0$.

The ratio of intensities at primary versus secondary maxima is $\boxed{9.00}$.

Section 37.4 Phasor Addition of Waves

P37.21 (a) We can use $\sin A + \sin B = 2\sin\left(\frac{A}{2}+\frac{B}{2}\right)\cos\left(\frac{A}{2}-\frac{B}{2}\right)$ to find the sum of the two sine functions to be

$$E_1 + E_2 = (24.0\ \text{kN/C})\sin(15x - 4.5t + 35.0°)\cos 35.0°$$
$$E_1 + E_2 = (19.7\ \text{kN/C})\sin(15x - 4.5t + 35.0°)$$

Thus, the total wave has amplitude $\boxed{19.7\ \text{kN/C}}$ and has a constant phase difference of $\boxed{35.0°}$ from the first wave.

(b) In units of kN/C, the resultant phasor is

$$\mathbf{E}_R = \mathbf{E}_1 + \mathbf{E}_2 = (12.0\hat{\mathbf{i}}) + (12.0\cos 70.0°\,\hat{\mathbf{i}} + 12.0\sin 70.0\hat{\mathbf{j}}) = 16.1\hat{\mathbf{i}} + 11.3\hat{\mathbf{j}}$$

$$\mathbf{E}_R = \sqrt{(16.1)^2 + (11.3)^2} \text{ at } \tan^{-1}\left(\frac{11.3}{16.1}\right) = \boxed{19.7\ \text{kN/C at } 35.0°}$$

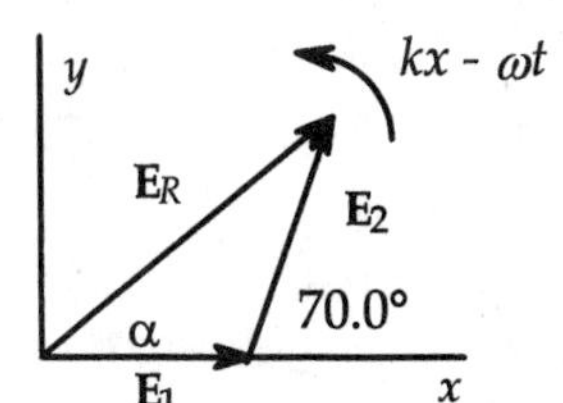

FIG. P37.21(b)

(c)
$$\mathbf{E}_R = 12.0\cos 70.0°\,\hat{\mathbf{i}} + 12.0\sin 70.0°\,\hat{\mathbf{j}}$$
$$+15.5\cos 80.0°\,\hat{\mathbf{i}} - 15.5\sin 80.0°\,\hat{\mathbf{j}}$$
$$+17.0\cos 160°\,\hat{\mathbf{i}} + 17.0\sin 160°\,\hat{\mathbf{j}}$$
$$\mathbf{E}_R = -9.18\hat{\mathbf{i}} + 1.83\hat{\mathbf{j}} = \boxed{9.36\ \text{kN/C at } 169°}$$

The wave function of the total wave is $E_P = (9.36\ \text{kN/C})\sin(15x - 4.5t + 169°)$.

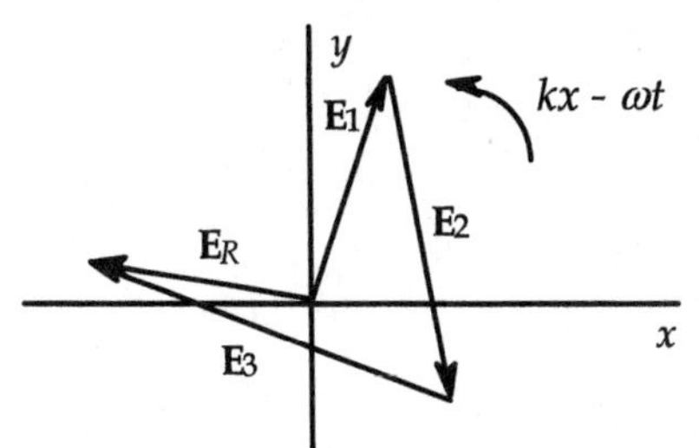

FIG. P37.21(c)

P37.22 (a)
$$\mathbf{E}_R = E_0\left[\hat{\mathbf{i}} + (\hat{\mathbf{i}}\cos 20.0° + \hat{\mathbf{j}}\sin 20.0°) + (\hat{\mathbf{i}}\cos 40.0° + \hat{\mathbf{j}}\sin 40.0°)\right]$$
$$\mathbf{E}_R = E_0\left[2.71\hat{\mathbf{i}} + 0.985\hat{\mathbf{j}}\right] = 2.88E_0 \text{ at } 20.0° = \boxed{2.88E_0 \text{ at } 0.349 \text{ rad}}$$
$$E_P = 2.88E_0\sin(\omega t + 0.349)$$

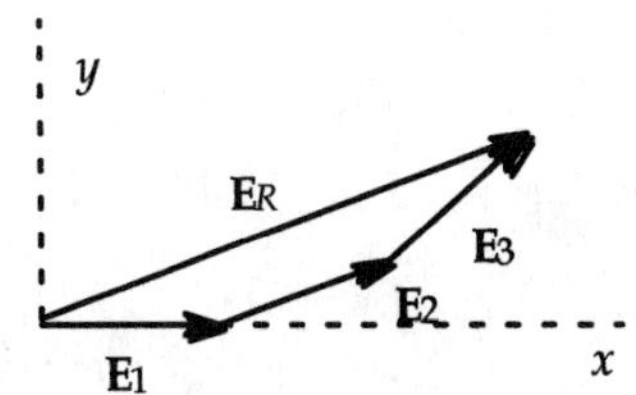

FIG. P37.22(a)

(b)
$$\mathbf{E}_R = E_0\left[\hat{\mathbf{i}} + (\hat{\mathbf{i}}\cos 60.0° + \hat{\mathbf{j}}\sin 60.0°) + (\hat{\mathbf{i}}\cos 120° + \hat{\mathbf{j}}\sin 120°)\right]$$
$$\mathbf{E}_R = E_0\left[1.00\hat{\mathbf{i}} + 1.73\hat{\mathbf{j}}\right] = 2.00E_0 \text{ at } 60.0° = \boxed{2.00E_0 \text{ at } \frac{\pi}{3} \text{ rad}}$$
$$E_P = 2.00E_0\sin\left(\omega t + \frac{\pi}{3}\right)$$

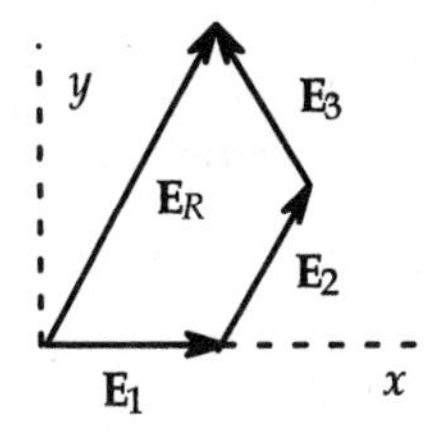

FIG. P37.22(b)

continued on next page

(c) $\mathbf{E}_R = E_0\left[\hat{\mathbf{i}} + \left(\hat{\mathbf{i}}\cos 120° + \hat{\mathbf{j}}\sin 120°\right) + \left(\hat{\mathbf{i}}\cos 240° + \hat{\mathbf{j}}\sin 240°\right)\right]$

$$\mathbf{E}_R = E_0\left[0\hat{\mathbf{i}} + 0\hat{\mathbf{j}}\right] = \boxed{0}$$

$$E_P = 0$$

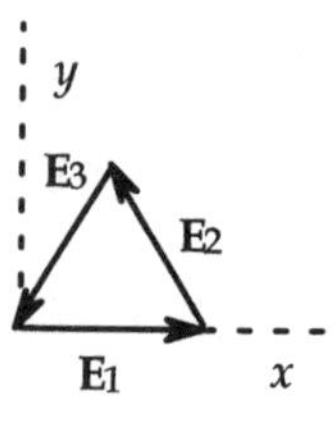

FIG. P37.22(c)

(d) $\mathbf{E}_R = E_0\left[\hat{\mathbf{i}} + \left(\hat{\mathbf{i}}\cos\frac{3\pi}{2} + \hat{\mathbf{j}}\sin\frac{3\pi}{2}\right) + \left(\hat{\mathbf{i}}\cos 3\pi + \hat{\mathbf{j}}\sin 3\pi\right)\right]$

$$\mathbf{E}_R = E_0\left[0\hat{\mathbf{i}} - 1.00\hat{\mathbf{j}}\right] = E_0 \text{ at } 270° = \boxed{E_0 \text{ at } \frac{3\pi}{2} \text{ rad}}$$

$$E_P = E_0 \sin\left(\omega t + \frac{3\pi}{2}\right)$$

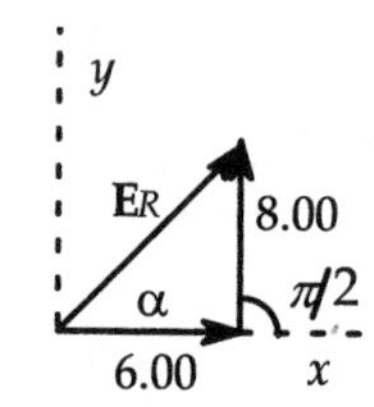

FIG. P37.22(d)

P37.23 $\mathbf{E}_R = 6.00\hat{\mathbf{i}} + 8.00\hat{\mathbf{j}} = \sqrt{(6.00)^2 + (8.00)^2} \text{ at } \tan^{-1}\left(\frac{8.00}{6.00}\right)$

$$\mathbf{E}_R = 10.0 \text{ at } 53.1° = 10.0 \text{ at } 0.927 \text{ rad}$$

$$E_P = \boxed{10.0\sin(100\pi t + 0.927)}$$

FIG. P37.23

P37.24 If $E_1 = E_{01}\sin\omega t$ and $E_2 = E_{02}\sin(\omega t + \phi)$, then by phasor addition, the amplitude of **E** is

$$E_0 = \sqrt{(E_{01} + E_{02}\cos\phi)^2 + (E_{02}\sin\phi)^2} = \boxed{\sqrt{E_{01}^2 + 2E_{01}E_{02}\cos\phi + E_{02}^2}}$$

and the phase angle is found from $\boxed{\sin\theta = \frac{E_{02}\sin\phi}{E_0}}$.

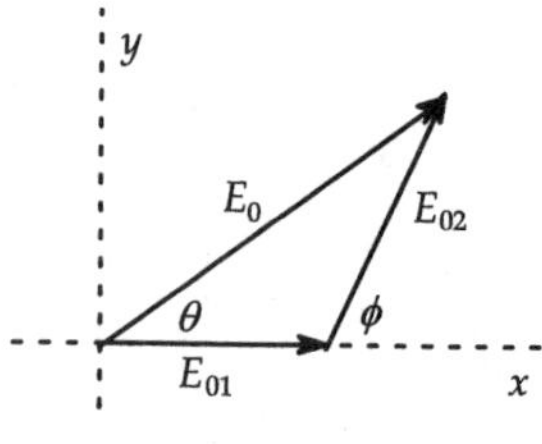

FIG. P37.24

P37.25 $\mathbf{E}_R = 12.0\hat{\mathbf{i}} + \left(18.0\cos 60.0°\,\hat{\mathbf{i}} + 18.0\sin 60.0°\,\hat{\mathbf{j}}\right)$

$$\mathbf{E}_R = 21.0\hat{\mathbf{i}} + 15.6\hat{\mathbf{j}} = 26.2 \text{ at } 36.6°$$

$$E_R = \boxed{26.2\sin(\omega t + 36.6°)}$$

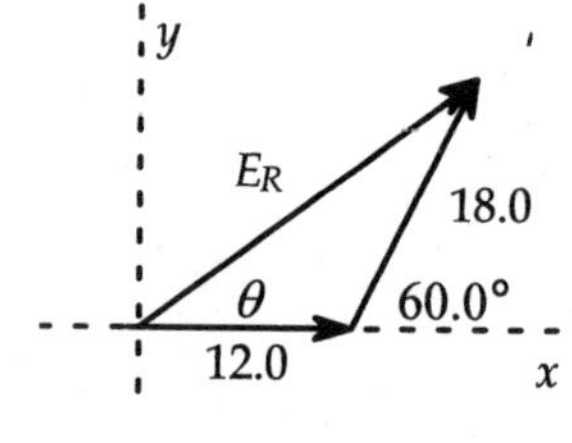

FIG. P37.25

P37.26 Constructive interference occurs where $m = 0, 1, 2, 3, \ldots$, for

$$\left(\frac{2\pi x_1}{\lambda} - 2\pi ft + \frac{\pi}{6}\right) - \left(\frac{2\pi x_2}{\lambda} - 2\pi ft + \frac{\pi}{8}\right) = 2\pi m \qquad \frac{2\pi(x_1 - x_2)}{\lambda} + \left(\frac{\pi}{6} - \frac{\pi}{8}\right) = 2\pi m$$

$$\frac{(x_1 - x_2)}{\lambda} + \frac{1}{12} - \frac{1}{16} = m \qquad \boxed{x_1 - x_2 = \left(m - \frac{1}{48}\right)\lambda \qquad m = 0, 1, 2, 3, \ldots}.$$

P37.27 See the figure to the right:

$$\boxed{\phi = \frac{\pi}{2}}.$$

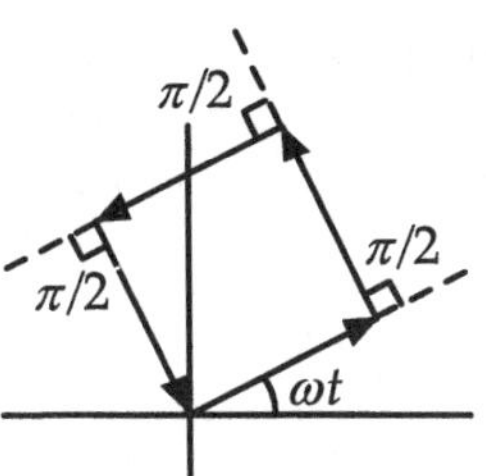

FIG. P37.27

P37.28 $E_R^2 = E_1^2 + E_2^2 - 2E_1E_2\cos\beta$ where $\beta = 180 - \phi$.

Since $I \propto E^2$

$$I_R = \boxed{I_1 + I_2 + 2\sqrt{I_1I_2}\cos\phi}.$$

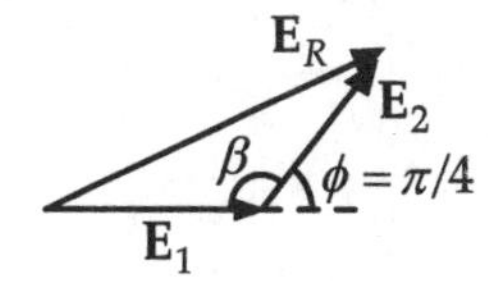

FIG. P37.28

P37.29 Take $\boxed{\phi = \frac{360°}{N}}$ where N defines the number of coherent sources. Then,

$$E_R = \sum_{m=1}^{N} E_0 \sin(\omega t + m\phi) = 0.$$

In essence, the set of N electric field components complete a full circle and return to zero.

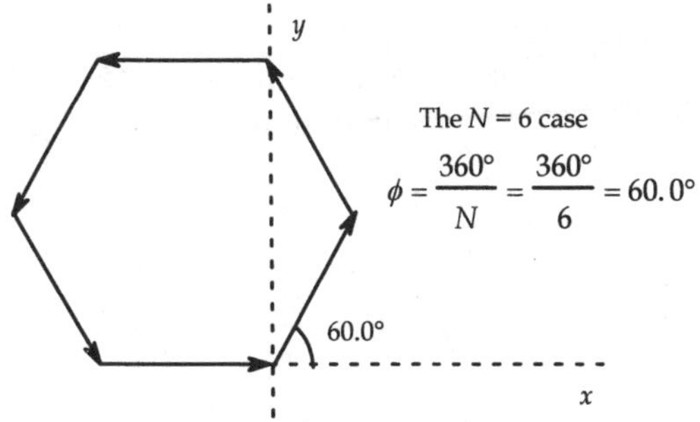

FIG. P37.29

Section 37.5 **Change of Phase Due to Reflection**

Section 37.6 **Interference in Thin Films**

P37.30 Light reflecting from the first surface suffers phase reversal. Light reflecting from the second surface does not, but passes twice through the thickness t of the film. So, for constructive interference, we require

$$\frac{\lambda_n}{2} + 2t = \lambda_n$$

where $\lambda_n = \frac{\lambda}{n}$ is the wavelength in the material.

Then $2t = \frac{\lambda_n}{2} = \frac{\lambda}{2n}$

$$\lambda = 4nt = 4(1.33)(115\text{ nm}) = \boxed{612\text{ nm}}.$$

P37.31 (a) The light reflected from the top of the oil film undergoes phase reversal. Since $1.45 > 1.33$, the light reflected from the bottom undergoes no reversal. For constructive interference of reflected light, we then have

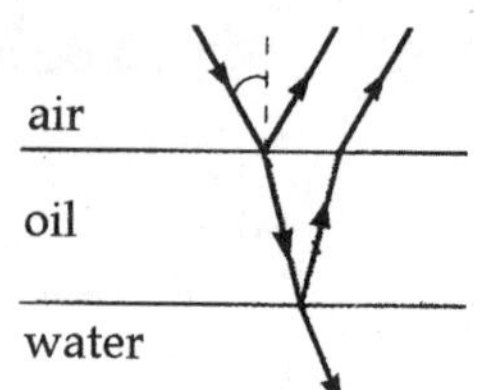

FIG. P37.31

$$2nt = \left(m + \frac{1}{2}\right)\lambda$$

or $$\lambda_m = \frac{2nt}{m+(1/2)} = \frac{2(1.45)(280\text{ nm})}{m+(1/2)}.$$

Substituting for m gives: $m = 0$, $\lambda_0 = 1\,620$ nm (infrared)

$m = 1$, $\lambda_1 = 541$ nm (green)

$m = 2$, $\lambda_2 = 325$ nm (ultraviolet).

Both infrared and ultraviolet light are invisible to the human eye, so the dominant color in reflected light is $\boxed{\text{green}}$.

(b) The dominant wavelengths in the transmitted light are those that produce destructive interference in the reflected light. The condition for destructive interference upon reflection is

$$2nt = m\lambda$$

or $$\lambda_m = \frac{2nt}{m} = \frac{812\text{ nm}}{m}.$$

Substituting for m gives: $m = 1$, $\lambda_1 = 812$ nm (near infrared)

$m = 2$, $\lambda_2 = 406$ nm (violet)

$m = 3$, $\lambda_3 = 271$ nm (ultraviolet).

Of these, the only wavelength visible to the human eye (and hence the dominate wavelength observed in the transmitted light) is 406 nm. Thus, the dominant color in the transmitted light is $\boxed{\text{violet}}$.

P37.32 Since $1 < 1.25 < 1.33$, light reflected both from the top and from the bottom surface of the oil suffers phase reversal.

For constructive interference we require $$2t = \frac{m\lambda_{\text{cons}}}{n}$$

and for destructive interference, $$2t = \frac{\left[m+(1/2)\right]\lambda_{\text{des}}}{n}.$$

Then $$\frac{\lambda_{\text{cons}}}{\lambda_{\text{dest}}} = 1 + \frac{1}{2m} = \frac{640\text{ nm}}{512\text{ nm}} = 1.25 \text{ and } m = 2.$$

Therefore, $$t = \frac{2(640\text{ nm})}{2(1.25)} = \boxed{512\text{ nm}}.$$

P37.33 Treating the anti-reflectance coating like a camera-lens coating,

$$2t = \left(m + \frac{1}{2}\right)\frac{\lambda}{n}.$$

Let $m = 0$: $t = \frac{\lambda}{4n} = \frac{3.00 \text{ cm}}{4(1.50)} = \boxed{0.500 \text{ cm}}$.

This anti-reflectance coating could be easily countered by changing the wavelength of the radar—to 1.50 cm—now creating maximum reflection!

P37.34 $2nt = \left(m + \frac{1}{2}\right)\lambda$ so $t = \left(m + \frac{1}{2}\right)\frac{\lambda}{2n}$

Minimum $t = \left(\frac{1}{2}\right)\frac{(500 \text{ nm})}{2(1.30)} = \boxed{96.2 \text{ nm}}$.

P37.35 Since the light undergoes a 180° phase change at each surface of the film, the condition for *constructive* interference is $2nt = m\lambda$, or $\lambda = \frac{2nt}{m}$. The film thickness is $t = 1.00 \times 10^{-5} \text{ cm} = 1.00 \times 10^{-7} \text{ m} = 100 \text{ nm}$. Therefore, the wavelengths intensified in the reflected light are

$$\lambda = \frac{2(1.38)(100 \text{ nm})}{m} = \frac{276 \text{ nm}}{m} \quad \text{where } m = 1, 2, 3, \ldots$$

or $\lambda_1 = 276 \text{ nm}$, $\lambda_2 = 138 \text{ nm}$, ... All reflection maxima are in the ultraviolet and beyond.

$\boxed{\text{No visible wavelengths are intensified.}}$

P37.36 (a) For maximum transmission, we want destructive interference in the light reflected from the front and back surfaces of the film.

If the surrounding glass has refractive index greater than 1.378, light reflected from the front surface suffers no phase reversal and light reflected from the back does undergo phase reversal. This effect by itself would produce destructive interference, so we want the distance down and back to be one whole wavelength in the film: $2t = \frac{\lambda}{n}$.

$$t = \frac{\lambda}{2n} = \frac{656.3 \text{ nm}}{2(1.378)} = \boxed{238 \text{ nm}}$$

(b) The filter will expand. As t increases in $2nt = \lambda$, so does $\boxed{\lambda \text{ increase}}$.

(c) Destructive interference for reflected light happens also for λ in $2nt = 2\lambda$,

or $\lambda = 1.378(238 \text{ nm}) = \boxed{328 \text{ nm}}$ (near ultraviolet).

P37.37 If the path length difference $\Delta = \lambda$, the transmitted light will be bright. Since $\Delta = 2d = \lambda$,

$$d_{\min} = \frac{\lambda}{2} = \frac{580 \text{ nm}}{2} = \boxed{290 \text{ nm}}.$$

P37.38 The condition for bright fringes is

$$2t+\frac{\lambda}{2n}=m\frac{\lambda}{n} \qquad m=1, 2, 3, \ldots.$$

From the sketch, observe that

$$t=R(1-\cos\theta)\approx R\left(1-1+\frac{\theta^2}{2}\right)=\frac{R}{2}\left(\frac{r}{R}\right)^2=\frac{r^2}{2R}.$$

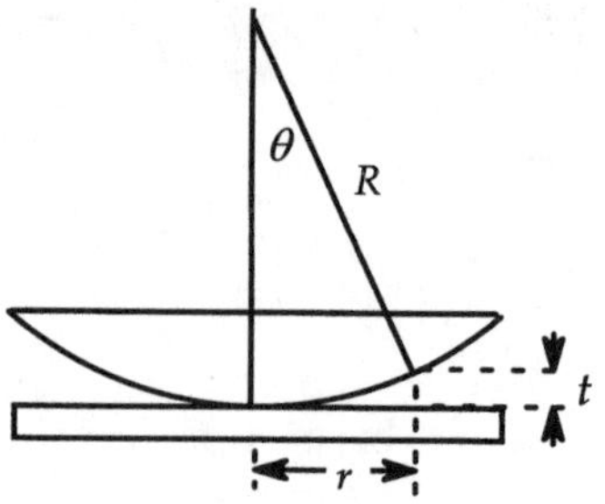

FIG. P37.38

The condition for a bright fringe becomes $\frac{r^2}{R}=\left(m-\frac{1}{2}\right)\frac{\lambda}{n}$.

Thus, for fixed m and λ, $nr^2=\text{constant}$.

Therefore, $n_{\text{liquid}}r_f^2=n_{\text{air}}r_i^2$ and $n_{\text{liquid}}=(1.00)\frac{(1.50\text{ cm})^2}{(1.31\text{ cm})^2}=\boxed{1.31}$.

P37.39 For destructive interference in the air,

$2t=m\lambda$.

For 30 dark fringes, including the one where the plates meet,

$$t=\frac{29(600\text{ nm})}{2}=8.70\times10^{-6}\text{ m}.$$

Therefore, the *radius* of the wire is

$$r=\frac{t}{2}=\frac{8.70\ \mu\text{m}}{2}=\boxed{4.35\ \mu\text{m}}.$$

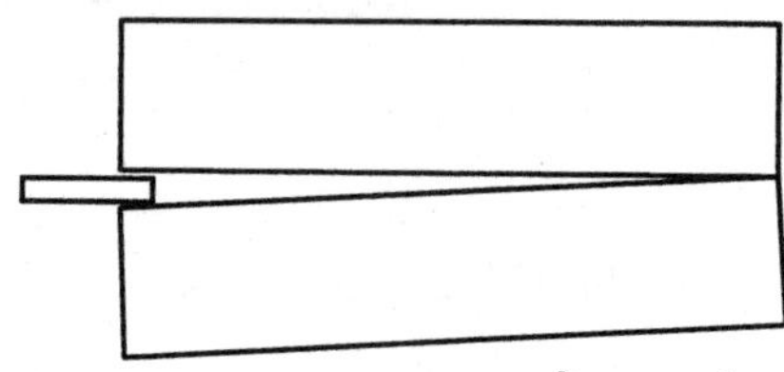

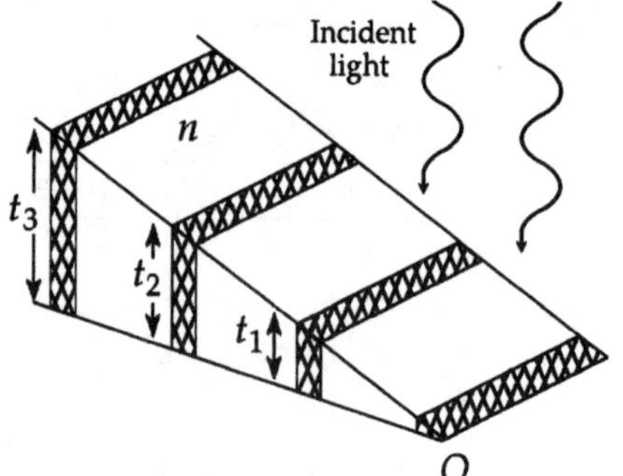

FIG. P37.39

P37.40 For total darkness, we want destructive interference for reflected light for both 400 nm and 600 nm. With phase reversal at just one reflecting surface, the condition for destructive interference is

$$2n_{\text{air}}t=m\lambda \qquad m=0, 1, 2, \ldots.$$

The least common multiple of these two wavelengths is 1 200 nm, so we get no reflected light at $2(1.00)t=3(400\text{ nm})=2(600\text{ nm})=1\,200\text{ nm}$, so $t=600\text{ nm}$ at this second dark fringe.

By similar triangles, $\frac{600\text{ nm}}{x}=\frac{0.050\,0\text{ mm}}{10.0\text{ cm}}$,

or the distance from the contact point is $x=\left(600\times10^{-9}\text{ m}\right)\left(\frac{0.100\text{ m}}{5.00\times10^{-5}\text{ m}}\right)=\boxed{1.20\text{ mm}}$.

Section 37.7 The Michelson Interferometer

P37.41 When the mirror on one arm is displaced by $\Delta\ell$, the path difference changes by $2\Delta\ell$. A shift resulting in the reversal between dark and bright fringes requires a path length change of one-half wavelength. Therefore, $2\Delta\ell = \frac{m\lambda}{2}$, where in this case, $m = 250$.

$$\Delta\ell = m\frac{\lambda}{4} = \frac{(250)(6.328\times10^{-7}\text{ m})}{4} = \boxed{39.6\ \mu\text{m}}$$

P37.42 Distance $= 2(3.82\times10^{-4}\text{ m}) = 1\,700\lambda$ $\qquad \lambda = 4.49\times10^{-7}\text{ m} = \boxed{449\text{ nm}}$

The light is $\boxed{\text{blue}}$.

P37.43 Counting light going both directions, the number of wavelengths originally in the cylinder is $m_1 = \frac{2L}{\lambda}$. It changes to $m_2 = \frac{2L}{\lambda/n} = \frac{2nL}{\lambda}$ as the cylinder is filled with gas. If N is the number of bright fringes passing, $N = m_2 - m_1 = \frac{2L}{\lambda}(n-1)$, or the index of refraction of the gas is

$$n = \boxed{1 + \frac{N\lambda}{2L}}$$

Additional Problems

***P37.44** (a) Where fringes of the two colors coincide we have $d\sin\theta = m\lambda = m'\lambda'$, requiring $\frac{\lambda}{\lambda'} = \frac{m'}{m}$.

(b) $\lambda = 430\text{ nm}$, $\lambda' = 510\text{ nm}$

$\therefore \frac{m'}{m} = \frac{430\text{ nm}}{510\text{ nm}} = \frac{43}{51}$, which cannot be reduced any further. Then $m = 51$, $m' = 43$.

$$\theta_m = \sin^{-1}\left(\frac{m\lambda}{d}\right) = \sin^{-1}\left[\frac{(51)(430\times10^{-9}\text{ m})}{0.025\times10^{-3}\text{ m}}\right] = 61.3°$$

$$y_m = L\tan\theta_m = (1.5\text{ m})\tan 61.3° = \boxed{2.74\text{ m}}$$

P37.45 The wavelength is $\lambda = \frac{c}{f} = \frac{3.00\times10^8\text{ m/s}}{60.0\times10^6\text{ s}^{-1}} = 5.00\text{ m}$.

Along the line AB the two traveling waves going in opposite directions add to give a standing wave. The two transmitters are exactly 2.00 wavelengths apart and the signal from B, when it arrives at A, will always be in phase with transmitter B. Since B is 180° out of phase with A, the two signals always interfere destructively at the position of A.

The first antinode (point of constructive interference) is located at distance

$\frac{\lambda}{4} = \frac{5.00\text{ m}}{4} = \boxed{1.25\text{ m}}$ from the node at A.

*P37.46 Along the line of length d joining the source, two identical waves moving in opposite directions add to give a standing wave. An antinode is halfway between the sources. If $\frac{d}{2} > \frac{\lambda}{2}$, there is space for two more antinodes for a total of three. If $\frac{d}{2} > \lambda$, there will be at least five antinodes, and so on. To repeat, if $\frac{d}{\lambda} > 0$, the number of antinodes is 1 or more. If $\frac{d}{\lambda} > 1$, the number of antinodes is 3 or more. If $\frac{d}{\lambda} > 2$, the number of antinodes is 5 or more. In general,

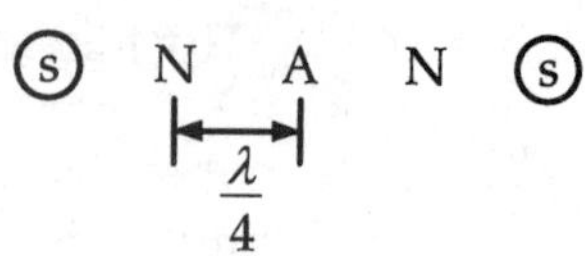

FIG. P37.46

The number of antinodes is 1 plus 2 times the greatest integer less than or equal to $\frac{d}{\lambda}$.

If $\frac{d}{2} < \frac{\lambda}{4}$, there will be no nodes. If $\frac{d}{2} > \frac{\lambda}{4}$, there will be space for at least two nodes, as shown in the picture. If $\frac{d}{2} > \frac{3\lambda}{4}$, there will be at least four nodes. If $\frac{d}{2} > \frac{5\lambda}{4}$ six or more nodes will fit in, and so on. To repeat, if $2d < \lambda$ the number of nodes is 0. If $2d > \lambda$ the number of nodes is 2 or more. If $2d > 3\lambda$ the number of nodes is 4 or more. If $2d > 5\lambda$ the number of nodes is 6 or more. Again, if $\left(\frac{d}{\lambda} + \frac{1}{2}\right) > 1$, the number of nodes is at least 2. If $\left(\frac{d}{\lambda} + \frac{1}{2}\right) > 2$, the number of nodes is at least 4. If $\left(\frac{d}{\lambda} + \frac{1}{2}\right) > 3$, the number of nodes is at least 6. In general,

the number of nodes is 2 times the greatest nonzero integer less than $\left(\frac{d}{\lambda} + \frac{1}{2}\right)$.

Next, we enumerate the zones of constructive interference. They are described by $d \sin\theta = m\lambda$, $m = 0, 1, 2, \ldots$ with θ counted as positive both left and right of the maximum at $\theta = 0$ in the center. The number of side maxima on each side is the greatest integer satisfying $\sin\theta \le 1$, $d1 \ge m\lambda$, $m \le \frac{d}{\lambda}$. So the total

number of bright fringes is one plus 2 times the greatest integer less than or equal to $\frac{d}{\lambda}$.

It is equal to the number of antinodes on the line joining the sources.

The interference minima are to the left and right at angles described by $d \sin\theta = \left(m + \frac{1}{2}\right)\lambda$, $m = 0, 1, 2, \ldots$. With $\sin\theta < 1$, $d1 > \left(m_{\max} + \frac{1}{2}\right)\lambda$, $m_{\max} < \frac{d}{\lambda} - \frac{1}{2}$ or $m_{\max} + 1 < \frac{d}{\lambda} + \frac{1}{2}$. Let $n = 1, 2, 3, \ldots$. Then the number of side minima is the greatest integer n less than $\frac{d}{\lambda} + \frac{1}{2}$. Counting both left and right, the number of dark fringes is two times the greatest positive integer less than $\left(\frac{d}{\lambda} + \frac{1}{2}\right)$. It is equal to the number of nodes in the standing wave between the sources.

P37.47 My middle finger has width $d = 2$ cm.

(a) Two adjacent directions of constructive interference for 600-nm light are described by

$$d\sin\theta = m\lambda$$
$$\theta_0 = 0$$
$$\left(2\times10^{-2}\text{ m}\right)\sin\theta_1 = 1\left(6\times10^{-7}\text{ m}\right)$$

Thus, $\theta_1 = 2\times10^{-3}$ degree

and $\theta_1 - \theta_0 \boxed{\sim 10^{-3}\text{ degree}}$.

(b) Choose $\theta_1 = 20°$

$$\left(2\times10^{-2}\text{ m}\right)\sin 20° = (1)\lambda$$
$$\lambda = 7\text{ mm}$$

Millimeter waves are $\boxed{\text{microwaves}}$.

$f = \dfrac{c}{\lambda}$: $\quad f = \dfrac{3\times10^{8}\text{ m/s}}{7\times10^{-3}\text{ m}}\boxed{\sim10^{11}\text{ Hz}}$

P37.48 If the center point on the screen is to be a dark spot rather than bright, passage through the plastic must delay the light by one-half wavelength. Calling the thickness of the plastic *t*.

$\dfrac{t}{\lambda} + \dfrac{1}{2} = \dfrac{t}{\lambda/n} = \dfrac{nt}{\lambda}$ or $t = \boxed{\dfrac{\lambda}{2(n-1)}}$ where n is the index of refraction for the plastic.

P37.49 No phase shift upon reflection from the upper surface (glass to air) of the film, but there will be a shift of $\dfrac{\lambda}{2}$ due to the reflection at the lower surface of the film (air to metal). The total phase difference in the two reflected beams is

then $\quad \delta = 2nt + \dfrac{\lambda}{2}$.

For constructive interference, $\delta = m\lambda$

or $\quad 2(1.00)t + \dfrac{\lambda}{2} = m\lambda$.

Thus, the film thickness for the mth order bright fringe is

$$t_m = \left(m - \frac{1}{2}\right)\frac{\lambda}{2} = m\left(\frac{\lambda}{2}\right) - \frac{\lambda}{4}$$

and the thickness for the $m-1$ bright fringe is:

$$t_{m-1} = (m-1)\left(\frac{\lambda}{2}\right) - \frac{\lambda}{4}.$$

Therefore, the change in thickness required to go from one bright fringe to the next is

$$\Delta t = t_m - t_{m-1} = \frac{\lambda}{2}.$$

continued on next page

To go through 200 bright fringes, the change in thickness of the air film must be:

$$200\left(\frac{\lambda}{2}\right)=100\lambda .$$

Thus, the increase in the length of the rod is

$$\Delta L=100\lambda=100\left(5.00\times10^{-7}\text{ m}\right)=5.00\times10^{-5}\text{ m}.$$

From $\Delta L=L_i\alpha\Delta t$

we have: $\alpha=\dfrac{\Delta L}{L_i\Delta T}=\dfrac{5.00\times10^{-5}\text{ m}}{(0.100\text{ m})(25.0^\circ\text{C})}=\boxed{20.0\times10^{-6}\ {}^\circ\text{C}^{-1}}.$

P37.50 Since $1<1.25<1.34$, light reflected from top and bottom surfaces of the oil undergoes phase reversal. The path difference is then $2t$, which must be equal to

$$m\lambda_n=\frac{m\lambda}{n}$$

for maximum reflection, with $m=1$ for the given first-order condition and $n=1.25$. So

$$t=\frac{m\lambda}{2n}=\frac{1(500\text{ nm})}{2(1.25)}=200\text{ nm}.$$

The volume we assume to be constant: $1.00\text{ m}^3=(200\text{ nm})A$

$$A=\frac{1.00\text{ m}^3}{200\left(10^{-9}\text{ m}\right)}=5.00\times10^6\text{ m}^2=\boxed{5.00\text{ km}^2}.$$

P37.51 One radio wave reaches the receiver R directly from the distant source at an angle θ above the horizontal. The other wave undergoes phase reversal as it reflects from the water at P.

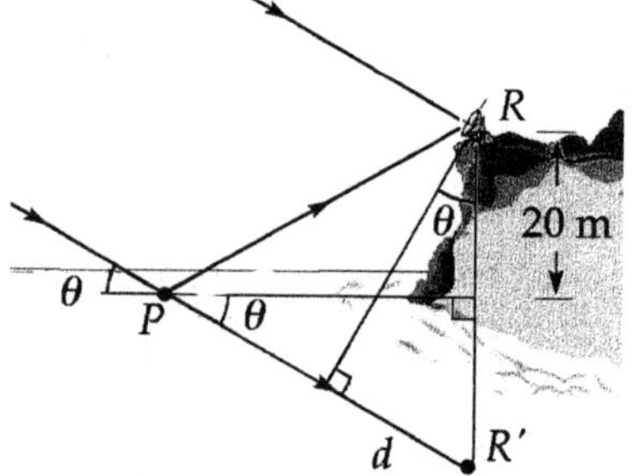

FIG. P37.51

Constructive interference first occurs for a path difference of

$$d=\frac{\lambda}{2} \qquad (1)$$

It is equally far from P to R as from P to R', the mirror image of the telescope.

The angles θ in the figure are equal because they each form part of a right triangle with a shared angle at R'.

So the path difference is $d=2(20.0\text{ m})\sin\theta=(40.0\text{ m})\sin\theta$.

The wavelength is $\lambda=\dfrac{c}{f}=\dfrac{3.00\times10^8\text{ m/s}}{60.0\times10^6\text{ Hz}}=5.00\text{ m}$.

Substituting for d and λ in Equation (1), $(40.0\text{ m})\sin\theta=\dfrac{5.00\text{ m}}{2}$.

Solving for the angle θ, $\sin\theta=\dfrac{5.00\text{ m}}{80.0\text{ m}}$ and $\boxed{\theta=3.58^\circ}$.

P37.52 For destructive interference, the path length must differ by $m\lambda$. We may treat this problem as a double slit experiment if we remember the light undergoes a $\frac{\pi}{2}$-phase shift at the mirror. The second slit is the mirror image of the source, 1.00 cm below the mirror plane. Modifying Equation 37.5,

$$y_{\text{dark}} = \frac{m\lambda L}{d} = \frac{1\left(5.00 \times 10^{-7}\text{ m}\right)(100\text{ m})}{\left(2.00 \times 10^{-2}\text{ m}\right)} = \boxed{2.50\text{ mm}}.$$

P37.53 $2\sqrt{(15.0\text{ km})^2 + h^2} = 30.175\text{ km}$

$(15.0\text{ km})^2 + h^2 = 227.63$

$h = \boxed{1.62\text{ km}}$

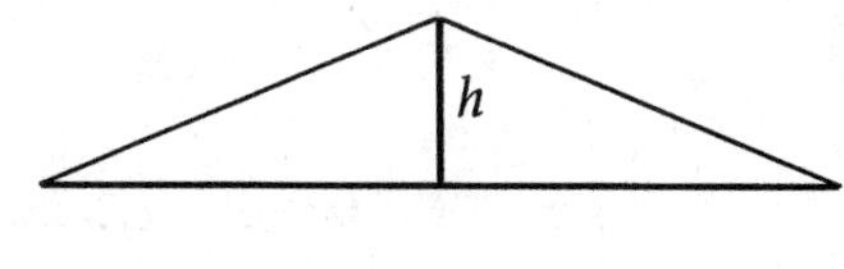

FIG. P37.53

P37.54 For dark fringes, $2nt = m\lambda$

and at the edge of the wedge, $t = \frac{84(500\text{ nm})}{2}$.

When submerged in water, $2nt = m\lambda$

$$m = \frac{2(1.33)(42)(500\text{ nm})}{500\text{ nm}}$$

so $m + 1 = \boxed{113\text{ dark fringes}}$.

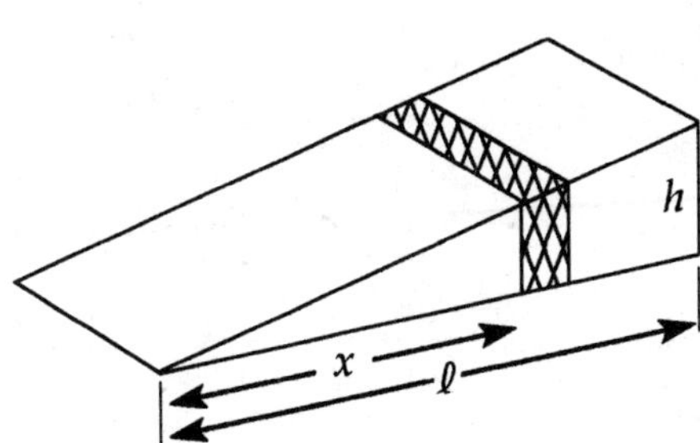

FIG. P37.54

P37.55 From Equation 37.13, $\frac{I}{I_{\max}} = \cos^2\left(\frac{\pi y d}{\lambda L}\right)$.

Let λ_2 equal the wavelength for which $\frac{I}{I_{\max}} \to \frac{I_2}{I_{\max}} = 0.640$.

Then $\lambda_2 = \frac{\pi y d/L}{\cos^{-1}(I_2/I_{\max})^{1/2}}$.

But $\frac{\pi y d}{L} = \lambda_1 \cos^{-1}\left(\frac{I_1}{I_{\max}}\right)^{1/2} = (600\text{ nm})\cos^{-1}(0.900) = 271\text{ nm}$.

Substituting this value into the expression for λ_2, $\lambda_2 = \frac{271\text{ nm}}{\cos^{-1}\left(0.640^{1/2}\right)} = \boxed{421\text{ nm}}$.

Note that in this problem, $\cos^{-1}\left(\frac{I}{I_{\max}}\right)^{1/2}$ must be expressed in radians.

P37.56 At entrance, $1.00\sin 30.0° = 1.38\sin\theta_2$ $\qquad \theta_2 = 21.2°$

Call t the unknown thickness. Then

$$\cos 21.2° = \frac{t}{a} \qquad a = \frac{t}{\cos 21.2°}$$

$$\tan 21.2° = \frac{c}{t} \qquad c = t\tan 21.2°$$

$$\sin\theta_1 = \frac{b}{2c} \qquad b = 2t\tan 21.2°\sin 30.0°$$

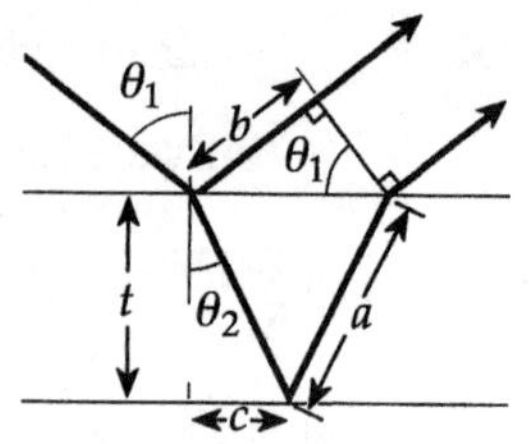

FIG. P37.56

The net shift for the second ray, including the phase reversal on reflection of the first, is

$$2an - b - \frac{\lambda}{2}$$

where the factor n accounts for the shorter wavelength in the film. For constructive interference, we require

$$2an - b - \frac{\lambda}{2} = m\lambda\,.$$

The minimum thickness will be given by $\qquad 2an - b - \frac{\lambda}{2} = 0\,.$

$$\frac{\lambda}{2} = 2an - b = 2\frac{nt}{\cos 21.2°} - 2t(\tan 21.2°)\sin 30.0°$$

$$\frac{590\text{ nm}}{2} = \left(\frac{2\times 1.38}{\cos 21.2°} - 2\tan 21.2°\sin 30.0°\right)t = 2.57t \qquad t = \boxed{115\text{ nm}}$$

P37.57 The shift between the two reflected waves is $\delta = 2na - b - \frac{\lambda}{2}$ where a and b are as shown in the ray diagram, n is the index of refraction, and the term $\frac{\lambda}{2}$ is due to phase reversal at the top surface. For constructive interference, $\delta = m\lambda$ where m has integer values. This condition becomes

$$2na - b = \left(m + \frac{1}{2}\right)\lambda \qquad (1)$$

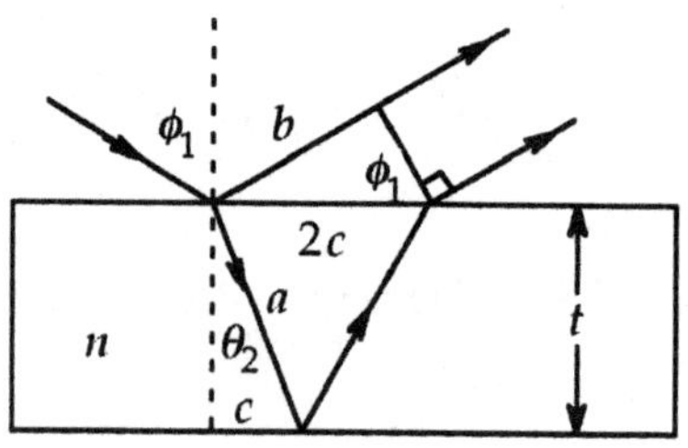

FIG. P37.57

From the figure's geometry, $\quad a = \dfrac{t}{\cos\theta_2}$

$$c = a\sin\theta_2 = \frac{t\sin\theta_2}{\cos\theta_2}$$

$$b = 2c\sin\phi_1 = \frac{2t\sin\theta_2}{\cos\theta_2}\sin\phi_1$$

Also, from Snell's law, $\quad \sin\phi_1 = n\sin\theta_2\,.$

Thus, $\quad b = \dfrac{2nt\sin^2\theta_2}{\cos\theta_2}\,.$

With these results, the condition for constructive interference given in Equation (1) becomes:

$$2n\left(\frac{t}{\cos\theta_2}\right) - \frac{2nt\sin^2\theta_2}{\cos\theta_2} = \frac{2nt}{\cos\theta_2}\left(1 - \sin^2\theta_2\right) = \left(m + \frac{1}{2}\right)\lambda$$

or $\qquad \boxed{2nt\cos\theta_2 = \left(m + \frac{1}{2}\right)\lambda}\,.$

P37.58 (a) Minimum: $2nt = m\lambda_2$ for $m = 0, 1, 2, \ldots$

Maximum: $2nt = \left(m' + \frac{1}{2}\right)\lambda_1$ for $m' = 0, 1, 2, \ldots$

for $\lambda_1 > \lambda_2$, $\left(m' + \frac{1}{2}\right) < m$

so $m' = m - 1$.

Then $2nt = m\lambda_2 = \left(m - \frac{1}{2}\right)\lambda_1$

$$2m\lambda_2 = 2m\lambda_1 - \lambda_1$$

so $\boxed{m = \frac{\lambda_1}{2(\lambda_1 - \lambda_2)}}$.

(b) $m = \frac{500}{2(500 - 370)} = 1.92 \to 2$ (wavelengths measured to ± 5 nm)

Minimum: $2nt = m\lambda_2$

$2(1.40)t = 2(370 \text{ nm})$ $t = 264$ nm

Maximum: $2nt = \left(m - 1 + \frac{1}{2}\right)\lambda = 1.5\lambda$

$2(1.40)t = 1.5(500 \text{ nm})$ $t = 268$ nm

Film thickness $= \boxed{266 \text{ nm}}$.

P37.59 From the sketch, observe that

$$x = \sqrt{h^2 + \left(\frac{d}{2}\right)^2} = \frac{\sqrt{4h^2 + d^2}}{2}.$$

Including the phase reversal due to reflection from the ground, the total shift between the two waves is $\delta = 2x - d - \frac{\lambda}{2}$.

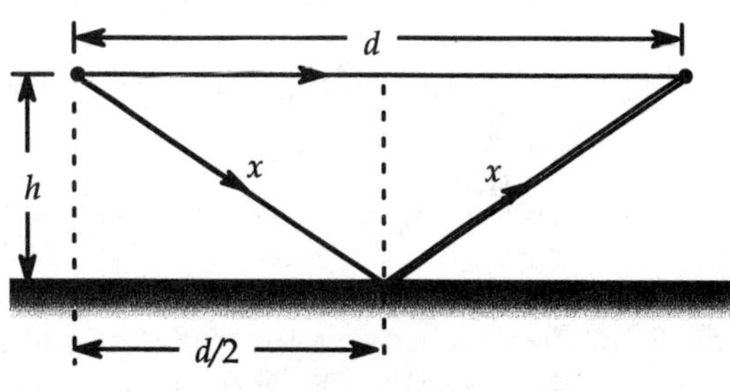

FIG. P37.59

(a) For constructive interference, the total shift must be an integral number of wavelengths, or $\delta = m\lambda$ where $m = 0, 1, 2, 3, \ldots$.

Thus, $2x - d = \left(m + \frac{1}{2}\right)\lambda$ or $\lambda = \frac{4x - 2d}{2m + 1}$.

For the longest wavelength, $m = 0$, giving $\lambda = 4x - 2d = \boxed{2\sqrt{4h^2 + d^2} - 2d}$.

(b) For destructive interference, $\delta = \left(m - \frac{1}{2}\right)\lambda$ where $m = 0, 1, 2, 3, \ldots$.

Thus, $2x - d = m\lambda$ or $\lambda = \frac{2x - d}{m}$.

For the longest wavelength, $m = 1$ giving $\lambda = 2x - d = \boxed{\sqrt{4h^2 + d^2} - d}$.

P37.60 Bright fringes occur when $2t = \frac{\lambda}{n}\left(m + \frac{1}{2}\right)$

and dark fringes occur when $2t = \left(\frac{\lambda}{n}\right)m$.

The thickness of the film at x is $t = \left(\frac{h}{\ell}\right)x$.

Therefore, $\boxed{x_{\text{bright}} = \frac{\lambda\ell}{2hn}\left(m + \frac{1}{2}\right)}$ and $\boxed{x_{\text{dark}} = \frac{\lambda\ell m}{2hn}}$.

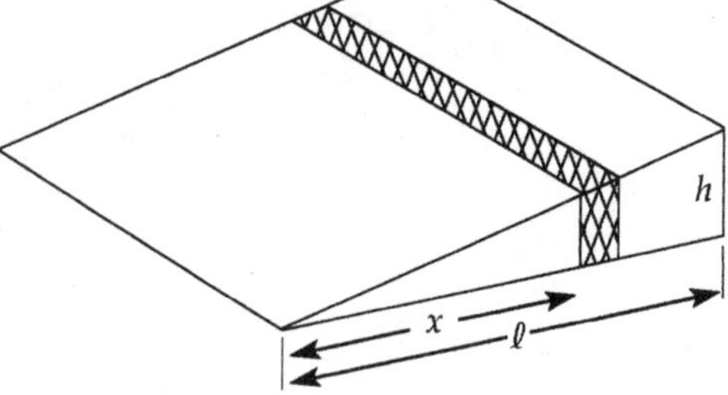

FIG. P37.60

P37.61 Call t the thickness of the film. The central maximum corresponds to zero phase difference. Thus, the added distance Δr traveled by the light from the lower slit must introduce a phase difference equal to that introduced by the plastic film. The phase difference ϕ is

$$\phi = 2\pi\left(\frac{t}{\lambda_a}\right)(n-1).$$

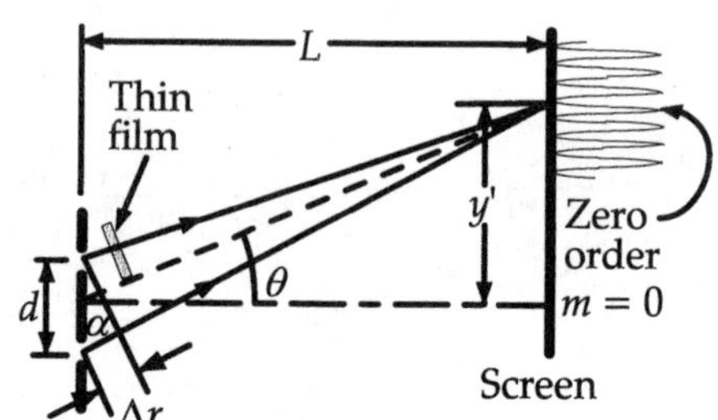

FIG. P37.61

The corresponding difference in **path length** Δr is

$$\Delta r = \phi\left(\frac{\lambda_a}{2\pi}\right) = 2\pi\left(\frac{t}{\lambda_a}\right)(n-1)\left(\frac{\lambda_a}{2\pi}\right) = t(n-1).$$

Note that the wavelength of the light does not appear in this equation. In the figure, the two rays from the slits are essentially parallel.

Thus the angle θ may be expressed as $\tan\theta = \frac{\Delta r}{d} = \frac{y'}{L}$.

Eliminating Δr by substitution, $\frac{y'}{L} = \frac{t(n-1)}{d}$ gives $\boxed{y' = \frac{t(n-1)L}{d}}$.

P37.62 The shift between the waves reflecting from the top and bottom surfaces of the film at the point where the film has thickness t is $\delta = 2tn_{\text{film}} + \frac{\lambda}{2}$, with the factor of $\frac{\lambda}{2}$ being due to a phase reversal at *one* of the surfaces.

For the dark rings (destructive interference), the total shift should be $\delta = \left(m + \frac{1}{2}\right)\lambda$ with $m = 0, 1, 2, 3, \ldots$. This requires that

$$t = \frac{m\lambda}{2n_{\text{film}}}.$$

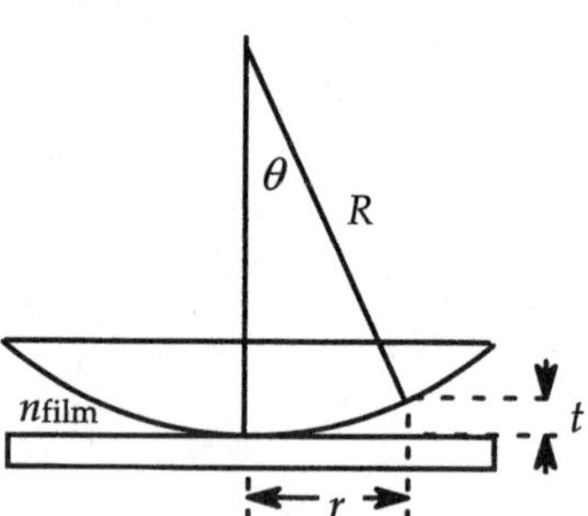

FIG. P37.62

To find t in terms of r and R, $R^2 = r^2 + (R-t)^2$ so $r^2 = 2Rt + t^2$.

Since t is much smaller than R, $t^2 \ll 2Rt$ and $r^2 \approx 2Rt = 2R\left(\frac{m\lambda}{2n_{\text{film}}}\right)$.

Thus, where m is an integer, $\boxed{r \approx \sqrt{\frac{m\lambda R}{n_{\text{film}}}}}$.

P37.63 (a) Constructive interference in the reflected light requires $2t = \left(m + \frac{1}{2}\right)\lambda$. The first bright ring has $m = 0$ and the 55th has $m = 54$, so at the edge of the lens

$$t = \frac{54.5\left(650 \times 10^{-9}\ \text{m}\right)}{2} = 17.7\ \mu\text{m}.$$

Now from the geometry in Figure 37.18, the distance from the center of curvature down to the flat side of the lens is

$$\sqrt{R^2 - r^2} = R - t \text{ or } R^2 - r^2 = R^2 - 2Rt + t^2$$

$$R = \frac{r^2 + t^2}{2t} = \frac{\left(5.00 \times 10^{-2}\ \text{m}\right)^2 + \left(1.77 \times 10^{-5}\ \text{m}\right)^2}{2\left(1.77 \times 10^{-5}\ \text{m}\right)} = \boxed{70.6\ \text{m}}$$

(b) $$\frac{1}{f} = (n-1)\left(\frac{1}{R_2} - \frac{1}{R_2}\right) = 0.520\left(\frac{1}{\infty} - \frac{1}{-70.6\ \text{m}}\right) \text{ so } f = \boxed{136\ \text{m}}$$

***P37.64** Light reflecting from the upper interface of the air layer suffers no phase change, while light reflecting from the lower interface is reversed 180°. Then there is indeed a dark fringe at the outer circumference of the lens, and a dark fringe wherever the air thickness t satisfies $2t = m\lambda$, $m = 0, 1, 2, \ldots$.

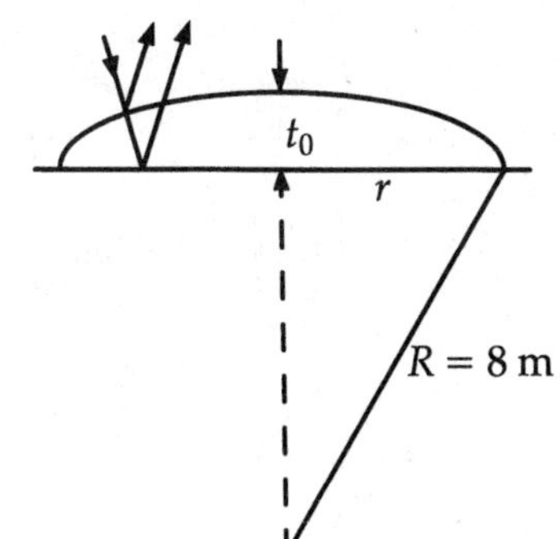

FIG. P37.64

(a) At the central dark spot $m = 50$ and

$$t_0 = \frac{50\lambda}{2} = 25\left(589 \times 10^{-9}\ \text{m}\right) = \boxed{1.47 \times 10^{-5}\ \text{m}}.$$

(b) In the right triangle,

$(8\ \text{m})^2 = r^2 + \left(8\ \text{m} - 1.47 \times 10^{-5}\ \text{m}\right)^2 = r^2 + (8\ \text{m})^2 - 2(8\ \text{m})\left(1.47 \times 10^{-5}\ \text{m}\right) + 2 \times 10^{-10}\ \text{m}^2$. The last term is negligible. $r = \sqrt{2(8\ \text{m})\left(1.47 \times 10^{-5}\ \text{m}\right)} = \boxed{1.53 \times 10^{-2}\ \text{m}}$

(c) $$\frac{1}{f} = (n-1)\left(\frac{1}{R_1} - \frac{1}{R_2}\right) = (1.50 - 1)\left(\frac{1}{\infty} - \frac{1}{8.00\ \text{m}}\right)$$

$$\boxed{f = -16.0\ \text{m}}$$

P37.65 For bright rings the gap t between surfaces is given by $2t = \left(m + \frac{1}{2}\right)\lambda$. The first bright ring has $m = 0$ and the hundredth has $m = 99$.

So, $t = \frac{1}{2}(99.5)\left(500 \times 10^{-9} \text{ m}\right) = 24.9\ \mu\text{m}$.

Call r_b the ring radius. From the geometry of the figure at the right,

$$t = r - \sqrt{r^2 - r_b^2} - \left(R - \sqrt{R^2 - r_b^2}\right)$$

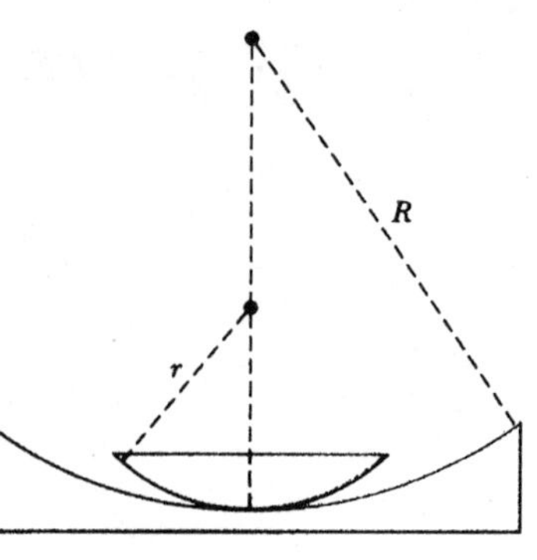

FIG. P37.65

Since $r_b \ll r$, we can expand in series:

$$t = r - r\left(1 - \frac{1}{2}\frac{r_b^2}{r^2}\right) - R + R\left(1 - \frac{1}{2}\frac{r_b^2}{R^2}\right) = \frac{1}{2}\frac{r_b^2}{r} - \frac{1}{2}\frac{r_b^2}{R}$$

$$r_b = \left[\frac{2t}{1/r - 1/R}\right]^{1/2} = \left[\frac{2\left(24.9 \times 10^{-6} \text{ m}\right)}{1/4.00 \text{ m} - 1/12.0 \text{ m}}\right]^{1/2} = \boxed{1.73 \text{ cm}}$$

P37.66

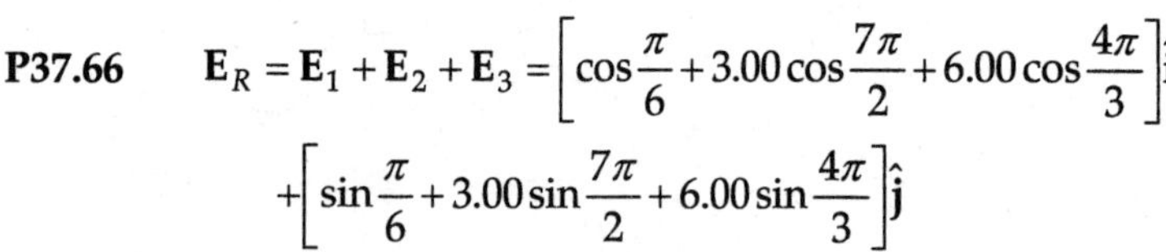

$$\mathbf{E}_R = \mathbf{E}_1 + \mathbf{E}_2 + \mathbf{E}_3 = \left[\cos\frac{\pi}{6} + 3.00\cos\frac{7\pi}{2} + 6.00\cos\frac{4\pi}{3}\right]\hat{\mathbf{i}} + \left[\sin\frac{\pi}{6} + 3.00\sin\frac{7\pi}{2} + 6.00\sin\frac{4\pi}{3}\right]\hat{\mathbf{j}}$$

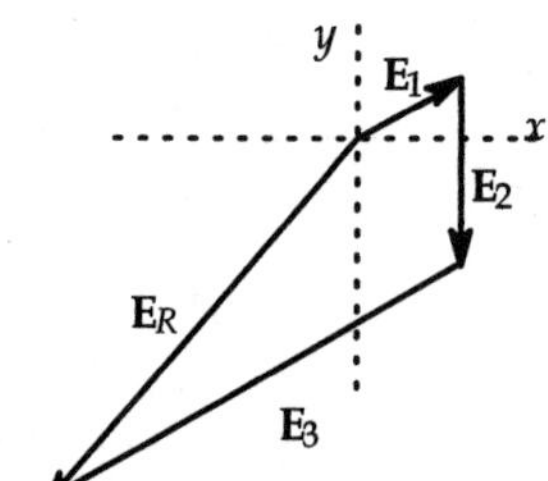

FIG. P37.66

$$\mathbf{E}_R = -2.13\hat{\mathbf{i}} - 7.70\hat{\mathbf{j}}$$

$$\mathbf{E}_R = \sqrt{(-2.13)^2 + (-7.70)^2} \text{ at } \tan^{-1}\left(\frac{-7.70}{-2.13}\right) = 7.99 \text{ at } 4.44 \text{ rad}$$

Thus, $E_P = \boxed{7.99\sin(\omega t + 4.44 \text{ rad})}$.

P37.67 (a) Bright bands are observed when $2nt = \left(m + \frac{1}{2}\right)\lambda$.

Hence, the first bright band ($m = 0$) corresponds to $nt = \frac{\lambda}{4}$.

Since $\frac{x_1}{x_2} = \frac{t_1}{t_2}$

we have $x_2 = x_1\left(\frac{t_2}{t_1}\right) = x_1\left(\frac{\lambda_2}{\lambda_1}\right) = (3.00 \text{ cm})\left(\frac{680 \text{ nm}}{420 \text{ nm}}\right) = \boxed{4.86 \text{ cm}}$.

(b) $t_1 = \frac{\lambda_1}{4n} = \frac{420 \text{ nm}}{4(1.33)} = \boxed{78.9 \text{ nm}}$

$t_2 = \frac{\lambda_2}{4n} = \frac{680 \text{ nm}}{4(1.33)} = \boxed{128 \text{ nm}}$

(c) $\theta \approx \tan\theta = \frac{t_1}{x_1} = \frac{78.9 \text{ nm}}{3.00 \text{ cm}} = \boxed{2.63 \times 10^{-6} \text{ rad}}$

***P37.68** Depth = one-quarter of the wavelength in plastic.

$$t=\frac{\lambda}{4n}=\frac{780\text{ nm}}{4(1.50)}=\boxed{130\text{ nm}}$$

P37.69 $2h\sin\theta=\left(m+\frac{1}{2}\right)\lambda$ bright

$2h\left(\frac{\Delta y}{2L}\right)=\frac{1}{2}\lambda$ so $h=\frac{L\lambda}{2\Delta y}=\frac{(2.00\text{ m})(606\times10^{-9}\text{ m})}{2(1.2\times10^{-3}\text{ m})}=\boxed{0.505\text{ mm}}$

***P37.70** Represent the light radiated from each slit to point P as a phasor. The two have equal amplitudes E. Since intensity is proportional to amplitude squared, they add to amplitude $\sqrt{3}E$. Then $\cos\theta=\frac{\sqrt{3}\,E/2}{E}$, $\theta=30°$. Next, the obtuse angle between the two phasors is $180-30-30=120°$, and $\phi=180-120°=60°$. The phase difference between the two phasors is caused by the path difference $\delta=\overline{SS_2}-\overline{SS_1}$ according to $\frac{\delta}{\lambda}=\frac{\phi}{360°}$, $\delta=\lambda\frac{60°}{360°}=\frac{\lambda}{6}$. Then

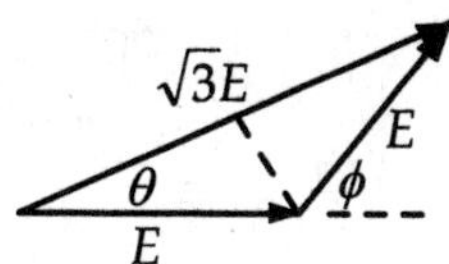

FIG. P37.70

$$\sqrt{L^2+d^2}-L=\frac{\lambda}{6}$$

$$L^2+d^2=L^2+\frac{2L\lambda}{6}+\frac{\lambda^2}{36}$$

The last term is negligible

$$d=\left(\frac{2L\lambda}{6}\right)^{1/2}=\sqrt{\frac{2(1.2\text{ m})620\times10^{-9}\text{ m}}{6}}=\boxed{0.498\text{ mm}}.$$

P37.71 Superposing the two vectors, $E_R=|\mathbf{E}_1+\mathbf{E}_2|$

$$E_R=|\mathbf{E}_1+\mathbf{E}_2|=\sqrt{\left(E_0+\frac{E_0}{3}\cos\phi\right)^2+\left(\frac{E_0}{3}\sin\phi\right)^2}=\sqrt{E_0^2+\frac{2}{3}E_0^2\cos\phi+\frac{E_0^2}{9}\cos^2\phi+\frac{E_0^2}{9}\sin^2\phi}$$

$$E_R=\sqrt{\frac{10}{9}E_0^2+\frac{2}{3}E_0^2\cos\phi}$$

Since intensity is proportional to the square of the amplitude,

$$I=\frac{10}{9}I_{\text{max}}+\frac{2}{3}I_{\text{max}}\cos\phi.$$

Using the trigonometric identity $\cos\phi=2\cos^2\frac{\phi}{2}-1$, this becomes

$$I=\frac{10}{9}I_{\text{max}}+\frac{2}{3}I_{\text{max}}\left(2\cos^2\frac{\phi}{2}-1\right)=\frac{4}{9}I_{\text{max}}+\frac{4}{3}I_{\text{max}}\cos^2\frac{\phi}{2},$$

or $$\boxed{I=\frac{4}{9}I_{\text{max}}\left(1+3\cos^2\frac{\phi}{2}\right)}.$$

ANSWERS TO EVEN PROBLEMS

P37.2 515 nm

P37.4 (a) 36.2°; (b) 5.08 cm; (c) 508 THz

P37.6 maxima at 0°, 29.1°, 76.3°; minima at 14.1° and 46.8°

P37.8 36.2 cm

P37.10 641

P37.12 6.33 mm/s

P37.14 see the solution

P37.16 (a) 1.29 rad; (b) 99.8 nm

P37.18 0.968

P37.20 (a) see the solution; (b) 9.00

P37.22 (a) $2.88E_0$ at 0.349 rad; (b) $2.00E_0$ at $\frac{\pi}{3}$ rad; (c) 0; (d) E_0 at $\frac{3\pi}{2}$ rad

P37.24 see the solution

P37.26 $x_1 - x_2 = \left(m - \frac{1}{48}\right)\lambda$ where $m = 0, 1, 2, 3, \ldots$

P37.28 see the solution

P37.30 612 nm

P37.32 512 nm

P37.34 96.2 nm

P37.36 (a) 238 nm; (b) λ increase; (c) 328 nm

P37.38 1.31

P37.40 1.20 mm

P37.42 449 nm; blue

P37.44 (a) see the solution; (b) 2.74 m

P37.46 number of antinodes = number of constructive interference zones = 1 plus 2 times the greatest positive integer $\le \frac{d}{\lambda}$
number of nodes = number of destructive interference zones = 2 times the greatest positive integer $< \left(\frac{d}{\lambda} + \frac{1}{2}\right)$

P37.48 $\frac{\lambda}{2(n-1)}$

P37.50 5.00 km^2

P37.52 2.50 mm

P37.54 113

P37.56 115 nm

P37.58 (a) see the solution; (b) 266 nm

P37.60 see the solution

P37.62 see the solution

P37.64 (a) 14.7 μm; (b) 1.53 cm; (c) −16.0 m

P37.66 $7.99\sin(\omega t + 4.44 \text{ rad})$

P37.68 130 nm

P37.70 0.498 mm

38

Diffraction Patterns and Polarization

CHAPTER OUTLINE

ANSWERS TO QUESTIONS

Q38.1 Audible sound has wavelengths on the order of meters or centimeters, while visible light has a wavelength on the order of half a micrometer. In this world of breadbox-sized objects, $\frac{\lambda}{a}$ is large for sound, and sound diffracts around behind walls with doorways. But $\frac{\lambda}{a}$ is a tiny fraction for visible light passing ordinary-size objects or apertures, so light changes its direction by only very small angles when it diffracts.

Another way of phrasing the answer: We can see by a small angle around a small obstacle or around the edge of a small opening. The side fringes in Figure 38.1 and the Arago spot in the center of Figure 38.3 show this diffraction. We cannot always hear around corners. Out-of-doors, away from reflecting surfaces, have someone a few meters distant face away from you and whisper. The high-frequency, short-wavelength, information-carrying components of the sound do not diffract around his head enough for you to understand his words.

Q38.2 The wavelength of light is extremely small in comparison to the dimensions of your hand, so the diffraction of light around an obstacle the size of your hand is totally negligible. However, sound waves have wavelengths that are comparable to the dimensions of the hand or even larger. Therefore, significant diffraction of sound waves occurs around hand-sized obstacles.

Q38.3 If you are using an extended light source, the gray area at the edge of the shadow is the penumbra. A bug looking up from there would see the light source partly but not entirely blocked by the book. If you use a point source of light, hold it and the book motionless, and look at very small angles out from the geometrical edge of the shadow, you may see a series of bright and dark bands produced by diffraction of light at the straight edge, as shown in the diagram.

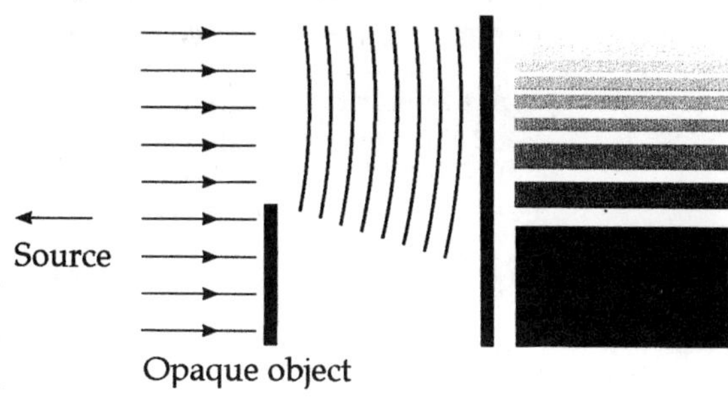

FIG. Q38.3

Q38.4 An AM radio wave has wavelength on the order of $\frac{3\times10^{8}\ \text{m/s}}{1\times10^{6}\ \text{s}^{-1}}\sim 300\ \text{m}$. This is large compared to the width of the mouth of a tunnel, so the AM radio waves can reflect from the surrounding ground as if the hole were not there. (In the same way, a metal screen forming the dish of a radio telescope can reflect radio waves as if it were solid, and a hole-riddled screen in the door of a microwave oven keeps the microwaves inside.) The wave does not "see" the hole. Very little of the radio wave energy enters the tunnel, and the AM radio signal fades. An FM radio wave has wavelength a hundred times smaller, on the order of a few meters. This is smaller than the size of the tunnel opening, so the wave can readily enter the opening. (On the other hand, the long wavelength of AM radio waves lets them diffract more around obstacles. Long-wavelength waves can change direction more in passing hills or large buildings, so in some experiments FM fades more than AM.)

Q38.5 The intensity of the light coming through the slit decreases, as you would expect. The central maximum increases in width as the width of the slit decreases. In the condition $\sin\theta=\frac{\lambda}{a}$ for destructive interference on each side of the central maximum, θ increases as a decreases.

Q38.6 It is shown in the correct orientation. If the horizontal width of the opening is equal to or less than the wavelength of the sound, then the equation $a\sin\theta=(1)\lambda$ has the solution $\theta=90°$, or has no solution. The central diffraction maximum covers the whole seaward side. If the vertical height of the opening is large compared to the wavelength, then the angle in $a\sin\theta=(1)\lambda$ will be small, and the central diffraction maximum will form a thin horizontal sheet.

Q38.7 The speaker is mounted incorrectly—it should be rotated by 90°. The speaker is mounted with its narrower dimension vertical. That means that the sound will diffract more vertically than it does horizontally. Mounting the speaker so that its thinner dimension is horizontal will give more diffraction spreading in the horizontal plane, broadcasting "important" information to the troops, instead of to the birds in the air and the worms in the ground, as the speaker was mounted in the movie.

Q38.8 We apply the equation $\theta_m=\frac{1.22\lambda}{D}$ for the resolution of a circular aperture, the pupil of your eye. Suppose your dark-adapted eye has pupil diameter $D=5\ \text{mm}$. An average wavelength for visible light is $\lambda=550\ \text{nm}$. Suppose the headlights are 2 m apart and the car is a distance L away. Then $\theta_m=\frac{2\ \text{m}}{L}=1.22\times1.1\times10^{-4}$ so $L\sim 10\ \text{km}$. The actual distance is less than this because the variable-temperature air between you and the car makes the light refract unpredictably. The headlights twinkle like stars.

Q38.9 Consider incident light nearly parallel to the horizontal ruler. Suppose it scatters from bumps at distance d apart to produce a diffraction pattern on a vertical wall a distance L away. At a point of height y, where $\theta=\frac{y}{L}$ gives the scattering angle θ, the character of the interference is determined by the shift δ between beams scattered by adjacent bumps, where $\delta=\frac{d}{\cos\theta}-d$. Bright spots appear for $\delta=m\lambda$, where 0, 1, 2, 3, ... For small θ, these equations combine and reduce to $m\lambda=\frac{y_m^2 d}{2L^2}$. Measurement of the heights y_m of bright spots allows calculation of the wavelength of the light.

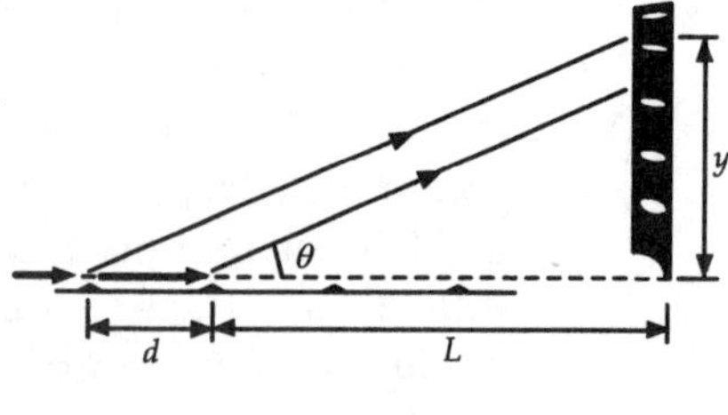

FIG. Q38.9

Q38.10 Yes, but no diffraction effects are observed because the separation distance between adjacent ribs is so much greater than the wavelength of x-rays. Diffraction does not limit the resolution of an x-ray image. Diffraction might sometimes limit the resolution of an ultrasonogram.

Q38.11 Vertical. Glare, as usually encountered when driving or boating, is horizontally polarized. Reflected light is polarized in the same plane as the reflecting surface. As unpolarized light hits a shiny horizontal surface, the atoms on the surface absorb and then reemit the light energy as a reflection. We can model the surface as containing conduction electrons free to vibrate easily along the surface, but not to move easily out of surface. The light emitted from a vibrating electron is partially or completely polarized along the plane of vibration, thus horizontally.

Q38.12 The earth has an atmosphere, while the moon does not. The nitrogen and oxygen molecules in the earth's atmosphere are of the right size to scatter short-wavelength (blue) light especially well, while there is nothing surrounding the moon to scatter light.

Q38.13 The little particles of dust diffusely reflect light from the light beam. Note that this is not necessarily *scattering*. Scattering is a resonance phenomenon—as when the O_2 and N_2 molecules in our atmosphere scatter blue light more than red. In general, light is visible when it enters your eye. Your eyes and brain are well prepared to make you think on a subconscious level that you can 'see' where light is coming from or sometimes 'see' light going past you, but really you see only light entering your eye.

Q38.14 Light from the sky is partially polarized. Light from the blue sky that is polarized at 90° to the polarization axis of the glasses will be blocked, making the sky look darker as compared to the clouds.

Q38.15 First think about the glass without a coin and about one particular point P on the screen. We can divide up the area of the glass into ring-shaped zones centered on the line joining P and the light source, with successive zones contributing alternately in-phase and out-of-phase with the light that takes the straight-line path to P. These Fresnel zones have nearly equal areas. An outer zone contributes only slightly less to the total wave disturbance at P than does the central circular zone. Now insert the coin. If P is in line with its center, the coin will block off the light from some particular number of zones. The first unblocked zone around its circumference will send light to P with significant amplitude. Zones farther out will predominantly interfere destructively with each other, and the Arago spot is bright. Slightly off the axis there is nearly complete destructive interference, so most of the geometrical shadow is dark. A bug on the screen crawling out past the edge of the geometrical shadow would in effect see the central few zones coming out of eclipse. As the light from them interferes alternately constructively and destructively, the bug moves through bright and dark fringes on the screen. The diffraction pattern is shown in Figure 38.3 in the text.

Q38.16 Since obsidian glass is opaque, a standard method of measuring incidence and refraction angles and using Snell's Law is ineffective. Reflect unpolarized light from the horizontal surface of the obsidian through a vertically polarized filter. Change the angle of incidence until you observe that none of the reflected light is transmitted through the filter. This means that the reflected light is completely horizontally polarized, and that the incidence and reflection angles are the polarization angle. The tangent of the polarization angle is the index of refraction of the obsidian.

Q38.17 The fine hair blocks off light that would otherwise go through a fine slit and produce a diffraction pattern on a distant screen. The width of the central maximum in the pattern is inversely proportional to the distance across the slit. When the hair is in place, it subtracts the same diffraction pattern from the projected disk of laser light. The hair produces a diffraction minimum that crosses the bright circle on the screen. The width of the minimum is inversely proportional to the diameter of the hair. The central minimum is flanked by narrower maxima and minima. Measure the width $2y$ of the central minimum between the maxima bracketing it, and use Equation 38.1 in the form $\frac{y}{L}=\frac{\lambda}{a}$ to find the width a of the hair.

Q38.18 The condition for constructive interference is that the three radio signals arrive at the city in phase. We know the speed of the waves (it is the speed of light c), the angular bearing θ of the city east of north from the broadcast site, and the distance d between adjacent towers. The wave from the westernmost tower must travel an extra distance $2d\sin\theta$ to reach the city, compared to the signal from the eastern tower. For each cycle of the carrier wave, the western antenna would transmit first, the center antenna after a time delay $\frac{d\sin\theta}{c}$, and the eastern antenna after an additional equal time delay.

SOLUTIONS TO PROBLEMS

Section 38.1 Introduction to Diffraction Patterns

Section 38.2 Diffraction Patterns from Narrow Slits

P38.1 $\sin\theta=\frac{\lambda}{a}=\frac{6.328\times10^{-7}}{3.00\times10^{-4}}=2.11\times10^{-3}$

$$\frac{y}{1.00\text{ m}}=\tan\theta\approx\sin\theta=\theta\ \text{(for small }\theta)$$

$$2y=\boxed{4.22\text{ mm}}$$

P38.2 The positions of the first-order minima are $\frac{y}{L}\approx\sin\theta=\pm\frac{\lambda}{a}$. Thus, the spacing between these two minima is $\Delta y=2\left(\frac{\lambda}{a}\right)L$ and the wavelength is

$$\lambda=\left(\frac{\Delta y}{2}\right)\left(\frac{a}{L}\right)=\left(\frac{4.10\times10^{-3}\text{ m}}{2}\right)\left(\frac{0.550\times10^{-3}\text{ m}}{2.06\text{ m}}\right)=\boxed{547\text{ nm}}.$$

P38.3 $\frac{y}{L}\approx\sin\theta=\frac{m\lambda}{a}$ $\qquad\Delta y=3.00\times10^{-3}\text{ nm}$

$\Delta m=3-1=2$ and $a=\frac{\Delta m\lambda L}{\Delta y}$

$$a=\frac{2(690\times10^{-9}\text{ m})(0.500\text{ m})}{(3.00\times10^{-3}\text{ m})}=\boxed{2.30\times10^{-4}\text{ m}}$$

P38.4 For destructive interference,

$$\sin\theta = m\frac{\lambda}{a} = \frac{\lambda}{a} = \frac{5.00\text{ cm}}{36.0\text{ cm}} = 0.139$$

and $\theta = 7.98°$

$$\frac{d}{L} = \tan\theta$$

gives $d = L\tan\theta = (6.50\text{ m})\tan 7.98° = 0.912\text{ m}$

$$d = \boxed{91.2\text{ cm}}\,.$$

P38.5 If the speed of sound is 340 m/s, $\lambda = \frac{v}{f} = \frac{340\text{ m/s}}{650\text{ s}^{-1}} = 0.523\text{ m}$.

Diffraction minima occur at angles described by $a\sin\theta = m\lambda$

$(1.10\text{ m})\sin\theta_1 = 1(0.523\text{ m})$ $\theta_1 = 28.4°$

$(1.10\text{ m})\sin\theta_2 = 2(0.523\text{ m})$ $\theta_2 = 72.0°$

$(1.10\text{ m})\sin\theta_3 = 3(0.523\text{ m})$ θ_3 nonexistent

Maxima appear straight ahead at $\boxed{0°}$ and left and right at an angle given approximately by

$(1.10\text{ m})\sin\theta_x = 1.5(0.523\text{ m})$ $\theta_x \boxed{\approx 46°}$.

There is no solution to $a\sin\theta = 2.5\lambda$, so our answer is already complete, with $\boxed{\text{three}}$ sound maxima.

P38.6 (a) $\sin\theta = \frac{y}{L} = \frac{m\lambda}{a}$

Therefore, for first minimum, $m = 1$ and

$$L = \frac{ay}{m\lambda} = \frac{(7.50\times10^{-4}\text{ m})(8.50\times10^{-4}\text{ m})}{(1)(587.5\times10^{-9}\text{ m})} = \boxed{1.09\text{ m}}\,.$$

(b) $w = 2y_1$ yields $y_1 = 0.850$ mm

$$w = 2(0.850\times10^{-3}\text{ m}) = \boxed{1.70\text{ mm}}$$

***P38.7** The rectangular patch on the wall is wider than it is tall. The aperture will be taller than it is wide. For horizontal spreading we have

$$\tan\theta_{\text{width}} = \frac{y_{\text{width}}}{L} = \frac{0.110\text{ m}/2}{4.5\text{ m}} = 0.012\,2$$

$$a_{\text{width}} \sin\theta_{\text{width}} = 1\lambda$$

$$a_{\text{width}} = \frac{632.8\times10^{-9}\text{ m}}{0.012\,2} = \boxed{5.18\times10^{-5}\text{ m}}$$

For vertical spreading, similarly

$$\tan\theta_{\text{height}} = \frac{0.006\text{ m}/2}{4.5\text{ m}} = 0.000\,667$$

$$a_{\text{height}} = \frac{1\lambda}{\sin\theta_h} = \frac{632.8\times10^{-9}\text{ m}}{0.000\,667} = \boxed{9.49\times10^{-4}\text{ m}}$$

P38.8 Equation 38.1 states that $\sin\theta = \frac{m\lambda}{a}$, where $m = \pm1, \pm2, \pm3, \ldots$. The requirement for $m = 1$ is from an analysis of the extra path distance traveled by ray 1 compared to ray 3 in Figure 38.5. This extra distance must be equal to $\frac{\lambda}{2}$ for destructive interference. When the source rays approach the slit at an angle β, there is a distance added to the path difference (of ray 1 compared to ray 3) of $\frac{a}{2}\sin\beta$ Then, for destructive interference,

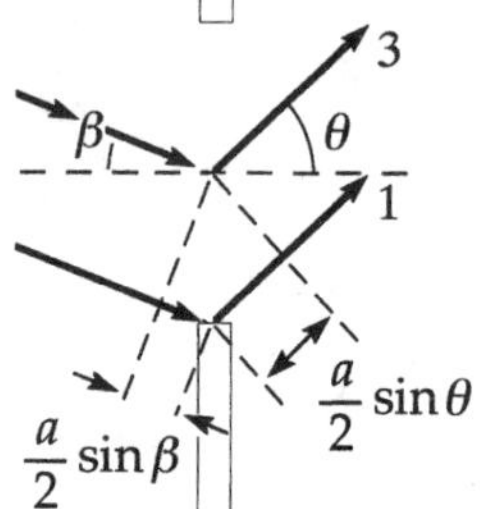

FIG. P38.8

$$\frac{a}{2}\sin\beta + \frac{a}{2}\sin\theta = \frac{\lambda}{2} \text{ so } \sin\theta = \frac{\lambda}{a} - \sin\beta.$$

Dividing the slit into 4 parts leads to the 2nd order minimum: $\sin\theta = \frac{2\lambda}{a} - \sin\beta.$

Dividing the slit into 6 parts gives the third order minimum: $\sin\theta = \frac{3\lambda}{a} - \sin\beta.$

Generalizing, we obtain the condition for the mth order minimum: $\sin\theta = \frac{m\lambda}{a} - \sin\beta.$

P38.9 $\sin\theta \approx \frac{y}{L} = \frac{4.10\times10^{-3}\text{ m}}{1.20\text{ m}}$

$$\frac{\beta}{2} = \frac{\pi a\sin\theta}{\lambda} = \frac{\pi\left(4.00\times10^{-4}\text{ m}\right)}{546.1\times10^{-9}\text{ m}}\left(\frac{4.10\times10^{-3}\text{ m}}{1.20\text{ m}}\right) = 7.86\text{ rad}$$

$$\frac{I}{I_{\max}} = \left[\frac{\sin(\beta/2)}{\beta/2}\right]^2 = \left[\frac{\sin(7.86)}{7.86}\right]^2 = \boxed{1.62\times10^{-2}}$$

38.10 (a) Double-slit interference maxima are at angles given by $d\sin\theta = m\lambda$.

For $m = 0$, $\theta_0 = \boxed{0°}$.

For $m = 1$, $(2.80\ \mu\text{m})\sin\theta = 1(0.501\,5\ \mu\text{m})$: $\theta_1 = \sin^{-1}(0.179) = \boxed{10.3°}$.

Similarly, for $m = 2, 3, 4, 5$ and 6, $\theta_2 = \boxed{21.0°}$, $\theta_3 = \boxed{32.5°}$, $\theta_4 = \boxed{45.8°}$,

$\theta_5 = \boxed{63.6°}$, and $\theta_6 = \sin^{-1}(1.07) =$ nonexistent.

Thus, there are $5 + 5 + 1 = \boxed{\text{11 directions for interference maxima}}$.

(b) We check for missing orders by looking for single-slit diffraction minima, at $a\sin\theta = m\lambda$.

For $m = 1$, $(0.700\ \mu\text{m})\sin\theta = 1(0.501\,5\ \mu\text{m})$ and $\theta_1 = 45.8°$.

Thus, there is no bright fringe at this angle. There are only $\boxed{\text{nine bright fringes}}$, at

$\boxed{\theta = 0°, \pm 10.3°, \pm 21.0°, \pm 32.5°, \text{ and } \pm 63.6°}$.

(c) $$I = I_{max}\left[\frac{\sin(\pi a\sin\theta/\lambda)}{\pi\sin\theta/\lambda}\right]^2$$

At $\theta = 0°$, $\frac{\sin\theta}{\theta} \to 1$ and $\frac{I}{I_{max}} \to \boxed{1.00}$.

At $\theta = 10.3°$, $$\frac{\pi a\sin\theta}{\lambda} = \frac{\pi(0.700\ \mu\text{m})\sin 10.3°}{0.501\,5\ \mu\text{m}} = 0.785\text{ rad} = 45.0°$$

$$\frac{I}{I_{max}} = \left[\frac{\sin 45.0°}{0.785}\right]^2 = \boxed{0.811}.$$

Similarly, at $\theta = 21.0°$, $\frac{\pi a\sin\theta}{\lambda} = 1.57\text{ rad} = 90.0°$ and $\frac{I}{I_{max}} = \boxed{0.405}$.

At $\theta = 32.5°$, $\frac{\pi a\sin\theta}{\lambda} = 2.36\text{ rad} = 135°$ and $\frac{I}{I_{max}} = \boxed{0.090\,1}$.

At $\theta = 63.6°$, $\frac{\pi a\sin\theta}{\lambda} = 3.93\text{ rad} = 225°$ and $\frac{I}{I_{max}} = \boxed{0.032\,4}$.

Section 38.3 **Resolution of Single-Slit and Circular Apertures**

P38.11 $$\sin\theta = \frac{\lambda}{a} = \frac{5.00\times10^{-7}\text{ m}}{5.00\times10^{-4}} = \boxed{1.00\times10^{-3}\text{ rad}}$$

P38.12 $\theta_{\min} = \frac{y}{L} = 1.22\frac{\lambda}{D}$

y = radius of star-image
L = length of eye
λ = 500 nm
D = pupil diameter
θ = half angle

$$y = \frac{(1.22)(5.00\times10^{-7})(0.030\,0)}{7.00\times10^{-3}} = \boxed{2.61\ \mu\text{m}}$$

P38.13 Undergoing diffraction from a circular opening, the beam spreads into a cone of half-angle

$$\theta_{\min} = 1.22\frac{\lambda}{D} = 1.22\left(\frac{632.8\times10^{-9}\ \text{m}}{0.005\,00\ \text{m}}\right) = 1.54\times10^{-4}\ \text{rad}.$$

The radius of the beam ten kilometers away is, from the definition of radian measure,

$$r_{\text{beam}} = \theta_{\min}\left(1.00\times10^{4}\ \text{m}\right) = 1.544\ \text{m}$$

and its diameter is $d_{\text{beam}} = 2r_{\text{beam}} = \boxed{3.09\ \text{m}}$.

***P38.14** When you are at the maximum range, the elves' eyes will be resolved by Rayleigh's criterion:

$$\frac{d}{L} = \theta_{\min} = 1.22\frac{\lambda}{D}$$

$$\frac{0.100\ \text{m}}{L} = 1.22\frac{660\times10^{-9}\ \text{m}}{7\times10^{-3}\ \text{m}} = 1.15\times10^{-4}$$

$$L = \frac{0.1\ \text{m}}{1.15\times10^{-4}} = \boxed{869\ \text{m}}$$

***P38.15** By Rayleigh's criterion: $\theta_{\min} = \frac{d}{L} = 1.22\frac{\lambda}{D}$, where $\theta_{\min}$ is the smallest angular separation of two objects for which they are resolved by an aperture of diameter D, d is the separation of the two objects, and L is the maximum distance of the aperture from the two objects at which they can be resolved.

Two objects can be resolved if their angular separation is greater than $\theta_{\min}$. Thus, $\theta_{\min}$ should be as small as possible. Therefore, the smaller of the two given wavelengths is easier to resolve, i.e. $\boxed{\text{violet}}$.

$$L = \frac{Dd}{1.22\lambda} = \frac{(5.20\times10^{-3}\ \text{m})(2.80\times10^{-2}\ \text{m})}{1.22\lambda} = \frac{1.193\times10^{-4}\ \text{m}^2}{\lambda}$$

Thus $L = 186$ m for $\lambda = 640$ nm, and $L = 271$ m for $\lambda = 440$ nm. The viewer can resolve adjacent tubes of violet in the range $\boxed{186\ \text{m to } 271\ \text{m}}$, but cannot resolve adjacent tubes of red in this range.

P38.16 $\theta_{\min} = 1.22\frac{\lambda}{D} = \frac{d}{L}$ $\quad 1.22\left(\frac{5.80\times10^{-7}\ \text{m}}{4.00\times10^{-3}\ \text{m}}\right) = \frac{d}{1.80\ \text{mi}}\left(\frac{1\ \text{mi}}{1\,609\ \text{m}}\right)$ $\quad d = \boxed{0.512\ \text{m}}$

The shortening of the wavelength inside the patriot's eye does not change the answer.

P38.17 By Rayleigh's criterion, two dots separated center-to-center by 2.00 mm would overlap

when $\theta_{\min} = \frac{d}{L} = 1.22\frac{\lambda}{D}$.

Thus, $L = \frac{dD}{1.22\lambda} = \frac{(2.00\times10^{-3}\text{ m})(4.00\times10^{-3}\text{ m})}{1.22(500\times10^{-9}\text{ m})} = \boxed{13.1\text{ m}}$.

P38.18 $D = 1.22\frac{\lambda}{\theta_{\min}} = \frac{1.22(5.00\times10^{-7})}{1.00\times10^{-5}}\text{ m} = \boxed{6.10\text{ cm}}$

***P38.19** The concave mirror of the spy satellite is probably about 2 m in diameter, and is surely not more than 5 m in diameter. That is the size of the largest piece of glass successfully cast to a precise shape, for the mirror of the Hale telescope on Mount Palomar. If the spy satellite had a larger mirror, its manufacture could not be kept secret, and it would be visible from the ground. Outer space is probably closer than your state capitol, but the satellite is surely above 200-km altitude, for reasonably low air friction. We find the distance between barely resolvable objects at a distance of 200 km, seen in yellow light through a 5-m aperture:

$$\frac{y}{L} = 1.22\frac{\lambda}{D}$$

$$y = (200\,000\text{ m})(1.22)\left(\frac{6\times10^{-7}\text{ m}}{5\text{ m}}\right) = 3\text{ cm}$$

(Considering atmospheric seeing caused by variations in air density and temperature, the distance between barely resolvable objects is more like $(200\,000\text{ m})(1\text{ s})\left(\frac{1°}{3\,600\text{ s}}\right)\left(\frac{\pi\text{ rad}}{180°}\right) = 97\text{ cm}$.) Thus the snooping spy satellite cannot see the difference between III and II or IV on a license plate. It cannot count coins spilled on a sidewalk, much less read the date on them.

P38.20 $1.22\frac{\lambda}{D} = \frac{d}{L}$ $\lambda = \frac{c}{f} = 0.020\,0\text{ m}$

$D = 2.10\text{ m}$ $L = 9\,000\text{ m}$

$$d = 1.22\frac{(0.020\,0\text{ m})(9\,000\text{ m})}{2.10\text{ m}} = \boxed{105\text{ m}}$$

P38.21 $\theta_{\min} = 1.22\frac{\lambda}{D} = 1.22\frac{(2.00\text{ m})}{(10.0\text{ m})} = \boxed{0.244\text{ rad} = 14.0°}$

P38.22 $L = 88.6\times10^{9}\text{ m}$, $D = 0.300\text{ m}$, $\lambda = 590\times10^{-9}\text{ m}$

(a) $1.22\frac{\lambda}{D} = \theta_{\min} = \boxed{2.40\times10^{-6}\text{ rad}}$

(b) $d = \theta_{\min}L = \boxed{213\text{ km}}$

Section 38.4 **The Diffraction Grating**

P38.23 $d = \dfrac{1.00 \text{ cm}}{2\,000} = \dfrac{1.00 \times 10^{-2} \text{ m}}{2\,000} = 5.00\ \mu\text{m}$

$$\sin\theta = \frac{m\lambda}{d} = \frac{1\left(640 \times 10^{-9} \text{ m}\right)}{5.00 \times 10^{-6} \text{ m}} = 0.128 \qquad \theta = \boxed{7.35°}$$

P38.24 The principal maxima are defined by

$$d\sin\theta = m\lambda \qquad m = 0, 1, 2, \ldots.$$

For $m = 1$, $\qquad \lambda = d\sin\theta$

where θ is the angle between the central ($m = 0$) and the first order ($m = 1$) maxima. The value of θ can be determined from the information given about the distance between maxima and the grating-to-screen distance. From the figure,

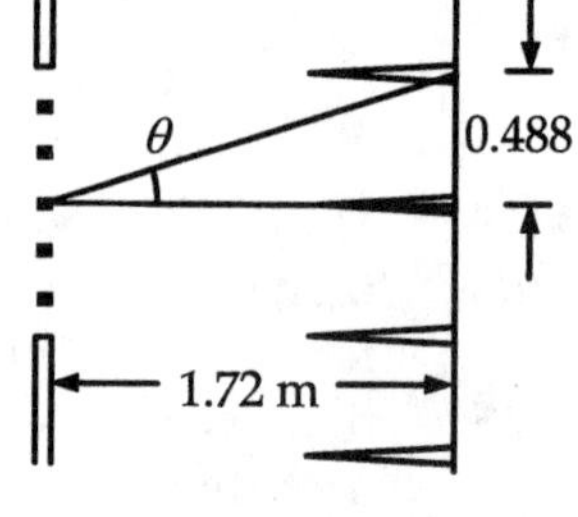

FIG. P38.24

$$\tan\theta = \frac{0.488 \text{ m}}{1.72 \text{ m}} = 0.284$$

so $\qquad \theta = 15.8°$

and $\qquad \sin\theta = 0.273$.

The distance between grating "slits" equals the reciprocal of the number of grating lines per centimeter

$$d = \frac{1}{5\,310 \text{ cm}^{-1}} = 1.88 \times 10^{-4} \text{ cm} = 1.88 \times 10^{3} \text{ nm}.$$

The wavelength is $\qquad \lambda = d\sin\theta = \left(1.88 \times 10^{3} \text{ nm}\right)(0.273) = \boxed{514 \text{ nm}}$.

P38.25 The grating spacing is $\qquad d = \dfrac{1.00 \times 10^{-2} \text{ m}}{4\,500} = 2.22 \times 10^{-6} \text{ m}$.

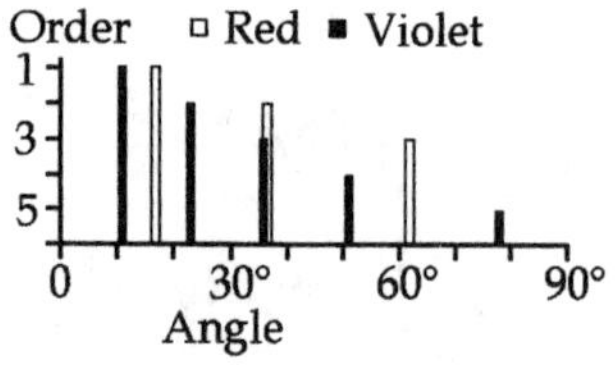

In the 1st-order spectrum, diffraction angles are given by

$\sin\theta = \dfrac{\lambda}{d}$: $\qquad \sin\theta_1 = \dfrac{656 \times 10^{-9} \text{ m}}{2.22 \times 10^{-6} \text{ m}} = 0.295$

so that for red $\qquad \theta_1 = 17.17°$

and for violet $\qquad \sin\theta_2 = \dfrac{434 \times 10^{-9} \text{ m}}{2.22 \times 10^{-6} \text{ m}} = 0.195$

so that $\qquad \theta_2 = 11.26°$.

FIG. P38.25

The angular separation is in first-order, $\qquad \Delta\theta = 17.17° - 11.26° = \boxed{5.91°}$.

In the second-order spectrum, $\qquad \Delta\theta = \sin^{-1}\left(\dfrac{2\lambda_1}{d}\right) - \sin^{-1}\left(\dfrac{2\lambda_2}{d}\right) = \boxed{13.2°}$.

Again, in the third order, $\qquad \Delta\theta = \sin^{-1}\left(\dfrac{3\lambda_1}{d}\right) - \sin^{-1}\left(\dfrac{3\lambda_2}{d}\right) = \boxed{26.5°}$.

Since the red does not appear in the fourth-order spectrum, the answer is complete.

P38.26 $\sin\theta = 0.350$: $d = \frac{\lambda}{\sin\theta} = \frac{632.8 \text{ nm}}{0.350} = 1.81 \times 10^3 \text{ nm}$

Line spacing $= \boxed{1.81\ \mu\text{m}}$

P38.27 (a) $d = \frac{1}{3\,660 \text{ lines/cm}} = 2.732 \times 10^{-4} \text{ cm} = 2.732 \times 10^{-6} \text{ m} = 2\,732 \text{ nm}$

$\lambda = \frac{d\sin\theta}{m}$: At $\theta = 10.09°$ $\lambda = \boxed{478.7 \text{ nm}}$

At $\theta = 13.71°$, $\lambda = \boxed{647.6 \text{ nm}}$

At $\theta = 14.77°$, $\lambda = \boxed{696.6 \text{ nm}}$

(b) $d = \frac{\lambda}{\sin\theta_1}$ and $2\lambda = d\sin\theta_2$ so $\sin\theta_2 = \frac{2\lambda}{d} = \frac{2\lambda}{\lambda/\sin\theta_1} = 2\sin\theta_1$.

Therefore, if $\theta_1 = 10.09°$ then $\sin\theta_2 = 2\sin(10.09°)$ gives $\theta_2 = \boxed{20.51°}$.

Similarly, for $\theta_1 = 13.71°$, $\theta_2 = \boxed{28.30°}$ and for $\theta_1 = 14.77°$, $\theta_2 = \boxed{30.66°}$.

P38.28 $\sin\theta = \frac{m\lambda}{d}$

Therefore, taking the ends of the visible spectrum to be $\lambda_v = 400$ nm and $\lambda_r = 750$ nm, the ends the different order spectra are:

End of second order: $\sin\theta_{2r} = \frac{2\lambda_r}{d} = \frac{1\,500 \text{ nm}}{d}$.

Start of third order: $\sin\theta_{3v} = \frac{3\lambda_v}{d} = \frac{1\,200 \text{ nm}}{d}$.

Thus, it is seen that $\boxed{\theta_{2r} > \theta_{3v} \text{ and these orders must overlap}}$ regardless of the value of the grating spacing *d*.

P38.29 (a) From Equation 38.12, $R = Nm$ where $N = (3\,000 \text{ lines/cm})(4.00 \text{ cm}) = 1.20 \times 10^4$ lines.

In the 1st order, $R = (1)(1.20 \times 10^4 \text{ lines}) = \boxed{1.20 \times 10^4}$.

In the 2nd order, $R = (2)(1.20 \times 10^4 \text{ lines}) = \boxed{2.40 \times 10^4}$.

In the 3rd order, $R = (3)(1.20 \times 10^4 \text{ lines}) = \boxed{3.60 \times 10^4}$.

(b) From Equation 38.11, $R = \frac{\lambda}{\Delta\lambda}$:

In the 3rd order, $\Delta\lambda = \frac{\lambda}{R} = \frac{400 \text{ nm}}{3.60 \times 10^4} = 0.011\,1 \text{ nm} = \boxed{11.1 \text{ pm}}$.

*P38.30 For a side maximum, $\tan\theta = \frac{y}{L} = \frac{0.4\ \mu\text{m}}{6.9\ \mu\text{m}}$

$$\theta = 3.32°$$

$d\sin\theta = m\lambda$ $\quad d = \frac{(1)(780\times10^{-9}\ \text{m})}{\sin 3.32°} = 13.5\ \mu\text{m}.$

The number of grooves per millimeter $= \frac{1\times10^{-3}\ \text{m}}{13.5\times10^{-6}\ \text{m}} = \boxed{74.2}$.

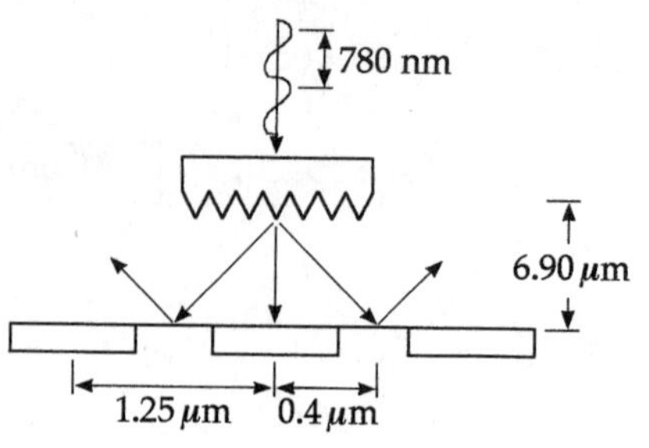

FIG. P38.30

P38.31 (a) $Nm = \frac{\lambda}{\Delta\lambda}$ $\quad N(1) = \frac{531.7\ \text{nm}}{0.19\ \text{nm}} = \boxed{2\,800}$

(b) $\frac{1.32\times10^{-2}\ \text{m}}{2\,800} = \boxed{4.72\ \mu\text{m}}$

P38.32 $d = \frac{1}{4\,200/\text{cm}} = 2.38\times10^{-6}\ \text{m} = 2\,380\ \text{nm}.$

$d\sin\theta = m\lambda$ or $\theta = \sin^{-1}\left(\frac{m\lambda}{d}\right)$ and $y = L\tan\theta = L\tan\left[\sin^{-1}\left(\frac{m\lambda}{d}\right)\right]$.

Thus, $\Delta y = L\left\{\tan\left[\sin^{-1}\left(\frac{m\lambda_2}{d}\right)\right] - \tan\left[\sin^{-1}\left(\frac{m\lambda_1}{d}\right)\right]\right\}$.

For $m = 1$, $\Delta y = (2.00\ \text{m})\left\{\tan\left[\sin^{-1}\left(\frac{589.6}{2\,380}\right)\right] - \tan\left[\sin^{-1}\left(\frac{589}{2\,380}\right)\right]\right\} = 0.554\ \text{mm}$.

For $m = 2$, $\Delta y = (2.00\ \text{m})\left\{\tan\left[\sin^{-1}\left(\frac{2(589.6)}{2\,380}\right)\right] - \tan\left[\sin^{-1}\left(\frac{2(589)}{2\,380}\right)\right]\right\} = 1.54\ \text{mm}$.

For $m = 3$, $\Delta y = (2.00\ \text{m})\left\{\tan\left[\sin^{-1}\left(\frac{3(589.6)}{2\,380}\right)\right] - \tan\left[\sin^{-1}\left(\frac{3(589)}{2\,380}\right)\right]\right\} = 5.04\ \text{mm}$.

Thus, the observed order must be $\boxed{m = 2}$.

P38.33 $d = \dfrac{1.00\times10^{-3}\text{ m/mm}}{250\text{ lines/mm}} = 4.00\times10^{-6}\text{ m} = 4\,000\text{ nm}$ $\qquad d\sin\theta = m\lambda \Rightarrow m = \dfrac{d\sin\theta}{\lambda}$

(a) The number of times a complete order is seen is the same as the number of orders in which the long wavelength limit is visible.

$$m_{\text{max}} = \frac{d\sin\theta_{\text{max}}}{\lambda} = \frac{(4\,000\text{ nm})\sin 90.0°}{700\text{ nm}} = 5.71$$

or $\boxed{\text{5 orders is the maximum}}$.

(b) The highest order in which the violet end of the spectrum can be seen is:

$$m_{\text{max}} = \frac{d\sin\theta_{\text{max}}}{\lambda} = \frac{(4\,000\text{ nm})\sin 90.0°}{400\text{ nm}} = 10.0$$

or $\boxed{\text{10 orders in the short-wavelength region}}$.

***P38.34** (a) The several narrow parallel slits make a diffraction grating. The zeroth- and first- order maxima are separated according to

$d\sin\theta = (1)\lambda \qquad \sin\theta = \dfrac{\lambda}{d} = \dfrac{632.8\times10^{-9}\text{ m}}{1.2\times10^{-3}\text{ m}}$

$\theta = \sin^{-1}(0.000\,527) = 0.000\,527\text{ rad}$

$y = L\tan\theta = (1.40\text{ m})(0.000\,527) = \boxed{0.738\text{ mm}}$.

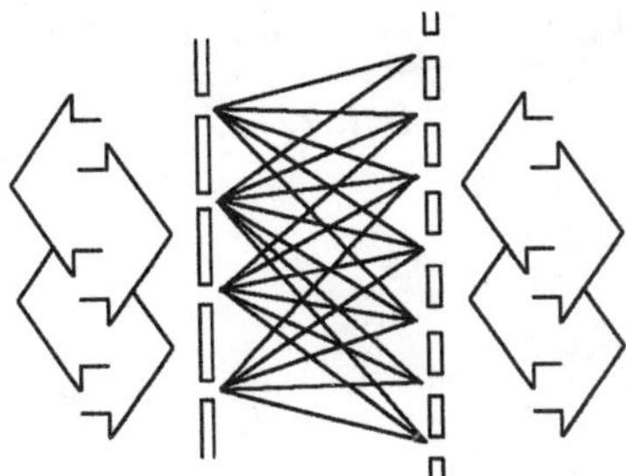

FIG. P38.34

(b) Many equally spaced transparent lines appear on the film. It is itself a diffraction grating. When the same light is sent through the film, it produces interference maxima separated according to

$d\sin\theta = (1)\lambda \qquad \sin\theta = \dfrac{\lambda}{d} = \dfrac{632.8\times10^{-9}\text{ m}}{0.738\times10^{-3}\text{ m}} = 0.000\,857$

$y = L\tan\theta = (1.40\text{ m})(0.000\,857) = 1.20\text{ mm}$

An image of the original set of slits appears on the screen. If the screen is removed, light diverges from the real images with the same wave fronts reconstructed as the original slits produced. Reasoning from the mathematics of Fourier transforms, Gabor showed that light diverging from any object, not just a set of slits, could be used. In the picture, the slits or maxima on the left are separated by 1.20 mm. The slits or maxima on the right are separated by 0.738 mm. The length difference between any pair of lines is an integer number of wavelengths. Light can be sent through equally well toward the right or toward the left.

Section 38.5 Diffraction of X-Rays by Crystals

P38.35 $2d\sin\theta = m\lambda$: $\qquad \lambda = \dfrac{2d\sin\theta}{m} = \dfrac{2(0.353\times10^{-9}\text{ m})\sin 7.60°}{1} = 9.34\times10^{-11}\text{ m} = \boxed{0.093\,4\text{ nm}}$

P38.36 $2d\sin\theta = m\lambda \Rightarrow d = \frac{m\lambda}{2\sin\theta} = \frac{(1)(0.129 \text{ nm})}{2\sin(8.15°)} = \boxed{0.455 \text{ nm}}$

P38.37 $2d\sin\theta = m\lambda$: $\sin\theta = \frac{m\lambda}{2d} = \frac{1(0.140\times10^{-9} \text{ m})}{2(0.281\times10^{-9} \text{ m})} = 0.249$

and $\boxed{\theta = 14.4°}$

P38.38 $\sin\theta_m = \frac{m\lambda}{2d}$: $\sin 12.6° = \frac{1\lambda}{2d} = 0.218$

$\sin\theta_2 = \frac{2\lambda}{2d} = 2(0.218)$ so $\theta_2 = 25.9°$

$\boxed{\text{Three}}$ other orders appear: $\theta_3 = \sin^{-1}(3\times0.218) = 40.9°$

$\theta_4 = \sin^{-1}(4\times0.218) = 60.8°$

$\theta_5 = \sin^{-1}(5\times0.218) = \text{nonexistent}$

P38.39 Figure 38.27 of the text shows the situation.

$2d\sin\theta = m\lambda$ or $\lambda = \frac{2d\sin\theta}{m}$

$m = 1$: $\lambda_1 = \frac{2(2.80 \text{ m})\sin 80.0°}{1} = \boxed{5.51 \text{ m}}$

$m = 2$: $\lambda_2 = \frac{2(2.80 \text{ m})\sin 80.0°}{2} = \boxed{2.76 \text{ m}}$

$m = 3$: $\lambda_3 = \frac{2(2.80 \text{ m})\sin 80.0°}{3} = \boxed{1.84 \text{ m}}$

Section 38.6 **Polarization of Light Waves**

P38.40 The average value of the cosine-squared function is one-half, so the first polarizer transmits $\frac{1}{2}$ the light. The second transmits $\cos^2 30.0° = \frac{3}{4}$.

$I_f = \frac{1}{2}\times\frac{3}{4}I_i = \boxed{\frac{3}{8}I_i}$

P38.41 $I = I_{\max}\cos^2\theta \quad\Rightarrow\quad \theta = \cos^{-1}\sqrt{\frac{I}{I_{\max}}}$

(a) $\frac{I}{I_{\max}} = \frac{1}{3.00} \quad\Rightarrow\quad \theta = \cos^{-1}\sqrt{\frac{1}{3.00}} = \boxed{54.7°}$

(b) $\frac{I}{I_{\max}} = \frac{1}{5.00} \quad\Rightarrow\quad \theta = \cos^{-1}\sqrt{\frac{1}{5.00}} = \boxed{63.4°}$

(c) $\frac{I}{I_{\max}} = \frac{1}{10.0} \quad\Rightarrow\quad \theta = \cos^{-1}\sqrt{\frac{1}{10.0}} = \boxed{71.6°}$

P38.42 (a) $\theta_1 = 20.0°$, $\theta_2 = 40.0°$, $\theta_3 = 60.0°$

$$I_f = I_i \cos^2(\theta_1 - 0°)\cos^2(\theta_2 - \theta_1)\cos^2(\theta_3 - \theta_2)$$

$$I_f = (10.0\text{ units})\cos^2(20.0°)\cos^2(20.0°)\cos^2(20.0°)$$

$$= \boxed{6.89\text{ units}}$$

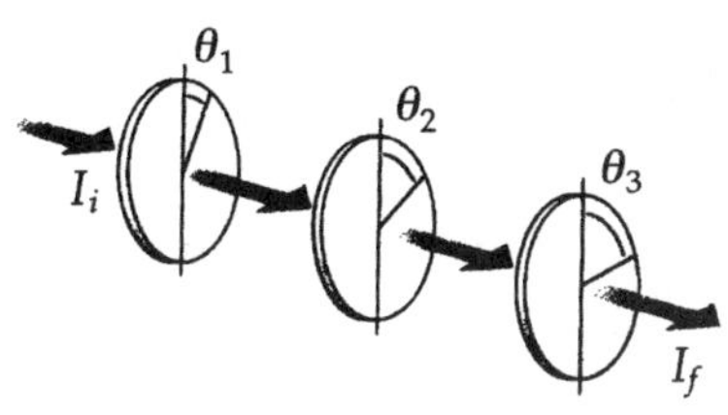

(b) $\theta_1 = 0°$, $\theta_2 = 30.0°$, $\theta_3 = 60.0°$

$$I_f = (10.0\text{ units})\cos^2(0°)\cos^2(30.0°)\cos^2(30.0°) = \boxed{5.63\text{ units}}$$

FIG. P38.42

P38.43 By Brewster's law, $n = \tan\theta_p = \tan(48.0°) = \boxed{1.11}$.

***P38.44** (a) At incidence, $n_1 \sin\theta_1 = n_2 \sin\theta_2$ and $\theta_1' = \theta_1$. For complete polarization of the reflected light,

$$(90 - \theta_1') + (90 - \theta_2) = 90°$$

$$\theta_1' + \theta_2 = 90 = \theta_1 + \theta_2$$

Then $n_1 \sin\theta_1 = n_2 \sin(90 - \theta_1) = n_2 \cos\theta_1$

$$\frac{\sin\theta_1}{\cos\theta_1} = \frac{n_2}{n_1} = \tan\theta_1$$

At the bottom surface, $\theta_3 = \theta_2$ because the normals to the surfaces of entry and exit are parallel.

FIG. P38.44(a)

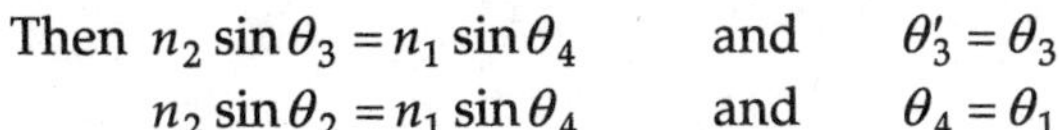

Then $n_2 \sin\theta_3 = n_1 \sin\theta_4$ and $\theta_3' = \theta_3$

$n_2 \sin\theta_2 = n_1 \sin\theta_4$ and $\theta_4 = \theta_1$

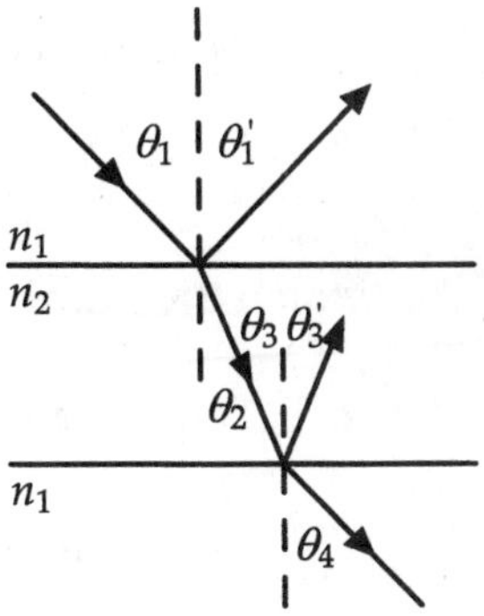

The condition for complete polarization of the reflected light is

$90 - \theta_3' + 90 - \theta_4 = 90°$ $\qquad$ $\theta_2 + \theta_1 = 90$

This is the same as the condition for θ_1 to be Brewster's angle at the top surface.

(b) We consider light moving in a plane perpendicular to the line where the surfaces of the prism meet at the unknown angle Φ. We require

$$n_1 \sin\theta_1 = n_2 \sin\theta_2$$

$$\theta_1 + \theta_2 = 90°$$

So $n_1 \sin(90 - \theta_2) = n_2 \sin\theta_2$ $\qquad$ $\dfrac{n_1}{n_2} = \tan\theta_2$

And $n_2 \sin\theta_3 = n_3 \sin\theta_4$ $\qquad$ $\theta_3 + \theta_4 = 90°$

$n_2 \sin\theta_3 = n_3 \cos\theta_3$ $\qquad$ $\tan\theta_3 = \dfrac{n_3}{n_2}$

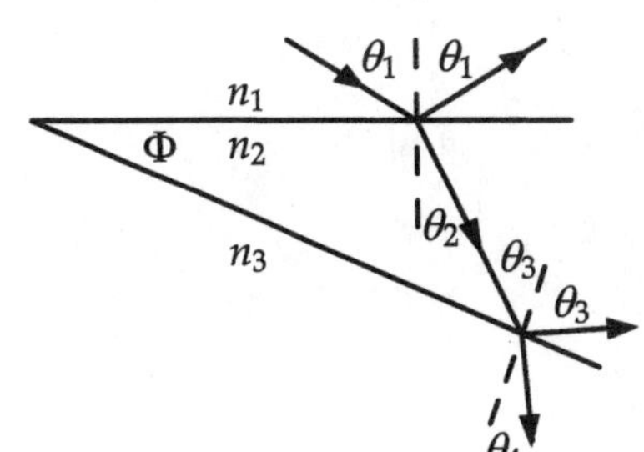

FIG. P38.44(b)

In the triangle made by the faces of the prism and the ray in the prism,

$$\Phi + 90 + \theta_2 + (90 - \theta_3) = 180.$$

So one particular apex angle is required, and it is

$$\Phi = \theta_3 - \theta_2 = \boxed{\tan^{-1}\left(\frac{n_3}{n_2}\right) - \tan^{-1}\left(\frac{n_1}{n_2}\right)}.$$

Here a negative result is to be interpreted as meaning the same as a positive result.

P38.45 $\sin\theta_c = \frac{1}{n}$ or $n = \frac{1}{\sin\theta_c} = \frac{1}{\sin 34.4°} = 1.77$.

Also, $\tan\theta_p = n$. Thus, $\theta_p = \tan^{-1}(n) = \tan^{-1}(1.77) = \boxed{60.5°}$.

P38.46 $\sin\theta_c = \frac{1}{n}$ and $\tan\theta_p = n$

Thus, $\sin\theta_c = \frac{1}{\tan\theta_p}$ or $\boxed{\cot\theta_p = \sin\theta_c}$.

P38.47 Complete polarization occurs at Brewster's angle $\tan\theta_p = 1.33$ $\theta_p = 53.1°$.

Thus, the Moon is $\boxed{36.9°}$ above the horizon.

Additional Problems

P38.48 For incident unpolarized light of intensity I_{max}:

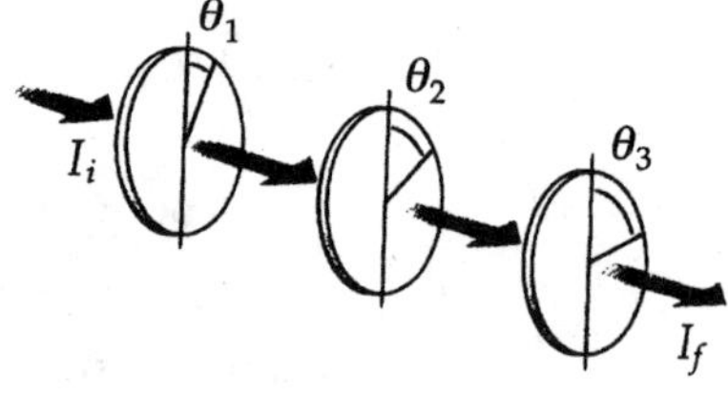

FIG. P38.48

After transmitting 1st disk: $I = \frac{1}{2} I_{\text{max}}$.

After transmitting 2nd disk: $I = \frac{1}{2} I_{\text{max}} \cos^2\theta$.

After transmitting 3rd disk: $I = \frac{1}{2} I_{\text{max}} \cos^2\theta \cos^2(90° - \theta)$.

where the angle between the first and second disk is $\theta = \omega t$.

Using trigonometric identities $\cos^2\theta = \frac{1}{2}(1 + \cos 2\theta)$

and $\cos^2(90° - \theta) = \sin^2\theta = \frac{1}{2}(1 - \cos 2\theta)$

we have $I = \frac{1}{2} I_{\text{max}} \left[\frac{(1 + \cos 2\theta)}{2}\right]\left[\frac{(1 - \cos 2\theta)}{2}\right]$

$$I = \frac{1}{8} I_{\text{max}}\left(1 - \cos^2 2\theta\right) = \frac{1}{8} I_{\text{max}}\left(\frac{1}{2}\right)(1 - \cos 4\theta).$$

Since $\theta = \omega t$, the intensity of the emerging beam is given by $\boxed{I = \frac{1}{16} I_{\text{max}}(1 - 4\omega t)}$.

P38.49 Let the first sheet have its axis at angle θ to the original plane of polarization, and let each further sheet have its axis turned by the same angle.

The first sheet passes intensity $I_{max}\cos^2\theta$.

The second sheet passes $I_{max}\cos^4\theta$

and the nth sheet lets through $I_{max}\cos^{2n}\theta \ge 0.90 I_{max}$ where $\theta = \dfrac{45°}{n}$.

Try different integers to find $\cos^{2\times 5}\left(\dfrac{45°}{5}\right) = 0.885$ $\cos^{2\times 6}\left(\dfrac{45°}{6}\right) = 0.902$.

(a) So $n = \boxed{6}$

(b) $\theta = \boxed{7.50°}$

P38.50 Consider vocal sound moving at 340 m/s and of frequency 3 000 Hz. Its wavelength is

$$\lambda = \frac{v}{f} = \frac{340 \text{ m/s}}{3\,000 \text{ Hz}} = 0.113 \text{ m}.$$

If your mouth, for horizontal dispersion, behaves similarly to a slit 6.00 cm wide, then $a\sin\theta = m\lambda$ predicts no diffraction minima. You are a nearly isotropic source of this sound. It spreads out from you nearly equally in all directions. On the other hand, if you use a megaphone with width 60.0 cm at its wide end, then $a\sin\theta = m\lambda$ predicts the first diffraction minimum at

$$\theta = \sin^{-1}\left(\frac{m\lambda}{a}\right) = \sin^{-1}\left(\frac{0.113 \text{ m}}{0.600 \text{ m}}\right) = 10.9°.$$

This suggests that the sound is radiated mostly toward the front into a diverging beam of angular diameter only about 20°. With less sound energy wasted in other directions, more is available for your intended auditors. We could check that a distant observer to the side or behind you receives less sound when a megaphone is used.

P38.51 The first minimum is at $a\sin\theta = (1)\lambda$.

This has no solution if $\dfrac{\lambda}{a} > 1$.

or if $a < \lambda = \boxed{632.8 \text{ nm}}$.

P38.52 $x = 1.22\dfrac{\lambda}{d}D = 1.22\left(\dfrac{5.00\times 10^{-7} \text{ m}}{5.00\times 10^{-3} \text{ m}}\right)\left(250\times 10^{3} \text{ m}\right) = \boxed{30.5 \text{ m}}$

$D = 250\times 10^{3}$ m

$\lambda = 5.00\times 10^{-7}$ m

$d = 5.00\times 10^{-3}$ m

P38.53 $d = \frac{1}{400\text{ mm}^{-1}} = 2.50 \times 10^{-6}\text{ m}$

(a) $d\sin\theta = m\lambda$ $\theta_a = \sin^{-1}\left(\frac{2 \times 541 \times 10^{-9}\text{ m}}{2.50 \times 10^{-6}\text{ m}}\right) = \boxed{25.6°}$

(b) $\lambda = \frac{541 \times 10^{-9}\text{ m}}{1.33} = 4.07 \times 10^{-7}\text{ m}$ $\theta_b = \sin^{-1}\left(\frac{2 \times 4.07 \times 10^{-7}\text{ m}}{2.50 \times 10^{-6}\text{ m}}\right) = \boxed{19.0°}$

(c) $d\sin\theta_a = 2\lambda$ $d\sin\theta_b = \frac{2\lambda}{n}$

$n\sin\theta_b = (1)\sin\theta_a$

P38.54 (a) $\lambda = \frac{v}{f}$: $\lambda = \frac{3.00 \times 10^8\text{ m/s}}{1.40 \times 10^9\text{ s}^{-1}} = 0.214\text{ m}$

$\theta_{\min} = 1.22\frac{\lambda}{D}$: $\theta_{\min} = 1.22\left(\frac{0.214\text{ m}}{3.60 \times 10^4\text{ m}}\right) = \boxed{7.26\ \mu\text{rad}}$

$\theta_{\min} = 7.26\ \mu\text{rad}\left(\frac{180 \times 60 \times 60\text{ s}}{\pi}\right) = \boxed{1.50\text{ arc seconds}}$

(b) $\theta_{\min} = \frac{d}{L}$: $d = \theta_{\min}L = (7.26 \times 10^{-6}\text{ rad})(26\,000\text{ ly}) = \boxed{0.189\text{ ly}}$

(c) $\theta_{\min} = 1.22\frac{\lambda}{D}$ $\theta_{\min} = 1.22\left(\frac{500 \times 10^{-9}\text{ m}}{12.0 \times 10^{-3}\text{ m}}\right) = \boxed{50.8\ \mu\text{rad}}$ (10.5 seconds of arc)

(d) $d = \theta_{\min}L = (50.8 \times 10^{-6}\text{ rad})(30.0\text{ m}) = 1.52 \times 10^{-3}\text{ m} = \boxed{1.52\text{ mm}}$

P38.55 With a grazing angle of 36.0°, the angle of incidence is 54.0°

$\tan\theta_p = n = \tan 54.0° = 1.38$.

In the liquid, $\lambda_n = \frac{\lambda}{n} = \frac{750\text{ nm}}{1.38} = \boxed{545\text{ nm}}$.

***P38.56** (a) Bragg's law applies to the space lattice of melanin rods. Consider the planes $d = 0.25\ \mu\text{m}$ apart. For light at near-normal incidence, strong reflection happens for the wavelength given by $2d\sin\theta = m\lambda$. The longest wavelength reflected strongly corresponds to $m = 1$:

$2(0.25 \times 10^{-6}\text{ m})\sin 90° = 1\lambda$ $\lambda = 500\text{ nm}$. This is the blue-green color.

(b) For light incident at grazing angle 60°, $2d\sin\theta = m\lambda$ gives $1\lambda = 2(0.25 \times 10^{-6}\text{ m})\sin 60° = 433\text{ nm}$. This is violet.

(c) Your two eyes receive light reflected from the feather at different angles, so they receive light incident at different angles and containing different colors reinforced by constructive interference.

continued on next page

(d) The longest wavelength that can be reflected with extra strength by these melanin rods is the one we computed first, 500 nm blue-green.

(e) If the melanin rods were farther apart (say 0.32 μm) they could reflect red with constructive interference.

P38.57 (a) $d\sin\theta = m\lambda$

or $d = \frac{m\lambda}{\sin\theta} = \frac{3(500\times10^{-9}\text{ m})}{\sin 32.0°} = 2.83\ \mu\text{m}$

Therefore, lines per unit length $= \frac{1}{d} = \frac{1}{2.83\times10^{-6}\text{ m}}$

or lines per unit length $= 3.53\times10^{5}\text{ m}^{-1} = \boxed{3.53\times10^{3}\text{ cm}^{-1}}$.

(b) $\sin\theta = \frac{m\lambda}{d} = \frac{m(500\times10^{-9}\text{ m})}{2.83\times10^{-6}\text{ m}} = m(0.177)$

For $\sin\theta \le 1.00$, we must have $m(0.177)\le 1.00$

or $m \le 5.66$.

Therefore, the highest order observed is $m = 5$.

Total number of primary maxima observed is $2m+1 = \boxed{11}$.

P38.58 For the air-to-water interface,

$$\tan\theta_p = \frac{n_{\text{water}}}{n_{\text{air}}} = \frac{1.33}{1.00} \qquad \theta_p = 53.1°$$

and $$(1.00)\sin\theta_p = (1.33)\sin\theta_2$$

$$\theta_2 = \sin^{-1}\left(\frac{\sin 53.1°}{1.33}\right) = 36.9°.$$

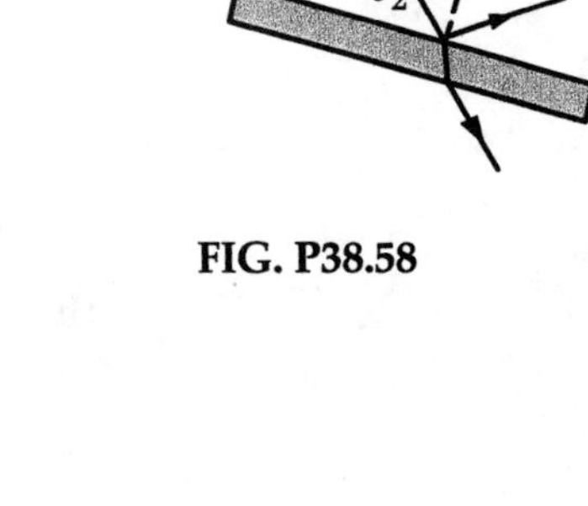

FIG. P38.58

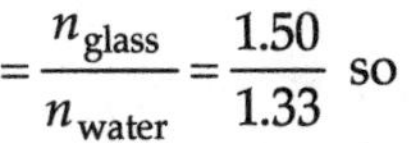

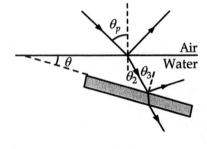

For the water-to-glass interface, $\tan\theta_p = \tan\theta_3 = \frac{n_{\text{glass}}}{n_{\text{water}}} = \frac{1.50}{1.33}$ so

$\theta_3 = 48.4°$.

The angle between surfaces is $\theta = \theta_3 - \theta_2 = \boxed{11.5°}$.

***P38.59** A central maximum and side maxima in seven orders of interference appear. If the seventh order is just at 90°,

$d\sin\theta = m\lambda \qquad d1 = 7(654\times10^{-9}\text{ m}) \qquad d = 4.58\ \mu\text{m}.$

If the seventh order is at less than 90°, the eighth order might be nearly ready to appear according to

$d1 = 8(654\times10^{-9}\text{ m}) \qquad d = 5.23\ \mu\text{m}.$

Thus $\boxed{4.58\ \mu\text{m} < d < 5.23\ \mu\text{m}}$.

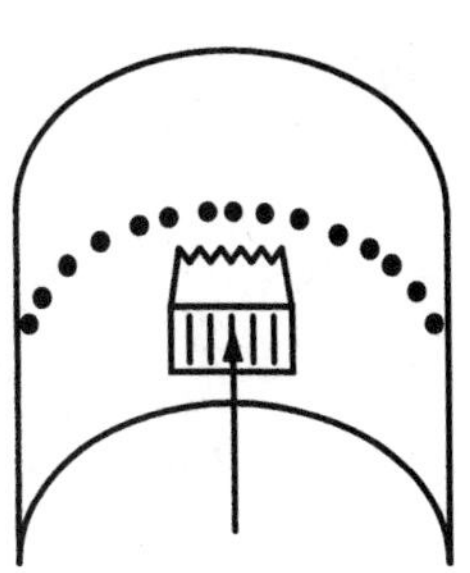
FIG. P38.59

P38.60 (a) We require $\theta_{\min} = 1.22\frac{\lambda}{D} = \frac{\text{radius of diffraction disk}}{L} = \frac{D}{2L}$.

Then $\boxed{D^2 = 2.44\lambda L}$.

(b) $D = \sqrt{2.44\left(500\times10^{-9}\text{ m}\right)(0.150\text{ m})} = \boxed{428\ \mu\text{m}}$

P38.61 The limiting resolution between lines $\theta_{\min} = 1.22\frac{\lambda}{D} = 1.22\frac{\left(550\times10^{-9}\text{ m}\right)}{\left(5.00\times10^{-3}\text{ m}\right)} = 1.34\times10^{-4}\text{ rad}$.

Assuming a picture screen with vertical dimension ℓ, the minimum viewing distance for no visible lines is found from $\theta_{\min} = \frac{\ell/485}{L}$. The desired ratio is then

$$\frac{L}{\ell} = \frac{1}{485\theta_{\min}} = \frac{1}{485\left(1.34\times10^{-4}\text{ rad}\right)} = \boxed{15.4}.$$

P38.62 (a) Applying Snell's law gives $n_2\sin\phi = n_1\sin\theta$. From the sketch, we also see that:

$\theta+\phi+\beta=\pi$, or $\phi=\pi-(\theta+\beta)$.

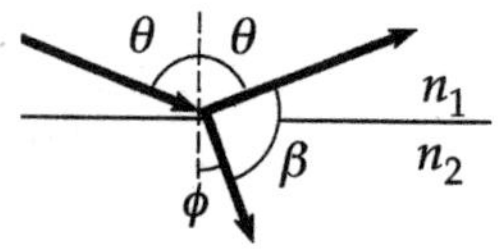

FIG. P38.62(a)

Using the given identity: $\sin\phi = \sin\pi\cos(\theta+\beta) - \cos\pi\sin(\theta+\beta)$,

which reduces to: $\sin\phi = \sin(\theta+\beta)$.

Applying the identity again: $\sin\phi = \sin\theta\cos\beta + \cos\theta\sin\beta$.

Snell's law then becomes: $n_2(\sin\theta\cos\beta + \cos\theta\sin\beta) = n_1\sin\theta$

or (after dividing by $\cos\theta$): $n_2(\tan\theta\cos\beta + \sin\beta) = n_1\tan\theta$.

Solving for $\tan\theta$ gives: $\boxed{\tan\theta = \frac{n_2\sin\beta}{n_1 - n_2\cos\beta}}$.

(b) If $\beta = 90.0°$, $n_1 = 1.00$, and $n_2 = n$, the above result becomes:

$\tan\theta = \frac{n(1.00)}{1.00-0}$, or $n = \tan\theta$, which is Brewster's law.

P38.63 (a) From Equation 38.1, $\theta = \sin^{-1}\left(\frac{m\lambda}{a}\right)$.

In this case $m=1$ and $\lambda = \frac{c}{f} = \frac{3.00\times10^8\text{ m/s}}{7.50\times10^9\text{ Hz}} = 4.00\times10^{-2}\text{ m}$.

Thus, $\theta = \sin^{-1}\left(\frac{4.00\times10^{-2}\text{ m}}{6.00\times10^{-2}\text{ m}}\right) = \boxed{41.8°}$.

continued on next page

(b) From Equation 38.4, $\frac{I}{I_{max}}=\left[\frac{\sin(\beta/2)}{\beta/2}\right]^2$ where $\beta=\frac{2\pi a\sin\theta}{\lambda}$.

When $\theta=15.0°$, $\beta=\frac{2\pi(0.060\,0\text{ m})\sin 15.0°}{0.040\,0\text{ m}}=2.44\text{ rad}$

and $\frac{I}{I_{max}}=\left[\frac{\sin(1.22\text{ rad})}{1.22\text{ rad}}\right]^2=\boxed{0.593}$.

(c) $\sin\theta=\frac{\lambda}{a}$ so $\theta=41.8°$:

This is the minimum angle subtended by the two sources at the slit. Let α be the half angle between the sources, each a distance $\ell=0.100$ m from the center line and a distance L from the slit plane. Then,

$$L=\ell\cot\alpha=(0.100\text{ m})\cot\left(\frac{41.8°}{2}\right)=\boxed{0.262\text{ m}}.$$

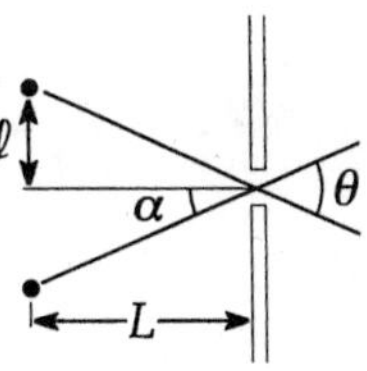

FIG. P38.63(c)

P38.64 $\frac{I}{I_{max}}=\frac{1}{2}\left(\cos^2 45.0°\right)\left(\cos^2 45.0°\right)=\boxed{\frac{1}{8}}$

P38.65 $d\sin\theta=m\lambda$

and, differentiating, $d(\cos\theta)d\theta=md\lambda$

or $d\sqrt{1-\sin^2\theta}\Delta\theta\approx m\Delta\lambda$

$$d\sqrt{1-\frac{m^2\lambda^2}{d^2}}\Delta\theta\approx m\Delta\lambda$$

so $\boxed{\Delta\theta\approx\frac{\Delta\lambda}{\sqrt{(d^2/m^2)-\lambda^2}}}$.

***P38.66** (a) The angles of bright beams diffracted from the grating are given by $(d)\sin\theta=m\lambda$. The angular dispersion is defined as the derivative $\frac{d\theta}{d\lambda}$: $(d)\cos\theta\frac{d\theta}{d\lambda}=m$ $\frac{d\theta}{d\lambda}=\frac{m}{d\cos\theta}$

(b) For the average wavelength 578 nm,

$d\sin\theta=m\lambda$ $\frac{0.02\text{ m}}{8\,000}\sin\theta=2\left(578\times10^{-9}\text{ m}\right)$

$$\theta=\sin^{-1}\frac{2\times578\times10^{-9}\text{ m}}{2.5\times10^{-6}\text{ m}}=27.5°$$

The separation angle between the lines is

$$\Delta\theta=\frac{d\theta}{d\lambda}\Delta\lambda=\frac{m}{d\cos\theta}\Delta\lambda=\frac{2}{2.5\times10^{-6}\text{ m}\cos 27.5°}2.11\times10^{-9}\text{ m}$$

$$=0.001\,90=0.001\,90\text{ rad}=0.001\,90\text{ rad}\left(\frac{180°}{\pi\text{ rad}}\right)=\boxed{0.109°}$$

***P38.67** (a) Constructive interference of light of wavelength λ on the screen is described by $d\sin\theta = m\lambda$ where $\tan\theta = \frac{y}{L}$ so $\sin\theta = \frac{y}{\sqrt{L^2+y^2}}$. Then $(d)y\left(L^2+y^2\right)^{-1/2} = m\lambda$. Differentiating with respect to y gives

$$d1\left(L^2+y^2\right)^{-1/2} + (d)y\left(-\frac{1}{2}\right)\left(L^2+y^2\right)^{-3/2}(0+2y) = m\frac{d\lambda}{dy}$$

$$\frac{d}{\left(L^2+y^2\right)^{1/2}} - \frac{(d)y^2}{\left(L^2+y^2\right)^{3/2}} = m\frac{d\lambda}{dy} = \frac{(d)L^2+(d)y^2-(d)y^2}{\left(L^2+y^2\right)^{3/2}}$$

$$\frac{d\lambda}{dy} = \frac{(d)L^2}{m\left(L^2+y^2\right)^{3/2}}$$

(b) Here $d\sin\theta = m\lambda$ gives $\frac{10^{-2}\text{ m}}{8\,000}\sin\theta = 1\left(550\times10^{-9}\text{ m}\right)$, $\theta = \sin^{-1}\left(\frac{0.55\times10^{-6}\text{ m}}{1.25\times10^{-6}\text{ m}}\right) = 26.1°$

$y = L\tan\theta = 2.40\text{ m}\tan 26.1° = 1.18\text{ m}$

Now $\frac{d\lambda}{dy} = \frac{dL^2}{m\left(L^2+y^2\right)^{3/2}} = \frac{1.25\times10^{-6}\text{ m}(2.40\text{ m})^2}{1\left((2.4\text{ m})^2+(1.18\text{ m})^2\right)^{3/2}} = 3.77\times10^{-7} = \boxed{3.77\text{ nm/cm}}$.

P38.68 For a diffraction grating, the locations of the principal maxima for wavelength λ are given by $\sin\theta = \frac{m\lambda}{d} \approx \frac{y}{L}$. The grating spacing may be expressed as $d = \frac{a}{N}$ where a is the width of the grating and N is the number of slits. Thus, the screen locations of the maxima become $y = \frac{NLm\lambda}{a}$. If two nearly equal wavelengths are present, the difference in the screen locations of corresponding maxima is

$$\Delta y = \frac{NLm(\Delta\lambda)}{a}.$$

For a single slit of width a, the location of the first diffraction minimum is $\sin\theta = \frac{\lambda}{a} \approx \frac{y}{L}$, or $y = \left(\frac{L}{a}\right)\lambda$. If the two wavelengths are to be just resolved by Rayleigh's criterion, $y = \Delta y$ from above. Therefore,

$\left(\frac{L}{a}\right)\lambda = \frac{NLm(\Delta\lambda)}{a}$ or the resolving power of the grating is $\boxed{R \equiv \frac{\lambda}{\Delta\lambda} = Nm}$.

P38.69 (a) The E and O rays, in phase at the surface of the plate, will have a phase difference

$$\theta=\left(\frac{2\pi}{\lambda}\right)\delta$$

after traveling distance d through the plate. Here δ is the difference in the *optical path* lengths of these rays. The optical path length between two points is the product of the actual path length d and the index of refraction. Therefore,

$$\delta=\left|dn_O-dn_E\right|.$$

The absolute value is used since $\frac{n_O}{n_E}$ may be more or less than unity. Therefore,

$$\theta=\left(\frac{2\pi}{\lambda}\right)\left|dn_O-dn_E\right|=\boxed{\left(\frac{2\pi}{\lambda}\right)d\left|n_O-n_E\right|}.$$

(b) $$d=\frac{\lambda\theta}{2\pi\left|n_O-n_E\right|}=\frac{\left(550\times10^{-9}\text{ m}\right)(\pi/2)}{2\pi\left|1.544-1.553\right|}=1.53\times10^{-5}\text{ m}=\boxed{15.3\ \mu\text{m}}$$

P38.70 (a) From Equation 38.4, $$\frac{I}{I_{\max}}=\left[\frac{\sin(\beta/2)}{\beta/2}\right]^2.$$

If we define $\phi\equiv\frac{\beta}{2}$ this becomes $$\frac{I}{I_{\max}}=\left[\frac{\sin\phi}{\phi}\right]^2.$$

Therefore, when $\frac{I}{I_{\max}}=\frac{1}{2}$ we must have $\frac{\sin\phi}{\phi}=\frac{1}{\sqrt{2}}$, or $\boxed{\sin\phi=\frac{\phi}{\sqrt{2}}}$.

(b) Let $y_1=\sin\phi$ and $y_2=\frac{\phi}{\sqrt{2}}$.

A plot of y_1 and y_2 in the range $1.00\le\phi\le\frac{\pi}{2}$ is shown to the right.

The solution to the transcendental equation is found to be $\boxed{\phi=1.39\text{ rad}}$.

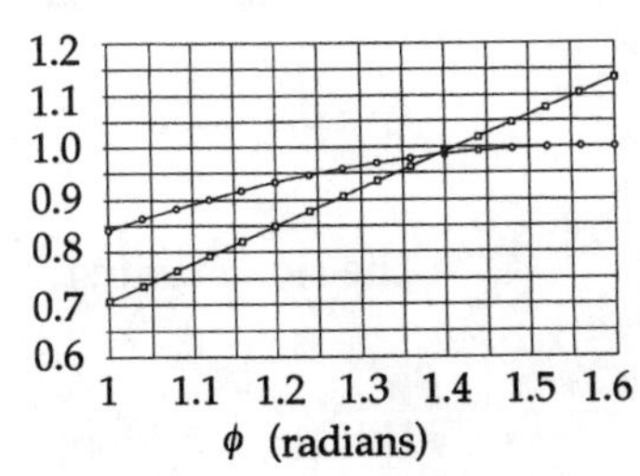

FIG. P38.70(b)

(c) $$\beta=\frac{2\pi a\sin\theta}{\lambda}=2\phi$$

gives $$\sin\theta=\left(\frac{\phi}{\pi}\right)\frac{\lambda}{a}=0.443\frac{\lambda}{a}.$$

If $\frac{\lambda}{a}$ is small, then $\theta\approx0.443\frac{\lambda}{a}$.

This gives the half-width, measured away from the maximum at $\theta=0$. The pattern is symmetric, so the full width is given by

$$\Delta\theta=0.443\frac{\lambda}{a}-\left(-0.443\frac{\lambda}{a}\right)=\boxed{\frac{0.886\lambda}{a}}.$$

P38.71

ϕ	$\sqrt{2}\sin\phi$	
1	1.19	bigger than ϕ
2	1.29	smaller than ϕ
1.5	1.41	smaller
1.4	1.394	
1.39	1.391	bigger
1.395	1.392	
1.392	1.391 7	smaller
1.391 5	1.391 54	bigger
1.391 52	1.391 55	bigger
1.391 6	1.391 568	smaller
1.391 58	1.391 563	
1.391 57	1.391 561	
1.391 56	1.391 558	
1.391 559	1.391 557 8	
1.391 558	1.391 557 5	
1.391 557	1.391 557 3	
1.391 557 4	1.391 557 4	

We get the answer to seven digits after 17 steps. Clever guessing, like using the value of $\sqrt{2}\sin\phi$ as the next guess for ϕ, could reduce this to around 13 steps.

P38.72 In $I = I_{max}\left[\frac{\sin(\beta/2)}{\beta/2}\right]^2$ find $\frac{dI}{d\beta} = I_{max}\left(\frac{2\sin(\beta/2)}{\beta/2}\right)\left[\frac{(\beta/2)\cos(\beta/2)(1/2)-\sin(\beta/2)(1/2)}{(\beta/2)^2}\right]$

and require that it be zero. The possibility $\sin\left(\frac{\beta}{2}\right)=0$ locates all of the minima and the central maximum, according to

$\frac{\beta}{2}=0,\ \pi,\ 2\pi,\ \ldots;$ $\beta=\frac{2\pi a\sin\theta}{\lambda}=0,\ 2\pi,\ 4\pi,\ \ldots\ ;\ a\sin\theta=0,\ \lambda,\ 2\lambda,\ \ldots.$

The side maxima are found from $\frac{\beta}{2}\cos\left(\frac{\beta}{2}\right)-\sin\left(\frac{\beta}{2}\right)=0$, or $\tan\left(\frac{\beta}{2}\right)=\frac{\beta}{2}$.

This has solutions $\boxed{\frac{\beta}{2}=4.493\,4}$, $\boxed{\frac{\beta}{2}=7.725\,3}$, and others, giving

(a) $\pi a\sin\theta=4.493\,4\lambda$ $\boxed{a\sin\theta=1.430\,3\lambda}$

(b) $\pi a\sin\theta=7.725\,3\lambda$ $\boxed{a\sin\theta=2.459\,0\lambda}$

P38.73 The first minimum in the single-slit diffraction pattern occurs at

$$\sin\theta = \frac{\lambda}{a} \approx \frac{y_{\min}}{L}.$$

Thus, the slit width is given by

$$a = \frac{\lambda L}{y_{\min}}.$$

For a minimum located at $y_{\min} = 6.36 \text{ mm} \pm 0.08 \text{ mm}$,

the width is

$$a = \frac{(632.8\times10^{-9}\text{ m})(1.00\text{ m})}{6.36\times10^{-3}\text{ m}} = \boxed{99.5\ \mu\text{m} \pm 1\%}.$$

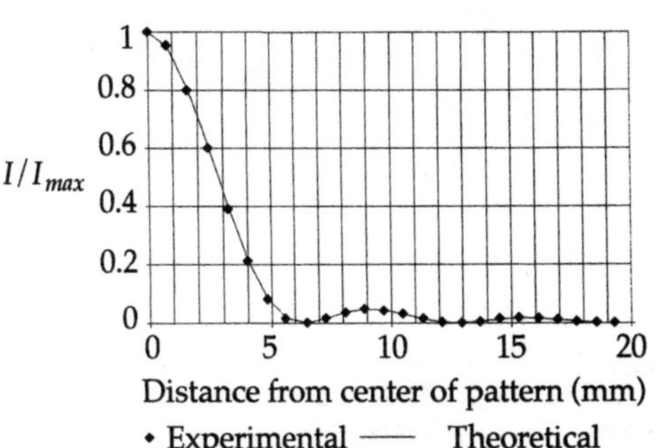

FIG. P38.73

ANSWERS TO EVEN PROBLEMS

P38.2 547 nm

P38.4 91.2 cm

P38.6 (a) 1.09 m; (b) 1.70 mm

P38.8 see the solution

P38.10 (a) 0°, 10.3°, 21.0°, 32.5°, 45.8°, 63.6°; (b) nine bright fringes at 0° and on either side at 10.3°, 21.0°, 32.5°, and 63.6°; (c) 1.00, 0.811, 0.405, 0.090 1, 0.032 4

P38.12 2.61 μm

P38.14 869 m

P38.16 0.512 m

P38.18 6.10 cm

P38.20 105 m

P38.22 (a) 2.40 μrad; (b) 213 km

P38.24 514 nm

P38.26 1.81 μm

P38.28 see the solution

P38.30 74.2 grooves/mm

P38.32 2

P38.34 (a) 0.738 mm; (b) see the solution

P38.36 0.455 nm

P38.38 3

P38.40 $\frac{3}{8}$

P38.42 (a) 6.89 units; (b) 5.63 units

P38.44 (a) see the solution; (b) For light confined to a plane, yes. $\left|\tan^{-1}\left(\frac{n_3}{n_2}\right) - \tan^{-1}\left(\frac{n_1}{n_2}\right)\right|$

P38.46 see the solution

P38.48 see the solution

P38.50 see the solution

P38.52 30.5 m

P38.54 (a) 1.50 sec; (b) 0.189 ly; (c) 10.5 sec; (d) 1.52 mm

P38.56 see the solution

P38.58 11.5°

P38.60 (a) see the solution; (b) 428 μm

P38.62 see the solution

P38.64 $\frac{1}{8}$

P38.66 (a) see the solution; (b) 0.109°

P38.68 see the solution

P38.70 (a) see the solution; (b) $\phi = 1.39$ rad; (c) see the solution

P38.72 (a) $a \sin\theta = 1.430\,3\lambda$; (b) $a \sin\theta = 2.459\,0\lambda$

39

Relativity

CHAPTER OUTLINE

ANSWERS TO QUESTIONS

Q39.1 The speed of light c and the speed v of their relative motion.

Q39.2 An ellipsoid. The dimension in the direction of motion would be measured to be scrunched in.

Q39.3 No. The principle of relativity implies that nothing can travel faster than the speed of light in a *vacuum*, which is 300 Mm/s. The electron would emit light in a conical shock wave of Cerenkov radiation.

Q39.4 The clock in orbit runs slower. No, they are not synchronized. Although they both tick at the same rate after return, a time difference has developed between the two clocks.

Q39.5 Suppose a railroad train is moving past you. One way to measure its length is this: You mark the tracks at the cowcatcher forming the front of the moving engine at 9:00:00 AM, while your assistant marks the tracks at the back of the caboose at the same time. Then you find the distance between the marks on the tracks with a tape measure. You and your assistant must make the marks simultaneously in your frame of reference, for otherwise the motion of the train would make its length different from the distance between marks.

Q39.6 (a) Yours does.

(b) His does.

(c) If the velocity of relative motion is constant, both observers have equally valid views.

Q39.7 Get a *Mr. Tompkins* book by George Gamow for a wonderful fictional exploration of this question. Driving home in a hurry, you push on the gas pedal not to increase your speed by very much, but rather to make the blocks get shorter. Big Doppler shifts in wave frequencies make red lights look green as you approach them and make car horns and car radios useless. High-speed transportation is very expensive, requiring huge fuel purchases. And it is dangerous, as a speeding car can knock down a building. Having had breakfast at home, you return hungry for lunch, but you find you have missed dinner. There is a five-day delay in transmission when you watch the Olympics in Australia on live television. It takes ninety-five years for sunlight to reach Earth. We cannot see the Milky Way; the fireball of the Big Bang surrounds us at the distance of Rigel or Deneb.

Q39.8 Nothing physically unusual. An observer riding on the clock does not think that you are *really* strange, either.

Q39.9 By a curved line. This can be seen in the middle of Speedo's world-line in Figure 39.12, where he turns around and begins his trip home.

Q39.10 According to $\mathbf{p} = \gamma m\mathbf{u}$, doubling the speed u will make the momentum of an object increase by the factor $2\left[\frac{c^2 - u^2}{c^2 - 4u^2}\right]^{1/2}$.

Q39.11 As the object approaches the speed of light, its kinetic energy grows without limit. It would take an infinite investment of work to accelerate the object to the speed of light.

Q39.12 There is no upper limit on the momentum of an electron. As more energy E is fed into the object without limit, its speed approaches the speed of light and its momentum approaches $\frac{E}{c}$.

Q39.13 Recall that when a spring of force constant k is compressed or stretched from its relaxed position a distance x, it stores elastic potential energy $U = \frac{1}{2}kx^2$. According to the special theory of relativity, any change in the total energy of the system is equivalent to a change in the mass of the system. Therefore, the mass of a compressed or stretched spring is greater than the mass of a relaxed spring by an amount $\frac{U}{c^2}$. The fractional change is typically unobservably small for a mechanical spring.

Q39.14 You see no change in your reflection at any speed you can attain. You cannot attain the speed of light, for that would take an infinite amount of energy.

Q39.15 Quasar light moves at three hundred million meters per second, just like the light from a firefly at rest.

Q39.16 A photon transports energy. The relativistic equivalence of mass and energy means that is enough to give it momentum.

Q39.17 Any physical theory must agree with experimental measurements within some domain. Newtonian mechanics agrees with experiment for objects moving slowly compared to the speed of light. Relativistic mechanics agrees with experiment for objects at all speeds. Thus the two theories must and do agree with each other for ordinary nonrelativistic objects. Both statements given in the question are formally correct, but the first is clumsily phrased. It seems to suggest that relativistic mechanics applies only to fast-moving objects.

Q39.18 The point of intersection moves to the right. To state the problem precisely, let us assume that each of the two cards moves toward the other parallel to the long dimension of the picture, with velocity of magnitude v. The point of intersection moves to the right at speed $\frac{2v}{\tan\phi} = 2v\cot\phi$, where ϕ is the small angle between the cards. As ϕ approaches zero, $\cot\phi$ approaches infinity. Thus the point of intersection can move with a speed faster than c if v is sufficiently large and ϕ sufficiently small. For example, take $v = 500$ m/s and $\phi = 0.000\,19°$. If you are worried about holding the cards steady enough to be sure of the angle, cut the edge of one card along a curve so that the angle will necessarily be sufficiently small at some place along the edge.

Let us assume the spinning flashlight is at the center of a grain elevator, forming a circular screen of radius R. The linear speed of the spot on the screen is given by $v = \omega R$, where ω is the angular speed of rotation of the flashlight. With sufficiently large ω and R, the speed of the spot moving on the screen can exceed c.

continued on next page

Neither of these examples violates the principle of relativity. Both cases are describing a point of intersection: in the first case, the intersection of two cards and in the second case, the intersection of a light beam with a screen. A point of intersection is not made of matter so it has no mass, and hence no energy. A bug momentarily at the intersection point could yelp, take a bite out of one card, or reflect the light. None of these actions would result in communication reaching another bug so soon as the intersection point reaches him. The second bug would have to wait for sound or light to travel across the distance between the first bug and himself, to get the message.

As a child, the author used an Erector set to build a superluminal speed generator using the intersecting-cards method. Can you get a visible dot to run across a computer screen faster than light? Want'a see it again?

Q39.19 In this case, both the relativistic and Galilean treatments would yield the same result: it is that the experimentally observed speed of one car with respect to the other is the sum of the speeds of the cars.

Q39.20 The hotter object has more energy per molecule than the cooler one. The equivalence of energy and mass predicts that each molecule of the hotter object will, on average, have a larger mass than those in the cooler object. This implies that given the same net applied force, the cooler object would have a larger acceleration than the hotter object would experience. In a controlled experiment, the difference will likely be too small to notice.

Q39.21 Special relativity describes inertial reference frames: that is, reference frames that are not accelerating. General relativity describes all reference frames.

Q39.22 The downstairs clock runs more slowly because it is closer to the Earth and hence in a stronger gravitational field than the upstairs clock.

Q39.23 The ants notice that they have a stronger sense of being pushed outward when they venture closer to the rim of the merry-go-round. If they wish, they can call this the effect of a stronger gravitational field produced by some mass concentration toward the edge of the disk. An ant named Albert figures out that the strong gravitational field makes measuring rods contract when they are near the rim of the disk. He shows that this effect precisely accounts for the discrepancy.

SOLUTIONS TO PROBLEMS

Section 39.1 The Principle of Galilean Relativity

P39.1 In the rest frame,

$$p_i = m_1 v_{1i} + m_2 v_{2i} = (2\,000 \text{ kg})(20.0 \text{ m/s}) + (1\,500 \text{ kg})(0 \text{ m/s}) = 4.00 \times 10^4 \text{ kg} \cdot \text{m/s}$$

$$p_f = (m_1 + m_2)v_f = (2\,000 \text{ kg} + 1\,500 \text{ kg})v_f$$

Since $p_i = p_f$, $$v_f = \frac{4.00 \times 10^4 \text{ kg} \cdot \text{m/s}}{2\,000 \text{ kg} + 1\,500 \text{ kg}} = 11.429 \text{ m/s}.$$

In the moving frame, these velocities are all reduced by +10.0 m/s.

$$v'_{1i} = v_{1i} - v' = 20.0 \text{ m/s} - (+10.0 \text{ m/s}) = 10.0 \text{ m/s}$$

$$v'_{2i} = v_{2i} - v' = 0 \text{ m/s} - (+10.0 \text{ m/s}) = -10.0 \text{ m/s}$$

$$v'_f = 11.429 \text{ m/s} - (+10.0 \text{ m/s}) = 1.429 \text{ m/s}$$

Our initial momentum is then

$$p'_i = m_1 v'_{1i} + m_2 v'_{2i} = (2\,000 \text{ kg})(10.0 \text{ m/s}) + (1\,500 \text{ kg})(-10.0 \text{ m/s}) = 5\,000 \text{ kg} \cdot \text{m/s}$$

and our final momentum is

$$p'_f = (2\,000 \text{ kg} + 1\,500 \text{ kg})v'_f = (3\,500 \text{ kg})(1.429 \text{ m/s}) = 5\,000 \text{ kg} \cdot \text{m/s}.$$

P39.2 (a) $v = v_T + v_B = \boxed{60.0 \text{ m/s}}$

(b) $v = v_T - v_B = \boxed{20.0 \text{ m/s}}$

(c) $v = \sqrt{v_T^2 + v_B^2} = \sqrt{20^2 + 40^2} = \boxed{44.7 \text{ m/s}}$

P39.3 The first observer watches some object accelerate under applied forces. Call the instantaneous velocity of the object $\mathbf{v}_1$. The second observer has constant velocity $\mathbf{v}_{21}$ relative to the first, and measures the object to have velocity $\mathbf{v}_2 = \mathbf{v}_1 - \mathbf{v}_{21}$.

The second observer measures an acceleration of $\mathbf{a}_2 = \dfrac{d\mathbf{v}_2}{dt} = \dfrac{d\mathbf{v}_1}{dt}$.

This is the same as that measured by the first observer. In this nonrelativistic case, they measure the same forces as well. Thus, the second observer also confirms that $\sum \mathbf{F} = m\mathbf{a}$.

P39.4 The laboratory observer notes Newton's second law to hold: $\mathbf{F}_1 = m\mathbf{a}_1$
(where the subscript 1 implies the measurement was made in the laboratory frame of reference). The observer in the accelerating frame measures the acceleration of the mass as $\mathbf{a}_2 = \mathbf{a}_1 - \mathbf{a}'$
(where the subscript 2 implies the measurement was made in the accelerating frame of reference, and the primed acceleration term is the acceleration of the accelerated frame with respect to the laboratory frame of reference). If Newton's second law held for the accelerating frame, that observer would then find valid the relation

$\mathbf{F}_2 = m\mathbf{a}_2$ or $\mathbf{F}_1 = m\mathbf{a}_2$

(since $\mathbf{F}_1 = \mathbf{F}_2$ and the mass is unchanged in each). But, instead, the accelerating frame observer will find that $\mathbf{F}_2 = m\mathbf{a}_2 - m\mathbf{a}'$ which is *not* Newton's second law.

Section 39.2 The Michelson-Morley Experiment

Section 39.3 Einstein's Principle of Relativity

Section 39.4 Consequences of the Special Theory of Relativity

P39.5 $L = L_p\sqrt{1 - \dfrac{v^2}{c^2}}$ $\qquad v = c\sqrt{1 - \left(\dfrac{L}{L_p}\right)^2}$

Taking $L = \dfrac{L_p}{2}$ where $L_p = 1.00$ m gives $\qquad v = c\sqrt{1 - \left(\dfrac{L_p/2}{L_p}\right)^2} = c\sqrt{1 - \dfrac{1}{4}} = \boxed{0.866c}$.

P39.6 $\Delta t = \dfrac{\Delta t_p}{\left[1 - (v/c)^2\right]^{1/2}}$ so $v = c\left[1 - \left(\dfrac{\Delta t_p}{\Delta t}\right)^2\right]^{1/2}$.

For $\Delta t = 2\Delta t_p$ $\qquad v = c\left[1 - \left(\dfrac{\Delta t_p}{2\Delta t_p}\right)^2\right]^{1/2} = c\left[1 - \dfrac{1}{4}\right]^{1/2} = \boxed{0.866c}$.

P39.7 (a) $\gamma = \dfrac{1}{\sqrt{1-(v/c)^2}} = \dfrac{1}{\sqrt{1-(0.500)^2}} = \dfrac{2}{\sqrt{3}}$

The time interval between pulses as measured by the Earth observer is

$$\Delta t = \gamma \Delta t_p = \frac{2}{\sqrt{3}}\left(\frac{60.0\text{ s}}{75.0}\right) = 0.924\text{ s}.$$

Thus, the Earth observer records a pulse rate of $\dfrac{60.0\text{ s/min}}{0.924\text{ s}} = \boxed{64.9/\text{min}}$.

(b) At a relative speed $v = 0.990c$, the relativistic factor γ increases to 7.09 and the pulse rate recorded by the Earth observer decreases to $\boxed{10.6/\text{min}}$. That is, the life span of the astronaut (reckoned by the duration of the total number of his heartbeats) is much longer as measured by an Earth clock than by a clock aboard the space vehicle.

***P39.8** (a) The $0.8c$ and the 20 ly are measured in the Earth frame,

so in this frame, $\Delta t = \dfrac{x}{v} = \dfrac{20\text{ ly}}{0.8c} = \dfrac{20\text{ ly}}{0.8c}\dfrac{1c}{1\text{ ly/yr}} = \boxed{25.0\text{ yr}}$.

(b) We see a clock on the meteoroid moving, so we do not measure proper time; that clock measures proper time.

$\Delta t = \gamma \Delta t_p$: $\Delta t_p = \dfrac{\Delta t}{\gamma} = \dfrac{25.0\text{ yr}}{1/\sqrt{1-v^2/c^2}} = 25.0\text{ yr}\sqrt{1-0.8^2} = 25.0\text{ yr}(0.6) = \boxed{15.0\text{ yr}}$

(c) Method one: We measure the 20 ly on a stick stationary in our frame, so it is proper length. The tourist measures it to be contracted to

$$L = \frac{L_p}{\gamma} = \frac{20\text{ ly}}{1/\sqrt{1-0.8^2}} = \frac{20\text{ ly}}{1.667} = \boxed{12.0\text{ ly}}.$$

Method two: The tourist sees the Earth approaching at $0.8c$

$$(0.8\text{ ly/yr})(15\text{ yr}) = \boxed{12.0\text{ ly}}.$$

Not only do distances and times differ between Earth and meteoroid reference frames, but within the Earth frame apparent distances differ from actual distances. As we have interpreted it, the 20-lightyear actual distance from the Earth to the meteoroid at the time of discovery must be a calculated result, different from the distance measured directly. Because of the finite maximum speed of information transfer, the astronomer sees the meteoroid as it was years previously, when it was much farther away. Call its apparent distance *d*. The time required for light to reach us from the newly-visible meteoroid is the lookback time $t = \dfrac{d}{c}$.

The astronomer calculates that the meteoroid has approached to be 20 ly away as it moved with constant velocity throughout the lookback time. We can work backwards to reconstruct her calculation:

$$d = 20\text{ ly} + 0.8ct = 20\text{ ly} + \frac{0.8cd}{c}$$

$$0.2d = 20\text{ ly}$$

$$d = 100\text{ ly}$$

Thus in terms of direct observation, the meteoroid we see covers 100 ly in only 25 years. Such an apparent superluminal velocity is actually observed for some jets of material emanating from quasars, because they happen to be pointed nearly toward the Earth. If we can watch events unfold on the meteoroid, we see them slowed by relativistic time dilation, but also greatly speeded up by the Doppler effect.

P39.9 $\Delta t = \gamma \Delta t_p = \dfrac{\Delta t_p}{\sqrt{1-v^2/c^2}}$ so $\Delta t_p = \left(\sqrt{1-\dfrac{v^2}{c^2}}\right)\Delta t \cong \left(1-\dfrac{v^2}{2c^2}\right)\Delta t$

and $\Delta t - \Delta t_p = \left(\dfrac{v^2}{2c^2}\right)\Delta t.$

If $v = 1\,000 \text{ km/h} = \dfrac{1.00\times 10^6 \text{ m}}{3\,600 \text{ s}} = 277.8 \text{ m/s}$

then $\dfrac{v}{c} = 9.26\times 10^{-7}$

and $\left(\Delta t - \Delta t_p\right) = \left(4.28\times 10^{-13}\right)(3\,600 \text{ s}) = 1.54\times 10^{-9} \text{ s} = \boxed{1.54 \text{ ns}}.$

P39.10 For $\dfrac{v}{c} = 0.990$, $\gamma = 7.09$

(a) The muon's lifetime as measured in the Earth's rest frame is

$$\Delta t = \frac{4.60 \text{ km}}{0.990c}$$

and the lifetime measured in the muon's rest frame is

$$\Delta t_p = \frac{\Delta t}{\gamma} = \frac{1}{7.09}\left[\frac{4.60\times 10^3 \text{ m}}{0.990\left(3.00\times 10^8 \text{ m/s}\right)}\right] = \boxed{2.18\ \mu\text{s}}.$$

(b) $L = L_p\sqrt{1-\left(\dfrac{v}{c}\right)^2} = \dfrac{L_p}{\gamma} = \dfrac{4.60\times 10^3 \text{ m}}{7.09} = \boxed{649 \text{ m}}$

P39.11 The spaceship is measured by the Earth observer to be length-contracted to

$L = L_p\sqrt{1-\dfrac{v^2}{c^2}}$ or $L^2 = L_p^2\left(1-\dfrac{v^2}{c^2}\right).$

Also, the contracted length is related to the time required to pass overhead by:

$L = vt$ or $L^2 = v^2t^2 = \dfrac{v^2}{c^2}(ct)^2.$

Equating these two expressions gives $L_p^2 - L_p^2\dfrac{v^2}{c^2} = (ct)^2\dfrac{v^2}{c^2}$

or $\left[L_p^2 + (ct)^2\right]\dfrac{v^2}{c^2} = L_p^2.$

Using the given values: $L_p = 300 \text{ m}$ and $t = 7.50\times 10^{-7} \text{ s}$

this becomes $\left(1.41\times 10^5 \text{ m}^2\right)\dfrac{v^2}{c^2} = 9.00\times 10^4 \text{ m}^2$

giving $v = \boxed{0.800c}.$

P39.12 (a) The spaceship is measured by Earth observers to be of length L, where

$$L = L_p\sqrt{1-\frac{v^2}{c^2}} \qquad \text{and} \qquad L = v\Delta t$$

$$v\Delta t = L_p\sqrt{1-\frac{v^2}{c^2}} \qquad \text{and} \qquad v^2\Delta t^2 = L_p^2\left(1-\frac{v^2}{c^2}\right).$$

Solving for v,
$$v^2\left(\Delta t^2+\frac{L_p^2}{c^2}\right) = L_p^2 \qquad \boxed{v = \frac{cL_p}{\sqrt{c^2\Delta t^2 + L_p^2}}}.$$

(b) The tanks move nonrelativistically, so we have $v = \dfrac{300\text{ m}}{75\text{ s}} = \boxed{4.00\text{ m/s}}$.

(c) For the data in problem 11,

$$v = \frac{c(300\text{ m})}{\sqrt{\left(3\times10^8\text{ m/s}\right)^2\left(0.75\times10^{-6}\text{ s}\right)^2 + (300\text{ m})^2}} = \frac{c(300\text{ m})}{\sqrt{225^2+300^2}\text{ m}} = 0.800c$$

in agreement with problem 11. For the data in part (b),

$$v = \frac{c(300\text{ m})}{\sqrt{\left(3\times10^8\text{ m/s}\right)^2(75\text{ s})^2 + (300\text{ m})^2}} = \frac{c(300\text{ m})}{\sqrt{\left(2.25\times10^{10}\right)^2+300^2}\text{ m}} = 1.33\times10^{-8}c = 4.00\text{ m/s}$$

in agreement with part (b).

P39.13 We find Cooper's speed:
$$\frac{GMm}{r^2} = \frac{mv^2}{r}.$$

Solving,
$$v = \left[\frac{GM}{(R+h)}\right]^{1/2} = \left[\frac{\left(6.67\times10^{-11}\right)\left(5.98\times10^{24}\right)}{\left(6.37\times10^6+0.160\times10^6\right)}\right]^{1/2} = 7.82\text{ km/s}.$$

Then the time period of one orbit,
$$T = \frac{2\pi(R+h)}{v} = \frac{2\pi\left(6.53\times10^6\right)}{7.82\times10^3} = 5.25\times10^3\text{ s}.$$

(a) The time difference for 22 orbits is $\Delta t - \Delta t_p = (\gamma-1)\Delta t_p = \left[\left(1-\dfrac{v^2}{c^2}\right)^{-1/2} - 1\right](22T)$

$$\Delta t - \Delta t_p \approx \left(1+\frac{1}{2}\frac{v^2}{c^2}-1\right)(22T) = \frac{1}{2}\left(\frac{7.82\times10^3\text{ m/s}}{3\times10^8\text{ m/s}}\right)^2 22\left(5.25\times10^3\text{ s}\right) = \boxed{39.2\ \mu\text{s}}.$$

(b) For one orbit, $\Delta t - \Delta t_p = \dfrac{39.2\ \mu\text{s}}{22} = 1.78\ \mu\text{s}$. The press report is $\boxed{\text{accurate to one digit}}$.

P39.14
$$\gamma = \frac{1}{\sqrt{1-\left(v^2/c^2\right)}} = 1.01 \qquad \text{so} \qquad \boxed{v = 0.140c}$$

P39.15 (a) Since your ship is identical to his, and you are at rest with respect to your own ship, its length is $\boxed{20.0 \text{ m}}$.

(b) His ship is in motion relative to you, so you measure its length contracted to $\boxed{19.0 \text{ m}}$.

(c) We have $L = L_p\sqrt{1-\frac{v^2}{c^2}}$

from which $\frac{L}{L_p} = \frac{19.0 \text{ m}}{20.0 \text{ m}} = 0.950 = \sqrt{1-\frac{v^2}{c^2}}$ and $\boxed{v = 0.312c}$.

***P39.16** In the Earth frame, Speedo's trip lasts for a time

$$\Delta t = \frac{\Delta x}{v} = \frac{20.0 \text{ ly}}{0.950 \text{ ly/yr}} = 21.05 \text{ yr}.$$

Speedo's age advances only by the proper time interval

$$\Delta t_p = \frac{\Delta t}{\gamma} = 21.05 \text{ yr}\sqrt{1-0.95^2} = 6.574 \text{ yr during his trip.}$$

Similarly for Goslo,

$$\Delta t_p = \frac{\Delta x}{v}\sqrt{1-\frac{v^2}{c^2}} = \frac{20.0 \text{ ly}}{0.750 \text{ ly/yr}}\sqrt{1-0.75^2} = 17.64 \text{ yr}.$$

While Speedo has landed on Planet X and is waiting for his brother, he ages by

$$\frac{20.0 \text{ ly}}{0.750 \text{ ly/yr}} - \frac{20.0 \text{ ly}}{0.950 \text{ ly/yr}} = 5.614 \text{ yr}.$$

Then $\boxed{\text{Goslo}}$ ends up older by $17.64 \text{ yr} - (6.574 \text{ yr} + 5.614 \text{ yr}) = \boxed{5.45 \text{ yr}}$.

P39.17 (a) $\Delta t = \gamma\Delta t_p = \frac{\Delta t_p}{\sqrt{1-(v/c)^2}} = \frac{15.0 \text{ yr}}{\sqrt{1-(0.700)^2}} = \boxed{21.0 \text{ yr}}$

(b) $d = v(\Delta t) = [0.700c](21.0 \text{ yr}) = [(0.700)(1.00 \text{ ly/yr})](21.0 \text{ yr}) = \boxed{14.7 \text{ ly}}$

(c) The astronauts see Earth flying out the back window at $0.700c$:

$d = v(\Delta t_p) = [0.700c](15.0 \text{ yr}) = [(0.700)(1.00 \text{ ly/yr})](15.0 \text{ yr}) = \boxed{10.5 \text{ ly}}$

(d) Mission control gets signals for 21.0 yr while the battery is operating, and then for 14.7 years after the battery stops powering the transmitter, 14.7 ly away:

$21.0 \text{ yr} + 14.7 \text{ yr} = \boxed{35.7 \text{ yr}}$

P39.18 The orbital speed of the Earth is as described by $\sum F = ma$: $\frac{Gm_S m_E}{r^2} = \frac{m_E v^2}{r}$

$$v = \sqrt{\frac{Gm_S}{r}} = \sqrt{\frac{\left(6.67\times10^{-11}\ \text{N}\cdot\text{m}^2/\text{kg}^2\right)\left(1.99\times10^{30}\ \text{kg}\right)}{1.496\times10^{11}\ \text{m}}} = 2.98\times10^4\ \text{m/s}.$$

The maximum frequency received by the extraterrestrials is

$$f_{obs} = f_{source}\sqrt{\frac{1+v/c}{1-v/c}} = \left(57.0\times10^6\ \text{Hz}\right)\sqrt{\frac{1+\left(2.98\times10^4\ \text{m/s}\right)/\left(3.00\times10^8\ \text{m/s}\right)}{1-\left(2.98\times10^4\ \text{m/s}\right)/\left(3.00\times10^8\ \text{m/s}\right)}} = 57.005\,66\times10^6\ \text{Hz}.$$

The minimum frequency received is

$$f_{obs} = f_{source}\sqrt{\frac{1-v/c}{1+v/c}} = \left(57.0\times10^6\ \text{Hz}\right)\sqrt{\frac{1-\left(2.98\times10^4\ \text{m/s}\right)/\left(3.00\times10^8\ \text{m/s}\right)}{1+\left(2.98\times10^4\ \text{m/s}\right)/\left(3.00\times10^8\ \text{m/s}\right)}} = 56.994\,34\times10^6\ \text{Hz}.$$

The difference, which lets them figure out the speed of our planet, is

$$(57.005\,66 - 56.994\,34)\times10^6\ \text{Hz} = \boxed{1.13\times10^4\ \text{Hz}}.$$

P39.19 (a) Let f_c be the frequency as seen by the car. Thus, $f_c = f_{source}\sqrt{\frac{c+v}{c-v}}$

and, if f is the frequency of the reflected wave, $f = f_c\sqrt{\frac{c+v}{c-v}}$.

Combining gives $\boxed{f = f_{source}\frac{(c+v)}{(c-v)}}$.

(b) Using the above result, $f(c-v) = f_{source}(c+v)$

which gives $(f - f_{source})c = (f + f_{source})v \approx 2f_{source}v$.

The beat frequency is then $f_{beat} = f - f_{source} = \frac{2f_{source}v}{c} = \boxed{\frac{2v}{\lambda}}$.

(c) $$f_{beat} = \frac{(2)(30.0\ \text{m/s})\left(10.0\times10^9\ \text{Hz}\right)}{3.00\times10^8\ \text{m/s}} = \frac{(2)(30.0\ \text{m/s})}{(0.030\,0\ \text{m})} = 2\,000\ \text{Hz} = \boxed{2.00\ \text{kHz}}$$

$$\lambda = \frac{c}{f_{source}} = \frac{3.00\times10^8\ \text{m/s}}{10.0\times10^9\ \text{Hz}} = 3.00\ \text{cm}$$

(d) $$v = \frac{f_{beat}\lambda}{2} \quad \text{so} \quad \Delta v = \frac{\Delta f_{beat}\lambda}{2} = \frac{(5\ \text{Hz})(0.030\,0\ \text{m})}{2} = \boxed{0.075\,0\ \text{m/s} \approx 0.2\ \text{mi/h}}$$

P39.20 (a) When the source moves away from an observer, the observed frequency is

$$f_{\text{obs}} = f_{\text{source}}\left(\frac{c - v_s}{c + v_s}\right)^{1/2} \quad \text{where } v_s = v_{\text{source}}.$$

When $v_s << c$, the binomial expansion gives

$$\left(\frac{c - v_s}{c + v_s}\right)^{1/2} = \left[1 - \left(\frac{v_s}{c}\right)\right]^{1/2}\left[1 + \left(\frac{v_s}{c}\right)\right]^{-1/2} \approx \left(1 - \frac{v_s}{2c}\right)\left(1 - \frac{v_s}{2c}\right) \approx \left(1 - \frac{v_s}{c}\right).$$

So, $$f_{\text{obs}} \approx f_{\text{source}}\left(1 - \frac{v_s}{c}\right).$$

The observed wavelength is found from $c = \lambda_{\text{obs}} f_{\text{obs}} = \lambda f_{\text{source}}$:

$$\lambda_{\text{obs}} = \frac{\lambda f_{\text{source}}}{f_{\text{obs}}} \approx \frac{\lambda f_{\text{source}}}{f_{\text{source}}(1 - v_s/c)} = \frac{\lambda}{1 - v_s/c}$$

$$\Delta\lambda = \lambda_{\text{obs}} - \lambda = \lambda\left(\frac{1}{1 - v_s/c} - 1\right) = \lambda\left(\frac{v_s/c}{1 - v_s/c}\right)$$

Since $1 - \frac{v_s}{c} \approx 1$, $$\boxed{\frac{\Delta\lambda}{\lambda} \approx \frac{v_{\text{source}}}{c}}.$$

(b) $$v_{\text{source}} = c\left(\frac{\Delta\lambda}{\lambda}\right) = c\left(\frac{20.0 \text{ nm}}{397 \text{ nm}}\right) = \boxed{0.050\,4c}$$

***P39.21** For the light as observed

$$f_{\text{obs}} = \frac{c}{\lambda_{\text{obs}}} = \sqrt{\frac{1 + v/c}{1 - v/c}}\, f_{\text{source}} = \sqrt{\frac{1 + v/c}{1 - v/c}}\, \frac{c}{\lambda_{\text{source}}}$$

$$\sqrt{\frac{1 + v/c}{1 - v/c}} = \frac{\lambda_{\text{source}}}{\lambda_{\text{obs}}} = \frac{650 \text{ nm}}{520 \text{ nm}} \qquad \frac{1 + v/c}{1 - v/c} = 1.25^2 = 1.562$$

$$1 + \frac{v}{c} = 1.562 - 1.562\frac{v}{c} \qquad \frac{v}{c} = \frac{0.562}{2.562} = 0.220$$

$$v = \boxed{0.220c} = 6.59 \times 10^7 \text{ m/s}$$

Section 39.5 **The Lorentz Transformation Equations**

***P39.22** Let Suzanne be fixed in reference from S and see the two light-emission events with coordinates $x_1 = 0$, $t_1 = 0$, $x_2 = 0$, $t_2 = 3\ \mu\text{s}$. Let Mark be fixed in reference frame S′ and give the events coordinate $x_1' = 0$, $t_1' = 0$, $t_2' = 9\ \mu\text{s}$.

(a) Then we have

$$t_2' = \gamma\left(t_2 - \frac{v}{c^2}x_2\right)$$

$$9\ \mu\text{s} = \frac{1}{\sqrt{1 - v^2/c^2}}(3\ \mu\text{s} - 0) \qquad \sqrt{1 - \frac{v^2}{c^2}} = \frac{1}{3}$$

$$\frac{v^2}{c^2} = \frac{8}{9} \qquad \boxed{v = 0.943c}$$

(b) $$x_2' = \gamma(x_2 - vt_2) = 3\left(0 - 0.943c \times 3 \times 10^{-6} \text{ s}\right)\left(\frac{3 \times 10^8 \text{ m/s}}{c}\right) = \boxed{2.55 \times 10^3 \text{ m}}$$

P39.23 $\gamma = \frac{1}{\sqrt{1-v^2/c^2}} = \frac{1}{\sqrt{1-0.995^2}} = 10.0$

We are also given: $L_1 = 2.00$ m, and $\theta = 30.0°$ (both measured in a reference frame moving relative to the rod).

Thus, $L_{1x} = L_1 \cos\theta_1 = (2.00 \text{ m})(0.867) = 1.73 \text{ m}$

and $L_{1y} = L_1 \sin\theta_1 = (2.00 \text{ m})(0.500) = 1.00 \text{ m}$

L_{2x} is a proper length, related to L_{1x} by $L_{1x} = \frac{L_{2x}}{\gamma}$.

Therefore, $L_{2x} = 10.0 L_{1x} = 17.3 \text{ m}$

and $L_{2y} = L_{1y} = 1.00 \text{ m}$.

(Lengths perpendicular to the motion are unchanged).

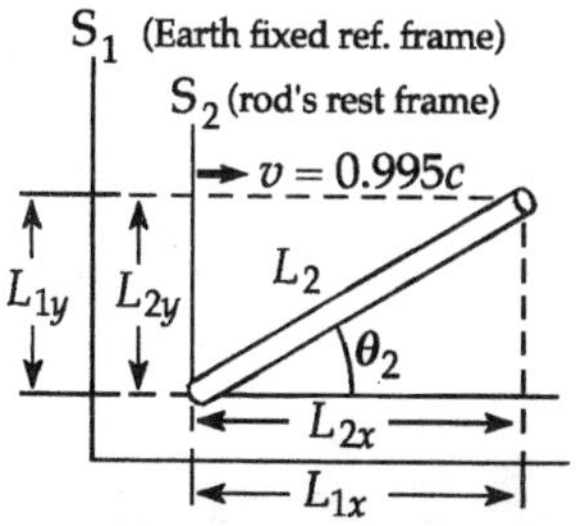

FIG. P39.23

(a) $L_2 = \sqrt{(L_{2x})^2 + (L_{2y})^2}$ gives $\boxed{L_2 = 17.4 \text{ m}}$

(b) $\theta_2 = \tan^{-1}\frac{L_{2y}}{L_{2x}}$ gives $\boxed{\theta_2 = 3.30°}$

***P39.24** Einstein's reasoning about lightning striking the ends of a train shows that the moving observer sees the event toward which she is moving, event B, as occurring first. The *S*-frame coordinates of the events we may take as $(x=0, y=0, z=0, t=0)$ and $(x=100 \text{ m}, y=0, z=0, t=0)$. Then the coordinates in S' are given by the Lorentz transformation. Event A is at $(x'=0, y'=0, z'=0, t'=0)$. The time of event B is

$$t' = \gamma\left(t - \frac{v}{c^2}x\right) = \frac{1}{\sqrt{1-0.8^2}}\left(0 - \frac{0.8c}{c^2}(100 \text{ m})\right) = 1.667\left(-\frac{80 \text{ m}}{3\times10^8 \text{ m/s}}\right) = -4.44\times10^{-7} \text{ s}.$$

The time elapsing before A occurs is $\boxed{444 \text{ ns}}$.

P39.25 (a) From the Lorentz transformation, the separations between the blue-light and red-light events are described by

$$\Delta x' = \gamma(\Delta x - v\Delta t) \qquad 0 = \gamma\left[2.00 \text{ m} - v\left(8.00\times10^{-9} \text{ s}\right)\right]$$

$$v = \frac{2.00 \text{ m}}{8.00\times10^{-9} \text{ s}} = \boxed{2.50\times10^8 \text{ m/s}} \qquad \gamma = \frac{1}{\sqrt{1-\left(2.50\times10^8 \text{ m/s}\right)^2/\left(3.00\times10^8 \text{ m/s}\right)^2}} = 1.81.$$

(b) Again from the Lorentz transformation, $x' = \gamma(x - vt)$:

$$x' = 1.81\left[3.00 \text{ m} - \left(2.50\times10^8 \text{ m/s}\right)\left(1.00\times10^{-9} \text{ s}\right)\right]$$

$$x' = \boxed{4.97 \text{ m}}.$$

(c) $t' = \gamma\left(t - \frac{v}{c^2}x\right)$:

$$t' = 1.81\left[1.00\times10^{-9} \text{ s} - \frac{\left(2.50\times10^8 \text{ m/s}\right)}{\left(3.00\times10^8 \text{ m/s}\right)^2}(3.00 \text{ m})\right]$$

$$t' = \boxed{-1.33\times10^{-8} \text{ s}}$$

Section 39.6 The Lorentz Velocity Transformation Equations

P39.26 u_x = Enterprise velocity

v = Klingon velocity

From Equation 39.16

$$u'_x = \frac{u_x - v}{1 - u_x v/c^2} = \frac{0.900c - 0.800c}{1-(0.900)(0.800)} = \boxed{0.357c}\,.$$

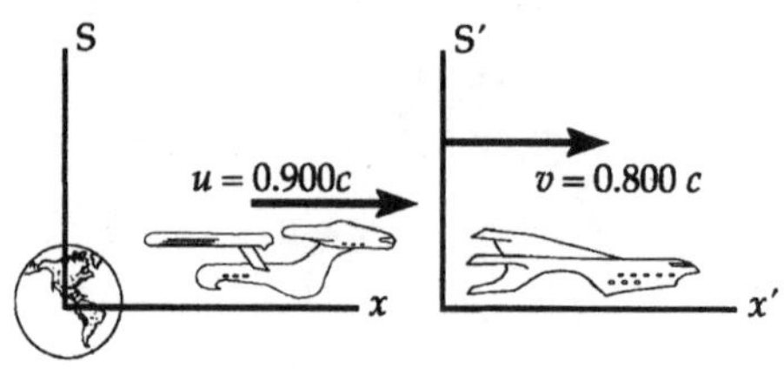

FIG. P39.26

P39.27 $$u'_x = \frac{u_x - v}{1 - u_x v/c^2} = \frac{-0.750c - 0.750c}{1-(-0.750)(0.750)} = \boxed{-0.960c}$$

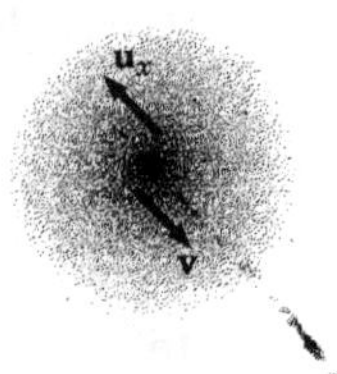

FIG. P39.27

***P39.28** Let frame S be the Earth frame of reference. Then $v = -0.7c$.

The components of the velocity of the first spacecraft are $u_x = (0.6c)\cos 50° = 0.386c$

and $u_y = (0.6c)\sin 50° = 0.459c$.

As measured from the S' frame of the second spacecraft,

$$u'_x = \frac{u_x - v}{1 - u_x v/c^2} = \frac{0.386c - (-0.7c)}{1 - \left[(0.386c)(-0.7c)/c^2\right]} = \frac{1.086c}{1.27} = 0.855c$$

$$u'_y = \frac{u_y}{\gamma\left(1 - u_x v/c^2\right)} = \frac{0.459c\sqrt{1-(0.7)^2}}{1-(0.386)(-0.7)} = \frac{0.459c(0.714)}{1.27} = 0.258c$$

The magnitude of $\mathbf{u}'$ is $\sqrt{(0.855c)^2 + (0.285c)^2} = \boxed{0.893c}$

and its direction is at $\tan^{-1}\dfrac{0.258c}{0.855c} = \boxed{16.8° \text{ above the } x'\text{-axis}}$.

Section 39.7 Relativistic Linear Momentum and the Relativistic Form of Newton's Laws

P39.29 (a) $p = \gamma m u$; for an electron moving at $0.010\,0c$,

$$\gamma = \frac{1}{\sqrt{1-(u/c)^2}} = \frac{1}{\sqrt{1-(0.010\,0)^2}} = 1.000\,05 \approx 1.00.$$

Thus, $$p = 1.00\left(9.11\times10^{-31}\text{ kg}\right)(0.010\,0)\left(3.00\times10^{8}\text{ m/s}\right)$$

$$p = \boxed{2.73\times10^{-24}\text{ kg}\cdot\text{m/s}}\,.$$

(b) Following the same steps as used in part (a),
we find at $0.500c$, $\gamma = 1.15$ and $p = \boxed{1.58\times10^{-22}\text{ kg}\cdot\text{m/s}}$.

(c) At $0.900c$, $\gamma = 2.29$ and $p = \boxed{5.64\times10^{-22}\text{ kg}\cdot\text{m/s}}$.

P39.30 Using the relativistic form,
$$p=\frac{mu}{\sqrt{1-(u/c)^2}}=\gamma\, mu$$

we find the difference Δp from the classical momentum, mu:
$$\Delta p=\gamma\, mu-mu=(\gamma-1)mu\,.$$

(a) The difference is 1.00% when $(\gamma-1)mu=0.010\,0\gamma\, mu$:
$$\gamma=\frac{1}{0.990}=\frac{1}{\sqrt{1-(u/c)^2}}$$

thus $1-\left(\frac{u}{c}\right)^2=(0.990)^2$, and
$$u=\boxed{0.141c}\,.$$

(b) The difference is 10.0% when $(\gamma-1)mu=0.100\gamma\, mu$:
$$\gamma=\frac{1}{0.900}=\frac{1}{\sqrt{1-(u/c)^2}}$$

thus $1-\left(\frac{u}{c}\right)^2=(0.900)^2$ and
$$u=\boxed{0.436c}\,.$$

P39.31 $\frac{p-mu}{mu}=\frac{\gamma\, mu-mu}{mu}=\gamma-1$:
$$\gamma-1=\frac{1}{\sqrt{1-(u/c)^2}}-1\approx 1+\frac{1}{2}\left(\frac{u}{c}\right)^2-1=\frac{1}{2}\left(\frac{u}{c}\right)^2$$
$$\frac{p-mu}{mu}=\frac{1}{2}\left(\frac{90.0\text{ m/s}}{3.00\times 10^{8}\text{ m/s}}\right)^2=\boxed{4.50\times 10^{-14}}$$

P39.32 $p=\frac{mu}{\sqrt{1-(u/c)^2}}$ becomes $1-\frac{u^2}{c^2}=\frac{m^2u^2}{p^2}$

which gives:
$$1=u^2\left(\frac{m^2}{p^2}+\frac{1}{c^2}\right)$$

or $c^2=u^2\left(\frac{m^2c^2}{p^2}+1\right)$ and
$$\boxed{u=\frac{c}{\sqrt{\left(m^2c^2/p^2\right)+1}}}\,.$$

P39.33 Relativistic momentum of the system of fragments must be conserved. For total momentum to be zero after as it was before, we must have, with subscript 2 referring to the heavier fragment, and subscript 1 to the lighter, $p_2=p_1$

or
$$\gamma_2 m_2 u_2=\gamma_1 m_1 u_1=\frac{2.50\times 10^{-28}\text{ kg}}{\sqrt{1-(0.893)^2}}\times(0.893c)$$

or
$$\frac{\left(1.67\times 10^{-27}\text{ kg}\right)u_2}{\sqrt{1-(u_2/c)^2}}=\left(4.960\times 10^{-28}\text{ kg}\right)c\,.$$

Proceeding to solve, we find
$$\left(\frac{1.67\times 10^{-27}}{4.960\times 10^{-28}}\frac{u_2}{c}\right)^2=1-\frac{u_2^2}{c^2}$$
$$12.3\frac{u_2^2}{c^2}=1 \text{ and } u_2=\boxed{0.285c}\,.$$

Section 39.8 **Relativistic Energy**

P39.34 $\Delta E = (\gamma_1 - \gamma_2)mc^2$

For an electron, $mc^2 = 0.511\text{ MeV}$

(a) $$\Delta E = \left(\sqrt{\frac{1}{(1-0.810)}} - \sqrt{\frac{1}{(1-0.250)}}\right)mc^2 = \boxed{0.582\text{ MeV}}$$

(b) $$\Delta E = \left(\sqrt{\frac{1}{1-(0.990)^2}} - \sqrt{\frac{1}{1-0.810}}\right)mc^2 = \boxed{2.45\text{ MeV}}$$

P39.35 $$\sum W = K_f - K_i = \left(\frac{1}{\sqrt{1-(v_f/c)^2}} - 1\right)mc^2 - \left(\frac{1}{\sqrt{1-(v_i/c)^2}}\right)mc^2$$

or $$\sum W = \left(\frac{1}{\sqrt{1-(v_f/c)^2}} - \frac{1}{\sqrt{1-(v_i/c)^2}}\right)mc^2$$

(a) $$\sum W = \left(\frac{1}{\sqrt{1-(0.750)^2}} - \frac{1}{\sqrt{1-(0.500)^2}}\right)(1.673\times10^{-27}\text{ kg})(2.998\times10^{8}\text{ m/s})^2$$

$$\sum W = \boxed{5.37\times10^{-11}\text{ J}}$$

(b) $$\sum W = \left(\frac{1}{\sqrt{1-(0.995)^2}} - \frac{1}{\sqrt{1-(0.500)^2}}\right)(1.673\times10^{-27}\text{ kg})(2.998\times10^{8}\text{ m/s})^2$$

$$\sum W = \boxed{1.33\times10^{-9}\text{ J}}$$

P39.36 The relativistic kinetic energy of an object of mass m and speed u is $K_r = \left(\frac{1}{\sqrt{1-u^2/c^2}} - 1\right)mc^2$.

For $u = 0.100c$, $$K_r = \left(\frac{1}{\sqrt{1-0.0100}} - 1\right)mc^2 = 0.005\,038mc^2.$$

The classical equation $K_c = \frac{1}{2}mu^2$ gives $$K_c = \frac{1}{2}m(0.100c)^2 = 0.005\,000mc^2$$

different by $$\frac{0.005\,038 - 0.005\,000}{0.005\,038} = 0.751\%.$$

For still smaller speeds the agreement will be still better.

P39.37 $E = \gamma mc^2 = 2mc^2$ or $\gamma = 2$.

Thus, $\dfrac{u}{c} = \sqrt{1 - \left(\dfrac{1}{\gamma}\right)^2} = \dfrac{\sqrt{3}}{2}$ or $u = \dfrac{c\sqrt{3}}{2}$.

The momentum is then $p = \gamma mu = 2m\left(\dfrac{c\sqrt{3}}{2}\right) = \left(\dfrac{mc^2}{c}\right)\sqrt{3}$

$$p = \left(\frac{938.3\text{ MeV}}{c}\right)\sqrt{3} = \boxed{1.63 \times 10^3 \ \frac{\text{MeV}}{c}}.$$

P39.38 (a) Using the classical equation, $K = \dfrac{1}{2}mv^2 = \dfrac{1}{2}(78.0\text{ kg})\left(1.06 \times 10^5 \text{ m/s}\right)^2 = \boxed{4.38 \times 10^{11}\text{ J}}$.

(b) Using the relativistic equation, $K = \left(\dfrac{1}{\sqrt{1-(v/c)^2}} - 1\right)mc^2$.

$$K = \left[\frac{1}{\sqrt{1 - \left(1.06 \times 10^5 / 2.998 \times 10^8\right)^2}} - 1\right](78.0\text{ kg})\left(2.998 \times 10^8 \text{ m/s}\right)^2 = \boxed{4.38 \times 10^{11}\text{ J}}$$

When $\dfrac{v}{c} << 1$, the binomial series expansion gives $\left[1 - \left(\dfrac{v}{c}\right)^2\right]^{-1/2} \approx 1 + \dfrac{1}{2}\left(\dfrac{v}{c}\right)^2$.

Thus, $\left[1 - \left(\dfrac{v}{c}\right)^2\right]^{-1/2} - 1 \approx \dfrac{1}{2}\left(\dfrac{v}{c}\right)^2$.

and the relativistic expression for kinetic energy becomes $K \approx \dfrac{1}{2}\left(\dfrac{v}{c}\right)^2 mc^2 = \dfrac{1}{2}mv^2$. That is, in the limit of speeds much smaller than the speed of light, the relativistic and classical expressions yield the same results.

P39.39 (a) $E_R = mc^2 = \left(1.67 \times 10^{-27}\text{ kg}\right)\left(2.998 \times 10^8 \text{ m/s}\right)^2 = 1.50 \times 10^{-10}\text{ J} = \boxed{938\text{ MeV}}$

(b) $E = \gamma mc^2 = \dfrac{1.50 \times 10^{-10}\text{ J}}{\left[1 - (0.950c/c)^2\right]^{1/2}} = 4.81 \times 10^{-10}\text{ J} = \boxed{3.00 \times 10^3\text{ MeV}}$

(c) $K = E - mc^2 = 4.81 \times 10^{-10}\text{ J} - 1.50 \times 10^{-10}\text{ J} = 3.31 \times 10^{-10}\text{ J} = \boxed{2.07 \times 10^3\text{ MeV}}$

P39.40 The relativistic density is

$$\frac{E_R}{c^2V} = \frac{mc^2}{c^2V} = \frac{m}{V} = \frac{m}{\left(L_p\right)\left(L_p\right)\left[L_p\sqrt{1-(u/c)^2}\right]} = \frac{8.00\text{ g}}{(1.00\text{ cm})^3\sqrt{1-(0.900)^2}} = \boxed{18.4\text{ g/cm}^3}.$$

P39.41 We must conserve both energy and relativistic momentum of the system of fragments. With subscript 1 referring to the $0.868c$ particle and subscript 2 to the $0.987c$ particle,

$$\gamma_1 = \frac{1}{\sqrt{1-(0.868)^2}} = 2.01 \text{ and } \gamma_2 = \frac{1}{\sqrt{1-(0.987)^2}} = 6.22.$$

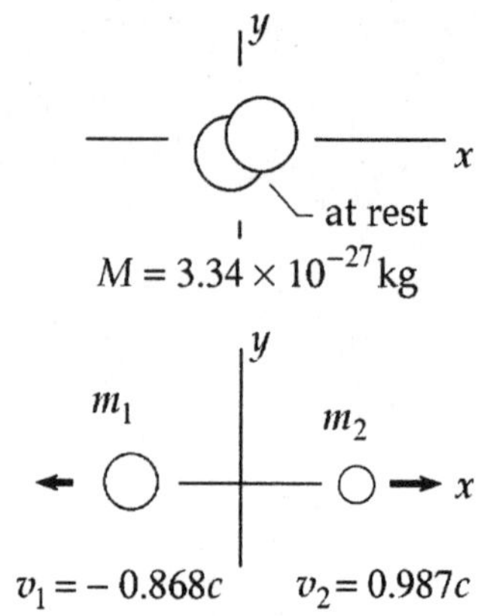

Conservation of energy gives $E_1 + E_2 = E_{\text{total}}$

which is $\gamma_1 m_1 c^2 + \gamma_2 m_2 c^2 = m_{\text{total}} c^2$

or $2.01m_1 + 6.22m_2 = 3.34 \times 10^{-27}$ kg.

This reduces to: $m_1 + 3.09m_2 = 1.66 \times 10^{-27}$ kg. (1)

Since the final momentum of the system must equal zero, $p_1 = p_2$

gives $\gamma_1 m_1 u_1 = \gamma_2 m_2 u_2$

or $(2.01)(0.868c)m_1 = (6.22)(0.987c)m_2$

which becomes $m_1 = 3.52m_2$. (2)

Solving (1) and (2) simultaneously, $m_1 = \boxed{8.84 \times 10^{-28} \text{ kg}}$ and $m_2 = \boxed{2.51 \times 10^{-28} \text{ kg}}$.

y
x
at rest
$M = 3.34 \times 10^{-27}$ kg
y
m_1
m_2
x
$v_1 = -0.868c$
$v_2 = 0.987c$

FIG. P39.41

***P39.42** Energy conservation: $\frac{1}{\sqrt{1-0^2}} 1\,400 \text{ kg}c^2 + \frac{900 \text{ kg}c^2}{\sqrt{1-0.85^2}} = \frac{Mc^2}{\sqrt{1-v^2/c^2}}$

$$3\,108 \text{ kg}\sqrt{1-\frac{v^2}{c^2}} = M.$$

Momentum conservation: $0 + \frac{900 \text{ kg}(0.85c)}{\sqrt{1-0.85^2}} = \frac{Mv}{\sqrt{1-v^2/c^2}}$

$$1\,452 \text{ kg}\sqrt{1-\frac{v^2}{c^2}} = \frac{Mv}{c}.$$

(a) Dividing gives $\frac{v}{c} = \frac{1\,452}{3\,108} = 0.467$ $\boxed{v = 0.467c}$.

(b) Now by substitution $3\,108 \text{ kg}\sqrt{1-0.467^2} = \boxed{M = 2.75 \times 10^3 \text{ kg}}$.

P39.43 $E = \gamma mc^2$ $p = \gamma mu$

$E^2 = \left(\gamma mc^2\right)^2$ $p^2 = (\gamma mu)^2$

$$E^2 - p^2c^2 = \left(\gamma mc^2\right)^2 - (\gamma mu)^2 c^2 = \gamma^2\left(\left(mc^2\right)^2 - (mc)^2u^2\right) = \left(mc^2\right)^2\left(1-\frac{u^2}{c^2}\right)\left(1-\frac{u^2}{c^2}\right)^{-1} = \left(mc^2\right)^2$$

Q.E.D.

P39.44 (a) $q(\Delta V) = K = (\gamma - 1)m_e c^2$

Thus, $\gamma = \frac{1}{\sqrt{1-(u/c)^2}} = 1 + \frac{q(\Delta V)}{m_e c^2}$ from which $\boxed{u = 0.302c}$.

(b) $K = (\gamma - 1)m_e c^2 = q(\Delta V) = \left(1.60 \times 10^{-19} \text{ C}\right)\left(2.50 \times 10^4 \text{ J/C}\right) = \boxed{4.00 \times 10^{-15} \text{ J}}$

P39.45 (a) $E=\gamma mc^2=20.0\text{ GeV}$ with $mc^2=0.511\text{ MeV}$ for electrons. Thus,

$$\gamma=\frac{20.0\times10^9\text{ eV}}{0.511\times10^6\text{ eV}}=\boxed{3.91\times10^4}.$$

(b) $$\gamma=\frac{1}{\sqrt{1-(u/c)^2}}=3.91\times10^4 \text{ from which } \boxed{u=0.999\,999\,999\,7c}$$

(c) $$L=L_p\sqrt{1-\left(\frac{u}{c}\right)^2}=\frac{L_p}{\gamma}=\frac{3.00\times10^3\text{ m}}{3.91\times10^4}=7.67\times10^{-2}\text{ m}=\boxed{7.67\text{ cm}}$$

***P39.46** (a) $$\mathcal{P}=\frac{\text{energy}}{\Delta t}=\frac{2\text{ J}}{100\times10^{-15}\text{ s}}=\boxed{2.00\times10^{13}\text{ W}}$$

(b) The kinetic energy of one electron with $v=0.999\,9c$ is

$$(\gamma-1)mc^2=\left(\frac{1}{\sqrt{1-0.999\,9^2}}-1\right)9.11\times10^{-31}\text{ kg}\left(3\times10^8\text{ m/s}\right)^2=69.7\left(8.20\times10^{-14}\text{ J}\right)$$

$$=5.72\times10^{-12}\text{ J}$$

Then we require $\frac{0.01}{100}2\text{ J}=N\left(5.72\times10^{-12}\text{ J}\right)$

$$N=\frac{2\times10^{-4}\text{ J}}{5.72\times10^{-12}\text{ J}}=\boxed{3.50\times10^7}.$$

P39.47 Conserving total momentum of the decaying particle system, $p_{\text{before decay}}=p_{\text{after decay}}=0$

$$p_v=p_\mu=\gamma m_\mu u=\gamma(207m_e)u.$$

Conservation of mass-energy for the system gives $E_\mu+E_v=E_\pi$: $\gamma m_\mu c^2+p_v c=m_\pi c^2$

$$\gamma(207m_e)+\frac{p_v}{c}=273m_e.$$

Substituting from the momentum equation above, $$\gamma(207m_e)+\gamma(207m_e)\frac{u}{c}=273m_e$$

or $\gamma\left(1+\frac{u}{c}\right)=\frac{273}{207}=1.32$: $\frac{1+u/c}{1-u/c}=1.74$ $\frac{u}{c}=0.270$.

Then, $K_\mu=(\gamma-1)m_\mu c^2=(\gamma-1)207\left(m_e c^2\right)$: $$K_\mu=\left(\frac{1}{\sqrt{1-(0.270)^2}}-1\right)207(0.511\text{ MeV})$$

$$K_\mu=\boxed{4.08\text{ MeV}}.$$

Also, $E_v=E_\pi-E_\mu$: $$E_v=m_\pi c^2-\gamma m_\mu c^2=(273-207\gamma)m_e c^2$$

$$E_v=\left(273-\frac{207}{\sqrt{1-(0.270)^2}}\right)(0.511\text{ MeV})$$

$$E_v=\boxed{29.6\text{ MeV}}$$

***P39.48** Let observer A hold the unprimed reference frame, with $u_1 = \frac{3c}{4}$ and $u_2 = -\frac{3c}{4}$. Let observer B be at rest in the primed frame with $u_1' = 0 = \frac{u_1 - v}{1 - u_1 v/c^2}$ $\qquad v = u_1 = \frac{3c}{4}$.

(a) Then $u_2' = \frac{u_2 - v}{1 - u_2 v/c^2} = \frac{-3c/4 - 3c/4}{1 - (-3c/4)(+3c/4)} = \frac{-1.5c}{1 + 9/16}$

speed $= |u_2'| = \frac{3c/2}{25/16} = \frac{24}{25}c = \boxed{0.960c}$.

(b) In the unprimed frame the objects, each of mass m, together have energy $\gamma mc^2 + \gamma mc^2 = 2\frac{mc^2}{\sqrt{1 - 0.75^2}} = 3.02mc^2$.

In the primed frame the energy is $\frac{mc^2}{\sqrt{1 - 0^2}} + \frac{mc^2}{\sqrt{1 - 0.96^2}} = 4.57mc^2$, greater by $\frac{4.57mc^2}{3.02mc^2} = \boxed{\text{1.51 times greater as measured by observer B}}$.

Section 39.9 **Mass and Energy**

P39.49 Let a 0.3-kg flag be run up a flagpole 7 m high.

We put into it energy $\qquad mgh = 0.3\ \text{kg}\left(9.8\ \text{m/s}^2\right)7\ \text{m} \approx 20\ \text{J}$.

So we put into it extra mass $\qquad \Delta m = \frac{E}{c^2} = \frac{20\ \text{J}}{\left(3 \times 10^8\ \text{m/s}\right)^2} = 2 \times 10^{-16}\ \text{kg}$

for a fractional increase of $\qquad \frac{2 \times 10^{-16}\ \text{kg}}{0.3\ \text{kg}} \boxed{\sim 10^{-15}}$.

P39.50 $E = 2.86 \times 10^5\ \text{J}$. Also, the mass-energy relation says that $E = mc^2$.

Therefore, $\qquad m = \frac{E}{c^2} = \frac{2.86 \times 10^5\ \text{J}}{\left(3.00 \times 10^8\ \text{m/s}\right)^2} = \boxed{3.18 \times 10^{-12}\ \text{kg}}$.

No, a mass loss of this magnitude (out of a total of 9.00 g) $\boxed{\text{could not be detected}}$.

P39.51 $\Delta m = \frac{E}{c^2} = \frac{\mathcal{P}\Delta t}{c^2} = \frac{0.800\left(1.00 \times 10^9\ \text{J/s}\right)(3.00\ \text{yr})\left(3.16 \times 10^7\ \text{s/yr}\right)}{\left(3.00 \times 10^8\ \text{m/s}\right)^2} = \boxed{0.842\ \text{kg}}$

P39.52 $\Delta m = \frac{E}{c^2} = \frac{mc(\Delta T)}{c^2} = \frac{\rho Vc(\Delta T)}{c^2} = \frac{\left(1\,030\ \text{kg/m}^3\right)\left(1.40 \times 10^9\right)\left(10^3\ \text{m}\right)^3 (4\,186\ \text{J/kg}\cdot{}^\circ\text{C})(10.0\ {}^\circ\text{C})}{\left(3.00 \times 10^8\ \text{m/s}\right)^2}$

$\Delta m = \boxed{6.71 \times 10^8\ \text{kg}}$

P39.53 $\mathcal{P} = \frac{dE}{dt} = \frac{d(mc^2)}{dt} = c^2\frac{dm}{dt} = 3.77\times10^{26}\text{ W}$

Thus, $\frac{dm}{dt} = \frac{3.77\times10^{26}\text{ J/s}}{(3.00\times10^{8}\text{ m/s})^2} = \boxed{4.19\times10^{9}\text{ kg/s}}$

P39.54 $2m_ec^2 = 1.02\text{ MeV}$ $\qquad E_\gamma \geq \boxed{1.02\text{ MeV}}$

Section 39.10 **The General Theory of Relativity**

***P39.55** (a) For the satellite $\sum F = ma$: $\frac{GM_Em}{r^2} = \frac{mv^2}{r} = \frac{m}{r}\left(\frac{2\pi r}{T}\right)^2$

$$GM_ET^2 = 4\pi^2r^3$$

$$r = \left(\frac{6.67\times10^{-11}\text{ N}\cdot\text{m}^2(5.98\times10^{24}\text{ kg})(43\,080\text{ s})^2}{\text{kg}^2 4\pi^2}\right)^{1/3}$$

$$r = \boxed{2.66\times10^{7}\text{ m}}$$

(b) $v = \frac{2\pi r}{T} = \frac{2\pi(2.66\times10^{7}\text{ m})}{43\,080\text{ s}} = \boxed{3.87\times10^{3}\text{ m/s}}$

(c) The small fractional decrease in frequency received is equal in magnitude to the fractional increase in period of the moving oscillator due to time dilation:

$$\text{fractional change in } f = -(\gamma - 1) = -\left(\frac{1}{\sqrt{1-(3.87\times10^3/3\times10^8)^2}} - 1\right)$$

$$= 1 - \left(1 - \frac{1}{2}\left[-\left(\frac{3.87\times10^3}{3\times10^8}\right)^2\right]\right) = \boxed{-8.34\times10^{-11}}$$

(d) The orbit altitude is large compared to the radius of the Earth, so we must use $U_g = -\frac{GM_Em}{r}$.

$$\Delta U_g = -\frac{6.67\times10^{-11}\text{ Nm}^2(5.98\times10^{24}\text{ kg})m}{\text{kg}^2\ 2.66\times10^{7}\text{ m}} + \frac{6.67\times10^{-11}\text{ Nm}(5.98\times10^{24}\text{ kg})m}{\text{kg}\ 6.37\times10^{6}\text{ m}}$$

$$= 4.76\times10^{7}\text{ J/kg}\,m$$

$$\frac{\Delta f}{f} = \frac{\Delta U_g}{mc^2} = \frac{4.76\times10^{7}\text{ m}^2/\text{s}^2}{(3\times10^{8}\text{ m/s})^2} = \boxed{+5.29\times10^{-10}}$$

(e) $-8.34\times10^{-11} + 5.29\times10^{-10} = \boxed{+4.46\times10^{-10}}$

Additional Problems

P39.56 (a) $d_{\text{earth}} = vt_{\text{earth}} = v\gamma t_{\text{astro}}$ so $(2.00\times10^6\text{ yr})c = v\dfrac{1}{\sqrt{1-v^2/c^2}}30.0\text{ yr}$

$$\sqrt{1-\frac{v^2}{c^2}} = \left(\frac{v}{c}\right)(1.50\times10^{-5}) \qquad 1-\frac{v^2}{c^2} = \frac{v^2(2.25\times10^{-10})}{c^2}$$

$$1 = \frac{v^2}{c^2}(1+2.25\times10^{-10}) \quad \text{so} \quad \frac{v}{c} = (1+2.25\times10^{-10})^{-1/2} = 1-\frac{1}{2}(2.25\times10^{-10})$$

$$\boxed{\frac{v}{c} = 1-1.12\times10^{-10}}$$

(b) $$K = \left(\frac{1}{\sqrt{1-v^2/c^2}}-1\right)mc^2 = \left(\frac{2.00\times10^6\text{ yr}}{30\text{ yr}}-1\right)(1\,000)(1\,000\text{ kg})(3\times10^8\text{ m/s})^2 = \boxed{6.00\times10^{27}\text{ J}}$$

(c) $$6.00\times10^{27}\text{ J} = 6.00\times10^{27}\text{ J}\left(\frac{13¢}{\text{kWh}}\right)\left(\frac{\text{k}}{10^3}\right)\left(\frac{\text{W}\cdot\text{s}}{\text{J}}\right)\left(\frac{\text{h}}{3\,600\text{ s}}\right) = \boxed{\$2.17\times10^{20}}$$

P39.57 (a) $10^{13}\text{ MeV} = (\gamma-1)m_pc^2$ so $\gamma = 10^{10}$

$v_p \approx c$ $\qquad t' = \dfrac{t}{\gamma} = \dfrac{10^5\text{ yr}}{10^{10}} = 10^{-5}\text{ yr} \sim \boxed{10^2\text{ s}}$

(b) $d' = ct' \boxed{\sim 10^8\text{ km}}$

P39.58 (a) When $K_e = K_p$, $\quad m_ec^2(\gamma_e-1) = m_pc^2(\gamma_p-1)$.

In this case, $\quad m_ec^2 = 0.511\text{ MeV}$, $m_pc^2 = 938\text{ MeV}$

and $\quad \gamma_e = \left[1-(0.750)^2\right]^{-1/2} = 1.511\,9$.

Substituting, $$\gamma_p = 1+\frac{m_ec^2(\gamma_e-1)}{m_pc^2} = 1+\frac{(0.511\text{ MeV})(1.511\,9-1)}{938\text{ MeV}} = 1.000\,279$$

but $$\gamma_p = \frac{1}{\left[1-(u_p/c)^2\right]^{1/2}}.$$

Therefore, $\quad u_p = c\sqrt{1-\gamma_p^{-2}} = \boxed{0.023\,6c}$.

(b) When $p_e = p_p$ $\quad \gamma_pm_pu_p = \gamma_em_eu_e$ or $\gamma_pu_p = \dfrac{\gamma_em_eu_e}{m_p}$.

Thus, $$\gamma_pu_p = \frac{(1.511\,9)(0.511\text{ MeV}/c^2)(0.750c)}{938\text{ MeV}/c^2} = 6.177\,2\times10^{-4}c$$

and $$\frac{u_p}{c} = 6.177\,2\times10^{-4}\sqrt{1-\left(\frac{u_p}{c}\right)^2}$$

which yields $\quad u_p = \boxed{6.18\times10^{-4}c} = 185\text{ km/s}$.

P39.59 (a) Since Mary is in the same reference frame, S', as Ted, she measures the ball to have the same speed Ted observes, namely $|u'_x| = \boxed{0.800c}$.

(b) $$\Delta t' = \frac{L_p}{|u'_x|} = \frac{1.80\times 10^{12}\text{ m}}{0.800\left(3.00\times 10^{8}\text{ m/s}\right)} = \boxed{7.50\times 10^{3}\text{ s}}$$

(c) $$L = L_p\sqrt{1-\frac{v^2}{c^2}} = \left(1.80\times 10^{12}\text{ m}\right)\sqrt{1-\frac{(0.600c)^2}{c^2}} = \boxed{1.44\times 10^{12}\text{ m}}$$

Since $v = 0.600c$ and $u'_x = -0.800c$, the velocity Jim measures for the ball is

$$u_x = \frac{u'_x + v}{1+u'_x v/c^2} = \frac{(-0.800c)+(0.600c)}{1+(-0.800)(0.600)} = \boxed{-0.385c}.$$

(d) Jim measures the ball and Mary to be initially separated by 1.44×10^{12} m. Mary's motion at $0.600c$ and the ball's motion at $0.385c$ nibble into this distance from both ends. The gap closes at the rate $0.600c + 0.385c = 0.985c$, so the ball and catcher meet after a time

$$\Delta t = \frac{1.44\times 10^{12}\text{ m}}{0.985\left(3.00\times 10^{8}\text{ m/s}\right)} = \boxed{4.88\times 10^{3}\text{ s}}.$$

***P39.60** (a) The charged battery stores energy $E = \mathscr{P}t = (1.20\text{ J/s})(50\text{ min})(60\text{ s/min}) = 3\,600\text{ J}$

so its mass excess is $$\Delta m = \frac{E}{c^2} = \frac{3\,600\text{ J}}{\left(3\times 10^{8}\text{ m/s}\right)^2} = \boxed{4.00\times 10^{-14}\text{ kg}}.$$

(b) $$\frac{\Delta m}{m} = \frac{4.00\times 10^{-14}\text{ kg}}{25\times 10^{-3}\text{ kg}} = \boxed{1.60\times 10^{-12}}\ \text{too small to measure.}$$

P39.61 $$\frac{\Delta mc^2}{mc^2} = \frac{4(938.78\text{ MeV}) - 3\,728.4\text{ MeV}}{4(938.78\text{ MeV})}\times 100\% = \boxed{0.712\%}$$

***P39.62** The energy of the first fragment is given by $E_1^2 = p_1^2c^2 + \left(m_1c^2\right)^2 = (1.75\text{ MeV})^2 + (1.00\text{ MeV})^2$

$E_1 = 2.02$ MeV.

For the second, $E_2^2 = (2.00\text{ MeV})^2 + (1.50\text{ MeV})^2$ $\qquad E_2 = 2.50$ MeV.

(a) Energy is conserved, so the unstable object had $E = 4.52$ MeV. Each component of momentum is conserved, so the original object moved with

$p^2 = p_x^2 + p_y^2 = \left(\frac{1.75\text{ MeV}}{c}\right)^2 + \left(\frac{2.00\text{ MeV}}{c}\right)^2$. Then for it

$$(4.52\text{ MeV})^2 = (1.75\text{ MeV})^2 + (2.00\text{ MeV})^2 + \left(mc^2\right)^2 \qquad \boxed{m = \frac{3.65\text{ MeV}}{c^2}}.$$

(b) Now $E = \gamma mc^2$ gives $4.52\text{ MeV} = \frac{1}{\sqrt{1-v^2/c^2}}3.65\text{ MeV}$ $\qquad 1-\frac{v^2}{c^2} = 0.654$, $\boxed{v = 0.589c}$.

P39.63 (a) Take the spaceship as the primed frame, moving toward the right at $v = +0.600c$.

Then $u'_x = +0.800c$, and $$u_x = \frac{u'_x + v}{1 + (u'_x v)/c^2} = \frac{0.800c + 0.600c}{1 + (0.800)(0.600)} = \boxed{0.946c}.$$

(b) $L = \dfrac{L_p}{\gamma}$: $$L = (0.200\text{ ly})\sqrt{1 - (0.600)^2} = \boxed{0.160\text{ ly}}$$

(c) The aliens observe the 0.160-ly distance closing because the probe nibbles into it from one end at $0.800c$ and the Earth reduces it at the other end at $0.600c$.

Thus, $$\text{time} = \frac{0.160\text{ ly}}{0.800c + 0.600c} = \boxed{0.114\text{ yr}}.$$

(d) $K = \left(\dfrac{1}{\sqrt{1 - u^2/c^2}} - 1\right)mc^2$: $$K = \left(\frac{1}{\sqrt{1 - (0.946)^2}} - 1\right)\left(4.00 \times 10^5\text{ kg}\right)\left(3.00 \times 10^8\text{ m/s}\right)^2$$

$$K = \boxed{7.50 \times 10^{22}\text{ J}}$$

P39.64 In this case, the proper time is T_0 (the time measured by the students on a clock at rest relative to them). The dilated time measured by the professor is: $\Delta t = \gamma T_0$

where $\Delta t = T + t$ Here T is the time she waits before sending a signal and t is the time required for the signal to reach the students.

Thus, we have: $$T + t = \gamma T_0. \qquad (1)$$

To determine the travel time t, realize that the distance the students will have moved beyond the professor before the signal reaches them is: $d = v(T + t)$.

The time required for the signal to travel this distance is: $$t = \frac{d}{c} = \left(\frac{v}{c}\right)(T + t).$$

Solving for t gives: $$t = \frac{(v/c)T}{1 - (v/c)}.$$

Substituting this into equation (1) yields: $$T + \frac{(v/c)T}{1 - (v/c)} = \gamma T_0$$

or $$\frac{T}{1 - v/c} = \gamma T_0.$$

Then $$T = T_0 \frac{1 - (v/c)}{\sqrt{1 - (v^2/c^2)}} = T_0 \frac{1 - (v/c)}{\sqrt{[1 + (v/c)][1 - (v/c)]}} = \boxed{T_0 \sqrt{\frac{1 - (v/c)}{1 + (v/c)}}}.$$

P39.65 Look at the situation from the instructors' viewpoint since they are at rest relative to the clock, and hence measure the proper time. The Earth moves with velocity $v = -0.280c$ relative to the instructors while the students move with a velocity $u' = -0.600c$ relative to Earth. Using the velocity addition equation, the velocity of the students relative to the instructors (and hence the clock) is:

$$u = \frac{v + u'}{1 + vu'/c^2} = \frac{(-0.280c) - (0.600c)}{1 + (-0.280c)(-0.600c)/c^2} = -0.753c \text{ (students relative to clock).}$$

(a) With a proper time interval of $\Delta t_p = 50.0\text{ min}$, the time interval measured by the students is:

$$\Delta t = \gamma\,\Delta t_p \qquad \text{with} \qquad \gamma = \frac{1}{\sqrt{1 - (0.753c)^2/c^2}} = 1.52\,.$$

Thus, the students measure the exam to last $T = 1.52(50.0\text{ min}) = \boxed{76.0\text{ minutes}}$.

(b) The duration of the exam as measured by observers on Earth is:

$$\Delta t = \gamma\,\Delta t_p \text{ with } \gamma = \frac{1}{\sqrt{1 - (0.280c)^2/c^2}} \text{ so } T = 1.04(50.0\text{ min}) = \boxed{52.1\text{ minutes}}.$$

P39.66 The energy which arrives in one year is

$$E = \mathcal{P}\,\Delta t = \left(1.79 \times 10^{17}\text{ J/s}\right)\left(3.16 \times 10^{7}\text{ s}\right) = 5.66 \times 10^{24}\text{ J}.$$

Thus, $m = \frac{E}{c^2} = \frac{5.66 \times 10^{24}\text{ J}}{\left(3.00 \times 10^{8}\text{ m/s}\right)^2} = \boxed{6.28 \times 10^{7}\text{ kg}}$.

P39.67 The observer measures the proper length of the tunnel, 50.0 m, but measures the train contracted to length

$$L = L_p\sqrt{1 - \frac{v^2}{c^2}} = 100\text{ m}\sqrt{1 - (0.950)^2} = 31.2\text{ m}$$

shorter than the tunnel by $50.0 - 31.2 = \boxed{18.8\text{ m}}$ so $\boxed{\text{it is completely within the tunnel.}}$.

P39.68 If the energy required to remove a mass m from the surface is equal to its rest energy mc^2,

then $\frac{GM_s m}{R_g} = mc^2$

and $R_g = \frac{GM_s}{c^2} = \frac{\left(6.67 \times 10^{-11}\text{ N}\cdot\text{m}^2/\text{kg}^2\right)\left(1.99 \times 10^{30}\text{ kg}\right)}{\left(3.00 \times 10^{8}\text{ m/s}\right)^2}$

$R_g = 1.47 \times 10^{3}\text{ m} = \boxed{1.47\text{ km}}$.

P39.69 (a) At any speed, the momentum of the particle is given by

$$p = \gamma mu = \frac{mu}{\sqrt{1-(u/c)^2}}.$$

Since $F = qE = \frac{dp}{dt}$:

$$qE = \frac{d}{dt}\left[mu\left(1-\frac{u^2}{c^2}\right)^{-1/2}\right]$$

$$qE = m\left(1-\frac{u^2}{c^2}\right)^{-1/2}\frac{du}{dt} + \frac{1}{2}mu\left(1-\frac{u^2}{c^2}\right)^{-3/2}\left(\frac{2u}{c^2}\right)\frac{du}{dt}.$$

So

$$\frac{qE}{m} = \frac{du}{dt}\left[\frac{1-u^2/c^2+u^2/c^2}{\left(1-u^2/c^2\right)^{3/2}}\right]$$

and

$$\boxed{a = \frac{du}{dt} = \frac{qE}{m}\left(1-\frac{u^2}{c^2}\right)^{3/2}}.$$

(b) For u small compared to c, the relativistic expression reduces to the classical $a = \frac{qE}{m}$. As u approaches c, the acceleration approaches zero, so that the object can never reach the speed of light.

(c)

$$\int_0^u \frac{du}{\left(1-u^2/c^2\right)^{3/2}} = \int_{t=0}^{t} \frac{qE}{m}dt \qquad \boxed{u = \frac{qEct}{\sqrt{m^2c^2+q^2E^2t^2}}}$$

$$x = \int_0^t u\,dt = qEc\int_0^t \frac{t\,dt}{\sqrt{m^2c^2+q^2E^2t^2}} \qquad \boxed{x = \frac{c}{qE}\left(\sqrt{m^2c^2+q^2E^2t^2}-mc\right)}$$

P39.70 (a) An observer at rest relative to the mirror sees the light travel a distance $D = 2d - x$, where $x = vt_S$ is the distance the ship moves toward the mirror in time t_S. Since this observer agrees that the speed of light is c, the time for it to travel distance D is

$$t_S = \frac{D}{c} = \frac{2d - vt_S}{c} \qquad t_S = \boxed{\frac{2d}{c+v}}.$$

(b) The observer in the rocket measures a length-contracted initial distance to the mirror of

$$L = d\sqrt{1-\frac{v^2}{c^2}}$$

and the mirror moving toward the ship at speed v. Thus, he measures the distance the light travels as $D = 2(L-y)$ where $y = \frac{vt}{2}$ is the distance the mirror moves toward the ship before the light reflects from it. This observer also measures the speed of light to be c, so the time for it to travel distance D is:

$$t = \frac{D}{c} = \frac{2}{c}\left[d\sqrt{1-\frac{v^2}{c^2}} - \frac{vt}{2}\right] \text{ so } (c+v)t = \frac{2d}{c}\sqrt{(c+v)(c-v)} \text{ or } t = \boxed{\frac{2d}{c}\sqrt{\frac{c-v}{c+v}}}.$$

***P39.71** Take the two colliding protons as the system

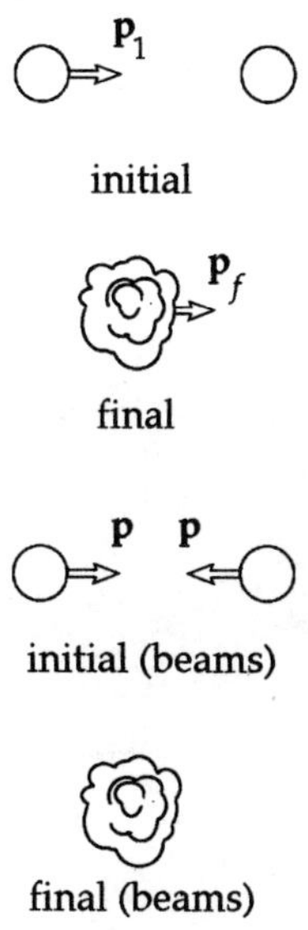

$E_1 = K + mc^2 \qquad E_2 = mc^2$

$E_1^2 = p_1^2c^2 + m^2c^4 \qquad p_2 = 0.$

In the final state, $E_f = K_f + Mc^2$: $E_f^2 = p_f^2c^2 + M^2c^4$.

By energy conservation, $E_1 + E_2 = E_f$, so

$$E_1^2 + 2E_1E_2 + E_2^2 = E_f^2$$

$$p_1^2c^2 + m^2c^4 + 2\left(K + mc^2\right)mc^2 + m^2c^4$$
$$= p_f^2c^2 + M^2c^4$$

By conservation of momentum, $p_1 = p_f$.

Then $$M^2c^4 = 2Kmc^2 + 4m^2c^4 = \frac{4Km^2c^4}{2mc^2} + 4m^2c^4$$

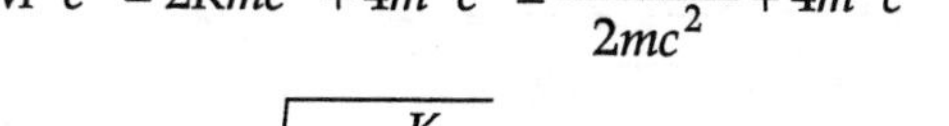

$$Mc^2 = 2mc^2\sqrt{1 + \frac{K}{2mc^2}}.$$

By contrast, for colliding beams we have

In the original state, $E_1 = K + mc^2$

$E_2 = K + mc^2.$

In the final state, $E_f = Mc^2$

$E_1 + E_2 = E_f$: $K + mc^2 + K + mc^2 = Mc^2$

$$Mc^2 = 2mc^2\left(1 + \frac{K}{2mc^2}\right).$$

$\mathbf{p}_1$

initial

$\mathbf{p}_f$

final

p **p**

initial (beams)

final (beams)

FIG. P39.71

***P39.72** Conservation of momentum γmu:

$$\frac{mu}{\sqrt{1 - u^2/c^2}} + \frac{m(-u)}{3\sqrt{1 - u^2/c^2}} = \frac{Mv_f}{\sqrt{1 - v_f^2/c^2}} = \frac{2mu}{3\sqrt{1 - u^2/c^2}}.$$

Conservation of energy γmc^2:

$$\frac{mc^2}{\sqrt{1 - u^2/c^2}} + \frac{mc^2}{3\sqrt{1 - u^2/c^2}} = \frac{Mc^2}{\sqrt{1 - v_f^2/c^2}} = \frac{4mc^2}{3\sqrt{1 - u^2/c^2}}.$$

To start solving we can divide: $v_f = \frac{2u}{4} = \frac{u}{2}$. Then

$$\frac{M}{\sqrt{1 - u^2/4c^2}} = \frac{4m}{3\sqrt{1 - u^2/c^2}} = \frac{M}{(1/2)\sqrt{4 - u^2/c^2}}$$

$$\boxed{M = \frac{2m\sqrt{4 - u^2/c^2}}{3\sqrt{1 - u^2/c^2}}}$$

Note that when $v \ll c$, this reduces to $M = \frac{4m}{3}$, in agreement with the classical result.

P39.73 (a) $L_0^2 = L_{0x}^2 + L_{0y}^2$ and $L^2 = L_x^2 + L_y^2$.

The motion is in the x direction: $L_y = L_{0y} = L_0 \sin\theta_0$

$$L_x = L_{0x}\sqrt{1-\left(\frac{v}{c}\right)^2} = (L_0 \cos\theta_0)\sqrt{1-\left(\frac{v}{c}\right)^2}.$$

Thus,
$$L^2 = L_0^2 \cos^2\theta_0\left[1-\left(\frac{v}{c}\right)^2\right] + L_0^2 \sin^2\theta_0 = L_0^2\left[1-\left(\frac{v}{c}\right)^2 \cos^2\theta_0\right]$$

or
$$\boxed{L = L_0\left[1-\left(\frac{v}{c}\right)^2 \cos^2\theta_0\right]^{1/2}}.$$

(b) $$\tan\theta = \frac{L_y}{L_x} = \frac{L_{0y}}{L_{0x}\sqrt{1-(v/c)^2}} = \boxed{\gamma\tan\theta_0}$$

P39.74 (b) Consider a hermit who lives on an asteroid halfway between the Sun and Tau Ceti, stationary with respect to both. Just as our spaceship is passing him, he also sees the blast waves from both explosions. Judging both stars to be stationary, this observer concludes that $\boxed{\text{the two stars blew up simultaneously}}$.

(a) We in the spaceship moving past the hermit do not calculate the explosions to be simultaneous. We measure the distance we have traveled from the Sun as

$$L = L_p\sqrt{1-\left(\frac{v}{c}\right)^2} = (6.00\text{ ly})\sqrt{1-(0.800)^2} = 3.60\text{ ly}.$$

We see the Sun flying away from us at 0.800c while the light from the Sun approaches at 1.00c. Thus, the gap between the Sun and its blast wave has opened at 1.80c, and the time we calculate to have elapsed since the Sun exploded is

$$\frac{3.60\text{ ly}}{1.80c} = 2.00\text{ yr}.$$

We see Tau Ceti as moving toward us at 0.800c, while its light approaches at 1.00c, only 0.200c faster. We measure the gap between that star and its blast wave as 3.60 ly and growing at 0.200c. We calculate that it must have been opening for

$$\frac{3.60\text{ ly}}{0.200c} = 18.0\text{ yr}$$

and conclude that $\boxed{\text{Tau Ceti exploded 16.0 years before the Sun}}$.

P39.75 Since the total momentum is zero before decay, it is necessary that after the decay

$$p_{\text{nucleus}} = p_{\text{photon}} = \frac{E_\gamma}{c} = \frac{14.0 \text{ keV}}{c}.$$

Also, for the recoiling nucleus, $E^2 = p^2c^2 + \left(mc^2\right)^2$ with $mc^2 = 8.60 \times 10^{-9} \text{ J} = 53.8 \text{ GeV}$.

Thus, $\left(mc^2 + K\right)^2 = (14.0 \text{ keV})^2 + \left(mc^2\right)^2$ or $\left(1 + \frac{K}{mc^2}\right)^2 = \left(\frac{14.0 \text{ keV}}{mc^2}\right)^2 + 1$.

So $1 + \frac{K}{mc^2} = \sqrt{1 + \left(\frac{14.0 \text{ keV}}{mc^2}\right)^2} \approx 1 + \frac{1}{2}\left(\frac{14.0 \text{ keV}}{mc^2}\right)^2$ (Binomial Theorem)

and $K \approx \frac{(14.0 \text{ keV})^2}{2mc^2} = \frac{\left(14.0 \times 10^3 \text{ eV}\right)^2}{2\left(53.8 \times 10^9 \text{ eV}\right)} = \boxed{1.82 \times 10^{-3} \text{ eV}}$.

P39.76 Take $m = 1.00 \text{ kg}$.

The classical kinetic energy is $K_c = \frac{1}{2}mu^2 = \frac{1}{2}mc^2\left(\frac{u}{c}\right)^2 = \left(4.50 \times 10^{16} \text{ J}\right)\left(\frac{u}{c}\right)^2$

and the actual kinetic energy is $K_r = \left(\frac{1}{\sqrt{1-(u/c)^2}} - 1\right)mc^2 = \left(9.00 \times 10^{16} \text{ J}\right)\left(\frac{1}{\sqrt{1-(u/c)^2}} - 1\right)$.

$\frac{u}{c}$	K_c (J)	K_r (J)
0.000	0.000	0.000
0.100	0.045×10^{16}	0.0453×10^{16}
0.200	0.180×10^{16}	0.186×10^{16}
0.300	0.405×10^{16}	0.435×10^{16}
0.400	0.720×10^{16}	0.820×10^{16}
0.500	1.13×10^{16}	1.39×10^{16}
0.600	1.62×10^{16}	2.25×10^{16}
0.700	2.21×10^{16}	3.60×10^{16}
0.800	2.88×10^{16}	6.00×10^{16}
0.900	3.65×10^{16}	11.6×10^{16}
0.990	4.41×10^{16}	54.8×10^{16}

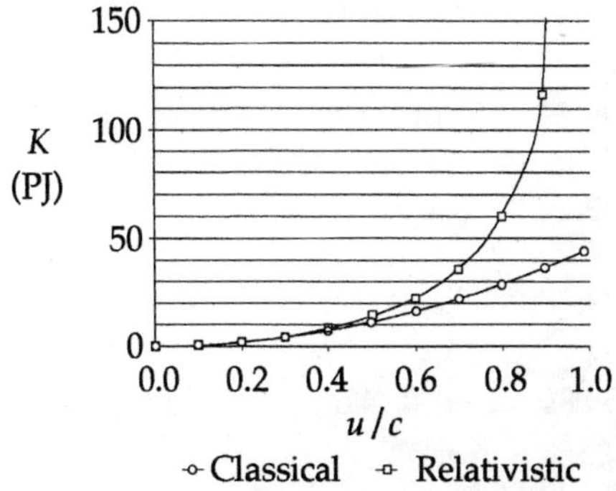

FIG. P39.76

$K_c = 0.990K_r$, when $\frac{1}{2}\left(\frac{u}{c}\right)^2 = 0.990\left[\frac{1}{\sqrt{1-(u/c)^2}} - 1\right]$, yielding $u = \boxed{0.115c}$.

Similarly, $K_c = 0.950K_r$ when $u = \boxed{0.257c}$

and $K_c = 0.500K_r$ when $u = \boxed{0.786c}$.

ANSWERS TO EVEN PROBLEMS

P39.2 (a) $60.0\ \text{m/s}$; (b) $20.0\ \text{m/s}$; (c) $44.7\ \text{m/s}$

P39.4 see the solution

P39.6 $0.866c$

P39.8 (a) 25.0 yr; (b) 15.0 yr; (c) 12.0 ly

P39.10 (a) $2.18\ \mu\text{s}$; (b) The moon sees the planet surface moving 649 m up toward it.

P39.12 (a) $\dfrac{cL_p}{\sqrt{c^2\Delta t^2 + L_p^2}}$; (b) $4.00\ \text{m/s}$; (c) see the solution

P39.14 $v = 0.140c$

P39.16 5.45 yr, Goslo is older

P39.18 11.3 kHz

P39.20 (a) see the solution; (b) $0.050\,4c$

P39.22 (a) $0.943c$; (b) 2.55 km

P39.24 B occurred 444 ns before A

P39.26 $0.357c$

P39.28 $0.893c$ at 16.8° above the x'-axis

P39.30 (a) $0.141c$; (b) $0.436c$

P39.32 see the solution

P39.34 (a) 0.582 MeV; (b) 2.45 MeV

P39.36 see the solution

P39.38 (a) 438 GJ; (b) 438 GJ

P39.40 $18.4\ \text{g/cm}^3$

P39.42 (a) $0.467c$; (b) 2.75×10^3 kg

P39.44 (a) $0.302c$; (b) 4.00 fJ

P39.46 (a) 20.0 TW; (b) 3.50×10^7 electrons

P39.48 (a) $0.960c$; (b) 1.51 times greater as measured by B.

P39.50 3.18×10^{-12} kg, not detectable

P39.52 6.71×10^8 kg

P39.54 1.02 MeV

P39.56 (a) $\dfrac{v}{c} = 1 - 1.12 \times 10^{-10}$; (b) 6.00×10^{27} J; (c) $\$2.17 \times 10^{20}$

P39.58 (a) $0.023\,6c$; (b) $6.18 \times 10^{-4}c$

P39.60 (a) 4.00×10^{-14} kg; (b) 1.60×10^{-12}

P39.62 (a) $\dfrac{3.65\ \text{MeV}}{c^2}$; (b) $v = 0.589c$

P39.64 see the solution

P39.66 6.28×10^7 kg

P39.68 1.47 km

P39.70 (a) $\dfrac{2d}{c+v}$; (b) $\dfrac{2d}{c}\sqrt{\dfrac{c-v}{c+v}}$

P39.72 $M = \dfrac{2m}{3}\sqrt{\dfrac{4 - u^2/c^2}{1 - u^2/c^2}}$

P39.74 (a) Tau Ceti exploded 16.0 yr before the Sun; (b) they exploded simultaneously

P39.76 see the solution, $0.115c$, $0.257c$, $0.786c$

40

Introduction to Quantum Physics

CHAPTER OUTLINE

ANSWERS TO QUESTIONS

Q40.1 Planck made two new assumptions: (1) molecular energy is quantized and (2) molecules emit or absorb energy in discrete irreducible packets. These assumptions contradict the classical idea of energy as continuously divisible. They also imply that an atom must have a definite structure—it cannot just be a soup of electrons orbiting the nucleus.

Q40.2 The first flaw is that the Rayleigh–Jeans law predicts that the intensity of short wavelength radiation emitted by a blackbody approaches infinity as the wavelength decreases. This is known as the *ultraviolet catastrophe*. The second flaw is the prediction much more power output from a black-body than is shown experimentally. The intensity of radiation from the blackbody is given by the area under the red $I(\lambda, T)$ *vs.* λ curve in Figure 40.5 in the text, not by the area under the blue curve.

Planck's Law dealt with both of these issues and brought the theory into agreement with the experimental data by adding an exponential term to the denominator that depends on $\frac{1}{\lambda}$. This both keeps the predicted intensity from approaching infinity as the wavelength decreases and keeps the area under the curve finite.

Q40.3 Our eyes are not able to detect all frequencies of energy. For example, all objects that are above 0 K in temperature emit electromagnetic radiation in the infrared region. This describes *everything* in a dark room. We are only able to see objects that emit or reflect electromagnetic radiation in the visible portion of the spectrum.

Q40.4 Most stars radiate nearly as blackbodies. Vega has a higher surface temperature than Arcturus. Vega radiates most intensely at shorter wavelengths.

Q40.5 No. The second metal may have a larger work function than the first, in which case the incident photons may not have enough energy to eject photoelectrons.

Q40.6 Comparing Equation 40.9 with the slope-intercept form of the equation for a straight line, $y = mx + b$, we see that the slope in Figure 40.11 in the text is Planck's constant h and that the y intercept is $-\phi$, the negative of the work function. If a different metal were used, the slope would remain the same but the work function would be different, Thus, data for different metals appear as parallel lines on the graph.

Q40.7 Wave theory predicts that the photoelectric effect should occur at any frequency, provided the light intensity is high enough. However, as seen in the photoelectric experiments, the light must have a sufficiently high frequency for the effect to occur.

Q40.8 The stopping voltage measures the kinetic energy of the most energetic photoelectrons. Each of them has gotten its energy from a single photon. According to Planck's $E = hf$, the photon energy depends on the frequency of the light. The intensity controls only the number of photons reaching a unit area in a unit time.

Q40.9 Let's do some quick calculations and see: 1.62 MHz is the highest frequency in the commercial AM band. From the relationship between the energy and the frequency, $E = hf$, the energy available from such a wave would be 1.07×10^{-27} J, or 6.68 neV. That is 9 orders of magnitude too small to eject electrons from the metal. The only thing this student could gain from this experiment is a hefty fine and a long jail term from the FCC. To get on the order of a few eV from this experiment, she would have to broadcast at a minimum frequency of 250 Thz, which is in the infrared region.

Q40.10 No. If an electron breaks free from an atom absorbing a photon, we say the atom is ionized. Ionization typically requires energy of several eV. As with the photoelectric effect in a solid metal, the light must have a sufficiently high frequency for a photon energy that is large enough. The gas can absorb energy from longer-wavelength light as it gains more internal energy of random motion of whole molecules.

Q40.11 Ultraviolet light has shorter wavelength and higher photon energy than visible light.

Q40.12 (c) UV light has the highest frequency of the three, and hence each photon delivers more energy to a skin cell. This explains why you can become sunburned on a cloudy day: clouds block visible light and infrared, but not much ultraviolet. You usually do not become sunburned through window glass, even though you can see the visible light from the Sun coming through the window, because the glass absorbs much of the ultraviolet and reemits it as infrared.

Q40.13 The Compton effect describes the *scattering* of photons from electrons, while the photoelectric effect predicts the ejection of electrons due to the *absorption* of photons by a material.

Q40.14 In developing a theory in accord with experimental evidence, Compton assumed that photons exhibited clear particle-like behavior, and that both energy and momentum are conserved in electron-photon interactions. Photons had previously been thought of as bits of waves.

Q40.15 The x-ray photon transfers some of its energy to the electron. Thus, its frequency must decrease.

Q40.16 A few photons would only give a few dots of exposure, apparently randomly scattered.

Q40.17 Light has both classical-wave and classical-particle characteristics. In single- and double-slit experiments light behaves like a wave. In the photoelectric effect light behaves like a particle. Light may be characterized as an electromagnetic wave with a particular wavelength or frequency, yet at the same time light may be characterized as a stream of photons, each carrying a discrete energy, *hf*. Since light displays *both* wave and particle characteristics, perhaps it would be fair to call light a "wavicle". It is customary to call a photon a quantum particle, different from a classical particle.

Q40.18 An electron has both classical-wave and classical-particle characteristics. In single- and double-slit diffraction and interference experiments, electrons behave like classical waves. An electron has mass and charge. It carries kinetic energy and momentum in parcels of definite size, as classical particles do. At the same time it has a particular wavelength and frequency. Since an electron displays characteristics of both classical waves and classical particles, it is neither a classical wave nor a classical particle. It is customary to call it a quantum particle, but another invented term, such as "wavicle", could serve equally well.

Q40.19 The discovery of electron diffraction by Davisson and Germer was a fundamental advance in our understanding of the motion of material particles. Newton's laws fail to properly describe the motion of an object with small mass. It moves as a wave, not as a classical particle. Proceeding from this recognition, the development of quantum mechanics made possible describing the motion of electrons in atoms; understanding molecular structure and the behavior of matter at the atomic scale, including electronics, photonics, and engineered materials; accounting for the motion of nucleons in nuclei; and studying elementary particles.

Q40.20 If we set $\frac{p^2}{2m} = q\Delta V$, which is the same for both particles, then we see that the electron has the smaller momentum and therefore the longer wavelength $\left(\lambda = \frac{h}{p}\right)$.

Q40.21 Any object of macroscopic size—including a grain of dust—has an undetectably small wavelength and does not exhibit quantum behavior.

Q40.22 A particle is represented by a wave packet of nonzero width. The width necessarily introduces uncertainty in the position of the particle. The width of the wave packet can be reduced toward zero only by adding waves of all possible wavelengths together. Doing this, however, results in loss of all information about the momentum and, therefore, the speed of the particle.

Q40.23 The *intensity* of electron waves in some small region of space determines the *probability* that an electron will be found in that region.

Q40.24 The wavelength of violet light is on the order of $\frac{1}{2}$ μm, while the de Broglie wavelength of an electron can be 4 orders of magnitude smaller. Would your height be measured more precisely with an unruled meter stick or with one engraved with divisions down to $\frac{1}{10}$ mm?

Q40.25 The spacing between repeating structures on the surface of the feathers or scales is on the order of 1/2 the wavelength of light. An optical microscope would not have the resolution to see such fine detail, while an electron microscope can. The electrons can have much shorter wavelength.

Q40.26 (a) The slot is blacker than any black material or pigment. Any radiation going in through the hole will be absorbed by the walls or the contents of the box, perhaps after several reflections. Essentially none of that energy will come out through the hole again. Figure 40.1 in the text shows this effect if you imagine the beam getting weaker at each reflection.

continued on next page

(b) The open slots between the glowing tubes are brightest. When you look into a slot, you receive direct radiation emitted by the wall on the far side of a cavity enclosed by the fixture; and you also receive radiation that was emitted by other sections of the cavity wall and has bounced around a few or many times before escaping through the slot. In Figure 40.1 in the text, reverse all of the arrowheads and imagine the beam getting stronger at each reflection. Then the figure shows the extra efficiency of a cavity radiator. Here is the conclusion of Kirchhoff's thermodynamic argument: ... energy radiated. A poor reflector—a good absorber—avoids rising in temperature by being an efficient emitter. Its emissivity is equal to its absorptivity: $e = a$. The slot in the box in part (a) of the question is a black body with reflectivity zero and absorptivity 1, so it must also be the most efficient possible radiator, to avoid rising in temperature above its surroundings in thermal equilibrium. Its emissivity in Stefan's law is $100\% = 1$, higher than perhaps 0.9 for black paper, 0.1 for light-colored paint, or 0.04 for shiny metal. Only in this way can the material objects underneath these different surfaces maintain equal temperatures after they come to thermal equilibrium and continue to exchange energy by electromagnetic radiation. By considering one blackbody facing another, Kirchhoff proved logically that the material forming the walls of the cavity made no difference to the radiation. By thinking about inserting color filters between two cavity radiators, he proved that the spectral distribution of blackbody radiation must be a universal function of wavelength, the same for all materials and depending only on the temperature. Blackbody radiation is a fundamental connection between the matter and the energy that physicists had previously studied separately.

SOLUTIONS TO PROBLEMS

Section 40.1 Blackbody Radiation and Planck's Hypothesis

P40.1 $$T = \frac{2.898 \times 10^{-3}\ \text{m}\cdot\text{K}}{560 \times 10^{-9}\ \text{m}} = \boxed{5.18 \times 10^{3}\ \text{K}}$$

P40.2 (a) $$\lambda_{\text{max}} = \frac{2.898 \times 10^{-3}\ \text{m}\cdot\text{K}}{T} \sim \frac{2.898 \times 10^{-3}\ \text{m}\cdot\text{K}}{10^{4}\ \text{K}} \boxed{\sim 10^{-7}\ \text{m}} \qquad \boxed{\text{ultraviolet}}$$

(b) $$\lambda_{\text{max}} \sim \frac{2.898 \times 10^{-3}\ \text{m}\cdot\text{K}}{10^{7}\ \text{K}} \boxed{\sim 10^{-10}\ \text{m}} \quad \boxed{\gamma - \text{ray}}$$

P40.3 Planck's radiation law gives intensity-per-wavelength. Taking E to be the photon energy and n to be the number of photons emitted each second, we multiply by area and wavelength range to have energy-per-time leaving the hole:

$$\mathcal{P} = \frac{2\pi hc^2(\lambda_2 - \lambda_1)\pi(d/2)^2}{\left[(\lambda_1 + \lambda_2)/2\right]^5\left(e^{2hc/[(\lambda_1+\lambda_2)k_BT]} - 1\right)} = En = nhf \qquad \text{where} \qquad E = hf = \frac{2hc}{\lambda_1 + \lambda_2}$$

$$n = \frac{\mathcal{P}}{E} = \frac{8\pi^2 cd^2(\lambda_2 - \lambda_1)}{(\lambda_1 + \lambda_2)^4\left(e^{2hc/[(\lambda_1+\lambda_2)k_BT]} - 1\right)}$$

$$= \frac{8\pi^2(3.00 \times 10^8\ \text{m/s})(5.00 \times 10^{-5}\ \text{m})^2(1.00 \times 10^{-9}\ \text{m})}{(1\,001 \times 10^{-9}\ \text{m})^4\left(e^{[2(6.626\times10^{-34}\ \text{J}\cdot\text{s})(3.00\times10^8\ \text{m/s})]/[(1\,001\times10^{-9}\ \text{m})(1.38\times10^{-23}\ \text{J/K})(7.50\times10^3\ \text{K})]} - 1\right)}$$

$$n = \frac{5.90 \times 10^{16}/\text{s}}{(e^{3.84} - 1)} = \boxed{1.30 \times 10^{15}/\text{s}}$$

P40.4 (a) $\mathcal{P} = eA\sigma T^4 = 1\left(20.0\times10^{-4}\text{ m}^2\right)\left(5.67\times10^{-8}\text{ W/m}^2\cdot\text{K}^4\right)(5\,000\text{ K})^4 = \boxed{7.09\times10^4\text{ W}}$

(b) $\lambda_{\max}T = \lambda_{\max}(5\,000\text{ K}) = 2.898\times10^{-3}\text{ m}\cdot\text{K} \Rightarrow \lambda_{\max} = \boxed{580\text{ nm}}$

(c) We compute: $\dfrac{hc}{k_BT} = \dfrac{\left(6.626\times10^{-34}\text{ J}\cdot\text{s}\right)\left(3.00\times10^8\text{ m/s}\right)}{\left(1.38\times10^{-23}\text{ J/K}\right)(5\,000\text{ K})} = 2.88\times10^{-6}\text{ m}$

The power per wavelength interval is $\mathcal{P}(\lambda) = AI(\lambda) = \dfrac{2\pi hc^2A}{\lambda^5\left[\exp(hc/\lambda k_BT)-1\right]}$, and

$$2\pi hc^2A = 2\pi\left(6.626\times10^{-34}\right)\left(3.00\times10^8\right)^2\left(20.0\times10^{-4}\right) = 7.50\times10^{-19}\text{ J}\cdot\text{m}^4/\text{s}$$

$$\mathcal{P}(580\text{ nm}) = \frac{7.50\times10^{-19}\text{ J}\cdot\text{m}^4/\text{s}}{\left(580\times10^{-9}\text{ m}\right)^5\left[\exp(2.88\ \mu\text{m}/0.580\ \mu\text{m})-1\right]} = \frac{1.15\times10^{13}\text{ J/m}\cdot\text{s}}{e^{4.973}-1}$$
$$= \boxed{7.99\times10^{10}\text{ W/m}}$$

(d)–(i) The other values are computed similarly:

	λ	$\dfrac{hc}{\lambda k_BT}$	$e^{hc/\lambda k_BT}-1$	$\dfrac{2\pi hc^2A}{\lambda^5}$	$\mathcal{P}(\lambda)$, W/m
(d)	1.00 nm	2882.6	7.96×10^{1251}	7.50×10^{26}	9.42×10^{-1226}
(e)	5.00 nm	576.5	2.40×10^{250}	2.40×10^{23}	1.00×10^{-227}
(f)	400 nm	7.21	1347	7.32×10^{13}	5.44×10^{10}
(c)	580 nm	4.97	143.5	1.15×10^{13}	7.99×10^{10}
(g)	700 nm	4.12	60.4	4.46×10^{12}	7.38×10^{10}
(h)	1.00 mm	0.00288	0.00289	7.50×10^{-4}	0.260
(i)	10.0 cm	2.88×10^{-5}	2.88×10^{-5}	7.50×10^{-14}	2.60×10^{-9}

(j) We approximate the area under the $\mathcal{P}(\lambda)$ versus λ curve, between 400 nm and 700 nm, as two trapezoids:

$$\mathcal{P} = \frac{\left[(5.44+7.99)\times10^{10}\text{ W/m}\right]\left[(580-400)\times10^{-9}\text{ m}\right]}{2}$$
$$+\frac{\left[(7.99+7.38)\times10^{10}\text{ W/m}\right]\left[(700-580)\times10^{-9}\text{ m}\right]}{2}$$

$\mathcal{P} = 2.13\times10^4\text{ W}$ so the power radiated as visible light is $\boxed{\text{approximately 20 kW}}$

P40.5 (a) $\mathcal{P} = eA\sigma T^4$, so

$$T = \left(\frac{\mathcal{P}}{eA\sigma}\right)^{1/4} = \left[\frac{3.77\times10^{26}\text{ W}}{1\left[4\pi\left(6.96\times10^8\text{ m}\right)^2\right]\left(5.67\times10^{-8}\text{ W/m}^2\cdot\text{K}^4\right)}\right]^{1/4} = \boxed{5.75\times10^3\text{ K}}$$

(b) $\lambda_{\max} = \dfrac{2.898\times10^{-3}\text{ m}\cdot\text{K}}{T} = \dfrac{2.898\times10^{-3}\text{ m}\cdot\text{K}}{5.75\times10^3\text{ K}} = 5.04\times10^{-7}\text{ m} = \boxed{504\text{ nm}}$

P40.6 $E = hf = \dfrac{hc}{\lambda} = \dfrac{(6.626\times10^{-34}\ \text{J}\cdot\text{s})(3.00\times10^{8}\ \text{m/s})}{589.3\times10^{-9}\ \text{m}} = 3.37\times10^{-19}\ \text{J/photon}$

$$n = \frac{\mathcal{P}}{E} = \frac{10.0\ \text{J/s}}{3.37\times10^{-19}\ \text{J/photon}} = \boxed{2.96\times10^{19}\ \text{photons/s}}$$

P40.7 (a) $E = hf = (6.626\times10^{-34}\ \text{J}\cdot\text{s})(620\times10^{12}\ \text{s}^{-1})\left(\dfrac{1.00\ \text{eV}}{1.60\times10^{-19}\ \text{J}}\right) = \boxed{2.57\ \text{eV}}$

(b) $E = hf = (6.626\times10^{-34}\ \text{J}\cdot\text{s})(3.10\times10^{9}\ \text{s}^{-1})\left(\dfrac{1.00\ \text{eV}}{1.60\times10^{-19}\ \text{J}}\right) = \boxed{1.28\times10^{-5}\ \text{eV}}$

(c) $E = hf = (6.626\times10^{-34}\ \text{J}\cdot\text{s})(46.0\times10^{6}\ \text{s}^{-1})\left(\dfrac{1.00\ \text{eV}}{1.60\times10^{-19}\ \text{J}}\right) = \boxed{1.91\times10^{-7}\ \text{eV}}$

(d) $\lambda = \dfrac{c}{f} = \dfrac{3.00\times10^{8}\ \text{m/s}}{620\times10^{12}\ \text{Hz}} = 4.84\times10^{-7}\ \text{m} = \boxed{484\ \text{nm, visible light (blue)}}$

$$\lambda = \frac{c}{f} = \frac{3.00\times10^{8}\ \text{m/s}}{3.10\times10^{9}\ \text{Hz}} = 9.68\times10^{-2}\ \text{m} = \boxed{9.68\ \text{cm, radio wave}}$$

$$\lambda = \frac{c}{f} = \frac{3.00\times10^{8}\ \text{m/s}}{46.0\times10^{6}\ \text{Hz}} = \boxed{6.52\ \text{m, radio wave}}$$

P40.8 Energy of a single 500-nm photon:

$$E_\gamma = hf = \frac{hc}{\lambda} = \frac{(6.626\times10^{-34}\ \text{J}\cdot\text{s})(3.00\times10^{8}\ \text{m/s})}{(500\times10^{-9}\ \text{m})} = 3.98\times10^{-19}\ \text{J}.$$

The energy entering the eye each second

$$E = \mathcal{P}\Delta t = IA\Delta t = (4.00\times10^{-11}\ \text{W/m}^2)\left[\frac{\pi}{4}(8.50\times10^{-3}\ \text{m})^2\right](1.00\ \text{s}) = 2.27\times10^{-15}\ \text{J}.$$

The number of photons required to yield this energy

$$n = \frac{E}{E_\gamma} = \frac{2.27\times10^{-15}\ \text{J}}{3.98\times10^{-19}\ \text{J/photon}} = \boxed{5.71\times10^{3}\ \text{photons}}.$$

P40.9 Each photon has an energy $E = hf = (6.626\times10^{-34})(99.7\times10^{6}) = 6.61\times10^{-26}\ \text{J}$.

This implies that there are $\dfrac{150\times10^{3}\ \text{J/s}}{6.61\times10^{-26}\ \text{J/photon}} = \boxed{2.27\times10^{30}\ \text{photons/s}}$.

P40.10 We take $\theta = 0.030\,0$ radians. Then the pendulum's total energy is

$$E = mgh = mg(L - L\cos\theta)$$

$$E = (1.00 \text{ kg})(9.80 \text{ m/s}^2)(1.00 - 0.999\,5) = 4.41 \times 10^{-3} \text{ J}$$

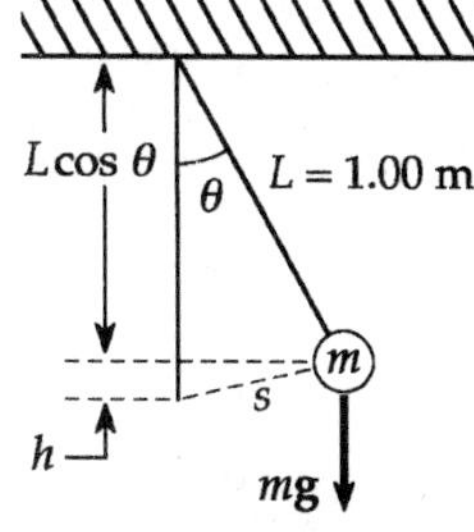

FIG. P40.10

The frequency of oscillation is $f = \frac{\omega}{2\pi} = \frac{1}{2\pi}\sqrt{\frac{g}{L}} = 0.498 \text{ Hz}$.

The energy is quantized, $E = nhf$.

Therefore, $n = \frac{E}{hf} = \frac{4.41 \times 10^{-3} \text{ J}}{(6.626 \times 10^{-34} \text{ J}\cdot\text{s})(0.498 \text{ s}^{-1})}$

$$= \boxed{1.34 \times 10^{31}}$$

P40.11 The radiation wavelength of $\lambda' = 500$ nm that is observed by observers on Earth is not the true wavelength, λ, emitted by the star because of the Doppler effect. The true wavelength is related to the observed wavelength using:

$\frac{c}{\lambda'} = \frac{c}{\lambda}\sqrt{\frac{1-(v/c)}{1+(v/c)}}$: $\lambda = \lambda'\sqrt{\frac{1-(v/c)}{1+(v/c)}} = (500 \text{ nm})\sqrt{\frac{1-(0.280)}{1+(0.280)}} = 375 \text{ nm}$.

The temperature of the star is given by $\lambda_{max}T = 2.898 \times 10^{-3} \text{ m}\cdot\text{K}$:

$T = \frac{2.898 \times 10^{-3} \text{ m}\cdot\text{K}}{\lambda_{max}}$: $T = \frac{2.898 \times 10^{-3} \text{ m}\cdot\text{K}}{375 \times 10^{-9}} = \boxed{7.73 \times 10^3 \text{ K}}$.

P40.12 Planck's radiation law is $I(\lambda, T) = \frac{2\pi hc^2}{\lambda^5\left(e^{hc/\lambda k_B T} - 1\right)}$.

Using the series expansion $e^x = 1 + x + \frac{x^2}{2!} + \frac{x^3}{3!} + \ldots$.

Planck's law reduces to $I(\lambda, T) = \frac{2\pi hc^2}{\lambda^5\left[(1 + hc/\lambda k_B T + \ldots) - 1\right]} \approx \frac{2\pi hc^2}{\lambda^5 (hc/\lambda k_B T)} = \frac{2\pi c k_B T}{\lambda^4}$

which is the Rayleigh-Jeans law, for very long wavelengths.

Section 40.2 The Photoelectric Effect

P40.13 (a) $\lambda_c = \frac{hc}{\phi} = \frac{(6.626 \times 10^{-34} \text{ J}\cdot\text{s})(3.00 \times 10^8 \text{ m/s})}{(4.20 \text{ eV})(1.60 \times 10^{-19} \text{ J/eV})} = \boxed{296 \text{ nm}}$

$$f_c = \frac{c}{\lambda_c} = \frac{3.00 \times 10^8 \text{ m/s}}{296 \times 10^{-9} \text{ m}} = \boxed{1.01 \times 10^{15} \text{ Hz}}$$

(b) $\frac{hc}{\lambda} = \phi + e\Delta V_S$: $\frac{(6.626 \times 10^{-34})(3.00 \times 10^8)}{180 \times 10^{-9}} = (4.20 \text{ eV})(1.60 \times 10^{-19} \text{ J/eV}) + (1.60 \times 10^{-19})\Delta V_S$

Therefore, $\boxed{\Delta V_S = 2.71 \text{ V}}$

P40.14 $K_{max} = \frac{1}{2}mv_{max}^2 = \frac{1}{2}(9.11\times10^{-31})(4.60\times10^5)^2 = 9.64\times10^{-20}\text{ J} = 0.602\text{ eV}$

(a) $\phi = E - K_{max} = \frac{1\,240\text{ eV}\cdot\text{nm}}{625\text{ nm}} - 0.602\text{ nm} = \boxed{1.38\text{ eV}}$

(b) $f_c = \frac{\phi}{h} = \frac{1.38\text{ eV}}{6.626\times10^{-34}\text{ J}\cdot\text{s}}\left(\frac{1.60\times10^{-19}\text{ J}}{1\text{ eV}}\right) = \boxed{3.34\times10^{14}\text{ Hz}}$

P40.15 (a) $\lambda_c = \frac{hc}{\phi}$

Li: $\lambda_c = \frac{(6.626\times10^{-34}\text{ J}\cdot\text{s})(3.00\times10^8\text{ m/s})}{(2.30\text{ eV})(1.60\times10^{-19}\text{ J/eV})} = 540\text{ nm}$

Be: $\lambda_c = \frac{(6.626\times10^{-34}\text{ J}\cdot\text{s})(3.00\times10^8\text{ m/s})}{(3.90\text{ eV})(1.60\times10^{-19}\text{ J/eV})} = 318\text{ nm}$

Hg: $\lambda_c = \frac{(6.626\times10^{-34}\text{ J}\cdot\text{s})(3.00\times10^8\text{ m/s})}{(4.50\text{ eV})(1.60\times10^{-19}\text{ J/eV})} = 276\text{ nm}$

$\lambda < \lambda_c$ for photo current. $\boxed{\text{Thus, only lithium will exhibit the photoelectric effect.}}$

(b) For lithium, $\frac{hc}{\lambda} = \phi + K_{max}$

$$\frac{(6.626\times10^{-34}\text{ J}\cdot\text{s})(3.00\times10^8\text{ m/s})}{400\times10^{-9}\text{ m}} = (2.30\text{ eV})(1.60\times10^{-19}) + K_{max}$$

$$K_{max} = 1.29\times10^{-19}\text{ J} = \boxed{0.808\text{ eV}}$$

P40.16 From condition (i), $hf = e(\Delta V_{S1}) + \phi_1$ and $hf = e(\Delta V_{S2}) + \phi_2$

$(\Delta V_{S1}) = (\Delta V_{S2}) + 1.48\text{ V}$.

Then $\phi_2 - \phi_1 = 1.48\text{ eV}$.

From condition (ii), $hf_{c1} = \phi_1 = 0.600hf_{c2} = 0.600\phi_2$

$\phi_2 - 0.600\phi_2 = 1.48\text{ eV}$

$\boxed{\phi_2 = 3.70\text{ eV}}$ $\boxed{\phi_1 = 2.22\text{ eV}}$.

P40.17 (a) $e\Delta V_S = \frac{hc}{\lambda} - \phi \rightarrow \phi = \frac{1\,240\text{ nm}\cdot\text{eV}}{546.1\text{ nm}} - 0.376\text{ eV} = \boxed{1.90\text{ eV}}$

(b) $e\Delta V_S = \frac{hc}{\lambda} - \phi = \frac{1\,240\text{ nm}\cdot\text{eV}}{587.5\text{ nm}} - 1.90\text{ eV} \rightarrow \boxed{\Delta V_S = 0.216\text{ V}}$

P40.18 The energy needed is $E = 1.00\text{ eV} = 1.60\times10^{-19}\text{ J}$.

The energy absorbed in time interval Δt is $E = \mathcal{P}\Delta t = IA\Delta t$

so $$\Delta t = \frac{E}{IA} = \frac{1.60\times10^{-19}\text{ J}}{\left(500\text{ J/s}\cdot\text{m}^2\right)\left[\pi\left(2.82\times10^{-15}\text{ m}\right)^2\right]} = 1.28\times10^{7}\text{ s} = \boxed{148\text{ days}}.$$

The gross failure of the classical theory of the photoelectric effect contrasts with the success of quantum mechanics.

P40.19 Ultraviolet photons will be absorbed to knock electrons out of the sphere with maximum kinetic energy $K_{\max} = hf - \phi$,

or $$K_{\max} = \frac{\left(6.626\times10^{-34}\text{ J}\cdot\text{s}\right)\left(3.00\times10^{8}\text{ m/s}\right)}{200\times10^{-9}\text{ m}}\left(\frac{1.00\text{ eV}}{1.60\times10^{-19}\text{ J}}\right) - 4.70\text{ eV} = 1.51\text{ eV}.$$

The sphere is left with positive charge and so with positive potential relative to $V = 0$ at $r = \infty$. As its potential approaches 1.51 V, no further electrons will be able to escape, but will fall back onto the sphere. Its charge is then given by

$$V = \frac{k_eQ}{r} \quad \text{or} \quad Q = \frac{rV}{k_e} = \frac{\left(5.00\times10^{-2}\text{ m}\right)\left(1.51\text{ N}\cdot\text{m/C}\right)}{8.99\times10^{9}\text{ N}\cdot\text{m}^2/\text{C}^2} = \boxed{8.41\times10^{-12}\text{ C}}.$$

P40.20 (a) By having the photon source move toward the metal, the incident photons are Doppler shifted to higher frequencies, and hence, higher energy.

(b) If $v = 0.280c$, $$f' = f\sqrt{\frac{1+v/c}{1-v/c}} = \left(7.00\times10^{14}\right)\sqrt{\frac{1.28}{0.720}} = 9.33\times10^{14}\text{ Hz}.$$

Therefore, $$\phi = \left(6.626\times10^{-34}\text{ J}\cdot\text{s}\right)\left(9.33\times10^{14}\text{ Hz}\right) = 6.18\times10^{-19}\text{ J} = \boxed{3.87\text{ eV}}.$$

(c) At $v = 0.900c$, $f = 3.05\times10^{15}\text{ Hz}$

and $$K_{\max} = hf - \phi = \left(6.626\times10^{-34}\text{ J}\cdot\text{s}\right)\left(3.05\times10^{15}\text{ Hz}\right)\left(\frac{1.00\text{ eV}}{1.60\times10^{-19}\text{ J}}\right) - 3.87\text{ eV} = \boxed{8.78\text{ eV}}.$$

Section 40.3 The Compton Effect

P40.21 $$E = \frac{hc}{\lambda} = \frac{\left(6.626\times10^{-34}\text{ J}\cdot\text{s}\right)\left(3.00\times10^{8}\text{ m/s}\right)}{700\times10^{-9}\text{ m}} = 2.84\times10^{-19}\text{ J} = \boxed{1.78\text{ eV}}$$

$$p = \frac{h}{\lambda} = \frac{6.626\times10^{-34}\text{ J}\cdot\text{s}}{700\times10^{-9}\text{ m}} = \boxed{9.47\times10^{-28}\text{ kg}\cdot\text{m/s}}$$

P40.22 (a) $\Delta\lambda = \frac{h}{m_e c}(1-\cos\theta)$: $\Delta\lambda = \frac{6.626\times10^{-34}}{(9.11\times10^{-31})(3.00\times10^{8})}(1-\cos 37.0°) = \boxed{4.88\times10^{-13}\text{ m}}$

(b) $E_0 = \frac{hc}{\lambda_0}$: $(300\times10^{3}\text{ eV})(1.60\times10^{-19}\text{ J/eV}) = \frac{(6.626\times10^{-34})(3.00\times10^{8}\text{ m/s})}{\lambda_0}$

$\lambda_0 = 4.14\times10^{-12}\text{ m}$

and $\lambda' = \lambda_0 + \Delta\lambda = 4.63\times10^{-12}\text{ m}$

$E' = \frac{hc}{\lambda'} = \frac{(6.626\times10^{-34}\text{ J}\cdot\text{s})(3.00\times10^{8}\text{ m/s})}{4.63\times10^{-12}\text{ m}} = 4.30\times10^{-14}\text{ J} = \boxed{268\text{ keV}}$

(c) $K_e = E_0 - E' = 300\text{ keV} - 268.5\text{ keV} = \boxed{31.5\text{ keV}}$

P40.23 With $K_e = E'$, $K_e = E_0 - E'$ gives $E' = E_0 - E'$

$E' = \frac{E_0}{2}$ and $\lambda' = \frac{hc}{E'}$ $\qquad$ $\lambda' = \frac{hc}{E_0/2} = 2\frac{hc}{E_0} = 2\lambda_0$

$\lambda' = \lambda_0 + \lambda_C(1-\cos\theta)$ $\qquad$ $2\lambda_0 = \lambda_0 + \lambda_C(1-\cos\theta)$

$1-\cos\theta = \frac{\lambda_0}{\lambda_C} = \frac{0.001\,60}{0.002\,43}$ $\qquad$ $\theta = \boxed{70.0°}$

P40.24 This is Compton scattering through 180°:

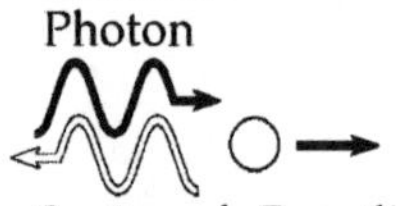

Incident Photon

Scattered Photon Recoiling Electron

FIG. P40.24

$$E_0 = \frac{hc}{\lambda_0} = \frac{(6.626\times10^{-34}\text{ J}\cdot\text{s})(3.00\times10^{8}\text{ m/s})}{(0.110\times10^{-9}\text{ m})(1.60\times10^{-19}\text{ J/eV})} = 11.3\text{ keV}$$

$$\Delta\lambda = \frac{h}{m_e c}(1-\cos\theta) = (2.43\times10^{-12}\text{ m})(1-\cos 180°) = 4.86\times10^{-12}\text{ m}$$

$\lambda' = \lambda_0 + \Delta\lambda = 0.115\text{ nm}$ so $\qquad$ $E' = \frac{hc}{\lambda'} = 10.8\text{ keV}$.

By conservation of momentum for the photon-electron system, $\frac{h}{\lambda_0}\hat{\mathbf{i}} = \frac{h}{\lambda'}(-\hat{\mathbf{i}}) + p_e\hat{\mathbf{i}}$

and $\qquad$ $p_e = h\left(\frac{1}{\lambda_0} + \frac{1}{\lambda'}\right)$

$$p_e = (6.626\times10^{-34}\text{ J}\cdot\text{s})\left(\frac{(3.00\times10^{8}\text{ m/s})/c}{1.60\times10^{-19}\text{ J/eV}}\right)\left(\frac{1}{0.110\times10^{-9}\text{ m}} + \frac{1}{0.115\times10^{-9}\text{ m}}\right) = \boxed{\frac{22.1\text{ keV}}{c}}.$$

By conservation of system energy, $\qquad$ $11.3\text{ keV} = 10.8\text{ keV} + K_e$

so that $\qquad$ $\boxed{K_e = 478\text{ eV}}$.

Check: $E^2 = p^2c^2 + m_e^2c^4$ or $\qquad$ $(m_ec^2 + K_e)^2 = (pc)^2 + (m_ec^2)^2$

$(511\text{ keV} + 0.478\text{ keV})^2 = (22.1\text{ keV})^2 + (511\text{ keV})^2$

$2.62\times10^{11} = 2.62\times10^{11}$

P40.25 (a) Conservation of momentum in the x direction gives: $p_\gamma = p'_\gamma \cos\theta + p_e \cos\phi$

or since $\theta = \phi$, $\frac{h}{\lambda_0} = \left(p_e + \frac{h}{\lambda'}\right)\cos\theta.$ [1]

Conservation of momentum in the y direction gives: $0 = p'_\gamma \sin\theta - p_e \sin\theta,$

which (neglecting the trivial solution $\theta = 0$) gives: $p_e = p'_\gamma = \frac{h}{\lambda'}.$ [2]

Substituting [2] into [1] gives: $\frac{h}{\lambda_0} = \frac{2h}{\lambda'}\cos\theta$, or $\lambda' = 2\lambda_0 \cos\theta.$ [3]

Then the Compton equation is $\lambda' - \lambda_0 = \frac{h}{m_e c}(1-\cos\theta)$

giving $2\lambda_0\cos\theta - \lambda_0 = \frac{h}{m_e c}(1-\cos\theta)$

or $2\cos\theta - 1 = \frac{hc}{\lambda_0}\frac{1}{m_e c^2}(1-\cos\theta).$

Since $E_\gamma = \frac{hc}{\lambda_0}$, this may be written as: $2\cos\theta - 1 = \left(\frac{E_\gamma}{m_e c^2}\right)(1-\cos\theta)$

which reduces to: $\left(2 + \frac{E_\gamma}{m_e c^2}\right)\cos\theta = 1 + \frac{E_\gamma}{m_e c^2}$

or $\cos\theta = \frac{m_e c^2 + E_\gamma}{2m_e c^2 + E_\gamma} = \frac{0.511 \text{ MeV} + 0.880 \text{ MeV}}{1.02 \text{ MeV} + 0.880 \text{ MeV}} = 0.732$ so that $\boxed{\theta = \phi = 43.0°}$.

(b) Using Equation (3): $E'_\gamma = \frac{hc}{\lambda'} = \frac{hc}{\lambda_0(2\cos\theta)} = \frac{E_\gamma}{2\cos\theta} = \frac{0.880 \text{ MeV}}{2\cos 43.0°} = 0.602 \text{ MeV} = \boxed{602 \text{ keV}}$.

Then, $p'_\gamma = \frac{E'_\gamma}{c} = \frac{0.602 \text{ MeV}}{c} = \boxed{3.21\times10^{-22} \text{ kg}\cdot\text{m/s}}$.

(c) From Equation (2), $p_e = p'_\gamma = \frac{0.602 \text{ MeV}}{c} = \boxed{3.21\times10^{-22} \text{ kg}\cdot\text{m/s}}$.

From energy conservation: $K_e = E_\gamma - E'_\gamma = 0.880 \text{ MeV} - 0.602 \text{ MeV} = 0.278 \text{ MeV} = \boxed{278 \text{ keV}}$.

P40.26 The energy of the incident photon is $E_0 = p_\gamma c = \dfrac{hc}{\lambda_0}$.

(a) Conserving momentum in the x direction gives

$$p_\lambda = p_e \cos\phi + p'_\gamma \cos\theta, \text{ or since } \phi = \theta,\ \frac{E_0}{c} = \left(p_e + p'_\gamma\right)\cos\theta. \qquad [1]$$

Conserving momentum in the y direction (with $\phi = 0$) yields

$$0 = p'_\gamma \sin\theta - p_e \sin\theta, \text{ or } p_e = p'_\gamma = \frac{h}{\lambda'}. \qquad [2]$$

Substituting Equation [2] into Equation [1] gives

$$\frac{E_0}{c} = \left(\frac{h}{\lambda'} + \frac{h}{\lambda'}\right)\cos\theta, \text{ or } \lambda' = \frac{2hc}{E_0}\cos\theta. \qquad [3]$$

By the Compton equation, $\lambda' - \lambda_0 = \dfrac{h}{m_e c}(1 - \cos\theta)$, $\quad \dfrac{2hc}{E_0}\cos\theta - \dfrac{2hc}{E_0} = \dfrac{h}{m_e c}(1 - \cos\theta)$

which reduces to $\quad \left(2m_e c^2 + E_0\right)\cos\theta = m_e c^2 + E_0$.

Thus, $\quad \boxed{\phi = \theta = \cos^{-1}\left(\dfrac{m_e c^2 + E_0}{2m_e c^2 + E_0}\right)}$.

(b) From Equation [3], $\quad \lambda' = \dfrac{2hc}{E_0}\cos\theta = \dfrac{2hc}{E_0}\left(\dfrac{m_e c^2 + E_0}{2m_e c^2 + E_0}\right)$.

Therefore, $\quad E'_\gamma = \dfrac{hc}{\lambda'} = \dfrac{hc}{(2hc/E_0)\left(m_e c^2 + E_0\right)/\left(2m_e c^2 + E_0\right)} = \boxed{\dfrac{E_0}{2}\left(\dfrac{2m_e c^2 + E_0}{m_e c^2 + E_0}\right)}$,

and $\quad p'_\gamma = \dfrac{E'_\gamma}{c} = \boxed{\dfrac{E_0}{2c}\left(\dfrac{2m_e c^2 + E_0}{m_e c^2 + E_0}\right)}$.

(c) From conservation of energy, $K_e = E_0 - E'_\gamma = E_0 - \dfrac{E_0}{2}\left(\dfrac{2m_e c^2 + E_0}{m_e c^2 + E_0}\right)$

or $\quad K_e = \dfrac{E_0}{2}\left(\dfrac{2m_e c^2 + 2E_0 - 2m_e c^2 - E_0}{m_e c^2 + E_0}\right) = \boxed{\dfrac{E_0^2}{2\left(m_e c^2 + E_0\right)}}$.

Finally, from Equation (2), $p_e = p'_\gamma = \boxed{\dfrac{E_0}{2c}\left(\dfrac{2m_e c^2 + E_0}{m_e c^2 + E_0}\right)}$.

***P40.27** The electron's kinetic energy is

$$K=\frac{1}{2}mv^2=\frac{1}{2}9.11\times10^{-31}\text{ kg}\left(2.18\times10^{6}\text{ m/s}\right)^2=2.16\times10^{-18}\text{ J}.$$

This is the energy lost by the photon, hf_0-hf'

$\frac{hc}{\lambda_0}-\frac{hc}{\lambda'}=2.16\times10^{-18}$ J. We also have

$$\lambda'-\lambda_0=\frac{h}{m_ec}(1-\cos\theta)=\frac{6.63\times10^{-34}\text{ Js s}}{9.11\times10^{-31}\text{ kg}\left(3\times10^{8}\text{ m}\right)}(1-\cos17.4°)$$

$$\lambda'=\lambda_0+1.11\times10^{-13}\text{ m}$$

(a) Combining the equations by substitution,

$$\frac{1}{\lambda_0}-\frac{1}{\lambda_0+0.111\text{ pm}}=\frac{2.16\times10^{-18}\text{ J s}}{6.63\times10^{-34}\text{ Js}\left(3\times10^{8}\text{ m}\right)}=1.09\times10^{7}/\text{m}$$

$$\frac{\lambda_0+0.111\text{ pm}-\lambda_0}{\lambda_0^2+\lambda_0(0.111\text{ pm})}=1.09\times10^{7}/\text{m}$$

$$0.111\text{ pm}=\left(1.09\times10^{7}/\text{m}\right)\lambda_0^2+1.21\times10^{-6}\lambda_0$$

$$1.09\times10^{7}\lambda_0^2+1.21\times10^{-6}\text{ m}\lambda_0-1.11\times10^{-13}\text{ m}^2=0$$

$$\lambda_0=\frac{-1.21\times10^{-6}\text{ m}\pm\sqrt{\left(1.21\times10^{-6}\text{ m}\right)^2-4\left(1.09\times10^{7}\right)\left(-1.11\times10^{-13}\text{ m}^2\right)}}{2\left(1.09\times10^{7}\right)}$$

only the positive answer is physical: $\lambda_0=\boxed{1.01\times10^{-10}\text{ m}}$.

(b) Then $\lambda'=1.01\times10^{-10}\text{ m}+1.11\times10^{-13}\text{ m}=1.01\times10^{-10}\text{ m}$.
Conservation of momentum in the transverse direction:

$$0=\frac{h}{\lambda'}\sin\theta-\gamma m_ev\sin\phi$$

$$\frac{6.63\times10^{-34}\text{ J}\cdot\text{s}}{1.01\times10^{-10}\text{ m}}\sin17.4°=\frac{9.11\times10^{-31}\text{ kg}\left(2.18\times10^{6}\text{ m/s}\right)\sin\phi}{\sqrt{1-\left(2.18\times10^{6}/3\times10^{8}\right)^2}}$$

$$1.96\times10^{-24}=1.99\times10^{-24}\sin\phi\qquad\phi=\boxed{81.1°}$$

P40.28 (a) Thanks to Compton we have four equations in the unknowns ϕ, v, and λ':

$$\frac{hc}{\lambda_0}=\frac{hc}{\lambda'}+\gamma m_e c^2-m_e c^2 \qquad \text{(energy conservation)} \qquad [1]$$

$$\frac{h}{\lambda_0}=\frac{h}{\lambda'}\cos 2\phi+\gamma m_e v\cos\phi \qquad \text{(momentum in } x \text{ direction)} \qquad [2]$$

$$0=\frac{h}{\lambda'}\sin 2\phi-\gamma m_e v\sin\phi \qquad \text{(momentum in } y \text{ direction)} \qquad [3]$$

$$\lambda'-\lambda_0=\frac{h}{m_e c}(1-\cos 2\phi) \qquad \text{(Compton equation).} \qquad [4]$$

Using $\sin 2\phi=2\sin\phi\cos\phi$ in Equation [3] gives $\gamma m_e v=\frac{2h}{\lambda'}\cos\phi$.

Substituting this into Equation [2] and using $\cos 2\phi=2\cos^2\phi-1$ yields

$$\frac{h}{\lambda_0}=\frac{h}{\lambda'}\left(2\cos^2\phi-1\right)+\frac{2h}{\lambda'}\cos^2\phi=\frac{h}{\lambda'}\left(4\cos^2\phi-1\right),$$

or $\lambda'=4\lambda_0\cos^2\phi-\lambda_0$. [5]

Substituting the last result into the Compton equation gives

$$4\lambda_0\cos^2\phi-2\lambda_0=\frac{h}{m_e c}\left[1-\left(2\cos^2\phi-1\right)\right]=2\frac{hc}{m_e c^2}\left(1-\cos^2\phi\right).$$

With the substitution $\lambda_0=\frac{hc}{E_0}$, this reduces to

$$\cos^2\phi=\frac{m_e c^2+E_0}{2m_e c^2+E_0}=\frac{1+x}{2+x} \text{ where } x\equiv\frac{E_0}{m_e c^2}.$$

For $x=\frac{0.700\text{ MeV}}{0.511\text{ MeV}}=1.37$, this gives $\phi=\cos^{-1}\sqrt{\frac{1+x}{2+x}}=\boxed{33.0°}$.

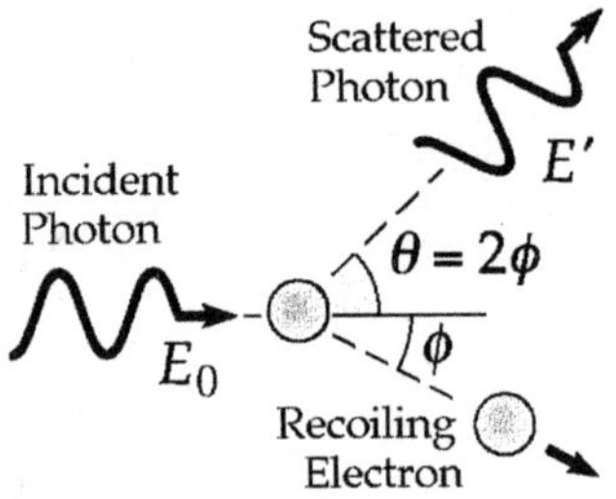

FIG. P40.28(a)

(b) From Equation [5], $\lambda'=\lambda_0\left(4\cos^2\phi-1\right)=\lambda_0\left[4\left(\frac{1+x}{2+x}\right)-1\right]=\lambda_0\left(\frac{2+3x}{2+x}\right)$.

Then, Equation [1] becomes

$$\frac{hc}{\lambda_0}=\frac{hc}{\lambda_0}\left(\frac{2+x}{2+3x}\right)+\gamma m_e c^2-m_e c^2 \text{ or } \frac{E_0}{m_e c^2}-\frac{E_0}{m_e c^2}\left(\frac{2+x}{2+3x}\right)+1=\gamma.$$

Thus, $\gamma=1+x-x\left(\frac{2+x}{2+3x}\right)$, and with $x=1.37$ we get $\gamma=1.614$.

Therefore, $\frac{v}{c}=\sqrt{1-\gamma^{-2}}=\sqrt{1-0.384}=0.785$ or $v=\boxed{0.785c}$.

P40.29 $\lambda' - \lambda = \dfrac{h}{m_e c}(1 - \cos\theta)$

$$\lambda'' - \lambda' = \frac{h}{m_e c}[1 - \cos(\pi - \theta)]$$

$$\lambda'' - \lambda = \frac{h}{m_e c} - \frac{h}{m_e c}\cos(\pi - \theta) + \frac{h}{m_e c} - \frac{h}{m_e c}\cos\theta$$

Now $\cos(\pi - \theta) = -\cos\theta$, so $\lambda'' - \lambda = 2\dfrac{h}{m_e c} = \boxed{0.004\,86 \text{ nm}}$.

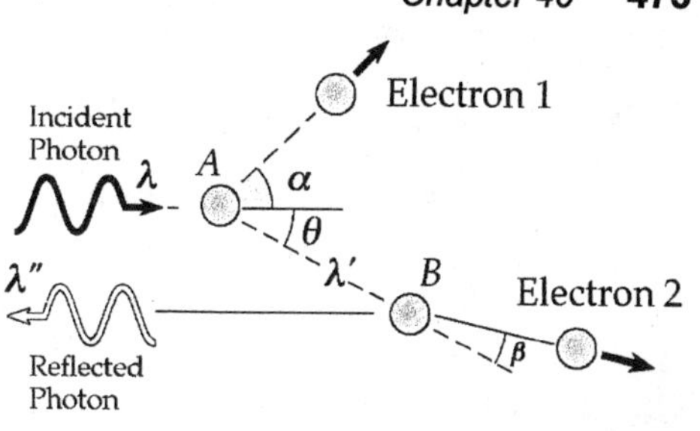

FIG. P40.29

P40.30 Maximum energy loss appears as maximum increase in wavelength, which occurs for scattering angle 180°. Then $\Delta\lambda = (1 - \cos 180°)\left(\dfrac{h}{mc}\right) = \dfrac{2h}{mc}$ where m is the mass of the target particle. The fractional energy loss is

$$\frac{E_0 - E'}{E_0} = \frac{hc/\lambda_0 - hc/\lambda'}{hc/\lambda_0} = \frac{\lambda' - \lambda_0}{\lambda'} = \frac{\Delta\lambda}{\lambda_0 + \Delta\lambda} = \frac{2h/mc}{\lambda_0 + 2h/mc}.$$

Further, $\lambda_0 = \dfrac{hc}{E_0}$, so $\dfrac{E_0 - E'}{E_0} = \dfrac{2h/mc}{hc/E_0 + 2h/mc} = \dfrac{2E_0}{mc^2 + 2E_0}$.

(a) For scattering from a free electron, $mc^2 = 0.511 \text{ MeV}$, so

$$\frac{E_0 - E'}{E_0} = \frac{2(0.511 \text{ MeV})}{0.511 \text{ MeV} + 2(0.511 \text{ MeV})} = \boxed{0.667}.$$

(b) For scattering from a free proton, $mc^2 = 938 \text{ MeV}$, and

$$\frac{E_0 - E'}{E_0} = \frac{2(0.511 \text{ MeV})}{938 \text{ MeV} + 2(0.511 \text{ MeV})} = \boxed{0.001\,09}.$$

Section 40.4 Photons and Electromagnetic Waves

***P40.31** With photon energy $10.0 \text{ eV} = hf$

$$f = \frac{10.0\left(1.6 \times 10^{-19} \text{ J}\right)}{6.63 \times 10^{-34} \text{ J} \cdot \text{s}} = 2.41 \times 10^{15} \text{ Hz}.$$

Any electromagnetic wave with frequency higher than 2.41×10^{15} Hz counts as ionizing radiation. This includes far ultraviolet light, x-rays, and gamma rays.

***P40.32** The photon energy is $E = \frac{hc}{\lambda} = \frac{6.63 \times 10^{-34}\ \text{J}\cdot\text{s}\left(3 \times 10^{8}\ \text{m/s}\right)}{633 \times 10^{-9}\ \text{m}} = 3.14 \times 10^{-19}\ \text{J}$. The power carried by the beam is $\left(2 \times 10^{18}\ \text{photons/s}\right)\left(3.14 \times 10^{-19}\ \text{J/photon}\right) = 0.628\ \text{W}$. Its intensity is the average Poynting vector $I = S_{\text{av}} = \frac{\mathscr{P}}{\pi r^2} = \frac{0.628\ \text{W}(4)}{\pi\left(1.75 \times 10^{-3}\ \text{m}\right)^2} = 2.61 \times 10^{5}\ \text{W/m}^2$.

(a) $S_{\text{av}} = \frac{1}{\mu_0} E_{\text{rms}} B_{\text{rms}} \sin 90° = \frac{1}{\mu_0} \frac{E_{\text{max}}}{\sqrt{2}} \frac{B_{\text{max}}}{\sqrt{2}}$. Also $E_{\text{max}} = B_{\text{max}} c$. So $S_{\text{av}} = \frac{E_{\text{max}}^2}{2\mu_0 c}$.

$$E_{\text{max}} = \left(2\mu_0 c S_{\text{av}}\right)^{1/2} = \left(2\left(4\pi \times 10^{-7}\ \text{Tm/A}\right)\left(3 \times 10^{8}\ \text{m/s}\right)\left(2.61 \times 10^{5}\ \text{W/m}^2\right)\right)^{1/2}$$

$$= \boxed{1.40 \times 10^{4}\ \text{N/C}}$$

$$B_{\text{max}} = \frac{1.40 \times 10^{4}\ \text{N/C}}{3 \times 10^{8}\ \text{m/s}} = \boxed{4.68 \times 10^{-5}\ \text{T}}$$

(b) Each photon carries momentum $\frac{E}{c}$. The beam transports momentum at the rate $\frac{\mathscr{P}}{c}$. It imparts momentum to a perfectly reflecting surface at the rate

$$\frac{2\mathscr{P}}{c} = \text{force} = \frac{2(0.628\ \text{W})}{3 \times 10^{8}\ \text{m/s}} = \boxed{4.19 \times 10^{-9}\ \text{N}}.$$

(c) The block of ice absorbs energy $mL = \mathscr{P}\Delta t$ melting

$$m = \frac{\mathscr{P}\Delta t}{L} = \frac{0.628\ \text{W}(1.5 \times 3\,600\ \text{s})}{3.33 \times 10^{5}\ \text{J/kg}} = \boxed{1.02 \times 10^{-2}\ \text{kg}}.$$

Section 40.5 The Wave Properties of Particles

P40.33 $$\lambda = \frac{h}{p} = \frac{h}{mv} = \frac{6.626 \times 10^{-34}\ \text{J}\cdot\text{s}}{\left(1.67 \times 10^{-27}\ \text{kg}\right)\left(1.00 \times 10^{6}\ \text{m/s}\right)} = \boxed{3.97 \times 10^{-13}\ \text{m}}$$

P40.34 (a) $$\frac{p^2}{2m} = (50.0)\left(1.60 \times 10^{-19}\ \text{J}\right)$$

$$p = 3.81 \times 10^{-24}\ \text{kg}\cdot\text{m/s}$$

$$\lambda = \frac{h}{p} = \boxed{0.174\ \text{nm}}$$

(b) $$\frac{p^2}{2m} = \left(50.0 \times 10^{3}\right)\left(1.60 \times 10^{-19}\ \text{J}\right)$$

$$p = 1.20 \times 10^{-22}\ \text{kg}\cdot\text{m/s}$$

$$\lambda = \frac{h}{p} = 5.49 \times 10^{-12}\ \text{m}$$

The relativistic answer is slightly more precise:

$$\lambda = \frac{h}{p} = \frac{hc}{\left[\left(mc^2 + K\right)^2 - m^2c^4\right]^{1/2}} = \boxed{5.37 \times 10^{-12}\ \text{m}}.$$

P40.35 (a) Electron: $\lambda = \frac{h}{p}$ and $K = \frac{1}{2}m_e v^2 = \frac{m_e^2 v^2}{2m_e} = \frac{p^2}{2m_e}$ so $p = \sqrt{2m_e K}$

and $$\lambda = \frac{h}{\sqrt{2m_e K}} = \frac{6.626 \times 10^{-34}\ \text{J}\cdot\text{s}}{\sqrt{2\left(9.11 \times 10^{-31}\ \text{kg}\right)(3.00)\left(1.60 \times 10^{-19}\ \text{J}\right)}}$$

$$\lambda = 7.09 \times 10^{-10}\ \text{m} = \boxed{0.709\ \text{nm}}.$$

(b) Photon: $\lambda = \frac{c}{f}$ and $E = hf$ so $f = \frac{E}{h}$

and $$\lambda = \frac{hc}{E} = \frac{\left(6.626 \times 10^{-34}\ \text{J}\cdot\text{s}\right)\left(3.00 \times 10^{8}\ \text{m/s}\right)}{3\left(1.60 \times 10^{-19}\ \text{J}\right)} = 4.14 \times 10^{-7}\ \text{m} = \boxed{414\ \text{nm}}.$$

P40.36 (a) The wavelength of a non-relativistic particle of mass m is given by $\lambda = \frac{h}{p} = \frac{h}{\sqrt{2mK}}$ where the kinetic energy K is in joules. If the neutron kinetic energy K_n is given in electron volts, its kinetic energy in joules is $K = \left(1.60 \times 10^{-19}\ \text{J/eV}\right)K_n$ and the equation for the wavelength becomes

$$\lambda = \frac{h}{\sqrt{2mK}} = \frac{6.626 \times 10^{-34}\ \text{J}\cdot\text{s}}{\sqrt{2\left(1.67 \times 10^{-27}\ \text{kg}\right)\left(1.60 \times 10^{-19}\ \text{J/eV}\right)K_n}} = \boxed{\frac{2.87 \times 10^{-11}}{\sqrt{K_n}}\ \text{m}}$$

where K_n is expressed in electron volts.

(b) If $K_n = 1.00\ \text{keV} = 1\,000\ \text{eV}$, then $\lambda = \frac{2.87 \times 10^{-11}}{\sqrt{1\,000}}\ \text{m} = 9.07 \times 10^{-13}\ \text{m} = \boxed{907\ \text{fm}}$.

P40.37 (a) $\lambda \sim 10^{-14}$ m or less. $p = \frac{h}{\lambda} \sim \frac{6.6 \times 10^{-34}\ \text{J}\cdot\text{s}}{10^{-14}\ \text{m}} = 10^{-19}\ \text{kg}\cdot\text{m/s}$ or more.

The energy of the electron is $E = \sqrt{p^2c^2 + m_e^2c^4} \sim \sqrt{\left(10^{-19}\right)^2\left(3 \times 10^8\right)^2 + \left(9 \times 10^{-31}\right)^2\left(3 \times 10^8\right)^4}$

or $E \sim 10^{-11}\ \text{J} \sim 10^{8}\ \text{eV}$ or more,

so that $K = E - m_e c^2 \sim 10^8\ \text{eV} - \left(0.5 \times 10^6\ \text{eV}\right) \boxed{\sim 10^8\ \text{eV}}$ or more.

(b) The electric potential energy of the electron-nucleus system would be

$$U_e = \frac{k_e q_1 q_2}{r} \sim \frac{\left(9 \times 10^9\ \text{N}\cdot\text{m}^2/\text{C}^2\right)\left(10^{-19}\ \text{C}\right)(-e)}{10^{-14}\ \text{m}} \sim -10^5\ \text{eV}.$$

With its $K + U_e >> 0$, $\boxed{\text{the electron would immediately escape the nucleus}}$.

P40.38 From the condition for Bragg reflection,

$$m\lambda = 2d\sin\theta = 2d\cos\left(\frac{\phi}{2}\right).$$

But $\quad d = a\sin\left(\frac{\phi}{2}\right)$

where a is the lattice spacing.

Thus, with $m = 1$, $\quad \lambda = 2a\sin\left(\frac{\phi}{2}\right)\cos\left(\frac{\phi}{2}\right) = a\sin\phi$

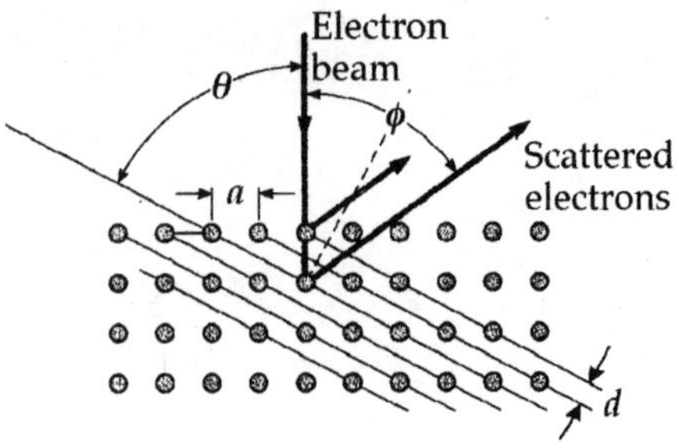

FIG. P40.38

$$\lambda = \frac{h}{p} = \frac{h}{\sqrt{2m_eK}} \qquad \lambda = \frac{6.626\times10^{-34}\ \text{J}\cdot\text{s}}{\sqrt{2\left(9.11\times10^{-31}\ \text{kg}\right)\left(54.0\times1.60\times10^{-19}\ \text{J}\right)}} = 1.67\times10^{-10}\ \text{m}.$$

Therefore, the lattice spacing is $a = \dfrac{\lambda}{\sin\phi} = \dfrac{1.67\times10^{-10}\ \text{m}}{\sin 50.0°} = 2.18\times10^{-10} = \boxed{0.218\ \text{nm}}$.

P40.39 (a) $\quad E^2 = p^2c^2 + m^2c^4$

with $E = hf$, $\quad p = \dfrac{h}{\lambda} \quad$ and $\quad mc = \dfrac{h}{\lambda_C}$

so $\quad h^2f^2 = \dfrac{h^2c^2}{\lambda^2} + \dfrac{h^2c^2}{\lambda_C^2} \quad$ and $\quad \left(\dfrac{f}{c}\right)^2 = \dfrac{1}{\lambda^2} + \dfrac{1}{\lambda_C^2} \quad$ (Eq. 1).

(b) For a photon $\quad \dfrac{f}{c} = \dfrac{1}{\lambda}$.

The third term $\dfrac{1}{\lambda_C}$ in Equation 1 for electrons and other massive particles shows that

$\boxed{\text{they will always have a different frequency from photons of the same wavelength}}$.

***P40.40** For the massive particle, $K = (\gamma - 1)mc^2$ and $\lambda_m = \dfrac{h}{p} = \dfrac{h}{\gamma mv}$. For the photon (which we represent as γ),

$E = K$ and $\lambda_\gamma = \dfrac{c}{f} = \dfrac{ch}{E} = \dfrac{ch}{K} = \dfrac{ch}{(\gamma-1)mc^2}$. Then the ratio is $\dfrac{\lambda_\gamma}{\lambda_m} = \dfrac{ch\gamma mv}{(\gamma-1)mc^2h} = \dfrac{\gamma}{\gamma-1}\dfrac{v}{c}$.

(a) $$\frac{\lambda_\gamma}{\lambda_m} = \frac{1(0.9)}{\sqrt{1-0.9^2}\left[\left(1/\sqrt{1-0.9^2}\right)-1\right]} = \boxed{1.60}$$

(b) $$\frac{\lambda_\gamma}{\lambda_m} = \frac{1(0.001)}{\sqrt{1-(0.001)^2}\left[\left(1/\sqrt{1-(0.001)^2}\right)-1\right]} = \boxed{2.00\times10^3}$$

(c) As $\dfrac{v}{c}\to 1$, $\gamma\to\infty$ and $\gamma - 1$ becomes nearly equal to γ. Then $\dfrac{\lambda_\gamma}{\lambda_m} \to \dfrac{\gamma}{\gamma}1 = \boxed{1}$.

(d) As $\dfrac{v}{c}\to 0$, $\left(1-\dfrac{v^2}{c^2}\right)^{-1/2} - 1 \approx 1 - \left(-\dfrac{1}{2}\right)\dfrac{v^2}{c^2} - 1 = \dfrac{1}{2}\dfrac{v^2}{c^2}$ and $\dfrac{\lambda_\gamma}{\lambda_m} \to 1\dfrac{v/c}{(1/2)\left(v^2/c^2\right)} = \dfrac{2c}{v} \to \boxed{\infty}$.

P40.41 $\lambda = \frac{h}{p}$ $\quad p = \frac{h}{\lambda} = \frac{6.626 \times 10^{-34}\ \text{J}\cdot\text{s}}{1.00 \times 10^{-11}\ \text{m}} = 6.63 \times 10^{-23}\ \text{kg}\cdot\text{m/s}$

(a) electrons: $K_e = \frac{p^2}{2m_e} = \frac{\left(6.63 \times 10^{-23}\right)^2}{2\left(9.11 \times 10^{-31}\right)}\ \text{J} = 15.1\ \text{keV}$

The relativistic answer is more precisely correct:

$$K_e = \sqrt{p^2c^2 + m_e^2c^4} - m_ec^2 = \boxed{14.9\ \text{keV}}.$$

(b) photons: $E_\gamma = pc = \left(6.63 \times 10^{-23}\right)\left(3.00 \times 10^8\right) = \boxed{124\ \text{keV}}$

P40.42 (a) The wavelength of the student is $\lambda = \frac{h}{p} = \frac{h}{mv}$. If w is the width of the diffracting aperture,

then we need $\quad w \le 10.0\lambda = 10.0\left(\frac{h}{mv}\right)$

so that $\quad v \le 10.0\frac{h}{mw} = 10.0\left(\frac{6.626 \times 10^{-34}\ \text{J}\cdot\text{s}}{(80.0\ \text{kg})(0.750\ \text{m})}\right) = \boxed{1.10 \times 10^{-34}\ \text{m/s}}.$

(b) Using $\Delta t = \frac{d}{v}$ we get: $\quad \Delta t \ge \frac{0.150\ \text{m}}{1.10 \times 10^{-34}\ \text{m/s}} = \boxed{1.36 \times 10^{33}\ \text{s}}.$

(c) $\boxed{\text{No}}$. The minimum time to pass through the door is over 10^{15} times the age of the Universe.

Section 40.6 **The Quantum Particle**

***P40.43** $E = K = \frac{1}{2}mu^2 = hf$ and $\lambda = \frac{h}{mu}$.

$$v_{\text{phase}} = f\lambda = \frac{mu^2}{2h}\frac{h}{mu} = \boxed{\frac{u}{2} = v_{\text{phase}}}.$$

This is different from the speed u at which the particle transports mass, energy, and momentum.

***P40.44** As a bonus, we begin by proving that the phase speed $v_p = \frac{\omega}{k}$ is not the speed of the particle.

$$v_p = \frac{\omega}{k} = \frac{\sqrt{p^2c^2 + m^2c^4}\,\hbar}{\hbar\gamma mv} = \frac{\sqrt{\gamma^2m^2v^2c^2 + m^2c^4}}{\sqrt{\gamma^2m^2v^2}} = c\sqrt{1 + \frac{c^2}{\gamma^2v^2}} = c\sqrt{1 + \frac{c^2}{v^2}\left(1 - \frac{v^2}{c^2}\right)} = c\sqrt{1 + \frac{c^2}{v^2} - 1} = \frac{c^2}{v}$$

In fact, the phase speed is larger than the speed of light. A point of constant phase in the wave function carries no mass, no energy, and no information.

Now for the group speed:

continued on next page

$$v_g = \frac{d\omega}{dk} = \frac{d\hbar\omega}{d\hbar k} = \frac{dE}{dp} = \frac{d}{dp}\sqrt{m^2c^4 + p^2c^2}$$

$$v_g = \frac{1}{2}\left(m^2c^4 + p^2c^2\right)^{-1/2}\left(0 + 2pc^2\right) = \sqrt{\frac{p^2c^4}{p^2c^2 + m^2c^4}}$$

$$v_g = c\sqrt{\frac{\gamma^2m^2v^2}{\gamma^2m^2v^2 + m^2c^2}} = c\sqrt{\frac{v^2/\left(1 - v^2/c^2\right)}{v^2/\left(1 - v^2/c^2\right) + c^2}} = c\sqrt{\frac{v^2/\left(1 - v^2/c^2\right)}{\left(v^2 + c^2 - v^2\right)/\left(1 - v^2/c^2\right)}} = v$$

It is this speed at which mass, energy, and momentum are transported.

Section 40.7 The Double-Slit Experiment Revisited

P40.45 (a) $\lambda = \frac{h}{mv} = \frac{6.626 \times 10^{-34}\ \text{J}\cdot\text{s}}{\left(1.67 \times 10^{-27}\ \text{kg}\right)\left(0.400\ \text{m/s}\right)} = \boxed{9.92 \times 10^{-7}\ \text{m}}$

(b) For destructive interference in a multiple-slit experiment, $d\sin\theta = \left(m + \frac{1}{2}\right)\lambda$, with $m = 0$ for the first minimum.

Then, $\theta = \sin^{-1}\left(\frac{\lambda}{2d}\right) = 0.028\ 4°$

so $\frac{y}{L} = \tan\theta$ $\quad y = L\tan\theta = (10.0\ \text{m})(\tan 0.028\ 4°) = \boxed{4.96\ \text{mm}}$.

(c) We cannot say the neutron passed through one slit. We can only say it passed through the slits.

P40.46 Consider the first bright band away from the center:

$d\sin\theta = m\lambda$ $\quad \left(6.00 \times 10^{-8}\ \text{m}\right)\sin\left(\tan^{-1}\left[\frac{0.400}{200}\right]\right) = (1)\lambda = 1.20 \times 10^{-10}\ \text{m}$

$\lambda = \frac{h}{m_ev}$ so $\quad m_ev = \frac{h}{\lambda}$

and $\quad K = \frac{1}{2}m_ev^2 = \frac{m_e^2v^2}{2m_e} = \frac{h^2}{2m_e\lambda^2} = e\Delta V$

$\Delta V = \frac{h^2}{2em_e\lambda^2}$ $\quad \Delta V = \frac{\left(6.626 \times 10^{-34}\ \text{J}\cdot\text{s}\right)^2}{2\left(1.60 \times 10^{-19}\ \text{C}\right)\left(9.11 \times 10^{-31}\ \text{kg}\right)\left(1.20 \times 10^{-10}\ \text{m}\right)^2} = \boxed{105\ \text{V}}$.

***P40.47** We find the speed of each electron from energy conservation in the firing process:

$0 = K_f + U_f = \frac{1}{2}mv^2 - \text{eV}$

$v = \sqrt{\frac{2eV}{m}} = \sqrt{\frac{2 \times 1.6 \times 10^{-19}\ \text{C}(45\ \text{V})}{9.11 \times 10^{-31}\ \text{kg}}} = 3.98 \times 10^6\ \text{m/s}$

The time of flight is $\Delta t = \frac{\Delta x}{v} = \frac{0.28\ \text{m}}{3.98 \times 10^6\ \text{m/s}} = 7.04 \times 10^{-8}\ \text{s}$. The current when electrons are 28 cm apart is $I = \frac{q}{t} = \frac{e}{\Delta t} = \frac{1.6 \times 10^{-19}\ \text{C}}{7.04 \times 10^{-8}\ \text{s}} = \boxed{2.27 \times 10^{-12}\ \text{A}}$.

Section 40.8 The Uncertainty Principle

P40.48 (a) $\Delta p\Delta x = m\Delta v\Delta x \geq \frac{\hbar}{2}$ so $\Delta v \geq \frac{h}{4\pi m\Delta x} = \frac{2\pi\,\text{J}\cdot\text{s}}{4\pi(2.00\text{ kg})(1.00\text{ m})} = \boxed{0.250\text{ m/s}}$.

(b) The duck might move by $(0.25\text{ m/s})(5\text{ s}) = 1.25\text{ m}$. With original position uncertainty of 1.00 m, we can think of Δx growing to $1.00\text{ m} + 1.25\text{ m} = \boxed{2.25\text{ m}}$.

P40.49 For the electron, $\Delta p = m_e\Delta v = (9.11\times10^{-31}\text{ kg})(500\text{ m/s})(1.00\times10^{-4}) = 4.56\times10^{-32}\text{ kg}\cdot\text{m/s}$

$$\Delta x = \frac{h}{4\pi\,\Delta p} = \frac{6.626\times10^{-34}\text{ J}\cdot\text{s}}{4\pi(4.56\times10^{-32}\text{ kg}\cdot\text{m/s})} = \boxed{1.16\text{ mm}}.$$

For the bullet, $\Delta p = m\Delta v = (0.020\,0\text{ kg})(500\text{ m/s})(1.00\times10^{-4}) = 1.00\times10^{-3}\text{ kg}\cdot\text{m/s}$

$$\Delta x = \frac{h}{4\pi\,\Delta p} = \boxed{5.28\times10^{-32}\text{ m}}.$$

P40.50 $\frac{\Delta y}{x} = \frac{\Delta p_y}{p_x}$ and $d\Delta p_y \geq \frac{h}{4\pi}$.

Eliminate Δp_y and solve for x.

$$x = 4\pi p_x(\Delta y)\frac{d}{h}: \qquad x = 4\pi(1.00\times10^{-3}\text{ kg})(100\text{ m/s})(1.00\times10^{-2}\text{ m})\frac{(2.00\times10^{-3}\text{ m})}{(6.626\times10^{-34}\text{ J}\cdot\text{s})}$$

The answer, $x = \boxed{3.79\times10^{28}\text{ m}}$, is 190 times greater than the diameter of the Universe!

P40.51 With $\Delta x = 2\times10^{-15}$ m m, the uncertainty principle requires $\Delta p_x \geq \frac{\hbar}{2\Delta x} = 2.6\times10^{-20}\text{ kg}\cdot\text{m/s}$.

The average momentum of the particle bound in a stationary nucleus is zero. The uncertainty in momentum measures the root-mean-square momentum, so we take $p_{rms} \approx 3\times10^{-20}\text{ kg}\cdot\text{m/s}$. For an electron, the non-relativistic approximation $p = m_e v$ would predict $v \approx 3\times10^{10}\text{ m/s}$, while v cannot be greater than c.

Thus, a better solution would be $E = \left[(m_e c^2)^2 + (pc)^2\right]^{1/2} \approx 56\text{ MeV} = \gamma m_e c^2$

$$\gamma \approx 110 = \frac{1}{\sqrt{1 - v^2/c^2}} \qquad \text{so} \qquad v \approx 0.999\,96c.$$

For a proton, $v = \frac{p}{m}$ gives $v = 1.8\times10^{7}\text{ m/s}$, less than one-tenth the speed of light.

***P40.52** (a) $K = \frac{1}{2}mv^2 = \frac{(mv)^2}{2m} = \frac{p^2}{2m}$

(b) To find the minimum kinetic energy, think of the minimum momentum uncertainty, and maximum position uncertainty of $10^{-15}\text{ m} = \Delta x$. We model the proton as moving along a straight line with $\Delta p\Delta x = \frac{\hbar}{2}$, $\Delta p = \frac{\hbar}{2\Delta x}$. The average momentum is zero. The average squared momentum is equal to the squared uncertainty:

$$K = \frac{p^2}{2m} = \frac{(\Delta p)^2}{2m} = \frac{\hbar^2}{4(\Delta x)^2 2m} = \frac{h^2}{32\pi^2(\Delta x)^2 m} = \frac{(6.63\times10^{-34}\text{ J}\cdot\text{s})^2}{32\pi^2(10^{-15}\text{ m})^2 1.67\times10^{-27}\text{ kg}} = 8.33\times10^{-13}\text{ J}$$

$$= \boxed{5.21\text{ MeV}}$$

P40.53 (a) At the top of the ladder, the woman holds a pellet inside a small region Δx_i. Thus, the uncertainty principle requires her to release it with typical horizontal momentum $\Delta p_x = m\Delta v_x = \dfrac{\hbar}{2\Delta x_i}$. It falls to the floor in a travel time given by $H = 0 + \frac{1}{2}gt^2$ as $t = \sqrt{\dfrac{2H}{g}}$, so the total width of the impact points is

$$\Delta x_f = \Delta x_i + (\Delta v_x)t = \Delta x_i + \left(\frac{\hbar}{2m\Delta x_i}\right)\sqrt{\frac{2H}{g}} = \Delta x_i + \frac{A}{\Delta x_i}$$

where $$A = \frac{\hbar}{2m}\sqrt{\frac{2H}{g}}.$$

To minimize Δx_f, we require $$\frac{d(\Delta x_f)}{d(\Delta x_i)} = 0 \qquad \text{or} \qquad 1 - \frac{A}{\Delta x_i^2} = 0$$

so $$\Delta x_i = \sqrt{A}.$$

The minimum width of the impact points is

$$(\Delta x_f)_{\min} = \left(\Delta x_i + \frac{A}{\Delta x_i}\right)\Bigg|_{\Delta x_i = \sqrt{A}} = 2\sqrt{A} = \boxed{\sqrt{\frac{2\hbar}{m}}\left(\frac{2H}{g}\right)^{1/4}}.$$

(b) $$(\Delta x_f)_{\min} = \left[\frac{2(1.0546\times 10^{-34}\text{ J}\cdot\text{s})}{5.00\times 10^{-4}\text{ kg}}\right]^{1/2}\left[\frac{2(2.00\text{ m})}{9.80\text{ m/s}^2}\right]^{1/4} = \boxed{5.19\times 10^{-16}\text{ m}}$$

Additional Problems

P40.54 $$\Delta V_S = \left(\frac{h}{e}\right)f - \frac{\phi}{e}$$

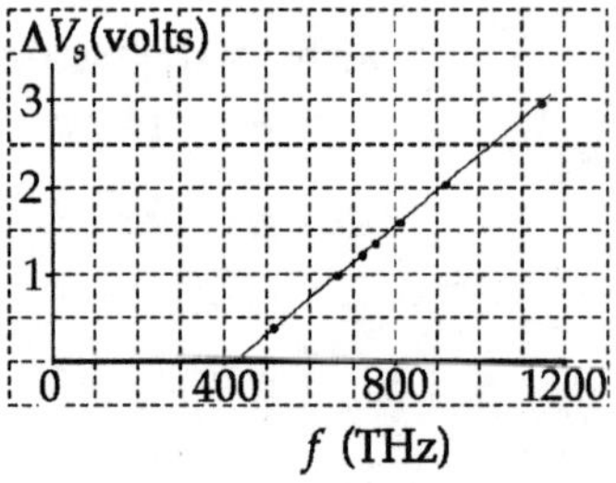

From two points on the graph $$0 = \left(\frac{h}{e}\right)(4.1\times 10^{14}\text{ Hz}) - \frac{\phi}{e}$$

and $$3.3\text{ V} = \left(\frac{h}{e}\right)(12\times 10^{14}\text{ Hz}) - \frac{\phi}{e}.$$

FIG. P40.54

Combining these two expressions we find:

(a) $\phi = \boxed{1.7\text{ eV}}$

(b) $\dfrac{h}{e} = \boxed{4.2\times 10^{-15}\text{ V}\cdot\text{s}}$

(c) At the cutoff wavelength $\dfrac{hc}{\lambda_c} = \phi = \left(\dfrac{h}{e}\right)\dfrac{ec}{\lambda_c}$

$$\lambda_c = (4.2\times 10^{-15}\text{ V}\cdot\text{s})(1.6\times 10^{-19}\text{ C})\frac{(3\times 10^8\text{ m/s})}{(1.7\text{ eV})(1.6\times 10^{-19}\text{ J/eV})} = \boxed{730\text{ nm}}$$

P40.55 We want an Einstein plot of K_{max} versus f

λ, nm	f, 10^{14} Hz	K_{max}, eV
588	5.10	0.67
505	5.94	0.98
445	6.74	1.35
399	7.52	1.63

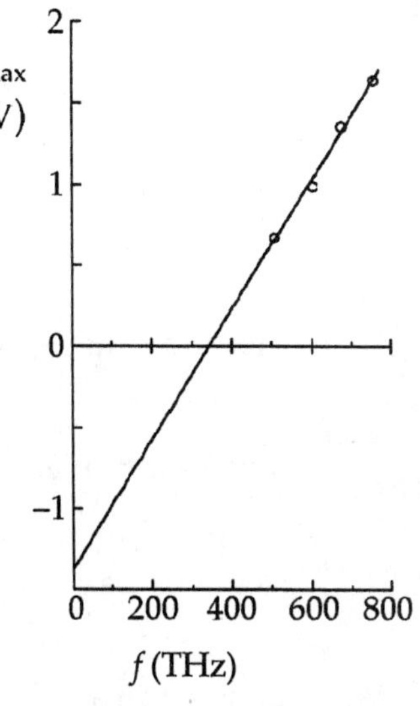

FIG. P40.55

(a) $$\text{slope} = \frac{0.402 \text{ eV}}{10^{14} \text{ Hz}} \pm 8\%$$

(b) $$e\Delta V_S = hf - \phi$$

$$h = (0.402)\left(\frac{1.60 \times 10^{-19} \text{ J}\cdot\text{s}}{10^{14}}\right) = \boxed{6.4 \times 10^{-34} \text{ J}\cdot\text{s} \pm 8\%}$$

(c) $$K_{max} = 0$$

at $f \approx 344 \times 10^{12}$ Hz

$$\phi = hf = 2.32 \times 10^{-19} \text{ J} = \boxed{1.4 \text{ eV}}$$

P40.56 From the path the electrons follow in the magnetic field, the maximum kinetic energy is seen to be:

$$K_{max} = \frac{e^2B^2R^2}{2m_e}.$$

From the photoelectric equation, $$K_{max} = hf - \phi = \frac{hc}{\lambda} - \phi.$$

Thus, the work function is $$\phi = \frac{hc}{\lambda} - K_{max} = \boxed{\frac{hc}{\lambda} - \frac{e^2B^2R^2}{2m_e}}.$$

P40.57 $$\Delta\lambda = \frac{h}{m_pc}(1-\cos\theta) = \frac{(6.626 \times 10^{-34} \text{ J}\cdot\text{s})}{(1.67 \times 10^{-27} \text{ kg})(3.00 \times 10^8 \text{ m/s})}(0.234) = 3.09 \times 10^{-16} \text{ m}$$

$$\lambda_0 = \frac{hc}{E_0} = \frac{(6.626 \times 10^{-34} \text{ J}\cdot\text{s})(3.00 \times 10^8 \text{ m/s})}{(200 \text{ MeV})(1.60 \times 10^{-13} \text{ J/MeV})} = 6.20 \times 10^{-15} \text{ m}$$

$$\lambda' = \lambda_0 + \Delta\lambda = 6.51 \times 10^{-15} \text{ m}$$

(a) $$E_\gamma = \frac{hc}{\lambda'} = \boxed{191 \text{ MeV}}$$

(b) $$K_p = \boxed{9.20 \text{ MeV}}$$

P40.58 Isolate the terms involving ϕ in Equations 40.13 and 40.14. Square and add to eliminate ϕ.

$$h^2\left[\frac{1}{\lambda_0^2}+\frac{1}{\lambda'^2}-\frac{2\cos\theta}{\lambda_0\lambda'}\right]=\gamma^2 m_e^2 v^2$$

Solve for $\frac{v^2}{c^2}=\frac{b}{\left(b+c^2\right)}$:

$$b=\frac{h^2}{m_e^2}\left[\frac{1}{\lambda_0^2}+\frac{1}{\lambda'^2}-\frac{2\cos\theta}{\lambda_0\lambda'}\right].$$

Substitute into Eq. 40.12:

$$1+\left(\frac{h}{m_e c}\right)\left[\frac{1}{\lambda_0}-\frac{1}{\lambda'}\right]=\gamma=\left(1-\frac{b}{b+c^2}\right)^{-1/2}=\sqrt{\frac{c^2+b}{c^2}}.$$

Square each side:

$$c^2+\frac{2hc}{m_e}\left[\frac{1}{\lambda_0}-\frac{1}{\lambda'}\right]+\frac{h^2}{m_e^2}\left[\frac{1}{\lambda_0}-\frac{1}{\lambda'}\right]^2=c^2+\left(\frac{h^2}{m_e^2}\right)\left[\frac{1}{\lambda_0^2}+\frac{1}{\lambda'^2}-\frac{2\cos\theta}{\lambda_0\lambda'}\right].$$

From this we get Eq. 40.11:

$$\lambda'-\lambda_0=\left(\frac{h}{m_e c}\right)[1-\cos\theta].$$

P40.59 Show that if all of the energy of a photon is transmitted to an electron, momentum will not be conserved.

Energy: $$\frac{hc}{\lambda_0}=\frac{hc}{\lambda'}+K_e=m_e c^2(\gamma-1)\text{ if }\frac{hc}{\lambda'}=0 \qquad (1)$$

Momentum: $$\frac{h}{\lambda_0}=\frac{h}{\lambda'}+\gamma m_e v=\gamma m_e v\text{ if }\lambda'=\infty \qquad (2)$$

From (1), $$\gamma=\frac{h}{\lambda_0 m_e c}+1 \qquad (3)$$

$$v=c\sqrt{1-\left(\frac{\lambda_0 m_e c}{h+\lambda_0 m_e c}\right)^2} \qquad (4)$$

Substitute (3) and (4) into (2) and show the inconsistency:

$$\frac{h}{\lambda_0}=\left(1+\frac{h}{\lambda_0 m_e c}\right)m_e c\sqrt{1-\left(\frac{\lambda_0 m_e c}{h+\lambda_0 m_e c}\right)^2}=\frac{\lambda_0 m_e c+h}{\lambda_0}\sqrt{\frac{h(h+2\lambda_0 m_e c)}{(h+\lambda_0 m_e c)^2}}=\frac{h}{\lambda_0}\sqrt{\frac{h+2\lambda_0 m_e c}{h}}.$$

This is impossible, so all of the energy of a photon cannot be transmitted to an electron.

P40.60 Begin with momentum expressions: $p=\frac{h}{\lambda}$, and $p=\gamma mv=\gamma mc\left(\frac{v}{c}\right)$.

Equating these expressions, $$\gamma\left(\frac{v}{c}\right)=\left(\frac{h}{mc}\right)\frac{1}{\lambda}=\frac{\lambda_C}{\lambda}.$$

Thus, $$\frac{(v/c)^2}{1-(v/c)^2}=\left(\frac{\lambda_C}{\lambda}\right)^2$$

or $$\left(\frac{v}{c}\right)^2=\left(\frac{\lambda_C}{\lambda}\right)^2-\left(\frac{\lambda_C}{\lambda}\right)^2\left(\frac{v}{c}\right)^2$$

$$\frac{v^2}{c^2}=\frac{(\lambda_C/\lambda)^2}{1+(\lambda_C/\lambda)^2}=\frac{1}{(\lambda/\lambda_C)^2+1}$$

giving $$\boxed{v=\frac{c}{\sqrt{1+(\lambda/\lambda_C)^2}}}.$$

P40.61 (a) Starting with Planck's law, $I(\lambda, T)=\dfrac{2\pi hc^2}{\lambda^5\left[e^{hc/\lambda k_BT}-1\right]}$

the total power radiated per unit area $\int_0^\infty I(\lambda, T)d\lambda=\int_0^\infty \dfrac{2\pi hc^2}{\lambda^5\left[e^{hc/\lambda k_BT}-1\right]}d\lambda$.

Change variables by letting $x=\dfrac{hc}{\lambda k_BT}$

and $dx=-\dfrac{hc\,d\lambda}{k_BT\lambda^2}$.

Note that as λ varies from $0\to\infty$, x varies from $\infty\to 0$.

Then $\int_0^\infty I(\lambda, T)d\lambda=-\dfrac{2\pi k_B^4T^4}{h^3c^2}\int_\infty^0 \dfrac{x^3}{(e^x-1)}dx=\dfrac{2\pi k_B^4T^4}{h^3c^2}\left(\dfrac{\pi^4}{15}\right)$.

Therefore, $\boxed{\int_0^\infty I(\lambda, T)d\lambda=\left(\dfrac{2\pi^5k_B^4}{15h^3c^2}\right)T^4=\sigma T^4}$.

(b) From part (a), $\sigma=\dfrac{2\pi^5k_B^4}{15h^3c^2}=\dfrac{2\pi^5\left(1.38\times10^{-23}\text{ J/K}\right)^4}{15\left(6.626\times10^{-34}\text{ J}\cdot\text{s}\right)^3\left(3.00\times10^8\text{ m/s}\right)^2}$

$\sigma=\boxed{5.67\times10^{-8}\text{ W/m}^2\cdot\text{K}^4}$.

P40.62 Planck's law states $I(\lambda, T)=\dfrac{2\pi hc^2}{\lambda^5\left[e^{hc/\lambda k_BT}-1\right]}=2\pi hc^2\lambda^{-5}\left[e^{hc/\lambda k_BT}-1\right]^{-1}$.

To find the wavelength at which this distribution has a maximum, compute

$$\frac{dI}{d\lambda}=2\pi hc^2\left\{-5\lambda^{-6}\left[e^{hc/\lambda k_BT}-1\right]^{-1}-\lambda^{-5}\left[e^{hc/\lambda k_BT}-1\right]^{-2}e^{hc/\lambda k_BT}\left(-\frac{hc}{\lambda^2k_BT}\right)\right\}=0$$

$$\frac{dI}{d\lambda}=\frac{2\pi hc^2}{\lambda^6\left[e^{hc/\lambda k_BT}-1\right]}\left\{-5+\frac{hc}{\lambda k_BT}\frac{e^{hc/\lambda k_BT}}{\left[e^{hc/\lambda k_BT}-1\right]}\right\}=0$$

Letting $x=\dfrac{hc}{\lambda k_BT}$, the condition for a maximum becomes $\dfrac{xe^x}{e^x-1}=5$.

We zero in on the solution to this transcendental equation by iterations as shown in the table below. The solution is found to be

x	$xe^x/(e^x-1)$
4.000 00	4.074 629 4
4.500 00	4.550 552 1
5.000 00	5.033 918 3
4.900 00	4.936 762 0
4.950 00	4.985 313 0
4.975 00	5.009 609 0
4.963 00	4.997 945 2
4.969 00	5.003 776 7
4.966 00	5.000 860 9

x	$xe^x/(e^x-1)$
4.964 50	4.999 403 0
4.965 50	5.000 374 9
4.965 00	4.999 889 0
4.965 25	5.000 132 0
4.965 13	5.000 015 3
4.965 07	4.999 957 0
4.965 10	4.999 986 2
4.965 115	5.000 000 8

$x=\dfrac{hc}{\lambda_{\max}k_BT}=4.965\,115$ and $\lambda_{\max}T=\dfrac{hc}{4.965\,115k_B}$.

continued on next page

Thus, $\lambda_{max}T = \dfrac{(6.626\,075\times10^{-34}\text{ J}\cdot\text{s})(2.997\,925\times10^{8}\text{ m/s})}{4.965\,115(1.380\,658\times10^{-23}\text{ J/K})} = \boxed{2.897\,755\times10^{-3}\text{ m}\cdot\text{K}}$.

This result is very close to Wien's experimental value of $\lambda_{max}T = 2.898\times10^{-3}\text{ m}\cdot\text{K}$ for this constant.

P40.63 (a) Planck's radiation law predicts maximum intensity at a wavelength λ_{max} we find from

$$\frac{dI}{d\lambda} = 0 = \frac{d}{d\lambda}\left\{2\pi hc^2\lambda^{-5}\left[e^{(hc/\lambda k_BT)}-1\right]^{-1}\right\}$$

$$0 = 2\pi hc^2\lambda^{-5}(-1)\left[e^{(hc/\lambda k_BT)}-1\right]^{-2}e^{(hc/\lambda k_BT)}\left(\frac{-hc}{\lambda^2 k_BT}\right) + 2\pi hc^2(-5)\lambda^{-6}\left[e^{(hc/\lambda k_BT)}-1\right]^{-1}$$

or
$$\frac{-hce^{(hc/\lambda k_BT)}}{\lambda^7 k_BT\left[e^{(hc/\lambda k_BT)}-1\right]^2} + \frac{5}{\lambda^6\left[e^{(hc/\lambda k_BT)}-1\right]} = 0$$

which reduces to
$$5\left(\frac{\lambda k_BT}{hc}\right)\left[e^{(hc/\lambda k_BT)}-1\right] = e^{(hc/\lambda k_BT)}.$$

Define $x = \dfrac{hc}{\lambda k_BT}$. Then we require $5e^x - 5 = xe^x$.

Numerical solution of this transcendental equation gives $x = 4.965$ to four digits. So $\lambda_{max} = \dfrac{hc}{4.965k_BT}$, in agreement with Wien's law.

The intensity radiated over all wavelengths is $\displaystyle\int_0^\infty I(\lambda,T)d\lambda = A + B = \int_0^\infty \frac{2\pi hc^2 d\lambda}{\lambda^5\left[e^{(hc/\lambda k_BT)}-1\right]}$.

Again, define $x = \dfrac{hc}{\lambda k_BT}$ so $\lambda = \dfrac{hc}{xk_BT}$ and $d\lambda = -\dfrac{hc}{x^2k_BT}dx$.

Then, $\displaystyle A + B = \int_{x=\infty}^{0} \frac{-2\pi hc^2x^5k_B^5T^5hcdx}{h^5c^5x^2k_BT(e^x-1)} = \frac{2\pi k_B^4T^4}{h^3c^2}\int_0^\infty \frac{x^3dx}{(e^x-1)}$.

The integral is tabulated as $\dfrac{\pi^4}{15}$, so (in agreement with Stefan's law) $A + B = \dfrac{2\pi^5k_B^4T^4}{15h^3c^2}$.

The intensity radiated over wavelengths shorter than λ_{max} is

$$\int_0^{\lambda_{max}} I(\lambda,T)d\lambda = A = \int_0^{\lambda_{max}} \frac{2\pi hc^2 d\lambda}{\lambda^5\left[e^{(hc/\lambda k_BT)}-1\right]}.$$

With $x = \dfrac{hc}{\lambda k_BT}$, this similarly becomes $\displaystyle A = \frac{2\pi k_B^4T^4}{h^3c^2}\int_{4.965}^{\infty}\frac{x^3dx}{e^x-1}$.

So the fraction of power or of intensity radiated at wavelengths shorter than λ_{max} is

$$\frac{A}{A+B} = \frac{\left(2\pi k_B^4T^4/h^3c^2\right)\left[\pi^4/15 - \int_0^{4.965}\left[x^3dx/(e^x-1)\right]\right]}{2\pi^5k_B^4T^4/15h^3c^2} = \boxed{1 - \frac{15}{\pi^4}\int_0^{4.965}\frac{x^3dx}{e^x-1}}.$$

continued on next page

(b) Here are some sample values of the integrand, along with a sketch of the curve:

x	$x^3\left(e^x-1\right)^{-1}$
0.000	0.00
0.100	9.51×10^{-3}
0.200	3.61×10^{-2}
1.00	0.582
2.00	1.25
3.00	1.42
4.00	1.19
4.90	0.883
4.965	0.860

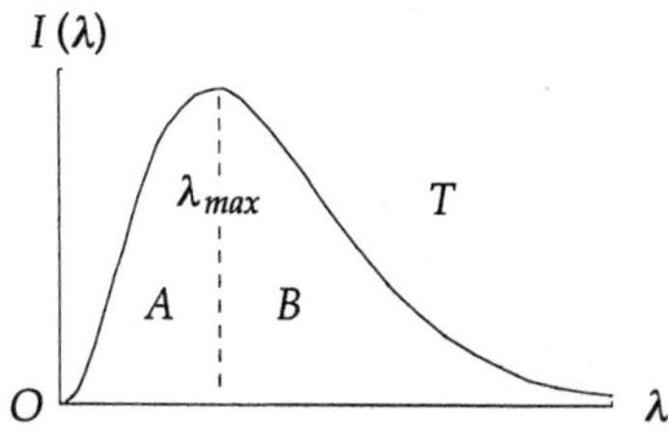

FIG. P40.63(b)

Approximating the integral by trapezoids gives $\dfrac{A}{A+B}\approx 1-\dfrac{15}{\pi^4}(4.870)=\boxed{0.250\,1}$.

P40.64 $p=mv=\sqrt{2mE}=\sqrt{2\left(1.67\times10^{-27}\text{ kg}\right)\left(0.040\,0\text{ eV}\right)\left(1.60\times10^{-19}\text{ J/eV}\right)}$

$\lambda=\dfrac{h}{mv}=1.43\times10^{-10}\text{ m}=\boxed{0.143\text{ nm}}$

This is of the same order of magnitude as the spacing between atoms in a crystal so diffraction should appear.

P40.65 $\lambda_C=\dfrac{h}{m_ec}$ and $\lambda=\dfrac{h}{p}$: $\qquad \dfrac{\lambda_C}{\lambda}=\dfrac{h/m_ec}{h/p}=\dfrac{p}{m_ec}$;

$E^2=c^2p^2+\left(m_ec^2\right)^2$: $\qquad p=\sqrt{\dfrac{E^2}{c^2}-\left(m_ec\right)^2}$

$$\frac{\lambda_C}{\lambda}=\frac{1}{m_ec}\sqrt{\frac{E^2}{c^2}-\left(m_ec\right)^2}=\sqrt{\frac{1}{\left(m_ec\right)^2}\left[\frac{E^2}{c^2}-\left(m_ec\right)^2\right]}=\sqrt{\left(\frac{E}{m_ec^2}\right)^2-1}$$

P40.66 (a) $mgy_i=\dfrac{1}{2}mv_f^2$

$v_f=\sqrt{2gy_i}=\sqrt{2\left(9.80\text{ m/s}^2\right)(50.0\text{ m})}=31.3\text{ m/s}$

$\lambda=\dfrac{h}{mv}=\dfrac{6.626\times10^{-34}\text{ J}\cdot\text{s}}{(75.0\text{ kg})(31.3\text{ m/s})}=\boxed{2.82\times10^{-37}\text{ m}}$ (not observable)

(b) $\Delta E\Delta t\ge\dfrac{\hbar}{2}$

so $\Delta E\ge\dfrac{6.626\times10^{-34}\text{ J}\cdot\text{s}}{4\pi\left(5.00\times10^{-3}\text{ s}\right)}=\boxed{1.06\times10^{-32}\text{ J}}$

(c) $\dfrac{\Delta E}{E}=\dfrac{1.06\times10^{-32}\text{ J}}{(75.0\text{ kg})\left(9.80\text{ m/s}^2\right)(50.0\text{ m})}=\boxed{2.87\times10^{-35}\%}$

P40.67 From the uncertainty principle $\Delta E \Delta t \geq \frac{\hbar}{2}$

or $\Delta\left(mc^2\right)\Delta t = \frac{\hbar}{2}$.

Therefore, $\frac{\Delta m}{m} = \frac{h}{4\pi c^2(\Delta t)m} = \frac{h}{4\pi(\Delta t)E_R}$

$$\frac{\Delta m}{m} = \frac{6.626 \times 10^{-34}\ \text{J}\cdot\text{s}}{4\pi\left(8.70 \times 10^{-17}\ \text{s}\right)(135\ \text{MeV})}\left(\frac{1\ \text{MeV}}{1.60 \times 10^{-13}\ \text{J}}\right) = \boxed{2.81 \times 10^{-8}}.$$

P40.68 $\Delta\lambda = \frac{h}{m_e c}(1 - \cos\theta) = \lambda' - \lambda_0$

$$E' = \frac{hc}{\lambda'} = \frac{hc}{\lambda_0 + \Delta\lambda} = hc\left[\lambda_0 + \frac{h}{m_e c}(1 - \cos\theta)\right]^{-1}$$

$$E' = \frac{hc}{\lambda_0}\left[1 + \frac{hc}{m_e c^2 \lambda_0}(1 - \cos\theta)\right]^{-1}$$

$$E' = \frac{hc}{\lambda_0}\left[1 + \frac{hc}{m_e c^2 \lambda_0}(1 - \cos\theta)\right]^{-1} = E_0\left[1 + \frac{E_0}{m_e c^2}(1 - \cos\theta)\right]^{-1}$$

P40.69 (a) The light is unpolarized. It contains both horizontal and vertical field oscillations.

(b) The interference pattern appears, but with diminished overall intensity.

(c) The results are the same in each case.

(d) The interference pattern appears and disappears as the polarizer turns, with alternately increasing and decreasing contrast between the bright and dark fringes. The intensity on the screen is precisely zero at the center of a dark fringe four times in each revolution, when the filter axis has turned by 45°, 135°, 225°, and 315° from the vertical.

(e) Looking at the overall light energy arriving at the screen, we see a low-contrast interference pattern. After we sort out the individual photon runs into those for trial 1, those for trial 2, and those for trial 3, we have the original results replicated: The runs for trials 1 and 2 form the two blue graphs in Figure 40.24 in the text, and the runs for trial 3 build up the red graph.

P40.70 Let u' represent the final speed of the electron and let $\gamma' = \left(1-\frac{u'^2}{c^2}\right)^{-1/2}$. We must eliminate β and u' from the three conservation equations:

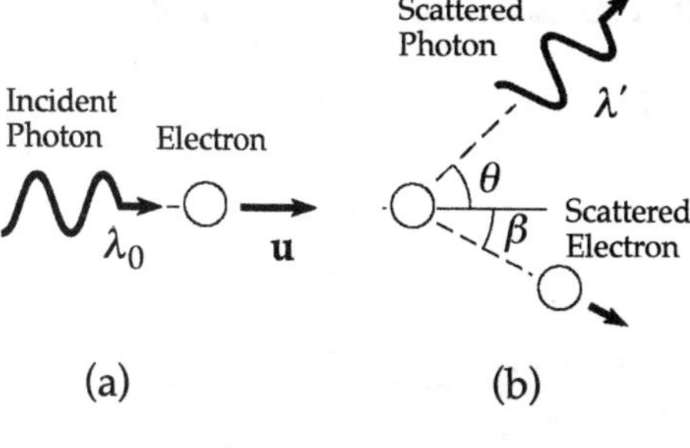

FIG. P40.70

$$\frac{hc}{\lambda_0}+\gamma m_e c^2 = \frac{hc}{\lambda'}+\gamma' m_e c^2 \qquad [1]$$

$$\frac{h}{\lambda_0}+\gamma m_e u - \frac{h}{\lambda'}\cos\theta = \gamma' m_e u' \cos\beta \qquad [2]$$

$$\frac{h}{\lambda'}\sin\theta = \gamma' m_e u' \sin\beta \qquad [3]$$

Square Equations [2] and [3] and add:

$$\frac{h^2}{\lambda_0^2}+\gamma^2 m_e^2 u^2+\frac{h^2}{\lambda'^2}+\frac{2h\gamma m_e u}{\lambda_0}-\frac{2h^2\cos\theta}{\lambda_0\lambda'}-\frac{2h\gamma m_e u\cos\theta}{\lambda'}=\gamma'^2 m_e^2 u'^2$$

$$\frac{h^2}{\lambda_0^2}+\frac{h^2}{\lambda'^2}+\gamma^2 m_e^2 u^2+\frac{2h\gamma m_e u}{\lambda_0}-\frac{2h\gamma m_e u\cos\theta}{\lambda'}-\frac{2h^2\cos\theta}{\lambda_0\lambda'}=\frac{m_e^2 u'^2}{1-u'^2/c^2}$$

Call the left-hand side b. Then $b-\frac{bu'^2}{c^2}=m_e^2 u'^2$ and $u'^2=\frac{b}{m_e^2+b/c^2}=\frac{c^2 b}{m_e^2 c^2+b}$.

Now square Equation [1] and substitute to eliminate γ':

$$\frac{h^2}{\lambda_0^2}+\gamma^2 m_e^2 c^2+\frac{h^2}{\lambda'^2}+\frac{2h\gamma m_e c}{\lambda_0}-\frac{2h^2}{\lambda_0\lambda'}-\frac{2h\gamma m_e c}{\lambda'}=\frac{m_e^2 c^2}{1-u'^2/c^2}=m_e^2 c^2+b.$$

So we have $\frac{h^2}{\lambda_0^2}+\frac{h^2}{\lambda'^2}+\gamma^2 m_e^2 c^2+\frac{2h\gamma m_e c}{\lambda_0}-\frac{2h\gamma m_e c}{\lambda'}-\frac{2h^2}{\lambda_0\lambda'}$

$$=m_e c^2+\frac{h^2}{\lambda_0^2}+\frac{h^2}{\lambda'^2}+\gamma^2 m_e^2 u^2+\frac{2h\gamma m_e u}{\lambda_0}-\frac{2h\gamma m_e u\cos\theta}{\lambda'}-\frac{2h^2\cos\theta}{\lambda_0\lambda'}$$

Multiply through by $\frac{\lambda_0\lambda'}{m_e^2 c^2}$

$$\lambda_0\lambda'\gamma^2+\frac{2h\lambda'\gamma}{m_e c}-\frac{2h\lambda_0\gamma}{m_e c}-\frac{2h^2}{m_e^2 c^2}=\lambda_0\lambda'+\frac{\lambda_0\lambda'\gamma^2 u^2}{m_e c^2}+\frac{2h\lambda' u\gamma}{m_e c^2}-\frac{2h\gamma\lambda_0 u\cos\theta}{m_e c^2}-\frac{2h^2\cos\theta}{m_e^2 c^2}$$

$$\lambda_0\lambda'\left(\gamma^2-1-\frac{\gamma^2 u^2}{c^2}\right)+\frac{2h\gamma\lambda'}{m_e c}\left(1-\frac{u}{c}\right)=\frac{2h\gamma\lambda_0}{m_e c}\left(1-\frac{u\cos\theta}{c}\right)+\frac{2h^2}{m_e^2 c^2}(1-\cos\theta)$$

The first term is zero. Then $\lambda'=\lambda_0\left(\frac{1-(u\cos\theta)/c}{1-u/c}\right)+\frac{h\gamma^{-1}}{m_e c}\left(\frac{1}{1-u/c}\right)(1-\cos\theta)$.

Since $\gamma^{-1}=\sqrt{1-\left(\frac{u}{c}\right)^2}=\sqrt{\left(1-\frac{u}{c}\right)\left(1+\frac{u}{c}\right)}$

this result may be written as $\boxed{\lambda'=\lambda_0\left(\frac{1-(u\cos\theta)/c}{1-u/c}\right)+\frac{h}{m_e c}\sqrt{\frac{1+u/c}{1-u/c}}(1-\cos\theta)}$.

It shows a specific combination of what looks like a Doppler shift and a Compton shift. This problem is about the same as the first problem in Albert Messiah's graduate text on quantum mechanics.

ANSWERS TO EVEN PROBLEMS

P40.2 (a) $\sim 10^{-7}$ m ultraviolet; (b) $\sim 10^{-10}$ m gamma ray

P40.4 (a) 70.9 kW; (b) 580 nm; (c) 7.99×10^{10} W/m; (d) 9.42×10^{-1226} W/m; (e) 1.00×10^{-227} W/m; (f) 5.44×10^{10} W/m; (g) 7.38×10^{10} W/m; (h) 0.260 W/m; (i) 2.60×10^{-9} W/m; (j) 20 kW

P40.6 2.96×10^{19} photons/s

P40.8 5.71×10^{3} photons

P40.10 1.34×10^{31}

P40.12 see the solution

P40.14 (a) 1.38 eV; (b) 334 THz

P40.16 Metal one: 2.22 eV, Metal two: 3.70 eV

P40.18 148 d, the classical theory is a gross failure

P40.20 (a) The incident photons are Doppler shifted to higher frequencies, and hence, higher energy; (b) 3.87 eV; (c) 8.78 eV

P40.22 (a) 488 fm; (b) 268 keV; (c) 31.5 keV

P40.24 $p_e = \dfrac{22.1 \text{ keV}}{c}$; $K_e = 478$ eV

P40.26 (a) $\cos^{-1}\left(\dfrac{m_ec^2 + E_0}{2m_ec^2 + E_0}\right)$;

(b) $E'_\gamma = \dfrac{E_0}{2}\left(\dfrac{2m_ec^2 + E_0}{m_ec^2 + E_0}\right)$,

$p'_\gamma = \dfrac{E_0}{2c}\left(\dfrac{2m_ec^2 + E_0}{m_ec^2 + E_0}\right)$;

(c) $K_e = \dfrac{E_0^2}{2\left(m_ec^2 + E_0\right)}$,

$p_e = \dfrac{E_0}{2c}\left(\dfrac{2m_ec^2 + E_0}{m_ec^2 + E_0}\right)$

P40.28 (a) 33.0°; (b) 0.785c

P40.30 (a) 0.667; (b) 0.001 09

P40.32 (a) 14.0 kV/m, 46.8 μT; (b) 4.19 nN; (c) 10.2 g

P40.34 (a) 0.174 nm; (b) 5.37 pm or 5.49 pm ignoring relativistic correction

P40.36 (a) see the solution; (b) 907 fm

P40.38 0.218 nm

P40.40 (a) 1.60; (b) 2.00×10^{3}; (c) 1; (d) ∞

P40.42 (a) 1.10×10^{-34} m/s; (b) 1.36×10^{33} s; (c) no

P40.44 see the solution

P40.46 105 V

P40.48 (a) 0.250 m/s; (b) 2.25 m

P40.50 3.79×10^{28} m, much larger than the diameter of the observable Universe

P40.52 (a) see the solution; (b) 5.21 MeV

P40.54 (a) 1.7 eV; (b) 4.2×10^{-15} V·s; (c) 730 nm

P40.56 $\dfrac{hc}{\lambda} - \dfrac{e^2B^2R^2}{2m_e}$

P40.58 see the solution

P40.60 see the solution

P40.62 see the solution

P40.64 0.143 nm, comparable to the distance between atoms in a crystal, so diffraction can be observed

P40.66 (a) 2.82×10^{-37} m; (b) 1.06×10^{-32} J; (c) 2.87×10^{-35}%

P40.68 see the solution

P40.70 see the solution

41

Quantum Mechanics

CHAPTER OUTLINE

ANSWERS TO QUESTIONS

Q41.1 A particle's wave function represents its state, containing all the information there is about its location and motion. The squared absolute value of its wave function tells where we would classically think of the particle as a spending most its time. $|\Psi|^2$ is the probability distribution function for the position of the particle.

Q41.2 The motion of the quantum particle does not consist of moving through successive points. The particle has no definite position. It can sometimes be found on one side of a node and sometimes on the other side, but never at the node itself. There is no contradiction here, for the quantum particle is moving as a wave. It is not a classical particle. In particular, the particle does not speed up to infinite speed to cross the node.

Q41.3 Consider a particle bound to a restricted region of space. If its minimum energy were zero, then the particle could have zero momentum and zero uncertainty in its momentum. At the same time, the uncertainty in its position would not be infinite, but equal to the width of the region. In such a case, the uncertainty product $\Delta x \Delta p_x$ would be zero, violating the uncertainty principle. This contradiction proves that the minimum energy of the particle is not zero.

Q41.4 The reflected amplitude decreases as U decreases. The amplitude of the reflected wave is proportional to the reflection coefficient, R, which is $1-T$, where T is the transmission coefficient as given in equation 41.20. As U decreases, C decreases as predicted by equation 41.21, T increases, and R decreases.

Q41.5 Consider the Heisenberg uncertainty principle. It implies that electrons initially moving at the same speed and accelerated by an electric field through the same distance *need not* all have the same measured speed after being accelerated. Perhaps the philosopher could have said "it is necessary for the very existence of science that the same conditions always produce the same results within the uncertainty of the measurements."

Q41.6 In quantum mechanics, particles are treated as wave functions, not classical particles. In classical mechanics, the kinetic energy is never negative. That implies that $E \geq U$. Treating the particle as a wave, the Schrödinger equation predicts that there is a nonzero probability that a particle can tunnel through a barrier—a region in which $E < U$.

Q41.7 Consider Figure 41.8, (a) and (b) in the text. In the square well with infinitely high walls, the particle's simplest wave function has strict nodes separated by the length L of the well. The particle's wavelength is $2L$, its momentum $\frac{h}{2L}$, and its energy $\frac{p^2}{2m} = \frac{h^2}{8mL^2}$. Now in the well with walls of only finite height, the wave function has nonzero amplitude at the walls. The wavelength is longer. The particle's momentum in its ground state is smaller, and its energy is less.

Q41.8 Quantum mechanically, the lowest kinetic energy possible for any bound particle is greater than zero. The following is a proof: If its minimum energy were zero, then the particle could have zero momentum and zero uncertainty in its momentum. At the same time, the uncertainty in its position would not be infinite, but equal to the width of the region in which it is restricted to stay. In such a case, the uncertainty product $\Delta x \Delta p_x$ would be zero, violating the uncertainty principle. This contradiction proves that the minimum energy of the particle is not zero. Any harmonic oscillator can be modeled as a particle or collection of particles in motion; thus it cannot have zero energy.

Q41.9 As Newton's laws are the rules which a particle of large mass follows in its motion, so the Schrödinger equation describes the motion of a quantum particle, a particle of small or large mass. In particular, the states of atomic electrons are confined-wave states with wave functions that are solutions to the Schrödinger equation.

SOLUTIONS TO PROBLEMS

Section 41.1 An Interpretation of Quantum Mechanics

P41.1 (a) $\psi(x) = Ae^{i\left(5.00\times10^{10}x\right)} = A\cos\left(5\times10^{10}x\right) + Ai\sin\left(5\times10^{10}x\right) = A\cos(kx) + Ai\sin(kx)$ goes through a full cycle when x changes by λ and when kx changes by 2π. Then $k\lambda = 2\pi$ where $k = 5.00\times10^{10}\ \text{m}^{-1} = \frac{2\pi}{\lambda}$. Then $\lambda = \frac{2\pi\ \text{m}}{\left(5.00\times10^{10}\right)} = \boxed{1.26\times10^{-10}\ \text{m}}$.

(b) $$p = \frac{h}{\lambda} = \frac{6.626\times10^{-34}\ \text{J}\cdot\text{s}}{1.26\times10^{-10}\ \text{m}} = \boxed{5.27\times10^{-24}\ \text{kg}\cdot\text{m/s}}$$

(c) $m_e = 9.11\times10^{-31}\ \text{kg}$

$$K = \frac{m_e^2v^2}{2m_e} = \frac{p^2}{2m} = \frac{\left(5.27\times10^{-24}\ \text{kg}\cdot\text{m/s}\right)^2}{\left(2\times9.11\times10^{-31}\ \text{kg}\right)} = 1.52\times10^{-17}\ \text{J} = \frac{1.52\times10^{-17}\ \text{J}}{1.60\times10^{-19}\ \text{J/eV}} = \boxed{95.5\ \text{eV}}$$

P41.2 Probability $$P = \int_{-a}^{a}|\psi(x)|^2 = \int_{-a}^{a}\frac{a}{\pi\left(x^2+a^2\right)}dx = \left(\frac{a}{\pi}\right)\left(\frac{1}{a}\right)\tan^{-1}\left(\frac{x}{a}\right)\Big|_{-a}^{a}$$

$$P = \frac{1}{\pi}\left[\tan^{-1}1 - \tan^{-1}(-1)\right] = \frac{1}{\pi}\left[\frac{\pi}{4} - \left(-\frac{\pi}{4}\right)\right] = \boxed{\frac{1}{2}}$$

Section 41.2 A Particle in a Box

P41.3 $E_1 = 2.00 \text{ eV} = 3.20 \times 10^{-19} \text{ J}$

For the ground-state, $E_1 = \dfrac{h^2}{8m_eL^2}$.

(a) $L = \dfrac{h}{\sqrt{8m_eE_1}} = 4.34 \times 10^{-10} \text{ m} = \boxed{0.434 \text{ nm}}$

(b) $\Delta E = E_2 - E_1 = 4\left(\dfrac{h^2}{8m_eL^2}\right) - \left(\dfrac{h^2}{8m_eL^2}\right) = \boxed{6.00 \text{ eV}}$

P41.4 For an electron wave to "fit" into an infinitely deep potential well, an integral number of half-wavelengths must equal the width of the well.

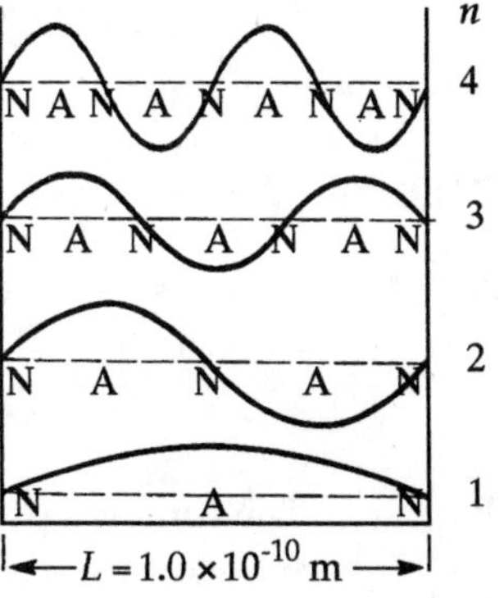

FIG. P41.4

$$\frac{n\lambda}{2} = 1.00 \times 10^{-9} \text{ m} \quad \text{so} \quad \lambda = \frac{2.00 \times 10^{-9}}{n} = \frac{h}{p}$$

(a) Since $K = \dfrac{p^2}{2m_e} = \dfrac{\left(h^2/\lambda^2\right)}{2m_e} = \dfrac{h^2}{2m_e}\dfrac{n^2}{\left(2 \times 10^{-9}\right)^2} = \left(0.377n^2\right) \text{ eV}$

For $K \approx 6 \text{ eV}$ $\boxed{n = 4}$

(b) With $n = 4$, $\boxed{K = 6.03 \text{ eV}}$

P41.5 (a) We can draw a diagram that parallels our treatment of standing mechanical waves. In each state, we measure the distance d from one node to another (N to N), and base our solution upon that:

Since $d_{\text{N to N}} = \dfrac{\lambda}{2}$ and $\lambda = \dfrac{h}{p}$

$$p = \frac{h}{\lambda} = \frac{h}{2d}.$$

Next, $K = \dfrac{p^2}{2m_e} = \dfrac{h^2}{8m_ed^2} = \dfrac{1}{d^2}\left[\dfrac{\left(6.626 \times 10^{-34} \text{ J}\cdot\text{s}\right)^2}{8\left(9.11 \times 10^{-31} \text{ kg}\right)}\right]$.

Evaluating, $K = \dfrac{6.02 \times 10^{-38} \text{ J}\cdot\text{m}^2}{d^2}$ $\quad K = \dfrac{3.77 \times 10^{-19} \text{ eV}\cdot\text{m}^2}{d^2}$.

In state 1, $d = 1.00 \times 10^{-10}$ m $\quad K_1 = 37.7$ eV.

In state 2, $d = 5.00 \times 10^{-11}$ m $\quad K_2 = 151$ eV.

In state 3, $d = 3.33 \times 10^{-11}$ m $\quad K_3 = 339$ eV.

In state 4, $d = 2.50 \times 10^{-11}$ m $\quad K_4 = 603$ eV.

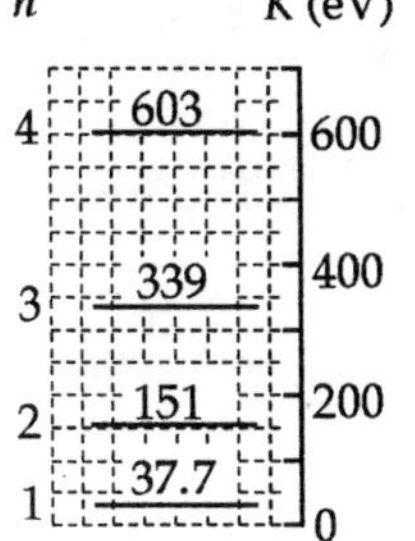

FIG. P41.5

continued on next page

(b) When the electron falls from state 2 to state 1, it puts out energy

$$E = 151\text{ eV} - 37.7\text{ eV} = 113\text{ eV} = hf = \frac{hc}{\lambda}$$

into emitting a photon of wavelength

$$\lambda = \frac{hc}{E} = \frac{\left(6.626\times10^{-34}\text{ J}\cdot\text{s}\right)\left(3.00\times10^{8}\text{ m/s}\right)}{(113\text{ eV})\left(1.60\times10^{-19}\text{ J/eV}\right)} = 11.0\text{ nm}.$$

The wavelengths of the other spectral lines we find similarly:

Transition	$4\to3$	$4\to2$	$4\to1$	$3\to2$	$3\to1$	$2\to1$
E(eV)	264	452	565	188	302	113
λ(nm)	4.71	2.75	2.20	6.60	4.12	11.0

P41.6 $\lambda = 2D$ for the lowest energy state

$$K = \frac{p^2}{2m} = \frac{h^2}{2m\lambda^2} = \frac{h^2}{8mD^2} = \frac{\left(6.626\times10^{-34}\text{ J}\cdot\text{s}\right)^2}{8\left[4\left(1.66\times10^{-27}\text{ kg}\right)\right]\left(1.00\times10^{-14}\text{ m}\right)^2} = 8.27\times10^{-14}\text{ J} = \boxed{0.517\text{ MeV}}$$

$$p = \frac{h}{\lambda} = \frac{h}{2D} = \frac{6.626\times10^{-34}\text{ J}\cdot\text{s}}{2\left(1.00\times10^{-14}\text{ m}\right)} = \boxed{3.31\times10^{-20}\text{ kg}\cdot\text{m/s}}$$

P41.7 $$\Delta E = \frac{hc}{\lambda} = \left(\frac{h^2}{8m_eL^2}\right)\left[2^2 - 1^2\right] = \frac{3h^2}{8m_eL^2}$$

$$L = \sqrt{\frac{3h\lambda}{8m_ec}} = 7.93\times10^{-10}\text{ m} = \boxed{0.793\text{ nm}}$$

P41.8 $$\Delta E = \frac{hc}{\lambda} = \left(\frac{h^2}{8m_eL^2}\right)\left[2^2 - 1^2\right] = \frac{3h^2}{8m_eL^2}$$

so $$L = \boxed{\sqrt{\frac{3h\lambda}{8m_ec}}}$$

P41.9 The confined proton can be described in the same way as a standing wave on a string. At level 1, the node-to-node distance of the standing wave is 1.00×10^{-14} m, so the wavelength is twice this distance: $\frac{h}{p} = 2.00\times10^{-14}$ m.

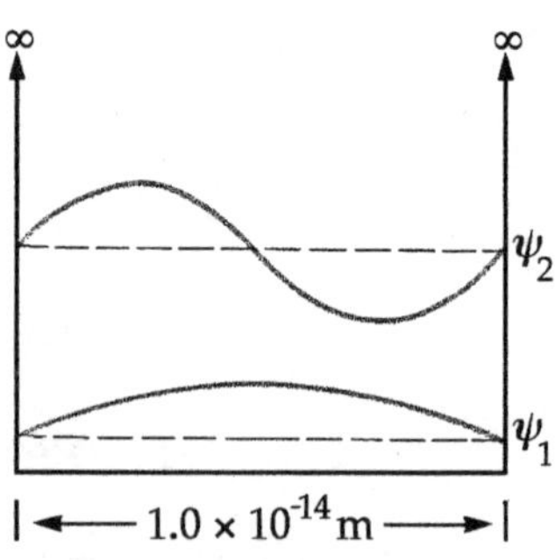

FIG. P41.9

The proton's kinetic energy is

$$K = \frac{1}{2}mv^2 = \frac{p^2}{2m} = \frac{h^2}{2m\lambda^2} = \frac{\left(6.626\times10^{-34}\text{ J}\cdot\text{s}\right)^2}{2\left(1.67\times10^{-27}\text{ kg}\right)\left(2.00\times10^{-14}\text{ m}\right)^2}$$

$$= \frac{3.29\times10^{-13}\text{ J}}{1.60\times10^{-19}\text{ J/eV}} = 2.05\text{ MeV}$$

continued on next page

In the first excited state, level 2, the node-to-node distance is half as long as in state 1. The momentum is two times larger and the energy is four times larger: $K = 8.22\text{ MeV}$.

The proton has mass, has charge, moves slowly compared to light in a standing wave state, and stays inside the nucleus. When it falls from level 2 to level 1, its energy change is

$2.05\text{ MeV} - 8.22\text{ MeV} = -6.16\text{ MeV}$.

Therefore, we know that a photon (a traveling wave with no mass and no charge) is emitted at the speed of light, and that it has an energy of $\boxed{+6.16\text{ MeV}}$.

Its frequency is $$f = \frac{E}{h} = \frac{(6.16\times10^{6}\text{ eV})(1.60\times10^{-19}\text{ J/eV})}{6.626\times10^{-34}\text{ J}\cdot\text{s}} = 1.49\times10^{21}\text{ Hz}.$$

And its wavelength is $$\lambda = \frac{c}{f} = \frac{3.00\times10^{8}\text{ m/s}}{1.49\times10^{21}\text{ s}^{-1}} = \boxed{2.02\times10^{-13}\text{ m}}.$$

This is a gamma ray, according to the electromagnetic spectrum chart in Chapter 34.

P41.10 The ground state energy of a particle (mass m) in a 1-dimensional box of width L is $E_1 = \dfrac{h^2}{8mL^2}$.

(a) For a proton $(m = 1.67\times10^{-27}\text{ kg})$ in a 0.200-nm wide box:

$$E_1 = \frac{(6.626\times10^{-34}\text{ J}\cdot\text{s})^2}{8(1.67\times10^{-27}\text{ kg})(2.00\times10^{-10}\text{ m})^2} = 8.22\times10^{-22}\text{ J} = \boxed{5.13\times10^{-3}\text{ eV}}.$$

(b) For an electron $(m = 9.11\times10^{-31}\text{ kg})$ in the same size box:

$$E_1 = \frac{(6.626\times10^{-34}\text{ J}\cdot\text{s})^2}{8(9.11\times10^{-31}\text{ kg})(2.00\times10^{-10}\text{ m})^2} = 1.51\times10^{-18}\text{ J} = \boxed{9.41\text{ eV}}.$$

(c) The electron has a much higher energy because it is much less massive.

P41.11 $$E_n = \left(\frac{h^2}{8mL^2}\right)n^2$$

$$E_1 = \frac{(6.626\times10^{-34}\text{ J}\cdot\text{s})^2}{8(1.67\times10^{-27}\text{ kg})(2.00\times10^{-14}\text{ m})^2} = 8.21\times10^{-14}\text{ J}$$

$E_1 = \boxed{0.513\text{ MeV}}$ $\quad E_2 = 4E_1 = \boxed{2.05\text{ MeV}}$ $\quad E_3 = 9E_1 = \boxed{4.62\text{ MeV}}$

$\boxed{\text{Yes}}$, the energy differences are $\sim 1\text{ MeV}$, which is a typical energy for a γ-ray photon.

***P41.12** (a) The energies of the confined electron are $E_n = \frac{h^2}{8m_eL^2}n^2$. Its energy gain in the quantum jump from state 1 to state 4 is $\frac{h^2}{8m_eL^2}\left(4^2-1^2\right)$ and this is the photon energy:

$$\frac{h^2 15}{8m_eL^2} = hf = \frac{hc}{\lambda}.\ \text{Then } 8m_ecL^2 = 15h\lambda \text{ and } \boxed{L = \left(\frac{15h\lambda}{8m_ec}\right)^{1/2}}.$$

(b) Let λ' represent the wavelength of the photon emitted: $\frac{hc}{\lambda'} = \frac{h^2}{8m_eL^2}4^2 - \frac{h^2}{8m_eL^2}2^2 = \frac{12h^2}{8m_eL^2}$.

Then $\frac{hc}{\lambda}\frac{\lambda'}{hc} = \frac{h^2 15\left(8m_eL^2\right)}{8m_eL^2 12h^2} = \frac{5}{4}$ and $\boxed{\lambda' = 1.25\lambda}$.

Section 41.3 **The Particle Under Boundary Conditions**

Section 41.4 **The Schrödinger Equation**

P41.13 We have $\psi = Ae^{i(kx-\omega t)}$ and $\frac{\partial^2\psi}{\partial x^2} = -k^2\psi$.

Schrödinger's equation: $\frac{\partial^2\psi}{\partial x^2} = -k^2\psi = -\frac{2m}{\hbar^2}(E-U)\psi$.

Since $k^2 = \frac{(2\pi)^2}{\lambda^2} = \frac{(2\pi p)^2}{h^2} = \frac{p^2}{\hbar^2}$ and $E-U = \frac{p^2}{2m}$.

$\boxed{\text{Thus this equation balances.}}$

P41.14 $\psi(x) = A\cos kx + B\sin kx$ $\qquad \frac{\partial\psi}{\partial x} = -kA\sin kx + kB\cos kx$

$\frac{\partial^2\psi}{\partial x^2} = -k^2A\cos kx - k^2B\sin kx$ $\qquad -\frac{2m}{\hbar}(E-U)\psi = -\frac{2mE}{\hbar^2}(A\cos kx + B\sin kx)$

Therefore the Schrödinger equation is satisfied if

$$\frac{\partial^2\psi}{\partial x^2} = \left(-\frac{2m}{\hbar^2}\right)(E-U)\psi \text{ or } -k^2(A\cos kx + B\sin kx) = \left(-\frac{2mE}{\hbar^2}\right)(A\cos kx + B\sin kx).$$

This is true as an identity (functional equality) for all x if $\boxed{E = \frac{\hbar^2k^2}{2m}}$.

***P41.15** (a) With $\psi(x) = A\sin(kx)$

$$\frac{d}{dx}A\sin kx = Ak\cos kx \quad \text{and} \quad \frac{d^2}{dx^2}\psi = -Ak^2\sin kx.$$

Then $$-\frac{\hbar^2}{2m}\frac{d^2\psi}{dx^2} = +\frac{\hbar^2k^2}{2m}A\sin kx = \frac{h^2\left(4\pi^2\right)}{4\pi^2\left(\lambda^2\right)(2m)}\psi = \frac{p^2}{2m}\psi = \frac{m^2v^2}{2m}\psi = \frac{1}{2}mv^2\psi = K\psi.$$

(b) With $\psi(x) = A\sin\left(\frac{2\pi x}{\lambda}\right) = A\sin kx$, the proof given in part (a) applies again.

P41.16 (a) $$\langle x\rangle=\int_0^L x\frac{2}{L}\sin^2\left(\frac{2\pi x}{L}\right)dx=\frac{2}{L}\int_0^L x\left(\frac{1}{2}-\frac{1}{2}\cos\frac{4\pi x}{L}\right)dx$$

$$\langle x\rangle=\frac{1}{L}\frac{x^2}{2}\bigg|_0^L-\frac{1}{L}\frac{L^2}{16\pi^2}\left[\frac{4\pi x}{L}\sin\frac{4\pi x}{L}+\cos\frac{4\pi x}{L}\right]_0^L=\boxed{\frac{L}{2}}$$

(b) $$\text{Probability}=\int_{0.490L}^{0.510L}\frac{2}{L}\sin^2\left(\frac{2\pi x}{L}\right)dx=\left[\frac{1}{L}x-\frac{1}{L}\frac{L}{4\pi}\sin\frac{4\pi x}{L}\right]_{0.490L}^{0.510L}$$

$$\text{Probability}=0.020-\frac{1}{4\pi}(\sin 2.04\pi-\sin 1.96\pi)=\boxed{5.26\times10^{-5}}$$

(c) $$\text{Probability}\left[\frac{x}{L}-\frac{1}{4\pi}\sin\frac{4\pi x}{L}\right]_{0.240L}^{0.260L}=\boxed{3.99\times10^{-2}}$$

(d) In the $n=2$ graph in Figure 41.4 (b), it is more probable to find the particle either near $x=\frac{L}{4}$ or $x=\frac{3L}{4}$ than at the center, where the probability density is zero.

Nevertheless, the symmetry of the distribution means that the average position is $\frac{L}{2}$.

P41.17 Normalization requires

$$\int_{\text{all space}}|\psi|^2dx=1 \qquad \text{or} \qquad \int_0^L A^2\sin^2\left(\frac{n\pi x}{L}\right)dx=1$$

$$\int_0^L A^2\sin^2\left(\frac{n\pi x}{L}\right)dx=A^2\left(\frac{L}{2}\right)=1 \qquad \text{or} \qquad \boxed{A=\sqrt{\frac{2}{L}}}.$$

P41.18 The desired probability is $$P=\int_0^{L/4}|\psi|^2dx=\frac{2}{L}\int_0^{L/4}\sin^2\left(\frac{2\pi x}{L}\right)dx$$

where $$\sin^2\theta=\frac{1-\cos 2\theta}{2}.$$

Thus, $$P=\left(\frac{x}{L}-\frac{1}{4\pi}\sin\frac{4\pi x}{L}\right)\bigg|_0^{L/4}=\left(\frac{1}{4}-0-0+0\right)=\boxed{0.250}.$$

P41.19 In $0\le x\le L$, the argument $\frac{2\pi x}{L}$ of the sine function ranges from 0 to 2π. The probability density $\left(\frac{2}{L}\right)\sin^2\left(\frac{2\pi x}{L}\right)$ reaches maxima at $\sin\theta=1$ and $\sin\theta=-1$ at

$$\frac{2\pi x}{L}=\frac{\pi}{2} \text{ and } \frac{2\pi x}{L}=\frac{3\pi}{2}.$$

∴ The most probable positions of the particle are at $\boxed{\text{at } x=\frac{L}{4} \text{ and } x=\frac{3L}{4}}$.

***P41.20** (a) Probability $=\int_0^{\ell}|\psi_1|^2\,dx=\frac{2}{L}\int_0^{\ell}\sin^2\left(\frac{\pi x}{L}\right)dx=\frac{1}{L}\int_0^{\ell}\left[1-\cos\left(\frac{2\pi x}{L}\right)\right]dx$

$$=\frac{1}{L}\left[x-\frac{L}{2\pi}\sin\left(\frac{2\pi x}{L}\right)\right]_0^{\ell}=\boxed{\frac{\ell}{L}-\frac{1}{2\pi}\sin\left(\frac{2\pi\ell}{L}\right)}$$

(b)

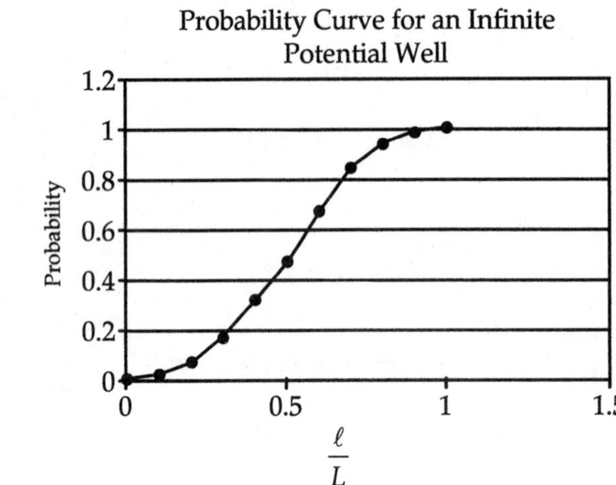

FIG. P41.20(b)

(c) The probability of finding the particle between $x=0$ and $x=\ell$ is $\frac{2}{3}$, and between $x=\ell$ and $x=L$ is $\frac{1}{3}$.

Thus, $\int_0^{\ell}|\psi_1|^2\,dx=\frac{2}{3}$

$$\therefore\ \frac{\ell}{L}-\frac{1}{2\pi}\sin\left(\frac{2\pi\ell}{L}\right)=\frac{2}{3},\qquad\text{or}\qquad u-\frac{1}{2\pi}\sin 2\pi u=\frac{2}{3}.$$

This equation for $\frac{\ell}{L}$ can be solved by homing in on the solution with a calculator, the result being $\frac{\ell}{L}=0.585$, or $\ell=\boxed{0.585L}$ to three digits.

P41.21 (a) The probability is $P=\int_0^{L/3}|\psi|^2\,dx=\int_0^{L/3}\frac{2}{L}\sin^2\left(\frac{\pi x}{L}\right)dx=\frac{2}{L}\int_0^{L/3}\left(\frac{1}{2}-\frac{1}{2}\cos\frac{2\pi x}{L}\right)dx$

$$P=\left(\frac{x}{L}-\frac{1}{2\pi}\sin\frac{2\pi x}{L}\right)\Bigg|_0^{L/3}=\left(\frac{1}{3}-\frac{1}{2\pi}\sin\frac{2\pi}{3}\right)=\left(\frac{1}{3}-\frac{\sqrt{3}}{4\pi}\right)=\boxed{0.196}.$$

(b) The probability density is symmetric about $x=\frac{L}{2}$. Thus, the probability of finding the particle between $x=\frac{2L}{3}$ and $x=L$ is the same 0.196. Therefore, the probability of finding it in the range $\frac{L}{3}\le x\le\frac{2L}{3}$ is $P=1.00-2(0.196)=\boxed{0.609}$.

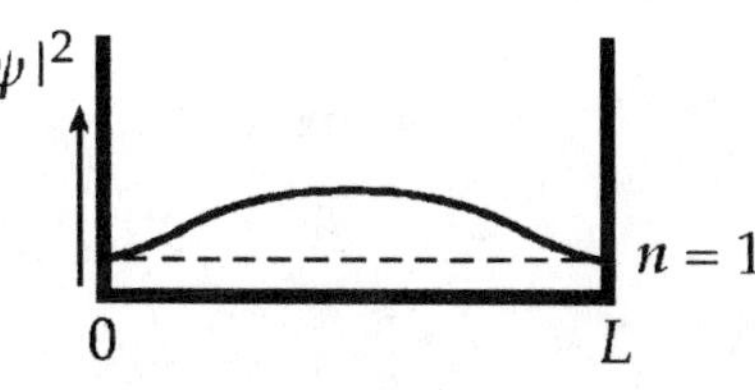

FIG. P41.21(b)

(c) Classically, the electron moves back and forth with constant speed between the walls, and the probability of finding the electron is the same for all points between the walls. Thus, the classical probability of finding the electron in any range equal to one-third of the available space is $P_{\text{classical}}=\boxed{\frac{1}{3}}$.

P41.22 (a) $\psi_1(x)=\sqrt{\frac{2}{L}}\cos\left(\frac{\pi x}{L}\right)$; $\qquad P_1(x)=|\psi_1(x)|^2=\frac{2}{L}\cos^2\left(\frac{\pi x}{L}\right)$

$\psi_2(x)=\sqrt{\frac{2}{L}}\sin\left(\frac{2\pi x}{L}\right)$; $\qquad P_2(x)=|\psi_2(x)|^2=\frac{2}{L}\sin^2\left(\frac{2\pi x}{L}\right)$

$\psi_3(x)=\sqrt{\frac{2}{L}}\cos\left(\frac{3\pi x}{L}\right)$; $\qquad P_3(x)=|\psi_3(x)|^2=\frac{2}{L}\cos^2\left(\frac{3\pi x}{L}\right)$

(b)

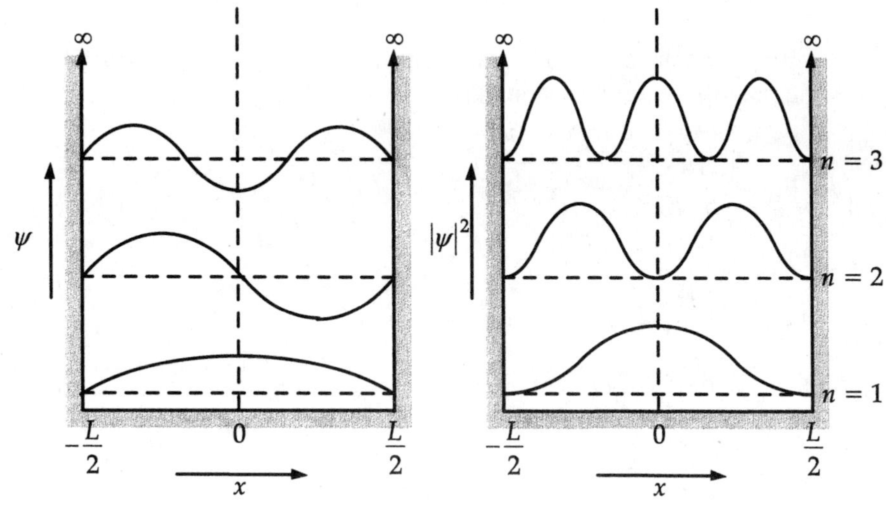

FIG. P41.22(b)

P41.23 Problem 43 in Chapter 16 helps students to understand how to draw conclusions from an identity

(a) $\psi(x) = A\left(1 - \frac{x^2}{L^2}\right)$ $\qquad \frac{d\psi}{dx} = -\frac{2Ax}{L^2}$ $\qquad \frac{d^2\psi}{dx^2} = -\frac{2A}{L}$

Schrödinger's equation $\quad \frac{d^2\psi}{dx^2} = -\frac{2m}{\hbar^2}(E-U)\psi$

becomes

$$-\frac{2A}{L^2} = -\frac{2m}{\hbar^2}EA\left(1-\frac{x^2}{L^2}\right) + \frac{2m}{\hbar^2}\frac{(-\hbar^2x^2)A(1-x^2/L^2)}{mL^2(L^2-x^2)}$$

$$-\frac{1}{L^2} = -\frac{mE}{\hbar^2} + \frac{mEx^2}{\hbar^2L^2} - \frac{x^2}{L^4}.$$

This will be true for all x if both $\quad \frac{1}{L^2} = \frac{mE}{\hbar^2}$

and $\quad \frac{mE}{\hbar^2L^2} - \frac{1}{L^4} = 0$

both these conditions are satisfied for a particle of energy $\quad \boxed{E = \frac{\hbar^2}{L^2m}}$.

(b) For normalization, $\quad 1 = \int_{-L}^{L} A^2\left(1-\frac{x^2}{L^2}\right)^2 dx = A^2\int_{-L}^{L}\left(1-\frac{2x^2}{L^2}+\frac{x^4}{L^4}\right)dx$

$$1 = A^2\left[x - \frac{2x^3}{3L^2} + \frac{x^5}{5L^4}\right]_{-L}^{L} = A^2\left[L - \frac{2}{3}L + \frac{L}{5} + L - \frac{2}{3}L + \frac{L}{5}\right] = A^2\left(\frac{16L}{15}\right) \qquad \boxed{A = \sqrt{\frac{15}{16L}}}.$$

(c) $$P = \int_{-L/3}^{L/3}\psi^2 dx = \frac{15}{16L}\int_{-L/3}^{L/3}\left(1-\frac{2x^2}{L^2}+\frac{x^4}{L^4}\right)dx = \frac{15}{16L}\left[x - \frac{2x^3}{3L^2} + \frac{x^5}{5L^5}\right]_{-L/3}^{L/3} = \frac{30}{16L}\left[\frac{L}{3} - \frac{2L}{81} + \frac{L}{1\,215}\right]$$

$$P = \frac{47}{81} = \boxed{0.580}$$

P41.24 (a) Setting the total energy E equal to zero and rearranging the Schrödinger equation to isolate the potential energy function gives

$$U(x) = \left(\frac{\hbar^2}{2m}\right)\frac{1}{\psi}\frac{d^2\psi}{dx^2}.$$

If $\quad \psi(x) = Axe^{-x^2/L^2}$.

Then $\quad \frac{d^2\psi}{dx^2} = (4Ax^3 - 6AxL^2)\frac{e^{-x^2/L^2}}{L^4}$

or $\quad \frac{d^2\psi}{dx^2} = \frac{(4x^2-6L^2)}{L^4}\psi(x)$

and $\quad \boxed{U(x) = \frac{\hbar^2}{2mL^2}\left(\frac{4x^2}{L^2} - 6\right)}$.

(b) See the figure to the right.

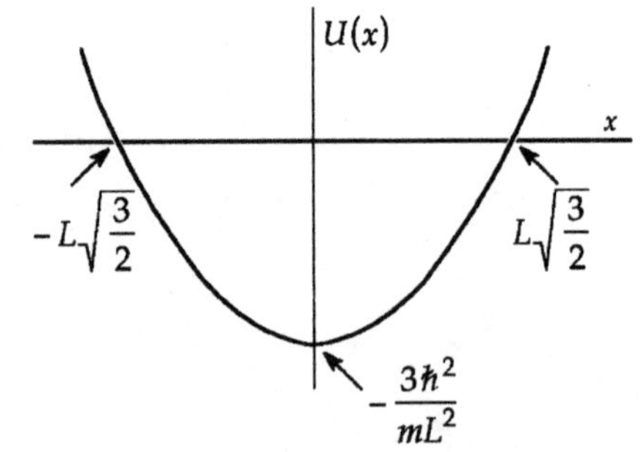

FIG. P41.24(b)

Section 41.5 A Particle in a Well of Finite Height

P41.25 (a) See figure to the right.

(b) The wavelength of the transmitted wave traveling to the left is the same as the original wavelength, which equals $\boxed{2L}$.

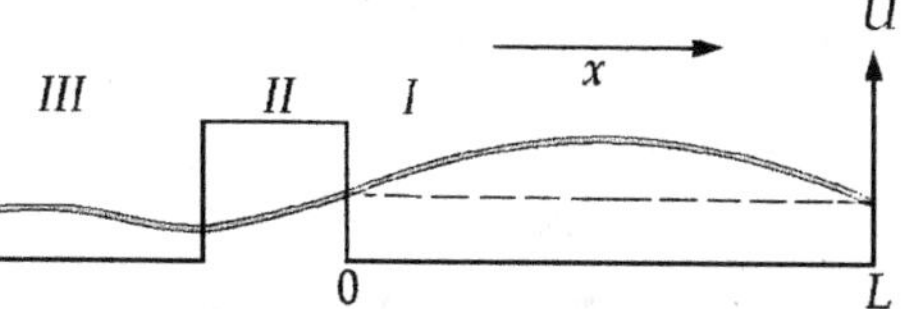

FIG. P41.25(a)

P41.26

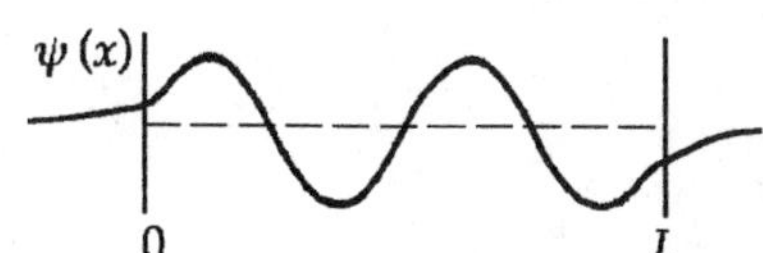

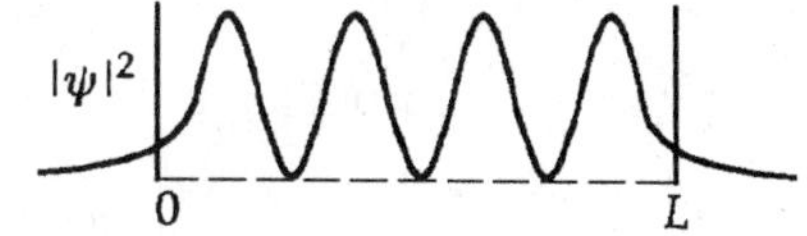

FIG. P41.26

Section 41.6 Tunneling Through a Potential Energy Barrier

P41.27 $T = e^{-2CL}$ where $C = \dfrac{\sqrt{2m(U-E)}}{\hbar}$

$$2CL = \frac{2\sqrt{2\left(9.11\times10^{-31}\right)\left(8.00\times10^{-19}\right)}}{1.055\times10^{-34}}\left(2.00\times10^{-10}\right) = 4.58$$

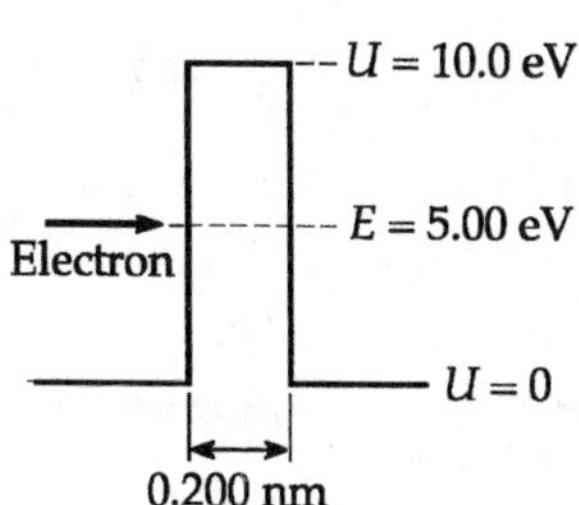

FIG. P41.27

(a) $T = e^{-4.58} = \boxed{0.010\,3}$, a 1% chance of transmission.

(b) $R = 1 - T = \boxed{0.990}$, a 99% chance of reflection.

P41.28

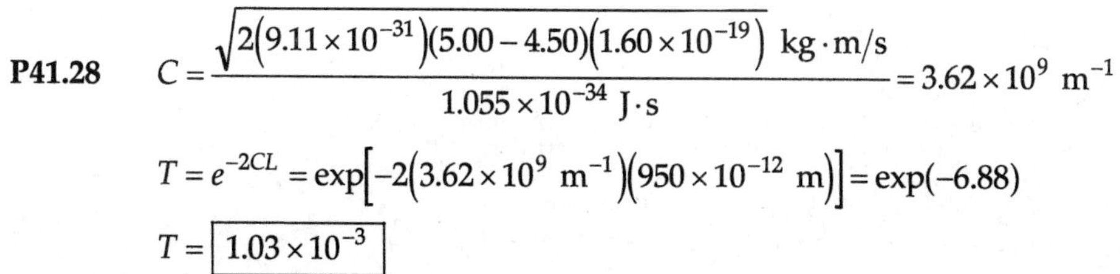

$$C = \frac{\sqrt{2\left(9.11\times10^{-31}\right)(5.00-4.50)\left(1.60\times10^{-19}\right)}\ \text{kg}\cdot\text{m/s}}{1.055\times10^{-34}\ \text{J}\cdot\text{s}} = 3.62\times10^{9}\ \text{m}^{-1}$$

$$T = e^{-2CL} = \exp\left[-2\left(3.62\times10^{9}\ \text{m}^{-1}\right)\left(950\times10^{-12}\ \text{m}\right)\right] = \exp(-6.88)$$

$$T = \boxed{1.03\times10^{-3}}$$

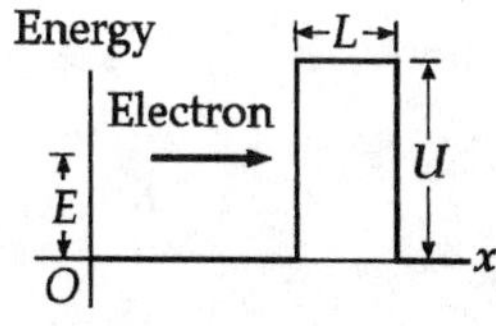

FIG. P41.28

P41.29 From problem 28, $C = 3.62\times10^{9}\ \text{m}^{-1}$

$$10^{-6} = \exp\left[-2\left(3.62\times10^{9}\ \text{m}^{-1}\right)L\right].$$

Taking logarithms, $\quad -13.816 = -2\left(3.62\times10^{9}\ \text{m}^{-1}\right)L.$

New $L = 1.91$ nm

$\Delta L = 1.91\ \text{nm} - 0.950\ \text{nm} = \boxed{0.959\ \text{nm}}$.

***P41.30** The original tunneling probability is $T = e^{-2CL}$ where

$$C = \frac{(2m(U-E))^{1/2}}{\hbar} = \frac{2\pi\left(2\times 9.11\times 10^{-31}\text{ kg}(20-12)1.6\times 10^{-19}\text{ J}\right)^{1/2}}{6.626\times 10^{-34}\text{ J}\cdot\text{s}} = 1.448\,1\times 10^{10}\text{ m}^{-1}.$$

The photon energy is $hf = \frac{hc}{\lambda} = \frac{1\,240\text{ eV}\cdot\text{nm}}{546\text{ nm}} = 2.27\text{ eV}$, to make the electron's new kinetic energy $12+2.27 = 14.27\text{ eV}$ and its decay coefficient inside the barrier

$$C' = \frac{2\pi\left(2\times 9.11\times 10^{-31}\text{ kg}(20-14.27)1.6\times 10^{-19}\text{ J}\right)^{1/2}}{6.626\times 10^{-34}\text{ J}\cdot\text{s}} = 1.225\,5\times 10^{10}\text{ m}^{-1}.$$

Now the factor of increase in transmission probability is

$$\frac{e^{-2C'L}}{e^{-2CL}} = e^{2L(C-C')} = e^{2\times 10^{-9}\text{ m}\times 0.223\times 10^{10}\text{ m}^{-1}} = e^{4.45} = \boxed{85.9}.$$

Section 41.7 The Scanning Tunneling Microscope

P41.31 With the wave function proportional to e^{-CL}, the transmission coefficient and the tunneling current are proportional to $|\psi|^2$, to e^{-2CL}.

Then,
$$\frac{I(0.500\text{ nm})}{I(0.515\text{ nm})} = \frac{e^{-2(10.0/\text{nm})(0.500\text{ nm})}}{e^{-2(10.0/\text{nm})(0.515\text{ nm})}} = e^{20.0(0.015)} = \boxed{1.35}.$$

P41.32 With transmission coefficient e^{-2CL}, the fractional change in transmission is

$$\frac{e^{-2(10.0/\text{nm})L} - e^{-2(10.0/\text{nm})(L+0.002\,00\text{ nm})}}{e^{-2(10.0/\text{nm})L}} = 1 - e^{-20.0(0.002\,00)} = 0.0392 = \boxed{3.92\%}.$$

Section 41.8 The Simple Harmonic Oscillator

P41.33 $\psi = Be^{-(m\omega/2\hbar)x^2}$ so $\frac{d\psi}{dx} = -\left(\frac{m\omega}{\hbar}\right)x\psi$ and $\frac{d^2\psi}{dx^2} = \left(\frac{m\omega}{\hbar}\right)^2 x^2\psi + \left(-\frac{m\omega}{\hbar}\right)\psi$.

Substituting into Equation 41.13 gives $\left(\frac{m\omega}{\hbar}\right)^2 x^2\psi + \left(-\frac{m\omega}{\hbar}\right)\psi = -\left(\frac{2mE}{\hbar^2}\right)\psi + \left(\frac{m\omega}{\hbar}\right)^2 x^2\psi$

which is satisfied provided that $E = \frac{\hbar\omega}{2}$.

P41.34 Problem 43 in Chapter 16 helps students to understand how to draw conclusions from an identity.

$\psi = Axe^{-bx^2}$ so $\dfrac{d\psi}{dx} = Ae^{-bx^2} - 2bx^2 Ae^{-bx^2}$

and $\dfrac{d^2\psi}{dx^2} = -2bxAe^{-bx^2} - 4bxAe^{-bx^2} + 4b^2x^3e^{-bx^2} = -6b\psi + 4b^2x^2\psi$.

Substituting into Equation 41.13, $-6b\psi + 4b^2x^2\psi = -\left(\dfrac{2mE}{\hbar}\right)\psi + \left(\dfrac{m\omega}{\hbar}\right)^2 x^2\psi$.

For this to be true as an identity, it must be true for all values of x.

So we must have both $-6b = -\dfrac{2mE}{\hbar^2}$ and $4b^2 = \left(\dfrac{m\omega}{\hbar}\right)^2$.

(a) Therefore $\boxed{b = \dfrac{m\omega}{2\hbar}}$

(b) and $E = \dfrac{3b\hbar^2}{m} = \boxed{\dfrac{3}{2}\hbar\omega}$.

(c) The wave function is that of the $\boxed{\text{first excited state}}$.

P41.35 The longest wavelength corresponds to minimum photon energy, which must be equal to the spacing between energy levels of the oscillator:

$$\frac{hc}{\lambda} = \hbar\omega = \hbar\sqrt{\frac{k}{m}} \text{ so } \lambda = 2\pi c\sqrt{\frac{m}{k}} = 2\pi\left(3.00\times10^{8}\text{ m/s}\right)\left(\frac{9.11\times10^{-31}\text{ kg}}{8.99\text{ N/m}}\right)^{1/2} = \boxed{600\text{ nm}}.$$

P41.36 (a) With $\psi = Be^{-(m\omega/2\hbar)x^2}$, the normalization condition $\int_{\text{all } x} |\psi|^2 dx = 1$

becomes $1 = \int_{-\infty}^{\infty} B^2 e^{-2(m\omega/2\hbar)x^2} dx = 2B^2\int_0^{\infty} e^{-(m\omega/\hbar)x^2} dx = 2B^2 \dfrac{1}{2}\sqrt{\dfrac{\pi}{m\omega/\hbar}}$

where Table B.6 in Appendix B was used to evaluate the integral.

Thus, $1 = B^2\sqrt{\dfrac{\pi\hbar}{m\omega}}$ and $\boxed{B = \left(\dfrac{m\omega}{\pi\hbar}\right)^{1/4}}$.

(b) For small δ, the probability of finding the particle in the range $-\dfrac{\delta}{2} < x < \dfrac{\delta}{2}$ is

$$\int_{-\delta/2}^{\delta/2} |\psi|^2 dx = \delta|\psi(0)|^2 = \delta B^2 e^{-0} = \boxed{\delta\left(\frac{m\omega}{\pi\hbar}\right)^{1/2}}.$$

***P41.37** (a) For the center of mass to be fixed, $m_1 v_1 + m_2 v_2 = 0$. Then $v = |v_1| + |v_2| = |v_1| + \frac{m_1}{m_2}|v_1| = \frac{m_2 + m_1}{m_2}|v_1|$ and $|v_1| = \frac{m_2 v}{m_1 + m_2}$. Similarly, $v = \frac{m_2}{m_1}|v_2| + |v_2|$ and $|v_2| = \frac{m_1 v}{m_1 + m_2}$. Then

$$\frac{1}{2}m_1 v_1^2 + \frac{1}{2}m_2 v_2^2 + \frac{1}{2}kx^2 = \frac{1}{2}\frac{m_1 m_2^2 v^2}{(m_1+m_2)^2} + \frac{1}{2}\frac{m_2 m_1^2 v^2}{(m_1+m_2)^2} + \frac{1}{2}kx^2$$

$$= \frac{1}{2}\frac{m_1 m_2 (m_1+m_2)}{(m_1+m_2)^2}v^2 + \frac{1}{2}kx^2 = \frac{1}{2}\mu v^2 + \frac{1}{2}kx^2$$

(b) $\frac{d}{dx}\left(\frac{1}{2}\mu v^2 + \frac{1}{2}kx^2\right) = 0$ because energy is constant

$$0 = \frac{1}{2}\mu 2v\frac{dv}{dx} + \frac{1}{2}k2x = \mu\frac{dx}{dt}\frac{dv}{dx} + kx = \mu\frac{dv}{dt} + kx.$$

Then $\mu a = -kx$, $a = -\frac{kx}{\mu}$. This is the condition for simple harmonic motion, that the acceleration of the equivalent particle be a negative constant times the excursion from equilibrium. By identification with $a = -\omega^2 x$, $\omega = \sqrt{\frac{k}{\mu}} = 2\pi f$ and $\boxed{f = \frac{1}{2\pi}\sqrt{\frac{k}{\mu}}}$.

P41.38 (a) With $\langle x \rangle = 0$ and $\langle p_x \rangle = 0$, the average value of x^2 is $(\Delta x)^2$ and the average value of p_x^2 is $(\Delta p_x)^2$. Then $\Delta x \ge \frac{\hbar}{2\Delta p_x}$ requires

$$E \ge \frac{p_x^2}{2m} + \frac{k}{2}\frac{\hbar^2}{4p_x^2} = \boxed{\frac{p_x^2}{2m} + \frac{k\hbar^2}{8p_x^2}}.$$

(b) To minimize this as a function of p_x^2, we require $\frac{dE}{dp_x^2} = 0 = \frac{1}{2m} + \frac{k\hbar^2}{8}(-1)\frac{1}{p_x^4}$.

Then $\frac{k\hbar^2}{8p_x^4} = \frac{1}{2m}$ so $p_x^2 = \left(\frac{2mk\hbar^2}{8}\right)^{1/2} = \frac{\hbar\sqrt{mk}}{2}$

and $E \ge \frac{\hbar\sqrt{mk}}{2(2m)} + \frac{k\hbar^2 2}{8\hbar\sqrt{mk}} = \frac{\hbar}{4}\sqrt{\frac{k}{m}} + \frac{\hbar}{4}\sqrt{\frac{k}{m}}$

$$E_{\min} = \frac{\hbar}{2}\sqrt{\frac{k}{m}} = \boxed{\frac{\hbar\omega}{2}}.$$

Additional Problems

P41.39 Suppose the marble has mass 20 g. Suppose the wall of the box is 12 cm high and 2 mm thick. While it is inside the wall,

$$U = mgy = (0.02 \text{ kg})(9.8 \text{ m/s}^2)(0.12 \text{ m}) = 0.023\,5 \text{ J}$$

and $$E = K = \frac{1}{2}mv^2 = \frac{1}{2}(0.02 \text{ kg})(0.8 \text{ m/s})^2 = 0.006\,4 \text{ J}.$$

Then $$C = \frac{\sqrt{2m(U-E)}}{\hbar} = \frac{\sqrt{2(0.02 \text{ kg})(0.017\,1 \text{ J})}}{1.055\times10^{-34} \text{ J}\cdot\text{s}} = 2.5\times10^{32} \text{ m}^{-1}$$

and the transmission coefficient is

$$e^{-2CL} = e^{-2\left(2.5\times10^{32}\right)\left(2\times10^{-3}\right)} = e^{-10\times10^{29}} = e^{-2.30\left(4.3\times10^{29}\right)} = 10^{-4.3\times10^{29}} = \boxed{\sim 10^{-10^{30}}}.$$

P41.40 (a) $\lambda = 2L = \boxed{2.00\times10^{-10} \text{ m}}$

(b) $p = \dfrac{h}{\lambda} = \dfrac{6.626\times10^{-34} \text{ J}\cdot\text{s}}{2.00\times10^{-10} \text{ m}} = \boxed{3.31\times10^{-24} \text{ kg}\cdot\text{m/s}}$

(c) $E = \dfrac{p^2}{2m} = \boxed{0.172 \text{ eV}}$

P41.41 (a) See the figure. (b) 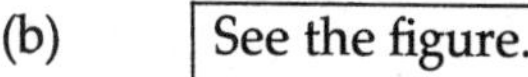

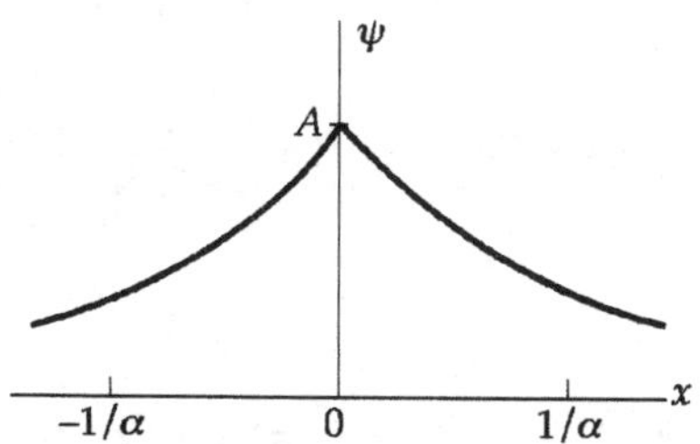

FIG. P41.41(a)

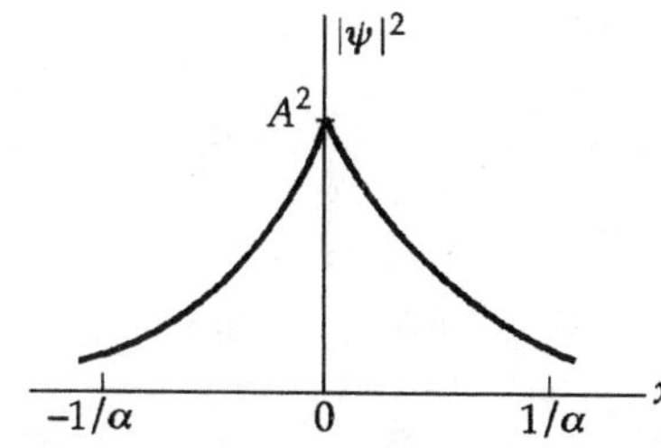

FIG. P41.41(b)

(c) ψ is continuous and $\psi \to 0$ as $x \to \pm\infty$. The function can be normalized. It describes a particle bound near $x = 0$.

(d) Since ψ is symmetric,

$$\int_{-\infty}^{\infty} |\psi|^2\, dx = 2\int_0^{\infty} |\psi|^2\, dx = 1$$

or $$2A^2 \int_0^{\infty} e^{-2\alpha x}\, dx = \left(\frac{2A^2}{-2\alpha}\right)\left(e^{-\infty} - e^0\right) = 1.$$

This gives $\boxed{A = \sqrt{\alpha}}$.

(e) $$P_{(-1/2\alpha)\to(1/2\alpha)} = 2\left(\sqrt{\alpha}\right)^2 \int_{x=0}^{1/2\alpha} e^{-2\alpha x}\, dx = \left(\frac{2\alpha}{-2\alpha}\right)\left(e^{-2\alpha/2\alpha} - 1\right) = \left(1 - e^{-1}\right) = \boxed{0.632}$$

P41.42 (a) Use Schrödinger's equation

$$\frac{\partial^2 \psi}{\partial x^2} = -\frac{2m}{\hbar^2}(E-U)\psi$$

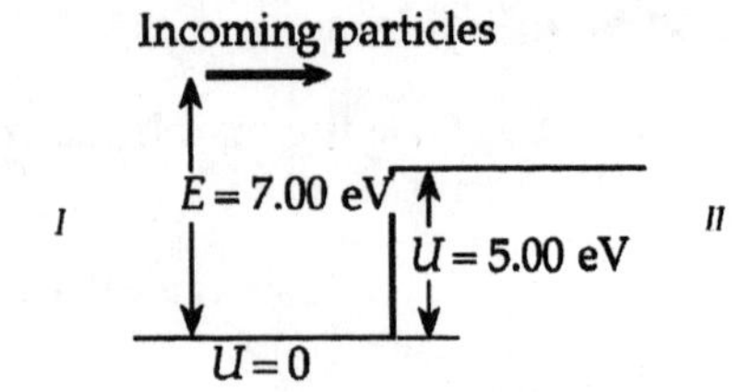

with solutions

$$\psi_1 = Ae^{ik_1x} + Be^{-ik_1x} \quad \text{[region } I\text{]}$$

$$\psi_2 = Ce^{ik_2x} \quad \text{[region } II\text{]}.$$

Incoming particles

I $E = 7.00$ eV $U = 5.00$ eV II

$U = 0$

FIG. P41.42(a)

Where $k_1 = \frac{\sqrt{2mE}}{\hbar}$

and $k_2 = \frac{\sqrt{2m(E-U)}}{\hbar}$.

Then, matching functions and derivatives at $x = 0$

$(\psi_1)_0 = (\psi_2)_0$ gives $A + B = C$

and $\left(\frac{d\psi_1}{dx}\right)_0 = \left(\frac{d\psi_2}{dx}\right)_0$ gives $k_1(A - B) = k_2 C$.

Then $B = \frac{1 - k_2/k_1}{1 + k_2/k_1} A$

and $C = \frac{2}{1 + k_2/k_1} A$.

Incident wave Ae^{ikx} reflects Be^{-ikx}, with probability $R = \frac{B^2}{A^2} = \frac{(1 - k_2/k_1)^2}{(1 + k_2/k_1)^2} = \boxed{\frac{(k_1 - k_2)^2}{(k_1 + k_2)^2}}$.

(b) With $E = 7.00$ eV

and $U = 5.00$ eV

$$\frac{k_2}{k_1} = \sqrt{\frac{E-U}{E}} = \sqrt{\frac{2.00}{7.00}} = 0.535.$$

The reflection probability is $R = \frac{(1 - 0.535)^2}{(1 + 0.535)^2} = \boxed{0.092\,0}$.

The probability of transmission is $T = 1 - R = \boxed{0.908}$.

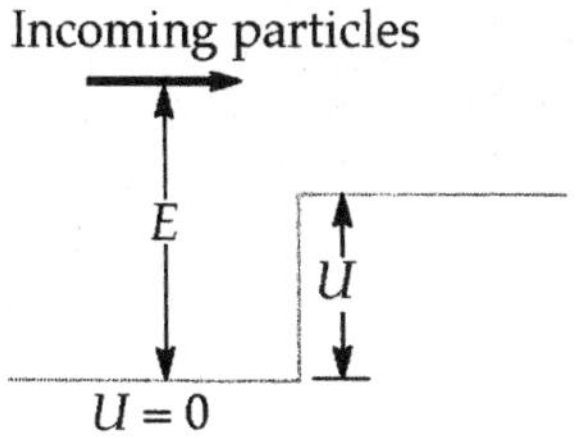

Incoming particles

E

U

$U = 0$

FIG. P41.43

P41.43 $R = \dfrac{(k_1 - k_2)^2}{(k_1 + k_2)^2} = \dfrac{(1 - k_2/k_1)^2}{(1 + k_2/k_1)^2}$

$\dfrac{\hbar^2 k^2}{2m} = E - U$ for constant U

$\dfrac{\hbar^2 k_1^2}{2m} = E$ since $U = 0$ (1)

$\dfrac{\hbar^2 k_2^2}{2m} = E - U$ (2)

Dividing (2) by (1), $\dfrac{k_2^2}{k_1^2} = 1 - \dfrac{U}{E} = 1 - \dfrac{1}{2} = \dfrac{1}{2}$ so $\dfrac{k_2}{k_1} = \dfrac{1}{\sqrt{2}}$

and therefore, $R = \dfrac{(1 - 1/\sqrt{2})^2}{(1 + 1/\sqrt{2})^2} = \dfrac{(\sqrt{2} - 1)^2}{(\sqrt{2} + 1)^2} = \boxed{0.029\,4}$.

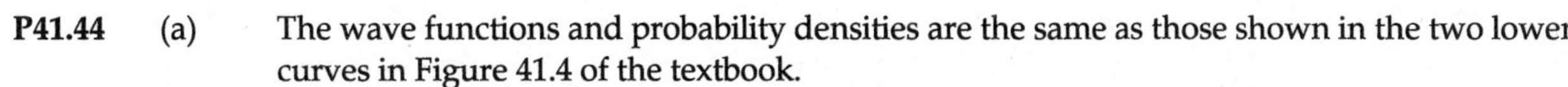

P41.44 (a) The wave functions and probability densities are the same as those shown in the two lower curves in Figure 41.4 of the textbook.

(b) $P_1 = \displaystyle\int_{0.150\text{ nm}}^{0.350\text{ nm}} |\psi_1|^2 dx = \left(\frac{2}{1.00\text{ nm}}\right)\int_{0.150}^{0.350} \sin^2\left(\frac{\pi x}{1.00\text{ nm}}\right) dx$

$= (2.00/\text{nm})\left[\dfrac{x}{2} - \dfrac{1.00\text{ nm}}{4\pi}\sin\left(\dfrac{2\pi x}{1.00\text{ nm}}\right)\right]_{0.150\text{ nm}}^{0.350\text{ nm}}$

In the above result we used $\int \sin^2 ax dx = \left(\frac{x}{2}\right) - \left(\frac{1}{4a}\right)\sin(2ax)$.

Therefore, $P_1 = (1.00/\text{nm})\left[x - \dfrac{1.00\text{ nm}}{2\pi}\sin\left(\dfrac{2\pi x}{1.00\text{ nm}}\right)\right]_{0.150\text{ nm}}^{0.350\text{ nm}}$

$P_1 = (1.00/\text{nm})\left\{0.350\text{ nm} - 0.150\text{ nm} - \dfrac{1.00\text{ nm}}{2\pi}\left[\sin(0.700\pi) - \sin(0.300\pi)\right]\right\} = \boxed{0.200}$.

(c) $P_2 = \dfrac{2}{1.00}\displaystyle\int_{0.150}^{0.350} \sin^2\left(\frac{2\pi x}{1.00}\right) dx = 2.00\left[\frac{x}{2} - \frac{1.00}{8\pi}\sin\left(\frac{4\pi x}{1.00}\right)\right]_{0.150}^{0.350}$

$P_2 = 1.00\left[x - \dfrac{1.00}{4\pi}\sin\left(\dfrac{4\pi x}{1.00}\right)\right]_{0.150}^{0.350} = 1.00\left\{(0.350 - 0.150) - \dfrac{1.00}{4\pi}\left[\sin(1.40\pi) - \sin(0.600\pi)\right]\right\}$

$= \boxed{0.351}$

(d) Using $E_n = \dfrac{n^2 h^2}{8mL^2}$, we find that $E_1 = \boxed{0.377\text{ eV}}$ and $E_2 = \boxed{1.51\text{ eV}}$.

P41.45 (a) $f=\frac{E}{h}=\frac{(1.80\text{ eV})}{(6.626\times10^{-34}\text{ J}\cdot\text{s})}\left(\frac{1.60\times10^{-19}\text{ J}}{1.00\text{ eV}}\right)=\boxed{4.34\times10^{14}\text{ Hz}}$

(b) $\lambda=\frac{c}{f}=\frac{3.00\times10^{8}\text{ m/s}}{4.34\times10^{14}\text{ Hz}}=6.91\times10^{-7}\text{ m}=\boxed{691\text{ nm}}$

(c) $\Delta E\Delta t\geq\frac{\hbar}{2}$ so $\Delta E\geq\frac{\hbar}{2\Delta t}=\frac{h}{4\pi(\Delta t)}=\frac{6.626\times10^{-34}\text{ J}\cdot\text{s}}{4\pi(2.00\times10^{-6}\text{ s})}=2.64\times10^{-29}\text{ J}=\boxed{1.65\times10^{-10}\text{ eV}}$

***P41.46** (a) Taking $L_x=L_y=L$, we see that the expression for E becomes

$$E=\frac{h^2}{8m_eL^2}\left(n_x^2+n_y^2\right).$$

For a normalizable wave function describing a particle, neither n_x nor n_y can be zero. The ground state, corresponding to $n_x=n_y=1$, has an energy of

$$E_{1,1}=\frac{h^2}{8m_eL^2}\left(1^2+1^2\right)=\boxed{\frac{h^2}{4m_eL^2}}.$$

The first excited state, corresponding to either $n_x=2$, $n_y=1$ or $n_x=1$, $n_y=2$, has an energy

$$E_{2,1}=E_{1,2}=\frac{h^2}{8m_eL^2}\left(2^2+1^2\right)=\boxed{\frac{5h^2}{8m_eL^2}}.$$

The second excited state, corresponding to $n_x=2$, $n_y=2$ has an energy of

$$E_{2,2}=\frac{h^2}{8m_eL^2}\left(2^2+2^2\right)=\boxed{\frac{h^2}{m_eL^2}}.$$

Finally, the third excited state, corresponding to either $n_x=1$, $n_y=3$ or $n_x=3$, $n_x=1$, has an energy

$$E_{1,3}=E_{3,1}=\frac{h^2}{8m_eL^2}\left(1^2+3^2\right)=\boxed{\frac{5h^2}{4m_eL^2}}.$$

(b) The energy difference between the second excited state and the ground state is given by

$$\Delta E=E_{2,2}-E_{1,1}=\frac{h^2}{m_eL^2}-\frac{h^2}{4m_eL^2}$$

$$=\boxed{\frac{3h^2}{4m_eL^2}}.$$

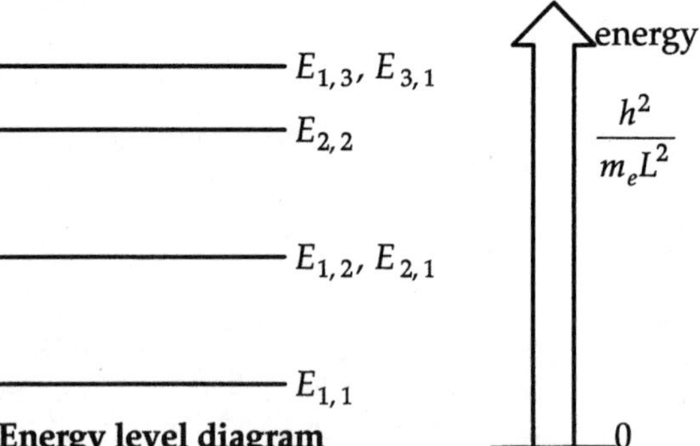

FIG. P41.46(b)

P41.47 $\langle x^2 \rangle = \int_{-\infty}^{\infty} x^2 |\psi|^2 dx$

For a one-dimensional box of width L, $\psi_n = \sqrt{\frac{2}{L}} \sin\left(\frac{n\pi x}{L}\right)$.

Thus, $\langle x^2 \rangle = \frac{2}{L} \int_0^L x^2 \sin^2\left(\frac{n\pi x}{L}\right) dx = \boxed{\frac{L^2}{3} - \frac{L^2}{2n^2\pi^2}}$ (from integral tables).

P41.48 (a) $\int_{-\infty}^{\infty} |\psi|^2 dx = 1$ becomes

$$A^2 \int_{-L/4}^{L/4} \cos^2\left(\frac{2\pi x}{L}\right) dx = A^2\left(\frac{L}{2\pi}\right)\left[\frac{\pi x}{L} + \frac{1}{4}\sin\left(\frac{4\pi x}{L}\right)\right]_{-L/4}^{L/4} = A^2\left(\frac{L}{2\pi}\right)\left[\frac{\pi}{2}\right] = 1$$

or $A^2 = \frac{4}{L}$ and $\boxed{A = \frac{2}{\sqrt{L}}}$.

(b) The probability of finding the particle between 0 and $\frac{L}{8}$ is

$$\int_0^{L/8} |\psi|^2 dx = A^2 \int_0^{L/8} \cos^2\left(\frac{2\pi x}{L}\right) dx = \frac{1}{4} + \frac{1}{2\pi} = \boxed{0.409}.$$

P41.49 For a particle with wave function

$\psi(x) = \sqrt{\frac{2}{a}} e^{-x/a}$ for $x > 0$

and 0 for $x < 0$.

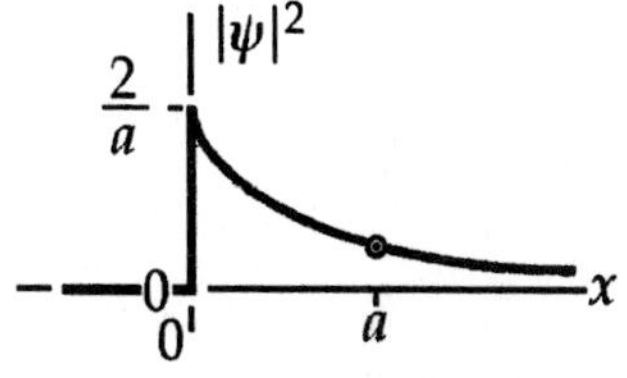

FIG. P41.49

(a) $|\psi(x)|^2 = 0,\ x < 0$ and $|\psi^2(x)| = \frac{2}{a} e^{-2x/a},\ x > 0$

(b) $\text{Prob}(x < 0) = \int_{-\infty}^{0} |\psi(x)|^2 dx = \int_{-\infty}^{0} (0) dx = \boxed{0}$

(c) Normalization $\int_{-\infty}^{\infty} |\psi(x)|^2 dx = \int_{-\infty}^{0} |\psi|^2 dx + \int_0^{\infty} |\psi|^2 dx = 1$

$$\int_{-\infty}^{0} 0\,dx + \int_0^{\infty}\left(\frac{2}{a}\right) e^{-2x/a} dx = 0 - e^{-2x/a}\Big|_0^{\infty} = -\left(e^{-\infty} - 1\right) = 1$$

$$\text{Prob}(0 < x < a) = \int_0^a |\psi|^2 dx = \int_0^a \left(\frac{2}{a}\right) e^{-2x/a} dx = -e^{-2x/a}\Big|_0^a = 1 - e^{-2} = \boxed{0.865}$$

P41.50 (a) The requirement that $\frac{n\lambda}{2}=L$ so $p=\frac{h}{\lambda}=\frac{nh}{2L}$ is still valid.

$$E=\sqrt{(pc)^2+(mc^2)^2} \Rightarrow E_n=\sqrt{\left(\frac{nhc}{2L}\right)^2+(mc^2)^2}$$

$$K_n=E_n-mc^2=\boxed{\sqrt{\left(\frac{nhc}{2L}\right)^2+(mc^2)^2}-mc^2}$$

(b) Taking $L=1.00\times10^{-12}$ m, $m=9.11\times10^{-31}$ kg, and $n=1$, we find $K_1=\boxed{4.69\times10^{-14}\text{ J}}$.

Nonrelativistic, $E_1=\frac{h^2}{8mL^2}=\frac{(6.626\times10^{-34}\text{ J}\cdot\text{s})^2}{8(9.11\times10^{-31}\text{ kg})(1.00\times10^{-12}\text{ m})^2}=6.02\times10^{-14}\text{ J}$.

Comparing this to K_1, we see that this value is too large by $\boxed{28.6\%}$.

P41.51 (a) $$U=\frac{e^2}{4\pi\in_0 d}\left[-1+\frac{1}{2}-\frac{1}{3}+\left(-1+\frac{1}{2}\right)+(-1)\right]=\frac{(-7/3)e^2}{4\pi\in_0 d}=\boxed{-\frac{7k_ee^2}{3d}}$$

(b) From Equation 41.12, $$K=2E_1=\frac{2h^2}{8m_e(9d^2)}=\boxed{\frac{h^2}{36m_ed^2}}.$$

(c) $E=U+K$ and $\frac{dE}{dd}=0$ for a minimum: $$\frac{7k_ee^2}{3d^2}-\frac{h^2}{18m_ed^3}=0$$

$$d=\frac{3h^2}{(7)(18k_ee^2m_e)}=\frac{h^2}{42m_ek_ee^2}=\frac{(6.626\times10^{-34})^2}{(42)(9.11\times10^{-31})(8.99\times10^9)(1.60\times10^{-19}\text{ C})^2}=\boxed{0.049\,9\text{ nm}}.$$

(d) Since the lithium spacing is a, where $Na^3=V$, and the density is $\frac{Nm}{V}$, where m is the mass of one atom, we get:

$$a=\left(\frac{Vm}{Nm}\right)^{1/3}=\left(\frac{m}{\text{density}}\right)^{1/3}=\left(\frac{1.66\times10^{-27}\text{ kg}\times7}{530\text{ kg}}\right)^{1/3}\text{ m}=2.80\times10^{-10}\text{ m}=\boxed{0.280\text{ nm}}$$

(5.62 times larger than c).

P41.52 (a) $\psi = Bxe^{-(m\omega/2\hbar)x^2}$

$$\frac{d\psi}{dx} = Be^{-(m\omega/2\hbar)x^2} + Bx\left(-\frac{m\omega}{2\hbar}\right)2xe^{-(m\omega/2\hbar)x^2} = Be^{-(m\omega/2\hbar)x^2} - B\left(\frac{m\omega}{\hbar}\right)x^2e^{-(m\omega/2\hbar)x^2}$$

$$\frac{d^2\psi}{dx^2} = Bx\left(-\frac{m\omega}{\hbar}\right)xe^{-(m\omega/2\hbar)x^2} - B\left(\frac{m\omega}{\hbar}\right)2xe^{-(m\omega/2\hbar)x^2} - B\left(\frac{m\omega}{\hbar}\right)x^2\left(-\frac{m\omega}{\hbar}\right)xe^{-(m\omega/2\hbar)x^2}$$

$$\frac{d^2\psi}{dx^2} = -3B\left(\frac{m\omega}{\hbar}\right)xe^{-(m\omega/2\hbar)x^2} + B\left(\frac{m\omega}{\hbar}\right)^2 x^3e^{-(m\omega/2\hbar)x^2}$$

Substituting into the Schrödinger Equation (41.13), we have

$$-3B\left(\frac{m\omega}{\hbar}\right)xe^{-(m\omega/2\hbar)x^2} + B\left(\frac{m\omega}{\hbar}\right)^2 x^3e^{-(m\omega/2\hbar)x^2} = -\frac{2mE}{\hbar^2}Bxe^{-(m\omega/2\hbar)x^2} + \left(\frac{m\omega}{\hbar}\right)^2 x^2Bxe^{-(m\omega/2\hbar)x^2}.$$

This is true if $-3\omega = -\frac{2E}{\hbar}$; it is true if $\boxed{E = \frac{3\hbar\omega}{2}}$.

(b) We never find the particle at $\boxed{x = 0}$ because $\psi = 0$ there.

(c) ψ is maximized if $\frac{d\psi}{dx} = 0 = 1 - x^2\left(\frac{m\omega}{\hbar}\right)$, which is true at $\boxed{x = \pm\sqrt{\frac{\hbar}{m\omega}}}$.

(d) We require $\int_{-\infty}^{\infty}|\psi|^2 dx = 1$:

$$1 = \int_{-\infty}^{\infty} B^2x^2e^{-(m\omega/\hbar)x^2}dx = 2B^2\int x^2e^{-(m\omega/\hbar)x^2}dx = 2B^2\frac{1}{4}\sqrt{\frac{\pi}{(m\omega/\hbar)^3}} = \frac{B^2}{2}\frac{\pi^{1/2}\hbar^{3/2}}{(m\omega)^{3/2}}.$$

Then $B = \frac{2^{1/2}}{\pi^{1/4}}\left(\frac{m\omega}{\hbar}\right)^{3/4} = \boxed{\left(\frac{4m^3\omega^3}{\pi\hbar^3}\right)^{1/4}}$.

(e) At $x = 2\sqrt{\frac{\hbar}{m\omega}}$, the potential energy is $\frac{1}{2}m\omega^2x^2 = \frac{1}{2}m\omega^2\left(\frac{4\hbar}{m\omega}\right) = 2\hbar\omega$. This is larger than the total energy $\frac{3\hbar\omega}{2}$, so there is $\boxed{\text{zero}}$ classical probability of finding the particle here.

(f) Probability $= |\psi|^2 dx = \left(Bxe^{-(m\omega/2\hbar)x^2}\right)^2\delta = \delta B^2x^2e^{-(m\omega/\hbar)x^2}$

$$\text{Probability} = \delta\frac{2}{\pi^{1/2}}\left(\frac{m\omega}{\hbar}\right)^{3/2}\left(\frac{4\hbar}{m\omega}\right)e^{-(m\omega/\hbar)4(\hbar/m\omega)} = \boxed{8\delta\left(\frac{m\omega}{\hbar\pi}\right)^{1/2}e^{-4}}$$

P41.53 (a) $\int_0^L |\psi|^2\,dx = 1$: $\quad A^2\int_0^L\left[\sin^2\left(\frac{\pi x}{L}\right)+16\sin^2\left(\frac{2\pi x}{L}\right)+8\sin\left(\frac{\pi x}{L}\right)\sin\left(\frac{2\pi x}{L}\right)\right]dx = 1$

$$A^2\left[\left(\frac{L}{2}\right)+16\left(\frac{L}{2}\right)+8\int_0^L \sin\left(\frac{\pi x}{L}\right)\sin\left(\frac{2\pi x}{L}\right)dx\right]=1$$

$$A^2\left[\frac{17L}{2}+16\int_0^L \sin^2\left(\frac{\pi x}{L}\right)\cos\left(\frac{\pi x}{L}\right)dx\right]=A^2\left[\frac{17L}{2}+\frac{16L}{3\pi}\sin^3\left(\frac{\pi x}{L}\right)\Bigg|_{x=0}^{x=L}\right]=1$$

$A^2=\frac{2}{17L}$, so the normalization constant is $\boxed{A=\sqrt{\frac{2}{17L}}}$.

(b) $\int_{-a}^{a}|\psi|^2\,dx=1$: $\quad \int_{-a}^{a}\left[|A|^2\cos^2\left(\frac{\pi x}{2a}\right)+|B|^2\sin^2\left(\frac{\pi x}{a}\right)+2|A||B|\cos\left(\frac{\pi x}{2a}\right)\sin\left(\frac{\pi x}{a}\right)\right]dx=1$

The first two terms are $|A|^2 a$ and $|B|^2 a$. The third term is:

$$2|A||B|\int_{-a}^{a}\cos\left(\frac{\pi x}{2a}\right)\left[2\sin\left(\frac{\pi x}{2a}\right)\cos\left(\frac{\pi x}{2a}\right)\right]dx=4|A||B|\int_{-a}^{a}\cos^2\left(\frac{\pi x}{2a}\right)\sin\left(\frac{\pi x}{2a}\right)dx$$

$$=\frac{8a|A||B|}{3\pi}\cos^3\left(\frac{\pi x}{2a}\right)\Bigg|_{-a}^{a}=0$$

so that $a\left(|A|^2+|B|^2\right)=1$, giving $\boxed{|A|^2+|B|^2=\frac{1}{a}}$.

***P41.54** (a) $\langle x\rangle_0=\int_{-\infty}^{\infty}x\left(\frac{a}{\pi}\right)^{1/2}e^{-ax^2}dx=\boxed{0}$, since the integrand is an odd function of x.

(b) $\langle x\rangle_1=\int_{-\infty}^{\infty}x\left(\frac{4a^3}{\pi}\right)^{1/2}x^2e^{-ax^2}dx=\boxed{0}$, since the integrand is an odd function of x.

(c) $\langle x\rangle_{01}=\int_{-\infty}^{\infty}x\frac{1}{2}(\psi_0+\psi_1)^2dx=\frac{1}{2}\langle x\rangle_0+\frac{1}{2}\langle x\rangle_1+\int_{-\infty}^{\infty}x\psi_0(x)\psi_1(x)dx$

The first two terms are zero, from (a) and (b). Thus:

$$\langle x\rangle_{01}=\int_{-\infty}^{\infty}x\left(\frac{a}{\pi}\right)^{1/4}e^{-ax^2/2}\left(\frac{4a^3}{\pi}\right)^{1/4}xe^{-ax^2/2}dx=2\left(\frac{2a^2}{\pi}\right)^{1/2}\int_0^{\infty}x^2e^{-ax^2}dx$$

$$=2\left(\frac{2a^2}{\pi}\right)^{1/2}\frac{1}{4}\left(\frac{\pi}{a^3}\right)^{1/2}\text{, from Table B.6}$$

$$=\boxed{\frac{1}{\sqrt{2a}}}$$

P41.55 With one slit open $P_1 = |\psi_1|^2$ or $P_2 = |\psi_2|^2$.

With both slits open, $P = |\psi_1 + \psi_2|^2$.

At a maximum, the wave functions are in phase $P_{max} = (|\psi_1| + |\psi_2|)^2$.

At a minimum, the wave functions are out of phase $P_{min} = (|\psi_1| - |\psi_2|)^2$.

Now $\frac{P_1}{P_2} = \frac{|\psi_1|^2}{|\psi_2|^2} = 25.0$, so $\frac{|\psi_1|}{|\psi_2|} = 5.00$

and $\frac{P_{max}}{P_{min}} = \frac{(|\psi_1| + |\psi_2|)^2}{(|\psi_1| - |\psi_2|)^2} = \frac{(5.00|\psi_2| + |\psi_2|)^2}{(5.00|\psi_2| - |\psi_2|)^2} = \frac{(6.00)^2}{(4.00)^2} = \frac{36.0}{16.0} = \boxed{2.25}$.

ANSWERS TO EVEN PROBLEMS

P41.2 $\frac{1}{2}$

P41.4 (a) 4; (b) 6.03 eV

P41.6 0.517 MeV, $3.31 \times 10^{-20}\ \text{kg} \cdot \text{m/s}$

P41.8 $\left(\frac{3h\lambda}{8m_e c}\right)^{1/2}$

P41.10 (a) 5.13 meV; (b) 9.41 eV; (c) The much smaller mass of the electron requires it to have much more energy to have the same momentum.

P41.12 (a) $\left(\frac{15h\lambda}{8m_e c}\right)^{1/2}$; (b) 1.25λ

P41.14 see the solution; $\frac{\hbar^2 k^2}{2m}$

P41.16 (a) $\frac{L}{2}$; (b) 5.26×10^{-5}; (c) 3.99×10^{-2}; (d) see the solution

P41.18 0.250

P41.20 (a) $\frac{\ell}{L} - \frac{1}{2\pi}\sin\left(\frac{2\pi\ell}{L}\right)$; (b) see the solution; (c) $0.585L$

P41.22 (a) $\psi_1(x) = \sqrt{\frac{2}{L}}\cos\left(\frac{\pi x}{L}\right)$;
$P_1(x) = \frac{2}{L}\cos^2\left(\frac{\pi x}{L}\right)$;
$\psi_2(x) = \sqrt{\frac{2}{L}}\sin\left(\frac{2\pi x}{L}\right)$;
$P_2(x) = \frac{2}{L}\sin^2\left(\frac{2\pi x}{L}\right)$;
$\psi_3(x) = \sqrt{\frac{2}{L}}\cos\left(\frac{3\pi x}{L}\right)$;
$P_3(x) = \frac{2}{L}\cos^2\left(\frac{3\pi x}{L}\right)$;
(b) see the solution

P41.24 (a) $\frac{\hbar^2}{2mL^2}\left(\frac{4x^2}{L^2} - 6\right)$; (b) see the solution

P41.26 see the solution

P41.28 1.03×10^{-3}

P41.30 85.9

P41.32 3.92%

P41.34 (a) see the solution; $b = \frac{m\omega}{2\hbar}$; (b) $E = \frac{3}{2}\hbar\omega$; (c) first excited state

P41.36 (a) $B = \left(\frac{m\omega}{\pi\hbar}\right)^{1/4}$; (b) $\delta\left(\frac{m\omega}{\pi\hbar}\right)^{1/2}$

P41.38 see the solution

P41.40 (a) 2.00×10^{-10} m; (b) 3.31×10^{-24} kg·m/s; (c) 0.172 eV

P41.42 (a) see the solution; (b) 0.0920, 0.908

P41.44 (a) see the solution; (b) 0.200; (c) 0.351; (d) 0.377 eV, 1.51 eV

P41.46 (a) $\frac{h^2}{4m_eL^2}, \frac{5h^2}{8m_eL^2}, \frac{h^2}{m_eL^2}, \frac{5h^2}{4m_eL^2}$; (b) see the solution, $\frac{3h^2}{4m_eL^2}$

P41.48 (a) $\frac{2}{\sqrt{L}}$; (b) 0.409

P41.50 (a) $\sqrt{\left(\frac{nhc}{2L}\right)^2 + m^2c^4} - mc^2$; (b) 46.9 fJ; 28.6%

P41.52 (a) $\frac{3\hbar\omega}{2}$; (b) $x = 0$; (c) $\pm\sqrt{\frac{\hbar}{m\omega}}$; (d) $\left(\frac{4m^3\omega^3}{\pi\hbar^3}\right)^{1/4}$; (e) 0; (f) $8\delta\left(\frac{m\omega}{\hbar\pi}\right)^{1/2} e^{-4}$

P41.54 (a) 0; (b) 0; (c) $(2a)^{-1/2}$

42

Atomic Physics

CHAPTER OUTLINE

ANSWERS TO QUESTIONS

Q42.1 Neon signs emit light in a bright-line spectrum, rather than in a continuous spectrum. There are many discrete wavelengths which correspond to transitions among the various energy levels of the neon atom. This also accounts for the particular color of the light emitted from a neon sign. You can see the separate colors if you look at a section of the sign through a diffraction grating, or at its reflection in a compact disk. A spectroscope lets you read their wavelengths.

Q42.2 One assumption is natural from the standpoint of classical physics: The electron feels an electric force of attraction to the nucleus, causing the centripetal acceleration to hold it in orbit. The other assumptions are in sharp contrast to the behavior of ordinary-size objects: The electron's angular momentum must be one of a set of certain special allowed values. During the time when it is in one of these quantized orbits, the electron emits no electromagnetic radiation. The atom radiates a photon when the electron makes a quantum jump from one orbit to a lower one.

Q42.3 If an electron moved like a hockey puck, it could have any arbitrary frequency of revolution around an atomic nucleus. If it behaved like a charge in a radio antenna, it would radiate light with frequency equal to its own frequency of oscillation. Thus, the electron in hydrogen atoms would emit a continuous spectrum, electromagnetic waves of all frequencies smeared together.

Q42.4 (a) Yes—provided that the energy of the photon is *precisely* enough to put the electron into one of the allowed energy states. Strangely—more precisely non-classically—enough, if the energy of the photon is not sufficient to put the electron into a particular excited energy level, the photon will not interact with the atom at all!

(b) Yes—a photon of any energy greater than 13.6 eV will ionize the atom. Any "extra" energy will go into kinetic energy of the newly liberated electron.

Q42.5 An atomic electron does not possess enough kinetic energy to escape from its electrical attraction to the nucleus. Positive ionization energy must be injected to pull the electron out to a very large separation from the nucleus, a condition for which we define the energy of the atom to be zero. The atom is a bound system. All this is summarized by saying that the total energy of an atom is negative.

Q42.6 From Equations 42.7, 42.8 and 42.9, we have $-|E| = -\frac{k_e e^2}{2r} = +\frac{k_e e^2}{2r} - \frac{k_e e^2}{r} = K + U_e$. Then $K = |E|$ and $U_e = -2|E|$.

Q42.7 Bohr modeled the electron as moving in a perfect circle, with zero uncertainity in its radial coordinate. Then its radial velocity is always zero with zero uncertainty. Bohr's theory violates the uncertainty principle by making the uncertainty product $\Delta r \Delta p_r$ be zero, less than the minimum allowable $\frac{\hbar}{2}$.

Q42.8 Fundamentally, three quantum numbers describe an orbital wave function because we live in three-dimensional space. They arise mathematically from boundary conditions on the wave function, expressed as a product of a function of r, a function of θ, and a function of ϕ.

Q42.9 Bohr's theory pictures the electron as moving in a flat circle like a classical particle described by $\sum F = ma$. Schrödinger's theory pictures the electron as a cloud of probability amplitude in the three-dimensional space around the hydrogen nucleus, with its motion described by a wave equation. In the Bohr model, the ground-state angular momentum is $1\hbar$; in the Schrödinger model the ground-state angular momentum is zero. Both models predict that the electron's energy is limited to discrete energy levels, given by $\frac{-13.606 \text{ eV}}{n^2}$ with $n = 1, 2, 3$.

Q42.10 The term *electron cloud* refers to the unpredictable location of an electron around an atomic nucleus. It is a cloud of probability amplitude. An electron in an *s* subshell has a spherically symmetric probability distribution. Electrons in *p*, *d*, and *f* subshells have directionality to their distribution. The shape of these electron clouds influences how atoms form molecules and chemical compounds.

Q42.11 The direction of the magnetic moment due to an orbiting charge is given by the right hand rule, but assumes a *positive* charge. Since the electron is negatively charged, its magnetic moment is in the opposite direction to its angular momentum.

Q42.12 Practically speaking, no. Ions have a net charge and the magnetic force $q(\mathbf{v} \times \mathbf{B})$ would deflect the beam, making it difficult to separate the atoms with different orientations of magnetic moments.

Q42.13 The deflecting force on an atom with a magnetic moment is proportional to the *gradient* of the magnetic field. Thus, atoms with oppositely directed magnetic moments would be deflected in *opposite* directions in an inhomogeneous magnetic field.

Q42.14 If the exclusion principle were not valid, the elements and their chemical behavior would be grossly different because every electron would end up in the lowest energy level of the atom. All matter would be nearly alike in its chemistry and composition, since the shell structures of all elements would be identical. Most materials would have a much higher density. The spectra of atoms and molecules would be very simple, and there would be very little color in the world.

Q42.15 The Stern-Gerlach experiment with hydrogen atoms shows that the component of an electron's spin angular momentum along an applied magnetic field can have only one of two allowed values. So does electron spin resonance on atoms with one unpaired electron.

Q42.16 The three elements have similar electronic configurations. Each has filled inner shells plus one electron in an *s* orbital. Their single outer electrons largely determine their chemical interactions with other atoms.

Q42.17 When a photon interacts with an atom, the atom's orbital angular momentum changes, thus the photon must carry orbital angular momentum. Since the allowed transitions of an atom are restricted to a change in angular momentum of $\Delta\ell = \pm 1$, the photon must have spin 1.

Q42.18 In a neutral helium atom, one electron can be modeled as moving in an electric field created by the nucleus and the other electron. According to Gauss's law, if the electron is above the ground state it moves in the electric field of a net charge of $+2e - 1e = +1e$ We say the nuclear charge is *screened* by the inner electron. The electron in a He^+ ion moves in the field of the unscreened nuclear charge of 2 protons. Then the potential energy function for the electron is about double that of one electron in the neutral atom.

Q42.19 At low density, the gas consists of essentially separate atoms. As the density increases, the atoms interact with each other. This has the effect of giving different atoms levels at slightly different energies, at any one instant. The collection of atoms can then emit photons in lines or bands, narrower or wider, depending on the density.

Q42.20 An atom is a quantum system described by a wave function. The electric force of attraction to the nucleus imposes a constraint on the electrons. The physical constraint implies mathematical boundary conditions on the wave functions, with consequent quantization so that only certain wave functions are allowed to exist. The Schrödinger equation assigns a definite energy to each allowed wave function. Each wave function is spread out in space, describing an electron with no definite position. If you like analogies, think of a classical standing wave on a string fixed at both ends. Its position is spread out to fill the whole string, but its frequency is one of a certain set of quantized values.

Q42.21 Each of the electrons must have at least one quantum number different from the quantum numbers of each of the other electrons. They can differ (in m_s) by being spin-up or spin-down. They can also differ (in ℓ) in angular momentum and in the general shape of the wave function. Those electrons with $\ell = 1$ can differ (in m_ℓ) in orientation of angular momentum—look at Figure Q42.21.

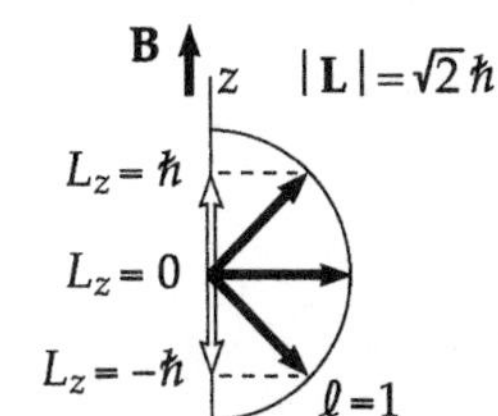

FIG. Q42.21

Q42.22 The Mosely graph shows that the reciprocal square root of the wavelength of K_α characteristic x-rays is a linear function of atomic number. Then measuring this wavelength for a new chemical element reveals its location on the graph, including its atomic number.

Q42.23 No. Laser light is collimated. The energy generally travels in the same direction. The intensity of a laser beam stays remarkably constant, independent of the distance it has traveled.

Q42.24 Stimulated emission coerces atoms to emit photons along a specific axis, rather than in the random directions of spontaneously emitted photons. The photons that are emitted through stimulation can be made to accumulate over time. The fraction allowed to escape constitutes the intense, collimated, and coherent laser beam. If this process relied solely on spontaneous emission, the emitted photons would not exit the laser tube or crystal in the same direction. Neither would they be coherent with one another.

Q42.25 (a) The terms "I define" and "this part of the universe" seem vague, in contrast to the precision of the rest of the statement. But the statement is true in the sense of being experimentally verifiable. The way to test the orientation of the magnetic moment of an electron is to apply a magnetic field to it. When that is done for any electron, it has precisely a 50% chance of being either spin-up or spin-down. Its spin magnetic moment vector must make one of two allowed angles with the applied magnetic field. They are given by $\cos\theta = \frac{S_z}{S} = \frac{1/2}{\sqrt{3}/2}$ and $\cos\theta = \frac{-1/2}{\sqrt{3}/2}$. You can calculate as many digits of the two angles allowed by "space quantization" as you wish.

(b) This statement may be true. There is no reason to suppose that an ant can comprehend the cosmos, and no reason to suppose that a human can comprehend all of it. Our experience with macroscopic objects does not prepare us to understand quantum particles. On the other hand, what seems strange to us now may be the common knowledge of tomorrow. Looking back at the past 150 years of physics, great strides in understanding the Universe—from the quantum to the galactic scale—have been made. Think of trying to explain the photoelectric effect using Newtonian mechanics. What seems strange sometimes just has an underlying structure that has not yet been described fully. On the other hand still, it has been demonstrated that a "hidden-variable" theory, that would model quantum uncertainty as caused by some determinate but fluctuating quantity, cannot agree with experiment.

SOLUTIONS TO PROBLEMS

Section 42.1 **Atomic Spectra of Gases**

P42.1 (a) Lyman series $\frac{1}{\lambda} = R\left(1 - \frac{1}{n_i^2}\right)$ $\quad n_i = 2, 3, 4, \ldots$

$$\frac{1}{\lambda} = \frac{1}{94.96\times 10^{-9}} = \left(1.097\times 10^{7}\right)\left(1 - \frac{1}{n_i^2}\right) \qquad \boxed{n_i = 5}$$

(b) Paschen series: $\frac{1}{\lambda} = R\left(\frac{1}{3^2} - \frac{1}{n_i^2}\right)$ $\quad n_i = 4, 5, 6, \ldots$

The shortest wavelength for this series corresponds to $n_i = \infty$ for ionization

$$\frac{1}{\lambda} = 1.097\times 10^{7}\left(\frac{1}{9} - \frac{1}{n_i^2}\right)$$

For $n_i = \infty$, this gives $\lambda = 820$ nm

This is larger than 94.96 nm, so this wave length $\boxed{\text{cannot be associated with the Paschen series}}$.

Balmer series: $\frac{1}{\lambda} = R\left(\frac{1}{2^2} - \frac{1}{n_i^2}\right)$ $\quad n_i = 3, 4, 5, \ldots$

$$\frac{1}{\lambda} = 1.097\times 10^{7}\left(\frac{1}{4} - \frac{1}{n_i^2}\right)$$ with $n_i = \infty$ for ionization, $\lambda_{\text{min}} = 365$ nm

Once again the shorter given wavelength $\boxed{\text{cannot be associated with the Balmer series}}$.

P42.2 (a) $\lambda_{\min} = \dfrac{hc}{E_{\max}}$

Lyman ($n_f = 1$): $\lambda_{\min} = \dfrac{hc}{|E_1|} = \dfrac{1\,240 \text{ eV}\cdot\text{nm}}{13.6 \text{ eV}} = \boxed{91.2 \text{ nm}}$ (Ultraviolet)

Balmer ($n_f = 2$): $\lambda_{\min} = \dfrac{hc}{|E_2|} = \dfrac{1\,240 \text{ eV}\cdot\text{nm}}{(1/4)13.6 \text{ eV}} = \boxed{365 \text{ nm}}$ (UV)

Paschen ($n_f = 3$): $\lambda_{\min} = \ldots = 3^2(91.2 \text{ nm}) = \boxed{821 \text{ nm}}$ (Infrared)

Bracket ($n_f = 4$): $\lambda_{\min} = \ldots = 4^2(91.2 \text{ nm}) = \boxed{1\,460 \text{ nm}}$ (IR)

(b) $E_{\max} = \dfrac{hc}{\lambda_{\min}}$

Lyman: $E_{\max} = \boxed{13.6 \text{ eV}}\left(= |E_1|\right)$

Balmer: $E_{\max} = \boxed{3.40 \text{ eV}}\left(= |E_2|\right)$

Paschen: $E_{\max} = \boxed{1.51 \text{ eV}}\left(= |E_3|\right)$

Brackett: $E_{\max} = \boxed{0.850 \text{ eV}}\left(= |E_4|\right)$

Section 42.2 Early Models of the Atom

P42.3 (a) For a classical atom, the centripetal acceleration is

$$a = \frac{v^2}{r} = \frac{1}{4\pi \in_0} \frac{e^2}{r^2 m_e}$$

$$E = -\frac{e^2}{4\pi \in_0 r} + \frac{m_e v^2}{2} = -\frac{e^2}{8\pi \in_0 r}$$

so $$\frac{dE}{dt} = \frac{e^2}{8\pi \in_0 r^2}\frac{dr}{dt} = \frac{-1}{6\pi \in_0}\frac{e^2 a^2}{c^3} = \frac{-e^2}{6\pi \in_0 c^3}\left(\frac{e^2}{4\pi \in_0 r^2 m_e}\right)^2.$$

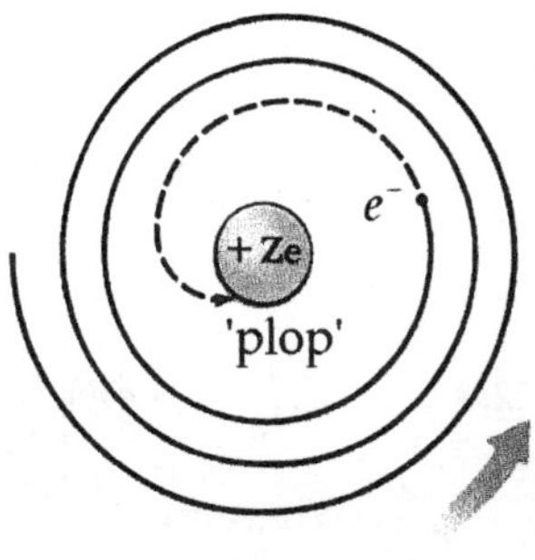

FIG. P42.3

Therefore, $$\frac{dr}{dt} = -\frac{e^4}{12\pi^2 \in_0^2 r^2 m_e^2 c^3}.$$

(b) $$-\int_{2.00\times10^{-10}\text{ m}}^{0} 12\pi^2 \in_0^2 r^2 m_e^2 c^3\, dr = e^4 \int_0^T dt \qquad \frac{12\pi^2 \in_0^2 m_e^2 c^3}{e^4} \left.\frac{r^3}{3}\right|_0^{2.00\times10^{-10}} = T = \boxed{8.46\times10^{-10} \text{ s}}$$

Since atoms last a lot longer than 0.8 ns, the classical laws (fortunately!) do not hold for systems of atomic size.

P42.4 (a) The point of closest approach is found when

$$E = K + U = 0 + \frac{k_e q_\alpha q_{\text{Au}}}{r}$$

or $$r_{\min} = \frac{k_e(2e)(79e)}{E}$$

$$r_{\min} = \frac{\left(8.99\times10^{9}\ \text{N}\cdot\text{m}^2/\text{C}^2\right)(158)\left(1.60\times10^{-19}\ \text{C}\right)^2}{(4.00\ \text{MeV})\left(1.60\times10^{-13}\ \text{J/MeV}\right)} = \boxed{5.68\times10^{-14}\ \text{m}}.$$

(b) The maximum force exerted on the alpha particle is

$$F_{\max} = \frac{k_e q_\alpha q_{\text{Au}}}{r_{\min}^2} = \frac{\left(8.99\times10^{9}\ \text{N}\cdot\text{m}^2/\text{C}^2\right)(158)\left(1.60\times10^{-19}\ \text{C}\right)^2}{\left(5.68\times10^{-14}\ \text{m}\right)^2} = \boxed{11.3\ \text{N}}$$ away from the nucleus.

Section 42.3 Bohr's Model of the Hydrogen Atom

P42.5 (a) $$v_1 = \sqrt{\frac{k_e e^2}{m_e r_1}}$$

where $r_1 = (1)^2 a_0 = 0.005\,29\ \text{nm} = 5.29\times10^{-11}\ \text{m}$

$$v_1 = \sqrt{\frac{\left(8.99\times10^{9}\ \text{N}\cdot\text{m}^2/\text{C}^2\right)\left(1.60\times10^{-19}\ \text{C}\right)^2}{\left(9.11\times10^{-31}\ \text{kg}\right)\left(5.29\times10^{-11}\ \text{m}\right)}} = \boxed{2.19\times10^{6}\ \text{m/s}}$$

(b) $$K_1 = \frac{1}{2}m_e v_1^2 = \frac{1}{2}\left(9.11\times10^{-31}\ \text{kg}\right)\left(2.19\times10^{6}\ \text{m/s}\right)^2 = 2.18\times10^{-18}\ \text{J} = \boxed{13.6\ \text{eV}}$$

(c) $$U_1 = -\frac{k_e e^2}{r_1} = -\frac{\left(8.99\times10^{9}\ \text{N}\cdot\text{m}^2/\text{C}^2\right)\left(1.60\times10^{-19}\ \text{C}\right)^2}{5.29\times10^{-11}\ \text{m}} = -4.35\times10^{-18}\ \text{J} = \boxed{-27.2\ \text{eV}}$$

P42.6 $$\Delta E = (13.6\ \text{eV})\left(\frac{1}{n_i^2} - \frac{1}{n_f^2}\right)$$

Where for $\Delta E > 0$ we have absorption and for $\Delta E < 0$ we have emission.

(i) for $n_i = 2$ and $n_f = 5$, $\Delta E = 2.86\ \text{eV}$ (absorption)

(ii) for $n_i = 5$ and $n_f = 3$, $\Delta E = -0.967\ \text{eV}$ (emission)

(iii) for $n_i = 7$ and $n_f = 4$, $\Delta E = -0.572\ \text{eV}$ (emission)

(iv) for $n_i = 4$ and $n_f = 7$, $\Delta E = 0.572\ \text{eV}$ (absorption)

(a) $E = \dfrac{hc}{\lambda}$ so the shortest wavelength is emitted in transition $\boxed{\text{ii}}$.

(b) The atom gains most energy in transition $\boxed{\text{i}}$.

(c) The atom loses energy in transitions $\boxed{\text{ii and iii}}$.

P42.7 (a) $r_2^2 = (0.052\,9\text{ nm})(2)^2 = \boxed{0.212\text{ nm}}$

(b) $$m_e v_2 = \sqrt{\frac{m_e k_e e^2}{r_2}} = \sqrt{\frac{(9.11\times10^{-31}\text{ kg})(8.99\times10^9\text{ N}\cdot\text{m}^2/\text{C}^2)(1.60\times10^{-19}\text{ C})^2}{0.212\times10^{-9}\text{ m}}}$$

$$m_e v_2 = \boxed{9.95\times10^{-25}\text{ kg}\cdot\text{m/s}}$$

(c) $$L_2 = m_e v_2 r_2 = (9.95\times10^{-25}\text{ kg}\cdot\text{m/s})(0.212\times10^{-9}\text{ m}) = \boxed{2.11\times10^{-34}\text{ kg}\cdot\text{m}^2/\text{s}}$$

(d) $$K_2 = \frac{1}{2}m_e v_2^2 = \frac{(m_e v_2)^2}{2m_e} = \frac{(9.95\times10^{-25}\text{ kg}\cdot\text{m/s})^2}{2(9.11\times10^{-31}\text{ kg})} = 5.43\times10^{-19}\text{ J} = \boxed{3.40\text{ eV}}$$

(e) $$U_2 = -\frac{k_e e^2}{r_2} = -\frac{(8.99\times10^9\text{ N}\cdot\text{m}^2/\text{C}^2)(1.60\times10^{-19}\text{ C})^2}{0.212\times10^{-9}\text{ m}} = -1.09\times10^{-18}\text{ J} = \boxed{-6.80\text{ eV}}$$

(f) $$E_2 = K_2 + U_2 = 3.40\text{ eV} - 6.80\text{ eV} = \boxed{-3.40\text{ eV}}$$

P42.8 We use $$E_n = \frac{-13.6\text{ eV}}{n^2}.$$

To ionize the atom when the electron is in the nth level,

it is necessary to add an amount of energy given by $$E = -E_n = \frac{13.6\text{ eV}}{n^2}.$$

(a) Thus, in the ground state where $n = 1$, we have $\boxed{E = 13.6\text{ eV}}$.

(b) In the $n = 3$ level, $$E = \frac{13.6\text{ eV}}{9} = \boxed{1.51\text{ eV}}.$$

P42.9 (b) $$\frac{1}{\lambda} = R\left(\frac{1}{n_f^2} - \frac{1}{n_i^2}\right) = (1.097\times10^7\text{ m}^{-1})\left(\frac{1}{2^2} - \frac{1}{6^2}\right) \text{ so } \boxed{\lambda = 410\text{ nm}}$$

(a) $$E = \frac{hc}{\lambda} = \frac{(6.626\times10^{-34}\text{ J}\cdot\text{s})(3.00\times10^8\text{ m/s})}{410\times10^{-9}\text{ m}} = 4.85\times10^{-19}\text{ J} = \boxed{3.03\text{ eV}}$$

(c) $$f = \frac{c}{\lambda} = \frac{3.00\times10^8}{410\times10^{-9}} = \boxed{7.32\times10^{14}\text{ Hz}}$$

P42.10 Starting with $\frac{1}{2}m_e v^2 = \frac{k_e e^2}{2r}$

we have $v^2 = \frac{k_e e^2}{m_e r}$

and using $r_n = \frac{n^2\hbar^2}{m_e k_e e^2}$

gives $v_n^2 = \frac{k_e e^2}{m_e\left(n^2\hbar^2/m_e k_e e^2\right)}$

or $v_n = \frac{k_e e^2}{n\hbar}$.

P42.11 Each atom gives up its kinetic energy in emitting a photon,

so $\frac{1}{2}mv^2 = \frac{hc}{\lambda} = \frac{\left(6.626\times10^{-34}\text{ J}\cdot\text{s}\right)\left(3.00\times10^{8}\text{ m/s}\right)}{\left(1.216\times10^{-7}\text{ m}\right)} = 1.63\times10^{-18}\text{ J}$

$v = \boxed{4.42\times10^{4}\text{ m/s}}$.

P42.12 The batch of excited atoms must make these six transitions to get back to state one: $2\rightarrow1$, and also $3\rightarrow2$ and $3\rightarrow1$, and also $4\rightarrow3$ and $4\rightarrow2$ and $4\rightarrow1$. Thus, the incoming light must have just enough energy to produce the $1\rightarrow4$ transition. It must be the third line of the Lyman series in the absorption spectrum of hydrogen. The absorbing atom changes from energy

$E_i = -\frac{13.6\text{ eV}}{1^2} = -13.6\text{ eV}$ to $E_f = -\frac{13.6\text{ eV}}{4^2} = -0.850\text{ eV}$,

so the incoming photons have wavelength

$$\lambda = \frac{hc}{E_f - E_i} = \frac{\left(6.626\times10^{-34}\text{ J}\cdot\text{s}\right)\left(3.00\times10^{8}\text{ m/s}\right)}{-0.850\text{ eV} - (-13.6\text{ eV})}\left(\frac{1.00\text{ eV}}{1.60\times10^{-19}\text{ J}}\right) = 9.75\times10^{-8}\text{ m} = \boxed{97.5\text{ nm}}.$$

P42.13 (a) The energy levels of a hydrogen-like ion whose charge number is Z are given by

$$E_n = (-13.6\text{ eV})\frac{Z^2}{n^2}.$$

Thus for Helium ($Z = 2$), the energy levels are

$$\boxed{E_n = -\frac{54.4\text{ eV}}{n^2} \quad n = 1, 2, 3, \ldots}.$$

(b) For He^+, $Z = 2$, so we see that the ionization energy (the energy required to take the electron from the $n = 1$ to the $n = \infty$ state) is

$$E = E_\infty - E_1 = 0 - \frac{(-13.6\text{ eV})(2)^2}{(1)^2} = \boxed{54.4\text{ eV}}.$$

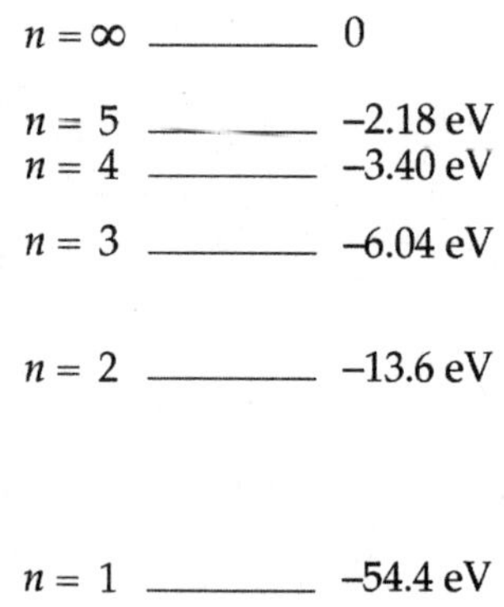

$n = \infty$	0
$n = 5$	–2.18 eV
$n = 4$	–3.40 eV
$n = 3$	–6.04 eV
$n = 2$	–13.6 eV
$n = 1$	–54.4 eV

FIG. P42.13

***P42.14** (a) $\frac{1}{\lambda}=Z^2R_H\left(\frac{1}{n_f^2}-\frac{1}{n_i^2}\right)$. The shortest wavelength, λ_s, corresponds to $n_i=\infty$, and the longest wavelength, λ_ℓ, to $n_i=n_f+1$.

$$\frac{1}{\lambda_s}=\frac{Z^2R_H}{n_f^2} \qquad (1)$$

$$\frac{1}{\lambda_\ell}=Z^2R_H\left[\frac{1}{n_f^2}-\frac{1}{(n_f+1)^2}\right]=\frac{Z^2R_H}{n_f^2}\left[1-\left(\frac{n_f}{n_f+1}\right)^2\right] \qquad (2)$$

Divide (1) and (2): $\frac{\lambda_s}{\lambda_\ell}=1-\left(\frac{n_f}{n_f+1}\right)^2$

$$\therefore\frac{n_f}{n_f+1}=\sqrt{1-\frac{\lambda_s}{\lambda_\ell}}=\sqrt{1-\frac{22.8\text{ nm}}{63.3\text{ nm}}}=0.800 \qquad \therefore n_f=4$$

From (1): $Z=\sqrt{\frac{n_f^2}{\lambda_sR_H}}=\sqrt{\frac{4^2}{(22.8\times10^{-9}\text{ m})(1.097\times10^7\text{ m}^{-1})}}=8.00$.

Hence $\boxed{\text{the ion is } O^{7+}}$.

(b) $$\lambda=\left\{(7.0208\times10^8\text{ m}^{-1})\left[\frac{1}{4^2}-\frac{1}{(4+k)^2}\right]\right\}^{-1},\ k=1,2,3,\ldots$$

Setting $k=2, 3, 4$ gives $\lambda=\boxed{41.0\text{ nm}, 33.8\text{ nm}, 30.4\text{ nm}}$.

P42.15 (a) The speed of the moon in its orbit is $v=\frac{2\pi r}{T}=\frac{2\pi(3.84\times10^8\text{ m})}{2.36\times10^6\text{ s}}=1.02\times10^3\text{ m/s}$.

So, $$L=mvr=(7.36\times10^{22}\text{ kg})(1.02\times10^3\text{ m/s})(3.84\times10^8\text{ m})=\boxed{2.89\times10^{34}\text{ kg}\cdot\text{m}^2/\text{s}}.$$

(b) We have $L=n\hbar$

or $$n=\frac{L}{\hbar}=\frac{2.89\times10^{34}\text{ kg}\cdot\text{m}^2/\text{s}}{1.055\times10^{-34}\text{ J}\cdot\text{s}}=\boxed{2.74\times10^{68}}.$$

(c) We have $n\hbar=L=mvr=m\left(\frac{GM_e}{r}\right)^{1/2}r$,

so $$r=\frac{\hbar^2}{m^2GM_e}n^2=Rn^2 \text{ and } \frac{\Delta r}{r}=\frac{(n+1)^2R-n^2R}{n^2R}=\frac{2n+1}{n^2}$$

which is approximately equal to $\frac{2}{n}=\boxed{7.30\times10^{-69}}$.

Section 42.4 The Quantum Model of the Hydrogen Atom

P42.16 The reduced mass of positronium is **less** than hydrogen, so the photon energy will be **less** for positronium than for hydrogen. This means that the wavelength of the emitted photon will be **longer** than 656.3 nm. On the other hand, helium has about the same reduced mass but more charge than hydrogen, so its transition energy will be **larger**, corresponding to a wavelength **shorter** than 656.3 nm.

All the factors in the given equation are constant for this problem except for the reduced mass and the nuclear charge. Therefore, the wavelength corresponding to the energy difference for the transition can be found simply from the ratio of mass and charge variables.

For hydrogen, $\mu = \dfrac{m_p m_e}{m_p + m_e} \approx m_e$. The photon energy is $\Delta E = E_3 - E_2$.

Its wavelength is $\lambda = 656.3$ nm, where $\lambda = \dfrac{c}{f} = \dfrac{hc}{\Delta E}$.

(a) For positronium, $\mu = \dfrac{m_e m_e}{m_e + m_e} = \dfrac{m_e}{2}$

so the energy of each level is one half as large as in hydrogen, which we could call "protonium". The photon energy is inversely proportional to its wavelength , so for positronium,

$$\lambda_{32} = 2(656.3 \text{ nm}) = \boxed{1.31\ \mu\text{m}} \text{ (in the infrared region).}$$

(b) For He^+, $\mu \approx m_e$, $q_1 = e$, and $q_2 = 2e$,

so the transition energy is $2^2 = 4$ times larger than hydrogen.

Then, $\lambda_{32} = \left(\dfrac{656}{4}\right) \text{nm} = \boxed{164 \text{ nm}}$ (in the ultraviolet region).

P42.17 (a) $\Delta x \Delta p \geq \dfrac{\hbar}{2}$ so if $\Delta x = r$, $\Delta p \geq \boxed{\dfrac{\hbar}{2r}}$.

(b) Choosing $\Delta p \approx \dfrac{\hbar}{r}$, $K = \dfrac{p^2}{2m_e} \approx \dfrac{(\Delta p)^2}{2m_e} = \boxed{\dfrac{\hbar^2}{2m_e r^2}}$

$U = \dfrac{-k_e e^2}{r}$, so $E = K + U \approx \boxed{\dfrac{\hbar^2}{2m_e r^2} - \dfrac{k_e e^2}{r}}$.

(c) To minimize E,

$$\frac{dE}{dr} = -\frac{\hbar^2}{m_e r^3} + \frac{k_e e^2}{r^2} = 0 \rightarrow r = \boxed{\frac{\hbar^2}{m_e k_e e^2} = a_0} \text{ (the Bohr radius).}$$

$$\text{Then, } E = \frac{\hbar^2}{2m_e}\left(\frac{m_e k_e e^2}{\hbar^2}\right)^2 - k_e e^2\left(\frac{m_e k_e e^2}{\hbar^2}\right) = -\frac{m_e k_e^2 e^4}{2\hbar^2} = \boxed{-13.6 \text{ eV}}.$$

Section 42.5 The Wave Functions of Hydrogen

P42.18 $\psi_{1s}(r)=\dfrac{1}{\sqrt{\pi a_0^3}}e^{-r/a_0}$ (Eq. 42.22)

$P_{1s}(r)=\dfrac{4r^2}{a_0^3}e^{-2r/a_0}$ (Eq. 42.25)

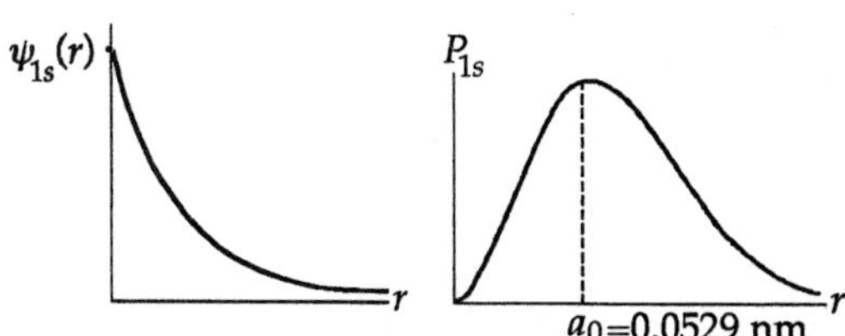

FIG. P42.18

P42.19 (a) $\int|\psi|^2 dV=4\pi\int_0^\infty|\psi|^2 r^2 dr=4\pi\left(\dfrac{1}{\pi a_0^3}\right)\int_0^\infty r^2 e^{-2r/a_0}dr$

Using integral tables, $\int|\psi|^2 dV=-\dfrac{2}{a_0^2}\left[e^{-2r/a_0}\left(r^2+a_0 r+\dfrac{a_0^2}{2}\right)\right]_0^\infty=\left(-\dfrac{2}{a_0^2}\right)\left(-\dfrac{a_0^2}{2}\right)=\boxed{1}$

so the wave function as given is normalized.

(b) $P_{a_0\,2\to 3a_0\,2}=4\pi\int_{a_0/2}^{3a_0/2}|\psi|^2 r^2 dr=4\pi\left(\dfrac{1}{\pi a_0^3}\right)\int_{a_0/2}^{3a_0/2}r^2 e^{-2r/a_0}dr$

Again, using integral tables,

$$P_{a_0\,2\to 3a_0\,2}=-\frac{2}{a_0^2}\left[e^{-2r/a_0}\left(r^2+a_0 r+\frac{a_0^2}{2}\right)\right]_{a_0/2}^{3a_0/2}=-\frac{2}{a_0^2}\left[e^{-3}\left(\frac{17a_0^2}{4}\right)-e^{-1}\left(\frac{5a_0^2}{4}\right)\right]=\boxed{0.497}.$$

P42.20 $\psi=\dfrac{1}{\sqrt{3}}\dfrac{1}{(2a_0)^{3/2}}\dfrac{r}{a_0}e^{-r/2a_0}$

so $P_r=4\pi r^2\left|\psi^2\right|=4\pi r^2\dfrac{r^2}{24a_0^5}e^{-r/a_0}.$

Set $\dfrac{dP}{dr}=\dfrac{4\pi}{24a_0^5}\left[4r^3e^{-r/a_0}+r^4\left(-\dfrac{1}{a_0}\right)e^{-r/a_0}\right]=0.$

Solving for r, this is a maximum at $\boxed{r=4a_0}$.

P42.21 $\psi=\dfrac{1}{\sqrt{\pi a_0^3}}e^{-r/a_0}$ $\qquad \dfrac{2}{r}\dfrac{d\psi}{dr}=\dfrac{-2}{r\sqrt{\pi a_0^5}}e^{-r/a_0}=-\dfrac{2}{ra_0}\psi$

$\dfrac{d^2\psi}{dr^2}=\dfrac{1}{\sqrt{\pi a_0^7}}e^{-r/a_0}=\dfrac{1}{a_0^2}\psi$ $\qquad -\dfrac{\hbar^2}{2m_e}\left(\dfrac{1}{a_0^2}-\dfrac{2}{ra_0}\right)\psi-\dfrac{e^2}{4\pi\epsilon_0 r}\psi=E\psi$

But $a_0=\dfrac{\hbar^2(4\pi\epsilon_0)}{m_e e^2}$

so $-\dfrac{e^2}{8\pi\epsilon_0 a_0}=E$

or $\boxed{E=-\dfrac{k_e e^2}{2a_0}}$.

This is true, so the Schrödinger equation is satisfied.

P42.22 The hydrogen ground-state radial probability density is

$$P(r)=4\pi r^2\left|\psi_{1s}\right|^2=\frac{4r^2}{a_0^3}\exp\left(-\frac{2r}{a_0}\right).$$

The number of observations at $2a_0$ is, by proportion

$$N=1\,000\frac{P(2a_0)}{P(a_0/2)}=1\,000\frac{(2a_0)^2}{(a_0/2)^2}\frac{e^{-4a_0/a_0}}{e^{-a_0/a_0}}=1\,000(16)e^{-3}=\boxed{797\text{ times}}.$$

Section 42.6 **Physical Interpretation of the Quantum Numbers**

Note: Problems 17 and 25 in Chapter 29 and Problem 68 in Chapter 30 can be assigned with this section.

P42.23 (a) In the $3d$ subshell, $n=3$ and $\ell=2$,

we have										
n	3	3	3	3	3	3	3	3	3	3
ℓ	2	2	2	2	2	2	2	2	2	2
m_ℓ	+2	+2	+1	+1	0	0	–1	–1	–2	–2
m_s	+1/2	–1/2	+1/2	–1/2	+1/2	–1/2	+1/2	–1/2	+1/2	–1/2

(A total of 10 states)

(b) In the $3p$ subshell, $n=3$ and $\ell=1$,

we have						
n	3	3	3	3	3	3
ℓ	1	1	1	1	1	1
m_ℓ	+1	+1	+0	+0	–1	–1
m_s	+1/2	–1/2	+1/2	–1/2	+1/2	–1/2

(A total of 6 states)

P42.24 (a) For the d state, $\ell=2$, $L=\boxed{\sqrt{6}\hbar}=2.58\times10^{-34}\text{ J}\cdot\text{s}$.

(b) For the f state, $\ell=3$, $L=\sqrt{\ell(\ell+1)}\hbar=\boxed{\sqrt{12}\hbar}=3.65\times10^{-34}\text{ J}\cdot\text{s}$.

P42.25 $L=\sqrt{\ell(\ell+1)}\hbar$: $4.714\times10^{-34}=\sqrt{\ell(\ell+1)}\left(\dfrac{6.626\times10^{-34}}{2\pi}\right)$

$$\ell(\ell+1)=\frac{\left(4.714\times10^{-4}\right)^2(2\pi)^2}{\left(6.626\times10^{-34}\right)^2}=1.998\times10^1\approx20=4(4+1)$$

so $\boxed{\ell=4}$.

P42.26 The 5th excited state has $n = 6$, energy $\frac{-13.6 \text{ eV}}{36} = -0.378 \text{ eV}$.

The atom loses this much energy: $\frac{hc}{\lambda} = \frac{(6.626 \times 10^{-34} \text{ J}\cdot\text{s})(3.00 \times 10^{8} \text{ m/s})}{(1\,090 \times 10^{-9} \text{ m})(1.60 \times 10^{-19} \text{ J/eV})} = 1.14 \text{ eV}$

to end up with energy $-0.378 \text{ eV} - 1.14 \text{ eV} = -1.52 \text{ eV}$

which is the energy in state 3: $-\frac{13.6 \text{ eV}}{3^3} = -1.51 \text{ eV}$.

While $n = 3$, ℓ can be as large as 2, giving angular momentum $\sqrt{\ell(\ell+1)}\hbar = \boxed{\sqrt{6}\hbar}$.

P42.27 (a) $n = 1$: For $n = 1$, $\ell = 0$, $m_\ell = 0$, $m_s = \pm\frac{1}{2}$

n	ℓ	m_ℓ	m_s
1	0	0	−1/2
1	0	0	+1/2

Yields 2 sets; $2n^2 = 2(1)^2 = \boxed{2}$

(b) $n = 2$: For $n = 2$,

we have

n	ℓ	m_ℓ	m_s
2	0	0	±1/2
2	1	−1	±1/2
2	1	0	±1/2
2	1	1	±1/2

yields 8 sets; $2n^2 = 2(2)^2 = \boxed{8}$

Note that the number is twice the number of m_ℓ values. Also, for each ℓ there are $(2\ell+1)$ different m_ℓ values. Finally, ℓ can take on values ranging from 0 to $n-1$.

So the general expression is $\text{number} = \sum_{0}^{n-1} 2(2\ell+1)$.

The series is an arithmetic progression: $2 + 6 + 10 + 14\ldots$

the sum of which is $\text{number} = \frac{n}{2}[2a + (n-1)d]$

where $a = 2$, $d = 4$: $\text{number} = \frac{n}{2}[4 + (n-1)4] = 2n^2$.

(c) $n = 3$: $2(1) + 2(3) + 2(5) = 2 + 6 + 10 = 18$ $2n^2 = 2(3)^2 = \boxed{18}$

(d) $n = 4$: $2(1) + 2(3) + 2(5) + 2(7) = 32$ $2n^2 = 2(4)^2 = \boxed{32}$

(e) $n = 5$: $32 + 2(9) = 32 + 18 = 50$ $2n^2 = 2(5)^2 = \boxed{50}$

P42.28 For a 3*d* state, $n=3$ and $\ell=2$.

Therefore, $L=\sqrt{\ell(\ell+1)}\hbar=\boxed{\sqrt{6}\hbar}=2.58\times10^{-34}\text{ J}\cdot\text{s}$

m_ℓ can have the values $-2, -1, 0, 1$, and 2

so $\boxed{L_z \text{ can have the values } -2\hbar,\ -\hbar,\ 0,\ \hbar \text{ and } 2\hbar}$.

Using the relation $\cos\theta=\dfrac{L_z}{L}$

we find the possible values of θ $\boxed{145°,\ 114°,\ 90.0°,\ 65.9°, \text{ and } 35.3°}$.

P42.29 (a) Density of a proton: $\rho=\dfrac{m}{V}=\dfrac{1.67\times10^{-27}\text{ kg}}{(4/3)\pi\left(1.00\times10^{-15}\text{ m}\right)^3}=\boxed{3.99\times10^{17}\text{ kg/m}^3}$.

(b) Size of model electron: $r=\left(\dfrac{3m}{4\pi\rho}\right)^{1/3}=\left(\dfrac{3\left(9.11\times10^{-31}\text{ kg}\right)}{4\pi\left(3.99\times10^{17}\text{ kg/m}^3\right)}\right)^{1/3}=\boxed{8.17\times10^{-17}\text{ m}}$.

(c) Moment of inertia: $I=\dfrac{2}{5}mr^2=\dfrac{2}{5}\left(9.11\times10^{-31}\text{ kg}\right)\left(8.17\times10^{-17}\text{ m}\right)^2=2.43\times10^{-63}\text{ kg}\cdot\text{m}^2$

$$L_z=I\omega=\frac{\hbar}{2}=\frac{Iv}{r}.$$

Therefore, $v=\dfrac{\hbar r}{2I}=\dfrac{\left(6.626\times10^{-34}\text{ J}\cdot\text{s}\right)\left(8.17\times10^{-17}\text{ m}\right)}{2\pi\left(2\times2.43\times10^{-63}\text{ kg}\cdot\text{m}^2\right)}=\boxed{1.77\times10^{12}\text{ m/s}}$.

(d) This is $\boxed{5.91\times10^3 \text{ times larger}}$ than the speed of light.

P42.30 In the N shell, $n=4$. For $n=4$, ℓ can take on values of 0, 1, 2, and 3. For each value of ℓ, m_ℓ can be $-\ell$ to ℓ in integral steps. Thus, the maximum value for m_ℓ is 3. Since $L_z=m_\ell\hbar$, the maximum value for L_z is $L_z=\boxed{3\hbar}$.

P42.31 The 3*d* subshell has $\ell=2$, and $n=3$. Also, we have $s=1$.

Therefore, we can have $\boxed{n=3,\ \ell=2;\ m_\ell=-2,\ -1,\ 0,\ 1,\ 2;\ s=1; \text{ and } m_s=-1,\ 0,\ 1}$

leading to the following table:

n	3	3	3	3	3	3	3	3	3	3	3	3	3	3	3
ℓ	2	2	2	2	2	2	2	2	2	2	2	2	2	2	2
m_ℓ	–2	–2	–2	–1	–1	–1	0	0	0	1	1	1	2	2	2
s	1	1	1	1	1	1	1	1	1	1	1	1	1	1	1
m_s	–1	0	1	–1	0	1	–1	0	1	–1	0	1	–1	0	1

Section 42.7 **The Exclusion Principle and the Periodic Table**

P42.32 (a) $\boxed{1s^2 2s^2 2p^4}$

(b) For the 1s electrons, $n = 1$, $\ell = 0$, $m_\ell = 0$, $m_s = +\frac{1}{2}$ and $-\frac{1}{2}$.

For the two 2s electrons, $n = 2$, $\ell = 0$, $m_\ell = 0$, $m_s = +\frac{1}{2}$ and $-\frac{1}{2}$.

For the four 2p electrons, $n = 2$; $\ell = 1$; $m_\ell = -1, 0$, or 1; and $m_s = +\frac{1}{2}$ or $-\frac{1}{2}$.

P42.33 The $\boxed{\text{4s subshell fills first}}$, for potassium and calcium, before the 3*d* subshell starts to fill for scandium through zinc. Thus, we would first suppose that $[\text{Ar}]3d^4 4s^2$ would have lower energy than $[\text{Ar}]3d^5 4s^1$. But the latter has more unpaired spins, six instead of four, and Hund's rule suggests that this could give the latter configuration lower energy. In fact it must, for $[\text{Ar}]3d^5 4s^1$ is the ground state for chromium.

P42.34 Electronic configuration: Sodium to Argon

$[1s^2 2s^2 2p^6]$	$+3s^1$	$\rightarrow$	Na^{11}
	$+3s^2$	$\rightarrow$	Mg^{12}
	$+3s^2 3p^1$	$\rightarrow$	Al^{13}
	$+3s^2 3p^2$	$\rightarrow$	Si^{14}
	$+3s^2 3p^3$	$\rightarrow$	P^{15}
	$+3s^2 3p^4$	$\rightarrow$	S^{16}
	$+3s^2 3p^5$	$\rightarrow$	Cl^{17}
	$+3s^2 3p^6$	$\rightarrow$	Ar^{18}
$[1s^2 2s^2 2p^6 3s^2 3p^6]4s^1$		$\rightarrow$	K^{19}

***P42.35** In the table of electronic configurations in the text, or on a periodic table, we look for the element whose last electron is in a 3*p* state and which has three electrons outside a closed shell. Its electron configuration then ends in $3s^2 3p^1$. The element is $\boxed{\text{aluminum}}$.

P42.36 (a) For electron one and also for electron two, $n = 3$ and $\ell = 1$. The possible states are listed here in columns giving the other quantum numbers:

electron	m_ℓ	1	1	1	1	1	1	1	1	1	1	0	0	0	0	0
one	m_s	$\frac{1}{2}$	$\frac{1}{2}$	$\frac{1}{2}$	$\frac{1}{2}$	$\frac{1}{2}$	$-\frac{1}{2}$	$-\frac{1}{2}$	$-\frac{1}{2}$	$-\frac{1}{2}$	$-\frac{1}{2}$	$\frac{1}{2}$	$\frac{1}{2}$	$\frac{1}{2}$	$\frac{1}{2}$	$\frac{1}{2}$
electron	m_ℓ	1	0	0	–1	–1	1	0	0	–1	–1	1	1	0	–1	–1
two	m_s	$-\frac{1}{2}$	$\frac{1}{2}$	$-\frac{1}{2}$	$\frac{1}{2}$	$-\frac{1}{2}$	$\frac{1}{2}$	$\frac{1}{2}$	$-\frac{1}{2}$	$\frac{1}{2}$	$-\frac{1}{2}$	$\frac{1}{2}$	$-\frac{1}{2}$	$-\frac{1}{2}$	$\frac{1}{2}$	$-\frac{1}{2}$
electron	m_ℓ	0	0	0	0	0	–1	–1	–1	–1	–1	–1	–1	–1	–1	–1
one	m_s	$-\frac{1}{2}$	$-\frac{1}{2}$	$-\frac{1}{2}$	$-\frac{1}{2}$	$-\frac{1}{2}$	$\frac{1}{2}$	$\frac{1}{2}$	$\frac{1}{2}$	$\frac{1}{2}$	$\frac{1}{2}$	$-\frac{1}{2}$	$-\frac{1}{2}$	$-\frac{1}{2}$	$-\frac{1}{2}$	$-\frac{1}{2}$
electron	m_ℓ	1	1	0	–1	–1	1	1	0	0	–1	1	1	0	0	–1
two	m_s	$\frac{1}{2}$	$-\frac{1}{2}$	$\frac{1}{2}$	$\frac{1}{2}$	$-\frac{1}{2}$	$\frac{1}{2}$	$-\frac{1}{2}$	$\frac{1}{2}$	$-\frac{1}{2}$	$-\frac{1}{2}$	$\frac{1}{2}$	$-\frac{1}{2}$	$\frac{1}{2}$	$-\frac{1}{2}$	$\frac{1}{2}$

There are thirty allowed states, since electron one can have any of three possible values for m_ℓ for both spin up and spin down, amounting to six states, and the second electron can have any of the other five states.

(b) Were it not for the exclusion principle, there would be $\boxed{36}$ possible states, six for each electron independently.

P42.37 (a)

$n+\ell$	1	2	3	4	5	6	7
subshell	1s	2s	$2p$, 3s	$3p$, 4s	$3d$, $4p$, 5s	$4d$, $5p$, 6s	$4f$, $5d$, $6p$, $7s$

(b) $Z = 15$:

Filled subshells:	$1s$, $2s$, $2p$, $3s$ (12 electrons)
Valence subshell:	3 electrons in $3p$ subshell
Prediction:	Valence $= +3$ or -5
Element is phosphorus,	Valence $= +3$ or -5 (Prediction correct)

$Z = 47$:

Filled subshells:	$1s$, $2s$, $2p$, $3s$, $3p$, $4s$, $3d$, $4p$, $5s$ (38 electrons)
Outer subshell:	9 electrons in $4d$ subshell
Prediction:	Valence $= -1$
Element is silver,	(Prediction fails) Valence is +1

$Z = 86$:

Filled subshells:	$1s$, $2s$, $2p$, $3s$, $3p$, $4s$, $3d$, $4p$, $5s$, $4d$, $5p$, $6s$, $4f$, $5d$, $6p$ (86 electrons)
Prediction	Outer subshell is full: inert gas
Element is radon, inert	(Prediction correct)

P42.38 Listing subshells in the order of filling, we have for element 110,

$1s^2 2s^2 2p^6 3s^2 3p^6 4s^2 3d^{10} 4p^6 5s^2 4d^{10} 5p^6 6s^2 4f^{14} 5d^{10} 6p^6 7s^2 5f^{14} 6d^8$.

In order of increasing principal quantum number, this is

$$\boxed{1s^2 2s^2 2p^6 3s^2 3p^6 3d^{10} 4s^2 4p^6 4d^{10} 4f^{14} 5s^2 5p^6 5d^{10} 5f^{14} 6s^2 6p^6 6d^8 7s^2}.$$

***P42.39** In the ground state of sodium, the outermost electron is in an *s* state. This state is spherically symmetric, so it generates no magnetic field by orbital motion, and has the same energy no matter whether the electron is spin-up or spin-down. The energies of the states $3p\uparrow$ and $3p\downarrow$ above 3*s* are $hf_1 = \frac{hc}{\lambda}$ and $hf_2 = \frac{hc}{\lambda_2}$.

The energy difference is

$$2\mu_B B = hc\left(\frac{1}{\lambda_1} - \frac{1}{\lambda_2}\right)$$

so $$B = \frac{hc}{2\mu_B}\left(\frac{1}{\lambda_1} - \frac{1}{\lambda_2}\right) = \frac{(6.63\times10^{-34}\text{ J}\cdot\text{s})(3\times10^{8}\text{ m/s})}{2(9.27\times10^{-24}\text{ J/T})}\left(\frac{1}{588.995\times10^{-9}\text{ m}} - \frac{1}{589.592\times10^{-9}\text{ m}}\right)$$

$$B = \boxed{18.4\text{ T}}.$$

Section 42.8 **More on Atomic Spectra: Visible and X-ray**

P42.40 (a) $\boxed{n=3,\ \ell=0,\ m_\ell=0}$

$\boxed{n=3,\ \ell=1,\ m_\ell=-1,\ 0,\ 1}$

For $\boxed{n=3,\ \ell=2,\ m_\ell=-2,\ -1,\ 0,\ 1,\ 2}$

(b) ψ_{300} corresponds to $E_{300} = -\frac{Z^2E_0}{n^2} = -\frac{2^2(13.6)}{3^2} = \boxed{-6.05\text{ eV}}$.

ψ_{31-1}, ψ_{310}, ψ_{311} have the same energy since *n* is the same.

ψ_{32-2}, ψ_{32-1}, ψ_{320}, ψ_{321}, ψ_{322} have the same energy since *n* is the same.

All states are degenerate.

P42.41 $E = \frac{hc}{\lambda} = e\Delta V$: $$\frac{(6.626\times10^{-34}\text{ J}\cdot\text{s})(3.00\times10^{8}\text{ m/s})}{(10.0\times10^{-9}\text{ m})} = (1.60\times10^{-19})\Delta V$$

$$\Delta V = \boxed{124\text{ V}}$$

P42.42 Some electrons can give all their kinetic energy $K_e = e\Delta V$ to the creation of a single photon of x-radiation, with

$$hf = \frac{hc}{\lambda} = e\Delta V$$

$$\lambda = \frac{hc}{e\Delta V} = \frac{(6.626\,1\times10^{-34}\text{ J}\cdot\text{s})(2.997\,9\times10^{8}\text{ m/s})}{(1.602\,2\times10^{-19}\text{ C})\Delta V} = \boxed{\frac{1\,240\text{ nm}\cdot\text{V}}{\Delta V}}$$

P42.43 Following Example 42.9 $E_\gamma = \frac{3}{4}(42-1)^2(13.6\text{ eV}) = 1.71\times10^4\text{ eV} = 2.74\times10^{-15}\text{ J}$

$f = 4.14\times10^{18}\text{ Hz}$

and $\lambda = \boxed{0.072\,5\text{ nm}}$.

P42.44 $E = \frac{hc}{\lambda} = \frac{1\,240\text{ eV}\cdot\text{nm}}{\lambda} = \frac{1.240\text{ keV}\cdot\text{nm}}{\lambda}$

For $\lambda_1 = 0.018\,5\text{ nm}$, $E = 67.11\text{ keV}$

$\lambda_2 = 0.020\,9\text{ nm}$, $E = 59.4\text{ keV}$

$\lambda_3 = 0.021\,5\text{ nm}$, $E = 57.7\text{ keV}$

FIG. P42.44

The ionization energy for the K shell is 69.5 keV, so the ionization energies for the other shells are:

$\boxed{\text{L shell} = 11.8\text{ keV}}$ $\boxed{\text{M shell} = 10.1\text{ keV}}$ $\boxed{\text{N shell} = 2.39\text{ keV}}$.

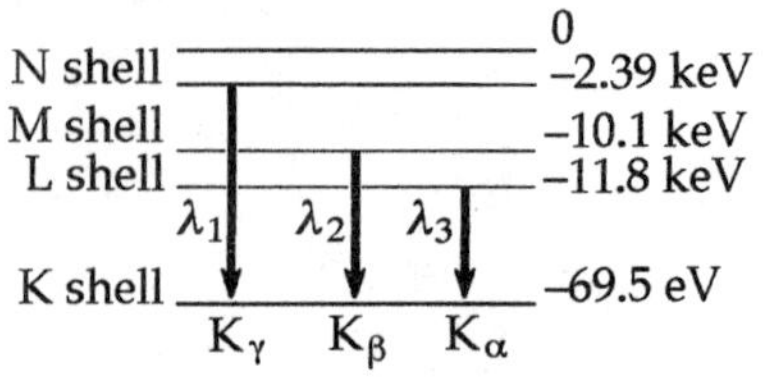

P42.45 The K_β x-rays are emitted when there is a vacancy in the ($n = 1$) K shell and an electron from the ($n = 3$) M shell falls down to fill it. Then this electron is shielded by nine electrons originally and by one in its final state.

$$\frac{hc}{\lambda} = -\frac{13.6(Z-9)^2}{3^2}\text{ eV} + \frac{13.6(Z-1)^2}{1^2}\text{ eV}$$

$$\frac{(6.626\times10^{-34}\text{ J}\cdot\text{s})(3.00\times10^8\text{ m/s})}{(0.152\times10^{-9}\text{ m})(1.60\times10^{-19}\text{ J/eV})} = (13.6\text{ eV})\left(-\frac{Z^2}{9} + \frac{18Z}{9} - \frac{81}{9} + Z^2 - 2Z + 1\right)$$

$$8.17\times10^3\text{ eV} = (13.6\text{ eV})\left(\frac{8Z^2}{9} - 8\right)$$

so $601 = \frac{8Z^2}{9} - 8$

and $Z = 26$ $\boxed{\text{Iron}}$.

Section 42.9 **Spontaneous and Stimulated Transitions**

Section 42.10 **Lasers**

P42.46 The photon energy is $E_4 - E_3 = (20.66 - 18.70)\text{ eV} = 1.96\text{ eV} = \frac{hc}{\lambda}$

$$\lambda = \frac{(6.626\times10^{-34}\text{ J}\cdot\text{s})(3.00\times10^8\text{ m/s})}{1.96(1.60\times10^{-19}\text{ J})} = \boxed{633\text{ nm}}.$$

P42.47 $f = \frac{E}{h} = \frac{0.117\text{ eV}}{6.630\times10^{-34}\text{ J}\cdot\text{s}}\left(\frac{1.60\times10^{-19}\text{ C}}{e}\right)\left(\frac{1\text{ J}}{1\text{ V}\cdot\text{C}}\right) = \boxed{2.82\times10^{13}\text{ s}^{-1}}$

$\lambda = \frac{c}{f} = \frac{3.00\times10^8\text{ m/s}}{2.82\times10^{13}\text{ s}^{-1}} = \boxed{10.6\ \mu\text{m}}$, $\boxed{\text{infrared}}$

P42.48 (a) $$I = \frac{\left(3.00\times10^{-3}\text{ J}\right)}{\left(1.00\times10^{-9}\text{ s}\right)\left[\pi\left(15.0\times10^{-6}\text{ m}\right)^2\right]} = \boxed{4.24\times10^{15}\text{ W/m}^2}$$

(b) $$\left(3.00\times10^{-3}\text{ J}\right)\frac{\left(0.600\times10^{-9}\text{ m}\right)^2}{\left(30.0\times10^{-6}\text{ m}\right)^2} = \boxed{1.20\times10^{-12}\text{ J}} = 7.50\text{ MeV}$$

P42.49 $$E = \mathcal{P}\Delta t = \left(1.00\times10^{6}\text{ W}\right)\left(1.00\times10^{-8}\text{ s}\right) = 0.010\,0\text{ J}$$

$$E_\gamma = hf = \frac{hc}{\lambda} = \frac{\left(6.626\times10^{-34}\right)\left(3.00\times10^{8}\right)}{694.3\times10^{-9}}\text{ J} = 2.86\times10^{-19}\text{ J}$$

$$N = \frac{E}{E_\gamma} = \frac{0.010\,0}{2.86\times10^{-19}} = \boxed{3.49\times10^{16}\text{ photons}}$$

***P42.50** (a) $$\frac{N_3}{N_2} = \frac{N_g e^{-E_3/(k_B\cdot 300\text{ K})}}{N_g e^{-E_2/(k_B\cdot 300\text{ K})}} = e^{-(E_3-E_2)/(k_B\cdot 300\text{ K})} = e^{-hc/\lambda(k_B\cdot 300\text{ K})}$$

where λ is the wavelength of light radiated in the $3\to2$ transition.

$$\frac{N_3}{N_2} = e^{-\left(6.63\times10^{-34}\text{ J}\cdot\text{s}\right)\left(3\times10^{8}\text{ m/s}\right)/\left(632.8\times10^{-9}\text{ m}\right)\left(1.38\times10^{-23}\text{ J/K}\right)(300\text{ K})}$$

$$\frac{N_3}{N_2} = e^{-75.9} = \boxed{1.07\times10^{-33}}$$

(b) $$\frac{N_u}{N_\ell} = e^{-(E_u-E_\ell)/k_BT}$$

where the subscript u refers to an upper energy state and the subscript ℓ to a lower energy state.

Since $E_u - E_\ell = E_{\text{photon}} = \dfrac{hc}{\lambda}$ $\qquad \dfrac{N_u}{N_\ell} = e^{-hc/\lambda k_BT}$.

Thus, we require $\qquad 1.02 = e^{-hc/\lambda k_BT}$

or $$\ln(1.02) = -\frac{\left(6.63\times10^{-34}\text{ J}\cdot\text{s}\right)\left(3\times10^{8}\text{ m/s}\right)}{\left(632.8\times10^{-9}\text{ m}\right)\left(1.38\times10^{23}\text{ J/K}\right)T}$$

$$T = -\frac{2.28\times10^{4}}{\ln(1.02)} = \boxed{-1.15\times10^{6}\text{ K}}.$$

A negative-temperature state is not achieved by cooling the system below 0 K, but by heating it above $T=\infty$, for as $T\to\infty$ the populations of upper and lower states approach equality.

(c) Because $E_u - E_\ell > 0$, and in any real equilibrium state $T > 0$,

$e^{-(E_u-E_\ell)/k_BT} < 1$ and $N_u < N_\ell$.

Thus, a population inversion cannot happen in thermal equilibrium.

***P42.51** (a) The light in the cavity is incident perpendicularly on the mirrors, although the diagram shows a large angle of incidence for clarity. We ignore the variation of the index of refraction with wavelength. To minimize reflection at a vacuum wavelength of 632.8 nm, the net phase difference between rays (1) and (2) should be 180°. There is automatically a 180° shift in one of the two rays upon reflection, so the extra distance traveled by ray (2) should be one whole wavelength:

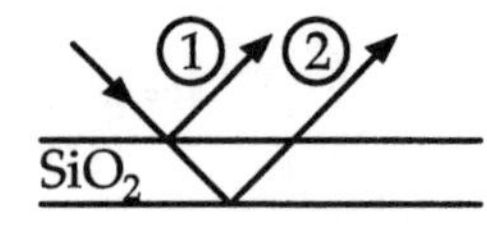

FIG. P42.51

$$2t = \frac{\lambda}{n}$$

$$t = \frac{\lambda}{2n} = \frac{632.8 \text{ nm}}{2(1.458)} = \boxed{217 \text{ nm}}$$

(b) The total phase difference should be 360°, including contributions of 180° by reflection and 180° by extra distance traveled

$$2t = \frac{\lambda}{2n}$$

$$t = \frac{\lambda}{4n} = \frac{543 \text{ nm}}{4(1.458)} = \boxed{93.1 \text{ nm}}$$

Additional Problems

***P42.52** (a) Using the same procedure that was used in the Bohr model of the hydrogen atom, we apply Newton's second law to the Earth. We simply replace the Coulomb force by the gravitational force exerted by the Sun on the Earth and find

$$G\frac{M_S M_E}{r^2} = M_E \frac{v^2}{r} \tag{1}$$

where v is the orbital speed of the Earth. Next, we apply the postulate that angular momentum of the Earth is quantized in multiples of $\hbar$:

$$M_E v r = n\hbar \qquad (n = 1, 2, 3, \ldots).$$

Solving for v gives

$$v = \frac{n\hbar}{M_E r}. \tag{2}$$

Substituting (2) into (1), we find

$$r = \frac{n^2\hbar^2}{GM_S M_E^2}. \tag{3}$$

continued on next page

(b) Solving (3) for n gives

$$n = \sqrt{GM_S r}\,\frac{M_E}{\hbar}. \qquad (4)$$

Taking $M_S = 1.99\times10^{30}$ kg, and $M_E = 5.98\times10^{24}$ kg, $r = 1.496\times10^{11}$ m, $G = 6.67\times10^{-11}\ \text{Nm}^2/\text{kg}^2$, and $\hbar = 1.055\times10^{-34}$ Js, we find

$$n = \boxed{2.53\times10^{74}}.$$

(c) We can use (3) to determine the radii for the orbits corresponding to the quantum numbers n and $n+1$:

$$r_n = \frac{n^2\hbar^2}{GM_S M_E^2} \quad \text{and} \quad r_{n+1} = \frac{(n+1)^2\hbar^2}{GM_S M_E^2}.$$

Hence, the separation between these two orbits is

$$\Delta r = \frac{\hbar^2}{GM_S M_E^2}\left[(n+1)^2 - n^2\right] = \frac{\hbar^2}{GM_S M_E^2}(2n+1).$$

Since n is very large, we can neglect the number 1 in the parentheses and express the separation as

$$\Delta r \approx \frac{\hbar^2}{GM_S M_E^2}(2n) = \boxed{1.18\times10^{-63}\ \text{m}}.$$

This number is *much smaller* than the radius of an atomic nucleus $\left(\sim10^{-15}\ \text{m}\right)$, so the distance between quantized orbits of the Earth is too small to observe.

***P42.53** (a) $\Delta E = \dfrac{e\hbar B}{m_e} = \dfrac{1.60\times10^{-19}\ \text{C}\left(6.63\times10^{-34}\ \text{J}\cdot\text{s}\right)(5.26\ \text{T})}{2\pi\left(9.11\times10^{-31}\ \text{kg}\right)}\left(\dfrac{\text{N}\cdot\text{s}}{\text{T}\cdot\text{C}\cdot\text{m}}\right)\left(\dfrac{\text{kg}\cdot\text{m}}{\text{N}\cdot\text{s}^2}\right) = 9.75\times10^{-23}\ \text{J}$

$= \boxed{609\ \mu\text{eV}}$

(b) $k_B T = \left(1.38\times10^{-23}\ \text{J/K}\right)\left(80\times10^{-3}\ \text{K}\right) = 1.10\times10^{-24}\ \text{J} = \boxed{6.90\ \mu\text{eV}}$

(c) $f = \dfrac{\Delta E}{h} = \dfrac{9.75\times10^{-23}\ \text{J}}{6.63\times10^{-34}\ \text{J}\cdot\text{s}} = \boxed{1.47\times10^{11}\ \text{Hz}}$

$\lambda = \dfrac{c}{f} = \dfrac{3\times10^{8}\ \text{m/s}}{1.47\times10^{11}\ \text{Hz}} = \boxed{2.04\times10^{-3}\ \text{m}}$

***P42.54** (a) Probability $= \displaystyle\int_r^\infty P_{1s}(r')dr' = \frac{4}{a_0^3}\int_r^\infty r'^2 e^{-2r'/a_0}dr' = \left[-\left(\frac{2r'^2}{a_0^2} + \frac{2r'}{a_0} + 1\right)e^{-2r'/a_0}\right]_r^\infty,$

using integration by parts, or Example 42.5

$$= \boxed{\left(\frac{2r^2}{a_0^2} + \frac{2r}{a_0} + 1\right)e^{-2r/a_0}}$$

continued on next page

(b)

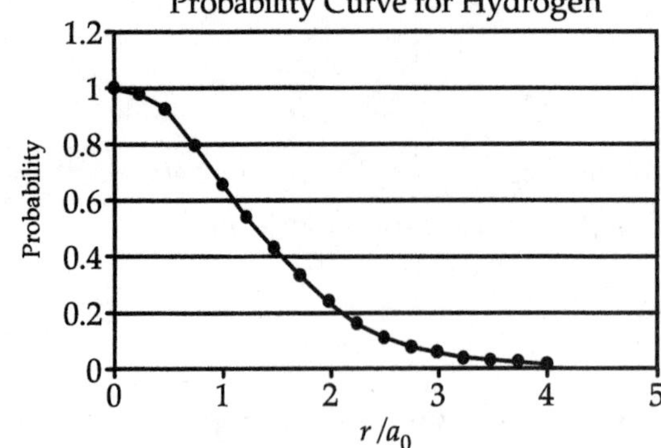

FIG. P42.66

(c) The probability of finding the electron inside or outside the sphere of radius r is $\frac{1}{2}$.

$$\therefore \left(\frac{2r^2}{a_0^2}+\frac{2r}{a_0}+1\right)e^{-2r/a_0}=\frac{1}{2} \text{ or } z^2+2z+2=e^z \text{ where } z=\frac{2r}{a_0}$$

One can home in on a solution to this transcendental equation for r on a calculator, the result being $r=\boxed{1.34a_0}$ to three digits.

P42.55 Let r represent the distance between the electron and the positron. The two move in a circle of radius $\frac{r}{2}$ around their center of mass with opposite velocities. The total angular momentum of the electron-positron system is quantized to according to

$$L_n=\frac{mvr}{2}+\frac{mvr}{2}=n\hbar$$

where $n=1, 2, 3, \ldots$.

For each particle, $\sum F=ma$ expands to $\frac{k_e e^2}{r^2}=\frac{mv^2}{r/2}$.

We can eliminate $v=\frac{n\hbar}{mr}$ to find $\frac{k_e e^2}{r}=\frac{2mn^2\hbar^2}{m^2r^2}$.

So the separation distances are $r=\frac{2n^2\hbar^2}{mk_e e^2}=2a_0n^2=\boxed{\left(1.06\times10^{-10}\text{ m}\right)n^2}$.

The orbital radii are $\frac{r}{2}=a_0n^2$, the same as for the electron in hydrogen.

The energy can be calculated from $E=K+U=\frac{1}{2}mv^2+\frac{1}{2}mv^2-\frac{k_e e^2}{r}$.

Since $mv^2=\frac{k_e e^2}{2r}$, $E=\frac{k_e e^2}{2r}-\frac{k_e e^2}{r}=-\frac{k_e e^2}{2r}=\frac{-k_e e^2}{4a_0n^2}=\boxed{-\frac{6.80\text{ eV}}{n^2}}$.

P42.56 (a) The energy difference between these two states is equal to the energy that is absorbed.

Thus, $E=E_2-E_1=\frac{(-13.6\text{ eV})}{4}-\frac{(-13.6\text{ eV})}{1}=10.2\text{ eV}=\boxed{1.63\times10^{-18}\text{ J}}$.

(b) $E=\frac{3}{2}k_BT$ or $T=\frac{2E}{3k_B}=\frac{2\left(1.63\times10^{-18}\text{ J}\right)}{3\left(1.38\times10^{-23}\text{ J/K}\right)}=\boxed{7.88\times10^4\text{ K}}$.

P42.57 $hf = \Delta E = \frac{4\pi^2 m k_e^2 e^4}{2h^2}\left(\frac{1}{(n-1)^2} - \frac{1}{n^2}\right)$

$$f = \frac{2\pi^2 m k_e^2 e^4}{h^3}\left(\frac{2n-1}{(n-1)^2 n^2}\right)$$

As n approaches infinity, we have f approaching $\frac{2\pi^2 m k_e^2 e^4}{h^3}\frac{2}{n^3}$

The classical frequency is $f = \frac{v}{2\pi r} = \frac{1}{2\pi}\sqrt{\frac{k_e e^2}{m}}\frac{1}{r^{3/2}}$

where $r = \frac{n^2 h^2}{4\pi m k_e e^2}$

Using this equation to eliminate r from the expression for f, $f = \frac{2\pi^2 m k_e^2 e^4}{h^3}\frac{2}{n^3}$

P42.58 (a) The energy of the ground state is: $E_1 = -\frac{hc}{\lambda_{\text{series limit}}} = -\frac{1\,240\text{ eV}\cdot\text{nm}}{152.0\text{ nm}} = \boxed{-8.16\text{ eV}}$.

From the wavelength of the Lyman α line: $E_2 - E_1 = \frac{hc}{\lambda} = \frac{1\,240\text{ nm}\cdot\text{eV}}{202.6\text{ nm}} = 6.12\text{ eV}$

$$E_2 = E_1 + 6.12\text{ eV} = \boxed{-2.04\text{ eV}}.$$

The wavelength of the Lyman β line gives: $E_3 - E_1 = \frac{1\,240\text{ nm}\cdot\text{eV}}{170.9\text{ nm}} = 7.26\text{ eV}$

so $E_3 = \boxed{-0.902\text{ eV}}$.

Next, using the Lyman γ line gives: $E_4 - E_1 = \frac{1\,240\text{ nm}\cdot\text{eV}}{162.1\text{ nm}} = 7.65\text{ eV}$

and $E_4 = \boxed{-0.508\text{ eV}}$.

From the Lyman δ line, $E_5 - E_1 = \frac{1\,240\text{ nm}\cdot\text{eV}}{158.3\text{ nm}} = 7.83\text{ eV}$

so $E_5 = \boxed{-0.325\text{ eV}}$.

(b) For the Balmer series, $\frac{hc}{\lambda} = E_i - E_2$, or $\lambda = \frac{1\,240\text{ nm}\cdot\text{eV}}{E_i - E_2}$.

For the α line, $E_i = E_3$ and so $\lambda_a = \frac{1\,240\text{ nm}\cdot\text{eV}}{(-0.902\text{ eV}) - (-2.04\text{ eV})} = \boxed{1\,090\text{ nm}}$.

Similarly, the wavelengths of the β line, γ line, and the short wavelength limit are found to be: $\boxed{811\text{ nm}}$, $\boxed{724\text{ nm}}$, and $\boxed{609\text{ nm}}$.

continued

(c) Computing 60.0% of the wavelengths of the spectral lines shown on the energy-level diagram gives:

$0.600(202.6\text{ nm}) = \boxed{122\text{ nm}}$, $0.600(170.9\text{ nm}) = \boxed{103\text{ nm}}$, $0.600(162.1\text{ nm}) = \boxed{97.3\text{ nm}}$, $0.600(158.3\text{ nm}) = \boxed{95.0\text{ nm}}$, and $0.600(152.0\text{ nm}) = \boxed{91.2\text{ nm}}$

These are seen to be the wavelengths of the α, β, γ, and δ lines as well as the short wavelength limit for the Lyman series in Hydrogen.

(d) The observed wavelengths could be the result of Doppler shift when the source moves away from the Earth. The required speed of the source is found from

$$\frac{f'}{f} = \frac{\lambda}{\lambda'} = \sqrt{\frac{1-(v/c)}{1+(v/c)}} = 0.600 \qquad \text{yielding} \qquad \boxed{v = 0.471c}.$$

P42.59 The wave function for the 2s state is given by Eq. 42.26: $\psi_{2s}(r) = \frac{1}{4\sqrt{2\pi}}\left(\frac{1}{a_0}\right)^{3/2}\left[2 - \frac{r}{a_0}\right]e^{-r/2a_0}$.

(a) Taking $r = a_0 = 0.529 \times 10^{-10}\text{ m}$

we find $\psi_{2s}(a_0) = \frac{1}{4\sqrt{2\pi}}\left(\frac{1}{0.529 \times 10^{-10}\text{ m}}\right)^{3/2}[2-1]e^{-1/2} = \boxed{1.57 \times 10^{14}\text{ m}^{-3/2}}$.

(b) $|\psi_{2s}(a_0)|^2 = \left(1.57 \times 10^{14}\text{ m}^{-3/2}\right)^2 = \boxed{2.47 \times 10^{28}\text{ m}^{-3}}$

(c) Using Equation 42.24 and the results to (b) gives $P_{2s}(a_0) = 4\pi a_0^2 |\psi_{2s}(a_0)|^2 = \boxed{8.69 \times 10^8\text{ m}^{-1}}$.

***P42.60** From Figure 42.20, a typical ionization energy is 8 eV. For internal energy to ionize most of the atoms we require

$$\frac{3}{2}k_BT = 8\text{ eV}: \qquad T = \frac{2 \times 8\left(1.60 \times 10^{-19}\text{ J}\right)}{3\left(1.38 \times 10^{-23}\text{ J/K}\right)} \boxed{\sim \text{between } 10^4\text{ K and } 10^5\text{ K}}.$$

P42.61 (a) $\left(3.00 \times 10^8\text{ m/s}\right)\left(14.0 \times 10^{-12}\text{ s}\right) = \boxed{4.20\text{ mm}}$

(b) $E = \frac{hc}{\lambda} = 2.86 \times 10^{-19}\text{ J}$

$$N = \frac{3.00\text{ J}}{2.86 \times 10^{-19}\text{ J}} = \boxed{1.05 \times 10^{19}\text{ photons}}$$

(c) $V = (4.20\text{ mm})\left[\pi(3.00\text{ mm})^2\right] = 119\text{ mm}^3$

$$n = \frac{1.05 \times 10^{19}}{119} = \boxed{8.82 \times 10^{16}\text{ mm}^{-3}}$$

P42.62 (a) The length of the pulse is $\Delta L = \boxed{c\Delta t}$.

(b) The energy of each photon is $E_\gamma = \frac{hc}{\lambda}$ so $N = \frac{E}{E_\gamma} = \boxed{\frac{E\lambda}{hc}}$.

(c) $V = \Delta L \pi \frac{d^2}{4}$ $\qquad n = \frac{N}{V} = \boxed{\left(\frac{4}{c\Delta t \pi d^2}\right)\left(\frac{E\lambda}{hc}\right)}$

***P42.63** The fermions are described by the exclusion principle. Two of them, one spin-up and one spin-down, will be in the ground energy level, with

$$d_{NN} = L = \frac{1}{2}\lambda,\ \lambda = 2L = \frac{h}{p},\ \text{and } p = \frac{h}{2L} \qquad K = \frac{1}{2}mv^2 = \frac{p^2}{2m} = \frac{h^2}{8mL^2}.$$

The third must be in the next higher level, with

$$d_{NN} = \frac{L}{2} = \frac{\lambda}{2},\ \lambda = L,\ \text{and } p = \frac{h}{L} \qquad K = \frac{p^2}{2m} = \frac{h^2}{2mL^2}.$$

The total energy is then $\frac{h^2}{8mL^2} + \frac{h^2}{8mL^2} + \frac{h^2}{2mL^2} = \boxed{\frac{3h^2}{4mL^2}}$.

P42.64 $\Delta z = \frac{at^2}{2} = \frac{1}{2}\left(\frac{F_z}{m_0}\right)t^2 = \frac{\mu_z(dB_z/dz)}{2m_0}\left(\frac{\Delta x}{v}\right)^2$ and $\mu_z = \frac{e\hbar}{2m_e}$

$$\frac{dB_z}{dz} = \frac{2m_0(\Delta z)v^2(2m_e)}{\Delta x^2 e\hbar} = \frac{2(108)\left(1.66\times10^{-27}\text{ kg}\right)\left(10^{-3}\text{ m}\right)\left(10^4\text{ m}^2/\text{s}^2\right)\left(2\times9.11\times10^{-31}\text{ kg}\right)}{\left(1.00\text{ m}^2\right)\left(1.60\times10^{-19}\text{ C}\right)\left(1.05\times10^{-34}\text{ J}\cdot\text{s}\right)}$$

$$\frac{dB_z}{dz} = \boxed{0.389\text{ T/m}}$$

P42.65 We use $\psi_{2s}(r) = \frac{1}{4}\left(2\pi a_0^3\right)^{-1/2}\left(2 - \frac{r}{a_0}\right)e^{-r/2a_0}$.

By Equation 42.24, $P(r) = 4\pi r^2\psi^2 = \frac{1}{8}\left(\frac{r^2}{a_0^3}\right)\left(2 - \frac{r}{a_0}\right)^2 e^{-r/a_0}$.

(a) $$\frac{dP(r)}{dr} = \frac{1}{8}\left[\frac{2r}{a_0^3}\left(2 - \frac{r}{a_0}\right)^2 - \frac{2r^2}{a_0^3}\left(\frac{1}{a_0}\right)\left(2 - \frac{r}{a_0}\right) - \frac{r^2}{a_0^3}\left(2 - \frac{r}{a_0}\right)^2\left(\frac{1}{a_0}\right)\right]e^{-r/a_0} = 0$$

or $$\frac{1}{8}\left(\frac{r}{a_0^3}\right)\left(2 - \frac{r}{a_0}\right)\left[2\left(2 - \frac{r}{a_0}\right) - \frac{2r}{a_0} - \frac{r}{a_0}\left(2 - \frac{r}{a_0}\right)\right]e^{-r/a_0} = 0.$$

The roots of $\frac{dP}{dr} = 0$ at $r = 0$, $r = 2a_0$ and $r = \infty$ are minima with $P(r) = 0$.

continued

Therefore we require $[.....]=4-\left(\frac{6r}{a_0}\right)+\left(\frac{r}{a_0}\right)^2=0$

with solutions $r=\left(3\pm\sqrt{5}\right)a_0$.

We substitute the last two roots into $P(r)$ to determine the most probable value:

When $r=\left(3-\sqrt{5}\right)a_0=0.763\,9a_0$, $P(r)=\frac{0.051\,9}{a_0}$.

When $r=\left(3+\sqrt{5}\right)a_0=5.236a_0$, $P(r)=\frac{0.191}{a_0}$.

Therefore, the most probable value of r is $\left(3+\sqrt{5}\right)a_0=\boxed{5.236a_0}$.

(b) $\int_0^\infty P(r)dr=\int_0^\infty \frac{1}{8}\left(\frac{r^2}{a_0^3}\right)\left(2-\frac{r}{a_0}\right)^2 e^{-r/a_0}dr$

Let $u=\frac{r}{a_0}$, $dr=a_0du$,

$$\int_0^\infty P(r)dr=\int_0^\infty \frac{1}{8}u^2\left(4-4u+u^2\right)e^{-u}dr=\int_0^\infty \frac{1}{8}\left(u^4-4u^3+4u^2\right)e^{-u}du=-\frac{1}{8}\left(u^4+4u^2+8u+8\right)e^{-u}\Big|_0^\infty=1$$

This is as required for normalization.

P42.66 $E=\frac{hc}{\lambda}=\frac{1\,240\text{ eV}\cdot\text{nm}}{\lambda}=\Delta E$

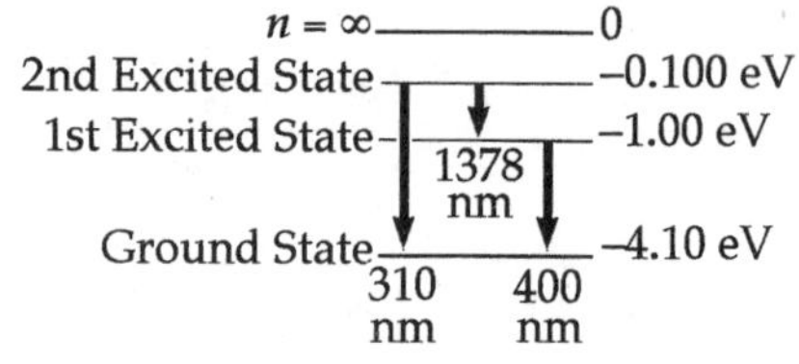

FIG. P42.66

$\lambda_1=310$ nm, so $\Delta E_1=4.00$ eV

$\lambda_2=400$ nm, $\Delta E_2=3.10$ eV

$\lambda_3=1\,378$ nm, $\Delta E_3=0.900$ eV

and the ionization energy $=4.10$ eV.

The energy level diagram having the fewest levels and consistent with these energies is shown at the right.

P42.67 With one vacancy in the K shell, excess energy

$$\Delta E\approx-(Z-1)^2(13.6\text{ eV})\left(\frac{1}{2^2}-\frac{1}{1^2}\right)=5.40\text{ keV}.$$

We suppose the outermost $4s$ electron is shielded by 22 electrons inside its orbit:

$$E_{\text{ionization}}\approx\frac{2^2(13.6\text{ eV})}{4^2}=3.40\text{ eV}.$$

Note the experimental ionization energy is 6.76 eV.

$$K=\Delta E-E_{\text{ionization}}\approx\boxed{5.39\text{ keV}}.$$

P42.68 (a) The configuration we may model as $\boxed{\text{SN}}\ \boxed{\text{NS}}$ has higher energy than $\boxed{\text{SN}}\ \boxed{\text{SN}}$. The higher energy state has antiparallel magnetic moments, so it has $\boxed{\text{parallel spins}}$ of the oppositely charged particles.

(b) $$E=\frac{hc}{\lambda}=9.42\times10^{-25}\text{ J}=\boxed{5.89\ \mu\text{eV}}$$

(c) $$\Delta E\Delta t\approx\frac{\hbar}{2}\text{ so }\Delta E\approx\frac{1.055\times10^{-34}\text{ J}\cdot\text{s}}{2\left(10^{7}\text{ yr}\right)\left(3.16\times10^{7}\text{ s/yr}\right)}\left(\frac{1.00\text{ eV}}{1.60\times10^{-19}\text{ J}}\right)=\boxed{1.04\times10^{-30}\text{ eV}}$$

P42.69 $$P=\int_{2.50a_0}^{\infty}\frac{4r^2}{a_0^3}e^{-2r/a_0}dr=\frac{1}{2}\int_{5.00}^{\infty}z^2e^{-z}dz\text{ where }z\equiv\frac{2r}{a_0}$$

$$P=-\frac{1}{2}\left(z^2+2z+2\right)e^{-z}\Big|_{5.00}^{\infty}=-\frac{1}{2}[0]+\frac{1}{2}(25.0+10.0+2.00)e^{-5}=\left(\frac{37}{2}\right)(0.006\,74)=\boxed{0.125}$$

P42.70 (a) One molecule's share of volume

$$\text{Al: }V=\frac{\text{mass per molecule}}{\text{density}}=\left(\frac{27.0\text{ g/mol}}{6.02\times10^{23}\text{ molecules/mol}}\right)\left(\frac{1.00\times10^{-6}\text{ m}^3}{2.70\text{ g}}\right)=1.66\times10^{-29}\text{ m}^3$$

$$\sqrt[3]{V}=\boxed{2.55\times10^{-10}\text{ m}\sim10^{-1}\text{ nm}}.$$

$$\text{U: }V=\left(\frac{238\text{ g}}{6.02\times10^{23}\text{ molecules}}\right)\left(\frac{1.00\times10^{-6}\text{ m}^3}{18.9\text{ g}}\right)=2.09\times10^{-29}\text{ m}^3$$

$$\sqrt[3]{V}=\boxed{2.76\times10^{-10}\text{ m}\sim10^{-1}\text{ nm}}.$$

(b) The outermost electron in any atom sees the nuclear charge screened by all the electrons below it. If we can visualize a single outermost electron, it moves in the electric field of net charge, $+Ze-(Z-1)e=+e$, the charge of a single proton, as felt by the electron in hydrogen. So the Bohr radius sets the scale for the outside diameter of every atom. An innermost electron, on the other hand, sees the nuclear charge unscreened, and the scale size of its (K-shell) orbit is $\frac{a_0}{Z}$.

P42.71 $\Delta E=2\mu_B B=hf$

so $$2\left(9.27\times10^{-24}\text{ J/T}\right)(0.350\text{ T})=\left(6.626\times10^{-34}\text{ J}\cdot\text{s}\right)f$$

and $$f=\boxed{9.79\times10^{9}\text{ Hz}}.$$

P42.72 $\psi_{25} = \frac{1}{4}(2\pi)^{-1/2}\left(\frac{1}{a_0}\right)^{3/2}\left(2-\frac{r}{a_0}\right)e^{-r/2a_0} = A\left(2-\frac{r}{a_0}\right)e^{-r/2a_0}$ $\qquad \frac{d\psi}{dr} = Ae^{-r/2a_0}\left(-\frac{2}{a_0}+\frac{r}{2a_0^2}\right)$

$$\frac{d^2\psi}{dr^2} = \left(\frac{Ae^{-r/2a_0}}{a_0^2}\right)\left(\frac{3}{2}-\frac{r}{4a_0}\right)$$

Substituting into Schrödinger's equation and dividing by $Ae^{-r/2a_0}$, we will have a solution if

$$-\frac{5}{4}\frac{\hbar^2}{m_e a_0^2}+\frac{k_e e^2}{a_0}+\frac{\hbar^2 r}{8m_e a_0^3}+\frac{2\hbar^2}{m_e a_0 r}-\frac{2k_e e^2}{r} = 2E-\frac{Er}{a_0}.$$

Now with $a_0 = \frac{\hbar^2}{m_e e^2 k_e}$, this reduces to

$$-\frac{m_e e^4 k_e^2}{8\hbar^2}\left(2-\frac{r}{a_0}\right) = E\left(2-\frac{r}{a_0}\right).$$

This is true, so ψ_{25} is a solution to the Schrödinger equation, provided $E = \frac{1}{4}E_1 = -3.40$ eV.

P42.73 (a) Suppose the atoms move in the $+x$ direction. The absorption of a photon by an atom is a completely inelastic collision, described by

$$mv_i\hat{\mathbf{i}}+\frac{h}{\lambda}\left(-\hat{\mathbf{i}}\right) = mv_f\hat{\mathbf{i}} \qquad \text{so} \qquad v_f - v_i = -\frac{h}{m\lambda}.$$

This happens promptly every time an atom has fallen back into the ground state, so it happens every $10^{-8}\text{ s} = \Delta t$. Then,

$$a = \frac{v_f - v_i}{\Delta t} = -\frac{h}{m\lambda\Delta t} \sim -\frac{6.626\times10^{-34}\text{ J}\cdot\text{s}}{\left(10^{-25}\text{ kg}\right)\left(500\times10^{-9}\text{ m}\right)\left(10^{-8}\text{ s}\right)} \sim \boxed{-10^6\text{ m/s}^2}.$$

(b) With constant average acceleration,

$$v_f^2 = v_i^2 + 2a\Delta x \qquad 0 \sim \left(10^3\text{ m/s}\right)^2 + 2\left(-10^6\text{ m/s}^2\right)\Delta x$$

so

$$\Delta x \sim \frac{\left(10^3\text{ m/s}\right)^2}{10^6\text{ m/s}^2}\boxed{\sim 1\text{ m}}.$$

P42.74 $\left\langle\frac{1}{r}\right\rangle = \int_0^\infty \frac{4r^2}{a_0^3}e^{-2r/a_0}\frac{1}{r}dr = \frac{4}{a_0^3}\int_0^\infty re^{-(2/a_0)r}dr = \frac{4}{a_0^3}\frac{1}{(2/a_0)^2} = \boxed{\frac{1}{a_0}}$

We compare this to $\frac{1}{\langle r\rangle} = \frac{1}{3a_0/2} = \frac{2}{3a_0}$, and find that the average reciprocal value is $\boxed{\text{NOT}}$ the reciprocal of the average value.

ANSWERS TO EVEN PROBLEMS

P42.2 (a) 91.2 nm, 365 nm, 821 nm, 1.46 μm; (b) 13.6 eV, 3.40 eV, 1.51 eV, 0.850 eV

P42.4 (a) 56.8 fm; (b) 11.3 N away from the nucleus

P42.6 (a) ii; (b) i; (c) ii and iii

P42.8 (a) 13.6 eV; (b)1.51 eV

P42.10 see the solution

P42.12 97.5 nm

P42.14 (a) O^{7+}; (b) 41.0 nm, 33.8 nm, 30.4 nm

P42.16 (a) 1.31 μm; (b) 164 nm

P42.18 see the solution

P42.20 $4a_0$

P42.22 797 times

P42.24 (a) $\sqrt{6}\hbar = 2.58\times10^{-34}$ J·s; (b) $\sqrt{12}\hbar = 3.65\times10^{-34}$ J·s

P42.26 $\sqrt{6}\hbar$

P42.28 $\sqrt{6}\hbar$; $-2\hbar, -\hbar, 0, \hbar, 2\hbar$; 145°, 114°, 90.0°, 65.9°, 35.3°

P42.30 $3\hbar$

P42.32 (a) $1s^2 2s^2 2p^4$;

(b)

n	1	1	2	2	2	2	2	2
ℓ	0	0	0	0	1	1	1	1
m_ℓ	0	0	0	0	1	1	0	−1
m_s	$\frac{1}{2}$	$-\frac{1}{2}$	$\frac{1}{2}$	$-\frac{1}{2}$	$\frac{1}{2}$	$-\frac{1}{2}$	$\frac{1}{2}$	$\frac{1}{2}$

P42.34 see the solution

P42.36 (a) see the solution; (b) 36 states instead of 30

P42.38 $1s^2 2s^2 2p^6 3s^2 3p^6 3d^{10} 4s^2 4p^6 4d^{10} 4f^{14} 5s^2 5p^6 5d^{10} 5f^{14} 6s^2 6p^6 6d^8 7s^2$

P42.40 (a) $\ell = 0$ with $m_\ell = 0$; $\ell = 1$ with $m_\ell = 1, 0,$ or 1; and $\ell = 2$ with $m_\ell = -2, -1, 0, 1, 2$; (b) −6.05 eV

P42.42 see the solution

P42.44 L shell 11.8 keV, M shell 10.1 keV, N shell 2.39 keV, see the solution

P42.46 see the solution

P42.48 (a) 4.24 PW/m^2; (b) 1.20 pJ = 7.50 MeV

P42.50 (a) 1.07×10^{-33}; (b) -1.15×10^{6} K; (c) negative temperatures do not describe systems in thermal equilibrium

P42.52 (a) see the solution; (b) 2.53×10^{74}; (c) 1.18×10^{-63} m, unobservably small

P42.54 (a) Probability $= \left(\dfrac{2r^2}{a_0^2} + \dfrac{2r}{a_0} + 1\right)e^{-2r/a_0}$; (b) see the solution; (c) $1.34a_0$

P42.56 (a) 10.2 eV = 1.63 aJ; (b) 7.88×10^{4} K

P42.58 (a) −8.16 eV, −2.04 eV, −0.902 eV, −0.508 eV, −0.325 eV; (b) 1 090 nm, 811 nm, 724 nm, 609 nm; (c) see the solution; (d) The spectrum could be that of hydrogen, Doppler shifted by motion away from us at speed $0.471c$.

P42.60 between 10^4 K and 10^5 K

P42.62 (a) $c\Delta t$; (b) $\dfrac{E\lambda}{hc}$; (c) $\dfrac{4E\lambda}{\Delta t \pi d^2 hc^2}$

P42.64 0.389 T/m

P42.66 Energy levels at 0, −0.100 eV, −1.00 eV, and −4.10 eV

P42.68 (a) parallel spins; (b) 5.89 μeV; (c) 1.04×10^{-30} eV

P42.70 (a) diameter $\sim 10^{-1}$ nm for both;
(b) A K-shell electron moves in an orbit with size on the order of $\frac{a_0}{Z}$

P42.72 see the solution

P42.74 $\frac{1}{a_0}$, no

43

Molecules and Solids

CHAPTER OUTLINE

ANSWERS TO QUESTIONS

Q43.1 Rotational, vibrational and electronic (as discussed in Chapter 42) are the three major forms of excitation. Rotational energy for a diatomic molecule is on the order of $\frac{\hbar^2}{2I}$, where I is the moment of inertia of the molecule. A typical value for a small molecule is on the order of $1\text{ meV} = 10^{-3}\text{ eV}$. Vibrational energy is on the order of hf, where f is the vibration frequency of the molecule. A typical value is on the order of 0.1 eV. Electronic energy depends on the state of an electron in the molecule and is on the order of a few eV. The rotational energy can be zero, but neither the vibrational nor the electronic energy can be zero.

Q43.2 The Pauli exclusion principle limits the number of electrons in the valence band of a metal, as no two electrons can occupy the same state. If the valence band is full, additional electrons must be in the conduction band, and the material can be a good conductor. For further discussion, see Q43.3.

Q43.3 The conductive properties of a material depend on the electron population of the conduction band of the material. If the conduction band is empty and a full valence band lies below the conduction band by an energy gap of a few eV, then the material will be an insulator. Electrons will be unable to move easily through the material in response to an applied electric field. If the conduction band is partly full, states are accessible to electrons accelerated by an electric field, and the material is a good conductor. If the energy gap between a full valence band and an empty conduction band is comparable to the thermal energy k_BT, the material is a semiconductor.

Q43.4 Thermal excitation increases the vibrational energy of the molecules. It makes the crystal lattice less orderly. We can expect it to increase the width of both the valence band and the conduction band, to decrease the gap between them.

Q43.5 First consider electric conduction in a metal. The number of conduction electrons is essentially fixed. They conduct electricity by having drift motion in an applied electric field superposed on their random thermal motion. At higher temperature, the ion cores vibrate more and scatter more efficiently the conduction electrons flying among them. The mean time between collisions is reduced. The electrons have time to develop only a lower drift speed. The electric current is reduced, so we see the resistivity increasing with temperature.

Now consider an intrinsic semiconductor. At absolute zero its valence band is full and its conduction band is empty. It is an insulator, with very high resistivity. As the temperature increases, more electrons are promoted to the conduction band, leaving holes in the valence band. Then both electrons and holes move in response to an applied electric field. Thus we see the resistivity decreasing as temperature goes up.

Q43.6 In a metal, there is no energy gap between the valence and conduction bands, or the conduction band is partly full even at absolute zero in temperature. Thus an applied electric field is able to inject a tiny bit of energy into an electron to promote it to a state in which it is moving through the metal as part of an electric current. In an insulator, there is a large energy gap between a full valence band and an empty conduction band. An applied electric field is unable to give electrons in the valence band enough energy to jump across the gap into the higher energy conduction band. In a semiconductor, the energy gap between valence and conduction bands is smaller than in an insulator. At absolute zero the valence band is full and the conduction band is empty, but at room temperature thermal energy has promoted some electrons across the gap. Then there are some mobile holes in the valence band as well as some mobile electrons in the conduction band.

Q43.7 Ionic bonds are ones between oppositely charged ions. A simple model of an ionic bond is the electrostatic attraction of a negatively charged latex balloon to a positively charged Mylar balloon.

Covalent bonds are ones in which atoms share electrons. Classically, two children playing a short-range game of catch with a ball models a covalent bond. On a quantum scale, the two atoms are sharing a wave function, so perhaps a better model would be two children using a single hula hoop.

Van der Waals bonds are weak electrostatic forces: the dipole-dipole force is analogous to the attraction between the opposite poles of two bar magnets, the dipole—induced dipole force is similar to a bar magnet attracting an iron nail or paper clip, and the dispersion force is analogous to an alternating-current electromagnet attracting a paper clip.

A hydrogen atom in a molecule is not ionized, but its electron can spend more time elsewhere than it does in the hydrogen atom. The hydrogen atom can be a location of net positive charge, and can weakly attract a zone of negative charge in another molecule.

Q43.8 Ionically bonded solids are generally poor electric conductors, as they have no free electrons. While they are transparent in the visible spectrum, they absorb infrared radiation. Physically, they form stable, hard crystals with high melting temperatures.

Q43.9 Covalently bonded solids are generally poor conductors, as they form structures in which the atoms share several electrons in the outer shell, leaving no room for conducting electrons. Depending on the structure of the solid, they are usually very hard and have high melting points.

Q43.10 Metals are good conductors, as the atoms have many free electrons in the conduction band. Metallic bonds allow the mixing of different metals to form alloys. Metals are opaque to visible light, and can be highly reflective. A metal can bend under stress instead of fracturing like ionically and covalently bonded crystals. The physical properties vary greatly depending on the composition.

Q43.11 The energy of the photon is given to the electron. The energy of a photon of visible light is sufficient to promote the electron from the lower-energy valence band to the higher-energy conduction band. This results in the additional electron in the conduction band and an additional hole—the energy state that the electron used to occupy—in the valence band.

Q43.12 Along with arsenic (As), any other element in group V, such as phosphorus (P), antimony (Sb), and bismuth (Bi), would make good donor atoms. Each has 5 valence electrons. Any element in group III would make good acceptor atoms, such as boron (B), aluminum, (Al), gallium (Ga), and indium (In). They all have only 3 valence electrons.

Q43.13 The two assumptions in the free-electron theory are that the conduction electrons are not bound to any particular atom, and that the nuclei of the atoms are fixed in a lattice structure. In this model, it is the "soup" of free electrons that are conducted through metals. The energy band model is more comprehensive than the free-electron theory. The energy band model includes an account of the more tightly bound electrons as well as the conduction electrons. It can be developed into a theory of the structure of the crystal and its mechanical and thermal properties.

Q43.14 A molecule containing two atoms of ${}^2\text{H}$, deuterium, has twice the mass of a molecule containing two atoms of ordinary hydrogen ${}^1\text{H}$. The atoms have the same electronic structure, so the molecules have the same interatomic spacing, and the same spring constant. Then the moment of inertia of the double-deuteron is twice as large and the rotational energies one-half as large as for ordinary hydrogen. Each vibrational energy level for D_2 is $\frac{1}{\sqrt{2}}$ times that of H_2.

Q43.15 Rotation of a diatomic molecule involves less energy than vibration. Absorption of microwave photons, of frequency $\sim 10^{11}$ Hz, excites rotational motion, while absorption of infrared photons, of frequency $\sim 10^{13}$ Hz, excites vibration in typical simple molecules.

Q43.16 Yes. A material can absorb a photon of energy greater than the energy gap, as an electron jumps into a higher energy state. If the photon does not have enough energy to raise the energy of the electron by the energy gap, then the photon will not be absorbed.

Q43.17 From the rotational spectrum of a molecule, one can easily calculate the moment of inertia of the molecule using Equation 43.7 in the text. Note that with this method, only the spacing between adjacent energy levels needs to be measured. From the moment of inertia, the size of the molecule can be calculated, provided that the structure of the molecule is known.

SOLUTIONS TO PROBLEMS

Section 43.1 Molecular Bonds

P43.1 (a) $$F = \frac{q^2}{4\pi \in_0 r^2} = \frac{\left(1.60\times10^{-19}\right)^2\left(8.99\times10^9\right)}{\left(5.00\times10^{-10}\right)^2}\text{ N} = \boxed{0.921\times10^{-9}\text{ N}}\text{ toward the other ion.}$$

(b) $$U = \frac{-q^2}{4\pi \in_0 r} = -\frac{\left(1.60\times10^{-19}\right)^2\left(8.99\times10^9\right)}{5.00\times10^{-10}}\text{ J} \approx \boxed{-2.88\text{ eV}}$$

P43.2 We are told $K + Cl + 0.7\text{ eV} \rightarrow K^+ + Cl^-$

and $Cl + e^- \rightarrow Cl^- + 3.6\text{ eV}$

or $Cl^- \rightarrow Cl + e^- - 3.6\text{ eV}$.

By substitution, $K + Cl + 0.7\text{ eV} \rightarrow K^+ + Cl + e^- - 3.6\text{ eV}$

$K + 4.3\text{ eV} \rightarrow K^+ + e^-$

or the ionization energy of potassium is $\boxed{4.3\text{ eV}}$.

P43.3 (a) Minimum energy of the molecule is found from

$$\frac{dU}{dr} = -12Ar^{-13} + 6Br^{-7} = 0 \text{ yielding } \boxed{r_0 = \left[\frac{2A}{B}\right]^{1/6}}.$$

(b)
$$E = U|_{r=\infty} - U|_{r=r_0} = 0 - \left[\frac{A}{4A^2/B^2} - \frac{B}{2A/B}\right] = -\left[\frac{1}{4} - \frac{1}{2}\right]\frac{B^2}{A} = \boxed{\frac{B^2}{4A}}$$

This is also the equal to the binding energy, the amount of energy given up by the two atoms as they come together to form a molecule.

(c)
$$r_0 = \left[\frac{2\left(0.124 \times 10^{-120}\text{ eV}\cdot\text{m}^{12}\right)}{1.488 \times 10^{-60}\text{ eV}\cdot\text{m}^6}\right]^{1/6} = 7.42 \times 10^{-11}\text{ m} = \boxed{74.2\text{ pm}}$$

$$E = \frac{\left(1.488 \times 10^{-60}\text{ eV}\cdot\text{m}^6\right)^2}{4\left(0.124 \times 10^{-120}\text{ eV}\cdot\text{m}^{12}\right)} = \boxed{4.46\text{ eV}}$$

***P43.4** (a) We add the reactions $K + 4.34\text{ eV} \rightarrow K^+ + e^-$

and $I + e^- \rightarrow I^- + 3.06\text{ eV}$

to obtain $K + I \rightarrow K^+ + I^- + (4.34 - 3.06)\text{ eV}$.

The activation energy is $\boxed{1.28\text{ eV}}$.

(b)
$$\frac{dU}{dr} = \frac{4\epsilon}{\sigma}\left[-12\left(\frac{\sigma}{r}\right)^{13} + 6\left(\frac{\sigma}{r}\right)^7\right]$$

At $r = r_0$ we have $\frac{dU}{dr} = 0$. Here $\left(\frac{\sigma}{r_0}\right)^{13} = \frac{1}{2}\left(\frac{\sigma}{r_0}\right)^7$

$$\frac{\sigma}{r_0} = 2^{-1/6} \qquad \sigma = 2^{-1/6}(0.305)\text{ nm} = \boxed{0.272\text{ nm} = \sigma}.$$

Then also

$$U(r_0) = 4\epsilon\left[\left(\frac{2^{-1/6}r_0}{r_0}\right)^{12} - \left(\frac{2^{-1/6}r_0}{r_0}\right)^6\right] + E_a = 4\epsilon\left[\frac{1}{4} - \frac{1}{2}\right] + E_a = -\epsilon + E_a$$

$$\epsilon = E_a - U(r_0) = 1.28\text{ eV} + 3.37\text{ eV} = \boxed{4.65\text{ eV} = \epsilon}$$

continued on next page

(c) $$F(r)=-\frac{dU}{dr}=\frac{4\in}{\sigma}\left[12\left(\frac{\sigma}{r}\right)^{13}-6\left(\frac{\sigma}{r}\right)^{7}\right]$$

To find the maximum force we calculate $\frac{dF}{dr}=\frac{4\in}{\sigma^2}\left[-156\left(\frac{\sigma}{r}\right)^{14}+42\left(\frac{\sigma}{r}\right)^{8}\right]=0$ when

$$\frac{\sigma}{r_{\text{rupture}}}=\left(\frac{42}{156}\right)^{1/6}$$

$$F_{\max}=\frac{4(4.65\text{ eV})}{0.272\text{ nm}}\left[12\left(\frac{42}{156}\right)^{13/6}-6\left(\frac{42}{156}\right)^{7/6}\right]=-41.0\text{ eV/nm}=-41.0\frac{1.6\times10^{-19}\text{ Nm}}{10^{-9}\text{ m}}$$
$$=-6.55\text{ nN}$$

Therefore the applied force required to rupture the molecule is $\boxed{+6.55\text{ nN}}$ away from the center.

(d) $$U(r_0+s)=4\in\left[\left(\frac{\sigma}{r_0+s}\right)^{12}-\left(\frac{\sigma}{r_0+s}\right)^{6}\right]+E_a=4\in\left[\left(\frac{2^{-1/6}r_0}{r_0+s}\right)^{12}-\left(\frac{2^{-1/6}}{r_0+s}\right)^{6}\right]+E_a$$
$$=4\in\left[\frac{1}{4}\left(1+\frac{s}{r_0}\right)^{-12}-\frac{1}{2}\left(1+\frac{s}{r_0}\right)^{-6}\right]+E_a$$
$$=4\in\left[\frac{1}{4}\left(1-12\frac{s}{r_0}+78\frac{s^2}{r_0^2}-\ldots\right)-\frac{1}{2}\left(1-6\frac{s}{r_0}+21\frac{s^2}{r_0^2}-\ldots\right)\right]+E_a$$
$$=\in-12\in\frac{s}{r_0}+78\in\frac{s^2}{r_0^2}-2\in+12\in\frac{s}{r_0}-42\in\frac{s^2}{r_0^2}+E_a+\ldots$$
$$=-\in+E_a+0\left(\frac{s}{r_0}\right)+36\in\frac{s^2}{r_0^2}+\ldots$$
$$U(r_0+s)\cong U(r_0)+\frac{1}{2}ks^2$$

where $k=\frac{72\in}{r_0^2}=\frac{72(4.65\text{ eV})}{(0.305\text{ nm})^2}=3\,599\text{ eV/nm}^2=\boxed{576\text{ N/m}}$.

P43.5 At the boiling or condensation temperature, $k_BT\approx10^{-3}\text{ eV}=10^{-3}\left(1.6\times10^{-19}\text{ J}\right)$

$$T\approx\frac{1.6\times10^{-22}\text{ J}}{1.38\times10^{-23}\text{ J/K}}\boxed{\sim10\text{ K}}.$$

Section 43.2 **Energy States and Spectra of Molecules**

P43.6 $$\mu = \frac{m_1 m_2}{m_1 + m_2} = \frac{132.9(126.9)}{132.9 + 126.9}\left(1.66 \times 10^{-27}\ \text{kg}\right) = 1.08 \times 10^{-25}\ \text{kg}$$

$$I = \mu r^2 = \left(1.08 \times 10^{-25}\ \text{kg}\right)\left(0.127 \times 10^{-9}\ \text{m}\right)^2 = 1.74 \times 10^{-45}\ \text{kg} \cdot \text{m}^2$$

(a) $$E = \frac{1}{2} I\omega^2 = \frac{(I\omega)^2}{2I} = \frac{J(J+1)\hbar^2}{2I}$$

$J = 0$ gives $E = 0$

$$J = 1 \text{ gives } E = \frac{\hbar^2}{I} = \frac{\left(6.626 \times 10^{-34}\ \text{J} \cdot \text{s}\right)^2}{4\pi^2\left(1.74 \times 10^{-45}\ \text{kg} \cdot \text{m}^2\right)} = 6.41 \times 10^{-24}\ \text{J} = \boxed{40.0\ \mu\text{eV}}$$

$$hf = 6.41 \times 10^{-24}\ \text{J} - 0 \text{ to } f = \boxed{9.66 \times 10^9\ \text{Hz}}$$

(b) $$f = \frac{E_1}{h} = \frac{\hbar^2}{hI} = \frac{h}{4\pi^2 \mu r^2} \propto r^{-2}$$ **If r is 10% too small, f is 20% too large.**

P43.7 For the HCl molecule in the $J = 1$ rotational energy level, we are given $r_0 = 0.127\,5$ nm.

$$E_{\text{rot}} = \frac{\hbar^2}{2I} J(J+1)$$

Taking $J = 1$, we have $$E_{\text{rot}} = \frac{\hbar^2}{I} = \frac{1}{2} I\omega^2 \text{ or } \omega = \sqrt{\frac{2\hbar^2}{I^2}} = \sqrt{2}\frac{\hbar}{I}.$$

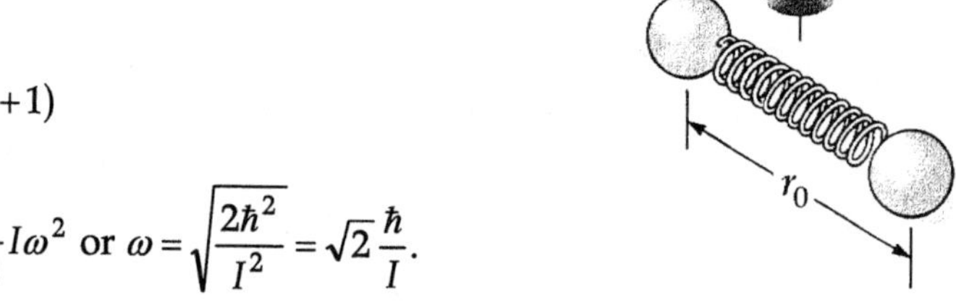

FIG. P43.7

The moment of inertia of the molecule is given by Equation 43.3.

$$I = \mu r_0^2 = \left(\frac{m_1 m_2}{m_1 + m_2}\right) r_0^2$$

$$I = \left[\frac{(1\ \text{u})(35\ \text{u})}{1\ \text{u} + 35\ \text{u}}\right] r_0^2 = (0.972\ \text{u})\left(1.66 \times 10^{-27}\ \text{kg/u}\right)\left(1.275 \times 10^{-10}\ \text{m}\right)^2 = 2.62 \times 10^{-47}\ \text{kg} \cdot \text{m}^2.$$

Therefore, $$\omega = \sqrt{2}\frac{\hbar}{I} = \sqrt{2}\frac{1.055 \times 10^{-34}\ \text{J} \cdot \text{s}}{2.62 \times 10^{-47}\ \text{kg} \cdot \text{m}^2} = \boxed{5.69 \times 10^{12}\ \text{rad/s}}.$$

P43.8 $$hf = \Delta E = \frac{\hbar^2}{2I}[2(2+1)] - \frac{\hbar^2}{2I}[1(1+1)] = \frac{\hbar^2}{2I}(4)$$

$$I = \frac{4(h/2\pi)^2}{2hf} = \frac{h}{2\pi^2 f} = \frac{6.626 \times 10^{-34}\ \text{J} \cdot \text{s}}{2\pi^2\left(2.30 \times 10^{11}\ \text{Hz}\right)} = \boxed{1.46 \times 10^{-46}\ \text{kg} \cdot \text{m}^2}$$

P43.9 $I = m_1 r_1^2 + m_2 r_2^2$ where $m_1 r_1 = m_2 r_2$ and $r_1 + r_2 = r$.

Then $r_1 = \frac{m_2 r_2}{m_1}$ so $\frac{m_2 r_2}{m_1} + r_2 = r$ and $r_2 = \frac{m_1 r}{m_1 + m_2}$.

Also, $r_2 = \frac{m_1 r_1}{m_2}$. Thus, $r_1 + \frac{m_1 r_1}{m_2} = r$ and $r_1 = \frac{m_2 r}{m_1 + m_2}$

$$I = m_1 \frac{m_2^2 r^2}{(m_1 + m_2)^2} + \frac{m_2 m_1^2 r^2}{(m_1 + m_2)^2} = \frac{m_1 m_2 r^2 (m_2 + m_1)}{(m_1 + m_2)^2} = \frac{m_1 m_2 r^2}{m_1 + m_2} = \boxed{\mu r^2}.$$

P43.10 (a) $$\mu = \frac{22.99(35.45)}{(22.99 + 35.45)}\left(1.66 \times 10^{-27}\text{ kg}\right) = 2.32 \times 10^{-26}\text{ kg}$$

$$I = \mu r^2 = \left(2.32 \times 10^{-26}\text{ kg}\right)\left(0.280 \times 10^{-9}\text{ m}\right)^2 = \boxed{1.81 \times 10^{-45}\text{ kg}\cdot\text{m}^2}$$

(b) $$\frac{hc}{\lambda} = \frac{\hbar^2}{2I}2(2+1) - \frac{\hbar^2}{2I}1(1+1) = \frac{3\hbar^2}{I} - \frac{\hbar^2}{I} = \frac{2\hbar^2}{I} = \frac{2h^2}{4\pi^2 I}$$

$$\lambda = \frac{c4\pi^2 I}{2h} = \frac{\left(3.00 \times 10^8\text{ m/s}\right)4\pi^2\left(1.81 \times 10^{-45}\text{ kg}\cdot\text{m}^2\right)}{2\left(6.626 \times 10^{-34}\text{ J}\cdot\text{s}\right)} = \boxed{1.62\text{ cm}}$$

P43.11 The energy of a rotational transition is $\Delta E = \left(\frac{\hbar^2}{I}\right)J$ where J is the rotational quantum number of the higher energy state (see Equation 43.7). We do not know J from the data. However,

$$\Delta E = \frac{hc}{\lambda} = \frac{\left(6.626 \times 10^{-34}\text{ J}\cdot\text{s}\right)\left(3.00 \times 10^8\text{ m/s}\right)}{\lambda}\left(\frac{1\text{ eV}}{1.60 \times 10^{-19}\text{ J}}\right).$$

For each observed wavelength,

λ (mm)	ΔE (eV)
0.120 4	0.010 32
0.096 4	0.012 88
0.080 4	0.015 44
0.069 0	0.018 00
0.060 4	0.020 56

The ΔE's consistently increase by 0.002 56 eV. $E_1 = \frac{\hbar^2}{I} = 0.002\,56\text{ eV}$

and $$I = \frac{\hbar^2}{E_1} = \frac{\left(1.055 \times 10^{-34}\text{ J}\cdot\text{s}\right)^2}{(0.002\,56\text{ eV})}\left(\frac{1\text{ eV}}{1.60 \times 10^{-19}\text{ J}}\right) = \boxed{2.72 \times 10^{-47}\text{ kg}\cdot\text{m}^2}.$$

For the HCl molecule, the internuclear radius is $r = \sqrt{\frac{I}{\mu}} = \sqrt{\frac{2.72 \times 10^{-47}}{1.62 \times 10^{-27}}}\text{ m} = 0.130\text{ nm}.$

P43.12 (a) Minimum amplitude of vibration of HI is

$$\frac{1}{2}kA^2=\frac{1}{2}hf: \quad A=\sqrt{\frac{hf}{k}}=\sqrt{\frac{(6.626\times10^{-34}\text{ J}\cdot\text{s})(6.69\times10^{13}/\text{s})}{320\text{ N/m}}}=1.18\times10^{-11}\text{ m}=\boxed{0.011\,8\text{ nm}}.$$

(b) For HF,
$$A=\sqrt{\frac{(6.626\times10^{-34}\text{ J}\cdot\text{s})(8.72\times10^{13}/\text{s})}{970\text{ N/m}}}=7.72\times10^{-12}\text{ m}=\boxed{0.007\,72\text{ nm}}.$$

Since HI has the smaller k, it is more weakly bound.

P43.13
$$\mu=\frac{m_1m_2}{m_1+m_2}=\frac{35}{36}\times1.66\times10^{-27}\text{ kg}=1.61\times10^{-27}\text{ kg}$$

$$\Delta E_{\text{vib}}=\hbar\sqrt{\frac{k}{\mu}}=(1.055\times10^{-34})\sqrt{\frac{480}{1.61\times10^{-27}}}=5.74\times10^{-20}\text{ J}=\boxed{0.358\text{ eV}}$$

P43.14 (a) The reduced mass of the O_2 is $\mu=\frac{(16\text{ u})(16\text{ u})}{(16\text{ u})+(16\text{ u})}=8\text{ u}=8(1.66\times10^{-27}\text{ kg})=1.33\times10^{-26}\text{ kg}$.

The moment of inertia is then $I=\mu r^2=(1.33\times10^{-26}\text{ kg})(1.20\times10^{-10}\text{ m})^2=1.91\times10^{-46}\text{ kg}\cdot\text{m}^2$.

The rotational energies are $E_{\text{rot}}=\frac{\hbar^2}{2I}J(J+1)=\frac{(1.055\times10^{-34}\text{ J}\cdot\text{s})^2}{2(1.91\times10^{-46}\text{ kg}\cdot\text{m}^2)}J(J+1)$.

Thus $E_{\text{rot}}=(2.91\times10^{-23}\text{ J})J(J+1)$.

And for $J=0, 1, 2,$ $E_{\text{rot}}=\boxed{0,\ 3.64\times10^{-4}\text{ eV},\ 1.09\times10^{-3}\text{ eV}}$.

(b)
$$E_{\text{vib}}=\left(v+\frac{1}{2}\right)\hbar\sqrt{\frac{k}{\mu}}=\left(v+\frac{1}{2}\right)(1.055\times10^{-34}\text{ J}\cdot\text{s})\sqrt{\frac{1\,177\text{ N/m}}{8(1.66\times10^{-27}\text{ kg})}}$$

$$E_{\text{vib}}=\left(v+\frac{1}{2}\right)(3.14\times10^{-20}\text{ J})\left(\frac{1\text{ eV}}{1.60\times10^{-19}\text{ J}}\right)=\left(v+\frac{1}{2}\right)(0.196\text{ eV})$$

For $v=0, 1, 2,$ $\boxed{E_{\text{vib}}=0.098\,2\text{ eV},\ 0.295\text{ eV},\ 0.491\text{ eV}}$.

P43.15 In Benzene, the carbon atoms are each 0.110 nm from the axis and each hydrogen atom is $(0.110+0.100\text{ nm})=0.210\text{ nm}$ from the axis. Thus, $I=\sum mr^2$:

$$I=6\left(1.99\times10^{-26}\text{ kg}\right)\left(0.110\times10^{-9}\text{ m}\right)^2+6\left(1.67\times10^{-27}\text{ kg}\right)\left(0.210\times10^{-9}\text{ m}\right)^2=1.89\times10^{-45}\text{ kg}\cdot\text{m}^2.$$

The allowed rotational energies are then

$$E_{\text{rot}}=\frac{\hbar^2}{2I}J(J+1)=\frac{\left(1.055\times10^{-34}\text{ J}\cdot\text{s}\right)^2}{2\left(1.89\times10^{-45}\text{ kg}\cdot\text{m}^2\right)}J(J+1)=\left(2.95\times10^{-24}\text{ J}\right)J(J+1)=\left(18.4\times10^{-6}\text{ eV}\right)J(J+1)$$

$$E_{\text{rot}}=\boxed{(18.4\ \mu\text{eV})J(J+1)\text{ where }J=0,\ 1,\ 2,\ 3,\ \ldots}$$

The first five of these allowed energies are: $E_{\text{rot}}=0$, $36.9\ \mu\text{eV}$, $111\ \mu\text{eV}$, $221\ \mu\text{eV}$, and $369\ \mu\text{eV}$.

***P43.16** We carry extra digits through the solution because part (c) involves the subtraction of two close numbers. The longest wavelength corresponds to the smallest energy difference between the rotational energy levels. It is between $J=0$ and $J=1$, namely $\frac{\hbar^2}{I}$

$$\lambda=\frac{hc}{\Delta E_{\min}}=\frac{hc}{\hbar^2/I}=\frac{4\pi^2Ic}{h}.$$ If μ is the reduced mass, then

$$I=\mu r^2=\mu\left(0.127\,46\times10^{-9}\text{ m}\right)^2=\left(1.624\,605\times10^{-20}\text{ m}^2\right)\mu$$

$$\therefore\lambda=\frac{4\pi^2\left(1.624\,605\times10^{-20}\text{ m}^2\right)\mu\left(2.997\,925\times10^8\text{ m/s}\right)}{6.626\,075\times10^{-34}\text{ J}\cdot\text{s}}=\left(2.901\,830\times10^{23}\text{ m/kg}\right)\mu \qquad (1)$$

(a) $$\mu_{35}=\frac{(1.007\,825\text{u})(34.968\,853\text{u})}{1.007\,825\text{u}+34.968\,853\text{u}}=0.979\,593\text{u}=1.626\,653\times10^{-27}\text{ kg}$$

From (1): $\lambda_{35}=\left(2.901\,830\times10^{23}\text{ m/kg}\right)\left(1.626\,653\times10^{-27}\text{ kg}\right)=\boxed{472\ \mu\text{m}}$

(b) $$\mu_{37}=\frac{(1.007\,825\text{u})(36.965\,903\text{u})}{1.007\,825\text{u}+36.965\,903\text{u}}=0.981\,077\text{u}=1.629\,118\times10^{-27}\text{ kg}$$

From (1): $\lambda_{37}=\left(2.901\,830\times10^{23}\text{ m/kg}\right)\left(1.629\,118\times10^{-27}\text{ kg}\right)=\boxed{473\ \mu\text{m}}$

(c) $\lambda_{37}-\lambda_{35}=472.742\,4\ \mu\text{m}-472.027\,0\ \mu\text{m}=\boxed{0.715\ \mu\text{m}}$

P43.17 $hf=\frac{h^2}{4\pi^2I}J$ where the rotational transition is from $J-1$ to J,

where $f=6.42\times10^{13}$ Hz and $I=1.46\times10^{-46}\text{ kg}\cdot\text{m}^2$ from Example 43.1.

$$J=\frac{4\pi^2If}{h}=\frac{4\pi^2\left(1.46\times10^{-46}\text{ kg}\cdot\text{m}^2\right)\left(6.42\times10^{13}/\text{s}\right)}{6.626\times10^{-34}\text{ J}\cdot\text{s}}=\boxed{558}$$

***P43.18** We find an average spacing between peaks by counting 22 gaps between 7.96×10^{13} Hz and 9.24×10^{13} Hz:

$$\Delta f=\frac{(9.24-7.96)10^{13}\text{ Hz}}{22}=0.058\,2\times10^{13}\text{ Hz}=\frac{1}{h}\left(\frac{h^2}{4\pi^2 I}\right)$$

$$I=\frac{h}{4\pi^2\Delta f}=\frac{6.63\times10^{-34}\text{ J}\cdot\text{s}}{4\pi^2 5.82\times10^{11}/\text{s}}=\boxed{2.9\times10^{-47}\text{ kg}\cdot\text{m}^2}$$

***P43.19** We carry extra digits through the solution because the given wavelengths are close together.

(a) $$E_{vJ}=\left(v+\frac{1}{2}\right)hf+\frac{\hbar^2}{2I}J(J+1)$$

$$\therefore E_{00}=\frac{1}{2}hf,\qquad E_{11}=\frac{3}{2}hf+\frac{\hbar^2}{I},\ E_{02}=\frac{1}{2}hf+\frac{3\hbar^2}{I}$$

$$\therefore E_{11}-E_{00}=hf+\frac{\hbar^2}{I}=\frac{hc}{\lambda}=\frac{(6.626\,075\times10^{-34}\text{ J}\cdot\text{s})(2.997\,925\times10^{8}\text{ m/s})}{2.211\,2\times10^{-6}\text{ m}}$$

$$\therefore hf+\frac{\hbar^2}{I}=8.983\,573\times10^{-20}\text{ J} \qquad (1)$$

$$E_{11}-E_{02}=hf-\frac{2\hbar^2}{I}=\frac{hc}{\lambda}=\frac{(6.626\,075\times10^{-34}\text{ J}\cdot\text{s})(2.997\,925\times10^{8}\text{ m/s})}{2.405\,4\times10^{-6}\text{ m}}$$

$$\therefore hf-\frac{2\hbar^2}{I}=8.258\,284\times10^{-20}\text{ J} \qquad (2)$$

Subtract (2) from (1): $\frac{3\hbar^2}{I}=7.252\,89\times10^{-21}\text{ J}$

$$\therefore I=\frac{3(1.054\,573\times10^{-34}\text{ J}\cdot\text{s})^2}{7.252\,89\times10^{-21}\text{ J}}=\boxed{4.60\times10^{-48}\text{ kg}\cdot\text{m}^2}$$

(b) From (1):

$$f=\frac{8.983\,573\times10^{-20}\text{ J}}{6.626\,075\times10^{-34}\text{ J}\cdot\text{s}}-\frac{(1.054\,573\times10^{-34}\text{ J}\cdot\text{s})^2}{(4.600\,060\times10^{-48}\text{ kg}\cdot\text{m}^2)(6.626\,075\times10^{-34}\text{ J}\cdot\text{s})}$$

$$=\boxed{1.32\times10^{14}\text{ Hz}}$$

(c) $I=\mu r^2$, where μ is the reduced mass:

$$\mu=\frac{1}{2}m_H=\frac{1}{2}(1.007\,825\text{u})=8.367\,669\times10^{-28}\text{ kg}.$$

So $r=\sqrt{\frac{I}{\mu}}=\sqrt{\frac{4.600\,060\times10^{-48}\text{ kg}\cdot\text{m}^2}{8.367\,669\times10^{-28}\text{ kg}}}=\boxed{0.0741\text{ nm}}$.

P43.20 The emission energies are the same as the absorption energies, but the final state must be below $(v=1,\ J=0)$. The transition must satisfy $\Delta J = \pm 1$, so it must end with $J=1$. To be lower in energy, it must be $(v=0,\ J=1)$. The emitted photon energy is therefore

$$hf_{\text{photon}} = \left(E_{\text{vib}}\big|_{v=1} + E_{\text{rot}}\big|_{J=0}\right) - \left(E_{\text{vib}}\big|_{v=0} + E_{\text{rot}}\big|_{J=1}\right) = \left(E_{\text{vib}}\big|_{v=1} - E_{\text{vib}}\big|_{v=0}\right) - \left(E_{\text{rot}}\big|_{J=1} - E_{\text{rot}}\big|_{J=0}\right)$$

$$hf_{\text{photon}} = hf_{\text{vib}} - hf_{\text{rot}}$$

Thus, $f_{\text{photon}} = f_{\text{vib}} - f_{\text{rot}} = 6.42 \times 10^{13}\ \text{Hz} - 1.15 \times 10^{11}\ \text{Hz} = \boxed{6.41 \times 10^{13}\ \text{Hz}}$.

P43.21 The moment of inertia about the molecular axis is $I_x = \frac{2}{5}mr^2 + \frac{2}{5}mr^2 = \frac{4}{5}m\left(2.00 \times 10^{-15}\ \text{m}\right)^2$.

The moment of inertia about a perpendicular axis is $I_y = m\left(\frac{R}{2}\right)^2 + m\left(\frac{R}{2}\right)^2 = \frac{m}{2}\left(2.00 \times 10^{-10}\ \text{m}\right)^2$.

The allowed rotational energies are $E_{\text{rot}} = \left(\frac{\hbar^2}{2I}\right)J(J+1)$, so the energy of the first excited state is $E_1 = \frac{\hbar^2}{I}$. The ratio is therefore

$$\frac{E_{1,x}}{E_{1,y}} = \frac{\left(\hbar^2/I_x\right)}{\left(\hbar^2/I_y\right)} = \frac{I_y}{I_x} = \frac{(1/2)m\left(2.00 \times 10^{-10}\ \text{m}\right)^2}{(4/5)m\left(2.00 \times 10^{-15}\ \text{m}\right)^2} = \frac{5}{8}\left(10^5\right)^2 = \boxed{6.25 \times 10^9}.$$

Section 43.3 **Bonding in Solids**

P43.22 Consider a cubical salt crystal of edge length 0.1 mm.

The number of atoms is $\left(\frac{10^{-4}\ \text{m}}{0.261 \times 10^{-9}\ \text{m}}\right)^3 \boxed{\sim 10^{17}}$.

This number of salt crystals would have volume $\left(10^{-4}\ \text{m}\right)^3\left(\frac{10^{-4}\ \text{m}}{0.261 \times 10^{-9}\ \text{m}}\right)^3 \boxed{\sim 10^5\ \text{m}^3}$.

If it is cubic, it has edge length 40 m.

P43.23 $$U = -\frac{\alpha k_e e^2}{r_0}\left(1 - \frac{1}{m}\right) = -(1.747\,6)\left(8.99 \times 10^9\right)\frac{\left(1.60 \times 10^{-19}\right)^2}{\left(0.281 \times 10^{-9}\right)}\left(1 - \frac{1}{8}\right) = -1.25 \times 10^{-18}\ \text{J} = \boxed{-7.84\ \text{eV}}$$

P43.24 Visualize a K^+ ion at the center of each shaded cube, a Cl^- ion at the center of each white one.

The distance *ab* is $\sqrt{2}(0.314\ \text{nm}) = \boxed{0.444\ \text{nm}}$.

Distance *ac* is $2(0.314\ \text{nm}) = \boxed{0.628\ \text{nm}}$.

Distance *ad* is $\sqrt{2^2 + \left(\sqrt{2}\right)^2}(0.314\ \text{nm}) = \boxed{0.769\ \text{nm}}$.

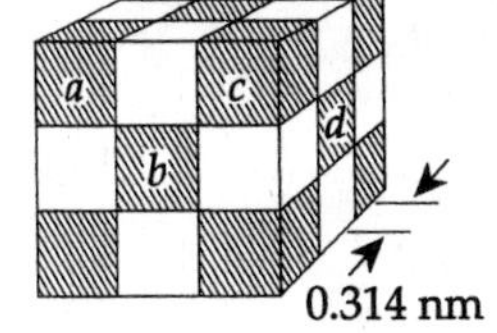

FIG. P43.24

P43.25 $U=-\frac{k_e e^2}{r}-\frac{k_e e^2}{r}+\frac{k_e e^2}{2r}+\frac{k_e e^2}{2r}-\frac{k_e e^2}{3r}-\frac{k_e e^2}{3r}+\frac{k_e e^2}{4r}+\frac{k_e e^2}{4r}-\ldots$

$$=-\frac{2k_e e^2}{r}\left(1-\frac{1}{2}+\frac{1}{3}-\frac{1}{4}+\ldots\right)$$

But, $\ln(1+x)=1-\frac{x^2}{2}+\frac{x^3}{3}-\frac{x^4}{4}+\ldots$

so, $U=-\frac{2k_e e^2}{r}\ln 2$, or $\boxed{U=-k_e\alpha\frac{e^2}{r} \text{ where } \alpha=2\ln 2}$.

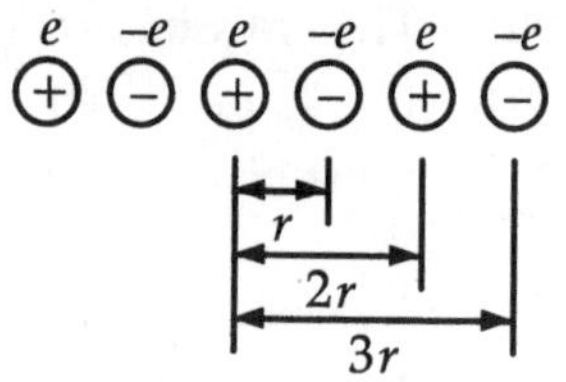

e −e e −e e −e

r

2r

3r

FIG. P43.25

Section 43.4 **Free-Electron Theory of Metals**

Section 43.5 **Band Theory of Solids**

P43.26 $E_F=\frac{h^2}{2m}\left(\frac{3n_e}{8\pi}\right)^{2/3}=\left[\frac{\left(6.626\times10^{-34}\text{ J}\cdot\text{s}\right)^2}{2\left(9.11\times10^{-31}\text{ kg}\right)\left(1.60\times10^{-19}\text{ J/eV}\right)}\right]\left(\frac{3}{8\pi}\right)^{2/3}n_e^{2/3}$

$E_F=\left(3.65\times10^{-19}\right)n_e^{2/3}$ eV with n measured in electrons/m^3.

P43.27 The density of conduction electrons n is given by $E_F=\frac{h^2}{2m}\left(\frac{3n_e}{8\pi}\right)^{2/3}$

or $$n_e=\frac{8\pi}{3}\left(\frac{2mE_F}{h^2}\right)^{3/2}=\frac{8\pi}{3}\frac{\left[2\left(9.11\times10^{-31}\text{ kg}\right)(5.48)\left(1.60\times10^{-19}\text{ J}\right)\right]^{3/2}}{\left(6.626\times10^{-34}\text{ J}\cdot\text{s}\right)^3}=5.80\times10^{28}\text{ m}^{-3}.$$

The number-density of silver atoms is

$$n_{Ag}=\left(10.6\times10^3\text{ kg/m}^3\right)\left(\frac{1\text{ atom}}{108\text{ u}}\right)\left(\frac{1\text{ u}}{1.66\times10^{-27}\text{ kg}}\right)=5.91\times10^{28}\text{ m}^{-3}.$$

So an average atom contributes $\frac{5.80}{5.91}=\boxed{0.981 \text{ electron to the conduction band}}$.

P43.28 (a) $\frac{1}{2}mv^2=7.05$ eV

$$v=\sqrt{\frac{2(7.05\text{ eV})\left(1.60\times10^{-19}\text{ J/eV}\right)}{9.11\times10^{-31}\text{ kg}}}=\boxed{1.57\times10^6\text{ m/s}}$$

(b) $\boxed{\text{Larger than }10^{-4}\text{ m/s by ten orders of magnitude.}}$ However, the energy of an electron at room temperature is typically $k_BT=\frac{1}{40}$ eV.

P43.29 For sodium, $M = 23.0\ \text{g/mol}$ and $\rho = 0.971\ \text{g/cm}^3$.

(a) $$n_e = \frac{N_A \rho}{M} = \frac{(6.02\times10^{23}\ \text{electrons/mol})(0.971\ \text{g/cm}^3)}{23.0\ \text{g/mol}}$$

$$n_e = 2.54\times10^{22}\ \text{electrons/cm}^3 = \boxed{2.54\times10^{28}\ \text{electrons/m}^3}$$

(b) $$E_F = \left(\frac{h^2}{2m}\right)\left(\frac{3n_e}{8\pi}\right)^{2/3} = \frac{(6.626\times10^{-34}\ \text{J}\cdot\text{s})^2}{2(9.11\times10^{-31}\ \text{kg})}\left[\frac{3(2.54\times10^{28}\ \text{m}^{-3})}{8\pi}\right]^{2/3} = 5.05\times10^{-19}\ \text{J} = \boxed{3.15\ \text{eV}}$$

P43.30 The melting point of silver is 1 234 K. Its Fermi energy at 300 K is 5.48 eV. The approximate fraction of electrons excited is

$$\frac{k_B T}{E_F} = \frac{(1.38\times10^{-23}\ \text{J/K})(1\,234\ \text{K})}{(5.48\ \text{eV})(1.60\times10^{-19}\ \text{J/eV})} \approx \boxed{2\%}.$$

P43.31 Taking $E_F = 5.48\ \text{eV}$ for sodium at 800 K,

$$f = \left[e^{(E-E_F)/k_BT} + 1\right]^{-1} = 0.950$$

$$e^{(E-E_F)/k_BT} = \frac{1}{0.950} - 1 = 0.052\,6$$

$$\frac{E-E_F}{k_BT} = \ln(0.052\,6) = -2.94$$

$$E - E_F = -2.94\frac{(1.38\times10^{-23})(800)\ \text{J}}{1.60\times10^{-19}\ \text{J/eV}} = -0.203\ \text{eV or } \boxed{E = 5.28\ \text{eV}}.$$

P43.32 $d = 1.00\ \text{mm}$, so $V = (1.00\times10^{-3}\ \text{m})^3 = 1.00\times10^{-9}\ \text{m}^3$.

The **density of states** is $g(E) = CE^{1/2} = \dfrac{8\sqrt{2}\pi m^{3/2}}{h^3}E^{1/2}$

or $$g(E) = \frac{8\sqrt{2}\pi(9.11\times10^{-31}\ \text{kg})^{3/2}}{(6.626\times10^{-34}\ \text{J}\cdot\text{s})^3}\sqrt{(4.00\ \text{eV})(1.60\times10^{-19}\ \text{J/eV})}$$

$$g(E) = 8.50\times10^{46}\ \text{m}^{-3}\cdot\text{J}^{-1} = 1.36\times10^{28}\ \text{m}^{-3}\cdot\text{eV}^{-1}.$$

So, the total number of electrons is

$$N = [g(E)](\Delta E)V = (1.36\times10^{28}\ \text{m}^{-3}\cdot\text{eV}^{-1})(0.025\,0\ \text{eV})(1.00\times10^{-9}\ \text{m}^3) = \boxed{3.40\times10^{17}\ \text{electrons}}.$$

P43.33 $E_{av} = \frac{1}{n_e}\int_0^\infty EN(E)dE$

At $T = 0$, $N(E) = 0$ for $E > E_F$;.

Since $f(E) = 1$ for $E < E_{EF}$ and $f(E) = 0$ for $E > E_F$, we can take $N(E) = CE^{1/2} = \frac{8\sqrt{2}\pi m_e^{3/2}}{h^3}E^{1/2}$

$$E_{av} = \frac{1}{n_e}\int_0^{E_F} CE^{3/2}dE = \frac{C}{n_e}\int_0^{E_F} E^{3/2}dE = \frac{2C}{5n_e}E_F^{5/2}.$$

But from Equation 43.24, $\frac{C}{n_e} = \frac{3}{2}E_F^{-3/2}$, so that $E_{av} = \left(\frac{2}{5}\right)\left(\frac{3}{2}E_F^{-3/2}\right)E_F^{5/2} = \boxed{\frac{3}{5}E_F}$.

P43.34 Consider first the wave function in x. At $x = 0$ and $x = L$, $\psi = 0$.

Therefore, $\sin k_x L = 0$ and $k_x L = \pi, 2\pi, 3\pi, \ldots$.

Similarly, $\sin k_y L = 0$ and $k_y L = \pi, 2\pi, 3\pi, \ldots$

$\sin k_z L = 0$ and $k_z L = \pi, 2\pi, 3\pi, \ldots$

$$\psi = A\sin\left(\frac{n_x \pi x}{L}\right)\sin\left(\frac{n_y \pi y}{L}\right)\sin\left(\frac{n_z \pi z}{L}\right).$$

From $\frac{\partial^2\psi}{\partial x^2} + \frac{\partial^2\psi}{\partial y^2} + \frac{\partial^2\psi}{\partial z^2} = \frac{2m_e}{\hbar^2}(U - E)\psi$, we have inside the box, where $U = 0$,

$$\left(-\frac{n_x^2\pi^2}{L^2} - \frac{n_y^2\pi^2}{L^2} - \frac{n_z^2\pi^2}{L^2}\right)\psi = \frac{2m_e}{\hbar^2}(-E)\psi \qquad \boxed{E = \frac{\hbar^2\pi^2}{2m_e L^2}\left(n_x^2 + n_y^2 + n_z^2\right) \qquad n_x, n_y, n_z = 1, 2, 3, \ldots}.$$

Outside the box we require $\psi = 0$.

The minimum energy state inside the box is $n_x = n_y = n_z = 1$, with $E = \frac{3\hbar^2\pi^2}{2m_e L^2}$

P43.35 (a) The density of states at energy E is $g(E) = CE^{1/2}$.

Hence, the required ratio is $\frac{g(8.50 \text{ eV})}{g(7.00 \text{ eV})} = \frac{C(8.50)^{1/2}}{C(7.00)^{1/2}} = \boxed{1.10}$.

(b) From Eq. 43.22, the number of occupied states having energy E is

$$N(E) = \frac{CE^{1/2}}{e^{(E - E_F)/k_B T} + 1}.$$

Hence, the required ratio is $\frac{N(8.50 \text{ eV})}{N(7.00 \text{ eV})} = \frac{(8.50)^{1/2}}{(7.00)^{1/2}}\left[\frac{e^{(7.00-7.00)/k_B T} + 1}{e^{(8.50-7.00)/k_B T} + 1}\right]$.

At $T = 300$ K, $k_B T = 4.14 \times 10^{-21}$ J $= 0.025\,9$ eV, $\frac{N(8.50 \text{ eV})}{N(7.00 \text{ eV})} = \frac{(8.50)^{1/2}}{(7.00)^{1/2}}\left[\frac{2.00}{e^{(1.50)/0.025\,9} + 1}\right]$.

And $\frac{N(8.50 \text{ eV})}{N(7.00 \text{ eV})} = \boxed{1.55 \times 10^{-25}}$.

Comparing this result with that from part (a), we conclude that very few states with $E > E_F$ are occupied.

Section 43.6 Electrical Conduction in Metals, Insulators, and Semiconductors

P43.36 (a) $E_g = 1.14 \text{ eV}$ for Si

$$hf = 1.14 \text{ eV} = (1.14 \text{ eV})\left(1.60\times10^{-19} \text{ J/eV}\right) = 1.82\times10^{-19} \text{ J so } f \geq \boxed{2.75\times10^{14} \text{ Hz}}$$

(b) $$c = \lambda f;\ \lambda = \frac{c}{f} = \frac{3.00\times10^{8} \text{ m/s}}{2.75\times10^{14} \text{ Hz}} = 1.09\times10^{-6} \text{ m} = \boxed{1.09\ \mu\text{m}}$$ (in the infrared region)

P43.37 Photons of energy greater than 2.42 eV will be absorbed. This means wavelength shorter than

$$\lambda = \frac{hc}{E} = \frac{\left(6.626\times10^{-34} \text{ J}\cdot\text{s}\right)\left(3.00\times10^{8} \text{ m/s}\right)}{2.42\times1.60\times10^{-19} \text{ J}} = 514 \text{ nm}.$$

All the hydrogen Balmer lines except for the red line at 656 nm will be absorbed.

P43.38 $$E_g = \frac{hc}{\lambda} = \frac{\left(6.626\times10^{-34} \text{ J}\cdot\text{s}\right)\left(3.00\times10^{8} \text{ m/s}\right)}{650\times10^{-9} \text{ m}} \text{ J} \approx \boxed{1.91 \text{ eV}}$$

P43.39 If $\lambda \leq 1.00\times10^{-6}$ m, then photons of sunlight have energy

$$E \geq \frac{hc}{\lambda_{\max}} = \frac{\left(6.626\times10^{-34} \text{ J}\cdot\text{s}\right)\left(3.00\times10^{8} \text{ m/s}\right)}{1.00\times10^{-6} \text{ m}}\left(\frac{1 \text{ eV}}{1.60\times10^{-19} \text{ J}}\right) = 1.24 \text{ eV}.$$

Thus, the energy gap for the collector material should be $\boxed{E_g \leq 1.24 \text{ eV}}$. Since Si has an energy gap $E_g \approx 1.14 \text{ eV}$, it will absorb radiation of this energy and greater. Therefore, $\boxed{\text{Si is acceptable}}$ as a material for a solar collector.

P43.40 If the photon energy is 5.5 eV or higher, the diamond window will absorb. Here,

$$(hf)_{\max} = \frac{hc}{\lambda_{\min}} = 5.5 \text{ eV}: \qquad \lambda_{\min} = \frac{hc}{5.5 \text{ eV}} = \frac{\left(6.626\times10^{-34} \text{ J}\cdot\text{s}\right)\left(3.00\times10^{8} \text{ m/s}\right)}{(5.5 \text{ eV})\left(1.60\times10^{-19} \text{ J/eV}\right)}$$

$$\lambda_{\min} = 2.26\times10^{-7} \text{ m} = \boxed{226 \text{ nm}}.$$

***P43.41** In the Bohr model we replace k_e by $\frac{k_e}{\kappa}$ and m_e by m^*. Then the radius of the first Bohr orbit,

$a_0 = \frac{\hbar^2}{m_e k_e e^2}$ in hydrogen, changes to

$$a' = \frac{\hbar^2\kappa}{m^* k_e e^2} = \left(\frac{m_e}{m^*}\right)\kappa\frac{\hbar^2}{m_e k_e e^2} = \left(\frac{m_e}{m^*}\right)\kappa a_0 = \left(\frac{m_e}{0.220 m_e}\right)11.7(0.052\,9 \text{ nm}) = \boxed{2.81 \text{ nm}}.$$

The energy levels are in hydrogen $E_n = -\frac{k_e e^2}{2a_0}\frac{1}{n^2}$ and here

$$E_n' = -\frac{k_e e^2}{\kappa 2a'}\frac{1}{n^2} = -\frac{k_e e^2}{\kappa 2\left(m_e/m^*\right)\kappa a_0} = -\left(\frac{m^*}{m_e}\right)\frac{E_n}{\kappa^2}$$

For $n = 1$, $E_1' = -0.220\frac{13.6 \text{ eV}}{11.7^2} = \boxed{-0.021\,9 \text{ eV}}$.

Section 43.7 Semiconductor Devices

P43.42 $I = I_0\left(e^{e(\Delta V)/k_BT} - 1\right)$. Thus, $e^{e(\Delta V)/k_BT} = 1 + \frac{I}{I_0}$

and $$\Delta V = \frac{k_BT}{e}\ln\left(1 + \frac{I}{I_0}\right).$$

At $T = 300\text{ K}$, $$\Delta V = \frac{\left(1.38\times10^{-23}\text{ J/K}\right)(300\text{ K})}{1.60\times10^{-19}\text{ C}}\ln\left(1+\frac{I}{I_0}\right) = (25.9\text{ mV})\ln\left(1+\frac{I}{I_0}\right).$$

(a) If $I = 9.00I_0$, $\Delta V = (25.9\text{ mV})\ln(10.0) = \boxed{59.5\text{ mV}}$.

(b) If $I = -0.900I_0$, $\Delta V = (25.9\text{ mV})\ln(0.100) = \boxed{-59.5\text{ mV}}$.

The basic idea behind a semiconductor device is that a large current or charge can be controlled by a small control voltage.

P43.43 The voltage across the diode is about 0.6 V. The voltage drop across the resistor is $(0.025\text{ A})(150\ \Omega) = 3.75\text{ V}$. Thus, $\varepsilon - 0.6\text{ V} - 3.8\text{ V} = 0$ and $\varepsilon = \boxed{4.4\text{ V}}$.

P43.44 First, we evaluate I_0 in $I = I_0\left(e^{e(\Delta V)/k_BT} - 1\right)$, given that $I = 200\text{ mA}$ when $\Delta V = 100\text{ mV}$ and $T = 300\text{ K}$.

$$\frac{e(\Delta V)}{k_BT} = \frac{\left(1.60\times10^{-19}\text{ C}\right)(0.100\text{ V})}{\left(1.38\times10^{-23}\text{ J/K}\right)(300\text{ K})} = 3.86 \text{ so } I_0 = \frac{I}{e^{e(\Delta V)/k_BT} - 1} = \frac{200\text{ mA}}{e^{3.86} - 1} = 4.28\text{ mA}$$

If $\Delta V = -100\text{ mV}$, $\frac{e(\Delta V)}{k_BT} = -3.86$; and the current will be

$$I = I_0\left(e^{e(\Delta V)/k_BT} - 1\right) = (4.28\text{ mA})\left(e^{-3.86} - 1\right) = \boxed{-4.19\text{ mA}}.$$

***P43.45** (a) The currents to be plotted are

$$I_D = \left(10^{-6}\text{ A}\right)\left(e^{\Delta V/0.025\text{ V}} - 1\right),$$
$$I_W = \frac{2.42\text{ V} - \Delta V}{745\ \Omega}$$

The two graphs intersect at $\Delta V = 0.200\text{ V}$. The currents are then

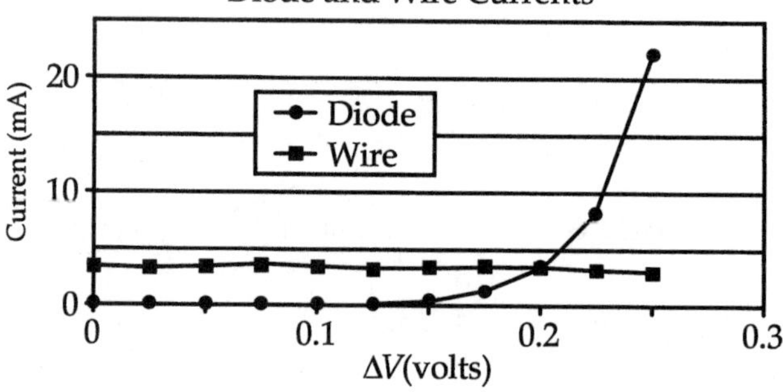

FIG. P43.45

$$I_D = \left(10^{-6}\text{ A}\right)\left(e^{0.200\text{ V}/0.025\text{ V}} - 1\right) = 2.98\text{ mA}$$

$$I_W = \frac{2.42\text{ V} - 0.200\text{ V}}{745\ \Omega} = 2.98\text{ mA}.$$ They agree to three digits.

$$\therefore I_D = I_W = \boxed{2.98\text{ mA}}$$

(b) $$\frac{\Delta V}{I_D} = \frac{0.200\text{ V}}{2.98\times10^{-3}\text{ A}} = \boxed{67.1\ \Omega}$$

(c) $$\frac{d(\Delta V)}{dI_D} = \left[\frac{dI_D}{d(\Delta V)}\right]^{-1} = \left[\frac{10^{-6}\text{ A}}{0.025\text{ V}}e^{0.200\text{ V}/0.025\text{ V}}\right]^{-1} = \boxed{8.39\ \Omega}$$

Section 43.8 **Superconductivity**

P43.46 (a) See the figure at right.

(b) For a surface current around the outside of the cylinder as shown,

$$B=\frac{N\mu_0 I}{\ell} \text{ or } NI=\frac{B\ell}{\mu_0}=\frac{(0.540\text{ T})\left(2.50\times10^{-2}\text{ m}\right)}{\left(4\pi\times10^{-7}\right)\text{ T}\cdot\text{m/A}}=\boxed{10.7\text{ kA}}.$$

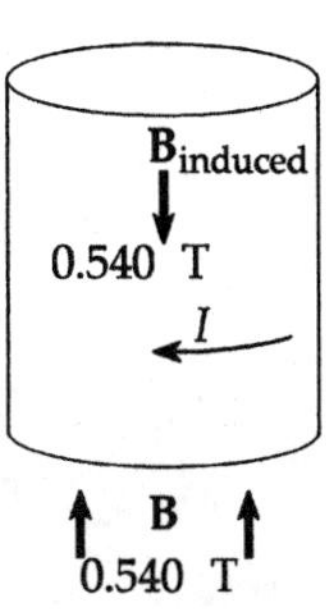

FIG. P43.46

P43.47 By Faraday's law (Equation 32.1), $\frac{\Delta\Phi_B}{\Delta t}=L\frac{\Delta I}{\Delta t}=A\frac{\Delta B}{\Delta t}$.

Thus, $\Delta I=\frac{A(\Delta B)}{L}=\frac{\pi(0.010\,0\text{ m})^2(0.020\,0\text{ T})}{3.10\times10^{-8}\text{ H}}=\boxed{203\text{ A}}$.

The direction of the induced current is such as to maintain the B–field through the ring.

P43.48 (a) $\Delta V=IR$

If $R=0$, then $\Delta V=0$, even when $I\neq0$.

(b) The graph shows a direct proportionality.

$$\text{Slope}=\frac{1}{R}=\frac{\Delta I}{\Delta V}=\frac{(155-57.8)\text{ mA}}{(3.61-1.356)\text{ mV}}=43.1\ \Omega^{-1}$$

$R=\boxed{0.023\,2\ \Omega}$

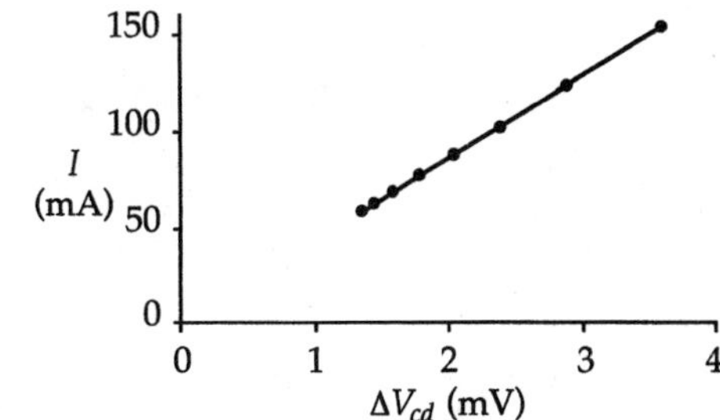

FIG. P43.48

(c) Expulsion of magnetic flux and therefore fewer current-carrying paths could explain the decrease in current.

Additional Problems

P43.49 (a) Since the interatomic potential is the same for both molecules, the spring constant is the same.

Then $f=\frac{1}{2\pi}\sqrt{\frac{k}{\mu}}$ where $\mu_{12}=\frac{(12\text{ u})(16\text{ u})}{12\text{ u}+16\text{ u}}=6.86\text{ u}$ and $\mu_{14}=\frac{(14\text{ u})(16\text{ u})}{14\text{ u}+16\text{ u}}=7.47\text{ u}$.

Therefore,

$$f_{14}=\frac{1}{2\pi}\sqrt{\frac{k}{\mu_{14}}}=\frac{1}{2\pi}\sqrt{\frac{k}{\mu_{12}}\left(\frac{\mu_{12}}{\mu_{14}}\right)}=f_{12}\sqrt{\frac{\mu_{12}}{\mu_{14}}}=\left(6.42\times10^{13}\text{ Hz}\right)\sqrt{\frac{6.86\text{ u}}{7.47\text{ u}}}=\boxed{6.15\times10^{13}\text{ Hz}}.$$

continued on next page

(b) The equilibrium distance is the same for both molecules.

$$I_{14} = \mu_{14} r^2 = \left(\frac{\mu_{14}}{\mu_{12}}\right)\mu_{12} r^2 = \left(\frac{\mu_{14}}{\mu_{12}}\right) I_{12}$$

$$I_{14} = \left(\frac{7.47\text{ u}}{6.86\text{ u}}\right)\left(1.46\times10^{-46}\text{ kg}\cdot\text{m}^2\right) = \boxed{1.59\times10^{-46}\text{ kg}\cdot\text{m}^2}$$

(c) The molecule can move to the $(v=1,\ J=9)$ state or to the $(v=1,\ J=11)$ state. The energy it can absorb is either

$$\Delta E = \frac{hc}{\lambda} = \left[\left(1+\frac{1}{2}\right)hf_{14} + 9(9+1)\frac{\hbar^2}{2I_{14}}\right] - \left[\left(0-\frac{1}{2}\right)hf_{14} + 10(10+1)\frac{\hbar^2}{2I_{14}}\right],$$

or $$\Delta E = \frac{hc}{\lambda} = \left[\left(1+\frac{1}{2}\right)hf_{14} + 11(11+1)\frac{\hbar^2}{2I_{14}}\right] - \left[\left(0+\frac{1}{2}\right)hf_{14} + 10(10+1)\frac{\hbar^2}{2I_{14}}\right].$$

The wavelengths it can absorb are then

$$\lambda = \frac{c}{f_{14} - 10\hbar/(2\pi I_{14})} \text{ or } \lambda = \frac{c}{f_{14} + 11\hbar/(2\pi I_{14})}.$$

These are: $$\lambda = \frac{3.00\times10^8\text{ m/s}}{6.15\times10^{13}\text{ Hz} - \left[10\left(1.055\times10^{-34}\text{ J}\cdot\text{s}\right)\right]/\left[2\pi\left(1.59\times10^{-46}\text{ kg}\cdot\text{m}^2\right)\right]} = \boxed{4.96\ \mu\text{m}}$$

and $$\lambda = \frac{3.00\times10^8\text{ m/s}}{6.15\times10^{13}\text{ Hz} + \left[11\left(1.055\times10^{-34}\text{ J}\cdot\text{s}\right)\right]/\left[2\pi\left(1.59\times10^{-46}\text{ kg}\cdot\text{m}^2\right)\right]} = \boxed{4.79\ \mu\text{m}}.$$

P43.50 For the N_2 molecule, $k = 2\,297$ N/m, $m = 2.32\times10^{-26}$ kg, $r = 1.20\times10^{-10}$ m, $\mu = \frac{m}{2}$

$$\omega = \sqrt{\frac{k}{\mu}} = 4.45\times10^{14}\text{ rad/s}, \qquad I = \mu r^2 = \left(1.16\times10^{-26}\text{ kg}\right)\left(1.20\times10^{-10}\text{ m}\right)^2 = 1.67\times10^{-46}\text{ kg}\cdot\text{m}^2.$$

For a rotational state sufficient to allow a transition to the first exited vibrational state,

$$\frac{\hbar^2}{2I}J(J+1) = \hbar\omega \text{ so } J(J+1) = \frac{2I\omega}{\hbar} = \frac{2\left(1.67\times10^{-46}\right)\left(4.45\times10^{14}\right)}{1.055\times10^{-34}} = 1\,410.$$

Thus $\boxed{J = 37}$.

P43.51 $\Delta E_{max} = 4.5\text{ eV} = \left(v+\frac{1}{2}\right)\hbar\omega$ so $\frac{(4.5\text{ eV})\left(1.6\times10^{-19}\text{ J/eV}\right)}{\left(1.055\times10^{-34}\text{ J}\cdot\text{s}\right)\left(8.28\times10^{14}\text{ s}^{-1}\right)} \ge \left(v+\frac{1}{2}\right)$

$8.25 > 7.5$ $\boxed{v = 7}$

P43.52 With 4 van der Waal bonds per atom pair or 2 electrons per atom, the total energy of the solid is

$$E = 2\left(1.74\times10^{-23}\text{ J/atom}\right)\left(\frac{6.02\times10^{23}\text{ atoms}}{4.00\text{ g}}\right) = \boxed{5.23\text{ J/g}}.$$

P43.53 The total potential energy is given by Equation 43.17: $U_{\text{total}} = -\alpha\dfrac{k_e e^2}{r} + \dfrac{B}{r^m}$.

The total potential energy has its minimum value U_0 at the equilibrium spacing, $r = r_0$. At this point, $\left.\dfrac{dU}{dr}\right|_{r=r_0} = 0$,

or $$\left.\frac{dU}{dr}\right|_{r=r_0} = \frac{d}{dr}\left.\left(-\alpha\frac{k_e e^2}{r} + \frac{B}{r^m}\right)\right|_{r=r_0} = \alpha\frac{k_e e^2}{r_0^2} - \frac{mB}{r_0^{m+1}} = 0.$$

Thus, $$B = \alpha\frac{k_e e^2}{m} r_0^{m-1}.$$

Substituting this value of B into U_{total}, $$U_0 = -\alpha\frac{k_e e^2}{r_0} + \alpha\frac{k_e e^2}{m} r_0^{m-1}\left(\frac{1}{r_0^m}\right) = \boxed{-\alpha\frac{k_e e^2}{r_0}\left(1 - \frac{1}{m}\right)}.$$

P43.54 Suppose it is a harmonic-oscillator potential well. Then, $\frac{1}{2}hf + 4.48\text{ eV} = \frac{3}{2}hf + 3.96\text{ eV}$ is the depth of the well below the dissociation point. We see $hf = 0.520\text{ eV}$, so the depth of the well is

$$\frac{1}{2}hf + 4.48\text{ eV} = \frac{1}{2}(0.520\text{ eV}) + 4.48\text{ eV} = \boxed{4.74\text{ eV}}.$$

P43.55 (a) For equilibrium, $\dfrac{dU}{dx} = 0$: $$\frac{d}{dx}\left(Ax^{-3} - Bx^{-1}\right) = -3Ax^{-4} + Bx^{-2} = 0$$

$x \to \infty$ describes one equilibrium position, but the stable equilibrium position is at $3Ax_0^{-2} = B$.

$$x_0 = \sqrt{\frac{3A}{B}} = \sqrt{\frac{3\left(0.150\text{ eV}\cdot\text{nm}^3\right)}{3.68\text{ eV}\cdot\text{nm}}} = \boxed{0.350\text{ nm}}$$

(b) The depth of the well is given by $$U_0 = U\big|_{x=x_0} = \frac{A}{x_0^3} - \frac{B}{x_0} = \frac{AB^{3/2}}{3^{3/2}A^{3/2}} - \frac{BB^{1/2}}{3^{1/2}A^{1/2}}$$

$$U_0 = U\big|_{x=x_0} = -\frac{2B^{3/2}}{3^{3/2}A^{1/2}} = -\frac{2(3.68\text{ eV}\cdot\text{nm})^{3/2}}{3^{3/2}\left(0.150\text{ eV}\cdot\text{nm}^3\right)^{1/2}} = \boxed{-7.02\text{ eV}}.$$

(c) $$F_x = -\frac{dU}{dx} = 3Ax^{-4} - Bx^{-2}$$

To find the maximum force, we determine finite x_m such that $\left.\dfrac{dF}{dx}\right|_{x=x_m} = 0$.

Thus, $\left[-12Ax^{-5} + 2Bx^{-3}\right]_{x=x_m} = 0$ so that $x_m = \left(\dfrac{6A}{B}\right)^{1/2}$.

Then $$F_{\max} = 3A\left(\frac{B}{6A}\right)^2 - B\left(\frac{B}{6A}\right) = -\frac{B^2}{12A} = -\frac{(3.68\text{ eV}\cdot\text{nm})^2}{12\left(0.150\text{ eV}\cdot\text{nm}^3\right)}$$

or $$F_{\max} = -7.52\text{ eV/nm}\left(\frac{1.60\times10^{-19}\text{ J}}{1\text{ eV}}\right)\left(\frac{1\text{ nm}}{10^{-9}\text{ m}}\right) = -1.20\times10^{-9}\text{ N} = \boxed{-1.20\text{ nN}}.$$

P43.56 (a) For equilibrium, $\frac{dU}{dx}=0$: $\frac{d}{dx}\left(Ax^{-3}-Bx^{-1}\right)=-3Ax^{-4}+Bx^{-2}=0$

$x\to\infty$ describes one equilibrium position, but the stable equilibrium position is at

$3Ax_0^{-2}=B$ or $\boxed{x_0=\sqrt{\frac{3A}{B}}}$.

(b) The depth of the well is given by $U_0=U|_{x=x_0}=\frac{A}{x_0^3}-\frac{B}{x_0}=\frac{AB^{3/2}}{3^{3/2}A^{3/2}}-\frac{BB^{1/2}}{3^{1/2}A^{1/2}}=\boxed{-2\sqrt{\frac{B^3}{27A}}}$.

(c) $F_x=-\frac{dU}{dx}=3Ax^{-4}-Bx^{-2}$

To find the maximum force, we determine finite x_m such that

$\left.\frac{dF_x}{dx}\right|_{x=x_m}=\left[-12Ax^{-5}+2Bx^{-3}\right]_{x=x_0}=0$ then $F_{max}=3A\left(\frac{B}{6A}\right)^2-B\left(\frac{B}{6A}\right)=\boxed{-\frac{B^2}{12A}}$.

P43.57 (a) At equilibrium separation, $r=r_e$, $\left.\frac{dU}{dr}\right|_{r=r_e}=-2aB\left[e^{-a(r_e-r_0)}-1\right]e^{-a(r_e-r_0)}=0$.

We have neutral equilibrium as $r_e\to\infty$ and stable equilibrium at $e^{-a(r_e-r_0)}=1$,

or $r_e=\boxed{r_0}$.

(b) At $r=r_0$, $U=0$. As $r\to\infty$, $U\to B$. The depth of the well is $\boxed{B}$.

(c) We expand the potential in a Taylor series about the equilibrium point:

$$U(r)\approx U(r_0)+\left.\frac{dU}{dr}\right|_{r=r_0}(r-r_0)+\frac{1}{2}\left.\frac{d^2U}{dr^2}\right|_{r=r_0}(r-r_0)^2$$

$$U(r)\approx 0+0+\frac{1}{2}(-2Ba)\left[-ae^{-2(r-r_0)}-ae^{-(r-r_0)}\left(e^{-2(r-r_0)}-1\right)\right]_{r=r_0}(r-r_0)^2\approx Ba^2(r-r_0)^2$$

This is of the form $\frac{1}{2}kx^2=\frac{1}{2}k(r-r_0)^2$

for a simple harmonic oscillator with $k=2Ba^2$.

Then the molecule vibrates with frequency $f=\frac{1}{2\pi}\sqrt{\frac{k}{\mu}}=\frac{a}{2\pi}\sqrt{\frac{2B}{\mu}}=\boxed{\frac{a}{\pi}\sqrt{\frac{B}{2\mu}}}$.

(d) The zero-point energy is $\frac{1}{2}\hbar\omega=\frac{1}{2}hf=\frac{ha}{\pi}\sqrt{\frac{B}{8\mu}}$.

Therefore, to dissociate the molecule in its ground state requires energy $\boxed{B-\frac{ha}{\pi}\sqrt{\frac{B}{8\mu}}}$.

P43.58

	$T=0$		$T=0.1T_F$		$T=0.2T_F$		$T=0.5T_F$	
$\frac{E}{E_F}$	$e^{[(E/E_F)-1](T_F/T)}$	$f(E)$	$e^{[(E/E_F)-1](T_F/T)}$	$f(E)$	$e^{[(E/E_F)-1](T_F/T)}$	$f(E)$	$e^{[(E/E_F)-1](T_F/T)}$	$f(E)$
0	$e^{-\infty}$	1.00	$e^{-10.0}$	1.000	$e^{-5.00}$	0.993	$e^{-2.00}$	0.881
0.500	$e^{-\infty}$	1.00	$e^{-5.00}$	0.993	$e^{-2.50}$	0.924	$e^{-1.00}$	0.731
0.600	$e^{-\infty}$	1.00	$e^{-4.00}$	0.982	$e^{-2.00}$	0.881	$e^{-0.800}$	0.690
0.700	$e^{-\infty}$	1.00	$e^{-3.00}$	0.953	$e^{-1.50}$	0.818	$e^{-0.600}$	0.646
0.800	$e^{-\infty}$	1.00	$e^{-2.00}$	0.881	$e^{-1.00}$	0.731	$e^{-0.400}$	0.599
0.900	$e^{-\infty}$	1.00	$e^{-1.00}$	0.731	$e^{-0.500}$	0.622	$e^{-0.200}$	0.550
1.00	e^{0}	0.500	e^{0}	0.500	e^{0}	0.500	e^{0}	0.500
1.10	$e^{+\infty}$	0.00	$e^{1.00}$	0.269	$e^{0.500}$	0.378	$e^{0.200}$	0.450
1.20	$e^{+\infty}$	0.00	$e^{2.00}$	0.119	$e^{1.00}$	0.269	$e^{0.400}$	0.401
1.30	$e^{+\infty}$	0.00	$e^{3.00}$	0.047 4	$e^{1.50}$	0.182	$e^{0.600}$	0.354
1.40	$e^{+\infty}$	0.00	$e^{4.00}$	0.018 0	$e^{2.00}$	0.119	$e^{0.800}$	0.310
1.50	$e^{+\infty}$	0.00	$e^{5.00}$	0.006 69	$e^{2.50}$	0.075 9	$e^{1.00}$	0.269

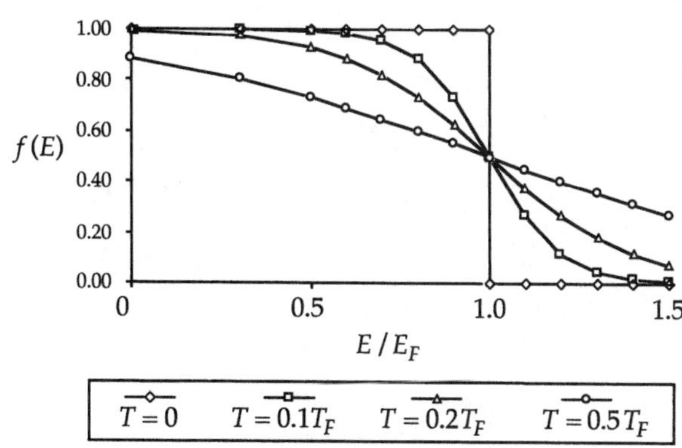

FIG. P43.58

P43.59 (a) There are 6 Cl^- ions at distance $r=r_0$. The contribution of these ions to the electrostatic potential energy is $\frac{-6k_e e^2}{r_0}$.

There are 12 Na^+ ions at distance $r=\sqrt{2}r_0$. Their contribution to the electrostatic potential energy is $\frac{+12k_e e^2}{\sqrt{2}r_0}$. Next, there are 8 Cl^- ions at distance $r=\sqrt{3}r_0$. These contribute a term of $\frac{-8k_e e^2}{\sqrt{3}r_0}$ to the electrostatic potential energy.

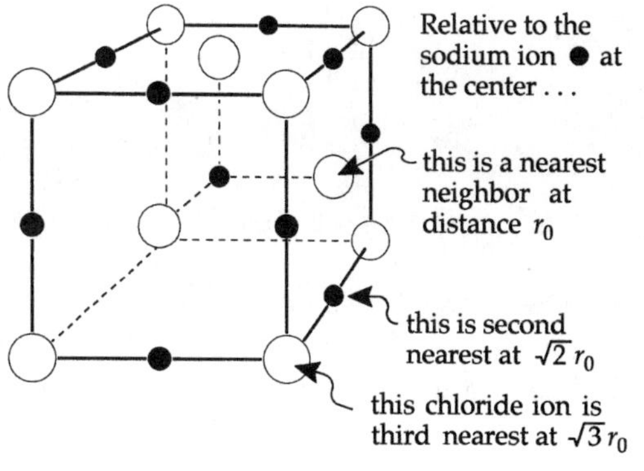

FIG. P43.59

To three terms, the electrostatic potential energy is:

$$U=\left(-6+\frac{12}{\sqrt{2}}-\frac{8}{\sqrt{3}}\right)\frac{k_e e^2}{r_0}=-2.13\frac{k_e e^2}{r_0} \text{ or } \boxed{U=-\alpha\frac{k_e e^2}{r_0} \text{ with } \alpha=2.13}.$$

continued on next page

(b) The fourth term consists of 6 Na^+ at distance $r = 2r_0$. Thus, to four terms,

$$U = (-2.13 + 3)\frac{k_e e^2}{r_0} = 0.866\frac{k_e e^2}{r_0}.$$

So we see that the electrostatic potential energy is not even attractive to 4 terms, and that the infinite series does not converge rapidly when groups of atoms corresponding to nearest neighbors, next-nearest neighbors, etc. are added together.

ANSWERS TO EVEN PROBLEMS

P43.2 4.3 eV

P43.4 (a) 1.28 eV; (b) $\sigma = 0.272$ nm, $\in = 4.65$ eV; (c) 6.55 nN; (d) 576 N/m

P43.6 (a) 40.0 μeV, 9.66 GHz; (b) If r is 10% too small, f is 20% too large.

P43.8 1.46×10^{-46} kg $\cdot$ m^2

P43.10 (a) 1.81×10^{-45} kg $\cdot$ m^2; (b) 1.62 cm

P43.12 (a) 11.8 pm; (b) 7.72 pm; HI is more loosely bound

P43.14 (a) 0, 364 μeV, 1.09 meV; (b) 98.2 meV, 295 meV, 491 meV

P43.16 (a) 472 μm; (b) 473 μm; (c) 0.715 μm

P43.18 2.9×10^{-47} kg $\cdot$ m^2

P43.20 only 64.1 THz

P43.22 (a) $\sim 10^{17}$; (b) $\sim 10^5$ m^3

P43.24 (a) 0.444 nm, 0.628 nm, 0.769 nm

P43.26 see the solution

P43.28 (a) 1.57 Mm/s; (b) larger by 10 orders of magnitude

P43.30 2%

P43.32 3.40×10^{17} electrons

P43.34 see the solution

P43.36 (a) 275 THz; (b) 1.09 μm

P43.38 1.91 eV

P43.40 226 nm

P43.42 (a) 59.5 mV; (b) –59.5 mV

P43.44 4.19 mA

P43.46 (a) see the solution; (b) 10.7 kA

P43.48 see the solution

P43.50 37

P43.52 5.23 J/g

P43.54 4.74 eV

P43.56 (a) $x_0 = \sqrt{\frac{3A}{B}}$; (b) $-2\sqrt{\frac{B^3}{27A}}$; (c) $-\frac{B^2}{12A}$

P43.58 see the solution

44

Nuclear Structure

CHAPTER OUTLINE

ANSWERS TO QUESTIONS

Q44.1 Because of electrostatic repulsion between the positively-charged nucleus and the $+2e$ alpha particle. To drive the α-particle into the nucleus would require extremely high kinetic energy.

Q44.2 There are 86 protons and 136 neutrons in the nucleus $^{222}_{86}\text{Rn}$. For the atom to be neutral, there must be 86 electrons orbiting the nucleus—the same as the number of protons.

Q44.3 All of these isotopes have the same number of protons in the nucleus. Neutral atoms have the same number of electrons. Isotopes only differ in the number of neutrons in the nucleus.

Q44.4 Nuclei with more nucleons than bismuth-209 are unstable because the electrical repulsion forces among all of the protons is stronger than the nuclear attractive force between nucleons.

Q44.5 The nuclear force favors the formation of neutron-proton pairs, so a stable nucleus cannot be too far away from having equal numbers of protons and neutrons. This effect sets the upper boundary of the zone of stability on the neutron-proton diagram. All of the protons repel one another electrically, so a stable nucleus cannot have too many protons. This effect sets the lower boundary of the zone of stability.

Q44.6 Nucleus Y will be more unstable. The nucleus with the higher binding energy requires more energy to be disassembled into its constituent parts.

Q44.7 Extra neutrons are required to overcome the increasing electrostatic repulsion of the protons. The neutrons participate in the net attractive effect of the nuclear force, but feel no Coulomb repulsion.

Q44.8 In the liquid-drop model the nucleus is modeled as a drop of liquid. The nucleus is treated as a whole to determine its binding energy and behavior. The shell model differs completely from the liquid-drop model, as it utilizes quantum states of the individual nucleons to describe the structure and behavior of the nucleus. Like the electrons that orbit the nucleus, each nucleon has a spin state to which the Pauli exclusion principle applies. Unlike the electrons, for protons and neutrons the spin and orbital motions are strongly coupled.

Q44.9 The liquid drop model gives a simpler account of a nuclear fission reaction, including the energy released and the probable fission product nuclei. The shell model predicts magnetic moments by necessarily describing the spin and orbital angular momentum states of the nucleons. Again, the shell model wins when it comes to predicting the spectrum of an excited nucleus, as the quantum model allows only quantized energy states, and thus only specific transitions.

Q44.10 ^{4}He, ^{16}O, ^{40}Ca, and ^{208}Pb.

Q44.11 If one half the number of radioactive nuclei decay in one year, then one half the remaining number will decay in the second year. Three quarters of the original nuclei will be gone, and one quarter will remain.

Q44.12 The statement is false. Both patterns show monotonic decrease over time, but with very different shapes. For radioactive decay, maximum activity occurs at time zero. Cohorts of people now living will be dying most rapidly perhaps forty years from now. Everyone now living will be dead within less than two centuries, while the mathematical model of radioactive decay tails off exponentially forever. A radioactive nucleus never gets old. It has constant probability of decay however long it has existed.

Q44.13 Since the samples are of the same radioactive isotope, their half-lives are the same. When prepared, sample A has twice the activity (number of radioactive decays per second) of sample B. After 5 half-lives, the activity of sample A is decreased by a factor of 2^5, and after 5 half-lives the activity of sample B is decreased by a factor of 2^5. So after 5 half-lives, the ratio of activities is still 2:1.

Q44.14 After one half-life, one half the radioactive atoms have decayed. After the second half-life, one half of the remaining atoms have decayed. Therefore $\frac{1}{2}+\frac{1}{4}=\frac{3}{4}$ of the original radioactive atoms have decayed after two half-lives.

Q44.15 The motion of a molecule through space does not affect anything inside the nucleus of an atom of the molecule. The half-life of a nucleus is based on nuclear stability which, as discussed in Questions 44.4 and Q44.5, is predominantly determined by Coulomb repulsion and nuclear forces, not molecular motion.

Q44.16 Long-lived progenitors at the top of each of the three natural radioactive series are the sources of our radium. As an example, thorium-232 with a half-life of 14 Gyr produces radium-228 and radium-224 at stages in its series of decays, shown in Figure 44.17.

Q44.17 A free neutron decays into a proton plus an electron and an antineutrino. This implies that a proton is more stable than a neutron, and in particular the proton has lower mass. Therefore a proton cannot decay into a neutron plus a positron and a neutrino. This reaction satisfies every conservation law except for energy conservation.

Q44.18 A neutrino has spin $\frac{1}{2}$ while a photon has spin 1. A neutrino interacts by the weak interaction while a photon is a quantum of the electromagnetic interaction.

Q44.19 Let us consider the carbon-14 decay used in carbon dating. ${}^{14}_{6}C \rightarrow {}^{14}_{7}N + e^{-} + \bar{\nu}$. The carbon-14 atom has 6 protons in the nucleus. The nitrogen-14 atom has 7 protons in the nucleus, but the additional + charge from the extra proton is canceled by the – charge of the ejected electron. Since charge is conserved in this (and every) reaction, the antineutrino must have zero charge.

Similarly, when nitrogen-12 decays into carbon-12, the nucleus of the carbon atom has one fewer protons, but the change in charge of the nucleus is balanced by the positive charge of the ejected positron. Again according to charge conservation, the neutrino must have no charge.

Q44.20 An electron has spin quantum number $\frac{1}{2}$. When a nucleus undergoes beta decay, an electron and antineutrino are ejected. With all nucleons paired, in their ground states the carbon-14, nitrogen-14, nitrogen-12, and carbon-12 nuclei have zero net angular momentum. Angular momentum is conserved in any process in an isolated system and in particular in the beta-decays of carbon-14 and nitrogen-12. Conclusion: the neutrino must have spin quantum number $\frac{1}{2}$, so that its z-component of angular momentum can be just $\frac{\hbar}{2}$ or $-\frac{\hbar}{2}$. A proton and a neutron have spin quantum number 1. For conservation of angular momentum in the beta-decay of a free neutron, an antineutrino must have spin quantum number $\frac{1}{2}$.

Q44.21 The alpha particle and the daughter nucleus carry equal amounts of momentum in opposite directions. Since kinetic energy can be written as $\frac{p^2}{2m}$, the small-mass alpha particle has much more of the decay energy than the recoiling nucleus.

Q44.22 Bullet and rifle carry equal amounts of momentum p. With a much smaller mass m, the bullet has much more kinetic energy $K = \frac{p^2}{2m}$. The daughter nucleus and alpha particle have equal momenta and the massive daughter nucleus, like the rifle, has a very small share of the energy released.

Q44.23 Yes. The daughter nucleus can be left in its ground state or sometimes in one of a set of excited states. If the energy carried by the alpha particle is mysteriously low, the daughter nucleus can quickly emit the missing energy in a gamma ray.

Q44.24 In a heavy nucleus each nucleon is strongly bound to its momentary neighbors. Even if the nucleus could step down in energy by shedding an individual proton or neutron, one individual nucleon is never free to escape. Instead, the nucleus can decay when two protons and two neutrons, strongly bound to one another but not to their neighbors, happen momentarily to have a lot of kinetic energy, to lie at the surface of the nucleus, to be headed outward, and to tunnel successfully through the potential energy barrier they encounter.

Q44.25 From $\sum F = ma$, or $qvB = \frac{mv^2}{r}$, or $qBr = mv$, a charged particle fired into a magnetic field is deflected into a path with radius proportional to its momentum. If they have equal kinetic energies K, the much greater mass m of the alpha particle gives it more momentum $mv = \sqrt{2mK}$ than an electron. Thus the electron undergoes greater deflection. This conclusion remains true if one or both particles are moving relativistically.

Q44.26 The alpha particle stops in the wood, while many beta particles can make it through to deposit some or all of their energy in the film emulsion.

Q44.27 The reaction energy is the amount of energy released as a result of a nuclear reaction. Equation 44.28 in the text implies that the reaction energy is (initial mass – final mass)c^2. The Q-value is taken as positive for an exothermic reaction.

Q44.28 Carbon-14 is produced when carbon-12 is bombarded by cosmic rays. Both carbon-12 and carbon-14 combine with oxygen to form the atmospheric CO_2 that plants absorb in respiration. When the plant dies, the carbon-14 is no longer replenished and decays at a known rate. Since carbon-14 is a beta-emitter, one only needs to compare the activity of a living plant to the activity of the sample to determine its age, since the activity of a radioactive sample exponentially decreases in time.

Q44.29 The samples would have started with more carbon-14 than we first thought. We would increase our estimates of their ages.

Q44.30 There are two factors that determine the uncertainty on dating an old sample. The first is the fact that the activity level decreases exponentially in time. After a long enough period of time, the activity will approach background radiation levels, making precise dating difficult. Secondly, the ratio of carbon-12 to carbon-14 in the atomsphere can vary over long periods of time, and this effect contributes additional uncertainty.

Q44.31 An α-particle is a helium nucleus: ${}^{4}_{2}\text{He}$

A β-particle is an electron or a positron: either e^- or e^+.

A γ-ray is a high-energy photon emitted when a nucleus makes a downward transition between two states.

Q44.32 I_z may have 6 values for $I = \frac{5}{2}$, namely $\frac{5}{2}, \frac{3}{2}, \frac{1}{2}, -\frac{1}{2}, -\frac{3}{2}$, and $-\frac{5}{2}$. Seven I_z values are possible for $I = 3$.

Q44.33 The frequency increases linearly with the magnetic field strength.

Q44.34 The decay of a radioactive nucleus at one particular moment instead of at another instant cannot be predicted and has no cause. Natural events are not just like a perfect clockworks. In history, the idea of a determinate mechanical Universe arose temporarily from an unwarranted wild extrapolation of Isaac Newton's account of planetary motion. Before Newton's time [really you can blame Pierre Simon de Laplace] and again now, no one thought of natural events as just like a perfect row of falling dominos. We can and do use the word "cause" more loosely to describe antecedent enabling events. One gear turning another is intelligible. So is the process of a hot dog getting toasted over a campfire, even though random molecular motion is at the essence of that process. In summary, we say that the future is not determinate. All natural events have causes in the ordinary sense of the word, but not necessarily in the contrived sense of a cause operating infallibly and predictably in a way that can be calculated. We have better reason now than ever before to think of the Universe as intelligible. First describing natural events, and second determining their causes form the basis of science, including physics but also scientific medicine and scientific bread-baking. The evidence alone of the past hundred years of discoveries in physics, finding causes of natural events from the photoelectric effect to x-rays and jets emitted by black holes, suggests that human intelligence is a good tool for figuring out how things go. Even without organized science, humans have always been searching for the causes of natural events, with explanations ranging from "the will of the gods" to Schrödinger's equation. We depend on the principle that things are intelligible as we make significant strides towards understanding the Universe. To hope that our search is not futile is the best part of human nature.

SOLUTIONS TO PROBLEMS

Section 44.1 **Some Properties of Nuclei**

P44.1 An iron nucleus (in hemoglobin) has a few more neutrons than protons, but in a typical water molecule there are eight neutrons and ten protons.

So protons and neutrons are nearly equally numerous in your body, each contributing mass (say) 35 kg:

$$35\text{ kg}\left(\frac{1\text{ nucleon}}{1.67\times10^{-27}\text{ kg}}\right)\boxed{\sim10^{28}\text{ protons}}$$

and $\boxed{\sim10^{28}\text{ neutrons}}$.

The electron number is precisely equal to the proton number, $\boxed{\sim10^{28}\text{ electrons}}$.

P44.2 $\frac{1}{2}mv^2=q\Delta V$ and $\frac{mv^2}{r}=qvB$

$2m\Delta V=qr^2B^2$: $r=\sqrt{\frac{2m\Delta V}{qB^2}}=\sqrt{\frac{2(1\,000\text{ V})}{(1.60\times10^{-19}\text{ C})(0.200\text{ T})^2}}\sqrt{m}$

$$r=\left(5.59\times10^{11}\text{ m}/\sqrt{\text{kg}}\right)\sqrt{m}$$

(a) For ^{12}C, $m=12$ u and $r=\left(5.59\times10^{11}\text{ m}/\sqrt{\text{kg}}\right)\sqrt{12\left(1.66\times10^{-27}\text{ kg}\right)}$

$$r=0.078\,9\text{ m}=\boxed{7.89\text{ cm}}.$$

For ^{13}C: $r=\left(5.59\times10^{11}\text{ m}/\sqrt{\text{kg}}\right)\sqrt{13\left(1.66\times10^{-27}\text{ kg}\right)}$

$$r=0.082\,1\text{ m}=\boxed{8.21\text{ cm}}.$$

(b) With $r_1=\sqrt{\frac{2m_1\Delta V}{qB^2}}$ and $r_2=\sqrt{\frac{2m_2\Delta V}{qB^2}}$

the ratio gives $\boxed{\frac{r_1}{r_2}=\sqrt{\frac{m_1}{m_2}}}$

$$\frac{r_1}{r_2}=\frac{7.89\text{ cm}}{8.21\text{ cm}}=0.961$$

and $\sqrt{\frac{m_1}{m_2}}=\sqrt{\frac{12\text{ u}}{13\text{ u}}}=0.961$

so they do agree.

P44.3 (a) $F = k_e \dfrac{Q_1 Q_2}{r^2} = \left(8.99\times10^9\ \text{N}\cdot\text{m}^2/\text{C}^2\right)\dfrac{(2)(6)\left(1.60\times10^{-19}\ \text{C}\right)^2}{\left(1.00\times10^{-14}\ \text{m}\right)^2} = \boxed{27.6\ \text{N}}$

(b) $a = \dfrac{F}{m} = \dfrac{27.6\ \text{N}}{6.64\times10^{-27}\ \text{kg}} = \boxed{4.17\times10^{27}\ \text{m/s}^2}$ away from the nucleus.

(c) $U = k_e \dfrac{Q_1 Q_2}{r} = \left(8.99\times10^9\ \text{N}\cdot\text{m}^2/\text{C}^2\right)\dfrac{(2)(6)\left(1.60\times10^{-19}\ \text{C}\right)^2}{\left(1.00\times10^{-14}\ \text{m}\right)} = 2.76\times10^{-13}\ \text{J} = \boxed{1.73\ \text{MeV}}$

P44.4 $E_\alpha = 7.70\ \text{MeV}$

(a) $d_{\min} = \dfrac{4k_e Z e^2}{mv^2} = \dfrac{2k_e Z e^2}{E_\alpha} = \dfrac{2\left(8.99\times10^9\right)(79)\left(1.60\times10^{-19}\right)^2}{7.70\left(1.60\times10^{-13}\right)} = 29.5\times10^{-15}\ \text{m} = \boxed{29.5\ \text{fm}}$

(b) The de Broglie wavelength of the α is

$$\lambda = \frac{h}{m_\alpha v_\alpha} = \frac{h}{\sqrt{2m_\alpha E_\alpha}} = \frac{6.626\times10^{-34}}{\sqrt{2\left(6.64\times10^{-27}\right)7.70\left(1.60\times10^{-13}\right)}} = 5.18\times10^{-15}\ \text{m} = \boxed{5.18\ \text{fm}}.$$

(c) Since $\boxed{\lambda \text{ is much less than the distance of closest approach}}$, the α may be considered a particle.

P44.5 (a) The initial kinetic energy of the alpha particle must equal the electrostatic potential energy at the distance of closest approach.

$$K_i = U_f = \frac{k_e qQ}{r_{\min}}$$

$$r_{\min} = \frac{k_e qQ}{K_i} = \frac{\left(8.99\times10^9\ \text{N}\cdot\text{m}^2/\text{C}^2\right)(2)(79)\left(1.60\times10^{-19}\ \text{C}\right)^2}{(0.500\ \text{MeV})\left(1.60\times10^{-13}\ \text{J/MeV}\right)} = \boxed{4.55\times10^{-13}\ \text{m}}$$

(b) Since $K_i = \dfrac{1}{2}m_\alpha v_i^2 = \dfrac{k_e qQ}{r_{\min}}$,

$$v_i = \sqrt{\frac{2k_e qQ}{m_\alpha r_{\min}}} = \sqrt{\frac{2\left(8.99\times10^9\ \text{N}\cdot\text{m}^2/\text{C}^2\right)(2)(79)\left(1.60\times10^{-19}\ \text{C}\right)^2}{(4.00\ \text{u})\left(1.66\times10^{-27}\ \text{kg/u}\right)\left(3.00\times10^{-13}\ \text{m}\right)}} = \boxed{6.04\times10^6\ \text{m/s}}.$$

P44.6 It must start with kinetic energy equal to $K_i = U_f = \frac{k_e qQ}{r_f}$. Here r_f stands for the sum of the radii of the ${}^{4}_{2}\text{He}$ and ${}^{197}_{79}\text{Au}$ nuclei, computed as

$$r_f = r_0 A_1^{1/3} + r_0 A_2^{1/3} = \left(1.20 \times 10^{-15}\text{ m}\right)\left(4^{1/3} + 197^{1/3}\right) = 8.89 \times 10^{-15}\text{ m}.$$

Thus, $K_i = U_f = \frac{\left(8.99 \times 10^{9}\text{ N}\cdot\text{m}^2/\text{C}^2\right)(2)(79)\left(1.60 \times 10^{-19}\text{ C}\right)^2}{8.89 \times 10^{-15}\text{ m}} = 4.09 \times 10^{-12}\text{ J} = \boxed{25.6\text{ MeV}}$.

P44.7 (a) $r = r_0 A^{1/3} = \left(1.20 \times 10^{-15}\text{ m}\right)(4)^{1/3} = \boxed{1.90 \times 10^{-15}\text{ m}}$

(b) $r = r_0 A^{1/3} = \left(1.20 \times 10^{-15}\text{ m}\right)(238)^{1/3} = \boxed{7.44 \times 10^{-15}\text{ m}}$

P44.8 From $r = r_0 A^{1/3}$, the radius of uranium is $r_U = r_0 (238)^{1/3}$.

Thus, if $r = \frac{1}{2} r_U$ then $r_0 A^{1/3} = \frac{1}{2} r_0 (238)^{1/3}$

from which $\boxed{A = 30}$.

P44.9 The number of nucleons in a star of two solar masses is

$$A = \frac{2\left(1.99 \times 10^{30}\text{ kg}\right)}{1.67 \times 10^{-27}\text{ kg/nucleon}} = 2.38 \times 10^{57}\text{ nucleons}.$$

Therefore $r = r_0 A^{1/3} = \left(1.20 \times 10^{-15}\text{ m}\right)\left(2.38 \times 10^{57}\right)^{1/3} = \boxed{16.0\text{ km}}$.

P44.10 $V = \frac{4}{3}\pi r^4 = \frac{4}{3}\pi (0.021\,5\text{ m})^3 = 4.16 \times 10^{-5}\text{ m}^3$

We take the nuclear density from Example 44.2

$$m = \rho V = \left(2.3 \times 10^{17}\text{ kg/m}^3\right)\left(4.16 \times 10^{-5}\text{ m}^3\right) = 9.57 \times 10^{12}\text{ kg}$$

and $F = G\frac{m_1 m_2}{r^2} = \left(6.67 \times 10^{-11}\text{ N}\cdot\text{m}^2/\text{kg}^2\right)\frac{\left(9.57 \times 10^{12}\text{ kg}\right)^2}{(1.00\text{ m})^2}$

$F = \boxed{6.11 \times 10^{15}\text{ N}}$ toward the other ball.

P44.11 The stable nuclei that correspond to magic numbers are:

Z magic: ${}_{2}\text{He}$ ${}_{8}\text{O}$ ${}_{20}\text{Ca}$ ${}_{28}\text{Ni}$ ${}_{50}\text{Sn}$ ${}_{82}\text{Pb}$

An artificially produced nucleus with $Z = 126$ might be more stable than other nuclei with lower values for Z, since this number of protons is magic.

N magic: ${}^{3}_{1}\text{T}$, ${}^{4}_{2}\text{He}$, ${}^{15}_{7}\text{N}$, ${}^{16}_{8}\text{O}$, ${}^{37}_{17}\text{Cl}$, ${}^{39}_{19}\text{K}$, ${}^{40}_{20}\text{Ca}$, ${}^{51}_{23}\text{V}$, ${}^{52}_{24}\text{Cr}$, ${}^{88}_{38}\text{Sr}$, ${}^{89}_{39}\text{Y}$, ${}^{90}_{40}\text{Zr}$, ${}^{136}_{54}\text{Xe}$, ${}^{138}_{56}\text{Ba}$, ${}^{139}_{57}\text{La}$, ${}^{140}_{58}\text{Ce}$, ${}^{141}_{59}\text{Pr}$, ${}^{142}_{60}\text{Nd}$, ${}^{208}_{82}\text{Pb}$, ${}^{209}_{83}\text{Bi}$, ${}^{210}_{84}\text{Po}$

***P44.12** (a) For even Z, even *N*, even *A*, the list begins ${}^{4}_{2}\text{He}$, ${}^{12}_{6}\text{C}$, and ends ${}^{194}_{78}\text{Pt}$, ${}^{196}_{78}\text{Pt}$, ${}^{202}_{80}\text{Hg}$, ${}^{208}_{82}\text{Pb}$, containing $\boxed{48}$ isotopes.

(b) The whole even Z, odd *N*, odd *A* list is ${}^{9}_{4}\text{Be}$, ${}^{129}_{54}\text{Xe}$, ${}^{195}_{78}\text{Pt}$, with $\boxed{3}$ entries.

(c) The odd Z, even *N*, odd *A* list has $\boxed{46}$ entries, represented as ${}^{1}_{1}\text{H}$, ${}^{7}_{3}\text{Li}$, ..., ${}^{203}_{81}\text{Tl}$, ${}^{205}_{81}\text{Tl}$, ${}^{209}_{83}\text{Bi}$.

(d) The odd Z, odd *N*, even *A* list has $\boxed{1}$ entry, ${}^{14}_{7}\text{N}$. Do not be misled into thinking that nature favors nuclei with even numbers of neutrons. The form of the question here forces a count with essentially equal numbers of odd-Z and even-Z nuclei. If we counted all of the stable nuclei we would find many even-even isotopes but also lots of even-Z odd-*N* nuclei and odd-Z even-*N* nuclei; we would find roughly equal numbers of these two kinds of odd-*A* nuclei. A nucleus with one odd neutron is no more likely to be unstable than a nucleus with one odd proton.

With the arbitrary 25% abundance standard, we can note that most elements have a single predominant isotope. Ni, Cu, Zn, Ga, Ge, Pd, Ag, Os, Ir, and Pt form a compact patch on the periodic table and have two common isotopes, as do some others. Tungsten is the only element with three isotopes over 25% abundance.

***P44.13** (a) $Z_1 = 8Z_2 \qquad N_1 = 5N_2$

$N_1 + Z_1 = 6(N_1 + Z_2)$ and $N_1 = Z_1 + 4$

Thus: $$N_1 + Z_1 = 6\left(\frac{1}{5}N_1 + \frac{1}{8}Z_1\right)$$

$$\therefore N_1 = \frac{5}{4}Z_1$$

$$\therefore Z_1 + 4 = \frac{5}{4}Z_1$$

$$\therefore Z_1 = 16$$

$$N_1 = Z_1 + 4 = 20,\ A_1 = Z_1 + N_1 = 36$$

$$N_2 = \frac{1}{5}N_1 = 4,\ Z_2 = \frac{1}{8}Z_1 = 2,\ A_2 = Z_2 + N_2 = 6$$

Hence: ${}^{36}_{16}\text{S}$ and ${}^{6}_{2}\text{He}$.

(b) ${}^{6}_{2}\text{He}$ is unstable. Two neutrons must be removed to make it stable $\left({}^{4}_{2}\text{He}\right)$.

Section 44.2 **Nuclear Binding Energy**

P44.14 Using atomic masses as given in Table A.3,

(a) For ${}^2_1\text{H}$: $\dfrac{-2.014\,102+1(1.008\,665)+1(1.007\,825)}{2}$

$$\frac{E_b}{A}=(0.001\,194\text{ u})\left(\frac{931.5\text{ MeV}}{\text{u}}\right)=\boxed{1.11\text{ MeV/nucleon}}.$$

(b) For ${}^4_2\text{He}$: $\dfrac{2(1.008\,665)+2(1.007\,825)-4.002\,603}{4}$

$$\frac{E_b}{A}=0.007\,59\text{ u}c^2=\boxed{7.07\text{ MeV/nucleon}}.$$

(c) For ${}^{56}_{26}\text{Fe}$: $30(1.008\,665)+26(1.007\,825)-55.934\,942=0.528\text{ u}$

$$\frac{E_b}{A}=\frac{0.528}{56}=0.009\,44\text{ u}c^2=\boxed{8.79\text{ MeV/nucleon}}.$$

(d) For ${}^{238}_{92}\text{U}$: $146(1.008\,665)+92(1.007\,825)-238.050\,783=1.934\,2\text{ u}$

$$\frac{E_b}{A}=\frac{1.934\,2}{238}=0.008\,13\text{ u}c^2=\boxed{7.57\text{ MeV/nucleon}}.$$

P44.15 $\Delta M=Zm_{\text{H}}+Nm_{\text{n}}-M$ $\qquad\dfrac{\text{BE}}{A}=\dfrac{\Delta M(931.5)}{A}$

Nuclei	Z	N	M in u	ΔM in u	$\dfrac{\text{BE}}{A}$ in MeV
${}^{55}\text{Mn}$	25	30	54.938 050	0.517 5	8.765
${}^{56}\text{Fe}$	26	30	55.934 942	0.528 46	8.790
${}^{59}\text{Co}$	27	32	58.933 200	0.555 35	8.768

$\therefore {}^{56}\text{Fe}$ has a greater $\dfrac{\text{BE}}{A}$ than its neighbors. This tells us finer detail than is shown in Figure 44.5.

P44.16 Use Equation 44.2.

The ${}^{23}_{11}\text{Na}$, $\quad\dfrac{E_b}{A}=8.11\text{ MeV/nucleon}$

and for ${}^{23}_{12}\text{Mg}$, $\quad\dfrac{E_b}{A}=7.90\text{ MeV/nucleon}$.

The binding energy per nucleon is greater for ${}^{23}_{11}\text{Na}$ by $\boxed{0.210\text{ MeV}}$. (There is less proton repulsion in Na^{23}.)

P44.17 (a) The neutron-to-proton ratio $\dfrac{A-Z}{Z}$ is greatest for $\boxed{{}^{139}_{55}\text{Cs}}$ and is equal to 1.53.

(b) $\boxed{{}^{139}\text{La}}$ has the largest binding energy per nucleon of 8.378 MeV.

(c) ${}^{139}\text{Cs}$ with a mass of 138.913 u. We locate the nuclei carefully on Figure 44.4, the neutron–proton plot of stable nuclei. $\boxed{\text{Cesium}}$ appears to be farther from the center of the zone of stability. Its instability means extra energy and extra mass.

P44.18 (a) The radius of the ^{40}Ca nucleus is: $R = r_0 A^{1/3} = \left(1.20 \times 10^{-15}\text{ m}\right)(40)^{1/3} = 4.10 \times 10^{-15}\text{ m}$.

The energy required to overcome electrostatic repulsion is

$$U = \frac{3k_e Q^2}{5R} = \frac{3\left(8.99 \times 10^9\text{ N}\cdot\text{m}^2/\text{C}^2\right)\left[20\left(1.60 \times 10^{-19}\text{ C}\right)\right]^2}{5\left(4.10 \times 10^{-15}\text{ m}\right)} = 1.35 \times 10^{-11}\text{ J} = \boxed{84.1\text{ MeV}}.$$

(b) The binding energy of $^{40}_{20}$Ca is

$$E_b = \left[20(1.007\,825\text{ u}) + 20(1.008\,665\text{ u}) - 39.962\,591\text{ u}\right](931.5\text{ MeV/u}) = \boxed{342\text{ MeV}}.$$

(c) The nuclear force is so strong that the binding energy greatly exceeds the minimum energy needed to overcome electrostatic repulsion.

P44.19 The binding energy of a nucleus is $E_b(\text{MeV}) = \left[ZM(\text{H}) + Nm_n - M\left({}^A_Z\text{X}\right)\right](931.494\text{ MeV/u})$.

For $^{15}_{8}$O: $E_b = \left[8(1.007\,825\text{ u}) + 7(1.008\,665\text{ u}) - 15.003\,065\text{ u}\right](931.494\text{ MeV/u}) = 111.96\text{ MeV}$.

For $^{15}_{7}$N: $E_b = \left[7(1.007\,825\text{ u}) + 8(1.008\,665\text{ u}) - 15.000\,109\text{ u}\right](931.494\text{ MeV/u}) = 115.49\text{ MeV}$.

Therefore, $\boxed{\text{the binding energy of } ^{15}_{7}\text{N is larger by 3.54 MeV}}$.

P44.20 Removal of a neutron from $^{43}_{20}$Ca would result in the residual nucleus, $^{42}_{20}$Ca. If the required separation energy is S_n, the overall process can be described by

$$\text{mass}\left({}^{43}_{20}\text{Ca}\right) + S_n = \text{mass}\left({}^{42}_{20}\text{Ca}\right) + \text{mass(n)}$$

$$S_n = (41.958\,618 + 1.008\,665 - 42.958\,767)\text{ u} = (0.008\,516\text{ u})(931.5\text{ MeV/u}) = \boxed{7.93\text{ MeV}}.$$

Section 44.3 **Nuclear Models**

P44.21 $\Delta E_b = E_{bf} - E_{bi}$

For $A = 200$, $\dfrac{E_b}{A} = 7.4\text{ MeV}$

so $E_{bi} = 200(7.4\text{ MeV}) = 1\,480\text{ MeV}$.

For $A \approx 100$, $\dfrac{E_b}{A} = 8.4\text{ MeV}$

so $E_{bf} = 2(100)(8.4\text{ MeV}) = 1\,680\text{ MeV}$.

$\Delta E_b = E_{bf} - E_{bi}$: $E_b = 1\,680\text{ MeV} - 1\,480\text{ MeV} = \boxed{200\text{ MeV}}$

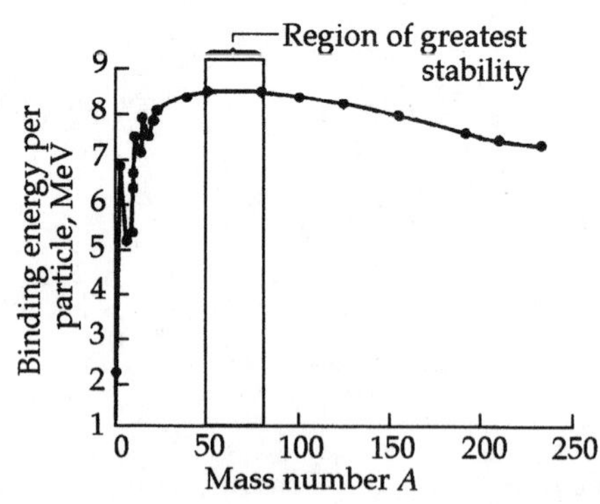

FIG. P44.21

P44.22 (a) The first term overstates the importance of volume and the second term *subtracts* this overstatement.

(b) For spherical volume $\frac{(4/3)\pi R^3}{4\pi R^2}=\boxed{\frac{R}{3}}$. For cubical volume $\frac{R^3}{6R^2}=\boxed{\frac{R}{6}}$.

The maximum binding energy or lowest state of energy is achieved by building "nearly" spherical nuclei.

P44.23 (a) "Volume" term: $E_1=C_1A=(15.7\text{ MeV})(56)=879\text{ MeV}$.

"Surface" term: $E_2=-C_2A^{2/3}=-(17.8\text{ MeV})(56)^{2/3}=-260\text{ MeV}$.

"Coulomb" term: $E_3=-C_3\frac{Z(Z-1)}{A^{1/3}}=-(0.71\text{ MeV})\frac{(26)(25)}{(56)^{1/3}}=-121\text{ MeV}$.

"Asymmetry" term: $E_4=C_4\frac{(A-2Z)^2}{A}=-(23.6\text{ MeV})\frac{(56-52)^2}{56}=-6.74\text{ MeV}$.

$\boxed{E_b=491\text{ MeV}}$

(b) $\frac{E_1}{E_b}=179\%;\ \frac{E_2}{E_b}=-53.0\%,\ \frac{E_3}{E_b}=-24.6\%;\ \frac{E_4}{E_b}=-1.37\%$

Section 44.4 **Radioactivity**

P44.24 $R=R_0e^{-\lambda t}=(6.40\text{ mCi})e^{-(\ln 2/8.04\text{ d})(40.2\text{ d})}=(6.40\text{ mCi})\left(e^{-\ln 2}\right)^5=(6.40\text{ mCi})\left(\frac{1}{2^5}\right)=\boxed{0.200\text{ mCi}}$

P44.25 $\frac{dN}{dt}=-\lambda N$

so $\lambda=\frac{1}{N}\left(-\frac{dN}{dt}\right)=\left(1.00\times10^{-15}\right)\left(6.00\times10^{11}\right)=6.00\times10^{-4}\text{ s}^{-1}$

$T_{1/2}=\frac{\ln 2}{\lambda}=\boxed{1.16\times10^3\text{ s}}(=19.3\text{ min})$

P44.26 $R=\lambda N=\left(\frac{\ln 2}{5.27\text{ yr}}\right)\left(\frac{1.00\text{ g}}{59.93\text{ g/mol}}\right)\left(6.02\times10^{23}\right)$

$R=\left(1.32\times10^{21}\text{ decays/yr}\right)\left(\frac{1\text{ yr}}{3.16\times10^7\text{ s}}\right)=\boxed{4.18\times10^{13}\text{ Bq}}$

P44.27 (a) From $R=R_0e^{-\lambda t}$,

$\lambda=\frac{1}{t}\ln\left(\frac{R_0}{R}\right)=\left(\frac{1}{4.00\text{ h}}\right)\ln\left(\frac{10.0}{8.00}\right)=5.58\times10^{-2}\text{ h}^{-1}=\boxed{1.55\times10^{-5}\text{ s}^{-1}}$

$T_{1/2}=\frac{\ln 2}{\lambda}=\boxed{12.4\text{ h}}$

(b) $N_0=\frac{R_0}{\lambda}=\frac{10.0\times10^{-3}\text{ Ci}}{1.55\times10^{-5}/\text{s}}\left(\frac{3.70\times10^{10}/\text{s}}{1\text{ Ci}}\right)=\boxed{2.39\times10^{13}\text{ atoms}}$

(c) $R=R_0e^{-\lambda t}=(10.0\text{ mCi})\exp\left(-5.58\times10^{-2}\times30.0\right)=\boxed{1.88\text{ mCi}}$

P44.28 $R = R_0 e^{-\lambda t}$ where $\lambda = \frac{\ln 2}{26.0 \text{ h}} = 0.026\,6 \text{ h}^{-1}$

$\frac{R}{R_0} = 0.100 = e^{-\lambda t}$ so $\ln(0.100) = -\lambda t$

$2.30 = \left(\frac{0.026\,6}{\text{h}}\right)t$ $\quad t = \boxed{86.4 \text{ h}}$

P44.29 The number of nuclei which decay during the interval will be $N_1 - N_2 = N_0\left(e^{-\lambda t_1} - e^{-\lambda t_2}\right)$.

First we find l: $\lambda = \frac{\ln 2}{T_{1/2}} = \frac{0.693}{64.8 \text{ h}} = 0.010\,7 \text{ h}^{-1} = 2.97 \times 10^{-6} \text{ s}^{-1}$

and $N_0 = \frac{R_0}{\lambda} = \frac{(40.0\ \mu\text{Ci})\left(3.70 \times 10^4 \text{ s}^{-1}/\mu\text{Ci}\right)}{2.97 \times 10^{-6} \text{ s}^{-1}} = 4.98 \times 10^{11} \text{ nuclei}$.

Substituting these values, $N_1 - N_2 = \left(4.98 \times 10^{11}\right)\left[e^{-(0.010\,7 \text{ h}^{-1})(10.0 \text{ h})} - e^{-(0.010\,7 \text{ h}^{-1})(12.0 \text{ h})}\right]$.

Hence, the number of nuclei decaying during the interval is $N_1 - N_2 = \boxed{9.47 \times 10^9 \text{ nuclei}}$.

P44.30 The number of nuclei which decay during the interval will be $N_1 - N_2 = N_0\left(e^{-\lambda t_1} - e^{-\lambda t_2}\right)$.

First we find λ: $\lambda = \frac{\ln 2}{T_{1/2}}$

so $e^{-\lambda t} = e^{\ln 2(-t/T_{1/2})} = 2^{-t/T_{1/2}}$

and $N_0 = \frac{R_0}{\lambda} = \frac{R_0 T_{1/2}}{\ln 2}$.

Substituting in these values $N_1 - N_2 = \frac{R_0 T_{1/2}}{\ln 2}\left(e^{-\lambda t_1} - e^{-\lambda t_2}\right) = \boxed{\frac{R_0 T_{1/2}}{\ln 2}\left(2^{-t_1/T_{1/2}} - 2^{-t_2/T_{1/2}}\right)}$.

***P44.31** We have all this information: $N_x(0) = 2.50 N_y(0)$

$N_x(3\text{d}) = 4.20 N_y(3\text{d})$

$N_x(0)e^{-\lambda_x 3\text{d}} = 4.20 N_y(0)e^{-\lambda_y 3\text{d}} = 4.20\frac{N_x(0)}{2.50}e^{-\lambda_y 3\text{d}}$

$e^{3\text{d}\lambda_x} = \frac{2.5}{4.2}e^{3\text{d}\lambda_y}$

$3\text{d}\lambda_x = \ln\left(\frac{2.5}{4.2}\right) + 3\text{d}\lambda_y$

$3\text{d}\frac{0.693}{T_{1/2\,x}} = \ln\left(\frac{2.5}{4.2}\right) + 3\text{d}\frac{0.693}{1.60 \text{ d}} = 0.781$

$T_{1/2\,x} = \boxed{2.66 \text{ d}}$

***P44.32** (a) $\frac{dN_2}{dt}$ = rate of change of N_2

= rate of production of N_2 – rate of decay of N_2

= rate of decay of N_1 – rate of decay of N_2

$= \lambda_1 N_1 - \lambda_2 N_2$

(b) From the trial solution

$$N_2(t) = \frac{N_{10}\lambda_1}{\lambda_1 - \lambda_2}\left(e^{-\lambda_2 t} - e^{-\lambda_1 t}\right)$$

$$\therefore \frac{dN_2}{dt} = \frac{N_{10}\lambda_1}{\lambda_1 - \lambda_2}\left(-\lambda_2 e^{-\lambda_2 t} + \lambda_1 e^{-\lambda_1 t}\right) \quad (1)$$

$$\therefore \frac{dN_2}{dt} + \lambda_2 N_2 = \frac{N_{10}\lambda_1}{\lambda_1 - \lambda_2}\left(-\lambda_2 e^{-\lambda_2 t} + \lambda_1 e^{-\lambda_1 t} + \lambda_2 e^{-\lambda_2 t} - \lambda_2 e^{-\lambda_1 t}\right)$$

$$= \frac{N_{10}\lambda_1}{\lambda_1 - \lambda_2}(\lambda_1 - \lambda_2)e^{-\lambda_1 t}$$

$$= \lambda_1 N_1$$

So $\frac{dN_2}{dt} = \lambda_1 N_1 - \lambda_2 N_2$ as required.

(c) The functions to be plotted are

$$N_1(t) = 1\,000 e^{-\left(0.223\,6 \text{ min}^{-1}\right)t}$$

$$N_2(t) = 1\,130.8\left[e^{-\left(0.223\,6 \text{ min}^{-1}\right)t} - e^{-\left(0.025\,9 \text{ min}^{-1}\right)t}\right]$$

From the graph: $t_m \approx \boxed{10.9 \text{ min}}$

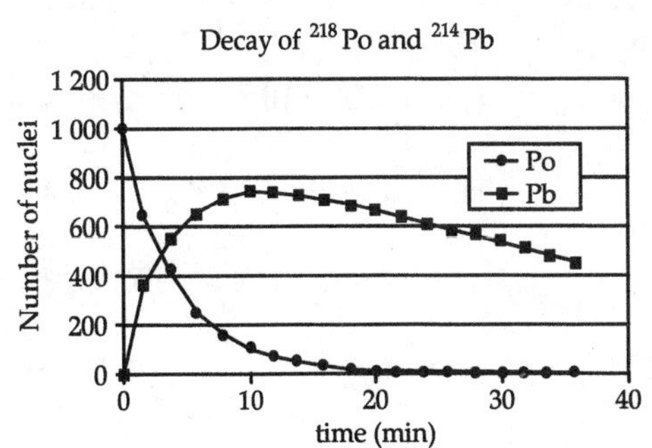

FIG. P44.32(c)

(d) From (1), $\frac{dN_2}{dt} = 0$ if $\lambda_2 e^{-\lambda_2 t} = \lambda_1 e^{-\lambda_1 t}$. $\therefore e^{(\lambda_1 - \lambda_2)t} = \frac{\lambda_1}{\lambda_2}$. Thus, $t = \boxed{t_m = \frac{\ln(\lambda_1/\lambda_2)}{\lambda_1 - \lambda_2}}$.

With $\lambda_1 = 0.223\,6 \text{ min}^{-1}$, $\lambda_2 = 0.025\,9 \text{ min}^{-1}$, this formula gives $t_m = \boxed{10.9 \text{ min}}$, in agreement with the result of part (c).

Section 44.5 The Decay Processes

P44.33 $Q = \left(M_{\text{U-238}} - M_{\text{Th-234}} - M_{\text{He-4}}\right)(931.5 \text{ MeV/u})$

$Q = (238.050\,783 - 234.043\,596 - 4.002\,603) \text{ u}(931.5 \text{ MeV/u}) = \boxed{4.27 \text{ MeV}}$

P44.34 (a) A gamma ray has zero charge and it contains no protons or neutrons. So for a gamma ray $Z=0$ and $A=0$. Keeping the total values of Z and A for the system conserved then requires $Z=28$ and $A=65$ for X. With this atomic number it must be nickel, and the nucleus must be in an exited state, so it is ${}^{65}_{28}\text{Ni}^*$.

(b) $\alpha={}^4_2\text{He}$ has $Z=2$ and $A=4$
so for X we require $Z=84-2=82$
for Pb and $A=215-4=211$, $X={}^{211}_{82}\text{Pb}$.

(c) A positron $e^+={}^{0}_{1}e$ has charge the same as a nucleus with $Z=1$. A neutrino ${}^0_0\nu$ has no charge. Neither contains any protons or neutrons. So X must have by conservation $Z=26+1=27$. It is Co. And $A=55+0=55$. It is ${}^{55}_{27}\text{Co}$.

Similar reasoning about balancing the sums of Z and A across the reaction reveals:

(d) ${}^{0}_{-1}e$

(e) ${}^1_1\text{H}$ (or p). Note that this process is a nuclear reaction, rather than radioactive decay. We can solve it from the same principles, which are fundamentally conservation of charge and conservation of baryon number.

P44.35 $N_C=\left(\dfrac{0.021\,0\text{ g}}{12.0\text{ g/mol}}\right)\left(6.02\times10^{23}\text{ molecules/mol}\right)$

$\left(N_C=1.05\times10^{21}\text{ carbon atoms}\right)$ of which 1 in 7.70×10^{11} is a ${}^{14}\text{C}$ atom

$(N_0)_{\text{C-14}}=1.37\times10^9$, $\lambda_{\text{C-14}}=\dfrac{\ln 2}{5\,730\text{ yr}}=1.21\times10^{-4}\text{ yr}^{-1}=3.83\times10^{-12}\text{ s}^{-1}$

$$R=\lambda N=\lambda N_0e^{-\lambda t}$$

At $t=0$, $R_0=\lambda N_0=\left(3.83\times10^{-12}\text{ s}^{-1}\right)\left(1.37\times10^9\right)\left[\dfrac{7(86\,400\text{ s})}{1\text{ week}}\right]=3.17\times10^3\text{ decays/week}$.

At time t, $R=\dfrac{837}{0.88}=951\text{ decays/week}$.

Taking logarithms, $\ln\dfrac{R}{R_0}=-\lambda t$ so $t=\dfrac{-1}{\lambda}\ln\left(\dfrac{R}{R_0}\right)$

$$t=\frac{-1}{1.21\times10^{-4}\text{ yr}^{-1}}\ln\left(\frac{951}{3.17\times10^3}\right)=\boxed{9.96\times10^3\text{ yr}}.$$

***P44.36** $N=N_0e^{-\lambda t}$ $\left|\dfrac{dN}{dt}\right|=R=\left|-\lambda N_0e^{-\lambda t}\right|=R_0e^{-\lambda t}$

$e^{-\lambda t}=\dfrac{R}{R_0}$ $e^{\lambda t}=\dfrac{R_0}{R}$ $\lambda t=\ln\left(\dfrac{R_0}{R}\right)=\dfrac{\ln 2}{T_{1/2}}t$ $t=T_{1/2}\dfrac{\ln(R_0/R)}{\ln 2}$

If $R=0.13$ Bq, $t=5\,730\text{ yr}\dfrac{\ln(0.25/0.13)}{0.693}=5\,406\text{ yr}$.

If $R=0.11$ Bq, $t=5\,730\text{ yr}\dfrac{\ln(0.25/0.11)}{0.693}=6\,787\text{ yr}$.

The range is most clearly written as $\boxed{\text{between } 5\,400\text{ yr and } 6\,800\text{ yr}}$, without understatement.

P44.37 $^3_1\text{H nucleus} \rightarrow {}^3_2\text{He nucleus} + e^- + \bar{\nu}$

becomes $^3_1\text{H nucleus} + e^- \rightarrow {}^3_2\text{He nucleus} + 2e^- + \bar{\nu}$.

Ignoring the slight difference in ionization energies,

we have $^3_1\text{H atom} \rightarrow {}^3_2\text{He atom} + \bar{\nu}$

$$3.016\,049\text{ u} = 3.016\,029\text{ u} + 0 + \frac{Q}{c^2}$$

$$Q = (3.016\,049\text{ u} - 3.016\,029\text{ u})(931.5\text{ MeV/u}) = 0.018\,6\text{ MeV} = \boxed{18.6\text{ keV}}$$

P44.38 (a) For e^+ decay,

$$Q = (M_X - M_Y - 2m_e)c^2 = [39.962\,591\text{ u} - 39.963\,999\text{ u} - 2(0.000\,549\text{ u})](931.5\text{ MeV/u})$$

$$Q = -2.33\text{ MeV}$$

Since $Q < 0$, the decay $\boxed{\text{cannot occur}}$ spontaneously.

(b) For alpha decay,

$$Q = (M_X - M_\alpha - M_Y)c^2 = [91.905\,287\text{ u} - 4.002\,603\text{ u} - 93.905\,088\text{ u}](931.5\text{ MeV/u})$$

$$Q = -2.24\text{ MeV}$$

Since $Q < 0$, the decay $\boxed{\text{cannot occur}}$ spontaneously.

(c) For alpha decay,

$$Q = (M_X - M_\alpha - M_Y)c^2 = [143.910\,083\text{ u} - 4.002\,603\text{ u} - 139.905\,434\text{ u}](931.5\text{ MeV/u})$$

$$Q = 1.91\text{ MeV}$$

Since $Q > 0$, the decay $\boxed{\text{can occur}}$ spontaneously.

P44.39 (a) $\boxed{e^- + p \rightarrow n + \nu}$

(b) For nuclei, $^{15}\text{O} + e^- \rightarrow {}^{15}\text{N} + \nu$.

Add seven electrons to both sides to obtain $\boxed{^{15}_8\text{O atom} \rightarrow {}^{15}_7\text{N atom} + \nu}$.

(c) From Table A.3, $m\left({}^{15}\text{O}\right) = m\left({}^{15}\text{N}\right) + \frac{Q}{c^2}$

$$\Delta m = 15.003\,065\text{ u} - 15.000\,109\text{ u} = 0.002\,956\text{ u}$$

$$Q = (931.5\text{ MeV/u})(0.002\,956\text{ u}) = \boxed{2.75\text{ MeV}}$$

Section 44.6 Natural Radioactivity

P44.40 (a) Let N be the number of ^{238}U nuclei and N' be ^{206}Pb nuclei.

Then $N = N_0 e^{-\lambda t}$ and $N_0 = N + N'$ so $N = (N+N')e^{-\lambda t}$ or $e^{\lambda t} = 1 + \frac{N'}{N}$.

Taking logarithms, $\lambda t = \ln\left(1 + \frac{N'}{N}\right)$ where $\lambda = \frac{\ln 2}{T_{1/2}}$.

Thus,
$$t = \left(\frac{T_{1/2}}{\ln 2}\right)\ln\left(1 + \frac{N'}{N}\right).$$

If $\frac{N}{N'} = 1.164$ for the $^{238}U \to {}^{206}Pb$ chain with $T_{1/2} = 4.47 \times 10^9$ yr, the age is:

$$t = \left(\frac{4.47 \times 10^9 \text{ yr}}{\ln 2}\right)\ln\left(1 + \frac{1}{1.164}\right) = \boxed{4.00 \times 10^9 \text{ yr}}.$$

(b) From above, $e^{\lambda t} = 1 + \frac{N'}{N}$. Solving for $\frac{N}{N'}$ gives $\frac{N}{N'} = \frac{e^{-\lambda t}}{1 - e^{-\lambda t}}$.

With $t = 4.00 \times 10^9$ yr and $T_{1/2} = 7.04 \times 10^8$ yr for the $^{235}U \to {}^{207}Pb$ chain,

$$\lambda t = \left(\frac{\ln 2}{T_{1/2}}\right)t = \frac{(\ln 2)(4.00 \times 10^9 \text{ yr})}{7.04 \times 10^8 \text{ yr}} = 3.938 \text{ and } \boxed{\frac{N}{N'} = 0.0199}.$$

With $t = 4.00 \times 10^9$ yr and $T_{1/2} = 1.41 \times 10^{10}$ yr for the $^{232}Th \to {}^{208}Pb$ chain,

$$\lambda t = \frac{(\ln 2)(4.00 \times 10^9 \text{ yr})}{1.41 \times 10^{10} \text{ yr}} = 0.1966 \text{ and } \boxed{\frac{N}{N'} = 4.60}.$$

P44.41

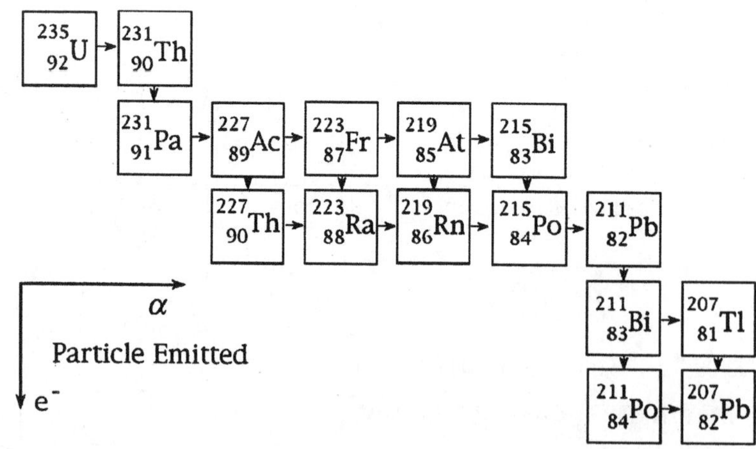

FIG. P44.41

P44.42 (a) $4.00\text{ pCi/L} = \left(\frac{4.00\times10^{-12}\text{ Ci}}{1\text{ L}}\right)\left(\frac{3.70\times10^{10}\text{ Bq}}{1\text{ Ci}}\right)\left(\frac{1.00\times10^{3}\text{ L}}{1\text{ m}^3}\right) = \boxed{148\text{ Bq/m}^3}$

(b) $N = \frac{R}{\lambda} = R\left(\frac{T_{1/2}}{\ln 2}\right) = \left(148\text{ Bq/m}^3\right)\left(\frac{3.82\text{ d}}{\ln 2}\right)\left(\frac{86\,400\text{ s}}{1\text{ d}}\right) = \boxed{7.05\times10^{7}\text{ atoms/m}^3}$

(c) $\text{mass} = \left(7.05\times10^{7}\text{ atoms/m}^3\right)\left(\frac{1\text{ mol}}{6.02\times10^{23}\text{ atoms}}\right)\left(\frac{222\text{ g}}{1\text{ mol}}\right) = 2.60\times10^{-14}\text{ g/m}^3$

Since air has a density of 1.20 kg/m^3, the fraction consisting of radon is

$\text{fraction} = \frac{2.60\times10^{-14}\text{ g/m}^3}{1\,200\text{ g/m}^3} = \boxed{2.17\times10^{-17}}$

***P44.43** (a) Let x, y denote the half-lives of the nuclei X, Y.

$\frac{R_X}{R_Y} = \frac{R_0 e^{-\lambda_X t}}{R_0 e^{-\lambda_Y t}} = e^{-(0.685\text{ h})(\ln 2)(1/x - 1/y)} = 1.04$, which gives

$\frac{1}{x} - \frac{1}{y} = -0.082\,603\,69\text{ h}^{-1}.$ (1)

From the data: $x - y = 77.2\text{ h}.$ (2)

Substitute (2) into (1): $\frac{1}{x} - \frac{1}{x - 77.2\text{ h}} = -0.082\,603\,69\text{ h}^{-1}.$

This reduces to the quadratic equation

$$x^2 - 77.2x - 934.6 = 0$$

which has solutions: $x = 87.84\text{ h}$ or -10.64 h.

Thus: $x = T_{1/2,\,X} = 87.84\text{ h} = \boxed{3.66\text{ days}}$ is the only physical root.

From (2): $y = T_{1/2,\,Y} = 87.84\text{ h} - 77.2\text{ h} = \boxed{10.6\text{ h}}$.

(b) From Table A.3, X is $\boxed{^{224}\text{Ra}}$ and Y is $\boxed{^{212}\text{Pb}}$.

(c) From Figure 44.18, ^{224}Ra decays to ^{212}Pb by $\boxed{\text{three}}$ successive alpha-decays.

P44.44 Number remaining: $N = N_0 e^{-(\ln 2)t/T_{1/2}}.$

Fraction remaining: $\frac{N}{N_0} = e^{-\lambda t} = e^{-(\ln 2)t/T_{1/2}}.$

(a) With $T_{1/2} = 3.82\text{ d}$ and $t = 7.00\text{ d}$, $\frac{N}{N_0} = e^{-(\ln 2)(7.00)/(3.82)} = \boxed{0.281}$.

(b) When $t = 1.00\text{ yr} = 365.25\text{ d}$, $\frac{N}{N_0} = e^{-(\ln 2)(365.25)/(3.82)} = \boxed{1.65\times10^{-29}}$.

(c) $\boxed{\text{Radon is continuously created}}$ as one daughter in the series of decays starting from the long-lived isotope ^{238}U.

Section 44.7 **Nuclear Reactions**

P44.45 $Q=\left[M_{^{27}\text{Al}}+M_\alpha-M_{^{30}\text{P}}-m_n\right]c^2$

$Q=[26.981\,539+4.002\,603-29.978\,314-1.008\,665]\text{ u}(931.5\text{ MeV/u})=\boxed{-2.64\text{ MeV}}$

P44.46 (a) For X, $A=24+1-4=21$

and $Z=12+0-2=10$, so X is $\boxed{^{21}_{10}\text{Ne}}$.

(b) $A=235+1-90-2=144$

and $Z=92+0-38-0=54$, so X is $\boxed{^{144}_{54}\text{Xe}}$.

(c) $A=2-2=0$

and $Z=2-1=+1$, so X must be a positron.

As it is ejected, so is a neutrino: $\boxed{X={}^{0}_{1}e^{+}}$ and $\boxed{X'={}^{0}_{0}\nu}$.

P44.47 (a) $^{197}_{79}\text{Au}+{}^{1}_{0}\text{n}\rightarrow{}^{198}_{79}\text{Au}^{*}\rightarrow{}^{198}_{80}\text{Hg}+{}^{0}_{-1}\text{e}+\overline{\nu}$

(b) Consider adding 79 electrons:

$^{197}_{79}\text{Au atom}+{}^{1}_{0}\text{n}\rightarrow{}^{198}_{80}\text{Hg atom}+\overline{\nu}+Q$

$Q=\left[M_{^{197}\text{Au}}+m_n-M_{^{198}\text{Hg}}\right]c^2$

$Q=[196.966\,552+1.008\,665-197.966\,752]\text{ u}(931.5\text{ MeV/u})=\boxed{7.89\text{ MeV}}$

P44.48 Neglect recoil of product nucleus, (i.e., do not require momentum conservation for the system of colliding particles). The energy balance gives $K_{\text{emerging}}=K_{\text{incident}}+Q$. To find Q:

$$Q=[(M_{\text{H}}+M_{\text{Al}})-(M_{\text{Si}}+m_n)]c^2$$

$$Q=[(1.007\,825+26.981\,539)-(26.986\,705+1.008\,665)]\text{ u}(931.5\text{ MeV/u})=-5.59\text{ MeV}$$

Thus, $K_{\text{emerging}}=6.61\text{ MeV}-5.59\text{ MeV}=\boxed{1.02\text{ MeV}}$.

P44.49 $^{9}_{4}\text{Be}+1.665\text{ MeV}\rightarrow{}^{8}_{4}\text{Be}+{}^{1}_{0}\text{n}$, so $M_{^{8}_{4}\text{Be}}=M_{^{9}_{4}\text{Be}}-\dfrac{Q}{c^2}-m_n$

$$M_{^{8}_{4}\text{Be}}=9.012\,182\text{ u}-\frac{(-1.665\text{ MeV})}{931.5\text{ MeV/u}}-1.008\,665\text{ u}=\boxed{8.005\,3\text{ u}}$$

$^{9}_{4}\text{Be}+{}^{1}_{0}\text{n}\rightarrow{}^{10}_{4}\text{Be}+6.812\text{ MeV}$, so $M_{^{10}_{4}\text{Be}}=M_{^{9}_{4}\text{Be}}+m_n-\dfrac{Q}{c^2}$

$$M_{^{10}_{4}\text{Be}}=9.012\,182\text{ u}+1.008\,665\text{ u}-\frac{6.812\text{ MeV}}{931.5\text{ MeV/u}}=\boxed{10.013\,5\text{ u}}$$

P44.50 (a) $^{10}_{5}\text{B} + ^{4}_{2}\text{He} \rightarrow ^{13}_{6}\text{C} + ^{1}_{1}\text{H}$

The product nucleus is $\boxed{^{13}_{6}\text{C}}$.

(b) $^{13}_{6}\text{C} + ^{1}_{1}\text{H} \rightarrow ^{10}_{5}\text{B} + ^{4}_{2}\text{He}$

The product nucleus is $\boxed{^{10}_{5}\text{B}}$.

P44.51 $^{236}_{92}\text{U} \rightarrow ^{90}_{37}\text{Rb} + ^{143}_{55}\text{Cs} + 3^{1}_{0}\text{n}$,

so $Q = \left[M_{^{236}_{92}\text{U}} - M_{^{90}_{37}\text{Rb}} - M_{^{143}_{55}\text{Cs}} - 3m_n\right]c^2$

From Table A.3,

$$Q = [236.045\,562 - 89.914\,809 - 142.927\,330 - 3(1.008\,665)]\text{u}(931.5 \text{ MeV/u}) = \boxed{165 \text{ MeV}}.$$

Section 44.8 **Nuclear Magnetic Resonance and Magnetic Resonance Imagining**

P44.52

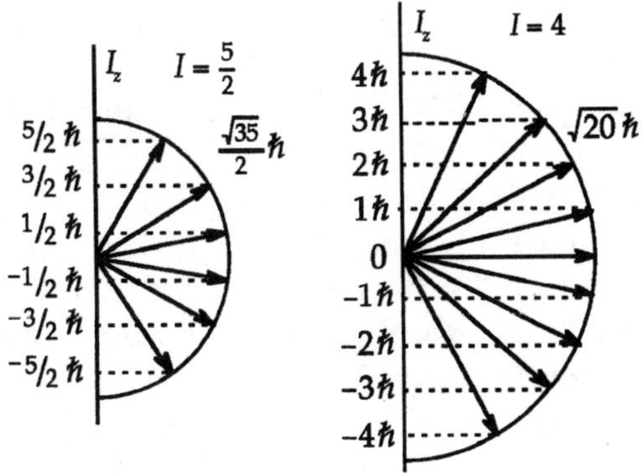

FIG. P44.52

P44.53 (a) $$f_n = \frac{|2\mu B|}{h} = \frac{2(1.913\,5)(5.05 \times 10^{-27} \text{ J/T})(1.00 \text{ T})}{6.626 \times 10^{-34} \text{ J}\cdot\text{s}} = \boxed{29.2 \text{ MHz}}$$

(b) $$f_p = \frac{2(2.792\,8)(5.05 \times 10^{-27} \text{ J/T})(1.00 \text{ T})}{6.626 \times 10^{-34} \text{ J}\cdot\text{s}} = \boxed{42.6 \text{ MHz}}$$

(c) In the Earth's magnetic field,

$$f_p = \frac{2(2.792\,8)(5.05 \times 10^{-27})(50.0 \times 10^{-6})}{6.626 \times 10^{-34}} = \boxed{2.13 \text{ kHz}}.$$

Additional Problems

***P44.54** (a) With m_n and v_n as the mass and speed of the neutrons, Eq. 9.23 of the text becomes, after making appropriate notational changes, for the two collisions $v_1 = \left(\frac{2m_n}{m_n + m_1}\right)v_n$,

$$v_2 = \left(\frac{2m_n}{m_n + m_2}\right)v_n$$

$$\therefore (m_n + m_2)v_2 = (m_n + m_1)v_1 = 2m_n v_n$$

$$\therefore m_n(v_2 - v_1) = m_1 v_1 - m_2 v_2$$

$$\therefore m_n = \frac{m_1 v_1 - m_2 v_2}{v_2 - v_1}$$

(b) $$m_n = \frac{(1\text{ u})(3.30\times 10^7\text{ m/s}) - (14\text{ u})(4.70\times 10^6\text{ m/s})}{4.70\times 10^6\text{ m/s} - 3.30\times 10^7\text{ m/s}} = \boxed{1.16\text{ u}}$$

P44.55 (a) $$Q = \left[M_{^9\text{Be}} + M_{^4\text{He}} - M_{^{12}\text{C}} - m_n\right]c^2$$

$$Q = [9.012\,182\text{ u} + 4.002\,603\text{ u} - 12.000\,000\text{ u} - 1.008\,665\text{ u}](931.5\text{ MeV/u}) = \boxed{5.70\text{ MeV}}$$

(b) $$Q = \left[2M_{^2\text{H}} - M_{^3\text{He}} - m_n\right]$$

$$Q = \left[2(2.014\,102) - 3.016\,029 - 1.008\,665\right]\text{u}(931.5\text{ MeV/u}) = \boxed{3.27\text{ MeV (exothermic)}}$$

P44.56 (a) At threshold, the particles have no kinetic energy relative to each other. That is, they move like two particles that have suffered a perfectly inelastic collision. Therefore, in order to calculate the reaction threshold energy, we can use the results of a perfectly inelastic collision. Initially, the projectile M_a moves with velocity v_a while the target M_X is at rest. We have from momentum conservation for the projectile-target system:

$$M_a v_a = (M_a + M_X)v_c.$$

The initial energy is: $E_i = \frac{1}{2}M_a v_a^2$.

The final kinetic energy is:

$$E_f = \frac{1}{2}(M_a + M_X)v_c^2 = \frac{1}{2}(M_a + M_X)\left[\frac{M_a v_a}{M_a + M_X}\right]^2 = \left[\frac{M_a}{M_a + M_X}\right]E_i.$$

From this, we see that E_f is always less than E_i and the change in energy, $E_f - E_i$, is given by

$$E_f - E_i = \left[\frac{M_a}{M_a + M_X} - 1\right]E_i = -\left[\frac{M_X}{M_a + M_X}\right]E_i.$$

This loss of kinetic energy in the isolated system corresponds to an increase in mass-energy during the reaction. Thus, the absolute value of this kinetic energy change is equal to $-Q$ (remember that Q is negative in an endothermic reaction). The initial kinetic energy E_i is the threshold energy E_{th}.

Therefore,
$$-Q = \left[\frac{M_X}{M_a + M_X}\right]E_{th}$$

or
$$E_{th} = -Q\left[\frac{M_X + M_a}{M_X}\right] = \boxed{-Q\left[1 + \frac{M_a}{M_X}\right]}.$$

continued on next page

(b) First, calculate the Q-value for the reaction: $Q=\left[M_{\text{N-14}}+M_{\text{He-4}}-M_{\text{O-17}}-M_{\text{H-1}}\right]c^2$

$$Q=[14.003\,074+4.002\,603-16.999\,132-1.007\,825]\text{u}(931.5\text{ MeV/u})=-1.19\text{ MeV}.$$

Then, $$E_{th}=-Q\left[\frac{M_X+M_a}{M_X}\right]=-(-1.19\text{ MeV})\left[1+\frac{4.002\,603}{14.003\,074}\right]=\boxed{1.53\text{ MeV}}.$$

P44.57 $^1_1\text{H}+{}^7_3\text{Li}\rightarrow{}^7_4\text{Be}+{}^1_0\text{n}$

$$Q=\left[(M_{\text{H}}+M_{\text{Li}})-(M_{\text{Be}}+M_{\text{n}})\right](931.5\text{ MeV/u})$$

$$Q=\left[(1.007\,825\text{ u}+7.016\,004\text{ u})-(7.016\,929\text{ u}+1.008\,665\text{ u})\right](931.5\text{ MeV/u})$$

$$Q=\left(-1.765\times10^{-3}\text{ u}\right)(931.5\text{ MeV/u})=-1.644\text{ MeV}$$

Thus, $$KE_{\min}=\left(1+\frac{m_{\text{incident projectile}}}{m_{\text{target nucleus}}}\right)|Q|=\left(1+\frac{1.007\,825}{7.016\,004}\right)(1.644\text{ MeV})=\boxed{1.88\text{ MeV}}.$$

P44.58 (a) $$N_0=\frac{\text{mass}}{\text{mass per atom}}=\frac{1.00\text{ kg}}{(239.05\text{ u})\left(1.66\times10^{-27}\text{ kg/u}\right)}=\boxed{2.52\times10^{24}}$$

(b) $$\lambda=\frac{\ln 2}{T_{1/2}}=\frac{\ln 2}{\left(2.412\times10^4\text{ yr}\right)\left(3.156\times10^7\text{ s/yr}\right)}=9.106\times10^{-13}\text{ s}^{-1}$$

$$R_0=\lambda N_0=\left(9.106\times10^{-13}\text{ s}^{-1}\right)\left(2.52\times10^{24}\right)=\boxed{2.29\times10^{12}\text{ Bq}}$$

(c) $$R=R_0e^{-\lambda t},\text{ so } t=\frac{-1}{\lambda}\ln\left(\frac{R}{R_0}\right)=\frac{1}{\lambda}\ln\left(\frac{R_0}{R}\right)$$

$$t=\frac{1}{9.106\times10^{-13}\text{ s}^{-1}}\ln\left(\frac{2.29\times10^{12}\text{ Bq}}{0.100\text{ Bq}}\right)=3.38\times10^{13}\text{ s}\left(\frac{1\text{ yr}}{3.156\times10^7\text{ s}}\right)=\boxed{1.07\times10^6\text{ yr}}$$

P44.59 (a) $^{57}_{27}\text{Co}\rightarrow{}^{57}_{26}\text{Fe}+{}^{0}_{+1}\text{e}+{}^0_0\nu$

The Q-value for this positron emission is $Q=\left[M_{^{57}\text{Co}}-M_{^{57}\text{Fe}}-2m_e\right]c^2$.

$$Q=[56.936\,296-56.935\,399-2(0.000\,549)]\text{u}(931.5\text{ MeV/u})=-0.187\text{ MeV}$$

Since $Q<0$, this reaction $\boxed{\text{cannot spontaneously occur}}$.

(b) $^{14}_6\text{C}\rightarrow{}^{14}_7\text{N}+{}^{0}_{-1}\text{e}+{}^0_0\bar{\nu}$

The Q-value for this e^- decay is $Q=\left[M_{^{14}\text{C}}-M_{^{14}\text{N}}\right]c^2$.

$$Q=[14.003\,242-14.003\,074]\text{u}(931.5\text{ MeV/u})=0.156\text{ MeV}=156\text{ keV}$$

Since $Q>0$, the decay $\boxed{\text{can spontaneously occur}}$.

(c) The energy released in the reaction of (b) is shared by the electron and neutrino. Thus, $\boxed{K_e\text{ can range from zero to 156 keV}}$.

P44.60 (a) $r = r_0 A^{1/3} = 1.20 \times 10^{-15} A^{1/3}$ m.

When $A = 12$, $r = \boxed{2.75 \times 10^{-15} \text{ m}}$.

(b) $F = \dfrac{k_e (Z-1)e^2}{r^2} = \dfrac{\left(8.99 \times 10^9 \text{ N} \cdot \text{m}^2/\text{C}^2\right)(Z-1)\left(1.60 \times 10^{-19} \text{ C}\right)^2}{r^2}$

When $Z = 6$ and $r = 2.75 \times 10^{-15}$ m, $F = \boxed{152 \text{ N}}$.

(c) $U = \dfrac{k_e q_1 q_2}{r} = \dfrac{k_e (Z-1)e^2}{r} = \dfrac{\left(8.99 \times 10^9\right)(Z-1)\left(1.6 \times 10^{-19}\right)^2}{r}$

When $Z = 6$ and $r = 2.75 \times 10^{-15}$ m, $U = 4.19 \times 10^{-13} \text{ J} = \boxed{2.62 \text{ MeV}}$.

(d) $A = 238$; $Z = 92$, $r = \boxed{7.44 \times 10^{-15} \text{ m}}$ $F = \boxed{379 \text{ N}}$

and $U = 2.82 \times 10^{-12} \text{ J} = \boxed{17.6 \text{ MeV}}$.

P44.61 (a) Because the reaction $p \to n + e^+ + \nu$ would violate the law of $\boxed{\text{conservation of energy}}$

$m_p = 1.007\,276$ u $m_n = 1.008\,665$ u $m_{e^+} = 5.49 \times 10^{-4}$ u.

Note that $m_n + m_{e^+} > m_p$.

(b) The $\boxed{\text{required energy can come from the electrostatic repulsion}}$ of protons in the nucleus.

(c) Add seven electrons to both sides of the reaction for nuclei ${}^{13}_{7}\text{N} \to {}^{13}_{6}\text{C} + e^+ + \nu$

to obtain the reaction for neutral atoms ${}^{13}_{7}\text{N atom} \to {}^{13}_{6}\text{C atom} + e^+ + e^- + \nu$

$$Q = c^2\left[m\left({}^{13}\text{N}\right) - m\left({}^{13}\text{C}\right) - m_{e^+} - m_{e^-} - m_\nu\right]$$

$$Q = (931.5 \text{ MeV/u})\left[13.005\,739 - 13.003\,355 - 2\left(5.49 \times 10^{-4}\right) - 0\right]\text{u}$$

$$Q = (931.5 \text{ MeV/u})\left(1.286 \times 10^{-3} \text{ u}\right) = \boxed{1.20 \text{ MeV}}$$

P44.62 (a) A least-square fit to the graph yields:

$$\lambda = -\text{slope} = -\left(-0.250 \text{ h}^{-1}\right) = 0.250 \text{ h}^{-1}$$

and

$$\ln(\text{cpm})\Big|_{t=0} = \text{intercept} = 8.30.$$

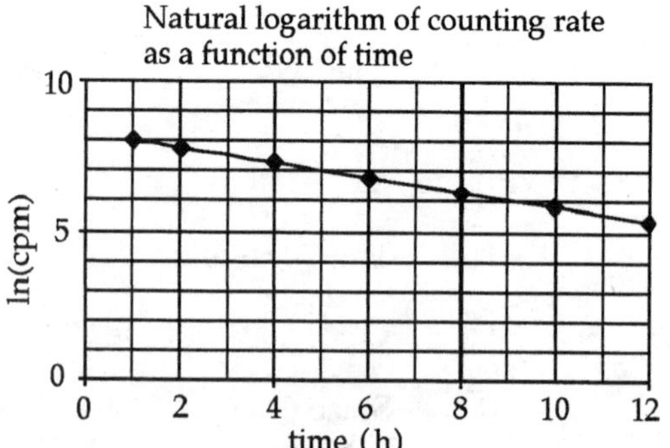

FIG. P44.62

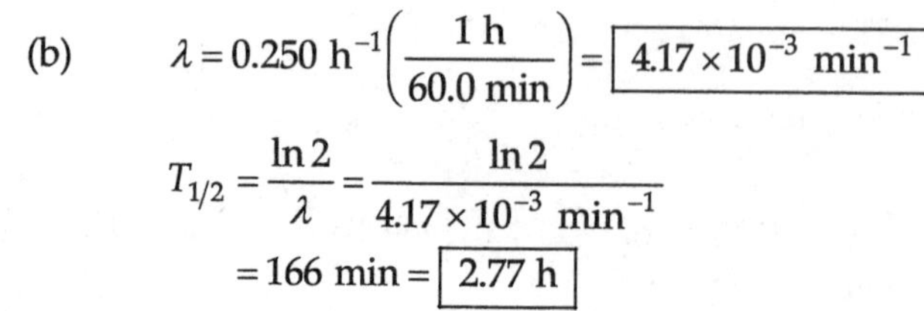

(b) $\lambda = 0.250 \text{ h}^{-1}\left(\dfrac{1 \text{ h}}{60.0 \text{ min}}\right) = \boxed{4.17 \times 10^{-3} \text{ min}^{-1}}$

$$T_{1/2} = \frac{\ln 2}{\lambda} = \frac{\ln 2}{4.17 \times 10^{-3} \text{ min}^{-1}}$$

$$= 166 \text{ min} = \boxed{2.77 \text{ h}}$$

continued on next page

(c) From (a), intercept $= \ln(\text{cpm})_0 = 8.30$.

Thus, $(\text{cpm})_0 = e^{8.30}$ counts/min $= \boxed{4.02\times10^3 \text{ counts/min}}$.

(d) $$N_0 = \frac{R_0}{\lambda} = \frac{1}{\lambda}\frac{(\text{cpm})_0}{\text{Eff}} = \frac{4.02\times10^3 \text{ counts/min}}{\left(4.17\times10^{-3}\text{ min}^{-1}\right)(0.100)} = \boxed{9.65\times10^6 \text{ atoms}}$$

P44.63 (a) The reaction is ${}^{145}_{61}\text{Pm} \to {}^{141}_{59}\text{Pr} + \alpha$

(b) $Q = (M_{\text{Pm}} - M_\alpha - M_{\text{Pr}})931.5 = (144.912\,744 - 4.002\,603 - 140.907\,648)931.5 = \boxed{2.32 \text{ MeV}}$

(c) The alpha and daughter have equal and opposite momenta $p_\alpha = p_d$

$$E_\alpha = \frac{p_\alpha^2}{2m_\alpha} \qquad E_d = \frac{p_d^2}{2m_d}$$

$$\frac{E_\alpha}{E_{\text{tot}}} = \frac{E_\alpha}{E_\alpha + E_d} = \frac{p_\alpha^2/2m_\alpha}{\left(p_\alpha^2/2m_\alpha\right)+\left(p_\alpha^2/2m_d\right)} = \frac{1/2m_\alpha}{(1/2m_\alpha)+(1/2m_d)} = \frac{m_d}{m_d+m_\alpha} = \frac{141}{141+4} = \boxed{97.2\%}$$ or 2.26 MeV.

This is carried away by the alpha.

P44.64 (a) If ΔE is the energy difference between the excited and ground states of the nucleus of mass M, and hf is the energy of the emitted photon, conservation of energy for the nucleus-photon system gives

$$\Delta E = hf + E_r. \tag{1}$$

Where E_r is the recoil energy of the nucleus, which can be expressed as

$$E_r = \frac{Mv^2}{2} = \frac{(Mv)^2}{2M}. \tag{2}$$

Since system momentum must also be conserved, we have

$$Mv = \frac{hf}{c}. \tag{3}$$

Hence, E_r can be expresses as $E_r = \dfrac{(hf)^2}{2Mc^2}$.

When $hf \ll Mc^2$

we can make the approximation that $hf \approx \Delta E$

so $E_r \approx \boxed{\dfrac{(\Delta E)^2}{2Mc^2}}$.

(b) $E_r = \dfrac{(\Delta E)^2}{2Mc^2}$ where $\Delta E = 0.014\,4$ MeV

and $Mc^2 = (57\text{ u})(931.5\text{ MeV/u}) = 5.31\times10^4$ MeV.

Therefore, $$E_r = \frac{\left(1.44\times10^{-2}\text{ MeV}\right)^2}{2\left(5.31\times10^4\text{ MeV}\right)} = \boxed{1.94\times10^{-3}\text{ eV}}.$$

P44.65 (a) One liter of milk contains this many ^{40}K nuclei:

$$N = (2.00\text{ g})\left(\frac{6.02\times10^{23}\text{ nuclei/mol}}{39.1\text{ g/mol}}\right)\left(\frac{0.011\,7}{100}\right) = 3.60\times10^{18}\text{ nuclei}$$

$$\lambda = \frac{\ln 2}{T_{1/2}} = \frac{\ln 2}{1.28\times10^{9}\text{ yr}}\left(\frac{1\text{ yr}}{3.156\times10^{7}\text{ s}}\right) = 1.72\times10^{-17}\text{ s}^{-1}$$

$$R = \lambda N = \left(1.72\times10^{-17}\text{ s}^{-1}\right)\left(3.60\times10^{18}\right) = \boxed{61.8\text{ Bq}}$$

(b) For the iodine, $R = R_0 e^{-\lambda t}$ with $\lambda = \dfrac{\ln 2}{8.04\text{ d}}$

$$t = \frac{1}{\lambda}\ln\left(\frac{R_0}{R}\right) = \frac{8.04\text{ d}}{\ln 2}\ln\left(\frac{2\,000}{61.8}\right) = \boxed{40.3\text{ d}}$$

P44.66 (a) For cobalt–56,

$$\lambda = \frac{\ln 2}{T_{1/2}} = \frac{\ln 2}{77.1\text{ d}}\left(\frac{365.25\text{ d}}{1\text{ yr}}\right) = 3.28\text{ yr}^{-1}.$$

The elapsed time from July 1054 to July 2003 is 949 yr.

$$R = R_0 e^{-\lambda t}$$

implies

$$\frac{R}{R_0} = e^{-\lambda t} = e^{-\left(3.28\text{ yr}^{-1}\right)(949\text{ yr})} = e^{-3\,116} = e^{-(\ln 10)1\,353} = \boxed{\sim 10^{-1\,353}}.$$

(b) For carbon–14,

$$\lambda = \frac{\ln 2}{5\,730\text{ yr}} = 1.21\times10^{-4}\text{ yr}^{-1}$$

$$\frac{R}{R_0} = e^{-\lambda t} = e^{-\left(1.21\times10^{-4}\text{ yr}^{-1}\right)(949\text{ yr})} = e^{-0.115} = \boxed{0.892}$$

P44.67 We have $N_{235} = N_{0,\,235}e^{-\lambda_{235}t}$

and $N_{238} = N_{0,\,238}e^{-\lambda_{238}t}$

$$\frac{N_{235}}{N_{238}} = 0.007\,25 = e^{\left(-(\ln 2)t/T_{h,\,235} + (\ln 2)t/T_{h,\,238}\right)}.$$

Taking logarithms,

$$-4.93 = \left(-\frac{\ln 2}{0.704\times10^{9}\text{ yr}} + \frac{\ln 2}{4.47\times10^{9}\text{ yr}}\right)t$$

or

$$-4.93 = \left(-\frac{1}{0.704\times10^{9}\text{ yr}} + \frac{1}{4.47\times10^{9}\text{ yr}}\right)(\ln 2)t$$

$$t = \frac{-4.93}{\left(-1.20\times10^{-9}\text{ yr}^{-1}\right)\ln 2} = \boxed{5.94\times10^{9}\text{ yr}}.$$

P44.68 (a) Add two electrons to both sides of the reaction to have it in energy terms:

$$4\,{}^1_1\text{H atom} \rightarrow {}^4_2\text{He atom} + Q \qquad Q = \Delta mc^2 = \left[4M_{{}^1_1\text{H}} - M_{{}^4_2\text{He}}\right]c^2$$

$$Q = \left[4(1.007\,825\text{ u}) - 4.002\,603\text{ u}\right](931.5\text{ MeV/u})\left(\frac{1.60\times10^{-13}\text{ J}}{1\text{ MeV}}\right) = \boxed{4.28\times10^{-12}\text{ J}}$$

(b) $$N = \frac{1.99\times10^{30}\text{ kg}}{1.67\times10^{-27}\text{ kg/atom}} = \boxed{1.19\times10^{57}\text{ atoms}} = 1.19\times10^{57}\text{ protons}$$

(c) The energy that could be created by this many protons in this reaction is:

$$\left(1.19\times10^{57}\text{ protons}\right)\left(\frac{4.28\times10^{-12}\text{ J}}{4\text{ protons}}\right) = 1.27\times10^{45}\text{ J}$$

$$\mathcal{P} = \frac{E}{\Delta t} \qquad \text{so} \qquad \Delta t = \frac{E}{\mathcal{P}} = \frac{1.27\times10^{45}\text{ J}}{3.77\times10^{26}\text{ W}} = 3.38\times10^{18}\text{ s} = \boxed{107\text{ billion years}}.$$

P44.69 $E = -\boldsymbol{\mu}\cdot\mathbf{B}$ so the energies are $E_1 = +\mu B$ and $E_2 = -\mu B$

$\mu = 2.792\,8\mu_n$ and $\mu_n = 5.05\times10^{-27}\text{ J/T}$

$$\Delta E = 2\mu B = 2(2.792\,8)\left(5.05\times10^{-27}\text{ J/T}\right)(12.5\text{ T}) = 3.53\times10^{-25}\text{ J} = \boxed{2.20\times10^{-6}\text{ eV}}.$$

P44.70 (a) $$\lambda = \frac{\ln 2}{T_{1/2}} = \frac{\ln 2}{5.27\text{ yr}}\left(\frac{1\text{ yr}}{3.156\times10^7\text{ s}}\right) = 4.17\times10^{-9}\text{ s}^{-1}$$

$$t = 30.0\text{ months} = (2.50\text{ yr})\left(\frac{3.156\times10^7\text{ s}}{1\text{ yr}}\right) = 7.89\times10^7\text{ s}$$

$$R = R_0e^{-\lambda t} = (\lambda N_0)e^{-\lambda t}$$

$$\text{so } N_0 = \left(\frac{R}{\lambda}\right)e^{\lambda t} = \left[\frac{(10.0\text{ Ci})\left(3.70\times10^{10}\text{ Bq/Ci}\right)}{4.17\times10^{-9}\text{ s}^{-1}}\right]e^{\left(4.17\times10^{-9}\text{ s}^{-1}\right)\left(7.89\times10^7\text{ s}\right)}$$

$$N_0 = 1.23\times10^{20}\text{ nuclei}$$

$$\text{Mass} = \left(1.23\times10^{20}\text{ atoms}\right)\left(\frac{59.93\text{ g/mol}}{6.02\times10^{23}\text{ atoms/mol}}\right) = 1.23\times10^{-2}\text{ g} = \boxed{12.3\text{ mg}}$$

(b) We suppose that each decaying nucleus promptly puts out both a beta particle and two gamma rays, for

$$Q = (0.310 + 1.17 + 1.33)\text{MeV} = 2.81\text{ MeV}$$

$$\mathcal{P} = QR = (2.81\text{ MeV})\left(1.6\times10^{-13}\text{ J/MeV}\right)\left(3.70\times10^{11}\text{ s}^{-1}\right) = \boxed{0.166\text{ W}}$$

P44.71 For an electric charge density $\rho = \dfrac{Ze}{(4/3)\pi R^3}$.

Using Gauss's Law inside the sphere,

$$E \cdot 4\pi r^2 = \frac{(4/3)\pi r^3}{\epsilon_0}\frac{Ze}{(4/3)\pi R^3}: \qquad E = \frac{1}{4\pi\epsilon_0}\frac{Zer}{R^3} \qquad (r \le R)$$

$$E = \frac{1}{4\pi\epsilon_0}\frac{Ze}{r^2} \qquad (r \ge R)$$

We now find the electrostatic energy: $U = \int_{r=0}^{\infty} \frac{1}{2}\epsilon_0 E^2 4\pi r^2 dr$

$$U = \frac{1}{2}\epsilon_0 \int_0^R \left(\frac{1}{4\pi\epsilon_0}\right)^2 \frac{Z^2e^2r^2}{R^6}4\pi r^2 dr + \frac{1}{2}\epsilon_0 \int_R^{\infty} \left(\frac{1}{4\pi\epsilon_0}\right)^2 \frac{Z^2e^2}{r^4}4\pi r^2 dr = \frac{Z^2e^2}{8\pi\epsilon_0}\left[\frac{R^5}{5R^6} + \frac{1}{R}\right]$$

$$= \boxed{\frac{3}{20}\frac{Z^2e^2}{\pi\epsilon_0 R}}$$

P44.72 (a) For the electron capture, ${}^{93}_{43}\text{Tc} + {}^{0}_{-1}\text{e} \rightarrow {}^{93}_{42}\text{Mo} + \gamma$.

The disintegration energy is $Q = \left[M_{^{93}\text{Tc}} - M_{^{93}\text{Mo}}\right]c^2$.

$$Q = [92.910\,2 - 92.906\,8]\text{u}(931.5 \text{ MeV/u}) = 3.17 \text{ MeV} > 2.44 \text{ MeV}$$

Electron capture is allowed $\boxed{\text{to all specified excited states}}$ in ${}^{93}_{42}\text{Mo}$.

For positron emission, ${}^{93}_{43}\text{Tc} \rightarrow {}^{93}_{42}\text{Mo} + {}^{0}_{+1}\text{e} + \gamma$.

The disintegration energy is $Q' = \left[M_{^{93}\text{Tc}} - M_{^{93}\text{Mo}} - 2m_e\right]c^2$.

$$Q' = [92.910\,2 - 92.906\,8 - 2(0.000\,549)]\text{u}(931.5 \text{ MeV/u}) = 2.14 \text{ MeV}$$

Positron emission can reach

$\boxed{\text{the 1.35, 1.48, and 2.03 MeV states}}$

but there is insufficient energy to reach the 2.44 MeV state.

(b) The daughter nucleus in both forms of decay is $\boxed{{}^{93}_{42}\text{Mo}}$.

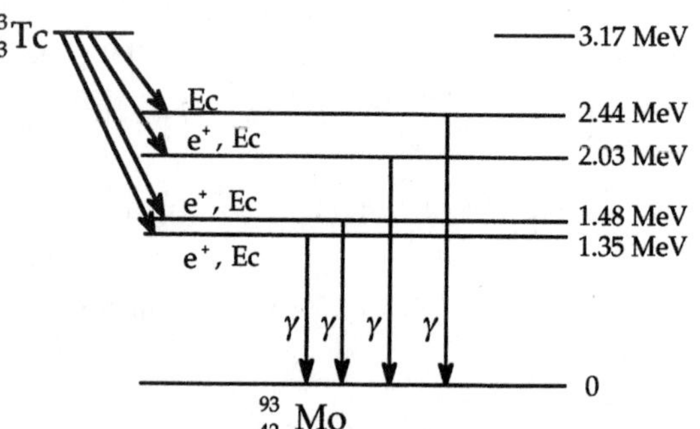

FIG. P44.72

P44.73 $K=\frac{1}{2}mv^2$,

so $$v=\sqrt{\frac{2K}{m}}=\sqrt{\frac{2(0.040\,0\text{ eV})(1.60\times10^{-19}\text{ J/eV})}{1.67\times10^{-27}\text{ kg}}}=2.77\times10^3\text{ m/s}.$$

The time for the trip is $t=\frac{x}{v}=\frac{1.00\times10^4\text{ m}}{2.77\times10^3\text{ m/s}}=3.61\text{ s}$.

The number of neutrons finishing the trip is given by $N=N_0e^{-\lambda t}$.

The fraction decaying is $1-\frac{N}{N_0}=1-e^{-(\ln 2)t/T_{1/2}}=1-e^{-(\ln 2)(3.61\text{ s}/624\text{ s})}=0.004\,00=\boxed{0.400\%}$.

P44.74 (a) If we assume all the ^{87}Sr came from ^{87}Rb,

then $N=N_0e^{-\lambda t}$

yields $t=\frac{-1}{\lambda}\ln\left(\frac{N}{N_0}\right)=\frac{T_{1/2}}{\ln 2}\ln\left(\frac{N_0}{N}\right)$

where $N=N_{\text{Rb-87}}$

and $N_0=N_{\text{Sr-87}}+N_{\text{Rb-87}}$

$$t=\frac{(4.75\times10^{10}\text{ yr})}{\ln 2}\ln\left(\frac{1.82\times10^{10}+1.07\times10^9}{1.82\times10^{10}}\right)=\boxed{3.91\times10^9\text{ yr}}.$$

(b) It could be $\boxed{\text{no older}}$. The rock could be younger if some ^{87}Sr were originally present.

P44.75 $R=R_0\exp(-\lambda t)$ lets us write $\ln R=\ln R_0-\lambda t$

which is the equation of a straight line with $|\text{slope}|=\lambda$.

The logarithmic plot shown in Figure P44.75 is fitted by $\ln R=8.44-0.262t$.

If t is measured in minutes, then decay constant λ is 0.262 per minute. The half–life is

$$T_{1/2}=\frac{\ln 2}{\lambda}=\frac{\ln 2}{0.262/\text{min}}=\boxed{2.64\text{ min}}.$$

The reported half–life of ^{137}Ba is 2.55 min. The difference reflects experimental uncertainties.

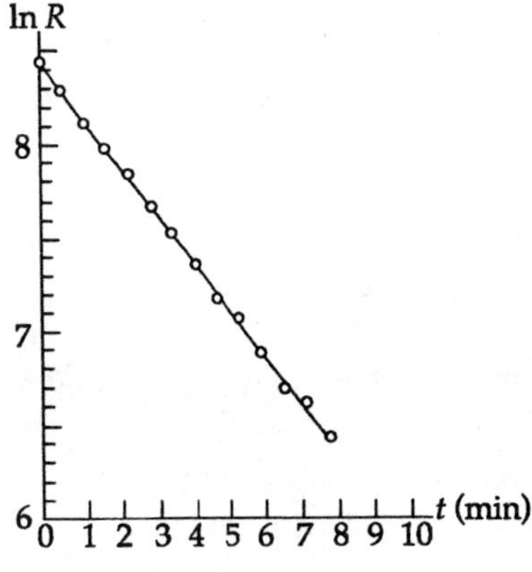

FIG. P44.75

ANSWERS TO EVEN PROBLEMS

P44.2 (a) 7.89 cm and 8.21 cm; (b) see the solution

P44.4 (a) 29.5 fm; (b) 5.18 fm; (c) see the solution

P44.6 25.6 MeV

P44.8 a nucleus such as ^{30}Si with $A=30$

P44.10 6.11 PN toward the other ball

P44.12 (a) 48; (b) 3; (c) 46; (d) 1

P44.14 (a) 1.11 MeV/nucleon;
(b) 7.07 MeV/nucleon;
(c) 8.79 MeV/nucleon;
(d) 7.57 MeV/nucleon

P44.16 0.210 MeV greater for ^{23}Na because it has less proton repulsion

P44.18 (a) 84.1 MeV; (b) 342 MeV; (c) The nuclear force of attraction dominates over electrical repulsion

P44.20 7.93 MeV

P44.22 (a) see the solution;
(b) $\frac{R}{3}$ and $\frac{R}{6}$; see the solution

P44.24 0.200 mCi

P44.26 41.8 TBq

P44.28 86.4 h

P44.30 $\frac{R_0 T_{1/2}}{\ln 2}\left(2^{-t_1/T_{1/2}} - 2^{-t_2/T_{1/2}}\right)$

P44.32 (a) see the solution; (b) see the solution;
(c) see the solution; 10.9 min;
(d) $t_m = \frac{\ln(\lambda_1/\lambda_2)}{\lambda_1 - \lambda_2}$; yes

P44.34 (a) $^{65}_{28}\text{Ni}^*$; (b) $^{211}_{82}\text{Pb}$; (c) $^{55}_{27}\text{Co}$; (d) $^{0}_{-1}\text{e}$;
(e) $^{1}_{1}\text{H}$

P44.36 between 5 400 yr and 6 800 yr

P44.38 (a) cannot occur; (b) cannot occur;
(c) can occur

P44.40 (a) 4.00 Gyr; (b) 0.019 9 and 4.60

P44.42 (a) 148 Bq/m^3; (b) 7.05×10^7 atoms/m^3;
(c) 2.17×10^{-17}

P44.44 (a) 0.281; (b) 1.65×10^{-29};
(c) see the solution

P44.46 (a) $^{21}_{10}\text{Ne}$; (b) $^{144}_{54}\text{Xe}$; (c) $^{0}_{1}\text{e}^+$ and $^{0}_{0}\nu$

P44.48 1.02 MeV

P44.50 (a) $^{13}_{6}\text{C}$; (b) $^{10}_{5}\text{B}$

P44.52 see the solution

P44.54 (a) see the solution; (b) 1.16 u

P44.56 (a) see the solution; (b) 1.53 MeV

P44.58 (a) 2.52×10^{24}; (b) 2.29 TBq; (c) 1.07 Myr

P44.60 (a) 2.75 fm; (b) 152 N; (c) 2.62 MeV;
(d) 7.44 fm, 379 N, 17.6 MeV

P44.62 (a) see the solution;
(b) 4.17×10^{-3} min^{-1}; 2.77 h;
(c) 4.02×10^3 counts/min;
(d) 9.65×10^6 atoms

P44.64 (a) see the solution; (b) 1.94 meV

P44.66 (a) $\sim 10^{-1\,353}$; (b) 0.892

P44.68 (a) 4.28 pJ; (b) 1.19×10^{57} atoms;
(c) 107 Gyr

P44.70 (a) 12.3 mg; (b) 0.166 W

P44.72 (a) electron capture to all; positron emission to the 1.35 MeV, 1.48 MeV, and 2.03 MeV states; (b) $^{93}_{42}\text{Mo}$; see the solution

P44.74 (a) 3.91 Gyr; (b) No older; it could be younger if some ^{87}Sr were originally present, contrary to our assumption.

45

Applications of Nuclear Physics

CHAPTER OUTLINE

ANSWERS TO QUESTIONS

Q45.1 A moderator is used to slow down neutrons released in the fission of one nucleus, so that they are likely to be absorbed by another nucleus to make it fission.

Q45.2 The hydrogen nuclei in water molecules have mass similar to that of a neutron, so that they can efficiently rob a fast-moving neutron of kinetic energy as they scatter it. Once the neutron is slowed down, a hydrogen nucleus can absorb it in the reaction $n + {}^{1}_{1}H \rightarrow {}^{2}_{1}H$.

Q45.3 The excitation energy comes from the binding energy of the extra nucleon.

Q45.4 The advantage of a fission reaction is that it can generate much more electrical energy per gram of fuel compared to fossil fuels. Also, fission reactors do not emit greenhouse gasses as combustion byproducts like fossil fuels—the only necessary environmental discharge is heat. The cost involved in producing fissile material is comparable to the cost of pumping, transporting and refining fossil fuel.

The disadvantage is that some of the products of a fission reaction are radioactive—and some of those have long half-lives. The other problem is that there will be a point at which enough fuel is spent that the fuel rods do not supply power economically and need to be replaced. The fuel rods are still radioactive after removal. Both the waste and the "spent" fuel rods present serious health and environmental hazards that can last for tens of thousands of years. Accidents and sabotage involving nuclear reactors can be very serious, as can accidents and sabotage involving fossil fuels.

Q45.5 The products of fusion reactors are generally not themselves unstable, while fission reactions result in a chain of reactions which almost all have some unstable products.

Q45.6 For the deuterium nuclei to fuse, they must be close enough to each other for the nuclear forces to overcome the Coulomb repulsion of the protons—this is why the ion density is a factor. The more time that the nuclei in a sample spend in close proximity, the more nuclei will fuse—hence the confinement time is a factor.

Q45.7 In a fusion reaction, the main idea is to get the nuclear forces, which act over very short distances, to overcome the Coulomb repulsion of the protons. Tritium has one more neutron in the nucleus, and thus increases the nuclear force, decreasing the necessary kinetic energy to obtain D–T fusion as compared to D–D fusion.

Q45.8 The biggest obstacle is power loss due to radiation. Remember that a high temperature must be maintained to keep the fuel in a reactive plasma state. If this kinetic energy is lost due to bremsstrahlung radiation, then the probability of nuclear fusion will decrease significantly. Additionally, each of the confinement techniques requires power input, thus raising the bar for sustaining a reaction in which the power output is greater than the power input.

Q45.9 Fusion of light nuclei to a heavier nucleus releases energy. Fission of a heavy nucleus to lighter nuclei releases energy. Both processes are steps towards greater stability on the curve of binding energy, Figure 44.5. The energy release per nucleon is typically greater for fusion, and this process is harder to control.

Q45.10 Advantages of fusion: high energy yield, no emission of greenhouse gases, fuel very easy to obtain, reactor can not go supercritical like a fission reactor, low amounts of radioactive waste.

Disadvantages: requires high energy input to sustain reaction, lithium and helium are scarce, neutrons released by reaction cause structural damage to reactor housing.

Q45.11 The fusion fuel must be heated to a very high temperature. It must be contained at a sufficiently high density for a sufficiently long time to achieve a reasonable energy output.

Q45.12 The first method uses magnetic fields to contain the plasma, reducing its contact with the walls of the container. This way, there is a reduction in heat loss to the environment, so that the reaction may be sustained over seconds.

The second method involves striking the fuel with high intensity, focused lasers from multiple directions, effectively imploding the fuel. This increases the internal pressure and temperature of the fuel to the point of ignition.

Q45.13 No. What is critical in radiation safety is the type of radiation encountered. The curie is a measure of the rate of decay, not the products of the decay or of their energies.

Q45.14 X-ray radiation can cause genetic damage in the developing fetus. If the damaged cells survive the radiation and reproduce, then the genetic errors will be replicated, potentially causing severe birth defects or death of the child.

Q45.15 For each additional dynode, a larger applied voltage is needed, and hence a larger output from a power supply—"infinite" amplification would not be practical. Nor would it be desirable: the goal is to connect the tube output to a simple counter, so a massive pulse amplitude is not needed. If you made the detector sensitive to weaker and weaker signals, you would make it more and more sensitive to background noise.

Q45.16 Sometimes the references are oblique indeed. Some must serve for more than one form of energy or mode of transfer. Here is one list:

kinetic: ocean currents
rotational kinetic: Earth turning
gravitational: water lifted up
elastic: Elastic energy is necessary for sound, listed below.
internal: by contrast to a chilly night; or in forging a chain
chemical: flames
sound: thunder
electrical transmission: lightning
electromagnetic radiation: heavens blazing; lightning
atomic electronic: In the blazing heavens, stars have different colors because of different predominant energy losses by atoms at their surfaces.
nuclear: The blaze of the heavens is produced by nuclear reactions in the cores of stars.

Remarkably, the word "energy" in this translation is an anachronism. Goethe wrote the song a few years before Thomas Young coined the term.

SOLUTIONS TO PROBLEMS

Section 45.1 Interactions Involving Neutrons

Section 45.2 Nuclear Fission

***P45.1** The energy is

$$3.30\times10^{10}\text{ J}\left(\frac{1\text{ eV}}{1.60\times10^{-19}\text{ J}}\right)\left(\frac{1\text{ U-235 nucleus}}{208\text{ MeV}}\right)\left(\frac{235\text{ g}}{6.02\times10^{23}\text{ nucleus}}\right)\left(\frac{\text{M}}{10^{6}}\right)=\boxed{0.387\text{ g}}\text{ of U-235.}$$

P45.2

$$\Delta m=(m_n+M_{\text{U}})-(M_{\text{Zr}}+M_{\text{Te}}+3m_n)$$

$$\Delta m=(1.008\,665\text{ u}+235.043\,923\text{ u})-(97.912\,7\text{ u}+134.916\,5\text{ u}+3(1.008\,665\text{ u}))$$

$$\Delta m=0.197\,39\text{ u}=3.28\times10^{-28}\text{ kg}\qquad\text{so}\qquad Q=\Delta mc^2=2.95\times10^{-11}\text{ J}=\boxed{184\text{ MeV}}$$

P45.3 Three different fission reactions are possible: $^{1}_{0}\text{n}+{}^{235}_{92}\text{U}\rightarrow{}^{90}_{38}\text{Sr}+{}^{144}_{54}\text{Xe}+2^{1}_{0}\text{n}$ $\boxed{^{144}_{54}\text{Xe}}$

$^{1}_{0}\text{n}+{}^{235}_{92}\text{U}\rightarrow{}^{90}_{38}\text{Sr}+{}^{143}_{54}\text{Xe}+3^{1}_{0}\text{n}$ $\boxed{^{143}_{54}\text{Xe}}$ $\qquad$ $^{1}_{0}\text{n}+{}^{235}_{92}\text{U}\rightarrow{}^{90}_{38}\text{Sr}+{}^{142}_{54}\text{Xe}+4^{1}_{0}\text{n}$ $\boxed{^{142}_{54}\text{Xe}}$

P45.4 $^{1}_{0}\text{n}+{}^{238}_{92}\text{U}\rightarrow{}^{239}_{92}\text{U}\rightarrow{}^{239}_{93}\text{Np}+e^-+\bar{\nu}$ $\qquad$ $^{239}_{93}\text{Np}\rightarrow{}^{239}_{94}\text{Pu}+e^-+\bar{\nu}$

P45.5 $^{1}_{0}\text{n}+{}^{232}_{90}\text{Th}\rightarrow{}^{233}_{90}\text{Th}\rightarrow{}^{233}_{91}\text{Pa}+e^-+\bar{\nu}$ $\qquad$ $^{233}_{91}\text{Pa}\rightarrow{}^{233}_{92}\text{U}+e^-+\bar{\nu}$

P45.6 (a)

$$Q=(\Delta m)c^2=\left[m_n+M_{\text{U235}}-M_{\text{Ba141}}-M_{\text{Kr92}}-3m_n\right]c^2$$

$$\Delta m=\left[(1.008\,665+235.043\,923)-(140.914\,4+91.926\,2+3\times1.008\,665)\right]\text{u}=0.185\,993\text{ u}$$

$$Q=(0.185\,993\text{ u})(931.5\text{ MeV/u})=\boxed{173\text{ MeV}}$$

(b)

$$f=\frac{\Delta m}{m_i}=\frac{0.185993\text{ u}}{236.05\text{ u}}=7.88\times10^{-4}=\boxed{0.078\,8\%}$$

***P45.7** (a) The initial mass is $1.007\,825\text{ u} + 11.009\,306\text{ u} = 12.017\,131\text{ u}$. The final mass is $3(4.002\,603\text{ u}) = 12.007\,809\text{ u}$. The rest mass annihilated is $\Delta m = 0.009\,322\text{ u}$. The energy created is $Q = \Delta mc^2 = 0.009\,322\text{ u}\left(\frac{931.5\text{ MeV}}{1\text{ u}}\right) = \boxed{8.68\text{ MeV}}$.

(b) The proton and the boron nucleus have positive charges. The colliding particles must have enough kinetic energy to approach very closely in spite of their electric repulsion.

P45.8 If the electrical power output of 1 000 MW is 40.0% of the power derived from fission reactions, the power output of the fission process is

$$\frac{1\,000\text{ MW}}{0.400} = \left(2.50\times10^{9}\text{ J/s}\right)\left(8.64\times10^{4}\text{ s/d}\right) = 2.16\times10^{14}\text{ J/d}.$$

The number of fissions per day is $\left(2.16\times10^{14}\text{ J/d}\right)\left(\frac{1\text{ fission}}{200\times10^{6}\text{ eV}}\right)\left(\frac{1\text{ eV}}{1.60\times10^{-19}\text{ J}}\right) = 6.74\times10^{24}\text{ d}^{-1}$.

This also is the number of ${}^{235}\text{U}$ nuclei used, so the mass of ${}^{235}\text{U}$ used per day is

$$\left(6.74\times10^{24}\text{ nuclei/d}\right)\left(\frac{235\text{ g/mol}}{6.02\times10^{23}\text{ nuclei/mol}}\right) = 2.63\times10^{3}\text{ g/d} = \boxed{2.63\text{ kg/d}}.$$

In contrast, a coal-burning steam plant producing the same electrical power uses more than $6\times10^{6}\text{ kg/d}$ of coal.

P45.9 The available energy to do work is 0.200 times the energy content of the fuel.

$$(1.00\text{ kg fuel})\left(0.034\,0\ {}^{235}\text{U/fuel}\right)\left(\frac{1\,000\text{ g}}{1\text{ kg}}\right)\left(\frac{1\text{ mol}}{235\text{ g}}\right)\left(6.02\times10^{23}/\text{mol}\right)\left(\frac{(208)\left(1.60\times10^{-13}\text{ J}\right)}{\text{fission}}\right) = 2.90\times10^{12}\text{ J}$$

$$\left(2.90\times10^{12}\text{ J}\right)(0.200) = 5.80\times10^{11}\text{ J} = \left(1.00\times10^{5}\text{ N}\right)\Delta r$$

$$\Delta r = 5.80\times10^{6}\text{ m} = \boxed{5.80\text{ Mm}}$$

Section 45.3 Nuclear Reactors

P45.10 (a) For a sphere: $V = \frac{4}{3}\pi r^3$ and $r = \left(\frac{3V}{4\pi}\right)^{1/3}$ so $\frac{A}{V} = \frac{4\pi r^2}{(4/3)\pi r^3} = \boxed{4.84V^{-1/3}}$.

(b) For a cube: $V = \ell^3$ and $\ell = V^{1/3}$ so $\frac{A}{V} = \frac{6\ell^2}{\ell^3} = \boxed{6V^{-1/3}}$.

(c) For a parallelepiped: $V = 2a^3$ and $a = \left(\frac{V}{2}\right)^{1/3}$ so $\frac{A}{V} = \frac{\left(2a^2 + 8a^2\right)}{2a^3} = \boxed{6.30V^{-1/3}}$.

(d) Therefore, the $\boxed{\text{sphere has the least leakage}}$ and the $\boxed{\text{parallelepiped has the greatest leakage}}$ for a given volume.

P45.11 mass of ^{235}U available $\approx (0.007)(10^9 \text{ metric tons})\left(\dfrac{10^6 \text{ g}}{1 \text{ metric ton}}\right) = 7\times 10^{12} \text{ g}$

number of nuclei $\approx \left(\dfrac{7\times 10^{12} \text{ g}}{235 \text{ g/mol}}\right)(6.02\times 10^{23} \text{ nuclei/mol}) = 1.8\times 10^{34} \text{ nuclei}$

The energy available from fission (at 208 MeV/event) is

$E \approx (1.8\times 10^{34} \text{ events})(208 \text{ MeV/event})(1.60\times 10^{-13} \text{ J/MeV}) = 6.0\times 10^{23} \text{ J}$.

This would last for a time interval of

$$\Delta t = \frac{E}{\mathcal{P}} \approx \frac{6.0\times 10^{23} \text{ J}}{7.0\times 10^{12} \text{ J/s}} = (8.6\times 10^{10} \text{ s})\left(\frac{1 \text{ yr}}{3.16\times 10^7 \text{ s}}\right) \approx \boxed{3\,000 \text{ yr}}.$$

P45.12 In one minute there are $\dfrac{60.0 \text{ s}}{1.20 \text{ ms}} = 5.00\times 10^4$ fissions.

So the rate increases by a factor of $(1.000\,25)^{50\,000} = \boxed{2.68\times 10^5}$.

P45.13 $\mathcal{P} = 10.0 \text{ MW} = 1.00\times 10^7 \text{ J/s}$

If each decay delivers $1.00 \text{ MeV} = 1.60\times 10^{-13} \text{ J}$, then the number of decays/s = $\boxed{6.25\times 10^{19} \text{ Bq}}$.

Section 45.4 Nuclear Fusion

P45.14 (a) The Q value for the D-T reaction is 17.59 MeV.

Specific energy content in fuel for D-T reaction:

$$\frac{(17.59 \text{ MeV})(1.60\times 10^{-13} \text{ J/MeV})}{(5 \text{ u})(1.66\times 10^{-27} \text{ kg/u})} = 3.39\times 10^{14} \text{ J/kg}$$

$$r_{DT} = \frac{(3.00\times 10^9 \text{ J/s})(3\,600 \text{ s/hr})}{(3.39\times 10^{14} \text{ J/kg})(10^{-3} \text{ kg/g})} = \boxed{31.9 \text{ g/h burning of D and T}}.$$

(b) Specific energy content in fuel for D-D reaction: $Q = \dfrac{1}{2}(3.27 + 4.03) = 3.65 \text{ MeV}$ average of two Q values

$$\frac{(3.65 \text{ MeV})(1.60\times 10^{-13} \text{ J/MeV})}{(4 \text{ u})(1.66\times 10^{-27} \text{ kg/u})} = 8.80\times 10^{13} \text{ J/kg}$$

$$r_{DD} = \frac{(3.00\times 10^9 \text{ J/s})(3\,600 \text{ s/hr})}{(8.80\times 10^{13} \text{ J/kg})(10^{-3} \text{ kg/g})} = \boxed{122 \text{ g/h burning of D}}.$$

P45.15 (a) At closest approach, the electrostatic potential energy equals the total energy E.

$$U_f = \frac{k_e(Z_1e)(Z_2e)}{r_{\min}} = E:$$

$$E = \frac{\left(8.99\times10^9\ \text{N}\cdot\text{m}^2/\text{C}^2\right)\left(1.6\times10^{-19}\ \text{C}\right)^2 Z_1Z_2}{1.00\times10^{-14}\ \text{m}} = \boxed{\left(2.30\times10^{-14}\ \text{J}\right)Z_1Z_2}.$$

(b) For both the D-D and the D-T reactions, $Z_1 = Z_2 = 1$. Thus, the minimum energy required in both cases is

$$E = \left(2.30\times10^{-14}\ \text{J}\right)\left(\frac{1\ \text{MeV}}{1.60\times10^{-13}\ \text{J}}\right) = \boxed{144\ \text{keV}}.$$

Section 45.4 in the text gives more accurate values for the critical ignition temperatures, of about 52 keV for D-D fusion and 6 keV for D-T fusion. The nuclei can fuse by tunneling. A triton moves more slowly than a deuteron at a given temperature. Then D-T collisions last longer than D-D collisions and have much greater tunneling probabilities.

P45.16 (a) $$r_f = r_\text{D} + r_\text{T} = \left(1.20\times10^{-15}\ \text{m}\right)\left[(2)^{1/3} + (3)^{1/3}\right] = \boxed{3.24\times10^{-15}\ \text{m}}$$

(b) $$U_f = \frac{k_e e^2}{r_f} = \frac{\left(8.99\times10^9\ \text{N}\cdot\text{m}^2/\text{C}^2\right)\left(1.60\times10^{-19}\ \text{C}\right)^2}{3.24\times10^{-15}\ \text{m}} = 7.10\times10^{-14}\ \text{J} = \boxed{444\ \text{keV}}$$

(c) Conserving momentum, $m_\text{D}v_i = (m_\text{D}+m_\text{T})v_f$, or $v_f = \left(\dfrac{m_\text{D}}{m_\text{D}+m_\text{T}}\right)v_i = \boxed{\dfrac{2}{5}v_i}$

(d) $K_i + U_i = K_f + U_f$:

$$K_i + 0 = \frac{1}{2}(m_\text{D}+m_\text{T})v_f^2 + U_f = \frac{1}{2}(m_\text{D}+m_\text{T})\left(\frac{m_\text{D}}{m_\text{D}+m_\text{T}}\right)^2 v_i^2 + U_f$$

$$K_i + 0 = \left(\frac{m_\text{D}}{m_\text{D}+m_\text{T}}\right)\left(\frac{1}{2}m_\text{D}v_i^2\right) + U_f = \left(\frac{m_\text{D}}{m_\text{D}+m_\text{T}}\right)K_i + U_f$$

$$\left(1 - \frac{m_\text{D}}{m_\text{D}+m_\text{T}}\right)K_i = U_f: \quad K_i = U_f\left(\frac{m_\text{D}+m_\text{T}}{m_\text{T}}\right) = \frac{5}{3}(444\ \text{keV}) = \boxed{740\ \text{keV}}$$

(e) $\boxed{\text{Possibly by tunneling.}}$

P45.17 (a) Average KE per particle is $\dfrac{3}{2}k_\text{B}T = \dfrac{1}{2}mv^2$.

Therefore, $$v_\text{rms} = \sqrt{\frac{3k_\text{B}T}{m}} = \sqrt{\frac{3\left(1.38\times10^{-23}\ \text{J/K}\right)\left(4.00\times10^8\ \text{K}\right)}{2\left(1.67\times10^{-27}\ \text{kg}\right)}} = \boxed{2.23\times10^6\ \text{m/s}}.$$

(b) $$t = \frac{x}{v} \sim \frac{0.1\ \text{m}}{10^6\ \text{m/s}} = \boxed{\sim10^{-7}\ \text{s}}$$

P45.18 (a) $V = \left(317 \times 10^6 \text{ mi}^3\right)\left(\frac{1\,609 \text{ m}}{1 \text{ mi}}\right)^3 = 1.32 \times 10^{18} \text{ m}^3$

$$m_{\text{water}} = \rho V = \left(10^3 \text{ kg/m}^3\right)\left(1.32 \times 10^{18} \text{ m}^3\right) = 1.32 \times 10^{21} \text{ kg}$$

$$m_{H_2} = \left(\frac{M_{H_2}}{M_{H_2O}}\right) m_{H_2O} = \left(\frac{2.016}{18.015}\right)\left(1.32 \times 10^{21} \text{ kg}\right) = 1.48 \times 10^{20} \text{ kg}$$

$$m_{\text{Deuterium}} = (0.030\,0\%) m_{H_2} = \left(0.030\,0 \times 10^{-2}\right)\left(1.48 \times 10^{20} \text{ kg}\right) = 4.43 \times 10^{16} \text{ kg}$$

The number of deuterium nuclei in this mass is

$$N = \frac{m_{\text{Deuterium}}}{m_{\text{Deuteron}}} = \frac{4.43 \times 10^{16} \text{ kg}}{(2.014 \text{ u})\left(1.66 \times 10^{-27} \text{ kg/u}\right)} = 1.33 \times 10^{43}.$$

Since two deuterium nuclei are used per fusion, ${}^2_1\text{H} + {}^2_1\text{H} \rightarrow {}^4_2\text{He} + Q$, the number of events is $\frac{N}{2} = 6.63 \times 10^{42}$.

The energy released per event is

$$Q = \left[M_{^2\text{H}} + M_{^2\text{H}} - M_{^4\text{He}}\right]c^2 = \left[2(2.014\,102) - 4.002\,603\right]\text{u}(931.5 \text{ MeV/u}) = 23.8 \text{ MeV}.$$

The total energy available is then

$$E = \left(\frac{N}{2}\right)Q = \left(6.63 \times 10^{42}\right)(23.8 \text{ MeV})\left(\frac{1.60 \times 10^{-13} \text{ J}}{1 \text{ MeV}}\right) = \boxed{2.53 \times 10^{31} \text{ J}}.$$

(b) The time this energy could possibly meet world requirements is

$$\Delta t = \frac{E}{\mathscr{P}} = \frac{2.53 \times 10^{31} \text{ J}}{100\left(7.00 \times 10^{12} \text{ J/s}\right)} = \left(3.61 \times 10^{16} \text{ s}\right)\left(\frac{1 \text{ yr}}{3.16 \times 10^7 \text{ s}}\right) = \boxed{1.14 \times 10^9 \text{ yr}} \sim 1 \text{ billion years}.$$

P45.19 (a) Including both ions and electrons, the number of particles in the plasma is $N = 2nV$ where n is the ion density and V is the volume of the container. Application of Equation 21.6 gives the total energy as

$$E = \frac{3}{2}Nk_BT = 3nVk_BT = 3\left(2.0 \times 10^{13} \text{ cm}^{-3}\right)\left[\left(50 \text{ m}^3\right)\left(\frac{10^6 \text{ cm}^3}{1 \text{ m}^3}\right)\right]\left(1.38 \times 10^{-23} \text{ J/K}\right)\left(4.0 \times 10^8 \text{ K}\right)$$

$$E = \boxed{1.7 \times 10^7 \text{ J}}$$

(b) From Table 20.2, the heat of vaporization of water is $L_v = 2.26 \times 10^6 \text{ J/kg}$. The mass of water that could be boiled away is

$$m = \frac{E}{L_v} = \frac{1.7 \times 10^7 \text{ J}}{2.26 \times 10^6 \text{ J/kg}} = \boxed{7.3 \text{ kg}}.$$

P45.20 (a) Lawson's criterion for the D-T reaction is $n\tau \geq 10^{14}\ \text{s/cm}^3$. For a confinement time of $\tau = 1.00\ \text{s}$, this requires a minimum ion density of $n = \boxed{10^{14}\ \text{cm}^{-3}}$.

(b) At the ignition temperature of $T = 4.5 \times 10^7\ \text{K}$ and the ion density found above, the plasma pressure is

$$P = 2nk_BT = 2\left[\left(10^{14}\ \text{cm}^{-3}\right)\left(\frac{10^6\ \text{cm}^3}{1\ \text{m}^3}\right)\right]\left(1.38 \times 10^{-23}\ \text{J/K}\right)\left(4.5 \times 10^7\ \text{K}\right) = \boxed{1.24 \times 10^5\ \text{J/m}^3}.$$

(c) The required magnetic energy density is then

$$u_B = \frac{B^2}{2\mu_0} \geq 10P = 10\left(1.24 \times 10^5\ \text{J/m}^3\right) = 1.24 \times 10^6\ \text{J/m}^3,$$

$$B \geq \sqrt{2\left(4\pi \times 10^{-7}\ \text{N/A}^2\right)\left(1.24 \times 10^6\ \text{J/m}^3\right)} = \boxed{1.77\ \text{T}}.$$

P45.21 Let the number of ^6Li atoms, each having mass 6.015 u, be N_6 while the number of ^7Li atoms, each with mass 7.016 u, is N_7.

Then, $$N_6 = 7.50\%\ \text{of}\ N_{\text{total}} = 0.075\,0\left(N_6 + N_7\right),\ \text{or}\ N_7 = \left(\frac{0.925}{0.075\,0}\right)N_6.$$

Also, $$\text{total mass} = \left[N_6(6.015\ \text{u}) + N_7(7.016\ \text{u})\right]\left(1.66 \times 10^{-27}\ \text{kg/u}\right) = 2.00\ \text{kg},$$

or $$N_6\left[(6.015\ \text{u}) + \left(\frac{0.925}{0.075\,0}\right)(7.016\ \text{u})\right]\left(1.66 \times 10^{-27}\ \text{kg/u}\right) = 2.00\ \text{kg}.$$

This yields $N_6 = \boxed{1.30 \times 10^{25}}$ as the number of ^6Li atoms and

$$N_7 = \left(\frac{0.925}{0.075\,0}\right)\left(1.30 \times 10^{25}\right) = \boxed{1.61 \times 10^{26}}$$ as the number of ^7Li atoms.

P45.22 The number of nuclei in 1.00 metric ton of trash is

$$N = 1\,000\ \text{kg}(1\,000\ \text{g/kg})\frac{6.02 \times 10^{23}\ \text{nuclei/mol}}{56.0\ \text{g/mol}} = 1.08 \times 10^{28}\ \text{nuclei}.$$

At an average charge of 26.0 e/nucleus, $$q = \left(1.08 \times 10^{28}\right)(26.0)\left(1.60 \times 10^{-19}\right) = 4.47 \times 10^{10}\ \text{C}.$$

Therefore $$t = \frac{q}{I} = \frac{4.47 \times 10^{10}}{1.00 \times 10^6} = 4.47 \times 10^4\ \text{s} = \boxed{12.4\ \text{h}}.$$

Section 45.5 **Radiation Damage**

P45.23 $N_0 = \dfrac{\text{mass present}}{\text{mass of nucleus}} = \dfrac{5.00 \text{ kg}}{(89.907\,7 \text{ u})(1.66\times10^{-27} \text{ kg/u})} = 3.35\times10^{25} \text{ nuclei}$

$$\lambda = \frac{\ln 2}{T_{1/2}} = \frac{\ln 2}{29.1 \text{ yr}} = 2.38\times10^{-2} \text{ yr}^{-1} = 4.52\times10^{-8} \text{ min}^{-1}$$

$$R_0 = \lambda N_0 = (4.52\times10^{-8} \text{ min}^{-1})(3.35\times10^{25}) = 1.52\times10^{18} \text{ counts/min}$$

$$\frac{R}{R_0} = e^{-\lambda t} = \frac{10.0 \text{ counts/min}}{1.52\times10^{18} \text{ counts/min}} = 6.60\times10^{-18}$$

and $\lambda t = -\ln(6.60\times10^{-18}) = 39.6$

giving $t = \dfrac{39.6}{\lambda} = \dfrac{39.6}{2.38\times10^{-2} \text{ yr}^{-1}} = \boxed{1.66\times10^{3} \text{ yr}}$.

P45.24 Source: 100 mrad of 2-MeV γ-rays/h at a 1.00-m distance.

(a) For γ-rays, dose in rem = dose in rad.

Thus a person would have to stand $\boxed{10.0 \text{ hours}}$ to receive 1.00 rem from a 100-mrad/h source.

(b) If the γ-radiation is emitted isotropically, the dosage rate falls off as $\dfrac{1}{r^2}$.

Thus a dosage 10.0 mrad/h would be received at a distance $r = \sqrt{10.0} \text{ m} = \boxed{3.16 \text{ m}}$.

P45.25 (a) The number of x-rays taken per year is

$n = (8 \text{ x-ray/d})(5 \text{ d/wk})(50 \text{ wk/yr}) = 2.0\times10^{3} \text{ x-ray/yr}$.

The average dose per photograph is $\dfrac{5.0 \text{ rem/yr}}{2.0\times10^{3} \text{ x-ray/yr}} = \boxed{2.5\times10^{-3} \text{ rem/x-ray}}$.

(b) The technician receives low-level background radiation at a rate of 0.13 rem/yr. The dose of 5.0 rem/yr received as a result of the job is

$\dfrac{5.0 \text{ rem/yr}}{0.13 \text{ rem/yr}} = \boxed{38 \text{ times background levels}}$.

P45.26 (a) $I = I_0 e^{-\mu x}$, so $x = \dfrac{1}{\mu}\ln\left(\dfrac{I_0}{I}\right)$

With $\mu = 1.59 \text{ cm}^{-1}$, the thickness when $I = \dfrac{I_0}{2}$ is $x = \dfrac{1}{1.59 \text{ cm}^{-1}}\ln(2) = \boxed{0.436 \text{ cm}}$.

(b) When $\dfrac{I_0}{I} = 1.00\times10^{4}$, $x = \dfrac{1}{1.59 \text{ cm}^{-1}}\ln(1.00\times10^{4}) = \boxed{5.79 \text{ cm}}$.

P45.27 $1\text{ rad} = 10^{-2}\ \text{J/kg}$ $\quad Q = mc\Delta T \quad$ $\mathcal{P}\Delta t = mc\Delta T$

$$\Delta t = \frac{mc\Delta T}{\mathcal{P}} = \frac{m(4186\ \text{J/kg}\cdot{}^\circ\text{C})(50.0^\circ\text{C})}{(10)(10^{-2}\ \text{J/kg}\cdot\text{s})(m)} = \boxed{2.09\times10^{6}\ \text{s}} \approx 24\ \text{days!}$$

Note that power is the product of dose rate and mass.

P45.28 $\frac{Q}{m} = \frac{\text{absorbed energy}}{\text{unit mass}} = (1\,000\ \text{rad})\frac{10^{-2}\ \text{J/kg}}{1\ \text{rad}} = 10.0\ \text{J/kg}$

The rise in body temperature is calculated from $Q = mc\Delta T$ where $c = 4186\ \text{J/kg}$ for water and the human body

$$\Delta T = \frac{Q}{mc} = (10.0\ \text{J/kg})\frac{1}{4186\ \text{J/kg}\cdot{}^\circ\text{C}} = \boxed{2.39\times10^{-3}\,{}^\circ\text{C}}\ \text{(Negligible).}$$

P45.29 If half of the 0.140-MeV gamma rays are absorbed by the patient, the total energy absorbed is

$$E = \frac{(0.140\ \text{MeV})}{2}\left[\left(\frac{1.00\times10^{-8}\ \text{g}}{98.9\ \text{g/mol}}\right)\left(\frac{6.02\times10^{23}\ \text{nuclei}}{1\ \text{mol}}\right)\right] = 4.26\times10^{12}\ \text{MeV}$$

$$E = \left(4.26\times10^{12}\ \text{MeV}\right)\left(1.60\times10^{-13}\ \text{J/MeV}\right) = 0.682\ \text{J}$$

Thus, the dose received is $\quad \text{Dose} = \frac{0.682\ \text{J}}{60.0\ \text{kg}}\left(\frac{1\ \text{rad}}{10^{-2}\ \text{J/kg}}\right) = \boxed{1.14\ \text{rad}}$.

P45.30 The nuclei initially absorbed are $\quad N_0 = \left(1.00\times10^{-9}\ \text{g}\right)\left(\frac{6.02\times10^{23}\ \text{nuclei/mol}}{89.9\ \text{g/mol}}\right) = 6.70\times10^{12}$.

The number of decays in time t is $\quad \Delta N = N_0 - N = N_0\left(1 - e^{-\lambda t}\right) = N_0\left(1 - e^{-(\ln 2)t/T_{1/2}}\right)$.

At the end of 1 year, $\quad \frac{t}{T_{1/2}} = \frac{1.00\ \text{yr}}{29.1\ \text{yr}} = 0.034\,4$

and $\quad \Delta N = N_0 - N = \left(6.70\times10^{12}\right)\left(1 - e^{-0.023\,8}\right) = 1.58\times10^{11}$.

The energy deposited is $\quad E = \left(1.58\times10^{11}\right)(1.10\ \text{MeV})\left(1.60\times10^{-13}\ \text{J/MeV}\right) = 0.027\,7\ \text{J}$.

Thus, the dose received is $\quad \text{Dose} = \left(\frac{0.027\,7\ \text{J}}{70.0\ \text{kg}}\right) = \boxed{3.96\times10^{-4}\ \text{J/kg}} = 0.039\,6\ \text{rad}$.

Section 45.6 Radiation Detectors

P45.31 (a) $\frac{E}{E_\beta} = \frac{(1/2)C(\Delta V)^2}{0.500\ \text{MeV}} = \frac{(1/2)\left(5.00\times10^{-12}\ \text{F}\right)\left(1.00\times10^{3}\ \text{V}\right)^2}{(0.500\ \text{MeV})\left(1.60\times10^{-13}\ \text{J/MeV}\right)} = \boxed{3.12\times10^{7}}$

(b) $N = \frac{Q}{e} = \frac{C(\Delta V)}{e} = \frac{\left(5.00\times10^{-12}\ \text{F}\right)\left(1.00\times10^{3}\ \text{V}\right)}{1.60\times10^{-19}\ \text{C}} = \boxed{3.12\times10^{10}\ \text{electrons}}$

P45.32 (a) $E_I = 10.0$ eV is the energy required to liberate an electron from a dynode. Let n_i be the number of electrons incident upon a dynode, each having gained energy $e(\Delta V)$ as it was accelerated to this dynode. The number of electrons that will be freed from this dynode is $N_i = n_i e\dfrac{\Delta V}{E_I}$:

At the first dynode, $n_i = 1$ and $N_1 = \dfrac{(1)e(100 \text{ V})}{10.0 \text{ eV}} = \boxed{10^1 \text{ electrons}}$.

(b) For the second dynode, $n_i = N_1 = 10^1$, so $N_2 = \dfrac{(10^1)e(100 \text{ V})}{10.0 \text{ eV}} = 10^2$.

At the third dynode, $n_i = N_2 = 10^2$ and $N_3 = \dfrac{(10^2)e(100 \text{ V})}{10.0 \text{ eV}} = 10^3$.

Observing the developing pattern, we see that the number of electrons incident on the seventh and last dynode is $n_7 = N_6 = \boxed{10^6}$.

(c) The number of electrons incident on the last dynode is $n_7 = 10^6$. The total energy these electrons deliver to that dynode is given by

$E = n_i e(\Delta V) = 10^6 e(700 \text{ V} - 600 \text{ V}) = \boxed{10^8 \text{ eV}}$.

P45.33 (a) The average time between slams is $60 \text{ min}/38 = 1.6$ min. Sometimes, the actual interval is nearly zero. Perhaps about equally as often, it is 2×1.6 min. Perhaps about half as often, it is 4×1.6 min. Somewhere around $5 \times 1.6 \text{ min} = \boxed{8.0 \text{ min}}$, the chances of randomness producing so long a wait get slim, so such a long wait might likely be due to mischief.

(b) The midpoints of the time intervals are separated by 5.00 minutes. We use $R = R_0 e^{-\lambda t}$. Subtracting the background counts,

$$337 - 5(15) = [372 - 5(15)]e^{-(\ln 2/T_{1/2})(5.00 \text{ min})}$$

or $\ln\left(\dfrac{262}{297}\right) = \ln(0.882) = -3.47 \text{ min}/T_{1/2}$ which yields $T_{1/2} = \boxed{27.6 \text{ min}}$.

(c) As in the random events in part (a), we imagine a ±5 count counting uncertainty. The smallest likely value for the half-life is then given by

$$\ln\left(\frac{262-5}{297+5}\right) = -3.47 \text{ min}/T_{1/2}, \text{ or } \left(T_{1/2}\right)_{\min} = 21.1 \text{ min}.$$

The largest credible value is found from

$$\ln\left(\frac{262+5}{297-5}\right) = -3.47 \text{ min}/T_{1/2}, \text{ yielding } \left(T_{1/2}\right)_{\max} = 38.8 \text{ min}.$$

Thus, $T_{1/2} = \left(\dfrac{38.8 + 21.1}{2}\right) \pm \left(\dfrac{38.8 - 21.1}{2}\right) \text{ min} = (30 \pm 9) \text{ min} = \boxed{30 \text{ min} \pm 30\%}$.

Section 45.7 **Uses of Radiation**

P45.34 The initial specific activity of ^{59}Fe in the steel,

$$(R/m)_0 = \frac{20.0\ \mu\text{Ci}}{0.200\ \text{kg}} = \frac{100\ \mu\text{Ci}}{\text{kg}}\left(\frac{3.70\times10^4\ \text{Bq}}{1\ \mu\text{Ci}}\right) = 3.70\times10^6\ \text{Bq/kg}.$$

After 1 000 h, $\frac{R}{m} = \left(\frac{R}{m}\right)_0 e^{-\lambda t} = \left(3.70\times10^6\ \text{Bq/kg}\right)e^{-(6.40\times10^{-4}\ \text{h}^{-1})(1\,000\ \text{h})} = 1.95\times10^6\ \text{Bq/kg}.$

The activity of the oil, $R_{\text{oil}} = \left(\frac{800}{60.0}\ \text{Bq/liter}\right)(6.50\ \text{liters}) = 86.7\ \text{Bq}.$

Therefore, $m_{\text{in oil}} = \frac{R_{\text{oil}}}{(R/m)} = \frac{86.7\ \text{Bq}}{1.95\times10^6\ \text{Bq/kg}} = 4.45\times10^{-5}\ \text{kg}.$

So that wear rate is $\frac{4.45\times10^{-5}\ \text{kg}}{1\,000\ \text{h}} = \boxed{4.45\times10^{-8}\ \text{kg/h}}.$

P45.35 The half-life of ^{14}O is 70.6 s, so the decay constant is $\lambda = \frac{\ln 2}{T_{1/2}} = \frac{\ln 2}{70.6\ \text{s}} = 0.009\,82\ \text{s}^{-1}$.

The ^{14}O nuclei remaining after five min is $N = N_0 e^{-\lambda t} = \left(10^{10}\right)e^{-(0.009\,82\ \text{s}^{-1})(300\ \text{s})} = 5.26\times10^8$.

The number of these in one cubic centimeter of blood is

$$N' = N\left(\frac{1.00\ \text{cm}^3}{\text{total vol. of blood}}\right) = \left(5.26\times10^8\right)\left(\frac{1.00\ \text{cm}^3}{2000\ \text{cm}^3}\right) = 2.63\times10^5$$

and their activity is $R = \lambda N' = \left(0.009\,82\ \text{s}^{-1}\right)\left(2.63\times10^5\right) = 2.58\times10^3\ \text{Bq}\ \boxed{\sim10^3\ \text{Bq}}.$

P45.36 (a) The number of photons is $\frac{10^4\ \text{MeV}}{1.04\ \text{MeV}} = 9.62\times10^3$. Since only 50% of the photons are detected, the number of ^{65}Cu nuclei decaying is twice this value, or 1.92×10^4. In two half-lives, three-fourths of the original nuclei decay, so $\frac{3}{4}N_0 = 1.92\times10^4$ and $N_0 = 2.56\times10^4$. This is 1% of the ^{65}Cu, so the number of ^{65}Cu is $2.56\times10^6\ \boxed{\sim10^6}$.

(b) Natural copper is 69.17% ^{63}Cu and 30.83% ^{65}Cu. Thus, if the sample contains N_{Cu} copper atoms, the number of atoms of each isotope is

$N_{63} = 0.691\,7N_{\text{Cu}}$ and $N_{65} = 0.308\,3N_{\text{Cu}}$.

Therefore, $\frac{N_{63}}{N_{65}} = \frac{0.691\,7}{0.308\,3}$ or $N_{63} = \left(\frac{0.6917}{0.3083}\right)N_{65} = \left(\frac{0.6917}{0.3083}\right)\left(2.56\times10^6\right) = 5.75\times10^6$.

The total mass of copper present is then $m_{\text{Cu}} = (62.93\ \text{u})N_{63} + (64.93\ \text{u})N_{65}$:

$$m_{\text{Cu}} = \left[(62.93)\left(5.75\times10^6\right) + (64.93)\left(2.56\times10^6\right)\right]\text{u}\left(1.66\times10^{-24}\ \text{g/u}\right)$$

$$= 8.77\times10^{-16}\ \text{g}\ \boxed{\sim10^{-15}\ \text{g}}$$

P45.37 (a) Starting with $N = 0$ radioactive atoms at $t = 0$, the rate of increase is (production – decay)

$$\frac{dN}{dt} = R - \lambda N \qquad \text{so} \qquad dN = (R - \lambda N)dt.$$

The variables are separable.

$$\int_0^N \frac{dN}{R - \lambda N} = \int_0^t dt: \qquad -\frac{1}{\lambda}\ln\left(\frac{R - \lambda N}{R}\right) = t$$

so $$\ln\left(\frac{R - \lambda N}{R}\right) = -\lambda t \qquad \text{and} \qquad \left(\frac{R - \lambda N}{R}\right) = e^{-\lambda t}.$$

Therefore, $$1 - \frac{\lambda}{R}N = e^{-\lambda t} \qquad N = \boxed{\frac{R}{\lambda}\left(1 - e^{-\lambda t}\right)}.$$

(b) The maximum number of radioactive nuclei would be $\boxed{\frac{R}{\lambda}}$.

Additional Problems

P45.38 (a) Suppose each ^{235}U fission releases 208 MeV of energy. Then, the number of nuclei that must have undergone fission is

$$N = \frac{\text{total release}}{\text{energy per nuclei}} = \frac{5 \times 10^{13}\ \text{J}}{(208\ \text{MeV})\left(1.60 \times 10^{-13}\ \text{J/MeV}\right)} = \boxed{1.5 \times 10^{24}\ \text{nuclei}}.$$

(b) $$\text{mass} = \left(\frac{1.5 \times 10^{24}\ \text{nuclei}}{6.02 \times 10^{23}\ \text{nuclei/mol}}\right)(235\ \text{g/mol}) \approx \boxed{0.6\ \text{kg}}$$

P45.39 (a) At 6×10^8 K, the average kinetic energy of a carbon atom is

$$\frac{3}{2}k_B T = (1.5)\left(8.62 \times 10^{-5}\ \text{eV/K}\right)\left(6 \times 10^8\ \text{K}\right) = \boxed{8 \times 10^4\ \text{eV}}$$

Note that 6×10^8 K is about $6^2 = 36$ times larger than 1.5×10^7 K, the core temperature of the Sun. This factor corresponds to the higher potential-energy barrier to carbon fusion compared to hydrogen fusion. It could be misleading to compare it to the temperature $\sim 10^8$ K required for fusion in a low-density plasma in a fusion reactor.

(b) The energy released is

$$E = \left[2m\left(\text{C}^{12}\right) - m\left(\text{Ne}^{20}\right) - m\left(\text{He}^4\right)\right]c^2$$

$$E = (24.000\,000 - 19.992\,440 - 4.002\,603)(931.5)\ \text{MeV} = \boxed{4.62\ \text{MeV}}$$

In the second reaction,

$$E = \left[2m\left(\text{C}^{12}\right) - m\left(\text{Mg}^{24}\right)\right](931.5)\ \text{MeV/u}$$

$$E = (24.000\,000 - 23.985\,042)(931.5)\ \text{MeV} = \boxed{13.9\ \text{MeV}}$$

continued on next page

(c) The energy released is the energy of reaction of the number of carbon nuclei in a 2.00-kg sample, which corresponds to

$$\Delta E = \left(2.00\times10^{3}\ \text{g}\right)\left(\frac{6.02\times10^{23}\ \text{atoms/mol}}{12.0\ \text{g/mol}}\right)\left(\frac{4.62\ \text{MeV/fusion event}}{2\ \text{nuclei/fusion event}}\right)\left(\frac{1\ \text{kWh}}{2.25\times10^{19}\ \text{MeV}}\right)$$

$$\Delta E = \frac{\left(1.00\times10^{26}\right)(4.62)}{2\left(2.25\times10^{19}\right)}\ \text{kWh} = \boxed{1.03\times10^{7}\ \text{kWh}}$$

P45.40 To conserve momentum, the two fragments must move in opposite directions with speeds v_1 and v_2 such that

$$m_1v_1 = m_2v_2 \qquad \text{or} \qquad v_2 = \left(\frac{m_1}{m_2}\right)v_1.$$

The kinetic energies after the break-up are then

$$K_1 = \frac{1}{2}m_1v_1^2 \qquad \text{and} \qquad K_2 = \frac{1}{2}m_2v_2^2 = \frac{1}{2}m_2\left(\frac{m_1}{m_2}\right)^2 v_1^2 = \left(\frac{m_1}{m_2}\right)K_1.$$

The fraction of the total kinetic energy carried off by m_1 is $\dfrac{K_1}{K_1+K_2} = \dfrac{K_1}{K_1+(m_1/m_2)K_1} = \boxed{\dfrac{m_2}{m_1+m_2}}$

and the fraction carried off by m_2 is $1-\dfrac{m_2}{m_1+m_2} = \boxed{\dfrac{m_1}{m_1+m_2}}.$

***P45.41** (a) $Q = 236.045\,562\text{u}c^2 - 86.920\,711\text{u}c^2 - 148.934\,370\text{u}c^2 = 0.190\,481\text{u}c^2 = \boxed{177\ \text{MeV}}$

Immediately after fission, this Q-value is the total kinetic energy of the fission products.

(b) $K_{\text{Br}} = \left(\dfrac{m_{\text{La}}}{m_{\text{Br}}+m_{\text{La}}}\right)Q$, from Problem 45.40.

$$= \left(\frac{149\ \text{u}}{87\ \text{u}+149\ \text{u}}\right)(177.4\ \text{MeV}) = \boxed{112\ \text{MeV}}$$

$$K_{\text{La}} = Q - K_{\text{Br}} = 177.4\ \text{MeV} - 112.0\ \text{MeV} = \boxed{65.4\ \text{MeV}}$$

(c)
$$v_{\text{Br}} = \sqrt{\frac{2K_{\text{Br}}}{m_{\text{Br}}}} = \sqrt{\frac{2\left(112\times10^{6}\ \text{eV}\right)\left(1.6\times10^{-19}\ \text{J/eV}\right)}{(87\ \text{u})\left(1.66\times10^{-27}\ \text{kg/u}\right)}} = \boxed{1.58\times10^{7}\ \text{m/s}}$$

$$v_{\text{La}} = \sqrt{\frac{2K_{\text{La}}}{m_{\text{La}}}} = \sqrt{\frac{2\left(65.4\times10^{6}\ \text{eV}\right)\left(1.6\times10^{-19}\ \text{J/eV}\right)}{(149\ \text{u})\left(1.66\times10^{-27}\ \text{kg/u}\right)}} = \boxed{9.20\times10^{6}\ \text{m/s}}$$

P45.42 For a typical ^{235}U, $Q = 208\text{ MeV}$; and the initial mass is 235 u. Thus, the fractional energy loss is

$$\frac{Q}{mc^2} = \frac{208\text{ MeV}}{(235\text{ u})(931.5\text{ MeV/u})} = 9.50\times10^{-4} = \boxed{0.095\,0\%}.$$

For the D-T fusion reaction, $Q = 17.6\text{ MeV}$.

The initial mass is $m = (2.014\text{ u}) + (3.016\text{ u}) = 5.03\text{ u}$.

The fractional loss in this reaction is $\dfrac{Q}{mc^2} = \dfrac{17.6\text{ MeV}}{(5.03\text{ u})(931.5\text{ MeV/u})} = 3.75\times10^{-3} = \boxed{0.375\%}$

$$\frac{0.375\%}{0.0950\%} = 3.95 \text{ or } \boxed{\text{the fractional loss in D-T is about 4 times that in } ^{235}\text{U fission}}.$$

P45.43 The decay constant is $\lambda = \dfrac{\ln 2}{T_{1/2}} = \dfrac{\ln 2}{(12.3\text{ yr})(3.16\times10^{7}\text{ s/yr})} = 1.78\times10^{-9}\text{ s}^{-1}$.

The tritium in the plasma decays at a rate of

$$R = \lambda N = \left(1.78\times10^{-9}\text{ s}^{-1}\right)\left[\left(\frac{2.00\times10^{14}}{\text{cm}^3}\right)\left(\frac{10^6\text{ cm}^3}{1\text{ m}^3}\right)\left(50.0\text{ m}^3\right)\right]$$

$$R = 1.78\times10^{13}\text{ Bq} = \left(1.78\times10^{13}\text{ Bq}\right)\left(\frac{1\text{ Ci}}{3.70\times10^{10}\text{ Bq}}\right) = \boxed{482\text{ Ci}}.$$

$\boxed{\text{The fission inventory is } \dfrac{4\times10^{10}\text{ Ci}}{482\text{ Ci}} \sim 10^8 \text{ times greater}}$ than this amount.

P45.44 Momentum conservation: $0 = m_{\text{Li}}\mathbf{v}_{\text{Li}} + m_\alpha \mathbf{v}_\alpha$, or, $m_{\text{Li}}v_{\text{Li}} = m_\alpha v_\alpha$.

Thus,
$$K_{\text{Li}} = \frac{1}{2}m_{\text{Li}}v_{\text{Li}}^2 = \frac{1}{2}\frac{(m_{\text{Li}}v_{\text{Li}})^2}{m_{\text{Li}}} = \frac{(m_\alpha v_\alpha)^2}{2m_{\text{Li}}} = \left(\frac{m_\alpha^2}{2m_{\text{Li}}}\right)v_\alpha^2$$

$$K_{\text{Li}} = \left(\frac{(4.002\,6\text{ u})^2}{2(7.016\,0\text{ u})}\right)\left(9.25\times10^6\text{ m/s}\right)^2 = (1.14\text{ u})\left(9.25\times10^6\text{ m/s}\right)^2$$

$$K_{\text{Li}} = 1.14\left(1.66\times10^{-27}\text{ kg}\right)\left(9.25\times10^6\text{ m/s}\right)^2 = 1.62\times10^{-13}\text{ J} = \boxed{1.01\text{ MeV}}.$$

P45.45 The complete fissioning of 1.00 gram of U^{235} releases

$$Q = \frac{(1.00\text{ g})}{235\text{ grams/mol}}\left(6.02\times10^{23}\text{ atoms/mol}\right)\left(200\text{ MeV/fission}\right)\left(1.60\times10^{-13}\text{ J/MeV}\right) = 8.20\times10^{10}\text{ J}.$$

If all this energy could be utilized to convert m kilograms of 20.0°C water to 400°C steam (see Chapter 20 of text for values),

then $Q = mc_w\,\Delta T + mL_v + mc_s\,\Delta T$

$$Q = m\left[(4186\text{ J/kg °C})(80.0\text{ °C}) + 2.26\times10^6\text{ J/kg} + (2010\text{ J/kg °C})(300\text{ °C})\right].$$

Therefore $m = \dfrac{8.20\times10^{10}\text{ J}}{3.20\times10^6\text{ J/kg}} = \boxed{2.56\times10^4\text{ kg}}$.

P45.46 When mass m of ^{235}U undergoes complete fission, releasing 200 MeV per fission event, the total energy released is:

$$Q=\left(\frac{m}{235\ \text{g/mol}}\right)N_A(200\ \text{MeV})$$ where N_A is Avogadro's number.

If all this energy could be utilized to convert a mass m_w of liquid water at T_c into steam at T_h, then,

$$Q=m_w\left[c_w(100°\text{C}-T_c)+L_v+c_s(T_h-100°\text{C})\right]$$

where c_w is the specific heat of liquid water, L_v is the latent heat of vaporization, and c_s is the specific heat of steam. Solving for the mass of water converted gives

$$m_w=\frac{Q}{\left[c_w(100°\text{C}-T_c)+L_v+c_s(T_h-100°\text{C})\right]}=\boxed{\frac{mN_A(200\ \text{MeV})}{(235\ \text{g/mol})\left[c_w(100°\text{C}-T_c)+L_v+c_s(T_h-100°\text{C})\right]}}.$$

P45.47 (a) The number of molecules in 1.00 liter of water (mass = 1 000 g) is

$$N=\left(\frac{1.00\times10^3\ \text{g}}{18.0\ \text{g/mol}}\right)(6.02\times10^{23}\ \text{molecules/mol})=3.34\times10^{25}\ \text{molecules}.$$

The number of deuterium nuclei contained in these molecules is

$$N'=(3.34\times10^{25}\ \text{molecules})\left(\frac{1\ \text{deuteron}}{3300\ \text{molecules}}\right)=1.01\times10^{22}\ \text{deuterons}.$$

Since 2 deuterons are consumed per fusion event, the number of events possible is $\frac{N'}{2}=5.07\times10^{21}$ reactions, and the energy released is

$$E_{\text{fusion}}=(5.07\times10^{21}\ \text{reactions})(3.27\ \text{MeV/reaction})=1.66\times10^{22}\ \text{MeV}$$

$$E_{\text{fusion}}=(1.66\times10^{22}\ \text{MeV})(1.60\times10^{-13}\ \text{J/MeV})=\boxed{2.65\times10^9\ \text{J}}.$$

(b) In comparison to burning 1.00 liter of gasoline, the energy from the fusion of deuterium is

$$\frac{E_{\text{fusion}}}{E_{\text{gasoline}}}=\frac{2.65\times10^9\ \text{J}}{3.40\times10^7\ \text{J}}=\boxed{78.0\ \text{times larger}}.$$

P45.48 (a) $\Delta V=4\pi r^2\Delta r=4\pi(14.0\times10^3\ \text{m})^2(0.05\ \text{m})=1.23\times10^8\ \text{m}^3\ \boxed{\sim10^8\ \text{m}^3}$

(b) The force on the next layer is determined by atmospheric pressure.

$W=P\Delta V=(1.013\times10^5\ \text{N/m}^2)(1.23\times10^8\ \text{m}^3)=1.25\times10^{13}\ \text{J}\ \boxed{\sim10^{13}\ \text{J}}$

(c) $1.25\times10^{13}\ \text{J}=\frac{1}{10}(\text{yield})$, so yield $=1.25\times10^{14}\ \text{J}\ \boxed{\sim10^{14}\ \text{J}}$

(d) $\frac{1.25\times10^{14}\ \text{J}}{4.2\times10^9\ \text{J/ton TNT}}=2.97\times10^4$ ton TNT $\sim10^4$ ton TNT

or $\boxed{\sim10\ \text{kilotons}}$

P45.49 (a) The thermal power transferred to the water is $\mathcal{P}_w = 0.970(\text{waste heat})$

$$\mathcal{P}_w = 0.970(3\,065 - 1\,000)\text{MW} = 2.00\times10^9 \text{ J/s}$$

r_w is the mass of water heated per hour:

$$r_w = \frac{\mathcal{P}_w}{c(\Delta T)} = \frac{(2.00\times10^9 \text{ J/s})(3600 \text{ s/h})}{(4186 \text{ J/kg}\cdot{}^\circ\text{C})(3.50\ {}^\circ\text{C})} = \boxed{4.91\times10^8 \text{ kg/h}}.$$

The volume used per hour is $\dfrac{4.91\times10^8 \text{ kg/h}}{1.00\times10^3 \text{ kg/m}^3} = \boxed{4.91\times10^5 \text{ m}^3\text{/h}}$.

(b) The ^{235}U fuel is consumed at a rate $r_f = \left(\dfrac{3\,065\times10^6 \text{ J/s}}{7.80\times10^{10} \text{ J/g}}\right)\left(\dfrac{1 \text{ kg}}{1\,000 \text{ g}}\right)\left(\dfrac{3\,600 \text{ s}}{1 \text{ h}}\right) = \boxed{0.141 \text{ kg/h}}$.

P45.50 The number of nuclei in 0.155 kg of ^{210}Po is

$$N_0 = \left(\frac{155 \text{ g}}{209.98 \text{ g/mol}}\right)(6.02\times10^{23} \text{ nuclei/mol}) = 4.44\times10^{23} \text{ nuclei}.$$

The half-life of ^{210}Po is 138.38 days, so the decay constant is given by

$$\lambda = \frac{\ln 2}{T_{1/2}} = \frac{\ln 2}{(138.38 \text{ d})(8.64\times10^4 \text{ s/d})} = 5.80\times10^{-8} \text{ s}^{-1}.$$

The initial activity is

$$R_0 = \lambda N_0 = (5.80\times10^{-8} \text{ s}^{-1})(4.44\times10^{23} \text{ nuclei}) = 2.58\times10^{16} \text{ Bq}.$$

The energy released in each ${}^{210}_{84}\text{Po} \to {}^{206}_{82}\text{Pb} + {}^{4}_{2}\text{He}$ reaction is

$$Q = \left[M_{{}^{210}_{84}\text{Po}} - M_{{}^{206}_{82}\text{Pb}} - M_{{}^{4}_{2}\text{He}}\right]c^2:$$

$$Q = [209.982\,857 - 205.974\,449 - 4.002\,603]\text{u}(931.5 \text{ MeV/u}) = 5.41 \text{ MeV}.$$

Thus, assuming a conversion efficiency of 1.00%, the initial power output of the battery is

$$\mathcal{P} = (0.010\,0)R_0Q = (0.010\,0)(2.58\times10^{16} \text{ decays/s})(5.41 \text{ MeV/decay})(1.60\times10^{-13} \text{ J/MeV}) = \boxed{223 \text{ W}}.$$

P45.51 (a) $V = \ell^3 = \dfrac{m}{\rho}$, so $\ell = \left(\dfrac{m}{\rho}\right)^{1/3} = \left(\dfrac{70.0 \text{ kg}}{18.7\times10^3 \text{ kg/m}^3}\right)^{1/3} = \boxed{0.155 \text{ m}}$

(b) Add 92 electrons to both sides of the given nuclear reaction. Then it becomes ${}^{238}_{92}\text{U atom} \to 8\,{}^{4}_{2}\text{He atom} + {}^{206}_{82}\text{Pb atom} + Q_{\text{net}}$.

$$Q_{\text{net}} = \left[M_{{}^{238}_{92}\text{U}} - 8M_{{}^{4}_{2}\text{He}} - M_{{}^{206}_{82}\text{Pb}}\right]c^2 = [238.050\,783 - 8(4.002\,603) - 205.974\,449]\text{u } (931.5 \text{ MeV/u})$$

$$Q_{\text{net}} = \boxed{51.7 \text{ MeV}}$$

(c) If there is a single step of decay, the number of decays per time is the decay rate R and the energy released in each decay is Q. Then the energy released per time is $\boxed{\mathcal{P} = QR}$. If there is a series of decays in steady state, the equation is still true, with Q representing the net decay energy.

continued on next page

(d) The decay rate for all steps in the radioactive series in steady state is set by the parent uranium:

$$N=\left(\frac{7.00\times10^{4}\ \text{g}}{238\ \text{g/mol}}\right)\left(6.02\times10^{23}\ \text{nuclei/mol}\right)=1.77\times10^{26}\ \text{nuclei}$$

$$\lambda=\frac{\ln 2}{T_{1/2}}=\frac{\ln 2}{4.47\times10^{9}\ \text{yr}}=1.55\times10^{-10}\ \frac{1}{\text{yr}}$$

$$R=\lambda N=\left(1.55\times10^{-10}\ \frac{1}{\text{yr}}\right)\left(1.77\times10^{26}\ \text{nuclei}\right)=2.75\times10^{16}\ \text{decays/yr},$$

so $$\mathscr{P}=QR=(51.7\ \text{MeV})\left(2.75\times10^{16}\ \frac{1}{\text{yr}}\right)\left(1.60\times10^{-13}\ \text{J/MeV}\right)=\boxed{2.27\times10^{5}\ \text{J/yr}}.$$

(e) dose in rem = dose in rad × RBE

$5.00\ \text{rem/yr}=(\text{dose in rad/yr})1.10$, giving $(\text{dose in rad/yr})=4.55\ \text{rad/yr}$

The allowed whole-body dose is then $(70.0\ \text{kg})(4.55\ \text{rad/yr})\left(\frac{10^{-2}\ \text{J/kg}}{1\ \text{rad}}\right)=\boxed{3.18\ \text{J/yr}}$.

P45.52 $E_T\equiv E(\text{thermal})=\frac{3}{2}k_BT=0.039\ \text{eV}$

$E_T=\left(\frac{1}{2}\right)^{n}E$ where $n\equiv$ number of collisions, and $0.039=\left(\frac{1}{2}\right)^{n}\left(2.0\times10^{6}\right)$.

Therefore, $n=25.6=\boxed{26\ \text{collisions}}$.

P45.53 Conservation of linear momentum and energy can be applied to find the kinetic energy of the neutron. We first suppose the particles are moving nonrelativistically.

The momentum of the alpha particle and that of the neutron must add to zero, so their velocities must be in opposite directions with magnitudes related by

$$m_n\mathbf{v}_n+m_\alpha\mathbf{v}_\alpha=0 \qquad \text{or} \qquad (1.008\,7\ \text{u})v_n=(4.002\,6\ \text{u})v_\alpha.$$

At the same time, their kinetic energies must add to 17.6 MeV

$$E=\frac{1}{2}m_nv_n^2+\frac{1}{2}m_\alpha v_\alpha^2=\frac{1}{2}(1.008\,7\ \text{u})v_n^2+\frac{1}{2}(4.002\,6)v_\alpha^2=17.6\ \text{MeV}.$$

Substitute $v_\alpha=0.252\,0v_n$: $$E=(0.504\,35\ \text{u})v_n^2+(0.127\,10\ \text{u})v_n^2=17.6\ \text{MeV}\left(\frac{1\ \text{u}}{931.494\ \text{MeV}/c^2}\right)$$

$$v_n=\sqrt{\frac{0.018\,9c^2}{0.631\,45}}=0.173c=5.19\times10^{7}\ \text{m/s}.$$

Since this speed is not too much greater than $0.1c$, we can get a reasonable estimate of the kinetic energy of the neutron from the classical equation,

$$K=\frac{1}{2}mv^2=\frac{1}{2}(1.008\,7\ \text{u})(0.173c)^2\left(\frac{931.494\ \text{MeV}/c^2}{\text{u}}\right)=14.1\ \text{MeV}.$$

continued on next page

For a more accurate calculation of the kinetic energy, we should use relativistic expressions. Conservation of momentum gives

$$\gamma_n m_n \mathbf{v}_n + \gamma_\alpha m_\alpha \mathbf{v}_\alpha = 0 \qquad 1.008\,7\frac{v_n}{\sqrt{1-v_n^2/c^2}} = 4.002\,6\frac{v_\alpha}{\sqrt{1-v_\alpha^2/c^2}}$$

yielding
$$\frac{v_\alpha^2}{c^2} = \frac{v_n^2}{15.746c^2 - 14.746v_n^2}.$$

Then
$$(\gamma_n - 1)m_n c^2 + (\gamma_\alpha - 1)m_\alpha c^2 = 17.6 \text{ MeV}$$

and
$$v_n = 0.171c, \text{ implying that } (\gamma_n - 1)m_n c^2 = \boxed{14.0 \text{ MeV}}.$$

P45.54 From Table A.3, the half-life of ^{32}P is 14.26 d. Thus, the decay constant is

$$\lambda = \frac{\ln 2}{T_{1/2}} = \frac{\ln 2}{14.26 \text{ d}} = 0.048\,6 \text{ d}^{-1} = 5.63 \times 10^{-7} \text{ s}^{-1}.$$

$$N_0 = \frac{R_0}{\lambda} = \frac{5.22 \times 10^6 \text{ decay/s}}{5.63 \times 10^{-7} \text{ s}^{-1}} = 9.28 \times 10^{12} \text{ nuclei}$$

At $t = 10.0$ days, the number remaining is

$$N = N_0 e^{-\lambda t} = \left(9.28 \times 10^{12} \text{ nuclei}\right) e^{-\left(0.048\,6 \text{ d}^{-1}\right)(10.0 \text{ d})} = 5.71 \times 10^{12} \text{ nuclei}$$

so the number of decays has been $N_0 - N = 3.57 \times 10^{12}$ and the energy released is

$$E = \left(3.57 \times 10^{12}\right)(700 \text{ keV})\left(1.60 \times 10^{-16} \text{ J/keV}\right) = 0.400 \text{ J}.$$

If this energy is absorbed by 100 g of tissue, the absorbed dose is

$$\text{Dose} = \left(\frac{0.400 \text{ J}}{0.100 \text{ kg}}\right)\left(\frac{1 \text{ rad}}{10^{-2} \text{ J/kg}}\right) = \boxed{400 \text{ rad}}.$$

P45.55 (a) The number of Pu nuclei in 1.00 kg $= \dfrac{6.02 \times 10^{23} \text{ nuclei/mol}}{239.05 \text{ g/mol}}(1\,000 \text{ g})$.

The total energy $= \left(25.2 \times 10^{23} \text{ nuclei}\right)(200 \text{ MeV}) = 5.04 \times 10^{26}$ MeV

$$E = \left(5.04 \times 10^{26} \text{ MeV}\right)\left(4.44 \times 10^{-20} \text{ kWh/MeV}\right) = \boxed{2.24 \times 10^7 \text{ kWh}}$$

or 22 million kWh.

(b) $E = \Delta m c^2 = (3.016\,049 \text{ u} + 2.014\,102 \text{ u} - 4.002\,603 \text{ u} - 1.008\,665 \text{ u})(931.5 \text{ MeV/u})$

$E = \boxed{17.6 \text{ MeV for each D-T fusion}}$

(c) $E_n = (\text{Total number of D nuclei})(17.6)\left(4.44 \times 10^{-20}\right)$

$$E_n = \left(6.02 \times 10^{23}\right)\left(\frac{1\,000}{2.014}\right)(17.6)\left(4.44 \times 10^{-20}\right) = \boxed{2.34 \times 10^8 \text{ kWh}}$$

continued on next page

(d) E_n = the number of C atoms in 1.00 kg × 4.20 eV

$$E_n = \left(\frac{6.02\times10^{26}}{12}\right)\left(4.20\times10^{-6}\text{ MeV}\right)\left(4.44\times10^{-20}\right) = \boxed{9.36\text{ kWh}}$$

(e) Coal is cheap at this moment in human history. We hope that safety and waste disposal problems can be solved so that nuclear energy can be affordable before scarcity drives up the price of fossil fuels.

P45.56 Add two electrons to both sides of the given reaction.

Then $4\ {}^1_1\text{H atom} \to {}^4_2\text{He atom} + Q$

where $Q = (\Delta m)c^2 = \left[4(1.007\,825) - 4.002603\right]\text{u}(931.5\text{ MeV/u}) = 26.7\text{ MeV}$

or $Q = (26.7\text{ MeV})\left(1.60\times10^{-13}\text{ J/MeV}\right) = 4.28\times10^{-12}\text{ J}$.

The proton fusion rate is then

$$\text{rate} = \frac{\text{power output}}{\text{energy per proton}} = \frac{3.77\times10^{26}\text{ J/s}}{\left(4.28\times10^{-12}\text{ J}\right)/(4\text{ protons})} = \boxed{3.53\times10^{38}\text{ protons/s}}.$$

P45.57 (a) $Q_{\text{I}} = [M_{\text{A}} + M_{\text{B}} - M_{\text{C}} - M_{\text{E}}]c^2$, and $Q_{\text{II}} = [M_{\text{C}} + M_{\text{D}} - M_{\text{F}} - M_{\text{G}}]c^2$

$Q_{\text{net}} = Q_{\text{I}} + Q_{\text{II}} = [M_{\text{A}} + M_{\text{B}} - M_{\text{C}} - M_{\text{E}} + M_{\text{C}} + M_{\text{D}} - M_{\text{F}} - M_{\text{G}}]c^2$

$Q_{\text{net}} = Q_{\text{I}} + Q_{\text{II}} = [M_{\text{A}} + M_{\text{B}} + M_{\text{D}} - M_{\text{E}} - M_{\text{F}} - M_{\text{G}}]c^2$

Thus, reactions may be added. Any product like C used in a subsequent reaction does not contribute to the energy balance.

(b) Adding all five reactions gives

$${}^1_1\text{H} + {}^1_1\text{H} + {}^{\ 0}_{-1}\text{e} + {}^1_1\text{H} + {}^1_1\text{H} + {}^{\ 0}_{-1}\text{e} \to {}^4_2\text{He} + 2\nu + Q_{\text{net}}$$

or $4\ {}^1_1\text{H} + 2\ {}^{\ 0}_{-1}\text{e} \to {}^4_2\text{He} + 2\nu + Q_{\text{net}}$.

Adding two electrons to each side $4\ {}^1_1\text{H atom} \to {}^4_2\text{He atom} + Q_{\text{net}}$.

Thus, $Q_{\text{net}} = \left[4M_{{}^1_1\text{H}} - M_{{}^4_2\text{He}}\right]c^2 = \left[4(1.007\,825) - 4.002\,603\right]\text{u}(931.5\text{ MeV/u}) = \boxed{26.7\text{ MeV}}$.

P45.58 (a) The mass of the pellet is $m = \rho V = \left(0.200 \text{ g/cm}^3\right)\left[\frac{4\pi}{3}\left(\frac{1.50\times 10^{-2}\text{ cm}}{2}\right)^3\right] = 3.53\times 10^{-7}\text{ g}$.

The pellet consists of equal numbers of ${}^2\text{H}$ and ${}^3\text{H}$ atoms, so the average molar mass is 2.50 and the total number of atoms is

$$N = \left(\frac{3.53\times 10^{-7}\text{ g}}{2.50\text{ g/mol}}\right)\left(6.02\times 10^{23}\text{ atoms/mol}\right) = 8.51\times 10^{16}\text{ atoms}\cdot$$

When the pellet is vaporized, the plasma will consist of $2N$particles (N nuclei and N electrons). The total energy delivered to the plasma is 1.00% of 200 kJ or 2.00 kJ. The temperature of the plasma is found from $E = (2N)\left(\frac{3}{2}k_BT\right)$ as

$$T = \frac{E}{3Nk_B} = \frac{2.00\times 10^3\text{ J}}{3\left(8.51\times 10^{16}\right)\left(1.38\times 10^{-23}\text{ J/K}\right)} = \boxed{5.68\times 10^8\text{ K}}.$$

(b) Each fusion event uses 2 nuclei, so $\frac{N}{2}$ events will occur. The energy released will be

$$E = \left(\frac{N}{2}\right)Q = \left(\frac{8.51\times 10^{16}}{2}\right)(17.59\text{ MeV})\left(1.60\times 10^{-13}\text{ J/MeV}\right) = 1.20\times 10^5\text{ J} = \boxed{120\text{ kJ}}.$$

P45.59 (a) The solar-core temperature of 15 MK gives particles enough kinetic energy to overcome the Coulomb-repulsion barrier to ${}_1^1\text{H} + {}_2^3\text{He} \to {}_2^4\text{He} + e^+ + \nu$, estimated as $\frac{k_e(e)(2e)}{r}$. The Coulomb barrier to Bethe's fifth and eight reactions is like $\frac{k_e(e)(7e)}{r}$, larger by $\frac{7}{2}$ times, so the required temperature can be estimated as $\frac{7}{2}\left(15\times 10^6\text{ K}\right) \approx \boxed{5\times 10^7\text{ K}}$.

(b) For ${}^{12}\text{C} + {}^1\text{H} \to {}^{13}\text{N} + Q$,

$Q_1 = (12.000\,000 + 1.007\,825 - 13.005\,739)(931.5\text{ MeV}) = \boxed{1.94\text{ MeV}}$

For the second step, add seven electrons to both sides to have: ${}^{13}\text{N atom} \to {}^{13}\text{C atom} + e^+ + e^- + Q$

$Q_2 = \left[13.005\,739 - 13.003\,355 - 2(0.000\,549)\right](931.5\text{ MeV}) = \boxed{1.20\text{ MeV}}$

$Q_3 = Q_7 = 2(0.000\,549)(931.5\text{ MeV}) = \boxed{1.02\text{ MeV}}$

$Q_4 = \left[13.003\,355 + 1.007\,825 - 14.003\,074\right](931.5\text{ MeV}) = \boxed{7.55\text{ MeV}}$

$Q_5 = \left[14.003\,074 + 1.007\,825 - 15.003\,065\right](931.5\text{ MeV}) = \boxed{7.30\text{ MeV}}$

$Q_6 = \left[15.003\,065 - 15.000\,109 - 2(0.000\,549)\right](931.5\text{ MeV}) = \boxed{1.73\text{ MeV}}$

$Q_8 = \left[15.000\,109 + 1.007\,825 - 12 - 4.002\,603\right](931.5\text{ MeV}) = \boxed{4.97\text{ MeV}}$

The sum is $\boxed{26.7\text{ MeV}}$, the same as for the proton-proton cycle.

(c) Not all of the energy released appears as internal energy in the star. When a neutrino is created, it will likely fly directly out of the star without interacting with any other particle.

P45.60 (a) $\frac{I_2}{I_1}=\frac{I_0e^{-\mu_2 x}}{I_0e^{-\mu_1 x}}=\boxed{e^{-(\mu_2-\mu_1)x}}$

(b) $\frac{I_{50}}{I_{100}}=e^{-(5.40-41.0)(0.100)}=e^{3.56}=\boxed{35.2}$

(c) $\frac{I_{50}}{I_{100}}=e^{-(5.40-41.0)(1.00)}=e^{35.6}=\boxed{2.89\times 10^{15}}$

Thus, a 1.00-cm aluminum plate has essentially removed the long-wavelength x-rays from the beam.

***P45.61** (a) The number of fissions ocurring in the zeroth, first, second, ... nth generation is

$$N_0,\ N_0K,\ N_0K^2,\ \ldots,\ N_0K^n.$$

The total number of fissions that have ocurred up to and including the nth generation is

$$N=N_0+N_0K+N_0K^2+\ldots+N_0K^n=N_0\left(1+K+K^2+\ldots+K^n\right).$$

Note that the factoring of the difference of two squares, $a^2-1=(a+1)(a-1)$, can be generalized to a difference of two quantities to any power,

$$a^3-1=\left(a^2+a+1\right)(a-1)$$

$$a^{n+1}-1=\left(a^n+a^{n-1}+\ldots+a^2+a+1\right)(a-1).$$

Thus $$K^n+K^{n-1}+\ldots+K^2+K+1=\frac{K^{n+1}-1}{K-1}$$

and $$\boxed{N=N_0\frac{K^{n+1}-1}{K-1}}.$$

(b) The number of U-235 nuclei is

$$N=5.50\text{ kg}\left(\frac{1\text{ atom}}{235\text{ u}}\right)\left(\frac{1\text{ u}}{1.66\times 10^{-27}\text{ kg}}\right)=1.41\times 10^{25}\text{ nuclei}.$$

We solve the equation from part (a) for n, the number of generations:

$$\frac{N}{N_0}(K-1)=K^{n+1}-1$$

$$\frac{N}{N_0}(K-1)+1=K^n(K)$$

$$n\ln K=\ln\left(\frac{N(K-1)/N_0+1}{K}\right)=\ln\left(\frac{N(K-1)}{N_0}+1\right)-\ln K$$

$$n=\frac{\ln\left(N(K-1)/N_0+1\right)}{\ln K}-1=\frac{\ln\left(1.41\times 10^{25}(0.1)/10^{20}+1\right)}{\ln 1.1}-1=99.2$$

Therefore time must be alotted for 100 generations:

$$\Delta t_b=100\left(10\times 10^{-9}\text{ s}\right)=\boxed{1.00\times 10^{-6}\text{ s}}.$$

continued on next page

(c) $$v=\sqrt{\frac{B}{\rho}}=\sqrt{\frac{150\times10^{9}\ \text{N/m}^2}{18.7\times10^{3}\ \text{kg/m}^3}}=\boxed{2.83\times10^{3}\ \text{m/s}}$$

(d) $$V=\frac{4}{3}\pi r^3=\frac{m}{\rho}$$

$$r=\left(\frac{3m}{4\pi\rho}\right)^{1/3}=\left(\frac{3(5.5\ \text{kg})}{4\pi\left(18.7\times10^{3}\ \text{kg/m}^3\right)}\right)^{1/3}=4.13\times10^{-2}\ \text{m}$$

$$\Delta t_d=\frac{r}{v}=\frac{4.13\times10^{-2}\ \text{m}}{2.83\times10^{3}\ \text{m/s}}=\boxed{1.46\times10^{-5}\ \text{s}}$$

(e) 14.6 μs is greater than 1 μs, so the entire bomb can fission. The destructive energy released is

$$1.41\times10^{25}\ \text{nuclei}\left(\frac{200\times10^{6}\ \text{eV}}{\text{fissioning nucleus}}\right)\left(\frac{1.6\times10^{-19}\ \text{J}}{1\ \text{eV}}\right)=4.51\times10^{14}\ \text{J}=4.51\times10^{14}\ \text{J}\left(\frac{1\ \text{ton TNT}}{4.2\times10^{9}\ \text{J}}\right)$$

$$=1.07\times10^{5}\ \text{ton TNT}$$

$$=\boxed{107\ \text{kilotons of TNT}}$$

What if? If the bomb did not have an "initiator" to inject 10^{20} neutrons at the moment when the critical mass is assembled, the number of generations would be

$$n=\frac{\ln\left(1.41\times10^{25}(0.1)/1+1\right)}{\ln 1.1}-1=582\ \text{requiring}\ 583\left(10\times10^{-9}\ \text{s}\right)=5.83\ \mu\text{s}.$$

This time is not very short compared with 14.6 μs, so this bomb would likely release much less energy.

ANSWERS TO EVEN PROBLEMS

P45.2 184 MeV

P45.4 see the solution

P45.6 (a) 173 MeV; (b) 0.078 8%

P45.8 2.63 kg/d

P45.10 (a) $4.84V^{-1/3}$; (b) $6V^{-1/3}$; (c) $6.30V^{-1/3}$; (d) the sphere has minimum loss and the parallelepiped maximum

P45.12 2.68×10^{5}

P45.14 (a) 31.9 g/h; (b) 122 g/h

P45.16 (a) 3.24 fm; (b) 444 keV; (c) $\frac{2}{5}v_i$; (d) 740 keV; (e) possibly by tunneling

P45.18 (a) 2.53×10^{31} J; (b) 1.14×10^{9} yr

P45.20 (a) 10^{14} cm^{-3}; (b) 1.24×10^{5} J/m^3; (c) 1.77 T

P45.22 12.4 h

P45.24 (a) 10.0 h; (b) 3.16 m

P45.26 (a) 0.436 cm; (b) 5.79 cm

P45.28 2.39×10^{-3} °C

P45.30 3.96×10^{-4} J/kg

P45.32 (a) 10; (b) 10^{6}; (c) 10^{8} eV

P45.34 4.45×10^{-8} kg/h

P45.36 (a) $\sim 10^6$; (b) $\sim 10^{-15}$ g

P45.38 (a) 1.5×10^{24}; (b) 0.6 kg

P45.40 see the solution

P45.42 The fractional loss in D-T is about 4 times that in ^{235}U fission

P45.44 1.01 MeV

P45.46 $$\frac{mN_A(200\text{ MeV})}{(235\text{ g/mol})\begin{bmatrix}c_w(100°\text{C}-T_c)+L_v\\+c_s(T_h-100°\text{C})\end{bmatrix}}$$

P45.48 (a) $\sim 10^8$ m^3; (b) $\sim 10^{13}$ J; (c) $\sim 10^{14}$ J; (d) ~ 10 kilotons

P45.50 223 W

P45.52 26 collisions

P45.54 400 rad

P45.56 3.53×10^{38} protons/s

P45.58 (a) 5.68×10^8 K; (b) 120 kJ

P45.60 (a) see the solution; (b) 35.2; (c) 2.89×10^{15}

46

Particle Physics and Cosmology

CHAPTER OUTLINE

ANSWERS TO QUESTIONS

Q46.1 Strong Force—Mediated by gluons.

Electromagnetic Force—Mediated by photons.

Weak Force—Mediated by W^+, W^-, and Z^0 bosons.

Gravitational Force—Mediated by gravitons.

Q46.2 The production of a single gamma ray could not satisfy the law of conservation of momentum, which must hold true in this—and every—interaction.

Q46.3 In the quark model, all hadrons are composed of smaller units called quarks. Quarks have a fractional electric charge and a baryon number of $\frac{1}{3}$. There are 6 types of quarks: up, down, strange, charmed, top, and bottom. Further, all *baryons* contain 3 quarks, and all *mesons* contain one quark and one anti-quark. *Leptons* are thought to be fundamental particles.

Q46.4 Hadrons are massive particles with structure and size. There are two classes of hadron: mesons and baryons. Hadrons are composed of quarks. Hadrons interact via the strong force.

Leptons are light particles with no structure or size. It is believed that leptons are fundamental particles. Leptons interact via the weak force.

Q46.5 Baryons are heavy hadrons with spin $\frac{1}{2}$ or $\frac{3}{2}$, are composed of three quarks, and have long lifetimes. Mesons are light hadrons with spin 0 or 1, are composed of a quark and an antiquark, and have short lifetimes.

Q46.6 Resonances are hadrons. They decay into strongly interacting particles such as protons, neutrons, and pions, all of which are hadrons.

Q46.7 The baryon number of a proton or neutron is one. Since baryon number is conserved, the baryon number of the kaon must be zero.

Q46.8 Decays by the weak interaction typically take 10^{-10} s or longer to occur. This is slow in particle physics.

Q46.9 The decays of the muon, tau, charged pion, kaons, neutron, lambda, charged sigmas, xis, and omega occur by the weak interaction. All have lifetimes longer than 10^{-13} s. Several produce neutrinos; none produce photons. Several violate strangeness conservation.

Q46.10 The decays of the neutral pion, eta, and neutral sigma occur by the electromagnetic interaction. These are three of the shortest lifetimes in Table 46.2. All produce photons, which are the quanta of the electromagnetic force. All conserve strangeness.

Q46.11 Yes, protons interact via the weak interaction; but the strong interaction predominates.

Q46.12 You can think of a conservation law as a superficial regularity which we happen to notice, as a person who does not know the rules of chess might observe that one player's two bishops are always on squares of opposite colors. Alternatively, you can think of a conservation law as identifying some stuff of which the universe is made. In classical physics one can think of both matter and energy as fundamental constituents of the world. We buy and sell both of them. In classical physics you can also think of linear momentum, angular momentum, and electric charge as basic stuffs of which the universe is made. In relativity we learn that matter and energy are not conserved separately, but are both aspects of the conserved quantity *relativistic total energy*. Discovered more recently, four conservation laws appear equally general and thus equally fundamental: Conservation of baryon number, conservation of electron-lepton number, conservation of tau-lepton number, and conservation of muon-lepton number. Processes involving the strong force and the electromagnetic force follow conservation of strangeness, charm, bottomness, and topness, while the weak interaction can alter the total S, C, B and T quantum numbers of an isolated system.

Q46.13 No. Antibaryons have baryon number −1, mesons have baryon number 0, and baryons have baryon number +1. The reaction cannot occur because it would not conserve baryon number, unless so much energy is available that a baryon-antibaryon pair is produced.

Q46.14 The Standard Model consists of quantum chromodynamics (to describe the strong interaction) and the electroweak theory (to describe the electromagnetic and weak interactions). The Standard Model is our most comprehensive description of nature. It fails to unify the two theories it includes, and fails to include the gravitational force. It pictures matter as made of six quarks and six leptons, interacting by exchanging gluons, photons, and W and Z bosons.

Q46.15 All baryons and antibaryons consist of three quarks. All mesons and antimesons consist of two quarks. Since quarks have spin quantum number $\frac{1}{2}$ and can be spin-up or spin-down, it follows that the three-quark baryons must have a half-integer spin, while the two-quark mesons must have spin 0 or 1.

Q46.16 Each flavor of quark can have colors, designated as red, green and blue. Antiquarks are colored antired, antigreen, and antiblue. A baryon consists of three quarks, each having a different color. By analogy to additive color mixing we call it colorless. A meson consists of a quark of one color and antiquark with the corresponding anticolor, making it colorless as a whole.

Q46.17 In 1961 Gell-Mann predicted the omega-minus particle, with quark composition sss. Its discovery in 1964 confirmed the quark theory.

Q46.18 The Ξ^- particle has, from Table 46.2, charge $-e$, spin $\frac{1}{2}$, $B=1$, $L_e = L_\mu = L_\tau = 0$, and strangeness -2. All of these are described by its quark composition dss (Table 46.5). The properties of the quarks from Table 46.3 let us add up charge: $-\frac{1}{3}e - \frac{1}{3}e - \frac{1}{3}e = -e$; spin $+\frac{1}{2} - \frac{1}{2} + \frac{1}{2} = \frac{1}{2}$, supposing one of the quarks is spin-down relative to the other two; baryon number $\frac{1}{3} + \frac{1}{3} + \frac{1}{3} = 1$; lepton numbers, charm, bottomness, and topness zero; and strangeness $0 - 1 - 1 = -2$.

Q46.19 The electroweak theory of Glashow, Salam, and Weinberg predicted the W^+, W^-, and Z particles. Their discovery in 1983 confirmed the electroweak theory.

Q46.20 Hubble determined experimentally that all galaxies outside the Local Group are moving away from us, with speed directly proportional to the distance of the galaxy from us.

Q46.21 Before that time, the Universe was too hot for the electrons to remain in any sort of stable orbit around protons. The thermal motion of both protons and electrons was too rapid for them to be in close enough proximity for the Coulomb force to dominate.

Q46.22 The Universe is vast and could on its own terms get along very well without us. But as the cosmos is immense, life appears to be immensely scarce, and therefore precious. We must do our work, growing corn to feed the hungry while preserving our planet for future generations. One person has singular abilities and opportunities for effort, faithfulness, generosity, honor, curiosity, understanding, and wonder. His or her place is to use those abilities and opportunities, unique in all the Universe.

SOLUTIONS TO PROBLEMS

Section 46.1 The Fundamental Forces in Nature

Section 46.2 Positrons and Other Antiparticles

P46.1 Assuming that the proton and antiproton are left nearly at rest after they are produced, the energy E of the photon must be

$$E = 2E_0 = 2(938.3 \text{ MeV}) = 1\,876.6 \text{ MeV} = 3.00 \times 10^{-10} \text{ J}.$$

Thus, $E = hf = 3.00 \times 10^{-10}$ J

$$f = \frac{3.00 \times 10^{-10} \text{ J}}{6.626 \times 10^{-34} \text{ J} \cdot \text{s}} = \boxed{4.53 \times 10^{23} \text{ Hz}}$$

$$\lambda = \frac{c}{f} = \frac{3.00 \times 10^8 \text{ m/s}}{4.53 \times 10^{23} \text{ Hz}} = \boxed{6.62 \times 10^{-16} \text{ m}}.$$

P46.2 The minimum energy is released, and hence the minimum frequency photons are produced, when the proton and antiproton are at rest when they annihilate.

That is, $E = E_0$ and $K = 0$. To conserve momentum, each photon must carry away one-half the energy.

Thus, $$E_{\text{min}} = \frac{2E_0}{2} = E_0 = 938.3 \text{ MeV} = hf_{\text{min}}.$$

Thus, $$f_{\text{min}} = \frac{(938.3 \text{ MeV})(1.60 \times 10^{-13} \text{ J/MeV})}{(6.626 \times 10^{-34} \text{ J}\cdot\text{s})} = \boxed{2.27 \times 10^{23} \text{ Hz}}$$

$$\lambda = \frac{c}{f_{\text{min}}} = \frac{3.00 \times 10^8 \text{ m/s}}{2.27 \times 10^{23} \text{ Hz}} = \boxed{1.32 \times 10^{-15} \text{ m}}.$$

P46.3 In $\gamma \to p^+ + p^-$,

we start with energy 2.09 GeV

we end with energy 938.3 MeV + 938.3 MeV + 95.0 MeV + K_2

where K_2 is the kinetic energy of the second proton.

Conservation of energy for the creation process gives $\boxed{K_2 = 118 \text{ MeV}}$.

Section 46.3 **Mesons and the Beginning of Particle Physics**

P46.4 The reaction is $\mu^+ + e^- \to \nu + \nu$

muon-lepton number before reaction: $(-1) + (0) = -1$

electron-lepton number before reaction: $(0) + (1) = 1$.

Therefore, after the reaction, the muon-lepton number must be –1. Thus, one of the neutrinos must be the anti-neutrino associated with muons, and one of the neutrinos must be the neutrino associated with electrons:

$$\boxed{\bar{\nu}_\mu} \quad \text{and} \quad \boxed{\nu_e}.$$

Then $$\mu^+ + e^- \to \bar{\nu}_\mu + \nu_e.$$

P46.5 The creation of a virtual Z^0 boson is an energy fluctuation $\Delta E = 93 \times 10^9$ eV. It can last no longer than $\Delta t = \frac{\hbar}{2\Delta E}$ and move no farther than

$$c(\Delta t) = \frac{hc}{4\pi \Delta E} = \frac{(6.626 \times 10^{-34} \text{ J}\cdot\text{s})(3.00 \times 10^8 \text{ m/s})}{4\pi(93 \times 10^9 \text{ eV})}\left(\frac{1 \text{ eV}}{1.60 \times 10^{-19} \text{ J}}\right) = 1.06 \times 10^{-18} \text{ m} = \boxed{\sim 10^{-18} \text{ m}}.$$

P46.6 A proton has rest energy 938.3 MeV. The time interval during which a virtual proton could exist is at most Δt in $\Delta E \Delta t = \frac{\hbar}{2}$. The distance it could move is at most

$$c\Delta t = \frac{\hbar c}{2\Delta E} = \frac{(1.055\times 10^{-34}\text{ J}\cdot\text{s})(3\times 10^{8}\text{ m/s})}{2(938.3)(1.6\times 10^{-13}\text{ J})}\boxed{\sim 10^{-16}\text{ m}}.$$

According to Yukawa's line of reasoning, this distance is the range of a force that could be associated with the exchange of virtual protons between high-energy particles.

P46.7 By Table 46.2, $M_{\pi^0} = 135\text{ MeV}/c^2$.

Therefore, $E_\gamma = \boxed{67.5\text{ MeV}}$ for each photon

$$p = \frac{E_\gamma}{c} = \boxed{67.5\text{ MeV}/c}$$

and $$f = \frac{E_\gamma}{h} = \boxed{1.63\times 10^{22}\text{ Hz}}.$$

P46.8 The time interval for a particle traveling with the speed of light to travel a distance of 3×10^{-15} m is

$$\Delta t = \frac{d}{v} = \frac{3\times 10^{-15}\text{ m}}{3\times 10^{8}\text{ m/s}} = \boxed{\sim 10^{-23}\text{ s}}.$$

P46.9 (a) $\Delta E = (m_n - m_p - m_e)c^2$

From Table A-3, $\Delta E = (1.008\,665 - 1.007\,825)(931.5) = \boxed{0.782\text{ MeV}}$.

(b) Assuming the neutron at rest, momentum conservation for the decay process implies $p_p = p_e$. Relativistic energy for the system is conserved

$$\sqrt{(m_pc^2)^2 + p_p^2c^2} + \sqrt{(m_ec^2)^2 + p_e^2c^2} = m_nc^2.$$

Since $p_p = p_e$, $\sqrt{(938.3)^2 + (pc)^2} + \sqrt{(0.511)^2 + (pc)^2} = 939.6\text{ MeV}$.

Solving the algebra, $pc = 1.19\text{ MeV}$.

If $p_ec = \gamma m_ev_ec = 1.19\text{ MeV}$, then $\frac{\gamma v_e}{c} = \frac{1.19\text{ MeV}}{0.511\text{ MeV}} = \frac{x}{\sqrt{1-x^2}} = 2.33$ where $x = \frac{v_e}{c}$.

Solving, $x^2 = (1-x^2)5.43$ and $x = \frac{v_e}{c} = 0.919$

$$\boxed{v_e = 0.919c}.$$

Then $m_pv_p = \gamma_em_ev_e$:

$$v_p = \frac{\gamma_em_ev_ec}{m_pc} = \frac{(1.19\text{ MeV})(1.60\times 10^{-13}\text{ J/MeV})}{(1.67\times 10^{-27})(3.00\times 10^{8}\text{ m/s})}$$

$$v_p = 3.80\times 10^{5}\text{ m/s} = \boxed{380\text{ km/s}}.$$

(c) $\boxed{\text{The electron is relativistic, the proton is not.}}$

Section 46.4 Classification of Particles

P46.10 In $? + p^+ \to n + \mu^+$, charge conservation requires the unknown particle to be neutral. Baryon number conservation requires baryon number = 0. The muon-lepton number of ? must be –1.

So the unknown particle must be $\boxed{\bar{\nu}_\mu}$.

P46.11 $\Omega^+ \to \bar{\Lambda}^0 + K^+$ $\quad$ $\bar{K}_S^0 \to \pi^+ + \pi^-$ $\quad$ (or $\pi^0 + \pi^0$)

$\bar{\Lambda}^0 \to \bar{p} + \pi^+$ $\quad$ $\bar{n} \to \bar{p} + e^+ + \nu_e$

Section 46.5 Conservation Laws

P46.12 (a) $p + \bar{p} \to \mu^+ + e^-$ $\quad \boxed{L_e}$ $\quad 0+0 \to 0+1$

and $\quad \boxed{L_\mu}$ $\quad 0+0 \to -1+0$

(b) $\pi^- + p \to p + \pi^+$ $\quad \boxed{\text{charge}}$ $\quad -1+1 \to +1+1$

(c) $p + p \to p + \pi^+$ $\quad \boxed{\text{baryon number}}$: $\quad 1+1 \to 1+0$

(d) $p + p \to p + p + n$ $\quad \boxed{\text{baryon number}}$: $\quad 1+1 \to 1+1+1$

(e) $\gamma + p \to n + \pi^0$ $\quad \boxed{\text{charge}}$ $\quad 0+1 \to 0+0$

P46.13 (a) Baryon number and charge are conserved, with values of $0+1 = 0+1$ and $1+1 = 1+1$ in both reactions.

(b) $\boxed{\text{Strangeness is } \textit{not} \text{ conserved}}$ in the second reaction.

P46.14 Baryon number conservation $\boxed{\text{allows the first and forbids the second}}$.

P46.15 (a) $\pi^- \to \mu^- + \boxed{\bar{\nu}_\mu}$ $\quad L_\mu$: $0 \to 1-1$

(b) $K^+ \to \mu^+ + \boxed{\nu_\mu}$ $\quad L_\mu$: $0 \to -1+1$

(c) $\boxed{\bar{\nu}_e} + p^+ \to n + e^+$ $\quad L_e$: $-1+0 \to 0-1$

(d) $\boxed{\nu_e} + n \to p^+ + e^-$ $\quad L_e$: $1+0 \to 0+1$

(e) $\boxed{\nu_\mu} + n \to p^+ + \mu^-$ $\quad L_\mu$: $1+0 \to 0+1$

(f) $\mu^- \to e^- + \boxed{\bar{\nu}_e} + \boxed{\nu_\mu}$ $\quad L_\mu$: $1 \to 0+0+1$ $\quad$ and $\quad L_e$: $0 \to 1-1+0$

P46.16 Momentum conservation for the decay requires the pions to have equal speeds.

The total energy of each is $\frac{497.7 \text{ MeV}}{2}$

so $E^2 = p^2c^2 + \left(mc^2\right)^2$ gives

$$(248.8 \text{ MeV})^2 = (pc)^2 + (139.6 \text{ MeV})^2.$$

Solving, $pc = 206 \text{ MeV} = \gamma\, mvc = \frac{mc^2}{\sqrt{1-(v/c)^2}}\left(\frac{v}{c}\right)$

$$\frac{pc}{mc^2} = \frac{206 \text{ MeV}}{139.6 \text{ MeV}} = \frac{1}{\sqrt{1-(v/c)^2}}\left(\frac{v}{c}\right) = 1.48$$

$$\frac{v}{c} = 1.48\sqrt{1-\left(\frac{v}{c}\right)^2}$$

and $\left(\frac{v}{c}\right)^2 = 2.18\left[1-\left(\frac{v}{c}\right)^2\right] = 2.18 - 2.18\left(\frac{v}{c}\right)^2$

$$3.18\left(\frac{v}{c}\right)^2 = 2.18$$

so $\frac{v}{c} = \sqrt{\frac{2.18}{3.18}} = 0.828$

and $\boxed{v = 0.828c}$.

P46.17

(a)	$p^+ \to \pi^+ + \pi^0$	$\boxed{\text{Baryon number}}$:	$1 \to 0+0$
(b)	$p^+ + p^+ \to p^+ + p^+ + \pi^0$	This reaction $\boxed{\text{can occur}}$.	
(c)	$p^+ + p^+ \to p^+ + \pi^+$	$\boxed{\text{Baryon number}}$ is violated:	$1+1 \to 1+0$
(d)	$\pi^+ \to \mu^+ + \nu_\mu$	This reaction $\boxed{\text{can occur}}$.	
(e)	$n^0 \to p^+ + e^- + \overline{\nu}_e$	This reaction $\boxed{\text{can occur}}$.	
(f)	$\pi^+ \to \mu^+ + n$	Violates $\boxed{\text{baryon number}}$:	$0 \to 0+1$
		Violates $\boxed{\text{muon-lepton number}}$:	$0 \to -1+0$

P46.18 (a) $p \to e^+ + \gamma$

Baryon number: $+1 \to 0 + 0$

$\Delta B \neq 0$, so baryon number conservation is violated.

(b) From conservation of momentum for the decay: $p_e = p_\gamma$.

Then, for the positron, $E_e^2 = (p_e c)^2 + E_{0,e}^2$

becomes $E_e^2 = (p_\gamma c)^2 + E_{0,e}^2 = E_\gamma^2 + E_{0,e}^2$.

From conservation of energy for the system: $E_{0,p} = E_e + E_\gamma$

or $E_e = E_{0,p} - E_\gamma$

so $E_e^2 = E_{0,p}^2 - 2E_{0,p}E_\gamma + E_\gamma^2$.

Equating this to the result from above gives $E_\gamma^2 + E_{0,e}^2 = E_{0,p}^2 - 2E_{0,p}E_\gamma + E_\gamma^2$

or $$E_\gamma = \frac{E_{0,p}^2 - E_{0,e}^2}{2E_{0,p}} = \frac{(938.3\text{ MeV})^2 - (0.511\text{ MeV})^2}{2(938.3\text{ MeV})} = \boxed{469\text{ MeV}}.$$

Thus, $$E_e = E_{0,p} - E_\gamma = 938.3\text{ MeV} - 469\text{ MeV} = \boxed{469\text{ MeV}}.$$

Also, $$p_\gamma = \frac{E_\gamma}{c} = \boxed{\frac{469\text{ MeV}}{c}}$$

and $$p_e = p_\gamma = \boxed{\frac{469\text{ MeV}}{c}}.$$

(c) The total energy of the positron is $E_e = 469\text{ MeV}$.

But, $$E_e = \gamma E_{0,e} = \frac{E_{0,e}}{\sqrt{1-(v/c)^2}}$$

so $$\sqrt{1-\left(\frac{v}{c}\right)^2} = \frac{E_{0,e}}{E_e} = \frac{0.511\text{ MeV}}{469\text{ MeV}} = 1.09 \times 10^{-3}$$

which yields: $\boxed{v = 0.999\,999\,4c}$.

P46.19 The relevant conservation laws are: $\Delta L_e = 0$

$\Delta L_\mu = 0$

and $\Delta L_\tau = 0$.

(a) $\pi^+ \to \pi^0 + e^+ + ?$ $\quad L_e:\ 0 \to 0 - 1 + L_e$ $\quad$ implies $L_e = 1$ $\quad$ and we have a $\boxed{\nu_e}$

(b) $? + p \to \mu^- + p + \pi^+$ $\quad L_\mu:\ L_\mu + 0 \to +1 + 0 + 0$ $\quad$ implies $L_\mu = 1$ $\quad$ and we have a $\boxed{\nu_\mu}$

continued on next page

(c) $\Lambda^0 \to \rho + \mu^- + ?$ L_μ: $0 \to 0 + 1 + L_\mu$ implies $L_\mu = -1$ and we have a $\boxed{\bar{\nu}_\mu}$

(d) $\tau^+ \to \mu^+ + ? + ?$ L_μ: $0 \to -1 + L_\mu$ implies $L_\mu = 1$ and we have a $\boxed{\nu_\mu}$

L_τ: $-1 \to 0 + L_\tau$ implies $L_\tau = -1$ and we have a $\boxed{\bar{\nu}_\tau}$

Conclusion for (d): $L_\mu = 1$ for one particle, and $L_\tau = -1$ for the other particle.

We have $\boxed{\nu_\mu}$

and $\boxed{\bar{\nu}_\tau}$.

Section 46.6 Strange Particles and Strangeness

P46.20 The $\rho^0 \to \pi^+ + \pi^-$ decay must occur via the strong interaction.

The $K_S^0 \to \pi^+ + \pi^-$ decay must occur via the weak interaction.

P46.21 (a) $\Lambda^0 \to p + \pi^-$ Strangeness: $-1 \to 0 + 0$ (strangeness is $\boxed{\text{not conserved}}$)

(b) $\pi^- + p \to \Lambda^0 + K^0$ Strangeness: $0 + 0 \to -1 + 1$ ($0 = 0$ and strangeness is $\boxed{\text{conserved}}$)

(c) $\bar{p} + p \to \overline{\Lambda^0} + \Lambda^0$ Strangeness: $0 + 0 \to +1 - 1$ ($0 = 0$ and strangeness is $\boxed{\text{conserved}}$)

(d) $\pi^- + p \to \pi^- + \Sigma^+$ Strangeness: $0 + 0 \to 0 - 1$ ($0 \neq -1$: strangeness is $\boxed{\text{not conserved}}$)

(e) $\Xi^- \to \Lambda^0 + \pi^-$ Strangeness: $-2 \to -1 + 0$ ($-2 \neq -1$ so strangeness is $\boxed{\text{not conserved}}$)

(f) $\Xi^0 \to p + \pi^-$ Strangeness: $-2 \to 0 + 0$ ($-2 \neq 0$ so strangeness is $\boxed{\text{not conserved}}$)

P46.22 (a) $\mu^- \to e^- + \gamma$ L_e: $0 \to 1 + 0$,

and L_μ: $1 \to 0$

(b) $n \to p + e^- + \nu_e$ L_e: $0 \to 0 + 1 + 1$

(c) $\Lambda^0 \to p + \pi^0$ Strangeness: $-1 \to 0 + 0$,

and charge: $0 \to +1 + 0$

(d) $p \to e^+ + \pi^0$ Baryon number: $+1 \to 0 + 0$

(e) $\Xi^0 \to n + \pi^0$ Strangeness: $-2 \to 0 + 0$

P46.23 (a) $\pi^- + p \to 2\eta$ violates conservation of baryon number as $0+1 \to 0$, not allowed.

(b) $K^- + n \to \Lambda^0 + \pi^-$

Baryon number, $0+1 \to 1+0$

Charge, $-1+0 \to 0-1$

Strangeness, $-1+0 \to -1+0$

Lepton number, $0 \to 0$

The interaction may occur via the strong interaction since all are conserved.

(c) $K^- \to \pi^- + \pi^0$

Strangeness, $-1 \to 0+0$

Baryon number, $0 \to 0$

Lepton number, $0 \to 0$

Charge, $-1 \to -1+0$

Strangeness is violated by one unit, but everything else is conserved. Thus, the reaction can occur via the weak interaction, but not the strong or electromagnetic interaction.

(d) $\Omega^- \to \Xi^- + \pi^0$

Baryon number, $1 \to 1+0$

Lepton number, $0 \to 0$

Charge, $-1 \to -1+0$

Strangeness, $-3 \to -2+0$

May occur by weak interaction, but not by strong or electromagnetic.

(e) $\eta \to 2\gamma$

Baryon number, $0 \to 0$

Lepton number, $0 \to 0$

Charge, $0 \to 0$

Strangeness, $0 \to 0$

No conservation laws are violated, but photons are the mediators of the electromagnetic interaction. Also, the lifetime of the η is consistent with the electromagnetic interaction.

P46.24 (a) $\Xi^- \to \Lambda^0 + \mu^- + \nu_\mu$

Baryon number:	$+1 \to +1+0+0$	Charge:	$-1 \to 0-1+0$
L_e:	$0 \to 0+0+0$	L_μ:	$0 \to 0+1+1$
L_τ:	$0 \to 0+0+0$	Strangeness:	$-2 \to -1+0+0$

Conserved quantities are: $\boxed{B\text{, charge, } L_e\text{, and } L_\tau}$

(b) $K_S^0 \to 2\pi^0$

Baryon number:	$0 \to 0$	Charge:	$0 \to 0$
L_e:	$0 \to 0$	L_μ:	$0 \to 0$
L_τ:	$0 \to 0$	Strangeness:	$+1 \to 0$

Conserved quantities are: $\boxed{B\text{, charge, } L_e\text{, } L_\mu\text{, and } L_\tau}$

(c) $K^- + p \to \Sigma^0 + n$

Baryon number:	$0+1 \to 1+1$	Charge:	$-1+1 \to 0+0$
L_e:	$0+0 \to 0+0$	L_μ:	$0+0 \to 0+0$
L_τ:	$0+0 \to 0+0$	Strangeness:	$-1+0 \to -1+0$

Conserved quantities are: $\boxed{S\text{, charge, } L_e\text{, } L_\mu\text{, and } L_\tau}$

(d) $\Sigma^0 + \Lambda^0 + \gamma$

Baryon number:	$+1 \to 1+0$	Charge:	$0 \to 0$
L_e:	$0 \to 0+0$	L_μ:	$0 \to 0+0$
L_τ:	$0 \to 0+0$	Strangeness:	$-1 \to -1+0$

Conserved quantities are: $\boxed{B\text{, } S\text{, charge, } L_e\text{, } L_\mu\text{, and } L_\tau}$

(e) $e^+ + e^- \to \mu^+ + \mu^-$

Baryon number:	$0+0 \to 0+0$	Charge:	$+1-1 \to +1-1$
L_e:	$-1+1 \to 0+0$	L_μ:	$0+0 \to +1-1$
L_τ:	$0+0 \to 0+0$	Strangeness:	$0+0 \to 0+0$

Conserved quantities are: $\boxed{B\text{, } S\text{, charge, } L_e\text{, } L_\mu\text{, and } L_\tau}$

(f) $\overline{p} + n \to \overline{\Lambda}^0 + \Sigma^-$

Baryon number:	$-1+1 \to -1+1$	Charge:	$-1+0 \to 0-1$
L_e:	$0+0 \to 0+0$	L_μ:	$0+0 \to 0+0$
L_τ:	$0+0 \to 0+0$	Strangeness:	$0+0 \to +1-1$

Conserved quantities are: $\boxed{B\text{, } S\text{, charge, } L_e\text{, } L_\mu\text{, and } L_\tau}$

P46.25 (a) $K^+ + p \rightarrow \underline{?} + p$

The strong interaction conserves everything.

Baryon number,	$0+1 \rightarrow B+1$	so	$B=0$
Charge,	$+1+1 \rightarrow Q+1$	so	$Q=+1$
Lepton numbers,	$0+0 \rightarrow L+0$	so	$L_e = L_\mu = L_\tau = 0$
Strangeness,	$+1+0 \rightarrow S+0$	so	$S=1$

The conclusion is that the particle must be positively charged, a non-baryon, with strangeness of $+1$. Of particles in Table 46.2, it can only be the $\boxed{K^+}$. Thus, this is an elastic scattering process.

The weak interaction conserves all but strangeness, and $\Delta S = \pm 1$.

(b) $\Omega^- \rightarrow \underline{?} + \pi^-$

Baryon number,	$+1 \rightarrow B+0$	so	$B=1$
Charge,	$-1 \rightarrow Q-1$	so	$Q=0$
Lepton numbers,	$0 \rightarrow L+0$	so	$L_e = L_\mu = L_\tau = 0$
Strangeness,	$-3 \rightarrow S+0$	so	$\Delta S = 1$: $S = -2$

The particle must be a neutral baryon with strangeness of –2. Thus, it is the $\boxed{\Xi^0}$.

(c) $K^+ \rightarrow \underline{?} + \mu^+ + \nu_\mu$

Baryon number,	$0 \rightarrow B+0+0$	so	$B=0$
Charge,	$+1 \rightarrow Q+1+0$	so	$Q=0$
Lepton numbers,	L_e, $0 \rightarrow L_e+0+0$	so	$L_e=0$
	L_μ, $0 \rightarrow L_\mu-1+1$	so	$L_\mu=0$
	L_τ, $0 \rightarrow L_\tau+0+0$	so	$L_\tau=0$
Strangeness,	$1 \rightarrow S+0+0$	so	$\Delta S = \pm 1$
			(for weak interaction): $S=0$

The particle must be a neutral meson with strangeness $=0 \Rightarrow \boxed{\pi^0}$.

Section 46.7 **Making Elementary Particles and Measuring Their Properties**

***P46.26** (a)

$$p_{\Sigma^+} = eBr_{\Sigma^+} = \frac{\left(1.602\,177\times10^{-19}\text{ C}\right)(1.15\text{ T})(1.99\text{ m})}{5.344\,288\times10^{-22}\,(\text{kg}\cdot\text{m/s})/(\text{MeV}/c)} = \boxed{\frac{686\text{ MeV}}{c}}$$

$$p_{\pi^+} = eBr_{\pi^+} = \frac{\left(1.602\,177\times10^{-19}\text{ C}\right)(1.15\text{ T})(0.580\text{ m})}{5.344\,288\times10^{-22}\,(\text{kg}\cdot\text{m/s})/(\text{MeV}/c)} = \boxed{\frac{200\text{ MeV}}{c}}$$

(b) Let φ be the angle made by the neutron's path with the path of the Σ^+ at the moment of decay. By conservation of momentum:

$$p_n\cos\varphi + (199.961\,581\text{ MeV}/c)\cos 64.5° = 686.075\,081\text{ MeV}/c$$

$$\therefore p_n\cos\varphi = 599.989\,401\text{ MeV}/c \quad (1)$$

$$p_n\sin\varphi = (199.961\,581\text{ MeV}/c)\sin 64.5° = 180.482\,380\text{ MeV}/c \quad (2)$$

From (1) and (2): $p_n = \sqrt{(599.989\,401\text{ MeV}/c)^2 + (180.482\,380\text{ MeV}/c)^2} = \boxed{627\text{ MeV}/c}$

(c)

$$E_{\pi^+} = \sqrt{\left(p_{\pi^+}c\right)^2 + \left(m_{\pi^+}c^2\right)^2} = \sqrt{(199.961\,581\text{ MeV})^2 + (139.6\text{ MeV})^2} = \boxed{244\text{ MeV}}$$

$$E_n = \sqrt{\left(p_nc\right)^2 + \left(m_nc^2\right)^2} = \sqrt{(626.547\,022\text{ MeV})^2 + (939.6\text{ MeV})^2} = \boxed{1\,130\text{ MeV}}$$

$$E_{\Sigma^+} = E_{\pi^+} + E_n = 243.870\,445\text{ MeV} + 1\,129.340\,219\text{ MeV} = \boxed{1\,370\text{ MeV}}$$

(d)

$$m_{\Sigma^+}c^2 = \sqrt{E_{\Sigma^+}^2 - \left(p_{\Sigma^+}c\right)^2} = \sqrt{(1\,373.210\,664\text{ MeV})^2 - (686.075\,081\text{ MeV})^2} = 1\,190\text{ MeV}$$

$$\therefore m_{\Sigma^+} = \boxed{1\,190\text{ MeV}/c^2}$$

$$E_{\Sigma^+} = \gamma m_{\Sigma^+}c^2,\text{ where } \gamma = \left(1-\frac{v^2}{c^2}\right)^{-1/2} = \frac{1\,373.210\,664\text{ MeV}}{1\,189.541\,303\text{ MeV}} = 1.154\,4$$

Solving for v, $v = \boxed{0.500c}$.

P46.27 Time-dilated lifetime:

$$T = \gamma T_0 = \frac{0.900\times10^{-10}\text{ s}}{\sqrt{1-v^2/c^2}} = \frac{0.900\times10^{-10}\text{ s}}{\sqrt{1-(0.960)^2}} = 3.214\times10^{-10}\text{ s}$$

$$\text{distance} = 0.960\left(3.00\times10^8\text{ m/s}\right)\left(3.214\times10^{-10}\text{ s}\right) = \boxed{9.26\text{ cm}}.$$

***P46.28** (a) Let $E_{\min}$ be the minimum total energy of the bombarding particle that is needed to induce the reaction. At this energy the product particles all move with the same velocity. The product particles are then equivalent to a single particle having mass equal to the total mass of the product particles, moving with the same velocity as each product particle. By conservation of energy:

$$E_{\min}+m_2c^2=\sqrt{\left(m_3c^2\right)^2+\left(p_3c\right)^2}. \qquad (1)$$

By conservation of momentum: $p_3=p_1$

$$\therefore \left(p_3c\right)^2=\left(p_1c\right)^2=E_{\min}^2-\left(m_1c^2\right)^2. \qquad (2)$$

Substitute (2) in (1): $E_{\min}+m_2c^2=\sqrt{\left(m_3c^2\right)^2+E_{\min}^2-\left(m_1c^2\right)^2}$.

Square both sides:

$$E_{\min}^2+2E_{\min}m_2c^2+\left(m_2c^2\right)^2=\left(m_3c^2\right)^2+E_{\min}^2-\left(m_1c^2\right)^2$$

$$\therefore E_{\min}=\frac{\left(m_3^2-m_1^2-m_2^2\right)c^2}{2m_2}$$

$$\therefore K_{\min}=E_{\min}-m_1c^2=\frac{\left(m_3^2-m_1^2-m_2^2-2m_1m_2\right)c^2}{2m_2}=\frac{\left[m_3^2-\left(m_1+m_2\right)^2\right]c^2}{2m_2}$$

Refer to Table 46.2 for the particle masses.

(b) $$K_{\min}=\frac{\left[4(938.3)\right]^2\text{ MeV}^2/c^2-\left[2(938.3)\right]^2\text{ MeV}^2/c^2}{2\left(938.3\text{ MeV}/c^2\right)}=\boxed{5.63\text{ GeV}}$$

(c) $$K_{\min}=\frac{(497.7+1\,115.6)^2\text{ MeV}^2/c^2-(139.6+938.3)^2\text{ MeV}^2/c^2}{2(938.3)\text{ MeV}/c^2}=\boxed{768\text{ MeV}}$$

(d) $$K_{\min}=\frac{\left[2(938.3)+135\right]^2\text{ MeV}^2/c^2-\left[2(938.3)\right]^2\text{ MeV}^2/c^2}{2(938.3)\text{ MeV}/c^2}=\boxed{280\text{ MeV}}$$

(e) $$K_{\min}=\frac{\left[\left(91.2\times10^3\right)^2-\left[(938.3+938.3)^2\right]\text{ MeV}^2/c^2\right]}{2(938.3)\text{ MeV}/c^2}=\boxed{4.43\text{ TeV}}$$

Section 46.8 **Finding Patterns in the Particles**

Section 46.9 **Quarks**

Section 46.10 **Multicolored Quarks**

Section 46.11 **The Standard Model**

P46.29 (a) The number of protons

$$N_p = 1\,000\text{ g}\left(\frac{6.02\times10^{23}\text{ molecules}}{18.0\text{ g}}\right)\left(\frac{10\text{ protons}}{\text{molecule}}\right) = 3.34\times10^{26}\text{ protons}$$

and there are $$N_n = 1\,000\text{ g}\left(\frac{6.02\times10^{23}\text{ molecules}}{18.0\text{ g}}\right)\left(\frac{8\text{ neutrons}}{\text{molecule}}\right) = 2.68\times10^{26}\text{ neutrons}.$$

So there are for electric neutrality $\boxed{3.34\times10^{26}\text{ electrons}}$.

The up quarks have number $2\left(3.34\times10^{26}\right)+2.68\times10^{26} = \boxed{9.36\times10^{26}\text{ up quarks}}$

and there are $2\left(2.68\times10^{26}\right)+3.34\times10^{26} = \boxed{8.70\times10^{26}\text{ down quarks}}$.

(b) Model yourself as 65 kg of water. Then you contain:

$$65\left(3.34\times10^{26}\right)\boxed{\sim10^{28}\text{ electrons}}$$

$$65\left(9.36\times10^{26}\right)\boxed{\sim10^{29}\text{ up quarks}}$$

$$65\left(8.70\times10^{26}\right)\boxed{\sim10^{29}\text{ down quarks}}.$$

Only these fundamental particles form your body. You have no strangeness, charm, topness or bottomness.

P46.30 (a)

	proton	u	u	d	total
strangeness	0	0	0	0	0
baryon number	1	1/3	1/3	1/3	1
charge	e	$2e/3$	$2e/3$	$-e/3$	e

(b)

	neutron	u	d	d	total
strangeness	0	0	0	0	0
baryon number	1	1/3	1/3	1/3	1
charge	0	$2e/3$	$-e/3$	$-e/3$	0

P46.31 Quark composition of proton = uud and of neutron = udd.
Thus, if we neglect binding energies, we may write

$$m_\text{p} = 2m_\text{u} + m_\text{d} \qquad (1)$$

and $$m_\text{n} = m_\text{u} + 2m_\text{d}. \qquad (2)$$

Solving simultaneously,

we find $$m_\text{u} = \frac{1}{3}\left(2m_\text{p} - m_\text{n}\right) = \frac{1}{3}\left[2\left(938\text{ MeV}/c^2\right) - 939.6\text{ meV}/c^2\right] = \boxed{312\text{ MeV}/c^2}$$

and from either (1) or (2), $m_\text{d} = \boxed{314\text{ MeV}/c^2}$.

P46.32 (a)

	K^0	d	$\bar{s}$	total
strangeness	1	0	1	1
baryon number	0	1/3	–1/3	0
charge	0	$-e/3$	$e/3$	0

(b)

	Λ^0	u	d	s	total
strangeness	–1	0	0	–1	–1
baryon number	1	1/3	1/3	1/3	1
charge	0	$2e/3$	$-e/3$	$-e/3$	0

P46.33 (a) $\pi^- + p \to K^0 + \Lambda^0$

In terms of constituent quarks: $\boxed{\bar{u}d + uud \to d\bar{s} + uds}$

up quarks: $-1+2 \to 0+1$, or $1 \to 1$

down quarks: $1+1 \to 1+1$, or $2 \to 2$

strange quarks: $0+0 \to -1+1$, or $0 \to 0$

(b) $\pi^+ + p \to K^+ + \Sigma^+$ $\boxed{\bar{d}u + uud \to u\bar{s} + uus}$

up quarks: $1+2 \to 1+2$, or $3 \to 3$

down quarks: $-1+1 \to 0+0$, or $0 \to 0$

strange quarks: $0+0 \to -1+1$, or $0 \to 0$

(c) $K^- + p \to K^+ + K^0 + \Omega^-$ $\boxed{\bar{u}s + uud \to u\bar{s} + d\bar{s} + sss}$

up quarks: $-1+2 \to 1+0+0$, or $1 \to 1$

down quarks: $0+1 \to 0+1+0$, or $1 \to 1$

strange quarks: $1+0 \to -1-1+3$, or $1 \to 1$

(d) $p + p \to K^0 + p + \pi^+ + \underline{?}$ $uud + uud \to d\bar{s} + uud + u\bar{d} + \underline{?}$

The quark combination of ? must be such as to balance the last equation for up, down, and strange quarks.

up quarks: $2+2 = 0+2+1+?$ (has 1 u quark)

down quarks: $1+1 = 1+1-1+?$ (has 1 d quark)

strange quarks: $0+0 = -1+0+0+?$ (has 1 s quark)

quark composition = uds = $\boxed{\Lambda^0 \text{ or } \Sigma^0}$

P46.34 In the first reaction, $\pi^- + p \to K^0 + \Lambda^0$, the quarks in the particles are: $\bar{u}d + uud \to d\bar{s} + uds$. There is a net of 1 up quark both before and after the reaction, a net of 2 down quarks both before and after, and a net of zero strange quarks both before and after. Thus, the reaction conserves the net number of each type of quark.

In the second reaction, $\pi^- + p \to K^0 + n$, the quarks in the particles are: $\bar{u}d + uud \to d\bar{s} + uds$. In this case, there is a net of 1 up and 2 down quarks before the reaction but a net of 1 up, 3 down, and 1 anti-strange quark after the reaction. Thus, the reaction does not conserve the net number of each type of quark.

P46.35 $\Sigma^0 + p \to \Sigma^+ + \gamma + X$

$dds + uud \to uds + 0 + ?$

The left side has a net 3d, 2u and 1s. The right-hand side has 1d, 1u, and 1s leaving 2d and 1u missing.

$\boxed{\text{The unknown particle is a neutron, udd.}}$

Baryon and strangeness numbers are conserved.

P46.36 Compare the given quark states to the entries in Tables 46.4 and 46.5:

(a) $suu = \boxed{\Sigma^+}$

(b) $\bar{u}d = \boxed{\pi^-}$

(c) $\bar{s}d = \boxed{K^0}$

(d) $ssd = \boxed{\Xi^-}$

P46.37 (a) $\bar{u}\bar{u}\bar{d}$: charge $= \left(-\frac{2}{3}e\right) + \left(-\frac{2}{3}e\right) + \left(\frac{1}{3}e\right) = \boxed{-e}$. This is the $\boxed{\text{antiproton}}$.

(b) $\bar{u}\bar{d}\bar{d}$: charge $= \left(-\frac{2}{3}e\right) + \left(\frac{1}{3}e\right) + \left(\frac{1}{3}e\right) = \boxed{0}$. This is the $\boxed{\text{antineutron}}$.

Section 46.12 **The Cosmic Connection**

P46.38 Section 39.4 says $f_{\text{observer}} = f_{\text{source}}\sqrt{\dfrac{1 + v_a/c}{1 - v_a/c}}$.

The velocity of approach, v_a, is the negative of the velocity of mutual recession: $v_a = -v$.

Then, $\dfrac{c}{\lambda'} = \dfrac{c}{\lambda}\sqrt{\dfrac{1 - v/c}{1 + v/c}}$ and $\boxed{\lambda' = \lambda\sqrt{\dfrac{1 + v/c}{1 - v/c}}}$.

P46.39 (a) $\lambda' = \lambda\sqrt{\dfrac{1 + v/c}{1 - v/c}}$ $\qquad 510\text{ nm} = 434\text{ nm}\sqrt{\dfrac{1 + v/c}{1 - v/c}}$

$$1.18^2 = \frac{1 + v/c}{1 - v/c} = 1.381$$

$$1 + \frac{v}{c} = 1.381 - 1.381\frac{v}{c} \qquad 2.38\frac{v}{c} = 0.381$$

$$\frac{v}{c} = 0.160 \quad \text{or} \quad v = \boxed{0.160c} = 4.80 \times 10^7 \text{ m/s}$$

(b) $v = HR$: $\qquad R = \dfrac{v}{H} = \dfrac{4.80 \times 10^7 \text{ m/s}}{17 \times 10^{-3} \text{ m/s}\cdot\text{ly}} = \boxed{2.82 \times 10^9 \text{ ly}}$

P46.40 (a) $\lambda_n' = \lambda_n\sqrt{\dfrac{1+v/c}{1-v/c}} = (Z+1)\lambda_n$ $\qquad \dfrac{1+v/c}{1-v/c} = (Z+1)^2$

$1+\dfrac{v}{c} = (Z+1)^2 - \left(\dfrac{v}{c}\right)(Z+1)^2$ $\qquad \left(\dfrac{v}{c}\right)\left(Z^2+2Z+2\right) = Z^2+2Z$

$$v = \boxed{c\left(\frac{Z^2+2Z}{Z^2+2Z+2}\right)}$$

(b) $R = \dfrac{v}{H} = \boxed{\dfrac{c}{H}\left(\dfrac{Z^2+2Z}{Z^2+2Z+2}\right)}$

P46.41 $v = HR$ $\qquad H = \dfrac{\left(1.7\times10^{-2}\ \text{m/s}\right)}{\text{ly}}$

(a) $v\left(2.00\times10^{6}\ \text{ly}\right) = 3.4\times10^{4}\ \text{m/s}$ $\qquad \lambda' = \lambda\sqrt{\dfrac{1+v/c}{1-v/c}} = 590(1.000\,113\,3) = \boxed{590.07\ \text{nm}}$

(b) $v\left(2.00\times10^{8}\ \text{ly}\right) = 3.4\times10^{6}\ \text{m/s}$ $\qquad \lambda' = 590\sqrt{\dfrac{1+0.011\,33}{1-0.011\,33}} = \boxed{597\ \text{nm}}$

(c) $v\left(2.00\times10^{9}\ \text{ly}\right) = 3.4\times10^{7}\ \text{m/s}$ $\qquad \lambda' = 590\sqrt{\dfrac{1+0.113\,3}{1-0.113\,3}} = \boxed{661\ \text{nm}}$

P46.42 (a) Wien's law: $\lambda_{\text{max}}T = 2.898\times10^{-3}\ \text{m}\cdot\text{K}.$

Thus, $\lambda_{\text{max}} = \dfrac{2.898\times10^{-3}\ \text{m}\cdot\text{K}}{T} = \dfrac{2.898\times10^{-3}\ \text{m}\cdot\text{K}}{2.73\ \text{K}} = 1.06\times10^{-3}\ \text{m} = \boxed{1.06\ \text{mm}}$.

(b) This is a $\boxed{\text{microwave}}$.

***P46.43** We suppose that the fireball of the Big Bang is a black body.

$I = e\sigma T^4 = (1)\left(5.67\times10^{-8}\ \text{W/m}^2\cdot\text{K}^4\right)(2.73\ \text{K})^4 = \boxed{3.15\times10^{-6}\ \text{W/m}^2}$

As a bonus, we can find the current power of direct radiation from the Big Bang in the section of the universe observable to us. If it is fifteen billion years old, the fireball is a perfect sphere of radius fifteen billion light years, centered at the point halfway between your eyes:

$$\mathcal{P} = IA = I(4\pi r^2) = \left(3.15\times10^{-6}\ \text{W/m}^2\right)(4\pi)\left(15\times10^{9}\ \text{ly}\right)^2\left(\frac{3\times10^{8}\ \text{m/s}}{1\ \text{ly/yr}}\right)^2\left(3.156\times10^{7}\ \text{s/yr}\right)^2$$

$\mathcal{P} = 7.98\times10^{47}\ \text{W}.$

P46.44 The density of the Universe is

$$\rho = 1.20\rho_c = 1.20\left(\frac{3H^2}{8\pi G}\right).$$

Consider a remote galaxy at distance r. The mass interior to the sphere below it is

$$M = \rho\left(\frac{4}{3}\pi r^3\right) = 1.20\left(\frac{3H^2}{8\pi G}\right)\left(\frac{4}{3}\pi r^3\right) = \frac{0.600H^2 r^3}{G}$$

both now and in the future when it has slowed to rest from its current speed $v = Hr$. The energy of this galaxy-sphere system is constant as the galaxy moves to apogee distance R:

$$\frac{1}{2}mv^2 - \frac{GmM}{r} = 0 - \frac{GmM}{R} \qquad \text{so} \qquad \frac{1}{2}mH^2r^2 - \frac{Gm}{r}\left(\frac{0.600H^2r^3}{G}\right) = 0 - \frac{Gm}{R}\left(\frac{0.600H^2r^3}{G}\right)$$

$$-0.100 = -0.600\frac{r}{R} \qquad \text{so} \qquad R = 6.00r.$$

The Universe will expand by a factor of $\boxed{6.00}$ from its current dimensions.

P46.45 (a) $k_B T \approx 2m_p c^2$

so $$T \approx \frac{2m_p c^2}{k_B} = \frac{2(938.3 \text{ MeV})}{(1.38\times10^{-23} \text{ J/K})}\left(\frac{1.60\times10^{-13} \text{ J}}{1 \text{ MeV}}\right)\boxed{\sim 10^{13} \text{ K}}$$

(b) $k_B T \approx 2m_e c^2$

so $$T \approx \frac{2m_e c^2}{k_B} = \frac{2(0.511 \text{ MeV})}{(1.38\times10^{-23} \text{ J/K})}\left(\frac{1.60\times10^{-13} \text{ J}}{1 \text{ MeV}}\right)\boxed{\sim 10^{10} \text{ K}}$$

***P46.46** (a) The Hubble constant is defined in $v = HR$. The distance R between any two far-separated objects opens at constant speed according to $R = vt$. Then the time t since the Big Bang is found from

$$v = Hvt \qquad 1 = Ht \qquad t = \frac{1}{H}.$$

(b) $$\frac{1}{H} = \frac{1}{17\times10^{-3} \text{ m/s}\cdot\text{ly}}\left(\frac{3\times10^8 \text{ m/s}}{1 \text{ ly/yr}}\right) = \boxed{1.76\times10^{10} \text{ yr}} = 17.6 \text{ billion years}$$

***P46.47** (a) Consider a sphere around us of radius R large compared to the size of galaxy clusters. If the matter M inside the sphere has the critical density, then a galaxy of mass m at the surface of the sphere is moving just at escape speed v according to

$$K+U_g=0 \qquad \frac{1}{2}mv^2-\frac{GMm}{R}=0.$$

The energy of the galaxy-sphere system is conserved, so this equation is true throughout the history of the Universe after the Big Bang, where $v=\frac{dR}{dt}$. Then

$$\left(\frac{dR}{dt}\right)^2=\frac{2GM}{R} \qquad \frac{dR}{dt}=R^{-1/2}\sqrt{2GM} \qquad \int_0^R\sqrt{R}\,dR=\sqrt{2GM}\int_0^T dt$$

$$\left.\frac{R^{3/2}}{3/2}\right|_0^R=\sqrt{2GM}\,t\Big|_0^T \qquad \frac{2}{3}R^{3/2}=\sqrt{2GM}\,T$$

$$T=\frac{2}{3}\frac{R^{3/2}}{\sqrt{2GM}}=\frac{2}{3}\frac{R}{\sqrt{2GM/R}}.$$

From above, $\sqrt{\frac{2GM}{R}}=v$

so $T=\frac{2}{3}\frac{R}{v}.$

Now Hubble's law says $v=HR.$

So $T=\frac{2}{3}\frac{R}{HR}=\frac{2}{3H}.$

(b) $$T=\frac{2}{3\left(17\times10^{-3}\text{ m/s}\cdot\text{ly}\right)}\left(\frac{3\times10^8\text{ m/s}}{1\text{ ly/yr}}\right)=\boxed{1.18\times10^{10}\text{ yr}}=11.8\text{ billion years}$$

***P46.48** In our frame of reference, Hubble's law is exemplified by $\mathbf{v}_1=H\mathbf{R}_1$ and $\mathbf{v}_2=H\mathbf{R}_2$. From these we may form the equations $-\mathbf{v}_1=-H\mathbf{R}_1$ and $\mathbf{v}_2-\mathbf{v}_1=H(\mathbf{R}_2-\mathbf{R}_1)$. These equations express Hubble's law as seen by the observer in the first galaxy cluster, as she looks at us to find $-\mathbf{v}_1=H(-\mathbf{R}_1)$ and as she looks at cluster two to find $\mathbf{v}_2-\mathbf{v}_1=H(\mathbf{R}_2-\mathbf{R}_1)$.

Section 46.13 **Problems and Perspectives**

P46.49 (a) $$L=\sqrt{\frac{\hbar G}{c^3}}=\sqrt{\frac{\left(1.055\times10^{-34}\text{ J}\cdot\text{s}\right)\left(6.67\times10^{-11}\text{ N}\cdot\text{m}^2/\text{kg}^2\right)}{\left(3.00\times10^8\text{ m/s}\right)^3}}=\boxed{1.61\times10^{-35}\text{ m}}$$

(b) This time is given as $T=\frac{L}{c}=\frac{1.61\times10^{-35}\text{ m}}{3.00\times10^8\text{ m/s}}=\boxed{5.38\times10^{-44}\text{ s}}$,

which is approximately equal to the ultra-hot epoch.

(c) Yes.

Additional Problems

P46.50 We find the number N of neutrinos:

$$10^{46}\text{ J} = N(6\text{ MeV}) = N\left(6\times 1.60\times 10^{-13}\text{ J}\right)$$

$$N = 1.0\times 10^{58}\text{ neutrinos}$$

The intensity at our location is

$$\frac{N}{A} = \frac{N}{4\pi r^2} = \frac{1.0\times 10^{58}}{4\pi\left(1.7\times 10^5\text{ ly}\right)^2}\left(\frac{1\text{ ly}}{\left(3.00\times 10^8\text{ m/s}\right)\left(3.16\times 10^7\text{ s}\right)}\right)^2 = 3.1\times 10^{14}\text{ m}^{-2}.$$

The number passing through a body presenting $5\,000\text{ cm}^2 = 0.50\text{ m}^2$

is then $$\left(3.1\times 10^{14}\ \frac{1}{\text{m}^2}\right)\left(0.50\text{ m}^2\right) = 1.5\times 10^{14}$$

or $$\boxed{\sim 10^{14}}.$$

***P46.51** A photon travels the distance from the Large Magellanic Cloud to us in 170 000 years. The hypothetical massive neutrino travels the same distance in 170 000 years plus 10 seconds:

$$c(170\,000\text{ yr}) = v(170\,000\text{ yr} + 10\text{ s})$$

$$\frac{v}{c} = \frac{170\,000\text{ yr}}{170\,000\text{ yr} + 10\text{ s}} = \frac{1}{1+\left\{10\text{ s}/\left[\left(1.7\times 10^5\text{ yr}\right)\left(3.156\times 10^7\text{ s/yr}\right)\right]\right\}} = \frac{1}{1+1.86\times 10^{-12}}$$

For the neutrino we want to evaluate mc^2 in $E = \gamma mc^2$:

$$mc^2 = \frac{E}{\gamma} = E\sqrt{1-\frac{v^2}{c^2}} = 10\text{ MeV}\sqrt{1-\frac{1}{\left(1+1.86\times 10^{-12}\right)^2}} = 10\text{ MeV}\sqrt{\frac{\left(1+1.86\times 10^{-12}\right)^2-1}{\left(1+1.86\times 10^{-12}\right)^2}}$$

$$mc^2 \approx 10\text{ MeV}\sqrt{\frac{2\left(1.86\times 10^{-12}\right)}{1}} = 10\text{ MeV}\left(1.93\times 10^{-6}\right) = 19\text{ eV}.$$

Then the upper limit on the mass is

$$m = \boxed{\frac{19\text{ eV}}{c^2}}$$

$$m = \frac{19\text{ eV}}{c^2}\left(\frac{\text{u}}{931.5\times 10^6\text{ eV}/c^2}\right) = 2.1\times 10^{-8}\text{ u}.$$

P46.52 (a) $\pi^- + \text{p} \to \Sigma^+ + \pi^0$ is forbidden by $\boxed{\text{charge conservation}}$.

(b) $\mu^- \to \pi^- + \nu_e$ is forbidden by $\boxed{\text{energy conservation}}$.

(c) $\text{p} \to \pi^+ + \pi^+ + \pi^-$ is forbidden by $\boxed{\text{baryon number conservation}}$.

P46.53 The total energy in neutrinos emitted per second by the Sun is:

$$(0.4)\left[4\pi\left(1.5\times10^{11}\right)^2\right]\text{W}=1.1\times10^{23}\text{ W}.$$

Over 10^9 years, the Sun emits 3.6×10^{39} J in neutrinos. This represents an annihilated mass

$$mc^2=3.6\times10^{39}\text{ J}$$

$$m=4.0\times10^{22}\text{ kg}.$$

About $\boxed{\text{1 part in 50 000 000}}$ of the Sun's mass, over 10^9 years, has been lost to neutrinos.

P46.54 $\text{p}+\text{p}\to\text{p}+\pi^++X$

We suppose the protons each have 70.4 MeV of kinetic energy. From conservation of momentum for the collision, particle X has zero momentum and thus zero kinetic energy. Conservation of system energy then requires

$$M_\text{p}c^2+M_\pi c^2+M_Xc^2=\left(M_\text{p}c^2+K_\text{p}\right)+\left(M_\text{p}c^2+K_\text{p}\right)$$

$$M_Xc^2=M_\text{p}c^2+2K_\text{p}-M_\pi c^2=938.3\text{ MeV}+2(70.4\text{ MeV})-139.6\text{ MeV}=939.5\text{ MeV}$$

X must be a neutral baryon of rest energy 939.5 MeV. Thus X is a $\boxed{\text{neutron}}$.

***P46.55** (a) If $2N$ particles are annihilated, the energy released is $2Nmc^2$. The resulting photon momentum is $p=\frac{E}{c}=\frac{2Nmc^2}{c}=2Nmc$. Since the momentum of the system is conserved, the rocket will have momentum $2Nmc$ directed opposite the photon momentum.

$$\boxed{p=2Nmc}$$

(b) Consider a particle that is annihilated and gives up its rest energy mc^2 to another particle which also has initial rest energy mc^2 (but no momentum initially).

$$E^2=p^2c^2+\left(mc^2\right)^2$$

Thus $\left(2mc^2\right)^2=p^2c^2+\left(mc^2\right)^2$.

Where p is the momentum the second particle acquires as a result of the annihilation of the first particle. Thus $4\left(mc^2\right)^2=p^2c^2+\left(mc^2\right)^2$, $p^2=3\left(mc^2\right)^2$. So $p=\sqrt{3}mc$.

This process is repeated N times (annihilate $\frac{N}{2}$ protons and $\frac{N}{2}$ antiprotons). Thus the total momentum acquired by the ejected particles is $\sqrt{3}Nmc$, and this momentum is imparted to the rocket.

$$\boxed{p=\sqrt{3}Nmc}$$

(c) Method (a) produces greater speed since $2Nmc>\sqrt{3}Nmc$.

P46.56 (a) $\Delta E \Delta t \approx \hbar$, and $\Delta t = \frac{r}{c} = \frac{1.4 \times 10^{-15}\text{ m}}{3 \times 10^{8}\text{ m/s}} = 4.7 \times 10^{-24}\text{ s}$

$$\Delta E \approx \frac{\hbar}{\Delta t} = \frac{1.055 \times 10^{-34}\text{ J}\cdot\text{s}}{4.7 \times 10^{-24}\text{ s}} = \left(2.3 \times 10^{-11}\text{ J}\right)\left(\frac{1\text{ MeV}}{1.60 \times 10^{-13}\text{ J}}\right) = 1.4 \times 10^{2}\text{ MeV}$$

$$m = \frac{\Delta E}{c^2} \approx 1.4 \times 10^{2}\text{ MeV}/c^2 \boxed{\sim 10^{2}\text{ MeV}/c^2}$$

(b) From Table 46.2, $m_\pi c^2 = 139.6\text{ MeV}$ $\boxed{\text{a pi-meson}}$.

P46.57 $m_\Lambda c^2 = 1115.6\text{ MeV}$ $\qquad \Lambda^0 \to \text{p} + \pi^-$

$m_p c^2 = 938.3\text{ MeV}$ $\qquad m_\pi c^2 = 139.6\text{ MeV}$

The difference between starting rest energy and final rest energy is the kinetic energy of the products.

$$K_p + K_\pi = 37.7\text{ MeV} \qquad \text{and} \qquad p_p = p_\pi = p$$

Applying conservation of relativistic energy to the decay process, we have

$$\left[\sqrt{(938.3)^2 + p^2c^2} - 938.3\right] + \left[\sqrt{(139.6)^2 + p^2c^2} - 139.6\right] = 37.7\text{ MeV}.$$

Solving the algebra yields

$$p_\pi c = p_p c = 100.4\text{ MeV}.$$

Then, $K_p = \sqrt{\left(m_p c^2\right)^2 + (100.4)^2} - m_p c^2 = \boxed{5.35\text{ MeV}}$

$$K_\pi = \sqrt{(139.6)^2 + (100.4)^2} - 139.6 = \boxed{32.3\text{ MeV}}.$$

P46.58 By relativistic energy conservation in the reaction, $E_\gamma + m_e c^2 = \frac{3m_e c^2}{\sqrt{1 - v^2/c^2}}$. (1)

By relativistic momentum conservation for the system, $\frac{E_\gamma}{c} = \frac{3m_e v}{\sqrt{1 - v^2/c^2}}$. (2)

Dividing (2) by (1), $X = \frac{E_\gamma}{E_\gamma + m_e c^2} = \frac{v}{c}$.

Subtracting (2) from (1), $m_e c^2 = \frac{3m_e c^2}{\sqrt{1 - X^2}} - \frac{3m_e c^2 X}{\sqrt{1 - X^2}}$.

Solving, $1 = \frac{3 - 3X}{\sqrt{1 - X^2}}$ and $X = \frac{4}{5}$ so $E_\gamma = 4m_e c^2 = \boxed{2.04\text{ MeV}}$.

P46.59 Momentum of proton is $qBr = (1.60 \times 10^{-19}\ \text{C})(0.250\ \text{kg/C}\cdot\text{s})(1.33\ \text{m})$

$p_p = 5.32 \times 10^{-20}\ \text{kg}\cdot m/s$ $\quad cp_p = 1.60 \times 10^{-11}\ \text{kg}\cdot\text{m}^2/\text{s}^2 = 1.60 \times 10^{-11}\ \text{J} = 99.8\ \text{MeV}$.

Therefore, $p_p = 99.8\ \text{MeV}/c$.

The total energy of the proton is $E_p = \sqrt{E_0^2 + (cp)^2} = \sqrt{(983.3)^2 + (99.8)^2} = 944\ \text{MeV}$.

For pion, the momentum qBr is the same (as it must be from conservation of momentum in a 2-particle decay).

$p_\pi = 99.8\ \text{MeV}/c$ $\quad E_{0\pi} = 139.6\ \text{MeV}$

$$E_\pi = \sqrt{E_0^2 + (cp)^2} = \sqrt{(139.6)^2 + (99.8)^2} = 172\ \text{MeV}$$

Thus, $E_{\text{total after}} = E_{\text{total before}} = \text{Rest energy}$.

Rest Energy of unknown particle $= 944\ \text{MeV} + 172\ \text{MeV} = 1\,116\ \text{MeV}$ (This is a Λ^0 particle!)

Mass $= \boxed{1\,116\ \text{MeV}/c^2}$.

P46.60 $\Sigma^0 \to \Lambda^0 + \gamma$

From Table 46.2, $m_\Sigma = 1\,192.5\ \text{MeV}/c^2$ and $m_\Lambda = 1115.6\ \text{MeV}/c^2$.

Conservation of energy in the decay requires

$$E_{0,\Sigma} = \left(E_{0,\Lambda} + K_\Lambda\right) + E_\gamma \quad \text{or} \quad 1\,192.5\ \text{MeV} = \left(1\,115.6\ \text{MeV} + \frac{p_\Lambda{}^2}{2m_\Lambda}\right) + E_\gamma.$$

System momentum conservation gives $|p_\Lambda| = |p_\gamma|$, so the last result may be written as

$$1\,192.5\ \text{MeV} = \left(1\,115.6\ \text{MeV} + \frac{p_\gamma{}^2}{2m_\Lambda}\right) + E_\gamma$$

or

$$1\,192.5\ \text{MeV} = \left(1\,115.6\ \text{MeV} + \frac{p_\gamma{}^2 c^2}{2m_\Lambda c^2}\right) + E_\gamma.$$

Recognizing that $m_\Lambda c^2 = 1\,115.6\ \text{MeV}$ and $p_\gamma c = E_\gamma$

we now have

$$1\,192.5\ \text{MeV} = 1\,115.6\ \text{MeV} + \frac{E_\gamma{}^2}{2(1\,115.6\ \text{MeV})} + E_\gamma.$$

Solving this quadratic equation, $E_\gamma = \boxed{74.4\ \text{MeV}}$.

P46.61 $\text{p} + \text{p} \to \text{p} + \text{n} + \pi^+$

The total momentum is zero before the reaction. Thus, all three particles present after the reaction may be at rest and still conserve system momentum. This will be the case when the incident protons have minimum kinetic energy. Under these conditions, conservation of energy for the reaction gives

$$2\left(m_p c^2 + K_p\right) = m_p c^2 + m_n c^2 + m_\pi c^2$$

so the kinetic energy of each of the incident protons is

$$K_p = \frac{m_n c^2 + m_\pi c^2 - m_p c^2}{2} = \frac{(939.6 + 139.6 - 938.3)\ \text{MeV}}{2} = \boxed{70.4\ \text{MeV}}.$$

P46.62 $\pi^- \to \mu^- + \bar{\nu}_\mu$: From the conservation laws for the decay,

$$m_\pi c^2 = 139.6\text{ MeV} = E_\mu + E_\nu \quad [1]$$

and $p_\mu = p_\nu$, $E_\nu = p_\nu c$: $E_\mu^2 = (p_\mu c)^2 + (105.7\text{ MeV})^2 = (p_\nu c)^2 + (105.7\text{ MeV})^2$

or $E_\mu^2 - E_\nu^2 = (105.7\text{ MeV})^2$. [2]

Since $E_\mu + E_\nu = 139.6\text{ MeV}$ [1]

and $(E_\mu + E_\nu)(E_\mu - E_\nu) = (105.7\text{ MeV})^2$ [2]

then $E_\mu - E_\nu = \dfrac{(105.7\text{ MeV})^2}{139.6\text{ MeV}} = 80.0$. [3]

Subtracting [3] from [1], $2E_\nu = 59.6\text{ MeV}$ and $\boxed{E_\nu = 29.8\text{ MeV}}$.

P46.63 The expression $e^{-E/k_BT}dE$ gives the fraction of the photons that have energy between E and $E + dE$. The fraction that have energy between E and infinity is

$$\frac{\int_E^\infty e^{-E/k_BT}dE}{\int_0^\infty e^{-E/k_BT}dE} = \frac{\int_E^\infty e^{-E/k_BT}(-dE/k_BT)}{\int_0^\infty e^{-E/k_BT}(-dE/k_BT)} = \frac{e^{-E/k_BT}\Big|_E^\infty}{e^{-E/k_BT}\Big|_0^\infty} = e^{-E/k_BT}.$$

We require T when this fraction has a value of 0.0100 (i.e., 1.00%)

and $E = 1.00\text{ eV} = 1.60 \times 10^{-19}\text{ J}$.

Thus, $0.010\,0 = e^{-(1.60\times10^{-19}\text{ J})/(1.38\times10^{-23}\text{ J/K})T}$

or $\ln(0.010\,0) = -\dfrac{1.60\times10^{-19}\text{ J}}{(1.38\times10^{-23}\text{ J/K})T} = -\dfrac{1.16\times10^4\text{ K}}{T}$ giving $T = \boxed{2.52\times10^3\text{ K}}$.

P46.64 (a) This diagram represents the annihilation of an electron and an antielectron. From charge and lepton-number conservation at either vertex, the exchanged particle must be an electron, $\boxed{e^-}$.

(b) This is the tough one. A neutrino collides with a neutron, changing it into a proton with release of a muon. This is a weak interaction. The exchanged particle has charge $+e$ and is a $\boxed{W^+}$.

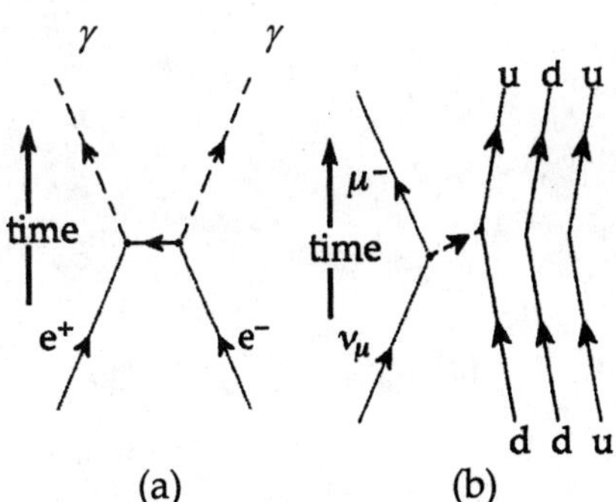

FIG. P46.64

P46.65 (a) The mediator of this weak interaction is a $\boxed{Z^0 \text{ boson}}$.

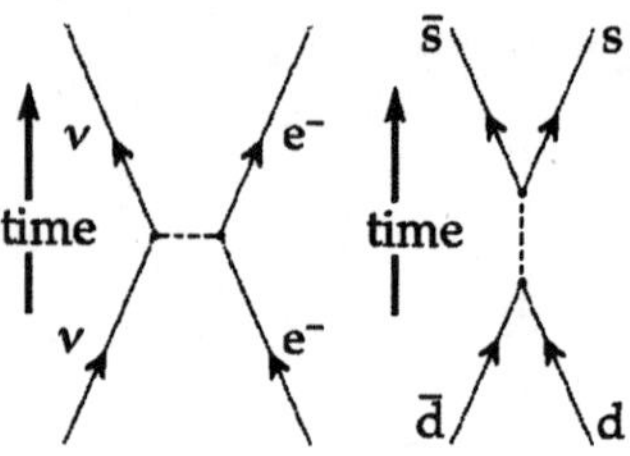

FIG. P46.65

(b) The Feynman diagram shows a down quark and its antiparticle annihilating each other. They can produce a particle carrying energy, momentum, and angular momentum, but zero charge, zero baryon number, and, it may be, no color charge. In this case the product particle is a $\boxed{\text{photon}}$.

For conservation of both energy and momentum in the collision we would expect two photons; but momentum need not be strictly conserved, according to the uncertainty principle, if the photon travels a sufficiently short distance before producing another matter-antimatter pair of particles, as shown in Figure P46.65. Depending on the color charges of the d and $\bar{\text{d}}$ quarks, the ephemeral particle could also be a $\boxed{\text{gluon}}$, as suggested in the discussion of Figure 46.14(b).

***P46.66** (a) At threshold, we consider a photon and a proton colliding head-on to produce a proton and a pion at rest, according to $\text{p}+\gamma \to \text{p}+\pi^0$. Energy conservation gives

$$\frac{m_\text{p}c^2}{\sqrt{1-u^2/c^2}}+E_\gamma = m_\text{p}c^2+m_\pi c^2.$$

Momentum conservation gives $\dfrac{m_\text{p}u}{\sqrt{1-u^2/c^2}}-\dfrac{E_\gamma}{c}=0.$

Combining the equations, we have

$$\frac{m_\text{p}c^2}{\sqrt{1-u^2/c^2}}+\frac{m_\text{p}c^2}{\sqrt{1-u^2/c^2}}\frac{u}{c}=m_\text{p}c^2+m_\pi c^2$$

$$\frac{938.3\text{ MeV}(1+u/c)}{\sqrt{(1-u/c)(1+u/c)}}=938.3\text{ MeV}+135.0\text{ MeV}$$

so $\dfrac{u}{c}=0.134$

and $E_\gamma = \boxed{127\text{ MeV}}$.

(b) $\lambda_{\max}T = 2.898\text{ mm}\cdot\text{K}$

$$\lambda_{\max}=\frac{2.898\text{ mm}\cdot\text{K}}{2.73\text{ K}}=\boxed{1.06\text{ mm}}$$

(c) $E_\gamma = hf = \dfrac{hc}{\lambda}=\dfrac{1\,240\text{ eV}\cdot 10^{-9}\text{ m}}{1.06\times10^{-3}\text{ m}}=\boxed{1.17\times10^{-3}\text{ eV}}$

continued on next page

(d) In the primed reference frame, the proton is moving to the right at $\frac{u'}{c} = 0.134$ and the photon is moving to the left with $hf' = 1.27 \times 10^{8}$ eV. In the unprimed frame, $hf = 1.17 \times 10^{-3}$ eV. Using the Doppler effect equation from Section 39.4, we have for the speed of the primed frame

$$1.27 \times 10^{8} = \sqrt{\frac{1+v/c}{1-v/c}}\, 1.17 \times 10^{-3}$$

$$\frac{v}{c} = 1 - 1.71 \times 10^{-22}$$

Then the speed of the proton is given by

$$\frac{u}{c} = \frac{u'/c + v/c}{1 + u'v/c^2} = \frac{0.134 + 1 - 1.71 \times 10^{-22}}{1 + 0.134\left(1 - 1.71 \times 10^{-22}\right)} = 1 - 1.30 \times 10^{-22}.$$

And the energy of the proton is

$$\frac{m_p c^2}{\sqrt{1-u^2/c^2}} = \frac{938.3 \text{ MeV}}{\sqrt{1-\left(1-1.30 \times 10^{-22}\right)^2}} = 6.19 \times 10^{10} \times 938.3 \times 10^{6} \text{ eV} = \boxed{5.81 \times 10^{19} \text{ eV}}.$$

ANSWERS TO EVEN PROBLEMS

P46.2 2.27×10^{23} Hz; 1.32 fm

P46.4 $\bar{\nu}_\mu$ and ν_e

P46.6 $\sim 10^{-16}$ m

P46.8 $\sim 10^{-23}$ s

P46.10 $\bar{\nu}_\mu$

P46.12 (a) electron lepton number and muon lepton number; (b) charge; (c) baryon number; (d) baryon number; (e) charge

P46.14 the second violates conservation of baryon number

P46.16 $0.828c$

P46.18 (a) see the solution; (b) 469 MeV; $\frac{469 \text{ MeV}}{c}$ for both; (c) $0.999\,999\,4c$

P46.20 see the solution

P46.22 (a) electron lepton number and muon lepton number; (b) electron lepton number; (c) strangeness and charge; (d) baryon number; (e) strangeness

P46.24 see the solution

P46.26 (a) $\frac{686 \text{ MeV}}{c}$ and $\frac{200 \text{ MeV}}{c}$; (b) 627 MeV/$c$; (c) 244 MeV, 1 130 MeV, 1 370 MeV; (d) 1 190 MeV/c^2, $0.500c$

P46.28 (a) see the solution; (b) 5.63 GeV; (c) 768 MeV; (d) 280 MeV; (e) 4.43 TeV

P46.30 see the solution

P46.32 see the solution

P46.34 see the solution

P46.36 (a) Σ^+; (b) π^-; (c) K^0; (d) Ξ^-

P46.38 see the solution

P46.40 (a) $v = c\left(\dfrac{Z^2 + 2Z}{Z^2 + 2Z + 2}\right)$; (b) $\dfrac{c}{H}\left(\dfrac{Z^2 + 2Z}{Z^2 + 2Z + 2}\right)$

P46.42 (a) 1.06 mm; (b) microwave

P46.44 6.00

P46.46 (a) see the solution; (b) 17.6 Gyr

P46.48 see the solution

P46.50 $\sim 10^{14}$

P46.52 (a) charge; (b) energy; (c) baryon number

P46.54 neutron

P46.56 (a) $\sim 10^2\ \text{MeV}/c^2$; (b) a pi-meson

P46.58 2.04 MeV

P46.60 74.4 MeV

P46.62 29.8 MeV

P46.64 (a) electron-position annihilation; e^-; (b) a neutrino collides with a neutron, producing a proton and a muon; W^+

P46.66 (a) 127 MeV; (b) 1.06 mm; (c) 1.17 meV; (d) 5.81×10^{19} eV